MW01038132

1992 - 1993

V.I.P. ADDRESS BOOK

1992 - 1993

V.I.P. ADDRESS BOOK

Edited by James M. Wiggins

Associated Media Companies Ltd.

Library of Congress Catalog Card Number 89-656029
(ISSN 1043-0261)
The V.I.P. address book/edited by James M. Wiggins
Bibliography: p.
Includes index.
1. Celebrities—Directories. 2. Celebrities—United States—Directories. 3. Social registers. 4. United States—Social registers.
I. Wiggins, James M., 1933- II. Title: VIP address book.
CT120.VI5 1990 920'.0025'73 - dc 89-656029
(ISSN 1043-0261)
International Standard Book Number 0-938731-09-2

TABLE OF CONTENTS

PREFACE

What a thing to be in the mouth of fame.

John Keats

A requirement for the title for this work, the **V.I.P. ADDRESS BOOK**, is a clear definition of who is a very important person and an understanding of the word "fame." What, or rather who, is a celebrity? And what really constitutes fame?

This work prefers to include in its definition of a V.I.P. emphasis on wide recognition complemented by achievement and/or position. In order to merit inclusion on the basis of achievement, men and women must distinguish themselves from their contemporaries through contributions to a chosen field, to human understanding or to mankind itself. While the names of such people may not be readily identifiable, the impact of their accomplishments is significant. Others have been included on the basis of their position. While many selected because of their position might also be selected by virtue of their accomplishments, their selections are assured by the positions or titles they hold. Such positions might relate to government, the military, business, law, or institutions and organizations devoted to educational and philanthropic aims.

Achievement can never be overemphasized. Achievement, regardless of the motivation, in one's occupation or line of endeavor, should always be a plus regardless of the impetus. Edmund Burke once noted that desire for fame can be a most positive force. He wrote, "Passion for fame; a passion which is the instinct of all great souls." There surely is nothing amoral about wanting or achieving fame. Desire for recognition is not restricted to athletes wanting larger contracts or television stars wanting their shows to have higher ratings. Percy Shelley felt that fame even has its place in the arts. He wrote, "Chameleons feed on light and air: Poets' food is love and fame." As well it might since poets (and others) often receive recognition/esteem from people only in their own areas.

Looking first at the term celebrity, some state that to be a celebrity one needs to be known outside one's field. If one is not readily recognizable to a large number of people then one is not a celebrity. This implies in these days of communication saturation by newspapers, magazines, radio and television that if most people do not recognize a person, he or she is simply not a celebrity. But restricting candidates for this reference work to only those who are clearly "recognizable" is ridiculous. This would exclude many - if not most - artists, composers, military leaders, scientists, religious leaders, explorers, politicians, writers, business leaders and legislators. The list would be left primarily with stars of television (actresses and actors, singers, newscasters), leaders of a handful of countries and well-known athletes.

Celebrity is considered synonymous with wide recognition, fame or renown. A secondary definition is a famous or well-publicized person. Although fashionable to belittle fame, Lord Byron noted fame does have its moment in the sun. He wrote:

Oh Fame! — if I e'er took delight in thy praises,
'Twas less for the sake of thy high-sounding phrases,
Than to see the bright eyes of the dear one discover,
She thought that I was not unworthy to love her.

Celebrities and very important people are often referred to as VIPs. While it is acknowledged that both have fame, it is said that a celebrity's fame is his or hers alone while a VIP's is largely positional. The argument goes that a celebrity would not need a qualifying identification while a VIP would require association with one's organization to be properly identified. Such a distinction lacks credibility. Is Ronald Reagan a celebrity because he was an actor or because he became President? He was a celebrity to movie buffs but his real identification came with the Presidency.

Efforts to distinguish between who is a celebrity and who is a VIP can end up as late-night collegiate discussions fueled by inexpensive wine and punctuated by faltering logic. Whether a person's impact is fleeting has little to do with achievement; attempts to establish limited definitions usually fail. To appreciate one's achievements, we must realize there may be only fleeting fame/celebrity time but endeavors can live long afterwards. The desire to leave a worthwhile contribution drives us to "make our mark." Edmund Spenser, wrote in his sonnet Amoretti:

One day I wrote her name upon the sand,
But came the waves and washed it away:
Again I wrote it with a second hand,
But came the tide, and made my pains his prey.
Vain man, said she, that dost in vain assay,
A mortal thing so to immortalize,
For I myself shall like to this decay,
And eke my name be wiped out likewise.
Not so, quoth I, let baser things devise,
To die in dust, but you shall live by fame:
My verse your virtues rare shall eternalize,
And in the heavens write your glorious name,
Where when as death shall all the world subdue,
Our love shall live, and later life renew.

The making of a mark, or name, in the sand can have different meanings. We must go our own way, dream our own dreams, seek our own goals. Robert Bridges, in his Ode to Music, said it best:

Rejoice ye dead, where'er your spirits dwell
Rejoice that yet on earth your fame is bright,
And that your names, remembered day and night,
Live on the lips of those who love you well.

James M. Wiggins, Editor

INTRODUCTION

Purpose of the Book

The purpose of the the **V.I.P. ADDRESS BOOK** is to provide readers a means of reaching Very Important People — Celebrities, Government Officials, Business Leaders, Entertainers, Sports Stars, Scientists and Artists.

It is genuinely hoped that people use this volume to write for information about an entrant's work or to express encouragement. Compliments and praise for one's efforts are always appreciated. Being at the top of one's chosen profession is no exception. And for those who are no longer active in a field, it is especially flattering to be contacted about one's past accomplishments.

Methodology

The determination of candidates for inclusion in this reference work has been a five-year process.

Committees of prominent and knowledgable people were brought together for discussions about who should be included. The nine major areas covered are Public Service, Adventure, Business, Religion, Education, Life and Leisure, Communications, Fine Arts, Sciences, Entertainment, Athletics.

Public Service includes World Leaders, Government Officials, Law Enforcement Officials and members of the Legal and Judicial fields.

Adventure includes Military Leaders (both U.S. and International), Astronauts and Cosmonauts, Heroes and Explorers.

Business, Religion and Education includes Financial and Labor Leaders as well as Businesspeople and Nobel Prize Winners in Economics and Peace.

Life and Leisure includes Fashion Design, Modeling, Beauty and Health Care and Social and Political Activists.

Communications encompasses Columnists, Commentators, Editors and Publishers, along with Editorial and Comic Book Cartoonists.

Fine Arts includes Architects, Artists, Opera, Ballet and Dance Performers, Conductors, Concert Artists, Composers (both classical and popular), Writers, Photographers and Nobel Literature Laureates.

Science covers Nobel Prize winners in Chemistry, Medicine and Physics, Engineers, Inventors, Earth and Space Scientists, Psychologists and Psychiatrists, Medical and Research Scientists.

Entertainment includes stars of Radio, Stage and Screen, Musicians, Cinematographers, Producers and Directors.

Sports includes all major spectator and participatory sports.

The challenge for the committees was to define the parameters of the people included and to prepare a list of candidates. This work was exhaustive with candidates running into many thousands. Once these lists were presented, the research staff began its detailed check and update procedures.

Locating the Addresses

In the last year, the candidates - or their designated representatives - were contacted in an effort to obtain the best mailing address. Some prefer home addresses, others prefer places of business and some prefer contact through agents. The actual task of finding appropriate addresses fell to a worldwide staff of experienced researchers and veteran investigative reporters. This work is ongoing to maintain the integrity of the information.

Before printing, we have attempted to verify each address and feel reasonably certain that the book is offering its readers the best way to reach listees.

People, however, do move, change jobs and change agents. Normally, the U.S. post office customarily forwards mail for up to six months. If the change is abrupt, mail may not be forwarded. We encourage users of this work to inform us if they find incorrect addresses. The **V.I.P. ADDRESS BOOK UPDATES**, an accompanying publication for this master volume, publishes updated and additional addresses on a regular basis.

Occupations and Titles

The category listed after a person's name is selected to best describe his/her most noteworthy accomplishment. No distinction is made whether the person still holds that position. It is felt that a person who made a name for herself or himself still retains that identity even if it was done several years ago.

Additional VIPs

While this volume contains addresses for more than 20,000 VIPs, it by no means exhausts the ranks of internationally prominent people. Often we were unable to confirm an address despite continuous efforts to do so. Because of this, some people have been omitted from this basic reference work.

The book's editors consider nominations for inclusion in later editions. Address corrections are welcome as well. We invite readers to participate in the nomination process and forms for this purpose are included in the back of the book.

We express our appreciation to the multitude of interested participants whose efforts have contributed to compilation of this reference work. It is an on-going project. It is also a project which people in a variety of fields for a variety of reasons can effectively utilize.

1992 - 1993
V.I.P. ADDRESS BOOK

Editor
James M. Wiggins

Managing Editor
Adele M. Cooke

Design Director
Lee Ann Nelson

Technical Director
Michael K. Maloy

Publisher
ASSOCIATED MEDIA COMPANIES LTD.
P.O. Box 10190
Marina del Rey, California 90295-8864
United States of America

TABLE OF ABBREVIATIONS

A

AA	Address Americas
AB	Alberta
AE	Address Europe
AFB	Air Force Base
AK	Alaska
AL	Alabama
AP	Address Pacific
Aly	Alley
APO	Army Post Office
AR	Arkansas
Arc	Arcade
AS	American Samoa
Assn	Association
Assoc	Associates
Ave	Avenue
AZ	Arizona

B

BC	British Columbia
Bd	Board
Beds	Bedfordshire
Berks	Berkshire
Bldg	Building
Blvd	Boulevard
Br	Branch
Bros	Brothers
Bucks	Buckinghamshire
BWI	British West Indies
Byp	Bypass

C

CA	California
Cambs	Cambridgeshire
Cir	Circle
CM	Mariana Islands
CMH	Medal of Honor Winner
CO	Colorado
Co	Company
Corp	Corporation
Cres	Crescent
Cswy	Causeway
CT	Connecticut
Ct	Court
Ctr	Center
Cts	Courts
CZ	Canal Zone

D

DC	District of Columbia
DE	Delaware
Dept	Department
Dis	District
Dr	Drive
Drwy	Driveway

E

E	East
Edin	Edinburgh
Expy	Expressway
Ext	Extended, Extension

F

Fedn	Federation
FL	Florida
FPO	Fleet Post Office
Ft	Fort
Fwy	Freeway

G

GA	Georgia
Gdns	Gardens
Glos	Gloucestershire
Grp	Group
Grv	Grove
Gt	Great
GU	Guam

H

Hants	Hampshire
Herts	Hertfordshire
HI	Hawaii
Hts	Heights
Hwy	Highway

I

IA	Iowa
ID	Idaho
IL	Illinois
IN	Indiana
Inc	Incorporated
Inst	Institute

J

Jr	Junior

K

KS	Kansas
KY	Kentucky

L

LA	Louisiana
Lancs	Lancashire
LB	Labrador
Lincs	Lincolnshire
Ln	Lane
Ltd	Limited

M

MA	Massachusetts
MB	Manitoba

MD	Maryland
ME	Maine
MI	Michigan
MN	Minnesota
MO	Missouri
Mon	Monmouthshire
MS	Mississippi
MT	Montana
Mt	Mount

N

N	North
NB	New Brunswick
NC	North Carolina
ND	North Dakota
NE	Northeast, Nebraska
NF	Newfoundland
NH	New Hampshire
NJ	New Jersey
NM	New Mexico
Northants	Northamptonshire
Notts	Nottinghamshire
NS	Nova Scotia
NSW	New South Wales
NT	Northwest Territories
NV	Nevada
NW	Northwest
NY	New York

O

OH	Ohio
OK	Oklahoma
ON	Ontario
OR	Oregon
Oxon	Oxfordshire

P

PA	Pennsylvania
Pkwy	Parkway
PE	Prince Edward Island
Pl	Place
Plz	Plaza
PO	Post Office
PQ	Province of Quebec
PR	Puerto Rico
Pt	Point

Q

Qld	Queensland

R

RD	Rural Delivery
Rd	Road
RI	Rhode Island
RR	Rural Route

S

S	South
SC	South Carolina
SD	South Dakota
SE	Southeast
SK	Saskatchewan
Spdwy	Speedway
Sq	Square
St	Saint, Street
SW	Southwest

T

Ter	Territory
Terr	Terrace
TN	Tennessee
Trl	Trail
Tpke	Turnpike
TX	Texas

U

Univ	University
US	United States
USSR	Soviet Union
UT	Utah

V

VA	Virginia
VC	Victoria Cross Winner
VI	Virgin Islands
VT	Vermont

W

W	West
WA	Washington
WI	Wisconsin
Worcs	Worcestershire
WV	West Virginia
WY	Wyoming

X-Y-Z

Yorks	Yorkshire
YT	Yukon

FORMS OF ADDRESSES

An important part of writing to people - regardless of their positions - is to properly address envelopes and the salutations of the enclosed letters.

Although the titles and positions of people listed in this directory are too numerous to cover, there are a number of people whose forms of address are worth noting.

The Table listed below is offered as a guide to enhance the likelihood of your letter being received in a favorable light.

POSITION	**ENVELOPE ADDRESS**	**SALUTATIONS**
Presidents of Countries	The President	Dear Mr./Madam President ---
Vice Presidents of Countries	The Vice President	Dear Mr./Madam Vice President ---
Cabinet Officers	The Honorable John/Jane Doe, Secretary of ---	Dear Mr./Madam, Secretary of ---
Judges	The Honorable John/Jane Doe, Judge, U.S. --- Court	Dear Judge ---
Senators	The Honorable John/Jane Doe, U.S. Senate	Dear Mr./Ms. Senator ---
Representatives	The Honorable John/Jane Doe, U.S. Representative	Dear Mr./Ms.---
U.S. Ambassadors	The Honorable John/Jane Doe, The (Country) Ambassador	Dear Mr./Ms. ---
Foreign Ambassadors	His/Her Excellency John/Jane Doe, Ambassador of ---	Dear Mr./Ms. Ambassador ---

POSITION	ENVELOPE ADDRESS	SALUTATIONS
Kings/Queens	His/Her Royal Highness --- , King/Queen of ---	Your Royal Highness ---
Military Leaders Attention should be given to the actual rank.	General/Admiral John/Jane Doe	Dear General/ Admiral ---
Governors	The Honorable John/Jane Doe, Governor of ----	Dear Governor ---
Mayors	The Honorable John/Jane Doe, Mayor of ---	Dear Mayor ---
The Clergy		
Catholics		
The Pope	His Eminence the Pope ---	Your Holiness ---
Cardinals	His Eminence, John Cardinal Doe	Dear Your Eminence Cardinal ---
Episcopalians	The Rt. Rev. John Doe	Dear Bishop ---
Protestants	The Rev. John Doe	Dear Mr./Ms. ---
Eastern Orthodox		
Patriach	His Holiness, the Patriach ---	Your Holiness ---
Jewish	Rabbi John Doe	Dear Rabbi ---

Forms of addresses can vary to almost impossible proportions. For instance, if the head of some Protestant churches holds degrees, you are supposed to add the degrees after the name on the envelope. But who knows which degrees someone holds? If you are a real stickler for proper protocol, you will need to obtain one of the many excellent reference books on etiquette or consult your local reference librarians for assistance.

Times are less formal so if you are polite and spell names correctly, your letter should be favorably received.

THE DIRECTORY of ADDRESS LISTINGS

Aames, Willie *Actor*
%Light Co, 901 Bringham Ave, Los Angeles, CA 90049
Aaron, Henry *Baseball Player*
1611 Adams Dr SW, Atlanta, GA 30311
Aaron, Tommy *Golfer*
%Stouffer Pine Isle Resort, PO Drawer 545, Buford, GA 30518
Aas, Roald *Speed Skater*
Enebakkvn 252, 1187 Oslo 11, Norway
Aase, Don *Baseball Player*
5055 Via Ricardo, Yorba Linda, CA 92686
Abakanowicz, Magdalena *Artist*
Al Stanow Zjednoczonych 16m53, 03-947 Warsaw, Poland
Abbado, Claudio *Conductor*
Piazzetta Bossi 1, 20121 Milan, Italy
Abbe, Elfriede M *Artist*
Applewood, Manchester Center, VT 05255
Abbott, Diahnne *Actress*
460 W Ave 46, Los Angeles, CA 90065
Abbott, Edward L *Financier*
%CenTrust Savings Bank, 101 E Flagler St, Miami, FL 33131
Abbott, George *Playwright, Theater Producer*
10 Rockefeller Plz, New York, NY 10020
Abbott, James A *Businessman*
%Northwest Airlines, Minneapolis-St Paul Airport, St Paul, MN 55111
Abbott, Jim *Baseball Player*
%California Angels, Anaheim Stadium, Anaheim, CA 92806
Abbott, John *Actor*
6424 Ivarene Ave, Los Angeles, CA 90068
Abbott, Philip *Actor*
%Barry Freed Co, 9255 Sunset Blvd, #603, Los Angeles, CA 90069
Abbott, Preston S *Psychologist*
801 N Pitt St, Alexandria, VA 22314
Abboud, A Robert *Businessman*
%First City Bancorp of Texas, 1001 Fannin St, #400, Houston, TX 77002
Abboud, Joseph *Fashion Designer*
650 5th Ave, New York, NY 10019
Abdelsayed, Archpriest Gabriel *Religious Leader*
%Coptic Orthodox Church, 427 West Side Ave, Jersey City, NJ 07304
Abdnor, James *Senator, SD*
%Small Business Administration, 1441 "L" St NW, Washington, DC 20416
Abdul Ahad Mohmand *Cosmonaut*
141 160 Svyosdny Gorodok, Moskovskoi Oblasti, Potchta Kosmonavtov, Russia
Abdul Majid Hamerd *Financier*
%Rafidain Bank, New Banks' St, Massarif, Baghdad, Iraq
Abdul, Paula *Singer, Dancer*
14046 Aubrey Rd, Beverly Hills, CA 90210
Abdul-Jabbar, Kareem *Basketball Player, Actor*
1170 Stone Canyon Rd, Los Angeles, CA 90077
Abdullah *Prince, Jordan*
%Royal Palace, Ammam, Jordan
Abdullah Ibn Abdul Aziz *Crown Prince, Saudi Arabia*
%Council of Ministers, Jeddah, Saudi Arabia
Abe, Hideo *Businessman*
%Fuji Electric, 1-1 Tanabe-Shinden, Kawasakiki, Kawasaki 210, Japan
Abe, Kobo *Writer*
1-22-10 Wakabacho, Chofu City, Tokyo, Japan
Abe, Yazuru *Businessman*
%Nisshin Steel, 3-4-1 Marunouchi, Chiyodaku, Tokyo 100, Japan
Abegg, Martin G *Educator*
%Bradley University, President's Office, Peoria, IL 61625
Abel, Robert, Jr *Ophthalmologist*
1300 Harrison St, Wilmington, DE 19806
Abell, Murray R *Pathologist*
%American Pathology Board, 5401 W Kennedy Blvd, #112, Tampa, FL 33623
Abelson, Alan *Editor*
%Barron's Magazine, 200 Liberty St, New York, NY 10281

A

Abelson, Philip H *Physical Chemist*
4244 50th St NW, Washington, DC 20016

Abelson, Robert P *Psychiatrist*
827 Whitney Ave, New Haven, CT 06511

Abely, Joseph F, Jr *Businessman*
%Sea-Land Corp, 10 Parsonage Rd, Edison, NJ 08837

Aberastain, Jose M *Ballet Instructor*
%Southern Methodist University, Dance Division, Dallas, TX 75275

Aberconway of Bodnant, Baron *Businessman*
%English China Clays, John Keay House, Cornwall PL25 4DJ, England

Abercrombie, Neil *Representative, HI*
%House of Representatives, Washington, DC 20515

Abernathy, K Brooks *Businessman*
%Brunswick Corp, 1 Brunswick Plz, Skokie, IL 60077

Abernethy, Robert *Commentator*
%NBC-TV, 4001 Nebraska Ave NW, Washington, DC 20016

Abert, Donald B *Publisher*
%Milwaukee Journal, 333 W State St, Milwaukee, WI 53203

Ablon, Ralph E *Businessman*
%Ogden Corp, 277 Park Ave, New York, NY 10172

Ablon, Richard *Businessman*
%Ogden Corp, 277 Park Ave, New York, NY 10172

Abourezk, James G *Senator, SD*
1129 20th St NW, #500, Washington, DC 20036

Abraham, Edward P *Chemical Pathologist*
Badger's Wood, Bedwells Heath, Boars Hill, Oxford, England

Abraham, F Murray *Actor*
%STE Representation, 9301 Wilshire Blvd, #312, Beverly Hills, CA 90210

Abraham, Seth *Television Executive*
%Time Warner Sports, HBO, 1100 Ave of Americas, New York, NY 10036

Abrahams, Doris Cole *Theater Producer*
%Transart, 1501 Broadway, New York, NY 10036

Abrahamsen, Samuel *Educator*
%Brooklyn College, Judiac Studies Dept, Brooklyn, NY 11210

Abrahamson, James A *Air Force General, Businessman*
%Hughes Aircraft, 2000 El Segundo Blvd, El Segundo, CA 90245

Abram, John C *Businessman*
%Pacific Lighting Corp, 810 S Flower St, Los Angeles, CA 90060

Abram, Morris Berthold *Educator*
15 W 81st St, New York, NY 10024

Abramovitz, Max *Architect*
%Abramovitz Kingsland Schiff, 630 5th Ave, New York, NY 10111

Abramowitz, Morton *Diplomat*
%US Embassy, 110 Ataturk Blvd, Ankara, Turkey

Abrams, Martin B *Businessman*
%Mego Corp, 41 Madison Ave, New York, NY 10010

Abramson, Jerry *Mayor*
%Mayor's Office, City Hall, 601 W Jefferson St, Louisville, KY 40202

Abravanel, Maurice *Conductor*
%Utah Symphony, 123 W South Temple, Salt Lake City, UT 84101

Abroms, Edward M *Movie Director, Executive*
%EMA Enterprises, 1866 Marlowe St, Thousand Oaks, CA 91360

Abs, Hermann J *Financier*
Junghofstrasse 5-11, Frankfurt/Main, Germany

Abzug, Bella *Representative, NY*
76 Beaver St, New York, NY 10005

Acconci, Vito *Conceptual Artist*
%Sonnabend Gallery, 420 W Broadway, New York, NY 10013

Achebe, Chinua *Writer*
PO Box 53, Nsukka, Anambra State, Nigeria

Achica, George *Football Player*
%San Francisco 49ers, 4949 Centennial Blvd, Santa Clara, CA 95054

Acker, Joseph E, Jr *Cardiologist*
1928 Alcoa Hwy, Knoxville, TN 37920

Acker, Sharon *Actress*
%Fred Amsel Assoc, 6310 San Vicente Blvd, #407, Los Angeles, CA 90048

A

Ackerman, Bettye *Actress*
302 N Alpine Dr, Beverly Hills, CA 90210

Ackerman, Gary L *Representative, NY*
%House of Representatives, Washington, DC 20515

Ackerman, Helen Page *Librarian*
310 20th St, Santa Monica, CA 90402

Ackerman, Roger G *Businessman*
%Corning Inc, Houghton Park, Corning, NY 14831

Ackley, Gardner *Government Official, Educator*
907 Berkshire Rd, Ann Arbor, MI 48104

Ackman, Fred *Businessman*
%Superior Oil, First City National Bank Bldg, Houston, TX 77001

Ackroyd, David *Actor*
%Harry Gold Assoc, 3500 W Olive Ave, #1400, Burbank, CA 91505

Acton, Loren W *Astronaut*
%Lockheed Research Lab, 3251 Hanover St, Palo Alto, CA 94305

Acuff, Roy *Singer*
PO Box 4623, Nashville, TN 37216

Aczel, Janos D *Mathematician*
300 Regina St N, Ste 2-1908, Waterloo ON N2J 4H2, Canada

Ada, James *Governor, GU*
%Governor's Office, Government Offices, Agana, GU 96910

Adair, Paul N (Red) *Oil Well Firefighter*
8705 Katy Fwy, #302, Houston, TX 77024

Adam, Helen *Poet*
223 E 82nd St, New York, NY 10028

Adam, Ray C *Businessman*
%NL Industries, 1230 Ave of Americas, New York, NY 10020

Adamany, David W *Educator*
%Wayne State University, President's Office, Detroit, MI 48202

Adamek, Donna *Bowler*
%Ladies Professional Bowlers Assn, 7171 Cherryvale Blvd, Rockford, IL 61112

Adamle, Mike *Sportscaster*
%ABC-Sports, 1330 Ave of Americas, New York, NY 10019

Adams, Brock *Secretary, Transportation; Senator, WA*
1415 42nd Ave E, Seattle, WA 98102

Adams, Brooke *Actress*
975 Hancock Ave, #126, Los Angeles, CA 90069

Adams, Bryan *Singer*
406-68 Water St, Vancouver BC V6B 1A4, Canada

Adams, Charles F *Businessman*
%Raytheon Co, 141 Spring St, Lexington, MA 02173

Adams, Don *Actor*
%Ted Witzer Talent Agency, 6310 San Vicente Blvd, Los Angeles, CA 90048

Adams, Edie *Actress*
8040 Ocean Terr, Los Angeles, CA 90046

Adams, Greg *Hockey Player*
%Vancouver Canucks, 199 N Renfrew St, Vancouver BC V5K 3N7, Canada

Adams, James L *Theologian*
60 Francis Ave, Cambridge, MA 02138

Adams, Jimmie V *Air Force General*
CINCPACAF, Hickam Air Force Base, HI 96853

Adams, Joey *Actor*
160 W 46th St, New York, NY 10036

Adams, John *Composer*
1509 Holly St, Berkeley, CA 94703

Adams, John H *Religious Leader*
%African Methodist Church, Box 19039, Germantown Station, Philadelphia, PA 19138

Adams, Julie *Actress*
%Lew Sherrell Agency, 1354 Los Robles, Palm Springs, CA 92262

Adams, Julius *Football Player*
%New England Patriots, Sullivan Stadium, Foxboro, MA 02035

Adams, Laurence J *Businessman*
%Martin Marietta Corp, 6801 Rockledge Dr, Bethesda, MD 20817

Adams, Lucian *WW II Army Hero (CMH)*
4323 Valleyfield, San Antonio, TX 78222

A

Adams, Mason *Actor*
2006 Stradella Rd, Los Angeles, CA 90077

Adams, Maud *Actress*
9589 Stuart Ln, Beverly Hills, CA 90210

Adams, Michael *Basketball Player*
%Washington Bullets, Capital Centre, 1 Truman Dr, Landover, MD 20785

Adams, Noah *Commentator*
%National Public Radio, 2025 "M" St NW, Washington, DC 20006

Adams, Richard *Writer*
26 Church St, Whitechurch, Hants, England

Adams, Richard N *Anthropologist*
%University of Texas, Anthropology Dept, Austin, TX 78712

Adams, Robert *Sculptor*
Rangers Hall, Great Maplestead, Halstead, Essex, England

Adams, Robert M, Jr *Anthropologist*
5805 S Dorchester Ave, Chicago, IL 60637

Adams, Stanley *Lyricist*
3 Orchard Ln, Kings Point, NY 11024

Adams, Stanley T *Korean War Army Hero (CMH)*
9526 N Fairway Blvd, Sun Lake, AZ 85224

Adams, William C *Businessman*
%Federal-Mogul Corp, 26555 Northwestern Hwy, Southfield, MI 48034

Adams, William R *Historian*
PO Box 1987, St Augustine, FL 32084

Adams, William W *Businessman*
%Armstrong World Industries, West Liberty St, Lancaster, PA 17604

Adamson, James C *Astronaut*
%NASA, Johnson Space Ctr, Houston, TX 77058

Adamson, John W *Hematologist*
%University of Washington, Medical Dept, Seattle, WA 98195

Adcock, Joe *Baseball Player*
PO Box 385, Coushatta, LA 71019

Adderley, Herb *Football Player*
%Green Bay Packers, 1265 Lombardi Ave, Green Bay, WI 54303

Adderley, Terence E *Businessman*
%Kelly Services, 999 W Big Beaver Rd, Troy, MI 48084

Addis, Don *Cartoonist (Bent Offerings)*
%Creators Syndicate, 5777 W Century Blvd, #700, Los Angeles, CA 90067

Addison, Edward L *Businessman*
%Southern Co, 64 Perimeter Cir E, Atlanta, GA 30346

Addison, John *Composer*
1948 Pacific Dr, Pacific Palisades, CA 90272

Ade, King Sunny *Singer*
%Island Records, 444 Madison Ave, New York, NY 10022

Adel, Arthur *Physicist*
PO Box 942, Flagstaff, AZ 86002

Adelizzi, Robert F *Financier*
%Home Federal Savings & Loan, 707 Broadway, San Diego, CA 92101

Adelman, Irma G *Economist*
10 Rosemont Ave, Berkeley, CA 94708

Adelman, Kenneth L *Government Official*
%Arms Control & Disarmament Agency, State Department, Washington, DC 20451

Adelman, Rick *Basketball Coach*
%Portland Trail Blazers, 700 NE Multnomah St, Portland, OR 97232

Adelson, Mervyn L *Television Executive*
%Lorimar-Telepictures, 3970 Overland Ave, Culver City, CA 90232

Aders, Robert O *Businessman*
1750 "K" St NW, Washington, DC 20006

Adjani, Isabelle *Actress*
%Irene Murroni, 33 Rue Marbeuf, 75008 Paris, France

Adler, Freda S *Criminologist*
30 Waterside Plz, New York, NY 10010

Adler, Frederick R *Financier*
%Adler & Shaykin, 325 Park Ave, New York, NY 10022

Adler, Larry *Concert Mouth Organist*
%Michael Bakewell, 118 Tottenham Court Rd, London W1, England

Adler, Lou *Actor, Movie Director*
%Ode Sounds & Visuals, 3969 Villa Costera, Malibu, CA 90265
Adler, Louis Kootz *Businessman*
3680 Inwood Dr, Houston, TX 77019
Adler, Mortimer J *Writer, Educator*
1320 N State Pkwy, Chicago, IL 60610
Adler, Renata *Writer*
%International Famous Agency, 1301 Ave of Americas, New York, NY 10019
Adler, Richard *Composer, Lyricist*
8 E 83rd St, New York, NY 10028
Adler, Robert *Businessman*
%United Sciences of America, Dallas, TX 75248
Adler, Stella *Actress, Director*
%Stella Adler Theater, 1653 N Argyle Ave, Los Angeles, CA 90028
Adolfo *Fashion Designer*
%Adolfo Inc, 36 E 57th St, New York, NY 10022
Adrian, Iris *Actress*
3341 Floyd Terr, Los Angeles, CA 90068
Adriani, John *Physician*
67 N Park Pl, New Orleans, LA 70124
Afanasyev, Viktor *Cosmonaut*
141 160 Svyosdny Gorodok, Moskovskoi Oblasti, Potchta Kosmonavtov, Russia
Affleck, James G *Businessman*
%American Cyanamid Co, 1 Cyanamid Plz, Wayne, NJ 07470
Africk, Jack *Businessman*
%United States Tobacco Co, 100 W Putnam Ave, Greenwich, CT 06830
Aga Khan IV, Prince Karim *Spiritual Leader*
Aiglemont, 60270 Gouvieux, France
Agajanian, Ben *Football Player*
3940 E Broadway, Long Beach, CA 90803
Agam, Yaacov *Artist*
26 Rue Boulard, Paris, France
Agar, John *Actor*
639 N Hollywood Way, Burbank, CA 91505
Agase, Alex *Football Player, Coach*
1837 Roosevelt St, Ypsilanti, MI 48197
Agassi, Andre *Tennis Player*
%International Management Grp, 1 Erieview Plz, Cleveland, OH 44114
Agee, William M *Businessman*
%Morrison Knudsen Corp, Morrison Knudsen Plz, Boise, ID 83707
Aghayan, Ray *Costume Designer*
706 N Linden Dr, Beverly Hills, CA 90210
Agnelli, Giovanni *Businessman*
%Fiat SpA, Corso G Marconi 10/20, 10125 Turin, Italy
Agnelli, Umberto *Businessman*
%Fiat SpA, Corson G Marconi 10/20, 10125 Turin, Italy
Agnew, Harold M *Physicist*
322 Punta Baja, Solana Beach, CA 92075
Agnew, James K *Businessman*
%McCann Erikson Inc, 495 Lexington Ave, New York, NY 10017
Agnew, Ray *Football Player*
%New England Patriots, Sullivan Stadium, Foxboro, MA 02035
Agnew, Rudolph I J *Businessman*
%Consolidated Gold Fields, 49 Moongate, London EC2R 6BQ, England
Agnew, Spiro T *Vice President*
78 Columbia Dr, Rancho Mirage, CA 92270
Agria, John J *Educator*
%University of Dubuque, President's Office, Dubuque, IA 52001
Agt, Andries A M Van *Prime Minister, Netherlands*
Joanneslaan 10, Nijmegen, Netherlands
Aguirre y Gonzalo, Jose Maria *Financier*
%Banco Espanol de Credito, Paseo de la Castellana 7, Madrid 1, Spain
Aguirre, Hank *Baseball Player*
31101 Sunset Dr, Franklin, MI 48205
Aguirre, Mark *Basketball Player*
%Detroit Pistons, Palace, 1 Championship Dr, Auburn Hills, MI 48057

Ahlfors, Lars V *Mathematician*
160 Commonwealth Ave, Boston, MA 02116

Ahmanson, William H *Financier*
%H F Ahmanson Co, 3731 Wilshire Blvd, Los Angeles, CA 90010

Ahmed Fares, Muhammad *Cosmonaut, Syria*
141 160 Svyosdny Gorodok, Moskovskoi Oblasti, Potchta Kosmonavtov, Russia

Aho, Lauri *Publisher*
Kaartintorpantie 6-A, Helsinki, Finland

Aidman, Charles *Actor*
525 N Palm Dr, Beverly Hills, CA 90210

Aiello, Danny *Actor*
%Artists Agency, 10000 Santa Monica Blvd, #305, Los Angeles, CA 90067

Aiken, Joan *Writer*
The Hermitage, Petworth, West Sussex GU28 OAB, England

Aikman, Troy *Football Player*
%Dallas Cowboys, 1 Cowboys Pkwy, Irving, TX 75063

Ailes, Roger E *Publisher*
%Ailes Communications, 440 Park Ave S, New York, NY 10016

Ailes, Stephen *Government Official*
4521 Wetherill Rd, Bethesda, MD 20816

Aimee, Anouk *Actress*
%Artmedia, 10 Ave George V, 75008 Paris, France

Ainge, Danny *Basketball Player*
%Portland Trail Blazers, 700 NE Multnomah St, Portland, OR 97232

Ainsleigh, H Gordon *Distance Runner*
17119 Placer Hills Rd, Meadow Vista, CA 95722

Ainsworth-Land, George T *Philosopher*
230 North St, Buffalo, NY 14201

Aishwarya Rajya Laxmi Devi Rana *Queen, Nepal*
%Narayanhity Royal Palace, Kathmandu, Nepal

Aitay, Victor *Concert Violinist*
212 Oak Knoll Terr, Highland Park, IL 60035

Aitken, Webster *Concert Pianist*
128 Christopher St, New York, NY 10014

Akaka, Daniel K *Senator, HI*
%US Senate, Washington, DC 20510

Akama, Yoshihiro *Financier*
%Mitsubishi Trust & Banking, 4-5 Marunouchi, Tokyo 100, Japan

Akashi, Toshio *Financier*
%Sanwa Bank, 4-10 Fushimimachi, Higashiku, Osaka 541, Japan

Akbar, Taufik *Astronaut, Indonesia*
Jalan Sukasenang V/48, Bandung 40124, Indonesia

Akers, Fred *Football Coach*
%Purdue University, Athletic Dept, West Lafayette, IN 47907

Akers, John F *Businessman*
%International Business Machines Corp, Old Orchard Rd, Armonk, NY 10504

Akers, Thomas D *Astronaut*
%NASA, Johnson Space Ctr, Houston, TX 77058

Akhmadulina, Bella *Poet*
%Union of Writers, Ul Vorovskogo 20, Moscow G-69, Russia

Akihito *Emperor, Japan*
%Imperial Palace, Tokyo, Japan

Akins, Claude *Actor*
%William Morris Agency, 151 El Camino, Beverly Hills, CA 90212

Akins, James E *Diplomat*
2904 Garfield Terr, Washington, DC 20008

Akita, Masaya *Businessman*
%Daido Steel, 11-18 Nishiki, Nakaku, Nagoya 460, Japan

Akiyama, Kazuyoshi *Conductor*
%Vancouver Symphony, 400 E Broadway, Vancouver BC V5T 1X2, Canada

Akiyoshi, Toshiko *Jazz Pianist, Conductor*
38 W 94th St, New York, NY 10025

Aksenov, Vladimir *Cosmonaut*
141 160 Svyosdny Gorodok, Moskovskoi Oblasti, Potchta Kosmonavtov, Russia

Aksyonov, Vassili P *Writer*
4434 Lingan Rd NW, Washington, DC 20007

Al-Tuckmachi, Tariq *Financier*
%Rafidain Bank, New Banks' St, Massarif, Baghdad, Iraq

Aladjem, Silvio *Obstetrician, Gynecologist*
2160 S 1st St, Maywood, IL 60153

Alan, Buddy *Singer*
1225 N Chester Ave, Bakersfield, CA 93308

Alarcon, Arthur L *Judge*
%US Court of Appeals, 312 N Spring St, Los Angeles, CA 90012

Albanese, Licia *Opera Singer*
800 Park Ave, New York, NY 10021

Albani, Thomas J *Businessman*
%Allegheny International, 2 Oliver Plz, Pittsburgh, PA 15230

Albeck, Stan *Basketball Coach*
%Bradley University, Athletic Dept, Peoria, IL 61625

Albee, Arden L *Geologist*
2040 Midlothian Dr, Altadena, CA 91001

Albee, Edward *Writer*
14 Harrison St, New York, NY 10013

Alberghetti, Anna Maria *Actress, Singer*
2337 Benedict Canyon Dr, Beverly Hills, CA 90210

Albers, Hans *Businessman*
%BASF AG, Carl-Bosch-Strasse 38, 6700 Ludwigshafen, Germany

Albert *Prince, Monaco*
%Palais de Monaco, 98015 Monte Carlo 518, Monaco

Albert, Carl B *Representative, OK; Speaker*
827 E Osage, McAlester, OK 74501

Albert, Eddie *Actor*
719 Amalfi Dr, Pacific Palisades, CA 90272

Albert, Edward *Actor*
27320 Winding Way, Malibu, CA 90265

Albert, Frankie *Football Player*
1 Stanford Dr, Rancho Mirage, CA 92270

Albert, Marv *Sportscaster*
%NBC-Sports, 30 Rockefeller Plz, New York, NY 10112

Alberthal, Lester M, Jr *Businessman*
%Electronic Data Systems Corp, 7171 Forest Ln, Dallas, TX 75230

Albertson, Joseph A *Businessman*
%Albertson's Inc, 250 Parkcenter Blvd, Boise, ID 83726

Alberty, Robert Arnold *Chemist*
7 Old Dee Rd, Cambridge, MA 02138

Albrecht, Gerd *Conductor*
%Mariedi Anders Mgmt, 535 El Camino Del Mar, San Francisco, CA 94121

Albrecht, Ronald F *Anesthesiologist*
28 Salem Ln, Evanston, IL 60203

Albright, David B *Financier*
%TransOhio Financial Corp, 1 Penton Plz, Cleveland, OH 44114

Albright, Harry W, Jr *Financier*
%Dime Savings Bank, 589 5th Ave, New York, NY 10017

Albright, Jack L *Animal Scientist*
188 Blueberry Ln, West Lafayette, IN 47906

Albright, Lola *Actress*
235 N Valley, #136, Burbank, CA 91505

Albright, Malvin Marr (Zsissly) *Artist*
1500 N Lake Shore Dr, Chicago, IL 60610

Albright, Tenley *Figure Skater*
Carlton House, 2 Commonwealth Ave, Boston, MA 02117

Albritton, Dave *Track Athlete*
3115 Salem Ave, Dayton, OH 45406

Albuquerque, Lita *Artist*
305 Boyd St, Los Angeles, CA 90013

Alcott, Amy *Golfer*
%Little Women Enterprises, PO Box 956, Pacific Palisades, CA 90272

Alda, Alan *Actor*
%Martin Bregman Productions, 641 Lexington Ave, #1400, New York, NY 10022

Alden, Ginger *Model, Actress*
4152 Royal Crest Pl, Memphis, TN 38138

Alden, Norman *Actor*
%Irv Schechter Co, 9300 Wilshire Blvd, #410, Beverly Hills, CA 90212

Alden, Raymond M *Businessman*
%United Telecommunications, 2330 Johnson Dr, Westwood, KS 66205

Alder, Berni J *Theoretical Physicist*
%Lawrence Radiation Laboratory, PO Box 808, Livermore, CA 94550

Alderman, Darrell *Drag Racing Driver*
%D A Construction Co, 8145 Flemingsburg Rd, Morehead, KY 40351

Aldisert, Ruggero J *Judge*
6144 Calle Real, Santa Barbara, CA 93117

Aldiss, Brian W *Writer*
Woodlands, Foxcombe Rd, Boars Hill, Oxford OX1 5DL, England

Aldredge, Theoni V *Costume Designer*
425 Lafayette St, New York, NY 10003

Aldrich, Bailey *Judge*
%McCormack Post Office-Courthouse, Boston, MA 02109

Aldrich, Hulbert Stratton *Financier*
1088 Park Ave, New York, NY 10028

Aldridge, Robert A *Businessman*
%Kobrand Corp, 134 E 40th St, New York, NY 10016

Aldrin, Edwin E (Buzz), Jr *Astronaut*
%Starcraft Enterprises, 233 Emerald Bay, Laguna Beach, CA 92651

Alechinsky, Pierre *Artist*
2 Bis Rue Henri Barbusse, 78380 Bougival, France

Aleksandrov, Anatoly *Physicist*
%Kurchatov Atomic Energy Institute, Ul Korchatova 46, Moscow, Russia

Aletter, Frank *Actor*
5430 Corbin Ave, Tarzana, CA 91356

Alexander, Clifford L, Jr *Government Official*
%Alexander Assoc, 400 "C" St NE, Washington, DC 20002

Alexander, Denise *Actress*
%Knofsky, 7967 W 4th St, Los Angeles, CA 90048

Alexander, Donald C *Government Official*
2801 New Mexico Ave NW, Washington, DC 20007

Alexander, J David, Jr *Educator*
%Pomona College, President's Office, Claremont, CA 91711

Alexander, Jane *Actress*
Gordon Rd, RR 2, Carmel, NY 10512

Alexander, Jason *Actor*
329 N Weatherly Dr, #101, Beverly Hills, CA 90211

Alexander, John *Artist*
PO Box 600, Amagansett, NY 11930

Alexander, Karen *Model*
%Pauline's Model Agency, 444 Madison Ave, New York, NY 10022

Alexander, Kenneth *Editorial Cartoonist*
1182 Glen Rd, Lafayette, CA 94549

Alexander, Lamar *Secretary, Education; Governor, TN*
%Department of Education, 400 Maryland Ave SW, Washington, DC 20202

Alexander, Norman E *Businessman*
%Sun Chemical Corp, 200 Park Ave, New York, NY 10166

Alexander, Peter *Artist*
9 1/2 Wavecrest Ave, Venice CA 90291

Alexander, R B *Publisher*
%Business Week Magazine, 1221 Ave of Americas, New York, NY 10020

Alexander, Robert M *Air Force General*
Director of Plans, Hq USAF, Washington, DC 20330

Alexander, Shana *Journalist*
%CBS-TV, 524 W 57th St, New York, NY 10019

Alexander, William V, Jr *Representative, AR*
811 W Hale Ave, Osceola, AR 72370

Alexandroff, Mirron *Educator*
%Columbia College, President's Office, Chicago, IL 60605

Alexandrov, Alexander *Cosmonaut, Bulgaria*
Omourtag, Northern Bulgaria, Bulgaria

Alexis, Kim *Model*
%Elite Model Mgmt, 111 E 22nd St, New York, NY 10010

Alfieri, Janet *Cartoonist (Suburban Cowgirls)*
%Tribune Media Services, 64 E Concord St, Orlando, FL 32801
Alfonso, Kristian *Actress*
%Milton B Suchin Co, 201 N Robertson Blvd, #A, Beverly Hills, CA 90211
Alfonzo Ravard, Rafael *Businessman*
%Petroleos de Venezuela, Edif Petroleos de Venezuela, Caracas, Venezuela
Alford, William *Writer*
31 Athens St, Cambridge, MA 02138
Alfven, Hannes O G *Nobel Physics Laureate*
%University of California, Engineering Dept, La Jolla, CA 92093
Ali Haider Khan Bangash *WW II Pakistani Army Hero (VC)*
PO Hangu, Tehsil Hangu, Distt Kohat Mohallah, Khan Bari, Pakistan
Ali Samatar, Mohammed *General, Prime Minister, Somalia*
%Prime Minister's Office, Mogadishu, Somalia
Ali, Muhammad *Boxer*
PO Box 187, Berrien Springs, MI 49103
Alia, Ramiz *President, Albania*
%President's Office, Tirana, Albania
Aliber, James A *Financier*
%First Federal of Michigan, 1001 Woodward Ave, Detroit, MI 48226
Alibrandi, Joseph F *Businessman*
%Whittaker Corp, 10880 Wilshire Blvd, Los Angeles, CA 90024
Alioto, Joseph L *Mayor, Attorney*
111 Sutter St, #2100, San Francisco, CA 94104
Alito, Samuel A, Jr *Judge*
%US Court of Appeals, US Courthouse, PO Box 999, Newark, NJ 07101
Aliyev, Geidar A *Government Official, Russia*
%Moscow City Committee, 6 Staraya Ploschchad, Moscow, Russia
Allain, William A *Governor, MS*
401 Capitol St, Jackson, MS 39201
Allaire, Paul A *Businessman*
%Xerox Corp, PO Box 1600, Stamford, CT 06904
Allais, Maurice *Nobel Economics Laureate*
15 Rue des Gate-Ceps, 92210 Saint Cloud, France
Allam, Mark Whittier *Veterinarian*
211 E 5th St, Media, PA 19063
Allan, J D *Businessman*
%Stelco, Toronto-Dominion Ctr, Toronto ON M5K 1J4, Canada
Allan, Jed *Actor*
4965 Medina Dr, Woodland Hills, CA 91364
Allan, William *Artist*
327 Melrose, Mill Valley, CA 94941
Allard, Linda *Fashion Designer*
%Ellen Tracy Blouse Corp, 575 7th Ave, New York, NY 10018
Allard, Wayne *Representative, CO*
%House of Representatives, Washington, DC 20515
Allen, Andrew M *Astronaut*
%NASA, Johnson Space Ctr, Houston, TX 77058
Allen, Betty *Classical, Opera Singer*
645 St Nicholas Ave, New York, NY 10030
Allen, Bill *Bowler*
%Professional Bowlers Assn, 1720 Merriman Rd, Akron, OH 44313
Allen, Chad *Actor*
%Savage Agency, 6212 Banner Ave, Los Angeles, CA 90038
Allen, Charles R *Businessman*
%TRW Inc, 1900 Richmond Rd, Cleveland, OH 44124
Allen, Corey *Actor*
8642 Hollywood Blvd, Los Angeles, CA 90046
Allen, Darryl F *Businessman*
%Libbey-Owens-Ford Co, 811 Madison Ave, Toledo, OH 43695
Allen, Debbie *Singer, Songwriter, Dancer*
%Raymond Katz Enterprises, 9255 Sunset Blvd, Los Angeles, CA 90069
Allen, Duane *Singer (Oak Ridge Boys)*
%Oak Ridge Boys, 329 Rockland Rd, Hendersonville, TN 37075
Allen, Ethan *Baseball Player*
Stratford Hill Apartments, #40-C, Chapel Hill, NC 27514

Allen, Fred T *Businessman*
%Pitney Bowes, Walter H Wheeler Jr Dr, Stamford, CT 06904

Allen, George, Jr *Representative, VA*
%House of Representatives, Washington, DC 20515

Allen, Gordon E *Businessman*
%Cluett Peabody Co, 510 5th Ave, New York, NY 10036

Allen, Herbert, Sr *Investor, Businessman*
%Allen & Co, 711 5th Ave, 9th Floor, New York, NY 10022

Allen, Howard P *Businessman*
%Southern California Edison, 2244 Walnut Grove Ave, Rosemead, CA 91770

Allen, Ivan, Jr *Businessman*
3700 Northside Dr, Atlanta, GA 30305

Allen, Joan *Actress*
%International Creative Mgmt, 8899 Beverly Blvd, Los Angeles, CA 90048

Allen, Joseph P *Astronaut*
%Space Industries Int'l, 711 W Bay Area Blvd, #320, Webster, TX 77598

Allen, Karen *Actress*
122 E 10th St, New York, NY 10013

Allen, Lew *Research Scientist*
%Jet Propulsion Labs, 4800 Oak Grove Dr, Pasadena, CA 91109

Allen, Marcus *Football Player*
%Los Angeles Raiders, 332 Center St, El Segundo, CA 90245

Allen, Martin *Businessman*
%Computervision Corp, 15 Crosby Dr, Bedford, MA 01730

Allen, Marty *Comedian, Promoter*
5750 Wilshire Blvd, #580, Los Angeles, CA 90036

Allen, Maryon P *Senator, AL*
3215 Cliff Rd, Birmingham, AL 35205

Allen, Mel *Sportscaster*
%Major League Baseball Productions, 1212 Ave of Americas, New York, NY 10036

Allen, Nancy *Actress*
%Agency for Performing Arts, 9000 Sunset Blvd, #1200, Los Angeles, CA 90069

Allen, Peter *Singer, Songwriter*
652 Neptune Ave, Encinitas, CA 92024

Allen, Phillip Richard *Actor*
%Gersh Agency, 232 N Canon Dr, Beverly Hills, CA 90210

Allen, Raymond B *Educator*
14136 Wadsworth Ct, Annandale, VA 22003

Allen, Rex *Actor*
PO Box 430, Sonoita, AZ 85637

Allen, Richard V *Government Official*
905 16th St NW, Washington, DC 20006

Allen, Richie *Baseball Player*
PO Box 204, Sellersville, PA 18960

Allen, Robert E *Businessman*
%American Telephone & Telegraph, 550 Madison Ave, New York, NY 10022

Allen, Robert G *Real Estate Investor, Writer*
%Allen Grp, 145 S Center St, Provo, UT 84601

Allen, Ron W *Businessman*
%Delta Air Lines, Hartsfield International Airport, Atlanta, GA 30320

Allen, Sian Barbara *Actress*
1622 Sierra Bonita Ave, Los Angeles, CA 90046

Allen, Steve *Comedian, Writer*
15201 Burbank Blvd, #B, Van Nuys, CA 91411

Allen, Thomas *Opera Singer*
%John Coast Ltd, 1 Park Close, Knightsbridge, London SW1X 7PQ, England

Allen, Tim *Actor*
%Messina & Baker, 8961 Sunset Blvd, #C, Los Angeles, CA 90069

Allen, Wayne *Businessman*
%Phillips Petroleum, Phillips Bldg, Bartlesville, OK 74044

Allen, Willard M *Physician*
14180 Burntwoods Rd, Glenwood, MD 21738

Allen, William R, Jr *Businessman*
%Union Equity Co-operative Exchange, 2300 N 10th St, Enid, OK 73702

Allen, Woody *Actor, Comedian, Director*
%Rollins/Joffre Mgmt, 130 W 57th St, New York, NY 10019

Allende, Fernando *Actor*
%Yvette Bikoff Agency, 8721 Santa Monica Blvd, #21, West Hollywood, CA 90067

Aller, Lawrence H *Astronomer*
18118 W Kingsport Dr, Malibu, CA 90265

Allers, Franz *Conductor*
%Columbia Artists Mgmt Inc, 165 W 57th St, New York, NY 10019

Alley, Gene *Baseball Player*
10236 Steuben Dr, Glen Allen, VA 23060

Alley, Kirstie *Actress*
Barrett Benson McCartt Weston, 9320 Wilshire Blvd, #301, Beverly Hills, CA 90212

Alley, William J *Businessman*
%American Brands Inc, 245 Park Ave, New York, NY 10167

Allfrey, Vincent G *Biochemist*
24 Winthrop Ct, Tenafly, NJ 07670

Allison, Bobby *Auto Racing Driver*
140 Church St, Hueytown, AL 35023

Allison, Davey *Auto Racing Driver*
%NASCAR, 1801 Speedway Blvd, Daytona Beach, FL 32015

Allison, Glenn *Bowler*
%Professional Bowlers Assn, 1720 Merriman Rd, Akron, OH 44313

Allison, Mose *Jazz Pianist, Composer*
34 Dogwood Dr, Smithtown, NY 11787

Allison, Stacy *Mountaineer*
7431 N Foss, Portland, OR 97203

Allison, Wick *Publisher*
%National Review Magazine, 150 E 35th St, New York, NY 10016

Alliss, Peter *Sportscaster*
%Mark McCormack, 1 Erieview Plz, #1300, Cleveland, OH 44144

Allman, Greg *Singer, Songwriter*
PO Box 4332, Marietta, GA 30061

Allott, Gordon L *Senator, CO*
3427 S Race St, Englewood, CO 80110

Allport, Christopher *Actor*
%Susan Smith Assoc, 121 N San Vicente Blvd, Beverly Hills, CA 90211

Allport, Denis Ivor *Businessman*
%Metal Box, Queens House, Forbury Rd, Reading RG1 3JH, England

Allred, Gloria R *Attorney*
6380 Wilshire Blvd, #1404, Los Angeles, CA 90048

Allumbaugh, Byron *Businessman*
%Ralphs Grocery Co, PO Box 54143, Los Angeles, CA 90054

Allyson, June *Actress*
1651 Foothill Rd, Ojai, CA 93023

Almeida, Laurindo *Jazz Guitarist, Composer*
4104 Witzel Dr, Sherman Oaks, CA 91423

Almen, Lowell G *Religious Leader*
%Evangelical Lutheran Church, 8765 W Higgins Rd, Chicago, IL 60631

Almendros, Nestor *Cinematographer*
%Smith/Gosnell/Nicholson, 1515 Palisades Dr, #N, Pacific Palisades, CA 90272

Almodovar, Pedro *Movie Director*
%Official Body of Spanish Cinema, San Mateo 4, Madrid 28004, Spain

Alonso, Alicia *Ballerina*
%Cuban National Ballet, Havana, Cuba

Alonso, Maria Conchita *Actress*
PO Box 537, Beverly Hills, CA 90213

Alonzo, John *Cinematographer*
310 Avondale Ave, Los Angeles, CA 90049

Alpert, Herb *Musician*
31930 Pacific Coast Hwy, Malibu, CA 90265

Alpert, Hollis *Writer*
PO Box 142, Shelter Island, NY 11964

Alsop, Robert C *Businessman*
%Stanhome Inc, 333 Western Ave, Westfield, MA 01085

Alston, James O *Businessman*
%Jim Walter Corp, 1500 N Dale Mabry Hwy, Tampa, FL 33607

Alt, Carol *Model*
%Elite Model Mgmt, 111 E 22nd St, New York, NY 10010

A

Alter, Hobie *Surfboard, Boat Designer*
PO Box 1008, Oceanside, CA 92054

Altimari, Frank X *Judge*
%US Court of Appeals, Uniondale Ave & Hempstead Trnpk, Uniondale, NY 11533

Altman, Sidney *Nobel Chemistry Laureate*
%Yale University, Chemistry Dept, New Haven, CT 06520

Altman, Steven *Educator*
%University of Central Florida, President's Office, Orlando, FL 32816

Altman, Stuart H *Educator*
%Brandeis University, President's Office, Waltham, MA 02554

Altmeyer, Jeannine *Opera Singer*
%Metropolitan Opera Assn, Lincon Center Plz, New York, NY 10023

Alvarado, Natividad (Naty) *Handball Player*
%Equitable of Iowa, 2700 N Main, Santa Ana, CA 92701

Alvary, Lorenzo *Opera Singer*
20 Ocean Lane Dr, Key Biscayne, FL 33149

Alvine, Robert *Businessman*
%Uniroyal Inc, World Headquarters, Middlebury, CT 06749

Alworth, Lance *Football Player*
%Del Mar Corporate Ctr, 990 Highland Dr, #300, Solana Beach, CA 92075

Alyn, Kirk *Actor*
PO Box 200, Sun City, CA 92381

Alzado, Lyle *Football Player, Actor*
%Irv Schecter Co, 9300 Wilshire Blvd, #410, Beverly Hills, CA 90212

Amador, Jorge *Writer*
Rua Alagoinhas 33, Rio Vermelho-Salvador, Bahia, Brazil

Amanpour, Christiane *News Correspondent*
%Cable News Network, 1 CNN Center, PO Box 105366, Atlanta, GA 30348

Amara, Lucine *Opera Singer*
260 West End Ave, New York, NY 10023

Amateau, Rodney *Movie Director*
133 1/2 S Linden Dr, Beverly Hills, CA 90212

Amaya, Armando *Sculptor*
Lopex 137, Depto 1, Mexico City 06070 CP, Mexico

Ambasz, Emilio *Architect*
632 Broadway, New York, NY 10012

Ambler, Eric *Writer*
%Campbell Thomson McLaughlin, 31 Newington Green, London N16 9PU, England

Ambler, J D *Businessman*
%Texaco Ltd, 1 Knightsbridge Green, London SW1X 7QJ, England

Amdahl, Gene M *Businessman, Computer Engineer*
15250 Peach Hill Rd, Saratoga, CA 95070

Ameche, Don *Actor*
633 Ocean Ave, Santa Monica, CA 90402

Ameling, Elly *Classical Singer*
%Sheldon Soffer Mgmt, 130 W 56th St, New York, NY 10019

Amelio, Gilbert F *Businessman*
%National Semiconductor Corp, 7900 Semiconductor Dr, Santa Clara, CA 95052

Amerman, John W *Businessman*
%Mattel USA, 5150 Rosecrans Ave, Hawthorne, CA 90250

Ames, Bernard N *Businessman*
%Kidde Inc, Park 80 W, Plaza 2, Saddle Brook, NJ 07662

Ames, Bruce N *Biochemist*
1324 Spruce St, Berkeley, CA 94709

Ames, Ed *Actor, Singer*
1457 Claridge Dr, Beverly Hills, CA 90210

Ames, Frank Anthony *Concert Percussionist*
%National Symphony Orchestra, Kennedy Ctr, Washington, DC 20566

Ames, Leon *Actor*
23388 Mulholland Dr, Woodland Hills, CA 91364

Ames, Louise Bates *Child Psychologist*
283 Edwards St, New Haven, CT 06511

Amies, Hardy *Fashion Designer*
14 Savile Row, London SW1, England

Amis, Kingsley *Writer*
%Jonathan Clowes Co, 19 Jeffrey's Pl, London NW1, England

Amis, Suzy *Actress, Model*
%InterTalent Agency, 131 S Rodeo Dr, #300, Beverly Hills, CA 90212

Amling, Warren E *Football Player*
%General Delivery, London, OH 43140

Ammaccapane, Danielle *Golfer*
%Ladies Professional Golf Assn, 2570 Volusia Ave, #B, Daytona Beach, FL 32114

Ammerman, Craig L *Publisher*
%Philadelphia Bulletin, 30th & Market, Philadelphia, PA 19101

Ammons, A R *Poet*
606 Hanshaw Rd, Ithaca, NY 14850

Amory, Cleveland *Writer*
%Fund for the Animals, 200 W 57th St, New York, NY 10019

Amos, John B *Businessman*
%American Family Corp, 1932 Wynnton Rd, Columbus, GA 31906

Amos, Paul S *Businessman*
%American Family Corp, 1932 Wynnton Rd, Columbus, GA 31906

Amos, Wally (Famous) *Businessman*
PO Box 897, Kailua, HI 96734

Amran, David Werner, III *Composer, Conductor*
461 6th Ave, New York, NY 10011

Amsterdam, Gustave G *Financier*
%Bankers' Securities Corp, 1401 Walnut St, Philadelphia, PA 19131

Amsterdam, Morey *Comedian*
1012 N Hillcrest Rd, Beverly Hills, CA 90210

Ana-Alicia *Actress*
%Century Artists, 9744 Wilshire Blvd, #308, Beverly Hills, CA 90212

Anagnostopoulos, Constantine E *Heart Surgeon*
1555 N Astor St, Chicago, IL 60610

Anaya, Toney *Governor, NM*
%MALDEF, 634 S Spring, Los Angeles, CA 90014

Anderegg, Karen *Businesswoman, Editor*
%Clinique Laboratories Inc, 767 5th Ave, New York, NY 10022

Anders, William A *Astronaut, Businessman*
%General Dynamics Corp, Pierre Laclede Ctr, St Louis, MO 63105

Andersen Watts, Teresa *Sychronized Swimmer*
2582 Marsha Way, San Jose, CA 95125

Andersen, Adel Edward *Farm Coalition Executive*
1700 Crescent Ln, McLean, VA 22101

Andersen, Anthony L *Businessman*
%H B Fuller Co, 2400 Energy Park Dr, St Paul, MN 55108

Andersen, Elmer L *Governor, MN; Businessman*
1483 Bussard Ct, Arden Hills, MN 55112

Andersen, Greta *Channel Swimmer*
3561 Farquhar Ave, Los Alamitos, CA 90720

Andersen, Hjalmar *Speed Skater*
%Velferden for Handelsflaten, Trondheimsvn 2, 0560 Oslo 5, Norway

Andersen, Ib *Ballet Dancer*
%New York City Ballet, Lincoln Ctr, New York, NY 10023

Andersen, John *Publisher*
%Chicago Sun-Times, 401 N Wabash, Chicago, IL 60611

Andersen, Ladell *Basketball Coach*
%Brigham Young University, Athletic Dept, Provo, UT 84602

Andersen, Mogens *Artist*
Strandagervej 28, 2900 Hellerup, Copenhagen, Denmark

Andersen, Morton *Football Player*
%New Orleans Saints, 6928 Saints Dr, Metairie, LA 70003

Andersen, Reidar *Ski Jumper*
%National Ski Hall of Fame, PO Box 191, Ishpeming, MI 49849

Andersin, Hans *Businessman*
%Valmet Corp, Punanotkonkatu 2, PL 155, 99131 Helsinki 13, Finland

Anderson, A Chris *Financier*
%Drexel Burham Lambert Inc, 60 Broad St, New York, NY 10004

Anderson, Arnold S *Businessman*
%Woolworth Corp, 233 Broadway, New York, NY 10279

Anderson, Barbara *Actress*
10140 Angelo Cir, Beverly Hills, CA 90210

Anderson, Beaufort T — *WW II Army Hero (CMH)*
22105 Ranchitis Dr, Salinas, CA 93908

Anderson, Bill — *Singer*
1114 17th Ave S, #203, Nashville, TN 37212

Anderson, Brad — *Cartoonist (Marmaduke)*
422 Santa Marina Ct, Escondido, CA 92025

Anderson, C Elmer — *Governor, MN*
624 N 3rd St, Brainerd, MN 56401

Anderson, Daryl — *Actor*
5923 Wilbur Ave, Tarzana, CA 91356

Anderson, David E — *Businessman*
%General Telephone Co, 100 Wilshire Blvd, Santa Monica, CA 90146

Anderson, Duwayne M — *Polar Scientist*
188 Koster Row, Amherst, NY 14226

Anderson, Eric — *Singer, Songwriter*
%Vanguard Recording Society, 71 W 23rd St, New York, NY 10010

Anderson, Forrest H — *Governor, MT*
1712 Jerome Pl, Helena, MT 59601

Anderson, Gary — *Football Player*
%San Diego Chargers, 9449 Friars Rd, San Diego, CA 92108

Anderson, Gary — *Marksman*
%National Rifle Assn, 1600 Rhode Island NW, Washington, DC 20036

Anderson, Glenn — *Hockey Player*
%Toronto Maple Leafs, 60 Carleton St, Toronto ON M5B 1L1, Canada

Anderson, Glenn M — *Representative, CA*
%House of Representatives, Washington, DC 20515

Anderson, Gordon M — *Businessman*
%Santa Fe International Corp, PO Box 4000, Alhambra, CA 91802

Anderson, Greg — *Basketball Player*
%Denver Nuggets, McNicholas Arena, 1635 Clay St, Denver, CO 80204

Anderson, Harry — *Comedian, Actor*
%Creative Artists Agency, 9830 Wilshire Blvd, Beverly Hills, CA 90212

Anderson, Harry W — *Businessman*
%Saga Corp, 1 Saga Ln, Menlo Park, CA 95025

Anderson, Ian — *Musician*
%Chrysalis Records, 9255 Sunset Blvd, Los Angeles, CA 90069

Anderson, Jack — *Columnist*
1531 "P" St NW, Washington, DC 20005

Anderson, James F — *Religious Leader*
1420 W Long Lake Rd, Bloomfield Hills, MI 48013

Anderson, James K — *Financier*
%Pacific First Federal Savings Bank, 11th & Pacific, Tacoma, WA 98401

Anderson, John — *Actor*
%Agency for Performing Arts, 9000 Sunset Blvd, #1200, Los Angeles, CA 90069

Anderson, John — *Football Player*
%Green Bay Packers, 1265 Lombardi Ave, Green Bay, WI 54303

Anderson, John B — *Representative, Presidential Candidate*
3917 Massachusetts Ave NW, Washington, DC 20016

Anderson, John E — *Attorney*
%Kindel & Anderson, 555 S Flower St, #2601, Los Angeles, CA 90071

Anderson, John, Jr — *Governor, KS*
16609 W 133rd, Olathe, KS 66062

Anderson, June — *Opera Singer*
%Columbia Artists Mgmt Inc, 165 W 57th St, New York, NY 10019

Anderson, Kenny — *Football Player*
%Cincinnati Bengals, 200 Riverfront Stadium, Cincinnati, OH 45202

Anderson, Kenny — *Basketball Player*
%New Jersey Nets, Meadowlands Arena, East Rutherford, NJ 07073

Anderson, Laurie — *Performance Artist*
%Warner Bros Records, 3 E 54th St, New York, NY 10022

Anderson, Lindsay — *Movie Director*
9 Stirling Mansions, Canfield Gdns, London NW6 3JT, England

Anderson, Loni — *Actress*
%BR Ranch, 1001 Indiantown Rd, Jupiter, FL 33458

Anderson, Lynn — *Singer*
4925 Tyne Valley Blvd, Nashville, TN 37220

Anderson, Marian *Singer*
Marianna Farms, Joe's Hill Rd, Danbury, CT 06811
Anderson, Melissa Sue *Actress*
20722 Pacific Coast Hwy, Malibu, CA 90265
Anderson, Melody *Actress*
%Gersh Agency, 232 N Canon Dr, Beverly Hills, CA 90210
Anderson, Michael J *Movie Director*
%Director's Guild, 7950 Sunset Blvd, Los Angeles, CA 90046
Anderson, Michael, Jr *Actor*
%Henderson/Hogan Agency, 246 S Beverly Dr, #102, Beverly Hills, CA 90210
Anderson, N Christian *Editor*
%Orange County Register, 625 N Grand Ave, Santa Ana, CA 92711
Anderson, Neal *Football Player*
%Chicago Bears, 250 N Washington Rd, Lake Forest, IL 60045
Anderson, Ottis *Football Player*
%New York Giants, Giants Stadium, East Rutherford, NJ 07073
Anderson, Paul *Weightlifter*
%Paul Anderson Youth Home, 1603 McIntosh St, Vidalia, GA 30474
Anderson, Philip W *Nobel Physics Laureate*
%Bell Telephone Laboratories, Murray Hill, NJ 07974
Anderson, Poul *Writer*
3 Las Palomas, Orinda, CA 94563
Anderson, R Lanier, III *Judge*
%US Court of Appeals, 56 Forsyth St NW, Atlanta, GA 30303
Anderson, Reid *Ballet Dancer, Artistic Director*
%National Ballet of Canada, 157 King St E, Toronto ON M5C 1G9, Canada
Anderson, Renee *Actress*
2052 Paramount Dr, Los Angeles, CA 90068
Anderson, Richard *Actor*
10120 Cielo Dr, Beverly Hills, CA 90210
Anderson, Richard Dean *Actor*
%International Creative Mgmt, 8899 Beverly Blvd, Los Angeles, CA 90048
Anderson, Richard L *Businessman*
%Brown Grp, 8400 Maryland Ave, St Louis, MO 63105
Anderson, Robert *Businessman*
%Rockwell International, 600 Grant St, Pittsburgh, PA 15219
Anderson, Robert E *Businessman*
%Mattel Inc, 5150 Rosecrans Blvd, Hawthorne, CA 90250
Anderson, Robert O *Businessman*
PO Box 1000, Roswell, NM 88201
Anderson, Robert W *Writer*
%General Delivery, Roxbury, CT 06783
Anderson, Roger E *Financier*
%Regina Wells, Continental Bank, 231 S LaSalle St, Chicago, IL 60693
Anderson, Ron *Basketball Player*
%Philadelphia 76ers, PO Box 25040, Veterans Stadium, Philadelphia, PA 19147
Anderson, Ross *Journalist*
%Seattle Times, Fairview Ave N & John St, Seattle, WA 98111
Anderson, Roy A *Businessman*
%Lockheed Corp, 2555 N Hollywood Way, Burbank, CA 91520
Anderson, Sigurd *Governor, SD*
313 W 7th Ave, Webster, SD 57274
Anderson, Sparky (George L) *Baseball Manager*
PO Box 6415, Thousand Oaks, CA 91360
Anderson, Stephen H *Judge*
%US Court of Appeals, Federal Bldg, 125 S State St, Salt Lake City, UT 84138
Anderson, W French *Medical Researcher*
%National Institutes of Health, 9000 Rockville Pike, Bethesda, MD 20892
Anderson, Webster *Vietnam War Army Hero (CMH)*
Rt 2, Box 17-H, Winnsboro, SC 29180
Anderson, Wendell R *Governor/Senator, MN*
%Larkin & Hoffman, 1700 First Bank Pl W, Minneapolis, MN 55402
Anderson, Weston *Physicist*
%Varian Assoc, 611 Hansen Way, Palo Alto, CA 94303
Anderson, William R *Representative, TN: Navy Officer*
400 N Capitol St NW, Washington, DC 20001

Andersson, Benny *Singer (ABBA), Composer*
%ABBA, PO Box 26072, 100 41 Stockholm, Sweden

Andersson, Bibi *Actress*
Tyko Vagen 28, Lidingo, Sweden

Andersson, Lennart *Businessman*
%Oljekonsumenternas Forbund Eleonomisk Forening, Warfvinges Vag 25, Sweden

Andewelt, Roger B *Judge*
%US Claims Court, 717 Madison Pl NW, Washington, DC 20005

Andonova, Ludmila *Track Athlete*
%Olympic Committee, Rue Anghel Kantchev 4, 1000 Sofia, Bulgaria

Andre the Giant *Wrestler*
%World Wrestling Federation, TitanSports, 1055 Summer St, Stamford, CT 06905

Andre, Carl *Sculptor*
PO Box 10001, Cooper Station, New York, NY 10003

Andreas, Dwayne O *Businessman*
%Archer Daniels Midland Co, 4666 Faries Pkwy, Decatur, IL 62525

Andreotti, Giulio *Prime Minister, Italy*
Piazza Montecitorio 13, 00186 Rome, Italy

Andres Oteyza, Jose *Businessman*
%Pemex, Ave Marina Nacional 329, Mexico 17 DF, Mexico

Andres, Jerry *Businessman*
%Happy Trails Resorts, 17200 W Bell Rd, Suprise, AZ 85374

Andres, William A *Businessman*
%Dayton-Hudson Co, 777 Nicollet Mall, Minneapolis, MN 55402

Andress, James G *Businessman*
%Sterling Drug, 90 Park Ave, New York, NY 10016

Andress, Ursula *Actress*
Danikofenweg 95, 3072 Ostermudingen, Switzerland

Andretti, Mario *Auto Racing Driver*
53 Victory Ln, Nazareth, PA 18064

Andrew *Prince, England*
Buckingham Palace, London SW1, England

Andrews, Anthony *Actor*
%Peters Fraser Dunlop, Chelsea Harbor, Lots Rd, London SW10 OXF, England

Andrews, Dana *Actor*
1021 N Crescent Heights Blvd, #306, Los Angeles, CA 90046

Andrews, Glenn *Representative, AL*
1205 Champaign St, Anniston, AL 36201

Andrews, James E *Religious Leader*
%Presbyterian Church (USA), 100 Witherspoon St, Louisville, KY 40202

Andrews, John H *Architect*
32 Florida Rd, Palm Beach NSW 2108, Australia

Andrews, Julie *Actress*
%Triad Artists, 10100 Santa Monica Blvd, #1600, Los Angeles, CA 90067

Andrews, Mark *Senator, ND*
%General Delivery, Mapleton, ND 58059

Andrews, Maxene *Singer*
%Bugle Boy Productions, 5119 Gaviota Ave, Encino, CA 91436

Andrews, Michael A *Representative, TX*
%House of Representatives, Washington, DC 20515

Andrews, Nelson C *Businessman*
%Brookside Properties, 224 White Bridge Rd, Nashville, TN 37209

Andrews, Patty *Singer*
PO Box 1793, Encino, CA 91316

Andrews, R F *Religious Leader*
%Free Methodist Church, PO Box 535002, Winona Lake, IN 46590

Andrews, Robert E *Representative, NJ*
%House of Representatives, Washington, DC 20515

Andrews, Theresa *Swimmer*
2004 Homewood Rd, Annapolis, MD 21402

Andrews, Thomas H *Representative, ME*
%House of Representatives, Washington, DC 20515

Andrews, Tige *Actor*
4914 Encino Terr, Encino, CA 91316

Andrews, William F *Businessman*
%Scovill Inc, 500 Chase Pkwy, Waterbury, CT 06708

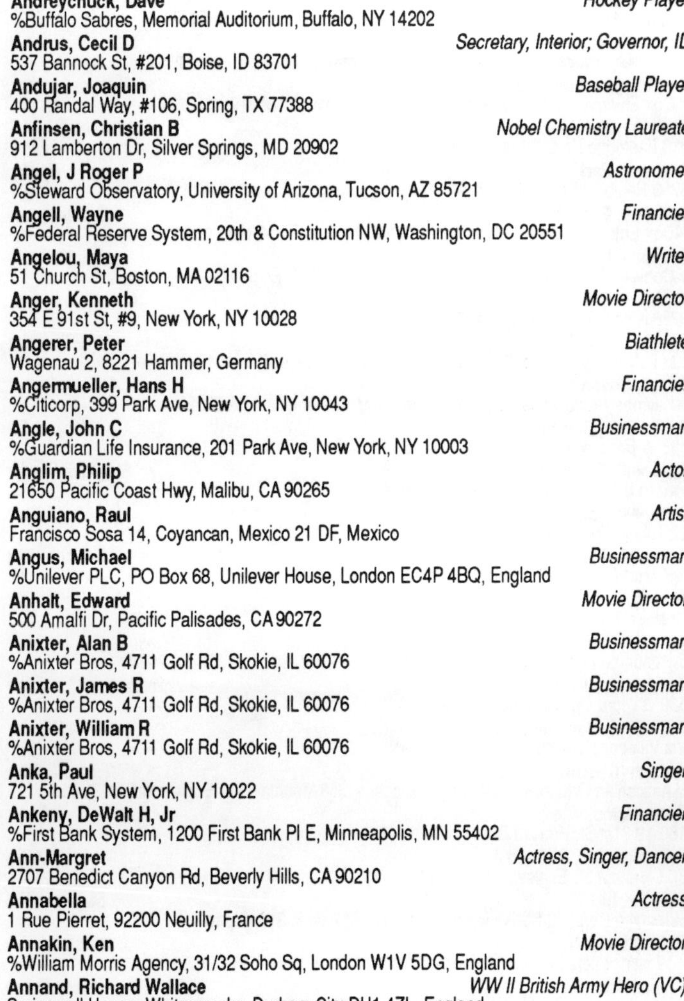

Andreychuck, Dave *Hockey Player*
%Buffalo Sabres, Memorial Auditorium, Buffalo, NY 14202
Andrus, Cecil D *Secretary, Interior; Governor, ID*
537 Bannock St, #201, Boise, ID 83701
Andujar, Joaquin *Baseball Player*
400 Randal Way, #106, Spring, TX 77388
Anfinsen, Christian B *Nobel Chemistry Laureate*
912 Lamberton Dr, Silver Springs, MD 20902
Angel, J Roger P *Astronomer*
%Steward Observatory, University of Arizona, Tucson, AZ 85721
Angell, Wayne *Financier*
%Federal Reserve System, 20th & Constitution NW, Washington, DC 20551
Angelou, Maya *Writer*
51 Church St, Boston, MA 02116
Anger, Kenneth *Movie Director*
354 E 91st St, #9, New York, NY 10028
Angerer, Peter *Biathlete*
Wagenau 2, 8221 Hammer, Germany
Angermueller, Hans H *Financier*
%Citicorp, 399 Park Ave, New York, NY 10043
Angle, John C *Businessman*
%Guardian Life Insurance, 201 Park Ave, New York, NY 10003
Anglim, Philip *Actor*
21650 Pacific Coast Hwy, Malibu, CA 90265
Anguiano, Raul *Artist*
Francisco Sosa 14, Coyancan, Mexico 21 DF, Mexico
Angus, Michael *Businessman*
%Unilever PLC, PO Box 68, Unilever House, London EC4P 4BQ, England
Anhalt, Edward *Movie Director*
500 Amalfi Dr, Pacific Palisades, CA 90272
Anixter, Alan B *Businessman*
%Anixter Bros, 4711 Golf Rd, Skokie, IL 60076
Anixter, James R *Businessman*
%Anixter Bros, 4711 Golf Rd, Skokie, IL 60076
Anixter, William R *Businessman*
%Anixter Bros, 4711 Golf Rd, Skokie, IL 60076
Anka, Paul *Singer*
721 5th Ave, New York, NY 10022
Ankeny, DeWalt H, Jr *Financier*
%First Bank System, 1200 First Bank Pl E, Minneapolis, MN 55402
Ann-Margret *Actress, Singer, Dancer*
2707 Benedict Canyon Rd, Beverly Hills, CA 90210
Annabella *Actress*
1 Rue Pierret, 92200 Neuilly, France
Annakin, Ken *Movie Director*
%William Morris Agency, 31/32 Soho Sq, London W1V 5DG, England
Annand, Richard Wallace *WW II British Army Hero (VC)*
Springwell House, Whitesmocks, Durham City DH1 4ZL, England
Annaud, Jean-Jacques *Movie Director*
55 Rue de Varenne, 75007 Paris, France
Anne *Princess, England*
Gatecombe Park, Gloucestershire, England
Annenberg, Walter H *Publisher, Diplomat*
71231 Tamarisk Ln, Rancho Mirage, CA 92270
Annis, Francesca *Actress*
2 Vicarage Ct, London W8, England
Annunzio, Frank *Representative, IL*
%House of Representatives, Washington, DC 20515
Ansara, Michael *Actor*
4624 Park Mirasol, Calabasas, CA 91302
Anschutz, Philip F *Businessman*
%Anschutz Corp, 555 17th St, Denver, CO 80202
Anspach, Susan *Actress*
473 16th St, Santa Monica, CA 90402
Ant, Adam *Singer*
PO Box 4QT, London W1A, England

Antall, Josef *Prime Minister, Hungary*
%Prime Minister's Office, Kossuth L.yer 1-3, H Budapest V, Hungary

Antes, Horst *Artist*
Hohenbergstrasse 11, 7500 Karlsruhe 41, Germany

Anthony, Barbara Cox *Businesswoman*
%Cox Enterprises, 1400 Lake Hearn Dr NE, Atlanta, GA 30319

Anthony, Beryl, Jr *Representative, AR*
710 Eastridge Dr, El Dorado, AR 71730

Anthony, Earl *Bowler*
6750 Regional St, Dublin, CA 94566

Anthony, Garner *Businessman*
%Cox Enterprises, 1400 Lake Hearn Dr NE, Atlanta, GA 30319

Anthony, Lysette *Actresss*
%Conway, Eagle House, 109 Jermyn St, London SW1, England

Anthony, Ray *Orchestra Leader*
9288 Kinglet Dr, Los Angeles, CA 90069

Antoci, Mario J *Financier*
%H F Ahmanson & Co, 3731 Wilshire Blvd, Los Angeles, CA 90010

Anton, Susan *Actress, Singer*
%Kalimba Productions, 1990 Westwood Blvd, Los Angeles, CA 90025

Antonakos, Stephen *Artist*
435 W Broadway, New York, NY 10012

Antonelli, Ferdinando Cardinal *Religious Leader*
Piazza S Calisto 16, 00153 Rome, Italy

Antonelli, Johnny *Baseball Player*
22 Tobey Woods, Pittsford, NY 14534

Antonini, Joseph E *Businessman*
%K Mart Corp, 3100 W Big Beaver Rd, Troy, MI 48084

Antonio *Spanish Dancer*
Coslada 7, Madrid, Spain

Antonio, Jim *Actor*
%Henderson/Hogan Agency, 247 S Beverly Dr, #102, Beverly Hills, CA 90210

Antonio, Lou *Actor*
530 Gaylord Dr, Burbank, CA 91505

Antonioni, Michelangelo *Movie Director*
Via Vincenzo Tiberio 18, Rome XVI, Italy

Antoun (Khouri), Bishop *Religious Leader*
%Antiochian Orthodox Christian Archdiocese, 358 Mountain Rd, Englewood, NJ 07631

Antuofermo, Vito *Boxer*
160-19 81st St, Howard Beach, NY 11414

Anuszkiewicz, Richard J *Artist*
76 Chestnut St, Englewood, NJ 07631

Aoi, Joichi *Businessman*
%Toshiba Corp, 72 Horikawacho, Saiwaiku, Kawasaki 210, Japan

Aoki, Chieko N *Businesswoman*
%Westin Hotels Co, Westin Building, 2001 6th Ave, Seattle, WA 98121

Aoki, Ikuro *Businessman*
%Kanebo Ltd, 1-2-2 Umeda, Kitaku, Osaka 530, Japan

Aoki, Rocky *Boat Racing Driver, Businessman*
%Benihana of Tokyo, 8685 NW 53rd Terr, Miami, FL 33166

Aoshika, Meishi *Financier*
%Joyo Bank, 2-5-5 Minamimachi, Mito City 310, Japan

Aouita, Said *Track Athlete*
%Abdejil Bencheikh, 9 Rue Soivissi, Loubira, Rabat, Morocco

Aparicio, Luis *Baseball Player*
Calle 67, #26-82, Maracaibo, Venezuela

Apfalter, Heribert *Businessman*
%Voest-Alpine, Muldenstrasse 5, 4010 Linz, Austria

Apodaca, Jerry *Governor, NM*
1328 Camino Corrales, Santa Fe, NM 87501

Aponte Martinez, Luis Cardinal *Religious Leader*
%Arzobispado, Calle San Jorge 201, Santurce, PR 00912

Appel, Karel *Artist*
Galerie Statler, 51 Rue de Seine, Paris, France

Appleberry, James B *Educator*
515 E Ford St, Pittsburg, KS 66762

Applegate, Christina *Actress*
%Tami Lynn, 4527 Park Allegra, Calabasas, CA 91302

Applegate, Douglas *Representative, OH*
Rt 3, Berkeley Pl, Steubenville, OH 43952

Appleton, James R *Educator*
%University of Redlands, President's Office, Redlands, CA 92373

Apps, Syl *Hockey Player*
185 Ontario St, #1303, Kingston ON N7L 2YZ, Canada

Apt, Jerome *Astronaut*
%NASA, Johnson Space Ctr, Houston, TX 77058

Apted, Michael *Movie Director*
1051 Villa View Dr, Pacific Palisades, CA 90272

Aquilino, Thomas J, Jr *Judge*
%US Court of International Trade, 1 Federal Plz, New York, NY 10007

Aquino, Corazon C *President, Philippines*
%President's Office, Malacanang Palace, Manila, Philippines

Arafat, Yasser *Head, Palestine Liberation Organization*
Palais Essaada La Marsa, Tunis, Tunisia

Aragall, Giacomo *Opera Singer*
%Robert Lombardo Assoc, 61 W 62nd St, New York, NY 10023

Aragon, Art *Boxer*
%Art Aragon Bail Bonds, 14444 Victory Blvd, Van Nuys, CA 91401

Aragones, Sergio *Cartoonist (Mad Comics)*
%Mad Magazine, 485 Madison Ave, New York, NY 10022

Arai, Kazuo *Businessman*
%Kao Corp, 14-10 Nihonbashi, Kayabacho, Chuoku, Tokyo 103, Japan

Arakawa, Ichiro *Businessman*
%Kanto Auto Works, Taura-Minatomachi, Yokosuka City 237, Japan

Arakawa, Masashi *Businessman*
%Hino Motors, 3-1-1 Hinodal, Hino City, Tokyo 191, Japan

Arakawa, Toyozo *Pottery Maker*
4-101, O-Hatacho, Tokyo, Japan

Aramburu, Juan Carlos Cardinal *Religious Leader*
Arzobispado, Suipacha 1034, Buenos Aires 1008, Argentina

Araskog, Rand V *Businessman*
%ITT Corp, 320 Park Ave, New York, NY 10022

Arbanas, Fred *Football Player*
11700 E 139th St, Kansas City, KS 64149

Arber, Werner *Nobel Medicine Laureate*
70 Klingelbergstrasse, 4000 Basel, Switzerland

Arbour, Al *Hockey Coach, Executive*
%New York Islanders, Nassau Coliseum, Uniondale, NY 11553

Arbus, Allan *Actor*
%Borinstein Oreck Bogart Agency, 8271 Melrose, #110, Los Angeles, CA 90046

Arcaro, Eddie *Thoroughbred Racing Jockey*
11111 Biscayne Blvd, Miami, FL 33161

Arcel, Ray *Boxing Trainer*
288 Lexington Ave, New York, NY 10016

Archer, Anne *Actress*
13201 Old Oak Ln, Los Angeles, CA 90049

Archer, Beverly *Actress*
%Stone Manners Agency, 9113 Sunset Blvd, Los Angeles, CA 90069

Archer, George *Golfer*
%Professional Golfers Assn, PO Box 109601, Palm Beach Gardens, FL 33410

Archer, Glenn L, Jr *Judge*
US Court of Appeals, 717 Madison Pl NW, Washington, DC 20439

Archer, John *Writer*
Old Vicarage, Grantchester, Cambridge, England

Archer, William R, Jr *Representative, TX*
%House of Representatives, Washington, DC 20515

Archerd, Army *Journalist*
%Variety Magazine, 5700 Wilshire Blvd, Los Angeles, CA 90036

Archibald, Nolan D *Businessman*
%Black & Decker Corp, 701 E Joppa Rd, Towson, MD 21204

Archiniegas, German *Writer, Diplomat*
%Universidad de Los Andes, Cra 1E-18A-10, Bogota, Colombia

Arciniega, Tomas A *Educator*
%California State College, President's Office, Bakersfield, CA 93311

Arden, John *Playwright*
%M Ramsay, 14-A Goodwin's Ct, St Martin's Ln, London WC2N 4LL, England

Arden, Toni *Singer*
34-34 75th St, Jackson Heights, NY 11372

Ardia, Stephen V *Businessman*
%Goulds Pumps, 240 Fall St, Seneca Falls, NY 13148

Ardolino, Emile *Movie Director, Producer*
2920 Neilson Way, #301, Santa Monica, CA 90405

Aregood, Richard L *Journalist*
%Philadelphia Daily News, 400 N Broad St, Philadelphia. PA 19101

Arendts, Wilhelm *Businessman*
%Papierwerke Waldhof Aschaffenburg, PWA-Haus, 8201 Raubling, Germany

Arens, Moshe *Government Official, Israel*
49 Hagderot, Saryon, Israel

Aretsky, Ken *Restauranteur*
%21 Club, 21 W 52nd St, New York, NY 10019

Argento, Dominick *Composer*
%University of Minnesota, Music Dept, Ferguson Hall, Minneapolis, MN 55455

Argyros, George L *Baseball Executive*
%Seattle Mariners, 100 S King St, Seattle, WA 98104

Arias Sanchez, Oscar *President, Costa Rica; Nobel Laureate*
%Casa Presidencial, San Jose, Costa Rica

Arias, Ricardo M *President, Panama*
Apdo 4549, Panama City, Panama

Arinze, Francis Cardinal *Religious Leader*
%Secretariat for Non-Christians, 00120 Vatican City, Italy

Aristide, Jean-Bertrand *President, Haiti*
%Palace du Gouvernement, Port-au-Prince, Haiti

Ariyaratne, Ahangamage *Agricutural Economist*
%Sarvodaya Shramadana, Sri Lanka

Ariyoshi, George *Governor, HI*
745 Fort St, 5th Fl, Honolulu, HI 96813

Ariyoshi, Shingo *Businessman*
%Mitsui Mining, 1-1-1 Nihonbashi Muromachi, Chuoku, Tokyo 103, Japan

Arizin, Paul *Basketball Player*
227 Lewis Rd, Springfield, PA 19064

Arkin, Adam *Actor*
50 Ridge Dr, Chappaqua, NY 10514

Arkin, Alan *Actor*
%Triad Artists, 10100 Santa Monica Blvd, #1600, Los Angeles, CA 90067

Arkoff, Samuel Z *Movie Producer*
3205 Oakdell Ln, Studio City, CA 91604

Arledge, Roone *Television Executive, Journalist*
%ABC-TV, 1330 Ave of Americas, New York, NY 10019

Arlen, Michael J *Writer*
%New Yorker Magazine 25 W 43rd St, New York, NY 10036

Arletty *Actress*
14 Rue de Rimuset, 75016 Paris, France

Armacost, Michael *Diplomat*
%US Embassy, 10-5 Akasaka 1-chome, Minatoku, Tokyo, Japan

Armacost, Samuel H *Financier*
%Weiss Peck Greer, 555 California, San Francisco, CA 94104

Arman *Sculptor*
430 Washington St, New York, NY 10013

Armani, Giorgio *Fashion Designer*
Palazzo Durini 24, 20122 Milan, Italy

Armas, Tony *Baseball Player*
Los Mercedes, #37, P Piruto-Edo, Anzoatequi, Venezuela

Armatrading, Joan *Singer*
%Running Dog Mgmt, 27 Queensdale Pl, London W11 45Q, England

Armedariz, Pedro, Jr *Actor*
%Diamond Artists, 9200 Sunset Blvd, #909, Los Angeles, CA 90069

Armey, Richard *Representative, TX*
%House of Representatives, Washington, DC 20515

Armitage, Karole *Choreographer, Dancer*
350 W 21st St, New York, NY 10011

Armitage, Kenneth *Artist*
22-A Avonmore Rd, London W14 8RR, England

Armitage, Richard L *Government Official*
%Secretary's Office, Department of Army, Pentagon, Washington, DC 20310

Armstrong, A James *Religious Leader*
%Broadway Methodist Church, 1100 W 42nd St, Indianapolis, IN 46208

Armstrong, Anne *Diplomat, Educator*
Armstrong Ranch, Armstrong, TX 78338

Armstrong, Bess *Actress*
%Agency for Performing Arts, 9000 Sunset Blvd, #1200, Los Angeles, CA 90069

Armstrong, Bruce *Football Player*
%New England Patriots, Sullivan Stadium, Foxboro, MA 02035

Armstrong, C Michael *Businessman*
%IBM World Trade Corp, 360 Hamilton Ave, White Plains, NY 10601

Armstrong, Garner Ted *Evangelist*
PO Box 2525, Tyler, TX 75710

Armstrong, Gillian *Movie Director*
%M&L Casting, 49 Darlinghurst Rd, Kings Cross NSW 2911, Australia

Armstrong, Neil A *Astronaut*
%CTA Inc, PO Box 436, Rt 123, Lebanon, OH 45036

Armstrong, R G *Actor*
3856 Reklaw Dr, Studio City, CA 91604

Armstrong, Richard Q *Businessman*
%Cluett Peabody Co, 510 5th Ave, New York, NY 10036

Armstrong, Robb *Cartoonist (Jump Start)*
%United Feature Syndicate, 200 Park Ave, New York, NY 10166

Armstrong, Valorie *Actress*
%Contemporary Artists, 132 S Lasky Dr, #B, Beverly Hills, CA 90212

Armstrong, Warren B *Educator*
%Wichita State University, President's Office, Wichita, KS 67208

Armstrong, William L *Senator, CO*
%US Senate, Washington, DC 20510

Arn, Edward *Governor, KS*
9434 E Bent Tree Cir, Wichita, KS 67226

Arnall, Ellis G *Governor, GA*
%Arnall Golden Gregory, 55 Park Pl, #400, Atlanta, GA 30335

Arnason, Hjorvardur H *Art Historian*
4 E 89th St, New York, NY 10028

Arnaz, Desi, Jr *Actor*
%Success Without Stress, PO Box 2000, Ojai, CA 93023

Arnaz, Lucie *Actress*
470 Main St, #K, Ridgefield, CT 06877

Arneson, Robert *Artist*
%University of California, Art Dept, Davis, CA 95616

Arnett, Peter *Correspondent*
%Cable News Network, 1 CNN Center, PO Box 105366, Atlanta, GA 30348

Arno, Ed *Cartoonist*
PO Box 4203, New York, NY 10017

Arnold, Anna Bing *Philanthropist*
%Anna Bing Arnold Foundation, 9700 W Pico Blvd, Los Angeles, CA 90035

Arnold, Daniel C *Financier*
%First City Bancorp of Texas, 1001 Fannin St, Houston, TX 77002

Arnold, Danny *Movie Producer, Director*
1293 Sunset Plaza Dr, Los Angeles, CA 90069

Arnold, Eddy *Singer*
PO Box 97, Franklin Rd, Brentwood, TN 37207

Arnold, Gary H *Movie Critic*
5133 N 1st St, Arlington, VA 22203

Arnold, Harry L, Jr *Dermatologist, Writer*
4340 Pahoa Ave, #3-C, Honolulu, HI 96816

Arnold, Jackson D *Navy Admiral*
%Cubic Corp, 9333 Balboa Ave, San Diego, CA 92123

Arnold, James R *Chemist*
%University of California, Space Institute, La Jolla, CA 92307

A

Arnold – Ash

Arnold, Jim *Football Player*
%Detroit Lions, Silverdome, 1200 Featherstone Rd, Pontiac, MI 48057

Arnold, Kristine *Singer*
%CBS Records, 51 W 52nd St, New York, NY 10019

Arnold, Malcolm *Composer*
%Faber Music Co, 3 Queen Sq, London WC1N 3AU, England

Arnold, Murray *Basketball Coach*
%Western Kentucky University, Athletic Dept, Bowling Green, KY 42101

Arnold, Richard S *Judge*
%US Court of Appeals, Court & Customs House, PO Box 429, Little Rock, AR 72203

Arnold, Roseanne Barr *Comedienne*
%William Morris Agency, 151 El Camino, Beverly Hills, CA 90212

Arnoldi, Charles *Artist*
721 Hampton Dr, Venice, CA 90291

Arnon, Daniel I *Biochemist*
28 Norwood Ave, Berkeley, CA 94707

Arns, Paulo E Cardinal *Religious Leader*
Rue Mococa 71, 01255 Sao Paulo SP, Brazil

Arnsparger, Bill *Football Coach, Administrator*
%University of Florida, Athletic Dept, Gainesville, FL 32611

Arnsten, Stefan *Actor*
1326 Dawnridge Dr, Beverly Hills, CA 90210

Arp, Halton C *Astronomer*
%Max Planck Institute for Physics/Radiology, 8036 Garching Munich, Germany

Arpel, Adrien *Beauty Consultant*
666 5th Ave, New York, NY 10103

Arpino, Gerald *Choreographer*
%City Center Joffrey Ballet, 130 W 56th St, New York, NY 10019

Arquette, Rosanna *Actress*
1201 Alta Loma Rd, Los Angeles, CA 90069

Arrington, Richard, Jr *Mayor*
%Mayor's Office, 710 20th St N, Birmingham, AL 35203

Arriola, Gus *Cartoonist (Gordo)*
PO Box 3275, Carmel, CA 93921

Arron, Henck *Prime Minister, Suriname*
%Prime Minister's Office, Paramaribo, Suriname

Arrow, Kenneth J *Nobel Economics Laureate*
580 Constanzo St, Stanford, CA 94305

Arroyo, Luis *Baseball Player*
Box 354, Penuelas, PR 00724

Arroyo, Martina *Opera Singer*
%Thea Dispeker, 59 E 54th St, New York, NY 10022

Arthur, Beatrice *Actress, Comedienne*
2000 Old Ranch Rd, Los Angeles, CA 90049

Arthur, Lloyd *Businessman*
%Indiana Farm Bureau Cooperative, 120 E Market, Indianapolis, IN 46204

Arthur, Maureen *Actress*
%Abrams Artists, 9200 Sunset Blvd, Los Angeles, CA 90069

Arthur, Stanley R *Navy Admiral*
Commander, 7th Fleet, FPO, AP 96601

Artschwager, Richard *Artist*
PO Box 99, Charlottesville, NY 12036

Artsebarsky, Anatoly *Cosmonaut*
141 160 Svyosdny Gorodok, Moskovskoi Oblasti, Potchta Kosmonavtov, Russia

Artyukhin, Yuri *Cosmonaut*
141 160 Svyosdny Gorodok, Moskovskoi Oblasti, Potchta Kosmonavtov, Russia

Artzt, Edwin L *Businessman*
%Procter & Gamble Co, 1 Procter & Gamble Plz, Cincinnati, OH 45202

Arum, Robert *Sports Promoter*
%Top Rank Inc, 919 3rd Ave, New York, NY 10022

Asby, Joseph W *Air Force General*
Commander, Air Training Command, Randolph Air Force Base, TX 78150

Ash, Mary Kay *Businesswoman*
%Mary Kay Cosmetics, 8787 Stemmons Fwy, Dallas, TX 75247

Ash, Roy L *Businessman, Government Official*
655 Funchal Rd, Los Angeles, CA 90024

Ashbery, John L *Writer*
%Georges Borchardt Inc, 136 E 57th St, New York, NY 10022
Ashbrook, Dana *Actor*
%Gersh Agency, 232 N Canon Dr, Beverly Hills, CA 90210
Ashbrook, Daphne *Actress*
1827 Canyon Dr, #6, Los Angeles, CA 90028
Ashbury, Beverly A *Religious Leader*
%Vanderbilt University, Religious Affairs Office, Nashville, TN 37204
Ashcroft, John *Governor, MO*
%Governor's Office, PO Box 720, Jefferson City, MO 65102
Ashe, Arthur *Tennis Player*
PO Box 447, Bedford Hills, NY 10507
Ashenfelter, Horace, III *Track Athlete*
100 Hawthorne Ave, Glen Ridge, NJ 07028
Asher, Frederick *Businessman*
405 Moraine Rd, Highland Park, IL 60035
Asher, Jane *Actress*
%Globe Theater, Shaftsbury Ave, London W1, England
Asher, Peter *Record Producer, Singer*
%Peter Asher Mgmt, 644 N Doheny Dr, Los Angeles, CA 90064
Asherson, Renee *Actress*
28 Elsworthy Rd, London NW3, England
Ashford, Matthew *Actor*
%J Michael Bloom Ltd, 9200 Sunset Blvd, #710, Los Angeles, CA 90069
Ashford, Nick *Singer (Ashford & Simpson)*
%George Schiffer, 1155 N La Cienega Blvd, Los Angeles, CA 90069
Ashkenazy, Vladimir *Concert Pianist, Conductor*
Sonnenhof 4, 6004 Lucerne, Switzerland
Ashley *Model*
%Ford Model Agency, 344 E 59th St, New York, NY 10022
Ashley, Elizabeth *Actress*
9010 Dorrington Ave, Los Angeles, CA 90048
Ashley, Merrill *Ballerina*
%New York City Ballet, Lincoln Ctr, New York, NY 10023
Ashmore, Edward *Fleet Admiral, England*
%National Westminster Bank, 26 Haymarket, London SW1, England
Ashmore, Harry S *Editor, Foundation Executive*
1373 E Valley Rd, Santa Barbara, CA 93108
Ashton, Harris J *Businessman*
%General Host Corp, 22 Gate House Rd, Stamford, CT 06904
Ashton, John *Actor*
22625 Town Crier Rd, Woodland Hills, CA 91367
Asimov, Isaac *Writer*
10 W 66th St, #33-A, New York, NY 10023
Askew, Reubin O *Governor, FL*
%Ackerman Senterfitt Edison, PO Box 231, Orlando, FL 32802
Askin, Leon *Actor*
625 N Rexford Dr, Beverly Hills, CA 90210
Asmis, Herbert *Businessman*
%Schering, Mullerstr 170-178, 1000 Berlin 65, Germany
Asner, Ed *Actor*
%Gores/Fields Agency, 10100 Santa Monica Blvd, #700, Los Angeles, CA 90067
Asp, Raymond J *Businessman*
%Geo A Hormel Co, 501 16th Ave NE, Austin, MN 55912
Aspin, Les *Representative, WI*
%House of Representatives, Washington, DC 20515
Asplin, Edward W *Businessman*
%Bemis Co, 800 Northstar Ctr, Minneapolis, MN 55402
Assad, Hafiz al- *President, Syria*
%Presidential Palace, Damascus, Syria
Assylmuratova, Altynai *Ballerina*
%Kirov Ballet Theatre, 1 Ploshchad Iskusstr, St Petersburg, Russia
Ast, Pat *Actress*
%Sanders Agency, 8831 Sunset Blvd, #304, Los Angeles, CA 90069
Astin, Allen V *Physicist*
5008 Battery Ln, Bethesda, MD 20814

Astin, John *Actor, Director*
%Light Co, 901 Bringham Ave, Los Angeles, CA 90049
Aston, James W *Financier*
5000 Royal Ln, Dallas, TX 75229
Astor, Brooke *Foundation Executive*
%Vincent Astor Foundation, 405 Park Ave, New York, NY 10022
Asturaga, Nova *Government Official, Nicaragua*
%Permanent Mission of Nicaragua, 820 2nd Ave, #801, New York, NY 10017
Atchison, David W *Religious Leader*
%Southern Baptist Convention, 5452 Grannywhite Pike, Brentwood, TN 37027
Atchley, Bill L *Educator*
%University of Pacific, President's Office, Stockton, CA 95211
Atherton, Alfred L, Jr *Diplomat*
%Department of State, 2201 "C" St NW, Washington, DC 20520
Atherton, David *Conductor*
%San Diego Symphony, 770 "B" St, #402, San Diego, CA 92101
Atherton, John W, Jr *Financier*
%City Federal Savings & Loan, Rt 2020296, Bedminister, NJ 07921
Athow, Kirk Leland *Plant Pathologist*
2104 Crestview Ct, Lafayette, IN 47905
Atienza Silvestre, Juan Antonio *Businessman*
%Empresa Nacional Siderurgica, Velazquez, #134, Madrid 6, Spain
Atiyeh, Victor *Governor, OR*
519 SW Park, Portland, OR 97205
Atkins, Chester G *Representative, MA*
%House of Representatives, Washington, DC 20515
Atkins, Chet *Guitarist*
1096 Lynwood Blvd, Nashville, TN 37215
Atkins, Christopher *Actor*
3751 Sunswept Dr, Studio City, CA 91604
Atkins, Doug *Football Player*
5312 E Sunset Rd, Knoxville, TN 37914
Atkins, Orin E *Businessman*
%Ashland Oil, 1409 Winchester Ave, Ashland, KY 41101
Atkins, Tom *Actor*
%STE Representation, 9301 Wilshire Blvd, #312, Beverly Hills, CA 90210
Atkinson, Ray N *Businessman*
%Guy F Atkinson Co, 10 W Orange Ave, South San Francisco, CA 94080
Atkinson, Richard C *Educator*
%University of California, Chancellor's Office, La Jolla, CA 92093
Atkinson, Rick *Journalist*
%Kansas City Times, 1729 Grand Ave, Kansas City, MO 64108
Atkov, Oleg Y *Cosmonaut*
141 160 Svyosdny Gorodok, Moskovskoi Oblasti, Potchta Kosmonavtov, Russia
Attenborough, David *Television Broadcaster, Writer*
5 Park Rd, Richmond, Surrey TW10 GNS, England
Attenborough, Richard *Actor, Director*
Beaver Lodge, Richmond Green, Surrey TW9 1NQ, England
Attkisson, Sharyl *Commentator*
%Cable News Network, 1 CNN Center, PO Box 105366, Atlanta, GA 30348
Attles, Al *Basketball Player, Coach*
%Golden State Warriors, Oakland Coliseum, Oakland, CA 94621
Atwater, H Brewster, Jr *Businessman*
%General Mills, 9200 Wayzata Blvd, Minneapolis, MN 55440
Atwood, J Leland *Businessman*
PO Box 157, Vista, CA 92083
Atwood, Margaret *Writer*
73 Sullivan St, Toronto ON M5T 1C2, Canada
Auberjonois, Rene *Actor*
448 S Arden Blvd, Los Angeles, CA 90020
Aubert, Pierre *President, Switzerland*
Palais Federal, 3003 Berne, Switzerland
Aubrey, James T *Movie Producer*
1426 Seabright Pl, Beverly Hills, CA 90210
Aubry, Cecile *Actress*
Le Moulin Bleu, 91410 Saint-Cyr, S/S Dourdan, France

Aubry, Eugene E *Architect*
%Morris/Aubry Architects, 3465 W Alabama St, Houston, TX 77027

Aubut, Marcel *Hockey Executive*
%Quebec Nordiques, 2205 Ave du Colisee, Quebec City PQ G1L 4W7, Canada

Auchincloss, Louis *Writer*
1111 Park Ave, New York, NY 10028

AuCoin, Les *Representative, OR*
%House of Representatives, Washington, DC 20515

Aucott, George W *Businessman*
%Firestone Tire & Rubber Co, 1200 Firestone Pkwy, Akron, OH 44317

Audran, Stephane *Actress*
95 Bis Rue de Chezy, 92200 Neuilly-sur-Seine, France

Auel, Jean M *Writer*
PO Box 430, Sherwood, OR 97140

Auer, Peter L *Plasma Physicist*
220 Devon Rd, Ithaca, NY 14850

Auerbach, Arnold J (Red) *Basketball Coach, Executive*
%Boston Celtics, 151 Merrimac St, Boston, MA 02114

Auerbach, Frank *Artist*
%Marlborough Fine Art Gallery, 6 Albermarle St, London W1X 3HF, England

Auerbach, Stanley I *Ecologist*
24 Wildwood Dr, Oak Ridge, TN 37830

Auger, Arleen *Opera Singer*
%Celia P Novo, 14 Townsend Ave, Hartsdale, NY 10530

Auger, Claudine *Actress*
%William Morris Agency, 151 El Camino, Beverly Hills, CA 90212

Augmon, Stacey *Basketball Player*
%Atlanta Hawks, 1 CNN Center, South Tower, Atlanta, GA 30303

Augstein, Rudolf *Publisher*
%Der Spiegel, Ost-West-Strasse, Hamburg 11, Germany

Augustain, Ira *Actor*
%Diamond Artists, 9200 Sunset Blvd, #909, Los Angeles, CA 90069

Augustine, Norman R *Businessman*
%Martin Marietta Corp, 6801 Rockledge Dr, Bethesda, MD 20817

Auker, Eldon *Baseball Player*
15 Sailfish Rd, Vero Beach, FL 32960

Aulby, Mike *Bowler*
8199 Wade Hill Ct, Indianapolis, IN 46256

Aumont, Jean-Pierre *Actor*
%L'Caster, 27 Rue de Richelier, 75001 Paris, France

Ausseil, Jean *Minister of State, Monaco*
%Minister of State's Office, Monaco-Ville, Monaco

Austin, Debbie *Golfer*
6733 Bittersweet Ln, Orlando, FL 32819

Austin, Denise *Physical Fitness Expert*
%Peter Pan Industries, 88 St Francis St, Newark, NJ 07105

Austin, John H, Jr *Businessman*
%Philadelphia Electric Co, 2301 Market St, Philadelphia, PA 19101

Austin, Philip E *Educator*
%Colorado State University, President's Office, Fort Collins, CO 80523

Austin, Tracy *Tennis Player*
1025 Thomas Jefferson St, #405-E, Washington, DC 20007

Austregesilo de Athayde, B M *Journalist*
Rua Cosme Velho 599, Rio de Janeiro RJ, Brazil

Austrian, Neil R *Businessman*
%Doyle Dane Bernbach, 437 Madison Ave, New York, NY 10022

Auth, Tony *Editorial Cartoonist*
1137 Rodman St, Philadelphia, PA 19147

Autry, Gene *Actor, Singer, Baseball Executive*
3171 Brookdale Rd, North Hollywood, CA 91604

Avalon, Frankie *Singer*
6311 DeSoto Ave, #1, Woodland Hills, CA 91367

Avedon, Richard *Photographer*
407 E 75th St, New York, NY 10021

Avery, Margaret *Actress*
2807 Pelham Pl, Los Angeles, CA 90068

A

Avery – Azzara

Avery, Phyllis *Actress*
914 S Barrington Ave, Los Angeles, CA 90049

Avery, R Stanton *Businessman*
%Avery International Grp, 150 N Orange Grove, Pasadena, CA 91103

Avery, Val *Actor*
84 Grove St, #19, New York, NY 10014

Avery, William H *Governor, KS*
Rt 2, Wakefield, KS 67487

Avery, William J *Businessman*
%Crown Cork & Seal Co, 9300 Ashton Rd, Philadelphia, PA 19136

Avila, Bobby *Baseball Player*
Navegantes FR-19, Reforma-Veracruz, Mexico

Avildsen, John G *Movie Director*
45 E 89th St, #37-A, New York, NY 10038

Avis, Warren E *Businessman*
%Liberty Financial, 5520 S State, Detroit, MI 48226

Awes, Gerald A *Businessman*
%Lucky Stores, 6300 Clark Ave, Dublin, GA 94568

Ax, Emmanuel *Concert Pianist*
175 Riverside Dr, New York, NY 10024

Axelrod, George *Playwright*
1840 Carla Ridge St, Beverly Hills, CA 90210

Axelrod, Julius *Nobel Medicine Laureate*
10401 Grosvenor Pl, Rockville, MD 20852

Axton, Hoyt *Singer*
%Lady Jane Music, PO Box 614, Tahoe City, CA 95730

Ay-O *Artist*
2-6-38 Matsuyama, Kiyoseshi, Tokyo, Japan

Ayang, Luc *Prime Minister, Cameroon*
%Prime Minister's Office, Yaounde, Cameroon

Ayckbourn, Alan *Playwright*
%M Ramsay, 14-A Goodwin's Ct, St Martin's Ln, London WC2N 4LL, England

Aycock, Alice *Artist*
62 Green St, New York, NY 10012

Aycock, Hugh D *Businessman*
%Nucor Corp, 4425 Randolph Rd, Charlotte, NC 28211

Ayers, Chuck *Cartoonist (Crankshaft)*
%Creators Syndicate, 5777 W Century Blvd, #700, Los Angeles, CA 90045

Ayers, Randy *Basketball Coach*
%Ohio State University, Athletic Dept, Columbus, OH 43210

Ayers, Richard H *Businessman*
%Stanley Works, 1000 Stanley Dr, New Britain, CT 06050

Aylward, Ronald L *Businessman*
%Interco Inc, 10 Broadway, St Louis, MO 63102

Aymond, Alphonse H *Businessman*
180 W Michigan Ave, Jackson, MI 49201

Ayres, Lew *Actor*
675 Walther Way, Los Angeles, CA 90049

Azar, Suzie *Mayor*
%Mayor's Office, City Hall, Civic Center Plaza, El Paso, TX 79901

Azcarraga, Emilio *Publisher*
%Televisa SA, Avda Chapultepec 28, 06 724 Mexico City, Mexico

Azcona Hoyo, Jose *President, Honduras*
%President's Office, Teguciagalpa, Honduras

Azenberg, Emanuel *Theater Producer*
165 W 46th St, New York, NY 10036

Azinger, Paul *Golfer*
4520 Bent Tree Blvd, Sarasota, FL 34241

Aziz, Tariq *Government Official, Iraq*
%Prime Minister's Office, Karadat Mariam, Baghdad, Iraq

Aznavour, Charles *Singer, Actor*
4 Rue de Ponthieu, 75008 Paris, France

Azoff, Irving *Record Company Executive*
%Azoff Records, Warner Bros Records, 3300 Warner Blvd, Burbank, CA 91505

Azzara, Candice *Actress*
%Gersh Agency, 232 N Canon Dr, Beverly Hills, CA 90210

B

Baba, Corneliu *Artist*
Uniunea Artistilor Plastici, Str Nicolae Iorga 42, Bucharest, Romania

Babangida, Ibrahim *Head of State; Army General, Nigeria*
%Supreme Military Council, Government Offices, Lagos, Nigeria

Babashoff, Shirley *Swimmer*
3929 Moss, Bakersfield, CA 93308

Babbidge, Homes D, Jr *Educator*
211 Girard Ave, Hartford, CT 06105

Babbitt, Bruce E *Governor, AZ*
1700 W Washington, Phoenix, AZ 85007

Babbitt, J Randolph *Labor Leader*
%Air Line Pilots Assn, 1625 Massachusetts Ave NW, Washington, DC 20036

Babbitt, Milton *Composer*
222 Western Way, Princeton, NJ 08540

Babcock, Barbara *Actress*
%STE Representation, 9301 Wilshire Blvd, #312, Beverly Hills, CA 90210

Babcock, Horace W *Astronomer*
%Hale Observatories, 813 Santa Barbara St, Pasadena, CA 91101

Babcock, Michael J *Businessman*
%Hooker Retail USA, 1120 Ave of Americas, New York, NY 10036

Babcock, Tim *Governor, MT*
%Ox Bow Ranch, PO Box 877, Helena, MT 59601

Babenco, Hector *Movie Director*
%Conselho Nacional de Cinema, Rua Mayrink Viega 28, Rio de Janeiro, Brazil

Babilonia, Tai *Figure Skater*
13889 Valley Vista, Sherman Oaks, CA 91423

Baca, John *Vietnam War Army Hero (CMH)*
14802 SE Valencia Dr, #63, Vancouver, WA 98684

Bacall, Lauren *Actress*
1 W 72nd St, #43, New York, NY 10023

Bacchus, Jim *Representative, FL*
%House of Representatives, Washington, DC 20515

Baccouche, Heidi *Prime Minister, Tunisia*
%Prime Minister's Office, Tunis, Tunisia

Bach, Barbara *Actress*
"Rocca Bella," 24 Ave Princess Grace, Monte Carlo, Monaco

Bach, Catherine *Actress*
14000 Davanna Terr, Sherman Oaks, CA 91403

Bach, Pamela *Actress*
%Artists Group, 1930 Century Park West, #403, Los Angeles, CA 90067

Bach, Richard *Writer*
%Eleanor Friede, Box "W", Bridgehampton, NY 11932

Bach, Steven K *Movie Producer*
2775 Outpost Dr, Los Angeles, CA 90068

Bachardy, Don *Screenwriter*
145 Adelaide Dr, Santa Monica, CA 90402

Bacher, Robert F *Physicist*
345 S Michigan Ave, Pasadena, CA 91106

Bachrach, Louis Fabian, Jr *Photographer*
44 Hunt St, Watertown, MA 02172

Bachrach, Louis K, Jr *Photographer*
41 Somerset Rd, West Newton, MA 02165

Backe, John D *Broadcast Executive*
224 Crest Rd, Ridgewood, NJ 07450

Backer, William *Businessman*
%Backer & Spielvogel Inc, 11 W 42nd St, New York, NY 10036

Backman, Jules *Economist, Writer*
59 Crane Rd, Scarsdale, NY 10583

Backman, Wally *Baseball Player*
160 SE 39th, Hillsboro, OR 97123

Backus, George E *Theoretical Geophysicist*
9362 La Jolla Farms Rd, La Jolla, CA 92037

Backus, John *Computer Programmer, Mathematician*
91 St Germaine Ave, San Francisco, CA 94114

Backus, Sharron *Softball Coach*
%University of California, Athletic Dept, Los Angeles, CA 90024

B

Bacon – Bailey

Bacon, Edmund N — *Architect*
2117 Locust St, Philadelphia, PA 19103

Bacon, Francis — *Artist*
%Marlborough Fine Art Ltd, 6 Albemarle St, London W1X 4BY, England

Bacon, James — *Columnist*
10982 Topeka Dr, Northridge, CA 91324

Bacon, Kevin — *Actor*
800 West End Ave, #7-A, New York, NY 10025

Bacon, Roger F — *Navy Admiral*
Assistant CNO, Undersea Warfare, Navy Department, Washington, DC 20350

Bacot, J Carter — *Financier*
%Bank of New York, 48 Wall St, New York, NY 10015

Badgro, Morris H (Red) — *Football Player*
1010 E Temperance St, Kent, WA 98031

Badham, John — *Movie Director*
%Badham-Cohen Group, 100 Universal City Plz, Universal City, CA 91608

Badillo, Herman — *Representative, NY*
405 W 259th St, Bronx, NY 10471

Badler, Jane — *Actress*
%Artists Agency, 10000 Santa Monica Blvd, #305, Los Angeles, CA 90067

Badouin I — *King, Belgium*
%Royal Palace, Brussels, Belgium

Badura-Skoda, Paul — *Concert Pianist*
Zuckerkandlgass 14, A-1190 Vienna, Austria

Baer, Kenneth P — *Businessman*
%CF Industries, Salem Lake Dr, Long Grove, IL 60047

Baer, Max, Jr — *Actor, Movie Producer, Director*
%Max Baer Productions, 10433 Wilshire Blvd, #104, Los Angeles, CA 90024

Baer, Parley — *Actor*
4967 Bilmoor Ave, Tarzana, CA 91365

Baez, Joan — *Singer*
934 Santa Cruz, Menlo Park, CA 94025

Bafile, Corrado Cardinal — *Religious Leader*
Via P Pancrazio Pfeiffer 10, 00193 Rome, Italy

Bagdasarian, Ross — *Actor*
1465 Lindacrest Dr, Beverly Hills, CA 90210

Bagdikian, Ben H — *Educator, Journalist*
217 Gravatt Dr, Berkeley, CA 94705

Baggetta, Vincent — *Actor*
4144 Crisp Canyon Rd, Sherman Oaks, CA 91403

Baggio, Sebastiano Cardinal — *Religious Leader*
Piazza Della Citta Leonina 9, 00193 Rome, Italy

Bagian, James P — *Astronaut*
%NASA, Johnson Space Ctr, Houston, TX 77058

Bagley, John — *Basketball Player*
92 Harral Ave, Bridgeport, CT 06604

Bagnell, Francis J — *Football Player*
2 Bala Plaza, #514, Bala Cynwyd, PA 19004

Bahouth, Peter — *Association Executive*
%Greenpeace, 1436 "U" St NW, Washington, DC 20007

Bahr, Egon — *Government Official, West Germany*
Bundeshaur, 5300 Bonn 1, Germany

Bahr, Matt — *Football Player*
%New York Giants, Giants Stadium, East Rutherford, NJ 07073

Bahr, Morton — *Labor Leader*
%Communications Workers Union, 1925 "K" St NW, Washington, DC 20006

Bahrenburg, Claeys — *Publisher*
%Hearst Corp, 959 8th Ave, New York, NY 10019

Bailar, Benjamin F — *Government Official*
101 S Wacker Dr, Chicago, IL 60606

Bailar, John C, Jr — *Chemist*
605 E Harding Dr, Urbana, IL 61801

Bailey, David — *Actor*
10 E 44th St, #700, New York, NY 10017

Bailey, David — *Photographer*
177 Gloucester Ave, London NW1 8LA, England

Bailey, Don *Representative, PA*
558 N Main St, Greensburg, PA 15601

Bailey, G W *Actor*
%Writers & Artists Agency, 11726 San Vicente Blvd, #300, Los Angeles, CA 90049

Bailey, Glenn W *Businessman*
%Bairnco Corp, 200 Park Ave, New York, NY 10166

Bailey, Irving W, II *Businessman*
%Capitol Holding Corp, 608 4th Ave, Louisville, KY 40232

Bailey, Jim *Entertainer*
%Lawrence/Keith, 1326 N Fairfax Ave, Los Angeles, CA 90046

Bailey, John *Cinematographer*
%United Talent, 9650 Wilshire Blvd, #500, Beverly Hills, CA 90212

Bailey, Johnny *Football Player*
%Chicago Bears, 250 N Washington Rd, Lake Forest, IL 60045

Bailey, Leonard H *Heart Surgeon*
%Loma Linda University, Medical School, Loma Linda, CA 92350

Bailey, Louis C *Businessman*
%Southwestern Bell Corp, 1 Bell Ctr, St Louis, MO 63101

Bailey, Paul *Writer*
32 Stephen's Gdns, London W2, England

Bailey, Philip *Singer*
%CBS Records, Sony Music, 1801 Century Park West, Los Angeles, CA 90067

Bailey, Ralph E *Businessman*
%E I du Pont de Nemours Co, 1807 Market St, Wilmington, DE 19898

Bailey, Razzy *Singer*
%Jim Halsey Co, 520 Georgetown Dr, Casselberry, FL 32707

Bailey, Thurl *Basketball Player*
%Minnesota Timberwolves, 500 City Pl, 730 Hennepin Ave, Minneapolis, MN 55403

Bailey, W J *Financier*
%Australia & New Zealand Banking Grp, 55 Collins, Melbourne, Australia

Bailey, Wendell *Representative, MO*
101 W 4th St, Willow Springs, MO 65793

Bailey, William *Artist*
223 E 10th St, New York, NY 10003

Bailey, William O *Businessman*
%Aetna Life & Casualty, 151 Farmington Ave, Hartford, CT 06156

Bailyn, Bernard *Historian*
170 Clifton St, Belmont, MA 02178

Bain, Barbara *Actress*
%Contemporary Artists, 132 Lasky Dr, #B, Beverly Hills, CA 90212

Bain, Conrad *Actor*
1230 Chickory Ln, Los Angeles, CA 90049

Bainbridge, Beryl *Actress, Writer*
42 Albert St, London NW1 7NU, England

Bainbridge, Kenneth T *Physicist*
5 Nobscot Rd, Weston, MA 02193

Baines, Harold *Baseball Player*
107 Trusty St, St Michaels, MD 21663

Bainton, Roland H *Educator*
363 St Ronan St, New Haven, CT 06511

Baio, Jimmy *Actor*
%Badgley Conner, 9229 Sunset Blvd, #607, Los Angeles, CA 90067

Baio, Scott *Actor*
11662 Duque Dr, Studio City, CA 91604

Baird, Charles F *Businessman*
%Inco Ltd, 1 First Canadian Pl, Toronto ON M5X 1C4, Canada

Baird, Joseph E *Businessman*
%Occidental Petroleum, 10889 Wilshire Blvd, Los Angeles, CA 90024

Baker Guadagnino, Kathy *Golfer*
%International Management Grp, 1 Erieview Plz, Cleveland, OH 44114

Baker, Al (Bubba) *Football Player*
%Cleveland Browns, Cleveland Stadium, Cleveland, OH 44286

Baker, Anita *Singer*
804 N Crescent Dr, Beverly Hills, CA 90210

Baker, Blanche *Actress*
70 Flower Ave, Hastings-on-Hudson, NY 10706

Baker, Bob R *Financier*
%First Columbia Financial Corp, 5850 S Ulster Cir, Denver, CO 80217

Baker, Buck *Auto Racing Driver*
5000 Currituck Dr, Charlotte, NC 28210

Baker, Buddy *Auto Racing Driver*
%NASCAR, 1801 Speedway Blvd, Daytona Beach, FL 32015

Baker, Calvin D *Financier*
%Atlantic Financial Federal, 50 Monument Rd, Bela Cynwyd, PA 19004

Baker, Carlos *Writer, Educator*
34 Allison Rd, Princeton, NJ 08540

Baker, Carroll *Actress*
%Abrams Artists, 9200 Sunset Blvd, #625, Los Angeles, CA 90069

Baker, D Kenneth *Educator*
495 E 12th St, Claremont, CA 91711

Baker, Dexter F *Businessman*
%Air Products & Chemicals, PO Box 538, Allentown, PA 18105

Baker, Diane *Actress*
PO Box 691501, Los Angeles, CA 90069

Baker, Dusty (Johnnie B) *Baseball Player*
633 Stonegate Dr S, San Francisco, CA 94080

Baker, Ellen Shulman *Astronaut*
%NASA, Johnson Space Ctr, Houston, TX 77058

Baker, George P *Educator*
4075 E Campbell Ave, Phoenix, AZ 85018

Baker, Graham *Movie Director*
10 Buckingham St, London WC2, England

Baker, Howard H, Jr *Senator, TN*
Baker Worthington Crossley Stansberry Woolf, 530 Gay SW, Knoxville, TN 37902

Baker, James A, III *Secretary, State*
%Department of State, 2201 "C" St NW, Washington, DC 20520

Baker, James K *Businessman*
%Arvin Industries, 1531 13th St, Columbus, IN 47201

Baker, Janet *Opera, Concert Singer*
450 Edgeware Rd, London W2, England

Baker, Joby *Actor*
%Artists Agency, 10000 Santa Monica Blvd, #305, Los Angeles, CA 90067

Baker, Joe Don *Actor*
23339 Hatteras St, Woodland Hills, CA 91367

Baker, John F, Jr *Vietnam War Army Hero (CMH)*
7400 Pirates Cove, #163, Las Vegas, NV 89128

Baker, John T *Publisher*
%JAMA Magazine, 535 N Dearborn St, Chicago, IL 60610

Baker, Jordan *Actress*
%J Michael Bloom Ltd, 9200 Sunset Blvd, #710, Los Angeles, CA 90069

Baker, Mark *Bowler*
12841 Newhope, Garden Grove, CA 92640

Baker, Michael A *Astronaut*
%NASA, Johnson Space Ctr, Houston, TX 77058

Baker, R Robinson *Surgeon*
8717 McDonogh Rd, McDonogh, MD 21208

Baker, Raymond *Actor*
%Triad Artists, 10100 Santa Monica Blvd, #1600, Los Angeles, CA 90067

Baker, Richard H *Representative, LA*
%House of Representatives, Washington, DC 20515

Baker, Russell W *Journalist, Columnist*
%New York Times, 229 W 43rd St, New York, NY 10036

Baker, Terry W *Football Player*
888 SW 5th Ave, Portland, OR 97204

Baker, Thane *Track Athlete*
2812 Bonnywood, Dallas, TX 75233

Baker, Thomas A *Air Force General*
Commander, 12th Air Force, Bergstrom Air Force Base, TX 78743

Baker, Warren J *Educator*
%California Poly University, President's Office, San Luis Obispo, CA 93407

Baker, William O *Research Chemist*
%Bell Telephone Laboratories, Murray Hill, NJ 07974

Bakewell, William *Actor*
1745 Selby Ave, #16, Los Angeles, CA 90024
Bakke, Allan *Social Activist*
%Mayo Clinic, 200 First St SW, Rochester, MN 55901
Bakken, Earl E *Businessman*
%Medtronic Inc, 7000 Central Ave NE, Minneapolis, MN 55432
Bakken, Jim *Football Player*
%St Louis University, Athletic Dept, St Louis, MO 63178
Bakker, Tammy *Religious Leader*
%New Covenant Church, Box 690788, Orlando, FL 32869
Bakshi, Ralph *Animator*
%Gang, 6400 Sunset Blvd, Los Angeles, CA 90028
Bakula, Scott *Actor*
%Henderson/Hogan Agency, 247 S Beverly Dr, #102, Beverly Hills, CA 90210
Balaguer, Joaquin *President, Dominican Republic*
Partido Reformista, Ensanche LA Fe, Santo Domingo, Dominican Republic
Balandin, Alexander *Cosmonaut*
141 160 Svyosdny Gorodok, Moskovskoi Oblasti, Potchta Kosmonavtov, Russia
Balas, Iolanda *Track Athlete*
%Olympic Committee, Str Vasile Conta 16, 1 Bucharest, Canada
Balassa, Bela *Economist*
2134 Wyoming Ave NW, Washington, DC 20008
Balderstone, James *Businessman*
Broken Hill Proprietary, 140 William St, Melbourne, Vic 3000, Australia
Baldessari, John *Conceptual Artist*
2001 1/2 Main St, Santa Monica, CA 90405
Baldock, Bobby R *Judge*
%US Court of Appeals, PO Box 2388, Roswell, NM 88202
Baldschun, Jack *Baseball Player*
492 Bader St, Green Bay, WI 54302
Baldwin, Alec *Actor*
%J Michael Bloom Ltd, 9200 Sunset Blvd, #710, Los Angeles, CA 90069
Baldwin, Howard *Hockey Executive*
%Hartford Whalers, 1 Civic Center Plz, Hartford, CT 06103
Baldwin, John A, Jr *Navy Admiral*
National Defense University, President's Office, Ft McNair, Washington, DC 20319
Baldwin, Phillip B *Judge*
%US Court of Appeals, 717 Madison Pl NW, Washington, DC 20439
Baldwin, Robert H B *Financier*
%Morgan Stanley Co, 1251 Ave of Americas, New York, NY 10020
Bales, Philip J *Businessman*
%Eastern Air Lines, Miami International Airport, Miami, FL 33148
Balfanz, John C *Ski Jumper*
7770 E Iliff Ave, #G, Denver, CO 80231
Baliles, Gerald L *Governor, VA*
%Hunton & Williams, PO Box 1535, Richmond, VA 23212
Ball, George L *Financier*
%J&W Seligman Co, 130 Liberty St, 24th Fl, New York, NY 10006
Ball, George W *Government Official*
860 United Nations Plz, New York, NY 10017
Ball, Robert M *Government Official*
7217 Park Terrace Dr, Alexandria, VA 22307
Ballard, Carroll *Movie Director*
PO Box 556, Mt Helena, CA 94574
Ballard, Del, Jr *Bowler*
%Professional Bowlers Assn, 1720 Merriman Rd, Akron, OH 44313
Ballard, Donald E *Vietnam War Navy Hero (CMH)*
801 NE 98th Terr, Kansas City, MO 64155
Ballard, J G *Writer*
36 Old Charlton Rd, Shepperton, Middlesex, England
Ballard, Robert D *Oceanographer; Titanic Discovery Mission*
538 Hatchville Rd, Hatchville, MA 02536
Ballesteros, Severiano *Golfer*
Ruiz Zorilla 16-2J, 39009 Santander, Spain
Ballestrero, Anastasio Cardinal *Religious Leader*
Via Arcivescovado 12, 10121 Turin, Italy

B

Ballhaus, William F *Aeronautical Engineer*
%Ames Research Ctr, Moffett Field, CA 94035

Balsam, Martin *Actor*
%Marshak-Wyckoff Assoc, 280 S Beverly Dr, #400, Beverly Hills, CA 90212

Balser, Glennon *Religious Leader*
%Advent Christian Church, PO Box 23152, Charlotte, NC 28212

Baltensweiler, Armin *Businessman*
%Sulzer Brothers Ltd, CH-8401 Winterthur, Switzerland

Balthus *Artist*
Grand Chalet Rossiniere, Canton de Vaux, Switzerland

Baltimore, David *Nobel Medicine Laureate*
28 Donnell St, Cambridge, MA 02138

Baltsa, Agnes *Opera Singer*
%Artist's Mgmt, Rutistrasse 52, CH-8044 Zurick-Gockhausen, Switzerland

Baltz, Lewis *Photographer*
70 Glen Dr, Sausalito, CA 94965

Balukas, Jean *Billiards Player*
9818 4th Ave, Brooklyn, NY 11209

Bama, Jim *Artist*
PO Box 148, Wapiti, WY 82450

Bamberger, George *Baseball Manager*
455 N Bath Club Blvd, North Redington Beach, FL 33720

Banach, Ed *Wrestler*
2128 Country Club Blvd, Ames, IA 50010

Banachowski, Andy *Volleyball Coach*
%University of California, Athletic Dept, Los Angeles, CA 90024

Banana, Canaan S *President, Zimbabwe*
%President's Office, Salisbury, Zimbabwe

Banaszynski, Jacqui *Journalist*
%St Paul Pioneer Press Dispatch, 345 Cedar St, St Paul, MN 55101

Banazek, Cas *Football Player*
2520 Nanette, San Carlos, CA 94070

Bancroft, Anne *Actress*
915 N Foothill Rd, Beverly Hills, CA 90210

Banda, Hastings K *President, Malawi*
%President's Office, Private Bag 388, Capital City, Lilongwe 3, Malawi

Bandaranaike, Sirimavo R D *Prime Minister, Sri Lanka*
65 Rosemead Pl, Colombo, Sri Lanka

Bando, Sal *Baseball Player*
104 W Juniper Ln, Mequon, WI 53092

Bandy, Moe *Singer*
%Woody Bowles Co, PO Box 40661, Nashville, TN 37204

Banfield, Edward C *Educator*
%Harvard University, Littauer Ctr, Cambridge, MA 02138

Bangemann, Martin *Government Official, West Germany*
%Economics Ministry, Villemomblerstrasse, 5300 Bonn, Germany

Bangerter, Dee R *Businessman*
%Winn Enterprises, 5500 E Santa Ana Canyon Rd, Anaheim, CA 92807

Bangerter, Lee R *Businessman*
%Winn Enterprises, 5500 E Santa Ana Canyon Rd, Anaheim, CA 92807

Bangerter, Norman H *Governor, UT*
%Governor's Office, State Capitol Bldg, #210, Salt Lake City, UT 84114

Bani Sadr, Abolhassan *Prime Minister, Iran*
16 Ave Pont Royal, 94230 Cachan, France

Bank, Aaron *WW II Army Hero*
239 Avenida Montalvo, San Clemente, CA 92672

Banks, Carl *Football Player*
%New York Giants, Giants Stadium, East Rutherford, NJ 07073

Banks, Chip *Football Player*
%Indianapolis Colts, 7001 W 56th St, Indianapolis, IN 46254

Banks, David R *Businessman*
%Beverly Enterprises, 873 S Fair Oaks Ave, Pasadena, CA 91105

Banks, Dennis *Indian Activist*
%General Delivery, Oglala, SD 57764

Banks, Ernie *Baseball Player*
PO Box 24302, Los Angeles, CA 90024

Banks, Kelcie *Boxer*
2322 Richton, #19, Houston, TX 77098

Banks, Russell *Businessman*
%Grow Grp, 200 Park Ave, New York, NY 10166

Banks, Ted *Track Coach*
%Riverside Community College, Athletic Dept, Riverside, CA 92506

Banks, Willie *Track Athlete*
2323 Benthey Ave, #305, Los Angeles, CA 90064

Bankston, Damon B *Businessman*
%Tidewater Inc, 1440 Canal St, New Orleans, LA 70112

Banky, Vilma *Actress*
316 N Rossmore Ave, Los Angeles, CA 90004

Bannen, Ian *Actor*
%Redway Ltd, 16 Berners St, London W1, England

Banner, Bob *Movie Producer, Director*
9037 Alto Cedro Dr, Beverly Hills, CA 90210

Bannister, Daniel R *Businessman*
%Dynalectron Corp, 1313 Dolley Madison Blvd, Madison, VA 22101

Bannister, Floyd *Baseball Player*
6701 Caball Dr, Paradise Valley, AZ 85253

Bannister, Roger *Track Athlete, Neurologist*
16 Edwardes Sq, London W8, England

Bannon, Jack *Actor*
5832 Nagle Ave, Van Nuys, CA 91401

Banois, Vincent J *Football Player*
24256 J Tamarack Trl, Southfield, MI 48075

Banowsky, William S *Educator, Businessman*
%Gaylord Broadcasting Co, PO Box 25125, Oklahoma City, OK 73125

Banta, Merle *Businessman*
%AM International, 128 E Randolph Dr, Chicago, IL 60601

Bantle, Louis F *Businessman*
%United States Tobacco Co, 100 W Putnam Ave, Greenwich, CT 06830

Bao, Joseph *Microsurgeon*
%University of Southern California, Medical School, Los Angeles, CA 90089

Baptista, Elieser *Businessman*
%Vale do Rio Doce, Ave Garca Aranha 25, 20 005 Rio de Janeiro, Brazil

Baquet, Dean P *Journalist*
%Chicago Tribune, 435 N Michigan Ave, Chicago, IL 60611

Bar-Illan, David *Concert Pianist*
%Columbia Artists Mgmt Inc, 165 W 57th St, New York, NY 10019

Bar-Josef, Ofer *Archeologist*
%Harvard University, Archeology Dept, Cambridge, MA 02138

Bar-Lev, Haim *Government Official, Israel*
%Israel Labor Party, PO Box 3263, 110 Haijarkon St, Tel-Aviv, Israel

Barach, Philip G *Businessman*
%US Shoe Corp, 1 Eastwood Dr, Cincinnati, OH 45227

Barany, Istvan *Swimmer*
I Attila Ut 87, Budapest 01012, Hungary

Barbara, Agatha *President, Malta*
%President's Office, The Palace, Valletta, Malta

Barbeau, Adrienne *Actress*
PO Box 1334, North Hollywood, CA 91604

Barber of Wentbridge, Baron *Financier*
%Standard Chartered Bank, 10 Clements Ln, London EC4N 7AB, England

Barber, G C *Businessman*
%Anchor Hocking Corp, 109 N Broad, Lancaster, OH 43130

Barber, Glynis *Actress*
%James Sharkey Mgmt, 15 Golden Sq, 3rd Fl, London W1R 3AG, England

Barber, Mike *Football Player*
%Cincinnati Bengals, 200 Riverfront Stadium, Cincinnati, OH 45202

Barber, Miller *Golfer*
PO Box 2202 Sherman, TX 75090

Barber, Red (W L) *Sportscaster*
3013 Brookmont Dr, Tallahassee, FL 32312

Barber, William E *Korean War Marine Corps Hero (CMH)*
15231 Chalon Cir, Irvine, CA 92714

Barbera – Barnard

Barbera, Joseph *Animator*
%Hanna-Barbera Productions, 3400 W Cahuenga Blvd, Los Angeles, CA 90068

Barbieri, Fedora *Opera Singer*
Viale Belfiore 9, Florence, Italy

Barbierri, Gato *Jazz Saxophonist*
PO Box 82, Great Neck, NY 11021

Barbour, John *Comedian, Writer*
%NBC-TV, 30 Rockefeller Plz, New York, NY 10020

Barco Vargas, Virgilio *President, Colombia*
%President's Office, Palacio de Narino, Correra 8, Bogota DE, Colombia

Bardot, Brigitte *Actress*
La Madrigue, 83990 St Tropez, Var, France

Bare, Bobby *Singer, Songwriter*
PO Box 2422, Hendersonville, TN 37077

Barenboim, Daniel *Conductor, Concert Pianist*
%Harold Holt Ltd, 134 Wigmore St, London W1, England

Bares, William G *Businessman*
%Lubrizol Corp, 29400 Lakeland Blvd, Wickliffe, OH 44092

Barfield, Jesse *Baseball Player*
4208 Canterwood Dr, Houston, TX 77068

Barfod, Hakon *Yachtsman*
Jon Ostensensv 15, 1360 Nesbru, Norway

Barfoot, Van T *WW II Army Hero (CMH)*
Leaning Oaks, Rt 1, Box 32-A, Ford, VA 23850

Barger, Thomas C *Businessman*
2685 Calle del Oro, La Jolla, CA 92307

Barkeley, Norman A, Jr *Businessman*
%Lear Siegler Inc, 2850 Ocean Park Blvd, Santa Monica, CA 90405

Barker, Bob *Actor*
1851 Outpost Dr, Los Angeles, CA 90068

Barker, Clive *Writer*
%Harper & Row, 10 E 53rd St, New York, NY 10022

Barker, Horace Albert *Biochemist*
561 Santa Clara Ave, Berkeley, CA 94707

Barker, Hugh A *Businessman*
%Public Service Co of Indiana, 100 E Main St, Plainfield, IN 46168

Barker, James R *Businessman*
%Moore McCormack Resources, 1 Landmark Sq, Stamford, CT 06901

Barker, Norman, Jr *Financier*
%First Interstate Bancorp, 707 Wilshire Blvd, Los Angeles, CA 90017

Barker, Richard A *Religious Leader*
%Orthodox Presbyterian Church, 7401 Old York Rd, Philadelphia, PA 19126

Barker, Robinson Franklin *Businessman*
8 Woodland Rd, Sewickley, PA 15143

Barkin, Ellen *Actress*
3007 Lake Glen Dr, Beverly Hills, CA 90210

Barkley, Charles *Basketball Player*
%Philadelphia 76ers, P0 Box 25040, Veterans Stadium, Philadelphia, PA 19147

Barkley, Paul C *Businessman*
%PS Group Inc, 3225 N Harbor Dr, San Diego, CA 92101

Barkman Tyler, Janie *Swimmer*
%Princeton University, Athletic Dept, Princeton, NJ 08544

Barksdale, James L *Businessman*
%Federal Express Corp, 2990 Airways Blvd, Memphis, TN 38194

Barksdale, Rhesa H *Judge*
%US Court of Appeals, 245 E Capitol St, Jackson, MS 39201

Barlick, Al *Baseball Umpire*
2071 N 6th, Springfield, IL 62702

Barlow, Thomas J *Businessman*
%Anderson Clayton Co, 1100 Louisiana, #3800, Houston, TX 77002

Barmore, Leon *Basketball Coach*
%Louisiana Tech University, Athletic Dept, Ruston, LA 71272

Barnard, Christian *Heart Surgeon*
Moorings, Flamingo Cres, Capetown, South Africa

Barnard, D Douglas, Jr *Representative, GA*
Milledge Rd, Augusta, GA 30904

Barnes, Binnie *Actress*
838 N Doheny Dr, #B, Los Angeles, CA 90069

Barnes, Carlyle F *Businessman*
%Barnes Grp, 123 Main St, Bristol, CT 06010

Barnes, Duncan *Editor*
%Field & Stream Magazine, 2 Park Ave, New York, NY 10016

Barnes, Edward Larrabee *Architect*
410 E 62nd St, New York, NY 10021

Barnes, Erich *Football Player*
255 W 85th St, New York, NY 10024

Barnes, George Elton *Businessman*
%Wayne Hummer Co, 175 W Jackson Blvd, Chicago, IL 60603

Barnes, Harry G, Jr *Diplomat*
%Department of State, 2201 "C" St NW, Washington, DC 20520

Barnes, J David *Financier*
%Mellon National Corp, Mellon Sq, Pittsburgh, PA 15230

Barnes, James E *Businessman*
%MAPCO Inc, PO Box 645, Tulsa, OK 74101

Barnes, Jhane *Fashion Designer*
19 W 55th St, New York, NY 10019

Barnes, Joanna *Actress*
%Progressive Artists Agency, 400 S Beverly Dr, #216, Beverly Hills, CA 90212

Barnes, Julian *Writer*
%A D Peters, 10 Buckingham St, London WC2N 6BU, England

Barnes, Leslie O *Businessman*
%Ryder System Inc, 3600 NW 82nd Ave, Miami, FL 33166

Barnes, Robert H *Psychiatrist*
%Texas Technical University, Medical School, Lubbock, TX 79409

Barnes, Wallace *Businessman*
%Barnes Grp, 123 Main St, Bristol, CT 06010

Barnes, Zane E *Businessman*
%Southwestern Bell Corp, 1 Bell Ctr, St Louis, MO 63101

Barnet, Will *Artist, Educator*
%National Arts Club, 15 Gramercy Park, New York, NY 10003

Barnett, Harlon *Football Player*
%Cleveland Browns, Cleveland Stadium, Cleveland, OH 44114

Barnett, Jim *Basketball Player*
7 Kittiwake Rd, Orinda, CA 94563

Barnett, Jonathan *Architect*
30 Park Ave, New York, NY 10016

Barnett, Marguerite Ross *Educator*
%University of Houston, President's Office, Houston, TX 77004

Barnett, Robert L *Businessman*
%Ameritek Corp, 225 W Randolph St, Chicago, IL 60606

Barnett, Sabrina *Model*
%Next Model Mgmt, 115 E 57th St, #1540, New York, NY 10022

Barnett, Tommy *Religious Leader*
%Phoenix First Assembly Church, 13613 N Cave Creek Rd, Phoenix, AZ 85022

Barnevik, Barney *Businessman*
%ASEA AB, 721 83 Vasteras, Sweden

Barnevik, Percy *Businessman*
%Sandvik AB Grp, 811 81, Sandviken, Sweden

Barney, Lem *Football Player*
%Michigan Consolidated Gas Co, 500 Griswold St, Detroit, MI 48226

Barney, R L *Businessman*
%Wendy's International, PO Box 256, Dublin, OH 43017

Barnidge, Tom *Editor*
%Sporting News, 1212 N Lindbergh Blvd, St Louis, MO 63166

Barnum, Harvey C, Jr *Vietnam War Marine Corps Hero (CMH)*
5410 Wycklow Ct, Alexandria, VA 22304

Barr, D W *Businessman*
%Moore Corp, 1 First Canadian Pl, Toronto ON M5X 1G5, Canada

Barr, Doug *Actor*
515 S Irving Blvd, Los Angeles, CA 90020

Barr, Joseph W *Secretary, Treasury*
Houyhnhnm Farm, Hume, VA 22639

B

Barr – Barry

Barr, Kenneth J *Businessman*
%Cyprus Minerals Co, 7200 S Alton Way, Englewood, CO 80155

Barr, Murray L *Anatomist, Geneticist*
452 Old Wonderland Rd, London ON N6K 3R2, Canada

Barr, Thomas D *Attorney*
%Cravath Swaine Moore, 1 Chase Manhattan Plz, New York, NY 10005

Barr, William P *Attorney General*
%Department of Justice, Constitution Ave & 10th St, Washington, DC 20530

Barragan, Luis *Architect*
Calle General Francisco Ramirez 14, Mexico 18 DF, Mexico

Barrasso, Tom *Hockey Player*
%Pittsburgh Penguins, Civic Arena, Pittsburgh, PA 15219

Barrault, Jean-Louis *Actor, Producer*
%Madeleine Renaud Agency, 18 Ave du President Wilson, 75116 Paris, France

Barrault, Marie-Christine *Actress*
19 Rue de Lisbonne, 75008 Paris, France

Barre, Raymond *Prime Minister, France*
4-6 Ave Emile-Acollas, Paris, France

Barreto, Bruno *Movie Director*
%Embrafilme, Rua Mayrink-Veiga 28, Rio de Janeiro 20090, Brazil

Barrett, Bill *Representative, NE*
%House of Representatives, Washington, DC 20515

Barrett, Charles M *Businessman*
%Western & Southern Life Insurance, 400 Broadway, Cincinnati, OH 45202

Barrett, Charles S *Physicist, Metallurgist*
%University of Denver, Metallurgy Materials Division, Denver, CO 80208

Barrett, James E *Judge*
%US Court of Appeals, PO Box 1288, Cheyenne, WY 82001

Barrett, Rona *Columnist*
1122 Tower Rd, Beverly Hills, CA 90210

Barrett, Tom H *Businessman*
%Goodyear Tire & Rubber Co, 1144 E Market St, Akron, OH 44316

Barrett, William *Philosopher*
34 Harwood Ave, North Tarrytown, NY 10591

Barrie, Barbara *Actress*
465 West End Ave, New York, NY 10024

Barrie, Dennis *Museum Director*
%Contemporary Arts Center, 115 E 5th St, Cincinnati, OH 45202

Barrie, George *Businessman*
%Faberge Inc, 1345 Ave of Americas, New York, NY 10019

Barris, Chuck *Television Producer*
9537 Charleyville Blvd, Beverly Hills, CA 90212

Barron, Arthur *Businessman*
%Gulf & Western Industries, 1 Gulf & Western Plz, New York, NY 10023

Barron, Donald J *Financier*
%Midland Bank, Poultry, London EC2P 2BX, England

Barron, Kenny *Jazz Musician*
%Joanne Klein, 130 W 28th St, New York, NY 10001

Barron, William W *Governor, WV*
Nassau House, #603, 301 N Ocean Blvd, Pompano Beach, FL 33062

Barrone, Gerald D *Financier*
%Coast Federal Savings, 855 S Hill St, Los Angeles, CA 90014

Barrow, Bernard *Actor*
%Don Buchwald Assoc, 10 E 44th St, New York, NY 10017

Barrows, Marjorie *Writer*
1615 Hinman Ave, Evanston, IL 60201

Barrs, Jay *Archer*
1666 South Extension, #17-104, Mesa, AZ 85202

Barry, Dave *Journalist*
%Miami Herald, 1 Herald Plz, Miami, FL 33101

Barry, Edward P, Jr *Air Force General*
Commander, Space/Missile Systems Division, Los Angeles Air Force Base, CA 90009

Barry, Gene *Actor*
622 N Maple Dr, Beverly Hills, CA 90210

Barry, J J *Labor Official*
%Int'l Brotherhood of Electrical Workers, 1125 15th St NW, Washington, DC 20005

Barry, John *Composer*
540 Centre Island Rd, Oyster Bay, NY 11771

Barry, Lynda *Cartoonist*
%Acme Features Syndicate, 2219 Main St, #E, Santa Monica, CA 90405

Barry, Patricia *Actress*
PO Box 49895, Los Angeles, CA 90049

Barry, Philip, Jr *Movie Producer, Writer*
PO Box 49895, Los Angeles, CA 90049

Barry, Sy (Seymour) *Cartoonist (Flash Gordon, Phantom)*
34 Saratoga Dr, Jericho, NY 11753

Barrymore, Drew *Actress*
%JAID, 3960 Laurel Canyon Blvd, #189, Studio City, CA 91604

Barrymore, John, III *Actor*
8036 Jovenita Canyon Rd, Los Angeles, CA 90046

Barschall, Henry H *Physicist*
1110 Tumalo Trl, Madison, WI 53711

Barstow, Richard *Choral Director*
200 W 54th St, New York, NY 10019

Bart, Lionel *Composer, Lyricist*
%Patricia McNaughton, 209 Fulham Rd, London W12, England

Bart, Peter *Editor*
%Variety Inc, 154 W 56th St, New York, NY 10036

Bartell, Dick *Baseball Player*
1118 Island Dr, Alameda, CA 94501

Barth, John *Writer*
%John Hopkins University, Writing Seminars, Baltimore, MD 21218

Barth, Richard *Businessman*
%Ciba-Geigy Corp, 444 Saw Mill Rd, Ardsley, NY 10502

Barth, Robert *Religious Leader*
%Churches of Christ in Christian Union, Box 30, Circleville, OH 43113

Barthelemy, Sidney J *Mayor*
%Mayor's Office, City Hall, 1300 Perdido St, New Orleans, LA 70112

Bartholomay, William C *Businessman, Baseball Executive*
%Frank B Hall Co, 549 Pleasantville Rd, Briarcliff Manor, NY 10510

Bartholomew, Frank H *Publisher*
General Delivery, Glenbrook, NV 89413

Bartholomew, Samuel W, Jr *Attorney*
%Federal National Mortgage Assn, 1133 15th St NW, Washington, DC 20005

Bartlett, Bonnie *Actress*
12805 Hortense St, Studio City, CA 91604

Bartlett, Boyd C *Businessman*
%Deere & Co, John Deere Rd, Moline, IL 61265

Bartlett, Dwight K, III *Businessman*
%Mutual of America, 666 5th Ave, New York, NY 10103

Bartlett, Hall *Movie Producer, Director*
861 Stone Canyon Rd, Los Angeles, CA 90024

Bartlett, Jennifer *Artist*
%Paula Cooper Gallery, 155 Wooster St, New York, NY 10012

Bartlett, Martine *Actress*
PO Box 32706, Tucson, AZ 85751

Bartlett, Neil *Chemist*
6 Oak Dr, Orinda, CA 94563

Bartlett, Paul D *Chemist*
%Texas Christian University, Chemistry Dept, Fort Worth, TX 76129

Bartlett, Steve *Mayor, Dallas; Representative, TX*
%Mayor's Office, City Hall, 1500 Marilla, Dallas, TX 75201

Bartlett, Walter E *Businessman, Publisher*
%Mutimedia Inc, 305 S Main St, Greenville, SC 29601

Bartley, Robert L *Editor*
%Wall Street Journal, 200 Liberty St, New York, NY 10281

Bartoe, John-David *Astronaut*
%Navy Research Lab, Code 4162, Washington, DC 20375

Bartoletti, Bruno *Conductor*
%Chicago Lyric Opera, 20 N Wacker Dr, Chicago, IL 60606

Barton, Alan R *Businessman*
%Mississippi Power Co, 2992 W Beach St, Gulfport, MS 39501

Barton, Bill *Co-Designer, Barbie Doll*
%Mattel Inc, 5150 W Rosecrans Ave, Hawthorne, CA 90250

Barton, Derek H R *Nobel Chemistry Laureate*
%Texas A&M University, Chemistry Dept, College Station, TX 77843

Barton, Greg *Kayak Athlete*
1770 Bedford Ln, #F, Newport Beach, CA 92660

Barton, Jacqueline *Chemist*
%Columbia University, Chemistry Dept, New York, NY 10027

Barton, James T *Financier*
%Prudential-Bache Securities, 100 Gold St, New York, NY 10292

Barton, Joe *Representative, TX*
%House of Representatives, Washington, DC 20515

Barton, Peter *Actor*
311 S Doheny Dr, #305, Los Angeles, CA 90048

Bartow, Gene *Basketball Coach*
%University of Alabama, Athletic Dept, Birmingham, AL 35294

Barty, Billy *Actor*
4502 Farmdale Ave, North Hollywood, CA 91602

Barucci, Piero *Financier*
%Monte dei Paschi di Siena Banking Grp, 53100 Siena, Italy

Baryshnikov, Mikhail *Ballet Dancer*
31 E 12th St, #5-D, New York, NY 10021

Barzini, Luigi *Journalist, Writer*
1055 Via Cassia, Tomba di Nerone, Rome, Italy

Barzun, Jacques *Educator*
597 5th Ave, New York, NY 10017

Bashir, Omar Hassan Ahmed *Prime Minister, Sudan*
%Prime Minister's Office, Khartoum, Sudan

Basia (Trzetizelewska) *Singer*
%CBS Records, Sony Music, 1801 Century Park West, Los Angeles, CA 90067

Basilio, Carmen *Boxer*
67 Boxwood Dr, Rochester, NY 14617

Basinger, Kim *Actress*
3960 Laurel Canyon Blvd, #114, Studio City, CA 91604

Baskin, Weems O, Jr *Track Coach*
501 Kalmia Dr, Columbia, SC 29205

Basov, Nikolai G *Nobel Physics Laureate*
%Lebedev Physical Institute, 53 Lenin Prospect, Moscow, Russia

Basquette, Lina *Actress*
Shadow Knoll Apartments, #1, Wheeling, WV 26003

Bass, Barbara *Businesswoman*
%I Magnin & Co, Geary & Stockton, San Francisco, CA 94108

Bass, Dick *Football Player*
%KMPC-Radio, 5858 Sunset Blvd, Los Angeles, CA 90028

Bass, Edward *Businessman*
%Bass Brothers Enterprises, 201 Main, Fort Worth, TX 76102

Bass, Lee *Businessman*
%Bass Brothers Enterprises, 201 Main, Fort Worth, TX 76102

Bass, Louis N *Agronomist, Plant Physiologist*
1117 Fairview, Fort Collins, CO 80521

Bass, Perry R *Businessman*
%Bass Brothers Enterprises, 201 Main, Fort Worth, TX 76102

Bass, Robert M *Businessman*
%Bass Brothers Enterprises, 201 Main, Fort Worth, TX 76102

Bass, Robert O *Businessman*
%Borg-Warner Corp, 200 S Michigan Ave, Chicago, IL 60604

Bass, Saul *Movie Director, Producer*
337 S Las Palmas Ave, Los Angeles, CA 90020

Bass, Sid *Businessman*
%Bass Brothers Enterprises, 201 Main, Fort Worth, TX 76102

Basset, Brian *Editorial Cartoonist*
%Seattle Times, Fairview & Johns, Seattle, WA 98111

Bassett, Edward P *Educator, Journalist*
%Northwestern University, Journalism School, Evanston, IL 60201

Bassett, J E, Jr *Businessman*
%Bassett Furniture Industries, PO Box 626, Bassett, VA 24055

Bassett, Leslie R *Composer*
1618 Harbal Dr, Ann Arbor, MI 48105

Bassett-Seguso, Carling *Tennis Player*
%Women's International Tennis Assn, 2665 S Bayshore Dr, Miami, FL 33133

Bassey, Shirley *Singer*
Villa Capricorn, 55 Via Campoine, CH-6816 Bissone, Switzerland

Bast, William *Screenwriter*
6691 Whitley Terr, Los Angeles, CA 90068

Basu, Asit Prakas *Statistician*
3709 W Rollins Rd, Columbia, MO 65201

Batalli Cosmovici, Cristiano *Astronaut, Italy*
%Istituto Fisica Spazio Interplanetario, CNR, 00044, Frascati, Italy

Batastini, Ralph C *Businessman*
%Greyhound Corp, Greyhound Tower, Phoenix, AZ 85077

Batchelor, Joy E *Animator*
%Educational Film Center, 5-7 Kean St, London WC2B 4AT, England

Bate, Anthony *Actor*
%Parker, 55 Park Ln, London W1, England

Batelle, Kenneth *Hairdresser*
%Kenneth Salon, 19 E 54th St, New York, NY 10022

Bateman, Herbert H *Representative, VA*
%House of Representatives, Washington, DC 20515

Bateman, Jason *Actor*
%InterTalent Agency, 131 S Rodeo Dr, 300, Beverly Hills, CA 90212

Bateman, Justine *Actress*
%Mad Prairie Dog Inc, 3960 Laurel Canyon Ave, #193, Studio City, CA 91604

Bateman, Robert *Artist*
Box 115, Fulford Harbour BC V0S 1C0, Canada

Bates, Alan *Actor*
122 Hamilton Terr, London NW8, England

Bates, Charles C *Oceanographer*
136 W La Pintura, Green Valley, AZ 85614

Bates, Edward B *Businessman*
46 Ironwood Rd, West Hartford, CT 06117

Bates, Kathy *Actress*
%Susan Smith Assoc, 121 San Vicente Blvd, Beverly Hills, CA 90211

Bates, Robert T *Labor Leader*
%Railroad Signalmen Brotherhood, 601 W Golf Rd, Mount Prospect, IL 60056

Bateson, Mary Catherine *Anthropologist*
%Amherst College, Anthropology-Sociology Dept, Amherst, MA 01002

Batey, Andrew *Architect*
%Batey & Mack, 84 Vandewater St, San Francisco, CA 94133

Bathgate, Andy *Hockey Player*
43 Brentwood Dr, Bramlee ON L6T 1R1, Canada

Batiuk, Tom *Cartoonist (Crankshaft)*
%Creators Syndicate, 5777 W Century Blvd, #700, Los Angeles, CA 90045

Batson, Arthur E, Jr *Labor Leader*
%Marine & Shipbuilding Workers Union, 5101 River Rd, Bethesda, MD 20816

Batten, James K *Publisher*
%Knight-Ridder Inc, 1 Herald Plz, Miami, FL 33101

Batten, William M *Businessman*
Locust Valley, Long Island, NY 11560

Battey, Charles W *Businessman*
%United Telecommunications, 2330 Johnson Dr, Westwood, KS 66205

Battle, Hinton *Dancer, Actor*
%Borinstein Bogart Agency, 8271 Melrose Ave, #110, Los Angeles, CA 90046

Battle, Kathleen *Opera Singer*
%Metropolitan Opera Assn, Lincoln Ctr, New York, NY 10023

Battle, Lucius D *Educator, Diplomat*
4856 Rockwood Pkwy NW, Washington, DC 20016

Battle, William C *Businessman*
%Fieldcrest Mills, 326 E Stadium Dr, Eden, NC 27288

Battram, Richard L *Businessman*
%May Department Stores, 611 Olive St, St Louis, MO 63101

Batts, Warren L *Businessman*
%Dart Inc, 2211 Sanders Rd, Northbrook, IL 60062

B

Baucus – Baxter

Baucus, Max S *Senator, MT*
%US Senate, Washington, DC 20510

Baudoin I *King, Belgium*
%Royal Palace of Laeken, Laeken-Brussels, Belgium

Baudry, Patrick *Spatinaute, France*
%Aerospatiale, Etablissement de Mureaux, 78133 Les Mureaux Cedex, France

Bauer, Belinda *Actress*
%Gersh Agency, 232 N Canon Dr, Beverly Hills, CA 90210

Bauer, David *Editor*
%Sport Magazine, 119 W 40th St, New York, NY 10018

Bauer, Gerard *Businessman*
%Jacobs Suchard, 107 Ave de Cour, 1007 Lausanne, Switzerland

Bauer, Hank *Baseball Player*
12705 W 108th St, Overland Park, KS 66210

Bauer, Jaime Lyn *Actress*
%Tyler Kjar Agency, 10653 Riverside Dr, Toluca Lake, CA 91602

Bauer, William J *Judge*
%US Court of Appeals, 219 S Dearborn St, Chicago, IL 60604

Baugh, John F *Businessman*
%Sysco Corp, 1177 West Loop S, Houston, TX 77027

Baugh, Laura *Golfer*
%Ladies Professional Golf Assn, 2570 Volusia Ave, #B, Daytona Beach, FL 32114

Baugh, Sammy *Football Player*
General Delivery, Rotan, TX 79546

Baughan, Maxie *Football Player, Coach*
%Minnesota Vikings, 9520 Viking Dr, Eden Prairie, MN 55344

Baughn, William *Educator*
%University of Colorado, President's Office, Boulder, CO 80309

Baum, Herbert M *Businessman*
%Campbell Soup Co, Campbell Pl, Camden, NJ 08101

Baum, Warren C *Economist*
%IBRD, 1818 "H" St NW, Washington, DC 20433

Baum, William Cardinal *Religious Leader*
%Congregation for Catholic Education, 3 Piazza Pio XII, Rome, Italy

Bauman, E J *Businessman*
%Blue Bell Inc, 335 Church Ct, Greensboro, NC 27420

Bauman, G Duncan *Publisher*
%St Louis Globe-Democrat, 710 N Tucker Blvd, St Louis, MO 63101

Bauman, Jon (Bowzer) *Singer*
PO Box 895, Times Square Station, New York, NY 10108

Bauman, R P *Businessman*
%Avco Corp, 1275 King St, Greenwich, CT 06830

Bauman, Robert P *Businessman*
%Textron Inc, 40 Westminster St, Providence, RI 02903

Baumann, Alex *Swimmer*
2617 Field St, Sudbury ON P3E 4X8, Canada

Baumann, Frank *Baseball Player*
7712 Sunray Ln, St Louis, MO 63123

Baumgartner, Bruce *Wrestler*
%Edinboro University, Athletic Dept, Edinboro, PA 16444

Baumgartner, William *Surgeon*
%Johns Hopkins Hospital, 600 N Wolfe St, Baltimore, MD 21205

Baumhart, Raymond C *Educator*
%Loyola University, President's Office, Chicago, IL 60611

Baumol, William J *Economist*
100 Bleecker St, #29-A, New York, NY 10012

Baunsgaard, Hilmar T I *Prime Minister, Denmark*
Blidahpark 34, 2900 Hellerup, Denmark

Bausch, Pina *Dancer, Choreographer*
%Wuppertal Dance Theatre, Spinnstrasse 4, 5600 Wuppertal 2, Germany

Bavaro, Mark *Football Player*
%New York Giants, Giants Stadium, East Rutherford, NJ 07073

Baxandall, Lee *Association Executive*
%Naturist Society, PO Box 132, Oshkosh, WI 54909

Baxter, Les *Orchestra Leader*
6430 Sunset Blvd, #1002, Los Angeles, CA 90028

Baxter, Meredith *Actress*
%Gores/Fields Agency, 10100 Santa Monica Blvd, #700, Los Angeles, CA 90067

Baxter, William F *Government Official*
%Shearman & Sterling, 53 Wall St, New York, NY 10005

Bay, Eugene A, Jr *Publisher*
%Field & Stream Magazine, 1515 Broadway, New York, NY 10036

Bay, Howard *Movie, Theatre Designer*
159 W 53rd St, New York, NY 10019

Bay, Willow *Model*
%Estee Lauder, 767 5th Ave, New York, NY 10022

Bayes, G E *Religious Leader*
%Free Methodist Church, PO Box 535002, Winona Lake, IN 46590

Bayh, Birch E, Jr *Senator, IN*
1 Indiana Sq, #240, Indianapolis, IN 46204

Bayh, Evan *Governor, IN*
%Governor's Office, State House, #206, Indianapolis, IN 46204

Bayi, Filbert *Track Athlete*
%Ministry of Information, Dar es Salaam, Tanzania 46204

Bayle, Jean-Michel *Motorcycle Racing Rider*
%General Delivery, Manosque, France

Baylor, Don *Baseball Player*
733 Sapphire Ave, Ventura, CA 93004

Baylor, Elgin *Basketball Player, Executive*
%Los Angeles Clippers, Sports Arena, 3939 S Figueroa St, Los Angeles, CA 90037

Bazelon, David L *Judge*
%US Court of Appeals, 717 Madison Pl NW, Washington, DC 20439

Beach, Edward L *WW II Navy Hero*
%Henry Holt Co, 521 5th Ave, New York, NY 10175

Beach, Morrison H *Businessman*
%Travelers Corp, 1 Tower Sq, Hartford, CT 06115

Beacham, Stephanie *Actress*
%Fraser & Dunlop, 91 Regent St, London W1R 8RU, England

Beal, Jack *Artist*
67 Vestry St, New York, NY 10013

Beal, John *Actor*
205 W 54th St, New York, NY 10019

Beale, Betty *Columnist*
2926 Garfield St NW, Washington, DC 20008

Beall, Charles C, Jr *Financier*
%Texas Commerce Bancshares Inc, 600 Travis St, Houston, TX 77002

Beall, Donald R *Businessman*
%Rockwell International Corp, 600 Grant St, Pittsburgh, PA 15219

Beals, Jennifer *Actress*
%International Creative Mgmt, 40 W 57th St, New York, NY 10019

Beals, Vaughn L, Jr *Businessman*
%Harley-Davidson Inc, 3700 W Juneau Ave, Milwaukee, WI 53208

Beam, C Arlen *Judge*
%US Court of Appeals, Federal Bldg, 100 Centennial Mall N, Lincoln, NE 68508

Beam, C Grier *Businessman*
%Carolina Freight Corp, North Carolina Hwy 150 E, Cherryville, NC 28021

Beaman, Alvin G *Businessman*
420 Jackson Blvd, Nashville, TN 37205

Beaman, Sally *Writer*
%Bantam Books, 666 5th Ave, New York, NY 10103

Beame, Abraham D *Mayor*
250 Broadway, New York, NY 10007

Bean, Alan L *Astronaut*
26 Sugarberry Cir, Houston, TX 77024

Bean, Andy *Golfer*
3216 Carleton Cir, Lakeland, FL 33803

Bean, Atherton *Businessman*
%International Multifoods Corp, PO Box 2942, Minneapolis, MN 55402

Bean, Orson *Actor, Comedian*
%Gage Group, 9255 Sunset Blvd, #515, Los Angeles, CA 90069

Bean, William B *Physician*
11 Rowland Ct, Iowa City, IA 52240

B

Beard – Beck

Beard, Alfred (Butch) *Basketball Player; Coach*
%Howard University, Athletic Dept, Washington, DC 20059

Beard, Eugene P *Businessman*
%Interpublic Grp of Companies, 1271 Ave of Americas, New York, NY 10020

Beard, Frank *Golfer*
%Professional Golfers Assn, PO Box 109601, Palm Beach Gardens, FL 33410

Beard, Percy *Track Athlete*
832 NW 22nd St, Gainesville, FL 32603

Beard, Ronald S *Attorney*
%Gibson Dunn Crutcher, 333 S Grand Ave, Los Angeles, CA 90071

Bearden, Gene *Baseball Player*
PO Box 176, Helena, AR 72342

Bearse, Amanda *Actress*
%Agency for Performing Arts, 9000 Sunset Blvd, #1200, Los Angeles, CA 90069

Beasley, Allyce *Actress*
2415 Castillian Dr, Los Angeles, CA 90068

Beasley, Bruce M *Artist*
322 Lewis St, Oakland, CA 94607

Beasley, Jere L *Governor, AL*
%Beasley Wilson Allen Mendelsohn, 207 Montgomery, 10th Fl, Montgomery, AL 36103

Beasley, William H, III *Businessman*
%Velsicol Chemical Corp, 61 W Burton Pl, Chicago, IL 60611

Beath, Hugh R *Businessman*
%John Blair Co, 1290 Ave of Americas, New York, NY 10104

Beathard, Bobby *Football Executive*
%San Diego Chargers, PO Box 20666, San Diego, CA 92120

Beatrix *Queen*
Huis Ten Bosch, The Hague, Netherlands

Beattie, Ann *Writer*
%Lynn Nesbit Mgmt, 40 W 57th St, New York, NY 10019

Beattie, Bob *Skier*
%World Wide Ski Corp, 402-D Pacific Ave, Aspen, CO 81612

Beatty, Ned *Actor*
2706 N Beachwood Dr, Los Angeles, CA 90068

Beatty, Warren *Actor, Movie Director, Producer*
13671 Mulholland Dr, Beverly Hills, CA 90210

Beau Jack *Boxer*
%5th St Boxing Gym, 501 Washington Ave, Miami Beach, FL 33139

Beaupre, Don *Hockey Player*
%Washington Capitals, Capital Centre, Landover, MD 20785

Beaver, Howard O, Jr *Businessman*
%Carpenter Technology Corp, 101 W Bern St, Reading, PA 19603

Beavogui, Louis Lansana *Prime Minister, Guinea*
%Prime Minister's Office, Conakry, Guinea

Beazley, John *Baseball Player*
23 Lymington Ct, Brentwood, TN 37027

Beban, Gary *Football Player*
%Coldwell Banker, Commercial Real Estate, 533 Fremont Ave, Los Angeles, CA 90071

Becaud, Gilbert *Singer*
4 Sq Leon-Blum, 92800 Puteaux, France

Bechtel, Riley *Businessman*
%Bechtel Grp, 50 Beale St, San Francisco, CA 94105

Bechtel, Stephen D, Jr *Businessman*
%Bechtel Grp, 50 Beale St, San Francisco, CA 94105

Beck, Aaron T *Psychiatrist*
133 S 36th St, #602, Philadelphia, PA 19104

Beck, Barry *Hockey Player*
%New York Rangers, 4 Pennsylvania Plz, New York, NY 10001

Beck, Chip *Golfer*
%Professional Golfers Assn, PO Box 12458, Palm Beach Gardens, FL 33410

Beck, Dave, Sr *Labor Leader*
16750 45th St NE, Seattle, WA 98150

Beck, Jeff *Singer, Guitarist (Yardbirds)*
%Ernest Chapman Mgmt, 11 Old Square Lincoln's Inn, London WC2, England

Beck, John *Actor*
%Camden ITG, 822 S Robertson, #200, Los Angeles, CA 90035

Beck, Julian *Theater Producer, Director*
800 West End Ave, New York, NY 10025

Beck, Kimberly *Actress*
11300 W Olympic Blvd, #610, Los Angeles, CA 90064

Beck, Marilyn *Columnist*
2132 El Roble Ln, Beverly Hills, CA 90210

Beck, Martin *Actor*
%Terry Lichtman Co, 12456 Ventura Blvd, Studio City, CA 91604

Beck, Michael *Actor*
%Harris & Goldberg Agency, 1999 Ave of Stars, #2850, Los Angeles, CA 90067

Beckel, Robert D *Air Force General*
Commander, 15th Air Force, March Air Force Base, CA 92518

Becker, Boris *Tennis Player*
%Karl-Heinz Becker, Nusslocherstrasse 51, 6906 Leimen, Germany

Becker, Edward R *Judge*
%US Court of Appeals, US Courthouse, 601 Market St, Philadelphia, PA 19106

Becker, Gert *Businessman*
%Degussa, Weissfrauenstrasse 9, 6000 Frankfurt 11, Germany

Becker, Isidore A *Businessman*
%Shenley Industries, 888 7th Ave, New York, NY 10106

Becker, Robert Jerome *Allergist*
229 N Hammes Ave, Joliet, IL 60435

Becket, MacDonald G *Architect*
%Becket Grp, 2501 Colorado Blvd, Santa Monica, CA 90404

Beckett, John R *Businessman*
%Transamerica Corp, 600 Montgomery St, San Francisco, CA 94111

Beckman, Arnold O *Businessman*
%SmithKline Beckman Corp, 1 Franklin Plz, Philadelphia, PA 19101

Becton, C W *Religious Leader*
%United Pentacostal Free Will Baptist Church, 8855 Dunn Rd, Hazelwood, MO 63042

Becton, Henry P *Businessman*
%Becton Dickinson Co, Mack Centre Dr, Paramus, NJ 07652

Bedelia, Bonnie *Actress*
1021 Georgina Ave, Santa Monica, CA 90402

Bedell, Berkley W *Representative, IA*
%General Delivery, Spirit Lake, IA 51360

Bedford, Brian *Actor*
%STE Representation, 9301 Wilshire Blvd, #312, Beverly Hills, CA 90210

Bedford, Sybille *Writer*
%Messrs Coutts, 1 Old Park Ln, London W1Y 4BS, England

Bednarik, Chuck *Football Player*
RD 4, Box 30, Coopersburg, PA 18036

Bednorz, J Georg *Nobel Physics Laureate*
%IBM Research Laboratory, Saumerstrasse 4, CH-8803 Ruschlikon, Switzerland

Bedrosian, John C *Businessman*
%National Medical Enterprises, 11620 Wilshire Blvd, Los Angeles, CA 90025

Bedrosian, Steve *Baseball Player*
5490 Cheisenwood Dr, Duluth, GA 30136

Bee, Molly *Actress, Singer*
PO Box 1310, Canyon City, CA 91351

Beebe, Robert Park *Yacht Designer*
PO Box 1452, Carmel, CA 93921

Beebe, William Thomas *Businessman*
%Delta Air Lines, Atlanta International Airport, Atlanta, GA 30320

Beene, Geoffrey *Fashion Designer*
550 7th Ave, New York, NY 10018

Beer, A M *Editor*
%The Spectator, 44 Frid St, Hamilton ON L8N 3G3, Canada

Beer, Samuel Hutchison *Political Scientist*
87 Lakeview Ave, Cambridge, MA 02138

Beering, Steven C *Educator*
%Purdue University, President's Office, Lafayette, IN 47907

Beers, William O *Businessman*
1 First National Plz, #2530, Chicago, IL 60603

Beery, Noah, Jr *Actor*
PO Box 108, Keene, CA 93531

B

Beeson – Bell

Beeson, Jack *Composer*
Seaforth Ln, Lloyd Neck, NY 11743

Beevers, Harry *Biologist*
46 South Circle Dr, Santa Cruz, CA 95060

Beezer, Robert R *Judge*
%US Court of Appeals, US Courthouse, 1010 5th Ave, Seattle, WA 98104

Begelman, David *Movie Producer*
705 N Linden Dr, Beverly Hills, CA 90210

Begg, Varyl *Fleet Admiral, England*
Copyhold Cottage, Chilbolton, Stockbridge, Hants, England

Beggs, James M *Space Engineer, Government Official*
%NASA, 400 Maryland Ave SW, Washington, DC 20546

Begin, Menachem *Prime Minister, Israel; Nobel Laureate*
1 Rosenbaum St, Tel-Aviv, Israel

Begley, Ed, Jr *Actor*
4158 Grand Ave, Ojai, CA 93023

Behnke, Wallace B, Jr *Businessman*
%Commonwealth Edison Co, 1 First National Plz, Chicago, IL 60690

Behrens, Hildegard *Opera Singer*
%Columbia Artists Mgmt Inc, 165 W 57th St, New York, NY 10019

Behrens, William W, Jr *Navy Admiral, Oceanographer*
1125 Friendly Way S, Saint Petersburg, FL 33705

Beilenson, Anthony C *Representative, CA*
%House of Representatives, Washington, DC 20515

Beilina, Nina *Concert Violinist*
400 W 43rd St, #7-D, New York, NY 10036

Beinecke, William S *Businessman*
%Sperry & Hutchinson Co, 330 Madison Ave, New York, NY 10017

Beisler, Randy *Football Player*
538 Eleanor Dr, Woodside, CA 94062

Beitz, Berthold *Businessman*
Hugel 15, 4300 Essen 1, Germany

Bejart, Maurice *Ballet Dancer, Choreographer*
%Twentieth Century Ballet, Lausanne, Switzerland

Bekavac, Nancy Y *Educator*
%Scripps College, President's Office, Claremont, CA 91711

Bel Geddes, Barbara *Actress*
15 Mill St, Putnam Valley, NY 10579

Bela, Magyari *Cosmonaut, Hungary*
18885 P Alffy 7-11, Budapest, Hungary

Belafonte, Harry *Singer*
300 West End Ave, New York, NY 10023

Belanger, Mark *Baseball Player*
2028 Pot Spring Rd, Timonium, MD 21093

Beldon, Sanford T *Publisher*
%Prevention Magazine, 33 E Minor St, Emmaus, PA 18049

Belford, Christina *Actress*
%Gores/Fields Agency, 10100 Santa Monica Blvd, #700, Los Angeles, CA 90067

Belichik, Bill *Football Coach*
%Cleveland Browns, Cleveland Stadium, Cleveland, OH 44114

Belita *Actress*
Crabtree Gdns, 42-46 Crabtree Ln, London SW6 6LW, England

Beliveau, Jean *Hockey Player*
%Montreal Canadiens, 2313 St Catherine St W, Montreal ON H3H 1N2, Canada

Bell, Archie *Singer*
%SLF Mgmt, 1831 Southmore St, Houston, TX 77004

Bell, Bobby *Football Player*
%Bobby Bell's Bar-B-Que, 7013 N Oak Trafficway, Kansas City, MO 64118

Bell, Buddy *Baseball Player*
6485 Hunters Trl, Cincinnati, OH 45243

Bell, Clyde R *Navy Admiral*
%Joint Strategic Target Planning, Pentagon, Washington, DC 20350

Bell, David E *Economist, Government Official*
%Ford Foundation, 320 E 43rd St, New York, NY 10017

Bell, George *Baseball Player*
%Toronto Blue Jays, PO Box 7777, Adelaide PO, Toronto ON M5C 2K7, Canada

Bell, Greg *Track Athlete*
110 12th St, Logansport, IN 46947

Bell, Griffin B *Attorney General*
%King & Spalding, 2500 Trust Company Tower, Atlanta, GA 30303

Bell, Gus (David R) *Baseball Player*
%Minuteman, 920 Race St, Cincinnati, OH 45202

Bell, James D *Diplomat*
14 Kite Hill Rd, Santa Cruz, CA 95060

Bell, Larry *Artist*
PO Box 495, Ranchos de Taos, NM 87557

Bell, Madison Smartt *Writer*
%Ticknor and Fields, 52 Vanderbilt Ave, New York, NY 10017

Bell, Marie *Actress*
32 Ave de Champs-Elysees, 75008 Paris, France

Bell, Michael *Actor*
%Cunningham-Escott-Dipene, 261 S Robertson Blvd, Beverly Hills, CA 90211

Bell, Robert *Businessman*
%Ralston Purina Co, Checkerboard Sq, St Louis, MO 63164

Bell, Terrel H *Secretary, Education*
%University of Utah, Education Dept, Salt Lake City, UT 84112

Bell, Thomas J *Businessman*
%Abitibi-Price Corp, Toronto-Dominion Ctr, Toronto ON M5K 1B3, Canada

Bell, Tom *Actor*
%International Creative Mgmt, 388-396 Oxford St, London W1, England

Bell, W Douglas *Businessman*
%State Mutual Life Assurance, 440 Lincoln St, Worcester, MA 01605

Bellamy, David *Botanist, Writer, Broadcaster*
Mill House, Bedburn, Bishop Auckland, Co Durham, England

Beller, Kathleen *Actress*
%Gores/Fields Agency, 10100 Santa Monica Blvd, #700, Los Angeles, CA 90067

Belli, Melvin *Attorney*
%Mark Hopkins Hotel, 1 Nob Hill, San Francisco, CA 94108

Bellingham, Norman *Rower*
328 Catalina Dr, Newport Beach, CA 92663

Bellini, Cal *Actor*
%Allen Goldstein Assoc, 5015 Lemona Ave, Sherman Oaks, CA 91423

Bellino, Joe *Football Player*
45 Hayden Ln, Bedford, MA 01730

Bellisario, Donald P *Television Producer*
%MCA/Universal Studios, 100 Universal City Plz, Universal City, CA 91608

Bellmon, Henry *Governor/Senator, OK*
Rt 1, Red Rock, OK 74651

Bellow, Saul *Nobel Literature Laureate*
%Committee on Social Thought, 1126 E 59th St, Chicago, IL 60637

Bellows, Brian *Hockey Player*
%Minnesota North Stars, 7901 Cedar Ave S, Bloomington, MN 55420

Bellson, Louis *Drummer*
Box 2608, Lake Havasu City, AZ 86405

Bellucci, Monica *Model*
%Elite Model Mgmt, 111 E 22nd St, New York, NY 10010

Belluschi, Pietro *Architect*
700 NW Rapidan Terr, Portland, OR 97210

Bellwood, Pamela *Actress*
%Harris & Goldberg Agency, 1999 Ave of Stars, #2850, Los Angeles, CA 90067

Belmondo, Jean-Paul *Actor*
77 Ave Donfert Rochereaux, 75016 Paris, France

Belote Hamlin, Melissa *Swimmer*
5409 Tripolis Ct, Burke, VA 22015

Belousova, Ludmila *Figure Skater*
Chalet Hubel, 3818 Grindelwald, Switzerland

Belushi, James *Actor*
%Whitehorse Productions, 9830 Wilshire Blvd, Beverly Hills, CA 90212

Belzberg, Hyman *Financier*
%First City Trust Co, Royal Ctr, 1055 W Georgia St, Vancouver BC, Canada

Belzberg, Samuel *Financier*
%First City Trust Co, Royal Ctr, 1055 W Georgia St, Vancouver BC, Canada

B

Belzberg, William *Financier*
%First City Trust Co, Royal Ctr, 1055 W Georgia St, Vancouver BC, Canada

Belzer, Alan *Businessman*
%Allied-Signal Inc, PO Box 4000-R, Morristown, NJ 07960

Beman, Deane *Golf Executive*
%Professional Golfer's Assn, Sawgrass, Ponte Vedra Beach, FL 32082

Ben Ami, Zine Abidine *President, Tunisia*
%President's Office, Tunis, Tunisia

Ben Haim, Paul *Composer*
11 Aharonovitz St, Tel-Aviv, Israel

Benacerraf, Baruj *Nobel Medicine Laureate*
111 Perkins St, Boston, MA 02130

Benard, Andre *Businessman*
%Eurotunnel, SA, Tour Franklin, Cedex 11, 92001 Paris-La-Define 8, France

Benatar, Pat *Singer*
%New Star, 60 W 70th St, New York, NY 10023

Benavidez, Roy P *Vietnam War Army Hero (CMH)*
1700 Byrne St, El Campo, TX 77437

Bench, Johnny *Baseball Player*
661 Reisling Knoll, Cincinnati, OH 45226

Benchley, Peter *Writer*
35 Boudinot St, Princeton, NJ 08540

Bencsik, Doris D *Businesswoman*
%Datapoint Corp, 9725 Datapoint Dr, San Antonio, TX 78284

Bender, Gary *Sportscaster*
%ABC-TV, Sports Dept, 1330 Ave of Americas, New York, NY 10019

Bender, Myron L *Chemist*
2514 Sheridan Rd, Evanston, IL 60201

Bender, Stanley *WW II Army Hero (CMH)*
PO Box 421, Fayetteville, WV 25840

Bendheim, Robert A *Businessman*
%M Lowenstein Corp, 1430 Broadway, New York, NY 10018

Benedek, Laslo *Movie Director*
70 Bank St, New York, NY 10014

Benedict, Alvin *Businessman*
%MGM Grand Hotels Inc, 3645 Las Vegas Blvd S, Las Vegas, NV 89109

Benedict, Dirk *Actor*
%Charter Mgmt, 9000 Sunset Blvd, #1112, Los Angeles, CA 90069

Benedict, Manson *Engineer*
2151 Gulf Shore Blvd N, Naples, FL 33940

Benedict, Paul *Actor*
%Gage Group, 9255 Sunset Blvd, #515, Los Angeles, CA 90069

Benedict, William *Actor*
1347 N Orange Grove Ave, Los Angeles, CA 90046

Beneke, Tex *Orchestra Leader*
%Hecker, 2275 Faust Ave, Long Beach, CA 90815

Benetton, Luciano *Businessman*
%Benetton SPA, Via Chiesa Ponzano 24, 31050 Ponzano Veneto, Italy

Benezet, Louis T *Educator*
%State University of New York, Human Development Dept, Stony Brook, NY 11794

Beng, Norbert *Businessman*
%Control Data Corp, 8100 34th Ave S, Minneapolis, MN 55420

Benglis, Lynda *Artist*
222 Bowery St, New York, NY 10012

Bengston, Billy Al *Artist*
110 Mildred Ave, Venice, CA 90291

Benichou, Jacques *Businessman*
%Snecma, 2 Blvd Victor, 75724 Paris Cedex 15, France

Bening, Annette *Actress*
13671 Mulholland Dr, Beverly Hills, CA 90210

Benjamin, Adam, Jr *Representative, IN*
6111 Ridge Rd, Gary, IN 46408

Benjamin, Benoit *Basketball Player*
%Seattle SuperSonics, 190 Queen Ann Ave N, Seattle, WA 98109

Benjamin, Curtis G *Publisher*
Kellogg Hill Rd, Weston, CT 06880

Benjamin, Joseph *Publisher*
%Psychology Today Magazine, 1 Park Ave, New York, NY 10016

Benjamin, Karl *Artist*
675 W 8th St, Claremont, CA 91711

Benjamin, Richard *Actor*
719 N Foothill Rd, Beverly Hills, CA 90210

Benn, Nigel *Boxer*
%World Sports Corp, 212 Tower Bridge Rd, London SE1 2UP, England

Benn, Tony *Government Official, England*
%House of Commons, Westminster, London SW1, England

Bennack, Frank A, Jr *Publisher*
%Hearst Corp, 959 8th Ave, New York, NY 10019

Bennett, Alan *Publisher*
%Savvy Magazine, 111 8th Ave, New York, NY 10011

Bennett, Bruce (Herman Brix) *Actor, Track Athlete*
2702 Forester Rd, Los Angeles, CA 90064

Bennett, Charles E *Representative, FL*
%House of Representatives, Washington, DC 20515

Bennett, Cornelius *Football Player*
%Buffalo Bills, 1 Bills Dr, Orchard Park, NY 14127

Bennett, David M *Navy Admiral*
Commander, Naval Surface Force Pacific, NAB Coronado, San Diego, CA 92155

Bennett, Emmett L *Classical Scholar*
%University of Wisconsin, Classics Dept, Madison, WI 53706

Bennett, Hywel *Actor*
%James Sharkey Assoc, 15 Golden Sq, London W1R 3AG, England

Bennett, Jack Franklin *Economist*
%Exxon Corp, 1251 Ave of Americas, New York, NY 10020

Bennett, Jill *Actress*
%Sharkey, 90 Regent St, London W1, England

Bennett, John Coleman *Theologian*
620 Plymouth Rd, Claremont, CA 91711

Bennett, Marion T *Judge*
%US Court of Appeals, 717 Madison Pl NW, Washington, DC 20439

Bennett, Nelson *Skier*
807 S 20th Ave, Yakima, WA 98902

Bennett, Otes, Jr *Businessman*
%North American Coal Corp, 12800 Shaker Blvd, Cleveland, OH 44120

Bennett, Richard Rodney *Composer*
%London Mgmt, Regent House, 235-241 Regent St, London W1A 2JT, England

Bennett, Robert *Businessman*
%Chromalloy Textile Apparel, 120 S Central Ave, St Louis, MO 63105

Bennett, Robert F *Governor, KS*
5315 W 96th, Prairie View, KS 66208

Bennett, Tony *Singer*
101 W 55th St, New York, NY 10019

Bennett, Tony *Football Player*
%Green Bay Packers, 1265 Lombardi Ave, Green Bay, WI 54303

Bennett, Wallace F *Senator, UT*
875 Donner Way, Salt Lake City, UT 84108

Bennett, Ward *Interior Designer*
%Dakota Hotel, 1 W 72nd St, PH-A, New York, NY 10023

Bennett, William G *Businessman*
%Circus Circus Enterprises, 2880 Las Vegas Blvd S, Las Vegas, NV 89109

Bennett, William J *Secretary, Education*
%National Drug Control Office, White House, Washington, DC 20500

Bennett, William John *Businessman*
1321 Sherbrooke St W, #F-41, Montreal PQ H3G 1J4, Canada

Bennett, William T, Jr *Diplomat*
%Department of State, 2201 "C" St NW, Washington, DC 20520

Bennis, Warren *Educator, Writer*
%University of Southern California, Management School, Los Angeles, CA 90007

Benoit Samuelson, Joan *Marathon Runner*
95 Lower Flying Point Rd, Freeport, ME 04032

Benschneider, Donald *Businessman*
%Countrymark Inc, 35 E Chestnut St, Columbus, OH 43216

B

Benson – Berg

Benson, Donald E *Businessman*
%MEI Corp, 710 Marquette Ave, Minneapolis, MN 55402

Benson, Erza Taft *Secretary, Agriculture; Religious Leader*
%Church of Latter Day Saints, 50 E North Temple, Salt Lake City, UT 84150

Benson, George *Jazz Guitarist*
19 Holomakani Pl, La Haina, HI 96761

Benson, Robby *Actor*
4839 Brewster Dr, Tarzana, CA 91356

Benson, Robert *Radio Executive*
%ABC Radio News, 1330 Ave of Americas, New York, NY 10019

Benson, Stephen *Editorial Cartoonist*
%Arizona Republic, 120 E Van Buren St, Phoenix, AZ 85004

Bentley, Clarence E *Financier*
%United Financial Grp, 10333 Harwin, Houston, TX 77036

Bentley, Eric *Writer*
194 Riverside Dr, New York, NY 10025

Bentley, Helen D *Representative, MD*
408 Chapelwood Ln, Lutherville, MD 21093

Bentley, John *Actor*
Wedgewood House, Peterworth, Sussex, England

Bentley, Stacey *Body Builder*
PO Box 26, Santa Monica, CA 90406

Benton, Barbi *Actress, Model*
%Joshua Gray Assoc, 6736 Laurel Canyon Blvd, North Hollywood, CA 91601

Benton, Fletcher *Artist*
250 Dore St, San Francisco, CA 94103

Benton, Jim *Football Player*
1401 Laurel, Pine Bluff, AR 71601

Benton, Robert *Movie Director*
%International Creative Mgmt, 40 W 57th St, New York, NY 10019

Bentsen, Donald L *Businessman*
%Tide Products Inc, 800 N Closner, Edinburg, TX 78539

Bentsen, Lloyd M, Jr *Senator, TX*
%US Senate, Washington, DC 20510

Benzer, Seymour *Biologist*
2075 Robin Rd, San Marino, CA 91108

Beradino, John *Actor*
1719 Ambassador Dr, Beverly Hills, CA 90210

Beran, Bruce *Coast Guard Admiral*
Commander, Pacific Area, US Coast Guard, Coast Guard Island, Alameda, CA 94501

Beran, Timothy *Financier*
%Barclays Bank, 54 Lombard St, London EC3P 3AH, England

Beras Rojas, Octavio Antonio Cardinal *Religious Leader*
Arzobispade, Apartado 186, Santo Domingo, Dominican Republic

Berbick, Trevor *Boxer*
%Carl King, Don King Productions, 32 E 69th St, New York, NY 10021

Bercu, Michaela *Model*
%Elite Model Mgmt, 111 E 22nd St, New York, NY 10010

Beregovoi, Georgi T *Cosmonaut*
141 160 Svyosdny Gorodok, Moskovskoi Oblasti, Potchta Kosmonavtov, Russia

Berenblum, Isaac *Pathologist*
%Weizmann Institute of Science, Rehovot, Israel

Berenger, Tom *Actor*
853 7th Ave, #9-A, New York, NY 10019

Berenson, Marisa *Actress*
%Chasin Agency, 190 N Canon Dr, #201, Beverly Hills, CA 90210

Beresford, Bruce *Movie Director*
3 Marathon Rd, #13, Darling Pt, Sydney NSW, Australia

Beretta, David *Businessman*
%Uniroyal Inc, 1230 Ave of Americas, New York, NY 10020

Bereuter, Douglas K *Representative, NE*
%House of Representatives, Washington, DC 20515

Berezovy, Anatoli *Cosmonaut*
141 160 Svyosdny Gorodok, Moskovskoi Oblasti, Potchta Kosmonavtov, Russia

Berg, Bengt *Businessman*
%Strarsforetag Grp, Hamngatan 6, 103 97, Stockholm, Sweden

Berg, Harold E *Businessman*
2011 Cummings Dr, Los Angeles, CA 90027

Berg, Jeffrey S *Businessman*
%International Creative Mgmt, 8899 Beverly Blvd, Los Angeles, CA 90048

Berg, John P *Businessman*
%Greif Bros Corp, 621 Pennsylvania Ave, Delaware, OH 43015

Berg, Milton *Financier*
%Steinhardt Partners, 605 3rd Ave, New York, NY 10158

Berg, Norbert R *Businessman*
%Control Data Corp, 8100 34th Ave S, Minneapolis, MN 55440

Berg, Patty *Golfer*
PO Box 9227, Fort Myers, FL 33902

Berg, Paul *Nobel Chemistry Laureate*
838 Santa Fe Ave, Stanford, CA 94305

Berganza, Teresa *Opera Singer*
Cafeto #5, Madrid 7, Spain

Berge, Ole M *Labor Leader*
%Maintenance of Way Brotherhood, 12050 Woodward Ave, Detroit, MI 48203

Berge, Pierre *Businessman*
%Yves Saint Laurent SA, 5 Ave Marceau, 75116 Paris, France

Bergen, Candice *Actress*
1134 Miradora Rd, Beverly Hills, CA 90210

Bergen, Polly *Actress*
%William Morris Agency, 151 El Camino, Beverly Hills, CA 90212

Bergen, William B *Aerospace Engineer*
%Rockwell International, 1700 E Imperial Hwy, El Segundo, CA 90245

Berger, Frank M *Biologist*
190 E 72nd St, New York, NY 10021

Berger, Helmut *Actor*
Via Stringher 43, Rome, Italy

Berger, John *Writer, Critic*
%Penguin Books, Harmondsworth, Middlesex, England

Berger, Peter *Sociologist*
%Boston University, Sociology Dept, Boston, MA 02215

Berger, Richard *Entertainment Executive*
%United Artists Corp, 10202 W Washington Blvd, Culver City, CA 90203

Berger, Senta *Actress*
Robert-Koch-Strasse 10, 8022 Grunwald, Germany

Berger, Thomas *Writer*
%Don Congdon Assoc, 111 5th Ave, New York, NY 10003

Bergere, Lee *Actor*
2267 Century Hill, Los Angeles, CA 90067

Berggren, Thommy *Actor*
%Swedish Film Institute, Kungsgatan 48, Stockholm C, Sweden

Berghaus, Ruth *Theatre Director*
%Deutsche Staatsoper, Unter Den Linden 7, 1086 Berlin, Germany

Bergland, Robert S *Secretary, Agriculture*
Rt 3, Roseau, MN 56751

Berglund, Paavo *Conductor*
Munkkiniemenranta 41, 00330 Helsinki 33, Finland

Bergman, Alan *Lyricist*
714 N Maple Dr, Beverly Hills, CA 90210

Bergman, Andrew *Playwright, Screenwriter*
555 W 57th St, #1230, New York, NY 10019

Bergman, Ingmar *Movie Director*
Titurelstrasse 2, 8000 Munich 8, Germany

Bergman, Klaus *Businessman*
%Allegheny Power System, 320 Park Ave, New York, NY 10022

Bergman, Marilyn *Lyricist*
714 N Maple Dr, Beverly Hills, CA 90210

Bergman, Martin *Movie Producer*
641 Lexington Ave, New York, NY 10022

Bergman, Sandahl *Actress*
9903 Santa Monica Blvd, #274, Beverly Hills, CA 90212

Bergmann, Arnfinn *Ski Jumper*
Nils Collett Vogtsv 58, 0765 Oslo 7, Norway

Bergonzi, Carlo *Opera Singer*
%A Ziliani, ALCI, Via Paolo da Cannobio 2, 120122 Milan, Italy

Bergquist, Curt *Immunologist*
%Allergon AB, Valinge 2090, S-262 92 Angelholm, Sweden

Bergquist, Kenneth P *Businessman*
3325 Foxbriar Ln, Cibolo, TX 78108

Bergsma, William L *Composer*
2328 Delmar Dr E, Seattle, WA 98102

Bergsten, C Fred *Economist*
4106 Sleepy Hollow Rd, Annandale, VA 22003

Bergstrom, K Sune *Nobel Medicine Laureate*
%Karolinska Institute, Stockholm, Sweden

Bergt, N G *Businessman*
%Western Air Lines, 6060 Avion Dr, Los Angeles, CA 90045

Berio, Luciano *Composer*
Il Colombaio, Radicondoli, Siena, Italy

Berkeley, Norborne, Jr *Financier*
41 Westcott Rd, Princeton, NJ 08540

Berkley, Richard L *Mayor*
%Mayor's Office, City Hall, 414 E 12th St, Kansas City, MO 64106

Berkoff, David *Swimmer*
%Harvard University, Athletic Dept, Cambridge, MA 02138

Berkowitz, Howard P *Businessman*
%Interstate Bakeries Corp, 12 E Armour Blvd, Kansas City, MO 64111

Berland, Kenneth K *Businessman*
%Melville Corp, 3000 Westchester Ave, Harrison, NY 10528

Berlant, Tony *Artist*
%LA Louver Gallery, 55 N Venice Blvd, Venice, CA 90291

Berle, Milton *Actor, Comedian*
711 N Alpine Dr, Beverly Hills, CA 90210

Berlin, Isaiah *Philosopher*
Headington House, Old High St, Headington, Oxford OX3 9HU, England

Berliner, Robert W *Physician*
36 Edgehill Terr, New Haven, CT 06511

Berlinger, Warren *Actor*
10642 Arnel Pl, Chatsworth, CA 91311

Berlitz, Charles F *Linguist, Writer, Archaeologist*
2816 NE 25th Ct, Fort Lauderdale, FL 33305

Berman, Chris *Sportscaster*
%ESPN, Sports Dept, ESPN Plz, Bristol, CT 06010

Berman, Howard L *Representative, CA*
%House of Representatives, Washington, DC 20515

Berman, Lazar *Concert Pianist*
%Jacques Leiser Artists, Dorchester Towers, 155 W 68th St, New York, NY 10023

Berman, Pandro S *Movie Producer*
914 N Roxbury Dr, Beverly Hills, CA 90210

Berman, Shelley *Comedian*
%Irvin Arthur Assoc, 9363 Wilshire Blvd, #212, Beverly Hills, CA 90210

Bernard, Crystal *Actress*
4511 St Clair, Studio City, CA 91604

Bernard, Ed *Actor*
7461 Beverly Blvd, #400, Los Angeles, CA 90036

Bernard, Jason *Actor*
%Agency for Performing Arts, 9000 Sunset Blvd, #1200, Los Angeles, CA 90069

Bernardin, Joseph Cardinal *Religious Leader*
%Archdiocese of Chicago, 1555 N State Pkwy, Chicago, IL 60610

Bernays, Edward L *Businessman*
7 Lowell St, Cambridge, MA 02138

Bernbach, William *Businessman*
870 United Nations Plz, New York, NY 10017

Berndt, Jens-Peter *Swimmer*
%Mission Bay Aquatic Center, 10333 Diego Dr, Boca Raton, FL 33428

Bernhard *Prince, Netherlands*
Soestdijk Palace, Baarn, Netherlands

Bernhard, Ruth *Photographer*
2982 Clay St, San Francisco, CA 94115

Bernhard, Sandra *Comedienne*
%Triad Artists, 10100 Santa Monica Blvd, #1600, Los Angeles, CA 90067
Bernhardt, Glenn R *Cartoonist*
PO Box 3772, Carmel, CA 93921
Bernier, Sylvie *Diver*
%Olympic Assn, Cite du Harve, Montreal PQ H3C 3R4, Canada
Berning, Susie *Golfer*
PO Box 321, Kailena Kona, HI 96745
Bernstein, Basil *Sociologist*
90 Farquhar Rd, Dulwich SE19 1LT, England
Bernstein, Carl *Journalist*
2753 Ontario Rd NW, Washington, DC 20009
Bernstein, Elmer *Composer*
%Gorfaine-Schwartz Agency, 3815 W Olive Dr, #201, Burbank, CA 91505
Bernstein, Harold P *Businessman*
%Northville Industries, Pinelawn Rd, Melville, NY 11747
Bernstein, Kenny *Auto Racing Driver*
1105 Seminole, Richardson, TX 75080
Bernstein, Richard B *Physical Chemist*
%Occidental Research Corp, PO Box 19601, Irvine, CA 92713
Bernstein, Robert L *Publisher*
20 Murray Hill Rd, Scarsdale, NY 10583
Bernthal, Harold G *Businessman*
%American Hospital Supply Corp, 1 American Plz, Evanston, IL 60201
Berra, Lawrence P (Yogi) *Baseball Player, Manager*
19 Highland Ave, Montclair, NJ 07042
Berri, Claude *Movie Director, Producer*
%Renn Productions, 10 Rue Lincoln, 75008 Paris, France
Berri, Nabih *Government Official, Lebanon*
%Ministry of Justice, Beirut, Lebanon
Berridge, Elizabeth *Actress*
%Writers & Artists Agency, 11726 San Vicente Blvd, #300, Los Angeles, CA 90049
Berrigan, Daniel *Clergyman, Social Activist*
220 W 98th St, #11-L, New York, NY 10025
Berruti, Livio *Track Athlete*
Via Avigliana 45, 10138 Torino, Italy
Berry, Bill *Skiing Writer*
839 N Center St, Reno, NV 89501
Berry, Chuck *Singer*
Berry Park, Buchner Rd, Wentzville, MO 63385
Berry, Harold J *Businessman*
%Schering-Plough Co, 1 Giralda Farms, Madison, NJ 07940
Berry, Jan *Singer (Jan & Dean)*
Rt 2, Box 23-W, Winters, CA 95694
Berry, Jim *Editorial Cartoonist*
%NEA Syndicate, 200 Park Ave, New York, NY 10166
Berry, Ken *Actor*
1900 Outpost Dr, Los Angeles, CA 90068
Berry, Kevin *Swimmer*
28 George St, Manly NSW 2295, Australia
Berry, Michael J *Chemist*
351 Tealwood St, Houston, TX 77024
Berry, Raymond E *Football Player, Coach*
%Detroit Lions, Silverdome, 1200 Featherstone Blvd, Detroit, MI 48057
Berry, Richard R *Businessman*
%Olin Corp, 120 Long Ridge Rd, Stamford, CT 06904
Berry, Walter *Basketball Player*
%Houston Rockets, Summit, Greenway Plaza, #10, Houston, TX 77046
Berry, Walter *Opera Singer*
Strassergasse 43-47, A-1150 Vienna, Austria
Berry, Wendell *Writer, Ecologist*
River Rd, Port Royal, KY 40058
Berry, William W *Businessman*
%Dominion Resources, 1 James River Plz, Richmond, VA 23261
Bers, Lipman *Mathematician*
111 Hunter Ave, New Rochelle, NY 10801

B

Bersen – Bhumibol Adulyadej

Bersen, Corbin *Actor*
2114 Kew Dr, Los Angeles, CA 90046

Berson, Jerome A *Chemist*
45 Bayberry Rd, Hamden, CT 06511

Berst, David *Sports Investigator*
%National Collegiate Athletic Assn, 6201 College Blvd, Overland Park, KS 66211

Bertelli, Angelo B *Football Player*
22 Springdale Ct, Clifton, NJ 07013

Bertinelli, Valerie *Actress*
PO Box 1984, Studio City, CA 91604

Bertoli, Paolo Cardinal *Religious Leader*
Piazza della Citta Leonina 1, 00193 Rome, Italy

Bertrand, Frederic H *Businessman*
%National Life Insurance, National Life Dr, Montpelier, VT 05604

Beruh, Joseph *Theater, Movie Producer*
1650 Broadway, New York, NY 10036

Berwanger, Jay (John J) *Football Player*
1245 Warren Ave, Downers Grove, IL 60515

Bess, Douglas R *Businessman*
%Avondale Mills, Avondale Ave, Sylacauga, AL 35150

Bessell, Ted *Actor*
1454 Stone Canyon Rd, Los Angeles, CA 90077

Bessmertnova, Natalia *Ballerina*
%State Academic Bolshoi Theatre, 1 Ploshchad Sverdlova, Moscow, Russia

Besson, Michel L *Businessman*
%CertainTeed Corp, PO Box 860, Valley Forge, PA 19482

Best, James *Actor*
470 S San Vicente Blvd, #104, Los Angeles, CA 90048

Bestor, Arthur Eugene *Historian*
%University of Washington, History Dept, Seattle, WA 98105

Bethe, Hans A *Nobel Physics Laureate*
%Cornell University, Nuclear Studies Laboratory, Ithaca, NY 14853

Bethune, Edwin R, Jr *Representative, AR*
210 E Vine St, Searcy, AR 72143

Bethune, Zina *Actress*
3096 Lake Hollywood Dr, Los Angeles, CA 90068

Bettenhausen, Gary *Auto Racing Driver*
2550 Tree Farm Rd, Martinsville, IN 46151

Bettis, Valerie *Dancer, Choreographer*
%Valerie Bettis Dance Studio, 22 W 15th St, New York, NY 10011

Bettmann, Otto L *Photo Archivist*
2600 S Ocean Blvd, Boca Raton, FL 33432

Bettors, Doug *Football Player*
%Miami Dolphins, 2269 NW 199th St, Miami, FL 33056

Betz Addie, Pauline *Tennis Player*
%Bidwell Friends School, Washington, DC 20000

Beutel, Bill *Commentator*
%WABC-TV, News Dept, 7 Lincoln Sq, New York, NY 10023

Bevan, Timothy H *Financier*
%Barclay's Bank, 54 Lombard St, London EC3P 3AH, England

Bevilacqua, Anthony J Cardinal *Religious Leader*
%Office of the Archbishop, 222 N 17th St, Philadelphia, PA 19103

Bevill, Tom *Representative, AL*
1600 Alabama Ave, Jasper, AL 35501

Bevis, Leslie *Actress*
%Artists Group, 1930 Century Park West, #403, Los Angeles, CA 90067

Bewkes, E Garrett, Jr *Businessman*
%American Bakeries Co, 100 Park Ave, New York, NY 10017

Beymer, Richard *Actor*
43367 16th St, #22, Lancaster, CA 93534

Bezombes, Roger *Artist*
3 Quai Saint-Michel, 75005 Paris, France

Bhandari Ram, Subadar *WW II Indian Army Hero (VC)*
Vill & Po Auhar, Teh Ghumarwin, Distt Bilaspur HP, India

Bhumibol Adulyadej *King, Thailand*
Chitralada Villa, Bangkok, Thailand

Bhutto, Benazir *Prime Minister, Pakistan*
%Pakistan People's Party, 70 Clifton Rd, Karachi, Pakistan

Biaggi, Mario *Representative, NY*
100 E Mosholu Pkwy, Bronx, NY 10458

Biaggini, Benjamin F *Businessman*
%Santa Fe Southern Pacific Corp, 224 S Michigan Ave, Chicago, IL 60604

Bialik, Mayim *Actress*
%Booh Schut Agency, 11350 Ventura Blvd, #206, Studio City, CA 91604

Biasucci, Dean *Football Player*
%Indianapolis Colts, 7001 W 56th St, Indianapolis, IN 46254

Bibb, John *Sports Editor*
%Nashville Tennessean, 1100 Broadway, Nashville, TN 37203

Bibby, Henry *Basketball Player, Coach*
%Oklahoma City Calvary, 1 Myriad Gardens, Oklahoma City, OK 73102

Bibby, Jim *Baseball Player*
RR 6, Box 402, Madison Heights, VA 24572

Bickerstaff, Bernie *Basketball Coach, Executive*
%Denver Nuggets, 1635 Clay St, Denver, CO 80204

Bickett, Duane *Football Player*
%Indianapolis Colts, 7001 W 56th St, Indianapolis, IN 46254

Bickner, Bruce P *Businessman*
%DeKalb AgResearch Inc, 3100 Sycamore Rd, DeKalb, IL 60115

Biddle, Melvin E *WW II Army Hero (CMH)*
918 Essex Dr, Anderson, IN 46013

Bide, Austin *Businessman*
%Glaxo Holdings, Clarger House, 6-12 Clarges St, London W1Y 8DH, England

Biden, Joseph R, Jr *Senator, DE*
6 Montchan Dr, Wilmington, DE 19807

Bidwell, William V *Football Executive*
%Phoenix Cardinals, PO Box 888, Phoenix, AZ 85001

Bieber, Owen *Labor Leader*
%United Auto Workers Union, 8000 E Jefferson Ave, Detroit, MI 48214

Biehn, Michael *Actor*
3737 Deervale Dr, Sherman Oaks, CA 91403

Bielecki, Krzysztof *Prime Minister, Poland*
%Prime Minister's Office, Ursad Rady Ministrow, 00-583 Warsaw, Poland

Biemiller, Andrew J *Representative, WI*
6805 Glenbrook Rd, Bethesda, MD 20014

Bieniemy, Eric *Football Player*
%University of Colorado, Athletic Dept, Boulder, CO 80309

Bierwirth, John C *Businessman*
%Grumman Corp, 1111 Stewart Ave, Bethpage, NY 11714

Bietila, Walter *Skier*
%General Delivery, Iron Mountain, MI 49801

Biffi, Giacomo Cardinal *Religious Leader*
Piazza Duomo 16, 20122 Milan, Italy

Bigeleisen, Jacob *Chemist*
PO Box 217, Saint James, NY 11780

Biggs, Tyrell *Boxer*
%Cross Country Concert Corp, 310 Madison Ave, New York, NY 10017

Bigley, Thomas Joseph *Navy Admiral*
423 Dillingham Blvd, Norfolk, VA 23511

Bignotti, George *Auto Racing Mechanic*
%Bignotti Enterprises, 7802 Eagle Creek Overlook Dr, Indianapolis, IN 46254

Bijan *Fashion Designer*
699 5th Ave, New York, NY 10022

Bikel, Theodore *Actor, Singer*
Honey Mill Rd, Georgetown, CT 06829

Bilandic, Michael *Mayor*
%Bilandic Neistein Richman Hauslinger Young, 33 N LaSalle, Chicago, IL 60602

Bilbray, James H *Representative, NV*
%House of Representatives, Washington, DC 20515

Bileck, Pam *Gymnast*
%SCATS, 5822 Research Dr, Huntington Beach, CA 92649

Biletnikoff, Fred *Football Player*
13734 Woodstock Pl, Valley Center, CA 92082

Bilheimer, Robert S *Religious Leader*
%Ecumenical Institute, St John's University, Collegeville, MN 56321
Bilirakis, Michael *Representative, FL*
%House of Representatives, Washington, DC 20515
Bill, Max *Architect, Artist*
Rebhusstrasse 50, 8126 Zumikon, Switzerland
Bill, Tony *Producer, Actor*
%Market Street Productions, 73 Market St, Venice, CA 90291
Biller, Moe *Labor Leader*
%American Postal Workers Union, 1300 "L" St NW, Washington, DC 20005
Billetdoux, Raphaele *Writer*
%Viking Press, 40 W 23rd St, New York, NY 10010
Billings, Marland P *Geologist*
Westside Rd, RFD, North Conway, NH 03860
Billingsley, Barbara *Actress*
PO Box 1320, Santa Monica, CA 90406
Billingsley, Hobie *Diving Coach*
%Indiana University, Athletic Dept, Bloomington, IN 47405
Billington, James H *Historian, Librarian*
%Library of Congress, 10 1st St SE, Washington, DC 20540
Bilson, Bruce *Television Director*
%Downwind Enterprises, 4444 Radford Ave, North Hollywood, CA 91607
Bilson, Malcolm *Concert Pianist*
132 N Sunset Dr, Ithaca, NY 14850
Binder, John *Religious Leader*
%North American Baptist Conference, 1 S 210 Summit, Oakbrook Terrace, IL 60181
Binder, Theodore *Physician*
Taos Canyon, Taos, NM 87571
Bing, Dave *Basketball Player*
%Bing Steel Inc, 1130 N Grand Blvd, Detroit, MI 48208
Bing, Ilse *Photographer*
210 Riverside Dr, #6-G, New York, NY 10025
Bing, R H *Mathematician*
%University of Texas, Mathematics Dept, Austin, TX 78712
Bing, Rudolf *Opera Producer*
Essex House, 160 Central Park South, New York, NY 10019
Bingaman, Jeff *Senator, NM*
PO Box 5775, Santa Fe, NM 87502
Binger, James H *Businessman*
%Honeywell Inc, Honeywell Plz, Minneapolis, MN 80901
Bingham, Barry, Jr *Editor, Publisher*
%Louisville Courier Journal & Times, 525 W Broadway, Louisville, KY 40202
Bingham, Charles W *Businessman*
%Weyerhaeuser Co, 33663 32nd St S, Tacoma, WA 98003
Bingham, Eula *Educator*
%University of Cincinnati, Graduate Studies Office, Cincinnati, OH 45221
Binnig, Gerd *Nobel Physics Laureate*
%IBM Research Laboratory, Saumerstrasse 4, CH-8803 Ruschlikon, Switzerland
Bintley, David *Choreographer*
%Royal Ballet, Convent Garden, London WL2E 9DD, England
Biondi, Frank J, Jr *Businessman*
%Viacom International Inc, 1211 Ave of Americas, New York, NY 10036
Biondi, Matt *Swimmer*
%Nicholas A Biondi, 1404 Rimer Dr, Moraga, CA 94556
Birch, Stanley F, Jr *Judge*
%US Court of Appeals, 56 Forsyth St NW, Atlanta, GA 30303
Bird, Billie *Actress*
%Gage Group, 9255 Sunset Blvd, #515, Los Angeles, CA 90069
Bird, Caroline *Writer, Social Activist*
60 Grammercy Park, New York, NY 10010
Bird, Joseph R *Businessman*
%Minnesota Mutual Life Insurance, 400 N Robert St, St Paul, MN 55101
Bird, Larry *Basketball Player*
%Boston Celtics, 151 Merrimac St, Boston, MA 02114
Birdsong, Otis *Basketball Player*
68 Hopper Farm Rd, Upper Saddle River, NJ 07458

Birenbaum, William M *Educator*
%Antioch College, President's Office, Yellow Springs, OH 45387
Birendra Bir Bikram Shah Dev *King, Nepal*
Narayanhity Royal Palace, Kathmandu, Nepal
Birk, Roger E *Businessman*
%Federal National Mortgage Assn, 1133 15th St NW, Washington, DC 20005
Birkin, Jane *Actress*
%M Israel, 56 Rue de Passy, 75016 Paris, France
Birks, John *Educator*
%University of Colorado, Boulder, CO 80309
Birman, Len *Actor*
%Michael Mann Mgmt, 8380 Melrose Ave, Los Angeles, CA 90069
Birmingham, Stephen *Writer*
%Brandt & Brandt, 1501 Broadway, New York, NY 10036
Birnbaum, Robert J *Businessman*
%Dechert Price Rhodes, 477 Madison Ave, New York, NY 10022
Birney, David *Actor*
%David Shapira Assoc, 15301 Ventura Blvd, #345, Sherman Oaks, CA 91403
Birney, Earle *Writer*
%McClelland & Stewart, 25 Hollinger Rd, Toronto ON M4B 3G2, Canada
Birren, James E *Gerontologist*
%University of Southern California, Andrus Ctr, Los Angeles, CA 90089
Birtwistle, Harrison *Composer*
%Alfred Kalmus Ltd, 2/3 Fareham St, London W1V 4DU, England
Bisar, Muhammad Abdul Rahman *Religious Leader*
%Grand Sheikh's Office, Al-Azhar Administration, Cairo, Egypt
Bish, Lawrence E *Businessman*
%Armstrong World Industries, W Liberty St, Lancaster, PA 17604
Bisher, Furman *Sportswriter*
3135 Rilman Rd NW, Atlanta, GA 30727
Bishop, Elvin *Singer*
%MCA Records, 70 Universal City Plz, Universal City, CA 91608
Bishop, Franklin G *Businessman*
%Matrix Corp, 230 Pegasus Ave, Northvale, NJ 07647
Bishop, J Michael *Nobel Medicine Laureate*
%University of California, G W Hooper Foundation, San Francisco, CA 94143
Bishop, Joey *Comedian*
534 Via Lido Nord, Newport Beach, CA 92663
Bishop, Keith *Football Player*
%Denver Broncos, 13655 E Dove Valley Pkwy, Englewood, CO 80112
Bishop, Ronald E *Businessman*
%National Life Insurance, National Life Dr, Montpelier, VT 05604
Bishop, Stephen *Singer; Songwriter*
231 Apollo Dr, Los Angeles, CA 90047
Bisoglio, Val *Actor*
7466 Beverly Blvd, #205, Los Angeles, CA 90036
Bisplinghoff, Raymond L *Aeronautical Engineer*
Tyco Laboratories, Tycor Park, Exeter, NH 03833
Bissell, Charles O *Editorial Cartoonist*
4221 Farrar Ave, Nashville, TN 37215
Bissell, Jean G *Judge*
%US Court of Appeals, 717 Madison Pl NW, Washington, DC 20439
Bissell, Phil *Cartoonist*
47 Shetland Rd, Rockport, MA 01966
Bissell, Whit *Actor*
10301 Chrysanthemum Ln, Los Angeles, CA 90077
Bisset, Jacqueline *Actress*
1815 Benedict Canyon Dr, Beverly Hills, CA 90210
Bissinger, Frederick L *Businessman*
11 West Way, Bronxville, NY 10708
Bista, Kirti Nidhi *Prime Minister, Nepal*
Gyaneshawor, Kathmandu, Nepal
Bixby, Bill *Actor*
%Brandon Assoc, 200 N Robertson, #223, Beverly Hills, CA 90211
Biya, Paul *President, Cameroon*
%President's Office, Yaounde, Cameroon

B

Bjedov-Gabrilo – Blackwell

Bjedov-Gabrilo, Djurdjica — *Swimmer*
Brace Santini 33, 5800 Split, Yugoslavia

Bjork, Anita — *Actress*
Baggensgatan 9, 1131 Stockholm, Sweden

Bjorklund, Anders — *Neurologist*
%University of Lund, Neurology Dept, Lund, Sweden

Bjorn, Anna — *Actress, Model*
%Paul Kohner Inc, 9169 Sunset Blvd, Los Angeles, CA 90069

Bjornstrand, Gunnar — *Actor*
Svalhas Alle 8-A, 18263 Djursholm, Sweden

Black, Cathleen P — *Publisher*
%American Newspaper Publishers Assn, 11600 Sunrise Valley Dr, Reston, VA 22091

Black, Charles L, Jr — *Attorney*
%Yale University, Law School, New Haven, CT 06520

Black, Clint — *Singer*
PO Box 299386, Houston, TX 77299

Black, Conrad — *Businessman*
%Hollinger Inc, 10 Toronto St, Toronto ON M5C 2B7, Canada

Black, Daniel J — *Businessman*
%Carter-Wallace Inc, 767 5th Ave, New York, NY 10153

Black, Eugene R — *Financier*
178 Columbia Hts, Brooklyn, NY 11201

Black, Fischer — *Economist*
%Goldman Sachs Co, 32 Old Slip, New York, NY 10005

Black, James W — *Nobel Medicine Laureate*
%King's College, London, England

Black, Joe Ed — *Golf Executive*
%Professional Golfers Assn, PO Box 109601, Palm Beach Gardens, FL 33410

Black, Karen — *Actress*
%Marshak-Wyckoff Assoc, 280 S Beverly Dr, #400, Beverly Hills, CA 90212

Black, Kent M — *Businessman*
%Rockwell International Corp, 600 Grant St, Pittsburgh, PA 15219

Black, Robert P — *Financier*
%Richmond Federal Reserve, 701 E Byrd St, Richmond, VA 23219

Black, Sena Ayn — *Actress*
%Sportscasting Period, 8489 W 3rd St, Los Angeles, CA 90048

Black, Shirley Temple — *Actress, Diplomat*
115 Lakeview Dr, Woodside, CA 94062

Black, Theodore H — *Businessman*
%Ingersoll-Rand Co, 20 Chestnut Ridge Rd, Woodcliff Lake, NJ 07675

Black, William H — *Financier*
%Morgan Stanley International, 1251 Ave of Americas, New York, NY 10020

Blackburn, Charles L — *Businessman*
%Maxus Energy Corp, 717 N Harwood St, Dallas, TX 75201

Blackford, David E — *Financier*
%Far West Financial Corp, 4001 MacArthur Blvd, Newport Beach, CA 92660

Blackie, William — *Businessman*
2305 Skyfarm Dr, Hillsborough, CA 94010

Blackman, Honor — *Actress*
%Michael Ladkin Mgmt, 11 S Wick Mews, London W2 1JG, England

Blackman, Robert L — *Football Coach*
8 Full Sweep, Palmetto Dr, Hilton Head Island, SC 29928

Blackman, Rolando — *Basketball Player*
%Dallas Mavericks, Reunion Arena, 777 Sports St, Dallas, TX 75207

Blackmun, Harry A — *Supreme Court Justice*
%US Supreme Court, 1 1st St NE, Washington, DC 20543

Blackstone, Harry — *Illusionist*
%David Belenzon Mgmt, PO Box 15428, San Diego, CA 92115

Blackwell, David J — *Businessman*
%Massachusetts Mutual Life Insurance, 1295 State St, Springfield, MA 01111

Blackwell, Earl — *Publisher, Writer*
171 W 57th St, #PH, New York, NY 10019

Blackwell, Ewell — *Baseball Player*
20 Moy Toy Ln, Brevard, NC 28712

Blackwell, Harolyn — *Opera Singer*
%Ken Benson, 165 W 57th St, New York, NY 10019

Blackwell, Lloyd P *Forester*
1212 Dubach St, Ruston, LA 71270

Blackwell, Lucien *Representative, PA*
%House of Representatives, Washington, DC 20515

Blackwell, Mr (Richard) *Fashion Designer*
531 S Windsor, Los Angeles, CA 90005

Blacque, Taurean *Actor*
%Gores/Fields Agency, 10100 Santa Monica Blvd, #700, Los Angeles, CA 90067

Blades, Bennie *Football Player*
%Detroit Lions, Silverdome, 1200 Featherstone Rd, Pontiac, MI 48057

Blaese, R Michael *Medical Researcher*
%National Cancer Institute, 9000 Rockville Pike, Bethesda, MD 20205

Blaha, John E *Astronaut*
%NASA, Johnson Space Ctr, Houston, TX 77058

Blair, Betsy *Actress*
11 Chalcot Gdns, England's Ln, London NW3, England

Blair, Bonnie *Speed Skater*
1907 W Springfield, Champaign, IL 61820

Blair, Linda *Actress*
8033 Sunset Blvd, #204, Los Angeles, CA 90046

Blair, William Draper, Jr *Conservationist*
%Nature Conservancy, 1800 N Kent St, Arlington, VA 22209

Blair, William McCormick, Jr *Attorney, Diplomat*
1156 15th St NW, Washington, DC 20005

Blair, William S *Publisher*
%Country Journal, 205 Main St, Brattleboro, VT 05301

Blais, Madeleine *Journalist*
%Miami Herald, 1 Herald Plz, Miami, FL 33101

Blake, Bud *Cartoonist (Tiger)*
PO Box 146, Damariscotta, ME 04543

Blake, George *Editor*
%Cincinnati Enquirer, 617 Vine St, Cincinnati, OH 45202

Blake, Hector (Toe) *Hockey Player*
206 Shearton Dr, Montreal West PQ H4X 1N4, Canada

Blake, Norman P, Jr *Businessman*
%USF&G Corp, 100 Light St, Baltimore, MD 21202

Blake, Robert *Actor*
11604 Dilling St, #8, North Hollywood, CA 91608

Blake, Rockwell *Opera Singer*
1 Onondaga Ln, Plattsburgh, NY 12901

Blake, Stewart Prestley *Businessman*
734 Bliss Rd, Longmeadow, MA 01106

Blakeley, Ronee *Actress*
8033 Sunset Blvd, #693, Los Angeles, CA 90046

Blakely, Ross M *Financier*
%Coast Federal Savings, 855 S Hope St, Los Angeles, CA 90014

Blakely, Susan *Actress*
%Harris & Goldberg Agency, 1999 Ave of Stars, #2850, Los Angeles, CA 90067

Blakemore, Colin B *Neurophysiologist, Physiologist*
%University Laboratory of Physiology, Parks Rd, Oxford OX1 3PT, England

Blakenham, Viscount *Businessman*
%S Pearson & Son, Millbank Tower, Millbank, London SW1P 4QZ, England

Blalack, Robert *Cinematographer*
%Praxis Film Works, 6918 Tujunga Ave, North Hollywood, CA 91605

Blalock, Jane *Golfer*
%Jane Blalock Co, 66 Long Wharf, Boston, MA 02110

Blampied, Peter J *Financier*
%Boston Five Cents Savings Bank, 10 School St, Boston, MA 02108

Blancas, Homero *Golfer*
%Homrand Inc, Randolph Golf Course, 600 S Alvernon, Tucson, AZ 85711

Blanch, E J *Businessman*
%Ford-Werke, Henry Ford Str 1, 5000 Koln 60, Germany

Blanchard, Elwood P *Businessman*
%E I DuPont de Nemours Co, 1007 Market St, Wilmington, DE 19898

Blanchard, Felix (Doc) *Football Player*
307 Stone Wood, San Antonio, TX 78216

Blanchard, Kenneth *Writer, Business Consultant*
2048 Aldergrove, #B, Escondido, CA 92025

Blanchard, Lawrence E, Jr *Businessman*
%Ethyl Corp, 330 S 4th St, Richmond, VA 23217

Blanchard, Nina *Model Agency Executive*
%Nina Blanchard Model Agency, 7060 Hollywood Blvd, Los Angeles, CA 90028

Blanchard, Susan *Actress*
900 Chapea Rd, Pasadena, CA 91107

Blanchard, Tim *Religious Leader*
%Conservative Baptist Assn, PO Box 66, Wheaton, IL 60189

Blanco-Cervantes, Raul *President, Costa Rica*
Apdo 918, San Jose, Costa Rica

Bland, Bobby (Blue) *Singer*
108 N Auburndale, #1010, Memphis, TN 38104

Blanda, George F *Football Player*
78001 Lago Dr, La Quinta, CA 92253

Blankers-Koen, Fanny *Track Athlete*
%Olympic Committee, Surinamestraat 33, 2585 La Harve, Netherlands

Blankfield, Mark *Actor*
%Gordon/Rosson Co, 12700 Ventura Blvd, #350, Studio City, CA 91604

Blanton, Ray *Governor, TN*
%WLAC Radio, 10 Music Cir E, Nashville, TN 37203

Blass, Bill *Fashion Designer*
%Bill Blass Ltd, 550 7th Ave, New York, NY 10018

Blass, Steve *Baseball Player*
1756 Quigg Dr, Pittsburgh, PA 15241

Blassie, Freddie *Wrestler*
%World Wrestling Federation, TitanSports, 1055 Summer St, Stamford, CT 06905

Blasucci, Richard *Actor*
10424 Bloomfield St, North Hollywood, CA 91602

Blatnick, Jeff *Wrestler*
848 Whitney Dr, Schenectady, NY 12309

Blatty, William Peter *Writer*
5841 Round Meadow, Woodland Hills, CA 91364

Blatz, Durand B *Businessman*
%Insilco Corp, 1000 Research Pkwy, Meriden, CT 06450

Blau, Peter M *Sociologist*
%State University of New York, Sociology Dept, Albany, NY 12222

Blaug, Mark *Economist*
%University of London, Economics School, London, England

Blaustein, Albert P *Attorney, Educator*
415 Barby Ln, Cherry Hill, NJ 08003

Blauvelt, Howard W *Businessman*
%Continental Oil Co, High Ridge Park, Stamford, CT 06904

Blaylock, Kenneth T *Labor Leader*
%American Government Employees Federation, 80 "F" St NW, Washington, DC 20001

Blaylock, Mookie *Basketball Player*
%New Jersey Nets, Meadowlands Arena, East Rutherford, NJ 07073

Blech, Henry *Conductor*
The Owls, 70 Leopold Rd, Wimbledon, London SW19 T5Q, England

Blegen, Judith *Opera Singer*
91 Central Park West, #1-B, New York, NY 10023

Bleiberg, Robert M *Editor*
%Barron's Magazine, 200 Liberty St, New York, NY 10281

Bleier, Rocky *Football Player*
%Rocky Bleier Enterprises, 580 Squaw Run Rd E, Pittsburgh, PA 15238

Bleifeld, Stanley *Sculptor*
27 Spring Valley Rd, Weston, CT 06883

Blessed, Brian *Actor*
%Miller Mgmt, 82 Broom Park, Teddington Middx TW11 9RR, England

Blethen, Frank A *Publisher*
%Seattle Times, Fairview & Johns, Seattle, WA 98111

Blethen, John A *Publisher*
%Seattle Times, Fairview & Johns, Seattle, WA 98111

Bliley, Thomas J, Jr *Representative, VA*
408 Henri Rd, Richmond, VA 23116

Bliss, Ray C *Government Official*
2535 Addyston Rd, Akron, OH 44313

Bloch, Erich *Government Official, Scientist*
%National Science Foundation, 1800 "C" St NW, Washington, DC 20550

Bloch, Felix *Nobel Physics Laureate*
1551 Emerson St, Palo Alto, CA 94301

Bloch, Henry W *Businessman*
%H & R Block Inc, 4410 Main St, Kansas City, MO 64111

Bloch, Konrad *Nobel Medicine Laureate*
38 Oxford St, Cambridge, MA 02138

Bloch, Richard A *Businessman*
%H & R Block Inc, 4410 Main St, Kansas City, MO 64111

Bloch, Robert *Writer*
2111 Sunset Crest Dr, Los Angeles, CA 90046

Blochwitz, Hans-Peter *Opera Singer*
%IMG Artists, 22 E 71st St, New York, NY 10021

Block, Herbert L (Herblock) *Editorial Cartoonist*
%Washington Post, 1150 15th St NW, Washington, DC 20005

Block, John *Secretary, Agriculture*
%Nat Am Wholesale Grocers Assn, 201 Park Washington St, Falls Church, VA 22046

Block, Joseph L *Businessman*
1325 Astor St, Chicago, IL 60610

Block, Leonard N *Businessman*
%Block Drug Co, 257 Cornelison Ave, Jersey City, NJ 07302

Block, Sherman *Law Enforcement Official*
%Los Angeles County Sheriffs Office, 211 W Temple, Los Angeles, CA 90012

Blodgett, F Caleb *Businessman*
%General Mills Inc, 9200 Wayzata Blvd, Minneapolis, MN 55440

Blodgett, J Alan *Financier*
%American Savings & Loan, 77 W 200th S, Salt Lake City, UT 84101

Bloembergen, Nicolaas *Nobel Physics Laureate*
%Harvard University, Pierce Hall, Cambridge, MA 02138

Blomquist, John E *Businessman*
%Reynolds Metals Co, 6601 Broad Street Rd, Richmond, VA 23261

Blood, Edward J *Skier*
RFD 2, Beech Hill, Durham, NH 03824

Bloom, Allan *Educator*
5807 Dorchester Ave, #10-E, Chicago, IL 60637

Bloom, Anne *Actress*
656 W Knoll Dr, #303, Los Angeles, CA 90069

Bloom, Claire *Actress*
15 Fawcett St, London SW10, England

Bloom, Harold *Educator*
179 Linden St, New Haven, CT 06511

Bloom, Lindsay *Actress*
PO Box 2188, Los Angeles, CA 90078

Bloom, Ursula *Writer*
191 Cranmer Ct, London SW3, England

Bloomfield, Coleman *Businessman*
%Minnesota Mutual Life Insurance, 400 N Robert St, St Paul, MN 55101

Bloostein, Allan J *Businessman*
%May Department Stores, 611 Olive St, St Louis, MO 63101

Blossom, Roberts *Actor*
%Gersh Agency, 232 N Canon Dr, Beverly Hills, CA 90210

Blount, Lisa *Actress*
3957 Albright Ave, Los Angeles, CA 90066

Blount, Mel *Football Player; Executive*
%National Football League, 410 Park Ave, New York, NY 10022

Blount, W Houston *Businessman*
%Vulcan Materials Co, 1 Metroplex Dr, Birmingham, AL 35209

Blount, Winton M *Postmaster General, Businessman*
%Blount Inc, 4520 Executive Park Dr, Montgomery, AL 36116

Blount, Winton M, III *Businessman*
%Blount Inc, 4520 Executive Park Dr, Montgomery, AL 36116

Blout, Elkan R *Biochemist*
1010 Memorial Dr, Cambridge, MA 02138

B

Blue, Forrest 4451 Ashton Dr, Sacramento, CA 95825	*Football Player*
Blue, Vida PO Box 1449, Pleasanton, CA 94566	*Baseball Player*
Bluford, Guion S, Jr %NASA, Johnson Space Ctr, Houston, TX 77058	*Astronaut*
Bluhm, Neil %JMB Realty Corp, 875 N Michigan Ave, Chicago, IL 60611	*Businessman*
Blum, Arlene %University of California, Biochemistry Dept, Berkeley, CA 94720	*Mountaineer*
Blumberg, Baruch S %Institute for Cancer Research, 7701 Burholme Ave, Philadelphia, PA 19111	*Nobel Medicine Laureate*
Blume, Judy %Bradbury Press, 2 Overhill Rd, Scarsdale, NY 10583	*Writer*
Blume, Peter Rt 1, Box 140, 2 Church Rd, Sherman, CT 06784	*Artist*
Blumenthal, W Michael %Unisys Corp, 1 Burroughs Pl, Detroit, MI 48232	*Secretary, Treasury; Businessman*
Bluth, Ray %Crestwood Bowl, 9822 Hwy 66, Crestwood, MO 63126	*Bowler*
Bly, Robert E 308 1st St, Moose Lake, MN 55767	*Poet, Psychologist*
Blyleven, Burt 18922 Canyon Dr, Villa Park, CA 92667	*Baseball Player*
Blyth, Ann 35325 Beach Rd, #PH, Capistrano Beach, CA 92624	*Actress*
Blyth, Myrna %Ladies Home Journal, 100 Park Ave, New York, NY 10017	*Editor*
Boardman, Thomas G %National Westminster Bank, 41 Lothbury, London EC2P 2BP, England	*Financier*
Boatman, Clark %Countrymark Inc, 35 E Chestnut St, Columbus, OH 43216	*Businessman*
Bobko, Karol J %Booz Allen Hamilton, 16811 El Camino Real, #130, Houston, TX 77058	*Astronaut*
Boccardi, Louis D %Associated Press, 50 Rockefeller Plz, New York, NY 10020	*Publisher*
Bochner, Hart 42 Haldeman Rd, Santa Monica, CA 90402	*Actor*
Bochner, Lloyd 42 Haldeman Rd, Santa Monica, CA 90402	*Actor*
Bochner, Salomon 4100 Greenbriar Ave, #239, Houston, TX 77098	*Mathematician*
Bochte, Bruce 3688 Hastings Ct, Lafayette, CA 94549	*Baseball Player*
Bock, Edward J 7 Huntleigh Woods, St Louis, MO 63131	*Businessman, Football Player*
Bock, Jerry 145 Wellington Ave, New Rochelle, NY 10804	*Composer*
Boddicker, Mike 56 Carter Dr, Framingham, MA 01701	*Baseball Player*
Boddie, Mayo %Boddie-Noell Enterprises, 2501 Sunset Dr, Rocky Mount, NC 27801	*Businessman*
Boddie, Nick %Boddie-Noell Enterprises, 2501 Sunset Dr, Rocky Mount, NC 27801	*Businessman*
Bode, Hendrick W %Harvard University, Pierce Hall, Cambridge, MA 02138	*Research Engineer*
Bode, Rolf %Smith/Gosnell/Nicholson, 1515 Palisades Dr, #N, Pacific Palisades, CA 90272	*Cinematographer*
Bodenstein, Dietrich H F A 536 Valley Rd, Charlottesville, VA 22903	*Biologist*
Bodett, Tom %Free Flight Productions, PO Box 1117, Homer, AK 99603	*Writer, Entertainer*
Bodian, David 3917 Cloverhill Rd, Baltimore, MD 21218	*Anatomist*
Bodine, Geoff %Levi Garrett Racing, Julian, NC 27283	*Auto Racing Driver*

Boe, Nils A *Judge; Governor, SD*
%US Court of International Trade, 1 Federal Plz, New York, NY 10007

Boeckman, Dee *Track Athlete*
16829 103rd Ave, Cactus Court, Sun City, AZ 85351

Boede, Marvin J *Labor Leader*
%Plumbing & Pipe Fitting Union, 901 Massachusetts NW, Washington, DC 20001

Boeheim, Jim *Basketball Coach*
%Syracus University, Athletic Dept, Syracuse, NY 13244

Boehlert, Sherwood L *Representative, NY*
4 Hubbardton Rd, New Hartford, NY 13413

Boehne, Edward G *Financier*
%Philadelphia Federal Reserve, 100 N 6th St, Philadelphia, PA 19105

Boehner, John A *Representative, OH*
%House of Representatives, Washington, DC 20515

Boekelheide, Virgil C *Chemist*
2017 Elk Dr, Eugene, OR 97403

Boesak, Allan *Religious Leader, Social Activist*
Bellville South, Cape Town, South Africa

Boeschenstein, William W *Businessman*
%Owens-Corning Fiberglas Corp, Fiberglas Tower, Toledo, OH 43659

Boesky, Ivan F *Financier*
%Ivan F Boesky Co, 650 5th Ave, New York, NY 10019

Boetticher, Budd *Movie Director*
23969 Green Haven Ln, Ramona, CA 92065

Boff, Leonardo *Theologian*
%Petropolis Institute for Philosophy, Petropolis, Rio de Janiero, Brazil

Bofill, Angela *Singer*
1385 York Ave, #6-B, New York, NY 10021

Bofill, Ricardo *Architect*
Taller de Arquitectura, Ave de la Industria 14, Barcelona, Spain

Bogardus, John A, Jr *Businessman*
%Alexander & Alexander Services, 1221 Ave of Americas, New York, NY 10036

Bogart, Paul *Television, Movie Director*
1033 N Carol Dr, #403, Los Angeles, CA 90069

Bogdanich, Walt *Journalist*
%Wall Street Journal, 22 Cortlandt St, New York, NY 10007

Bogdanovich, Peter *Movie Director*
212 Copa de Oro Rd, Los Angeles, CA 90077

Boggs, Danny J *Judge*
%US Court of Appeals, US Courthouse, 6th & Broadway, Louisville, KY 40202

Boggs, J Caleb *Governor/Senator, DE*
1203 Grinnell Rd, Wilmington, DE 19803

Boggs, Wade *Baseball Player*
14615 Village Glen Cir, Tampa, FL 33606

Bogorad, Lawrence *Biologist, Plant Physiologist*
%Harvard University, Biology Dept, Cambridge, MA 02138

Bogosian, Eric *Performance Artist*
230 Elizabeth St, New York, NY 10012

Bohannon, David D *Community Planner, Developer*
60 Hillsdale Mall, San Mateo, CA 94403

Bohay, Heidi *Actress*
%Agency for Performing Arts, 9000 Sunset Blvd, #1200, Los Angeles, CA 90069

Bohlin, John D *Space Scientist*
%NASA, Solar & Heliospherics Physics Division, Washington, DC 22546

Bohlmann, Ralph A *Religious Leader*
%Lutheran Church Missouri Synod, 1333 S Kirkwood, St Louis, MO 63122

Bohr, Aage N *Nobel Physics Laureate*
Strangader 34, 1-Sal, 1401 Copenhagen, Denmark

Boies, David *Attorney*
%Cravath Swaine Moore, 1 Chase Manhattan Plz, New York, NY 10005

Boisi, Geoffrey T *Financier*
%Goldman Sachs & Co, 55 Broad St, New York, NY 10004

Boiso, James O *Financier*
%J P Morgan Co, 23 Wall St, New York, NY 10015

Boisson, Andre *Businessman*
%Valeo, 64 Ave de la Grande Armee, 75848 Paris Cedex 17, France

B

Boitano – Bon Jovi

Boitano, Brian *Figure Skater*
%Leigh Steinberg, 2737 Dunleer Pl, Los Angeles, CA 90064

Boiteux, Jean *Swimmer*
51 Ave de Merignac, 33200 Bordeaux, Cauderan, France

Boivin, Leo *Hockey Player*
%Boston Bruins, 150 Causeway St, Boston, MA 02114

Bok, Bart J *Astronomer, Educator*
200 Sierra Vista Dr, Tucson, AZ 85719

Bok, Chip *Editorial Cartoonist*
709 Castle Blvd, Akron, OH 44313

Bok, Derek C *Educator*
%Harvard University, Law School, Cambridge, MA 02138

Bok, Sissela *Philosopher*
33 Elmwood Ave, Cambridge, MA 02138

Bol, Manute *Basketball Player*
%Philadelphia 76ers, PO Box 25040, Philadelphia, PA 19147

Bolack, Tom *Governor, NM*
3701 Bloomfield Hwy, Framington, NM 87401

Boland, Edward P *Representative, MA*
%House of Representatives, Washington, DC 20515

Bolcom, William E *Composer*
3080 Whitmore Lake Rd, Ann Arbor, MI 48105

Bolden, Charles F, Jr *Astronaut*
%NASA, Johnson Space Ctr, Houston, TX 77058

Bolduc, J P *Businessman*
%W R Grace Co, 1114 Ave of Americas, New York, NY 10036

Bolen, Bob *Mayor*
%Mayor's Office, City Hall, 1000 Throckmorton, Ft Worth, TX 76102

Bolen, David B *Diplomat*
26 Wesley Dr, Foxmeadow, Hockessin, DE 19707

Boles, Billy J *Air Force General*
Deputy Chief of Staff/Personnel, Hq USAF, Washington, DC 20330

Bolger, Jim *Prime Minister, New Zealand*
%National Party, Parliament, Wellington, New Zealand

Bolger, Thomas E *Businessman*
%Bell Atlantic Corp, 1600 Market St, Philadelphia, PA 19103

Boliek, Luther C *Financier*
%First Federal Savings & Loan, 301 College St, Greenville, SC 29602

Bolin, Bert *Meteorologist*
%University of Stockholm, Meteorological Institute, Stockholm, Sweden

Boling, Lawrence H *Businessman*
%Consolidated Papers Inc, 231 1st Ave S, Wisconsin Rapids, WI 54494

Bolkiah Mu'izuddin Waddaulah *Sultan, Brunei*
Istana Darui Hana, Brunei

Bolleau, Linda *Editorial Cartoonist*
%Frankfort State Journal, 321 W Main St, Frankfort, KY 40601

Bollen, Roger *Cartoonist (Animal Crackers, Catfish)*
8964 Little Mt, Mentor, OH 44060

Bolles, Richard N *Writer*
2135 Londonderry Ct, Walnut Creek, CA 94597

Bollettieri, Nick *Tennis Coach*
%Nick Bollettieri Tennis Academy, 5500 34th St W, Bradenton, FL 34210

Bolling, Tiffany *Actress*
10653 Riverside Dr, Toluca Lake, CA 91602

Bologna, Joseph *Actor*
613 N Arden Dr, Beverly Hills, CA 90210

Bolt, Robert *Writer*
%M Ramsay, 14-A Goodwin's Ct, St Martin's Ln, London WC2N 4LL, England

Bolwell, Harry J *Businessman*
%Midland-Ross Corp, 20600 Chagrin Blvd, Cleveland, OH 44122

Bombassaro, Gerald *Labor Leader*
%Tile Marble & Granite Cutters Union, 801 N Pitt St, Alexandria, VA 22314

Bombeck, Erma *Writer, Columnist*
%Universal Press Syndicate, 4900 Main St, Kansas City, MO 64112

Bon Jovi, Jon *Singer*
%Bon Jovi, PolyGram Records, 810 7th Ave, New York, NY 10019

Bonar, Ivan *Actor*
1356 N Gardner St, Los Angeles, CA 90046

Bond, Alan *Businessman, Yachtsman*
%Bond Holdings Ltd, 26 St George's, 17th Floor, Perth TCE 6000, Australia

Bond, Christopher S *Governor/Senator, MO*
14 S Jefferson Rd, Mexico, MO 65265

Bond, Edward *Playwright*
%M Ramsay, 14-A Goodwin's Ct, St Martin's Ln, London WC2N 1LL, England

Bond, John R H *Financier*
%Marine Midland Banks Inc, 1 Marine Midland Ctr, Buffalo, NY 14240

Bond, Julian *Civil Rights Activist*
361 Westview Dr SW, Atlanta, GA 30310

Bond, Richard C *Businessman*
412 Caversham Rd, Bryn Mawr, PA 19010

Bond, Richard N *Political Leader*
%Republican National Committee, 310 1st St SE, Washington, DC 20003

Bondar, Roberta *Astronaut, Canada*
%National Research Council, Montreal Rd, Ottawa ON K1A 0R6, Canada

Bondarchuk, Sergei F *Movie Director*
Gorky St 9, 75 Moscow 9, Russia

Bonde, Peder *Businessman*
%Alfa-Laval AB, PO Box 12150, 102 24 Stockholm, Sweden

Bondi, Hermann *Applied Mathematician*
60 Mill Ln, Impington, Cambridgeshire CB4 4XN, England

Bondlow, William F, Jr *Publisher*
%House & Garden Magazine, Conde Nast Bldg, 350 Madison Ave, New York, NY 10017

Bonds, Bobby *Baseball Player*
175 Lyndhurst, San Carlos, CA 94076

Bonds, Gary U S *Singer*
%MARS, 168 Orchid Dr, Pearl River, NY 10965

Bondurant, Bob *Auto Driving Instructor*
%School of High Performance Driving, Sears Point Raceway, Sonoma, CA 95476

Boner, William H *Mayor; Representative, TN*
%Mayor's Office, City Hall, 107 Court House, Nashville, TN 37201

Bonerz, Peter *Actor, Comedian*
3637 Lowry Rd, Los Angeles, CA 90027

Bonet, Lisa *Actress*
%William Morris Agency, 151 El Camino, Beverly Hills, CA 90212

Bongo, Albert-Bernard (Omar) *President, Gabon*
%President's Office, Boite Postale 546, Libreville, Gabon

Bonham-Carter, Helen *Actress*
%Jeremy Conway Ltd, Eagle House, 109 Jermyn St, London SW1, England

Boni, Robert E *Businessman*
%Armco Inc, 177 Madison Ave, Morristown, NJ 07960

Bonica, John J *Anesthesiologist*
4732 E Mercer Way, Mercer Island, WA 98040

Bonilla, Bobby *Baseball Player*
2648 Bainbridge Ave, Bronx, NY 10458

Bonior, David E *Representative, MI*
%House of Representatives, Washington, DC 20515

Bonker, Don L *Representative, WA*
%House of Representatives, Washington, DC 20515

Bonnefous, Jean-Pierre *Ballet Dancer, Choreographer*
%Indiana University, Ballet Dept, Music School, Bloomington, IN 47405

Bonner, Frank *Actor*
%Gores/Fields Agency, 10100 Santa Monica Blvd, #700, Los Angeles, CA 90067

Bonner, James *Biologist*
1914 Edgewood Dr, South Pasadena, CA 91030

Bonner, John F *Businessman*
%Pacific Gas & Electric Co, 77 Beale St, San Francisco, CA 94106

Bonner, Thomas N *Educator*
441 W Ferry, Detroit, MI 48202

Bonner, Zora D *Businessman*
%Tesoro Petroleum Co, 8700 Tesoro Dr, San Antonio, TX 78286

Bonnett, Neil *Auto Racing Driver*
%General Delivery, Hueytown, AL 35023

Bonney, J Dennis *Businessman*
%Chevron Corp, 225 Bush St, San Francisco, CA 94104

Bono, Sonny *Actor, Singer*
%Mayor's Office, 3200 E Tahquitz Canyon Way, Palm Springs, CA 92263

Bonoff, Karla *Singer*
1691 N Crescent Heights Blvd, Los Angeles, CA 90069

Bonsall, Joe *Singer (Oak Ridge Boys)*
%Oak Ridge Boys, 329 Rockland Rd, Hendersonville, TN 37075

Bonsignore, Joseph J *Publisher*
%Smithsonian Magazine, 900 Jefferson Dr SW, Washington, DC 20560

Bonvicini, Joan *Basketball Coach*
%University of Arizona, Athletic Dept, McKale Memorial Center, Tucson, AZ 85721

Bonynge, Richard *Conductor*
Chalet Monet, Rte de Sonloup, CH 1833 Les Avants, Switzerland

Boochever, Robert *Judge*
%US Court of Appeals, 125 S Grand Ave, Pasadena, CA 91109

Booher, Edward E *Publisher*
34 Wilson Rd, Princeton, NJ 08540

Booke, Sorrell *Actor*
PO Box 1105, Studio City, CA 91604

Booker, Henry G *Applied Physicist*
8696 Dunaway Dr, La Jolla, CA 92037

Bookout, John F, Jr *Businessman*
%Shell Oil Co, 1 Shell Plz, Houston, TX 77002

Boone, Bob *Baseball Player*
18571 Villa Dr, Villa Park, CA 92667

Boone, Debby *Actress*
%Resi, 15315 Magnolia Blvd, #208, Sherman Oaks, CA 91403

Boone, Mary *Artist Representative*
420 W Broadway, New York, NY 10012

Boone, Pat *Actor, Singer*
904 N Beverly Dr, Beverly Hills, CA 90210

Boorda, Jeremy M *Navy Admiral*
Deputy CNO, Military Personnel/Training, Navy Department, Washington, DC 20370

Boorman, John *Movie Director*
21 Thurlue Sq, London NW1, England

Boorstin, Daniel J *Historian*
3451 Ordway St NW, Washington, DC 20016

Boosler, Elayne *Comedienne*
11061 Wrightwood Ln, North Hollywood, CA 91604

Booth, Adrian *Actor*
3922 Glenridge Dr, Sherman Oaks, CA 91423

Booth, Douglas W *Businessman*
%Duke Power Co, 422 S Church St, Charlotte, NC 28242

Booth, George *Cartoonist*
PO Box 841, Stony Brook, NY 11790

Booth, I MacAllister *Businessman*
%Polaroid Corp, 549 Technology Sq, Cambridge, MA 02139

Booth, James *Actor*
%Hillard/Elkins, 8306 Wilshire Blvd, #438, Beverly Hills, CA 90211

Booth, Pat *Writer*
%Crown Publishers, 1 Park Ave, New York, NY 10016

Booth, Richard H *Businessman*
%Travelers Corp, 1 Tower Sq, Hartford, CT 06115

Booth, Shirley *Actress*
PO Box 103, Chatham, MA 02633

Booth, Wallace W *Businessman*
%Ducommun Inc, 611 W 6th St, #2500, Los Angeles, CA 90017

Boothe, Powers *Actor*
4319 Manson Ave, Woodland Hills, CA 91364

Borda, Richard J *Businessman*
%National Life Insurance, National Life Dr, Montpelier, VT 05604

Bordaberry Arocena, Juan Maria *President, Uruguay*
Joaquin Suarez 2868, Montevideo, Uruguay

Boren, David L *Governor/Senator, OK*
%US Senate, Washington, DC 20510

Borg Olivier, George *Prime Minister, Malta*
%House of Representatives, Valletta, Malta

Borg, Bjorn *Tennis Player*
%International Management Grp, 1 Erieview Plz, Cleveland, OH 44114

Borg, Kim *Opera Singer*
Osterbrogade 158, 2100 Copenhagen, Denmark

Borge, Victor *Musician, Comedian*
Field Point Park, Greenwich, CT 06830

Borgman, Jim *Editorial Cartoonist*
%Cincinnati Enquirer, 617 Vine St, Cincinnati, OH 45201

Borgnine, Ernest *Actor*
3055 Lake Glen Dr, Beverly Hills, CA 90210

Boris, Ruthanna *Ballerina, Choreographer*
%Center for Dance, 555 Pierce St, #1033, Albany, CA 94706

Bork, Robert H *Judge*
%American Enterprise Institute, 1150 17th St NW, Washington, DC

Borkh, Inge *Opera Singer*
Haus Weitblick, CH 9405 Wienacht, Switzerland

Borkowski, Francis T *Educator*
%University of South Florida, President's Office, Tampa, FL 33620

Borlaug, Norman *Nobel Peace Laureate*
15611 Ranchita Rd, Dallas, TX 75248

Borman, Frank *Astronaut*
Patlex Corp, 250 Cotorro Ct, Las Cruces, NM 88005

Borman, Paul *Businessman*
%Borman's Inc, 18718 Borman St, Detroit, MI 48232

Born, Allen *Businessman*
%Amax Inc, Amax Ctr, Greenwich, CT 06836

Bornstein, Steven M *Television Executive*
%ESPN, ESPN Plz, 935 Middle St, Bristol, CT 06010

Borofsky, Jonathan *Artist*
57 Market St, Venice, CA 90291

Boros, Julius *Golfer*
2900 NE 40th St, Fort Lauderdale, FL 33308

Borotra, Jean *Tennis Player*
35 Ave Foch, 75116 Paris, France

Borowy, Hank *Baseball Player*
210 W Passaic Ave, West Bloomfield, NJ 07003

Borra, Ermanno *Astrophysicist*
%Laval University, Astrophysics Dept, Quebec ON, Canada

Borski, Robert A *Representative, PA*
%House of Representatives, Washington, DC 20515

Bortoluzzi, Paolo *Ballet Dancer, Choreographer*
16 Ave Des Merles, 1150 Brussells, Belgium

Boryla, Vince *Basketball Player, Executive*
%Denver Nuggets, McNichols Arena, 1635 Clay St, Denver, CO 80204

Borysewicz, Eddy *Cycling Coach*
%Cycling Velodrome, Balboa Park, San Diego, CA 92136

Borzov, Valeri *Track Athlete*
Suvorov St 11-82, Kiev, Russia

Bosco, Philip *Actor*
%Artists Agency, 10000 Santa Monica Blvd, #305, Los Angeles, CA 90067

Bosetti, Rick *Baseball Player*
1233 Hill St, Anderson, CA 96007

Boskin, Michael J *Government Official*
%Council of Economic Advisers, Old Executive Office Bldg, Washington, DC 20500

Bosley, Bruce *Football Player*
246 W Santa Inez, Hillsborough, CA 94010

Bosley, Tom *Actor*
2822 Royston Pl, Beverly Hills, CA 90210

Bosman, Dick *Baseball Player*
3058 Landmark Blvd, #1202, Palm Harbor, FL 33563

Bossard, Andre *Law Enforcement Official*
%Interpol, 26 Rue Armengaud, 92210 Saint-Cloud, France

Bossidy, Lawrence A *Businessman*
%General Electric Co, 3135 Easton Tpke, Fairfield, CT 06431

B

Bosson - Boulting

Bosson, Barbara *Actress*
%Writers & Artists Agency, 11726 San Vicente Blvd, #300, Los Angeles, CA 90049

Bossy, Mike *Hockey Player*
%New York Islanders, Nassau Coliseum, Uniondale, NY 11553

Bostelle, Tom *Artist*
%Aeolian Palace Gallery, PO Box 8, Pocopson, PA 19366

Bostic, Jeff *Football Player*
%Washington Redskins, Dulles Airport, Box 17247, Washington, DC 20041

Bostic, Keith *Football Player*
%Indianapolis Colts, 7001 W 56th St, Indianapolis, IN 46254

Boston, Ralph *Track Athlete*
3301 Woodbine Ave, Knoxville, TN 37914

Bostwick, Barry *Actor*
2770 Hutton Dr, Beverly Hills, CA 90210

Boswell, Dave *Baseball Player*
309 Roxbury Ct, Joppa, MD 21085

Boswell, Thomas *Sportswriter*
%Washington Post, 1150 15th St NW, Washington, DC 20071

Botelho, Carlos *Artist*
Ave Joao XXI-3-3d-F, 1000 Lisbon, Portugal

Botero, Fernando *Artist*
5 Blvd du Palais, 75004 Paris, France

Botha, Pieter W *Prime Minister, South Africa*
Libertas, Bryntirion, Pretoria, South Africa

Botha, Roelof Frederik *Government Official, South Africa*
%Ministry of Foreign Affairs, Cape Town, South Africa

Botham, Ian *Cricket Player*
Epworth, South Humberside, England

Bothmer, Bernard V *Museum Curator, Egyptologist*
%Brooklyn Museum, 188 Eastern Pkwy, Brooklyn, NY 11238

Botstein, Leon *Educator*
%Bard College, President's Office, Annandale-on-Hudson, NY 12504

Bott, Raoul *Mathematician*
935 Memorial Dr, Cambridge, MA 02138

Bottari, Vic *Football Player*
%Bottari Holland Sweetman, 2150 Franklin St, Oakland, CA 94612

Bottoms, Joseph *Actor*
%Agency for Performing Arts, 9000 Sunset Blvd, #1200, Los Angeles, CA 90069

Bottoms, Samuel *Actor*
2386 Meyers Dr, Santa Rosa, CA 95401

Bottoms, Timothy *Actor*
532 Hot Springs Rd, Santa Barbara, CA 93108

Botvinnik, Mikhail *Chess Player*
3 Ja Frunzenskaya W 7, Flat 154, Moscow G-270, Russia

Botwinick, Michael *Museum Official*
%Brooklyn Museum, 188 Eastern Pkwy, Brooklyn, NY 11238

Bouchard, Emile J (Butch) *Hockey Player*
213 Marie-Victorin, Vercheres PQ J0L 2R0, Canada

Boucher, Frederick C (Rick) *Representative, VA*
%House of Representatives, Washington, DC 20515

Boucher, Gaetan *Speed Skater*
%Center Sportif, 3850 Edgar, St Hubert PQ J4T 368, Canada

Boucher, Pierre *Photographer*
L'Ermitage, 7 Ave Massoul, Faremountiers, 77120 Coulomiers, France

Boudreau, Lou *Baseball Player, Manager*
15600 Ellis Ave, Dolton, IL 60419

Boulding, Kenneth E *Behavioral Economist*
890 Willowbrook Rd, Boulder, CO 80302

Boulet, Gilles *Educator*
%University of Quebec, President's Office, Ste Foy PQ G1V 2M3, Canada

Boulez, Pierre *Composer, Conductor*
Postfach 22, Baden-Baden, Germany

Boulter, Beau *Representative, TX*
%House of Representatives, Washington, DC 20515

Boulting, Roy *Movie Producer, Director*
%Charter Film Productions, 8-A Glebe Pl, Chelsea, London SW3 5LB, England

Boulton, Robert G *Businessman*
%Gulf Resources & Chemical Corp, 1100 Milam Bldg, Houston, TX 77002

Bourdeaux, Michael *Religious Leader*
%Keston College, Heathfield Rd, Keston, Kent BR2 6BA, England

Bourgeois, Louise *Sculptor*
347 W 20th St, New York, NY 10011

Bourges-Maunoury, Maurice *Prime Minister, France*
67 Rue la Boetie, 75008 Paris, France

Bourjaily, Vance *Writer*
Redbird Farm, Rt 3, Iowa City, IA 52240

Bourke, William O *Businessman*
%Reynolds Metals Co, 6601 Broad Street Rd, Richmond, VA 23261

Bourland, Clifford *Track Athlete*
380 S Carmelina Ave, Brentwood, CA 90049

Bourns, Arthur Newcombe *Educator*
%McMaster University, Hamilton ON L8S 4L8, Canada

Bourque, Pierre *Horticulturist*
4101 E Sherbrooke St, Montreal PQ H1X 2B2, Canada

Bourque, Ray *Hockey Player*
%Boston Bruins, 150 Causeway St, Boston, MA 02114

Boussena, Sadek *Government Official, Algeria*
80 Rue Ahmad Ghermoul, Algiers, Algeria

Boutin, Bernard Louis *Mathematician*
174 Wallis Rd, Rye, NH 03870

Bouton, Jim *Baseball Player, Writer*
6 Myron Ct, Teaneck, NJ 07666

Boutros Ghali, Boutros *Government Official, Egypt*
%United Nations, Secretary-General's Office, UN Plaza, New York, NY 10017

Bouvet, Didier *Skier*
%Bouvet-Sports, 74360 Abondance, France

Bouwkamp, Gerald R *Businessman*
%Stanadyne Inc, 100 Deerfield Rd, Windson, CT 06095

Bovet, Daniel *Nobel Medicine Laureate*
Piazza San Apollinare 33, 00186 Rome, Italy

Bowa, Larry *Baseball Player*
1029 Morris Ave, Bryn Mawr, PA 19010

Bowden, Bobby *Football Coach*
%Florida State University, Athletic Dept, Tallahassee, FL 32306

Bowden, H K *Businessman*
%Canoca Ltd, Park House, 116 Park St, London W1Y 4NN, England

Bowdler, William G *Diplomat*
%Department of State, 2201 "C" St NW, Washington, DC 20520

Bowe, Rosemarie *Actress*
321 St Pierre Rd, Los Angeles, CA 90077

Bowen, Donald E *Educator*
%Stephen F Austin University, President's Office, Nacogdoches, TX 75962

Bowen, John S *Businessman*
%Benton & Bowles Inc, 909 3rd Ave, New York, NY 10022

Bowen, Otis R *Secretary, Health & Human Services*
%Health & Human Services Department, 200 Independence, Washington, DC 20201

Bowen, Richard *Educator*
%Idaho State University, President's Office, Pocatello, ID 83209

Bowen, W J *Businessman*
%Transco Energy Co, 2800 Post Oak Blvd, Houston, TX 77056

Bower, Antoinette *Actress*
%Brooke Dunn Oliver, 9165 Sunset Blvd, #202, Los Angeles, CA 90069

Bower, Rodney A *Labor Leader*
%Professional & Technical Engineers, 818 Roeder Rd, Silver Spring, MD 20910

Bowerman, William J *Businessman*
%Nike Inc, 3900 SW Murray Blvd, Beaverton, OR 97005

Bowers, Jack L *Businessman*
%Sanders Assoc, Daniel Webster Hwy, South Nashua, NH 03061

Bowers, John *Labor Leader*
%International Longshoremen's Assn, 17 Battery Pl, New York, NY 10004

Bowers, John W *Religious Leader*
%Foursquare Gospel Int'l Church, 1100 Glendale Blvd, Los Angeles, CA 90026

B

Bowersox, Kenneth D %NASA, Johnson Space Ctr, Houston, TX 77058	*Astronaut*
Bowie, David %Isolar, 641 5th Ave, #22-Q, New York, NY 10022	*Singer, Actor*
Bowie, Lester %ECM, 509 Madison Ave, New York, NY 10022	*Jazz Trumpeteer*
Bowie, Robert R 2801 New Mexico Ave NW, Washington, DC 20007	*Educator, Government Official*
Bowie, Sam 919 Lehman St, Lebanon, PA 17042	*Basketball Player*
Bowker, Albert H %University of Maryland, Public Affairs School, Adelphi, MD 20783	*Educator*
Bowker, Hilary %ABC-TV, News Dept, 1330 Ave of Americas, New York, NY 10019	*Commentator*
Bowker, Judi %William Morris Agency, 31/32 Soho Sq, London W1V SDG, England	*Actress*
Bowlen, Pat %Denver Broncos, 13655 E Dove Valley Pkwy, Englewood, CO 80112	*Football Executive*
Bowles, Lloyd S, Jr %Dallas Federal Financial Corp, 8333 Douglas Ave, Dallas, TX 75225	*Financier*
Bowles, Lloyd S, Sr %Dallas Federal Financial Corp, 8333 Douglas Ave, Dallas, TX 75225	*Financier*
Bowles, Paul 2117 Tanger Socco, Tangier, Morocco	*Composer, Writer*
Bowles, Samuel %University of Massachusetts, Economics Dept, Amherst, MA 01003	*Economist*
Bowlin, Patrick L %Open Bible Standard Churches, 2020 Bell Ave, Des Moines, IA 50315	*Religious Leader*
Bowman, Chris 5653 Kester Ave, Van Nuys, CA 91411	*Figure Skater*
Bowman, Pasco M, II %US Court of Appeals, US Courthouse, 811 Grand Ave, Kansas City, MO 64106	*Judge*
Bowman, Scotty %Pittsburgh Penguins, Civic Arena, Pittsburgh, PA 15219	*Hockey Coach*
Bownes, Hugh H %US Court of Appeals, Federal Courthouse, PO Box 311, Concord, NH 03301	*Judge*
Bowyer, C Stuart %University of California, Astronomy Dept, Berkeley, CA 94720	*Astronomer, Educator*
Boxcar Willie %Majic Promotions, 9265 Olde Eight Rd, Cleveland, OH 44067	*Singer, Songwriter*
Boxer, Barbara %House of Representatives, Washington, DC 20515	*Representative, CA*
Boxer, Stanley 37 E 18th St, New York, NY 10002	*Artist*
Boxleitner, Bruce 24500 John Colter Rd, Hidden Hills, CA 91302	*Actor*
Boy George (O'Dowd) 34-A Green Ln, Northwood, Middlesex, England	*Singer*
Boy, John Buckner %US Sugar Corp, 111 Ponce de Leon Ave, Clewiston, FL 33440	*Businessman*
Boyd, Alan S 2301 Connecticut Ave NW, Washington, DC 20008	*Secretary, Transportation*
Boyd, Charles G Commander, Air University, Maxwell Air Force Base, AL 36112	*Air Force General*
Boyd, Howard T 6042 Crab Orchard St, Houston, TX 77057	*Businessman*
Boyd, Jimmy %Light Co, 901 Bringham, Los Angeles, CA 90049	*Singer, Actor*
Boyd, Joseph A %Harris Corp, 1025 W NASA Blvd, Melbourne, FL 32919	*Businessman*
Boyd, Malcolm %St Augustine-By-the-Sea Episcopal Church, 1227 4th St, Santa Monica, CA 90401	*Religious Leader*
Boyd, Richard A %Fraternal Order of Police, 2100 Gardiner Ln, Louisville, KY 40205	*Labor Leader*
Boyd, Rob Whistler/Blackcomb Resort, Whistler BC, Canada	*Skier*

B

Boyd, William B *Businessman*
%American Standard Inc, 40 W 40th St, New York, NY 10018

Boyd, William C *Biochemist*
80 E Concord St, Boston, MA 02118

Boyer, Clete *Baseball Player*
100 Aleta Dr, Belleair Beach, FL 34635

Boyer, Ernest L *Educator, Government Official*
7016 Benjamin St, McLean, VA 22101

Boyer, Herbert W *Genetic Engineer, Biochemist*
%University of California, Biochemistry Dept, San Francisco, CA 94143

Boyer, Paul D *Chemist*
1033 Somera Rd, Los Angeles, CA 90024

Boykin, Robert H *Financier*
%Dallas Federal Reserve, 400 S Akard St, Dallas, TX 75222

Boykoff, Harry *Basketball Player*
11499 Thurston Cir, Los Angeles, CA 90049

Boyle Clune, Charlotte *Swimmer*
50 Brown's Grove, Box 31, Scottsville, NY 14546

Boyle, Barbara D *Movie Executive*
1160 San Vicente St, Los Angeles, CA 90049

Boyle, Dermont Alexander *Air Force Marshal, England*
Fair Gallop, Brighton Rd, Sway, Lymington, Hants, England

Boyle, Kay *Writer*
%A Watkins Inc, 77 Park Ave, New York, NY 10016

Boyle, Lara Flynn *Actress*
606 N Larchmont Blvd, #309, Los Angeles, CA 90004

Boyle, Richard J *Businessman*
%Chase Manhattan Corp, 1 Chase Manhattan Plz, New York, NY 10081

Boyle, T Coraghessan *Writer*
%University of Southern California, English Dept, Los Angeles, CA 90089

Boynton, Sandra *Graphic Artist*
%Recycled Paper Products, 3636 N Broadway, Chicago, IL 60613

Bozo, Dominque *Museum Official*
%Georges Pompidou Museum, 75191 Paris Cedex 04, France

Brabham, Geoff *Auto Racing Driver*
General Delivery, Noblesville, IN 46060

Brabham, Jack *Auto Racing Driver*
PO Box 149, Yagoona NSW 2199, Australia

Bracco, Lorraine *Actress*
PO Box 49, Palisades, NY 10964

Brace, William F *Geologist*
136 Lakeview Ave, Cambridge, MA 02138

Brachetti-Peretti, C L D A *Businessman*
%Anomina Petroli Italiana, Corso d'Italia 6, 00198 Rome, Italy

Brack, Reginald K, Jr *Publisher*
%Time Inc, Time-Life Bldg, Rcokefeller Center, New York, NY 10010

Bracken, Eddie *Actor*
%William Morris Agency, 151 El Camino, Beverly Hills, CA 90212

Bracken, Peg *Actress, Writer*
66 Kahana Pl, Lahaina, HI 96761

Bradbury, Malcolm *Writer*
%University of East Anglia, English School, Norwich, Norfolk, England

Bradbury, Norris E *Physicist*
1451 47th St, Los Alamos, NM 87544

Bradbury, Ray *Writer*
10265 Cheviot Dr, Los Angeles, CA 90064

Braddock, Richard S *Financier*
%Citicorp, 399 Park Ave, New York, NY 10043

Brademas, John *Educator; Representative, NY*
%New York University, President's Emeritus Office, New York, NY 10012

Braden, Vic *Tennis Coach*
22000 Trabuco Canyon Rd, Trabuco Canyon, CA 92678

Bradford, Barbara Taylor *Writer*
%Doubleday & Co, 245 Park Ave, New York, NY 10017

Bradford, Greg *Actor*
3752 Redwood Ave, Los Angeles, CA 90066

B

Bradlee - Brand

Bradlee, Benjamin C *Editor*
1721 21st St NW, Washington, DC 20009

Bradley, Bill *Senator, NJ; Basketball Player*
1605 Vauxhall Rd, Union, NJ 07083

Bradley, Dick *Sports Cartoonist*
%Sporting News, 1212 N Lindbergh, St Louis, MO 63132

Bradley, Ed *Commentator*
%CBS-TV, News Dept, 524 W 57th St, New York, NY 10019

Bradley, Pat *Golfer*
%Ladies Professional Golf Assn, 2570 Volusia Ave, #B, Daytona Beach, FL 32114

Bradley, Robert A *Physician*
2465 S Downing, Denver, CO 80210

Bradley, Tom *Mayor*
%Mayor's Office, City Hall, 200 N Spring St, Los Angeles, CA 90012

Bradman, Don *Cricket Player*
118 King William St, Adelaide SA, Australia

Bradshaw, Charles J *Businessman*
%Trans World Corp, 605 3rd Ave, New York, NY 10158

Bradshaw, Terry *Football Player*
Rt 1, Box 227, Gordonville, TX 76245

Brady, Nicholas F *Secretary, Treasury; Senator, NJ*
Black River Rd, Far Hills, NJ 07931

Brady, Patrick H *Vietnam War Army Hero (CMH), General*
Deputy Commanding General, 6th US Army, Presidio of San Francisco, CA 94129

Brady, Ray *Commentator*
%CBS-TV, 524 W 57th St, New York, NY 10019

Brady, William H *Businessman*
%William H Brady Co, 727 W Glendale Ave, Milwaukee, WI 53201

Braeden, Eric *Actor*
13723 Romany Dr, Pacific Palisades, CA 90272

Braga, Sonia *Actress*
295 Greenwich St, #11-B, New York, NY 10007

Bragg, Charles *Artist*
%Woodland Graphics, 9713 Santa Monica Blvd, #216, Beverly Hills, CA 90210

Bragg, Darrell Brent *Nutritionist*
%University of British Columbia, Vancouver BC V6T 2AZ, Canada

Bragg, Don *Track Athlete*
%D B Enterprises, PO Box 171, New Gretna, NJ 08224

Bragg, George L *Businessman*
%Telex Corp, 6422 E 41st St, Tulsa, OK 74135

Bragg, Melvyn *Writer*
12 Hampstead Hill Grdns, London NW3, England

Braidwood, Robert J *Archaeologist, Anthropologist*
%University of Chicago, Oriental Institute, Chicago, IL 60637

Brailsford, Marvin D *Army General*
DCG, Material Readiness, Hq AMC, 5001 Eisenhower Ave, Alexandria, VA 22333

Brainerd, Paul *Businessman*
%Aldus Corp, 411 Ist Ave S, #200, Seattle, WA 98104

Braman, Norman *Football Executive*
%Philadelphia Eagles, Veterans Stadium, Philadelphia, PA 19148

Branagh, Kenneth *Actor, Director*
Renaissance Theatre Co, 56 Kings Rd, Kingston-upon-Thames KT2 5HF, England

Branca, Ralph *Baseball Player*
%National Pension, 1025 Westchester, White Plains, NY 10604

Branch, C B *Businessman*
%Dow Chemical Co, 2030 Dow Ctr, Midland, TX 48640

Branch, Cliff *Football Player*
%Los Angeles Raiders, 332 Center St, El Segundo, CA 90245

Branch, Harllee, Jr *Businessman*
3106 Nancy Dr NW, Atlanta, GA 30327

Branch, William *Playwright*
53 Cortlandt Ave, New Rochelle, NY 10801

Brand, Frank A *Businessman*
%M/A-Com Inc, 7 New England Executive Park, Burlington, MA 01803

Brand, Oscar *Singer*
360 Central Park West, #16-G, New York, NY 10025

Brand, Robert *Theater Lighting Designer*
505 West End Ave, New York, NY 10024

Brand, Vance D *Astronaut*
%NASA, Johnson Space Ctr, Houston, TX 77058

Brandauer, Klaus Maria *Actor*
Bartensteingasse 8/9, 1010 Vienna, Austria

Brandenburg, Jim *Basketball Coach*
%San Diego State University, Athletic Dept, San Diego, CA 92182

Brandenstein, Daniel C *Astronaut*
%NASA, Johnson Space Ctr, Houston, TX 77058

Brandis, Jonathan *Actor*
%Herb Tannen Assoc, 1800 N Vine St, #120, Los Angeles, CA 90028

Brandner, J William *Publisher*
%Harcourt Brace Jovanovich Inc, 6277 Sea Harbor Dr, Orlando, FL 32821

Brando, Marlon *Actor*
Hawley Rd, Mundelein, IL 60060

Brandon, Clark *Actor*
%Jennings Assoc, 28035 Dorothy Dr, #210, Agoura, CA 91301

Brandon, Michael *Actor*
%Bernstein Fox Goldberg, 1875 Century Park East, #1300, Los Angeles, CA 90067

Brandon, Terrell *Basketball Player*
%Cleveland Cavaliers, PO Box 5000, Richfield, OH 44286

Brandow, Judy *Editor*
%Canadian Living Magazine, 50 Holly St, Toronto ON M4S 3B3, Canada

Brands, X *Actor*
17171 Roscoe Blvd, #104, Northridge, CA 91325

Brandt, Hank *Actor*
%Contemporary Artists, 132 Lasky Dr, #B, Beverly Hills, CA 90212

Brandt, Willy *Chancellor, West Germany; Nobel Laureate*
Erich Ollenhauerstr 1, 5300 Bonn 1, Germany

Branigan, Laura *Singer, Songwriter*
310 E 65th St, New York, NY 10021

Branitzki, Heinz *Businessman*
%Porsche Dr Ing HCF, Porchenstr 42, 7000 Stuttgart 40, Germany

Brannan, Charles F *Secretary, Agriculture*
3131 E Alameda Ave, Denver, CO 80239

Brannon, Del L *Financier*
%FirstSouth, 121 W 6th Ave, Pine Bluff, AK 71611

Branscomb, B Harvie *Educator*
1620 Chickering Rd, Nashville, TN 37215

Branscomb, Lewis M *Physicist*
%IBM Corp, Old Orchard Rd, Armonk, NY 10504

Branson, Richard *Businessman, Balloonist*
%Virgin Group PLC, 120 Campden Hill Rd, London W8 7AR, England

Branstad, Terry E *Governor, IA*
%Governor's Office, State Capitol Bldg, Des Moines, IA 50319

Brant, Tim *Sportscaster*
%ABC-TV, Sports Dept, 77 W 66th St, New York, NY 10023

Brasseur, Claude *Actor*
1 Rue Seguier, 75006 Paris, France

Brathwaite, Edward *Writer*
%University of West Indies, History Dept, Mona, Kingston 7, Jamaica

Bratkowski, Zeke *Football Player, Coach*
%Philadelphia Eagles, Veterans Stadium, Broad & Pattison, Philadelphia, PA 19148

Brauer, Arik *Artist*
%Joram Harel Mgmt, PO Box 145, 1013 Vienna, Austria

Brauer, Jerald Carl *Church Historian*
5620 S Blackstone Ave, Chicago, IL 60637

Braun, Lilian Jackson *Writer*
%Jove Books, Berkeley Publishing Grp, 200 Madison Ave, New York, NY 10016

Braun, Pinkas *Actor, Theater Director*
Unterdorf, CH 8261 Hemishofen/SH, Switzerland

Braver, Rita *Commentator*
%CBS-News, 2020 "M" St NW, Washington, DC 20036

Braverman, Bart *Actor*
%Allen Goldstein Assoc, 5015 Lemona Ave, Sherman Oaks, CA 91423

Braxton, Anthony *Jazz Guitarist, Composer*
2490 Channing Way, #406, Berkeley, CA 94704

Bray, R A *Businessman*
%Standard Oil Co (Ohio), Midland Bldg, Cleveland, OH 44115

Bray, William G *Representative, IN*
489 N Jefferson St, Martinsville, IN 46151

Brazelton, T Berry *Psychiatrist*
23 Hawthorn St, Cambridge, MA 02138

Brazier, Robert G *Businessman*
%Airborne Freight Corp, 3101 Western Ave, Seattle, WA 98121

Brazzi, Rosanno *Actor*
Via Gionanni Batta Martini 13, Rome, Italy

Bready, Richard L *Businessman*
%Nortek Inc, 50 Kennedy Plz, Providence, RI 02903

Bream, Julian *Concert Guitarist*
%Basil Douglas Ltd, 8 St George's Terr, London NW1 8XJ, England

Breathed, Berke *Cartoonist (Bloom County)*
%Washington Post Writers Grp, 1150 15th St NW, Washington, DC 20071

Breathitt, Edward T *Governor, KY*
%Norfolk Southern Corp, 1500 "K" St NW, #375, Washington, DC 20005

Breaux, John B *Senator, LA*
%US Senate, Washington, DC 20510

Brebbia, John Henry *Financier*
%First Western Financial Corp, 2700 W Sahara Ave, Las Vegas, NV 89102

Brecheen, Harry *Baseball Player*
1134 S Highschool, Ada, OK 74820

Breder, Charles M *Ichthyologist*
6275 Manasota Key Rd, Englewood, FL 33533

Breeden, Richard C *Government Official*
%Securities & Exchange Commission, 450 5th St NW, Washington, DC 20549

Breen, Bobby *Singer*
8102 SW 23rd Ct, North Lauderdale, FL 33068

Breen, George *Swimmer*
7-D Butternut Ct, Wilmington, DE 19810

Breen, John G *Businessman*
%Sherwin-Williams Co, 101 Prospect Ave NW, Cleveland, OH 44115

Breen, Steve *Editorial Cartoonist*
%Hemet News, PO Box 1107, Hemet, CA 92343

Breeze, Francis V *Businessman*
%PPG Industries, PPG Pl, Pittsburgh, PA 15272

Bregman, Buddy *Movie Director, Producer*
11288 Ventura Blvd, #700, Studio City, CA 91604

Breitkreutz, Emil *Track Athlete*
1404 Wilson Ave, San Marino, CA 91108

Breitschwerdt, Werner *Businessman*
%Daimler-Benz AG, Mercedesstrasse 136, 7000 Stuttgart 60, Germany

Breland, Mark *Boxer*
%Cross Country Concert Corp, 310 Madison Ave, New York, NY 10017

Bremer, Lucille *Actress*
8191 Via Mall Orca, La Jolla, CA 92037

Bremner, John B *Journalist, Educator*
2614 Orchard Ln, Lawrence, KS 66044

Bren, Donald L *Businessman*
%Irvine Co, 550 Newport Center Dr, Newport Beach, CA 92663

Brenan, Gerald *Writer*
Alhaurin El Grande, Malaga, Spain

Brendel, Alfred *Concert Pianist*
%Ingpen & Williams, 14 Kensington Ct, London W4, England

Brenden, Hallgeir *Nordic Skier*
General Delivery, 2417 Torberget, Norway

Brendsel, Leland C *Financier*
%Federal Home Loan Mortgage Corp, 1700 "G" St NW, Washington, DC 20552

Brengel, Fred L *Businessman*
%Johnson Controls Inc, 5757 N Green Bay Ave, Milwaukee, WI 53201

Brennan, Bernard F *Businessman*
%Montgomery Ward Co, 535 W Chicago Ave, Chicago, IL 60607

Brennan, Edward A *Businessman*
%Sears Roebuck Co, Sears Tower, Chicago, IL 60684
Brennan, Eileen *Actress*
PO Box 1777, Ojai, CA 93023
Brennan, James F *Hockey Executive*
%Boston Bruins, 150 Causeway St, Boston, MA 02114
Brennan, John A *Businessman*
%GAF Corp, 1361 Alps Rd, Wayne, NJ 07470
Brennan, Joseph E *Governor, Representative, ME*
104 France St, Portland, ME 04102
Brennan, Joseph R *Basketball Player*
9105 Colonial Rd, Brooklyn, NY 11209
Brennan, Melissa *Actress*
%Gage Group, 9255 Sunset Blvd, Los Angeles, CA 90069
Brennan, Peter J *Secretary, Labor*
2100 Massachusetts Ave, Washington, DC 20008
Brennan, Robert E *Horse Racing Executive, Businessman*
%First Jersey Securities, 50 Broadway, #1401, New York, NY 10004
Brennan, Terry *Football Player, Coach*
1349 Chestnut St, Wilmette, IL 60091
Brennan, William J, Jr *Supreme Court Justice*
%US Supreme Court, 1 1st St NE, Washington, DC 20543
Brenner, David *Comedian*
229 E 62nd St, New York, NY 10021
Brenner, Sydney *Molecular Biologist*
%MRC Molecular Genetics Unit, Hills Rd, Cambridge CB2 2QH, England
Brent Ashe, Eve *Actress*
%Joshua Gray Assoc, 6736 Laurel Canyon Blvd, #306, North Hollywood, CA 91601
Brescia, Richard *Radio Executive*
%CBS Radio Network, 51 W 52nd St, New York, NY 10019
Bresee, Bobbie *Actress*
%Barry Freed Co, 9255 Sunset Blvd, Los Angeles, CA 90069
Breslin, Jimmy *Journalist*
%Newsday, 780 3rd Ave, New York, NY 10017
Breslow, Lester *Physician*
10926 Verano Rd, Los Angeles, CA 90024
Breslow, Ronald C *Chemist*
275 Broad Ave, Englewood, NJ 07631
Bressler, Richard M *Businessman*
%Burlington Northern Inc, 999 3rd Ave, Seattle, WA 98104
Bresson, Robert *Movie Director*
49 Quai de Bourbon, 75004 Paris, France
Brest, Martin *Movie Director*
207 N Swall Dr, Beverly Hills, CA 90211
Brethen, Robert H *Businessman*
%Philips Industries, 4801 Springfield St, Dayton, OH 45401
Bretherick, John H, Jr *Businessman*
%Continental Corp, 180 Maiden Ln, New York, NY 10038
Bretoi, David *Financier*
%Beverly Hills Savings & Loan, 9401 Wilshire, Beverly Hills, CA 90212
Brett, George *Baseball Player*
%Kansas City Royals, Royals Stadium, PO Box 419969, Kansas City, MO 64141
Brett, Jeremy *Actor*
8322 Beverly Blvd, #202, Los Angeles, CA 90048
Breuer, Randy *Basketball Player*
%Minnesota Timberwolves, 500 City Pl, 730 Hennepin Ave, Minneapolis, MN 55403
Brewer, Albert P *Governor, AL*
%Samford University, Law School, 800 Lakeshsore Dr, Birmingham, AL 35229
Brewer, Edward E *Businessman*
%Cooper Tire & Rubber Co, Lima & Western, Findlay, OH 45840
Brewer, Gay *Golfer*
%Professional Golfers Assn, PO Box 109601, Palm Beach Gardens, FL 33410
Brewer, Leo *Chemist*
15 Vista del Orinda, Orinda, CA 94563
Brewer, Rowanne *Model*
%Elite Model Mgmt, 111 E 22nd St, 2nd Fl, New York, NY 10010

B

Brewer – Briloff

Brewer, Teresa *Singer*
394 Pinebrook Blvd, New Rochelle, NY 10803
Brewster, Bill *Representative, OK*
%House of Representatives, Washington, DC 20515
Breyer, Stephen *Judge*
%US Court of Appeals, McCormack Federal Bldg, Boston, MA 02109
Breytenbach, Breyten *Poet, Political Activist*
%Farrar Straus & Giroux, 19 Union Sq W, New York, NY 10003
Brian, David *Actor*
3922 Glenridge, Sherman Oaks, CA 92423
Brian, Earl W *Publisher*
%United Press International, 1400 "I" St NW, Washington, DC 20005
Brice, William J *Artist*
427 Beloit St, Los Angeles, CA 90049
Bricker, William H *Businessman*
%Maxus Energy Corp, 717 N Harwood St, Dallas, TX 75201
Brickfield, Cyril F *Association Official*
%AARP Federal Credit Union, 1901 "K" St NW, Washington, DC 20049
Brickhouse, Jack *Sportscaster*
%WGN-Continental Broadcasting Co, 2501 W Bradley Pl, Chicago, IL 60618
Bricklin, Daniel S *Computer Software Designer (VisiCalc)*
%Slate Corp, 15035 N 73rd St, Scottsdale, AZ 85260
Brickman, Paul *Movie Director, Screenwriter*
4116 Holly Knoll Dr, Los Angeles, CA 90027
Bricusse, Leslie *Composer*
1106 San Ysidro Dr, Beverly Hills, CA 90210
Bridges, Beau *Actor*
%Creative Artists Agency, 9830 Wilshire Blvd, Beverly Hills, CA 90212
Bridges, James L *Movie Director, Screenwriter*
449 Skyewiay Rd, Los Angeles, CA 90049
Bridges, Jeff *Actor*
436 Adelaide, Santa Monica, CA 90402
Bridges, Lloyd *Actor*
%William Morris Agency, 151 El Camino, Beverly Hills, CA 90212
Bridges, Roy D *Astronaut*
HQ AFSC/DR, Andrews Air Force Base, DC 20334
Bridges, Todd *Actor*
17260 Raven St, Northridge, CA 91306
Bridgewater, B A, Jr *Businessman*
%Brown Grp, 8400 Maryland Ave, St Louis, MO 63105
Brieant, Charles *Judge*
%US District Court, Courthouse, Foley Sq, New York, NY 10007
Briggs, Edward S *Navy Admiral*
29 Makalapa Dr, Honolulu, HI 96818
Briggs, Robert W *Biologist*
4318 Hector Dr, Bloomington, IN 47401
Bright, Harvey R (Bum) *Businessman*
4500 Lakeside Dr, Dallas, TX 75205
Bright, Myron H *Judge*
%US Court of Appeals, Federal Bldg, PO Box 2707, Fargo, ND 58108
Brightman, Sarah *Singer*
47 Greek St, London W1V 5LQ, England
Brignole, Michael J *Businessman*
%Redman Industries, 2550 Walnut Hill Ln, Dallas, TX 75229
Briles, Herschel F *WW II Army Hero (CMH)*
208 Mitchell Ave SW, Mitchellville, IA 50169
Briles, Nelson *Baseball Player*
1324 Clearview Dr, Greensburg, PA 15501
Brill, Fran *Actress*
%Writers & Artists Agency, 11726 San Vicente, #300, Los Angeles, CA 90049
Brill, Steven *Editor, Publisher*
%American Lawyer Magazine, 205 Lexington Ave, New York, NY 10022
Brill, Winston J *Bacteriologist*
%University of Wisconsin, Bacteriology Dept, Madison, WI 53706
Briloff, Abraham *Educator*
%Baruch College, Accounting Dept, New York, NY 10010

Brimley, Wilfred *Actor*
%Creative Artists Agency, 9830 Wilshire Blvd, Beverly Hills, CA 90212
Brimmer, Andrew F *Government Official, Economist*
%Brimmer Co, 2519 Connecticut Ave NW, Washington, DC 20008
Brimsek, Frank *Hockey Player*
1017 13th St N, Virginia, MN 55792
Brinckerhoff, Charles M *Businessman*
784 Park Ave, New York, NY 10021
Brinegar, Claude S *Secretary, Transportation*
2 Packsaddle Rd E, Rolling Hills, CA 90274
Brinegar, Paul *Actor*
17322 Halsey St, Granada Hills, CA 91344
Brink, Andre *Writer*
%Rhodes University, 6140 Grahamstown, South Africa
Brink, Frank, Jr *Biophysicist*
RR 2, Pleasant Valley Rd, Titusville, NJ 08560
Brink, K Robert *Publisher*
%Town & Country Magazine, 1700 Broadway, New York, NY 10019
Brink, R Alexander *Geneticist*
4237 Manitou Way, Madison, WI 53711
Brinkerhoff, Philip R *Financier*
%Financial Corp of Santa Barbara, 3908 State St, Santa Barbara, CA 93105
Brinkhous, Kenneth M *Pathologist*
524 Dogwood Dr, Chapel Hill, NC 27514
Brinkley, Christie *Model*
%Ford Model Agency, 344 E 59th St, New York, NY 10022
Brinkley, David *Commentator*
%ABC-News, 1717 De Sales St NW, Washington, DC 20036
Brinnin, John Malcolm *Writer, Educator*
King Caesar Rd, Duxbury, MA 02332
Brisco, Milo M *Businessman*
%Exxon Corp, 1251 Ave of Americas, New York, NY 10020
Brisco, Valerie *Track Athlete*
%World Class Mgmt, PO Box 21053, Long Beach, CA 90801
Briscoe, Dolph *Governor, TX*
338 Pecan St, Uvalde, TX 78801
Brisebois, Danielle *Actress*
950 N Kings Rd, Los Angeles, CA 90069
Briskin, Jacqueline *Writer*
%Delacorte Press, 666 5th Ave, New York, NY 10103
Brisse, Lou *Baseball Player*
1908 White Pine Dr, North Augusta, SC 29841
Britain, Radie *Composer*
1945 N Curson St, Los Angeles, CA 90046
Britt, May *Actress*
PO Box 525, Zephyr Cove, NV 89448
Britt, Russell W *Businessman*
%Wisconsin Electric Power Co, 231 W Michigan St, Milwaukee, WI 53201
Brittain, Alfred, III *Financier*
%Bankers Trust New York Corp, 16 Wall St, New York, NY 10005
Brittain, Perry G *Businessman*
%Texas Utilities Co, 2001 Bryan Tower, Dallas, TX 75201
Brittany, Morgan *Actress, Model*
3434 Cornell Rd, Agoura Hills, CA 91301
Britz, Jerilyn *Golfer*
%Ladies Professional Golf Assn, 2570 Volusia Ave, #B, Daytona Beach, FL 32114
Broad, Eli *Businessman*
%Kaufman & Broad Inc, 11601 Wilshire Blvd, Los Angeles, CA 90025
Broad, Morris N *Financier*
%American Savings & Loan Assn of Florida, 17801 NW 2nd Ave, Miami, FL 33169
Broad, Shepard *Financier*
%American Savings & Loan Assn of Florida, 17801 NW 2nd Ave, Miami, FL 33169
Broadbent, John Edward *Government Official, Canada*
%House of Commons, Ottawa ON K1A 0A6, Canada
Broadhead, James L *Businessman*
%GTE Corp, 1 Stamford Forum, Stamford, CT 06904

B

Broadhead, William McNulty *Representative, MI*
14320 Glastonbury St, Detroit, MI 48223

Broccoli, Albert R (Cubby) *Movie Producer*
809 Hillcrest Rd, Beverly Hills, CA 90210

Broches, Aron *Attorney*
2609 Tilden Pl NW, Washington, DC 20008

Brock, Karena Diane *Ballerina*
439 Abercorn, Savannah, GA 31401

Brock, Lou *Baseball Player*
12595 Durbin Dr, St Louis, MO 63141

Brock, Stan *Football Player*
%New Orleans Saints, 6928 Saints Dr, Metairie, LA 70032

Brock, William E *Secretary, Labor*
%Department of Labor, 200 Constitution Ave NW, Washington, DC 20210

Brockert, Richard C *Labor Leader*
%United Telegraph Workers, 701 Gude Dr, Rockville, MD 20850

Brockington, John *Football Player*
1205 Prospect, #550, La Jolla, CA 92037

Broder, David S *Columnist*
4024 N 27th St, Arlington, VA 22207

Broder, Samuel *Medical Administrator*
%National Cancer Institute, 9000 Rockville Pike, Bethesda, MD 20892

Brodie, H Keith H *Educator, Psychiatrist*
%Duke University, President's Office, Durham, NC 27706

Brodie, John *Football Player, Sportscaster*
2600 El Camino Real, Palo Alto, CA 94306

Brodsky, Joseph *Nobel Literature Laureate*
%Mount Holyoke College, English Dept, South Hadley, MA 01075

Brodsky, William J *Financier*
%Chicago Mercantile Exchange, 444 W Jackson Blvd, Chicaog, IL 60606

Brody, Alan J *Financier*
%Commodity Exchange, 4 World Trade Ctr, New York, NY 10048

Brody, Alexander J *Businessman*
%Ogilvy & Mather Worldwide, 2 E 48th St, New York, NY 10017

Brody, Clark L *Concert Clarinetist*
1621 Colfax St, Evanston, IL 60201

Brody, Jane E *Writer*
%New York Times, 229 W 43rd St, New York, NY 10036

Brody, Stuart S *Businessman*
%Cadoro Jewels, 389 5th Ave, New York, NY 10016

Broeg, Bob *Sportswriter*
%St Louis Post Dispatch, 900 N Tucker Blvd, St Louis, MO 63101

Broelsch, Christopher E *Surgeon*
%University of Chicago Medical Ctr, Dept of Surgery, Box 259, Chicago, IL 60637

Broglio, Ernie *Baseball Player*
2838 Via Carmen, San Jose, CA 95124

Brokaw, Gary *Basketball Player*
%Iona College, Athletic Dept, New Rochelle, NY 10801

Brokaw, Tom *Commentator*
941 Park Ave, #14-C, New York, NY 10025

Brolin, James *Actor*
2401 Colorado Ave, #160, Santa Monica, CA 90404

Brolin, Josh *Actor*
%International Creative Mgmt, 8899 Beverly Blvd, Los Angeles, CA 90048

Bromfield, John *Actor*
1750 Whittier Ave, Costa Mesa, CA 92627

Bromley, D Allan *Government Official, Physicist*
Science-Technology Policy Office, Old Executive Office Bldg, Washington,DC 20506

Bromwich, John *Tennis Player*
%International Tennis Hall of Fame, 194 Bellevue Ave, Newport, RI 02840

Bronars, Edward J *Marine Corps General*
%Navy Mutual Aid Assn, Arlington Annex, #G-070, Washington, DC 20370

Broner, Herbert J *Businessman*
%Mohasco Corp, 57 Lyon St, Amsterdam, NY 12010

Bronfman, Charles R *Businessman, Baseball Executive*
%Seagram Co, 1400 Peel St, Montreal PQ H3A 1S9, Canada

Bronfman, Edgar M *Businessman*
%Seagram Co, 1430 Peel St, Montreal PQ H3A 1S9, Canada

Bronfman, Yefin *Concert Pianist*
%International Creative Mgmt Artists, 40 W 57th St, New York, NY 10019

Bronson, Charles *Actor*
PO Box 2644, Malibu, CA 90265

Bronson, Oswald P, Sr *Educator*
%Bethune-Cookman College, President's Office, Daytona Beach, FL 32015

Bronson, Thomas *Businessman*
%Ideal Basic Industries, PO Box 8789, Denver, CO 80201

Brook, Peter *Movie, Theater Director*
%CIRT, 9 Rue du Cirque, 75008 Paris, France

Brooke, Edward W *Senator, MA*
%O'Connor & Hannan, 1919 Pennsylvania Ave NW, #800, Washington, DC 20006

Brooke, Hilary *Actress*
40 Via Casitas, Bonsall, CA 92003

Brooke, Walter *Actor*
4313 Ben Ave, North Hollywood, CA 91604

Brooker, Gary *Singer*
%Strongman Mgmt, Banda House, Cambridge Grove, London W6 8LE, England

Brooker, Robert E *Businessman*
1500 Sheridan Rd, Wilmette, IL 60091

Brookins, Gary *Editorial Cartoonist*
%Richmond Times-Dispatch, 333 E Grace St, Richmond, VA 23219

Brookner, Anita *Writer*
68 Elm Park Gardens, London SW10 9PB, England

Brooks, Albert *Actor, Director*
%Scotti Bros Moress Nanas, 212814 Pico Blvd, Santa Monica, CA 90405

Brooks, Avery *Actor*
%J Michael Bloom Ltd, 9200 Sunset Blvd, #710, Los Angeles, CA 90069

Brooks, Charles *Businessman*
%Standard Products Co, 2130 W 110th St, Cleveland, OH 44102

Brooks, Cleanth *Writer, Educator*
70 Ogden St, New Haven, CT 06511

Brooks, Donald M *Fashion, Theater Designer*
158 E 70th St, New York, NY 10021

Brooks, Elbert D *Educator*
911 Otter Creek Rd, Nashville, TN 37220

Brooks, Foster *Comedian*
18116 Chadron Cir, Encino, CA 91316

Brooks, Garth *Singer*
%Capitol Records, 1750 N Vine St, Los Angeles, CA 90028

Brooks, Gwendolyn *Writer*
7428 S Evans Ave, Chicago, IL 60619

Brooks, Harvey *Physicist*
46 Brewster St, Cambridge, MA 02138

Brooks, Jack B *Representative, TX*
1029 East Dr, Beaumont, TX 77706

Brooks, James *Football Player*
%Cincinnati Bengals, 200 Riverfront Stadium, Cincinnati, OH 44114

Brooks, James *Artist*
128 Neck Path, The Springs, East Hampton, NY 11937

Brooks, John E *Educator*
%College of Holy Cross, President's Office, Worcester, MA 01610

Brooks, John W *Businessman*
363 Cantitoe Rd, Bedford Hills, NY 10507

Brooks, Joseph *Movie Director, Producer, Screenwriter*
%Light & Sound Co, 41 E 74th St, #A, New York, NY 10021

Brooks, Joseph E *Businessman*
%Associated Dry Goods Corp, 417 5th Ave, New York, NY 10016

Brooks, Karen *Singer*
%Fritz/Turner Mgmt, 648 N Robertson Blvd, Los Angeles, CA 90069

Brooks, Mel *Movie Director, Actor*
%Brooksfilms, 20th Century Fox, 10201 W Pico Blvd, Los Angeles, CA 90035

Brooks, Phyllis *Actress*
PO Box 14, Rt 1-A, Cape Neddick, ME 03902

B

Brooks – Brown

Brooks, Rand *Actor*
440 W Broadway, Glendale, CA 91204

Brooks, Randy *Actor*
%Paul Kohner Inc, 9169 Sunset Blvd, Los Angeles, CA 90069

Brooks, Richard *Movie Director, Screenwriter*
2900 Deep Canyon Dr, Beverly Hills, CA 90210

Brookshier, Tom *Sportscaster*
%WIP-AM, 19th & Walnut Sts, Philadelphia, PA 19103

Broomfield, William S *Representative, MI*
570 Whethersfield Ln, Birmingham, MI 48010

Brophy, Brigid *Writer*
185 Old Brompton Rd, Flat 3, London SW5 0AN, England

Brophy, Kevin *Actor*
15010 Hamlin St, Van Nuys, CA 91411

Brophy, Theodore F *Businessman*
%GTE Corp, 1 Stamford Forum, Stamford, CT 06904

Brorby, Wade *Judge*
%US Court of Appeals, PO Box 1028, Cheyenne, WY 82001

Brosnan, Pierce *Actor*
PO Box 9851, Glendale, CA 91206

Brostek, Bern *Football Player*
%Los Angeles Rams, 2327 W Lincoln Ave, Anaheim, CA 92801

Brothers, Joyce *Psychologist*
1530 Palisade Ave, Fort Lee, NJ 07024

Brotje, Robert J, Jr *Businessman*
%Champion Spark Plug Co, 900 Upton Ave, Toldeo, OH 43661

Brough Clapp, Louise *Tennis Player*
1808 Voluntary Rd, Vista, CA 92083

Broun, Heywood Hale *Sportscaster, Columnist*
%CBS-TV, 51 W 52nd St, New York, NY 10019

Broussard, Steve *Football Player*
%Atlanta Falcons, Suwanee Rd, Suwanee, GA 30174

Brouwenstyn, Gerarda *Opera Singer*
3 Bachplein, Amsterdam, Netherlands

Browder, Glenn *Representative, AL*
%House of Representatives, Washington, DC 20515

Brower, David R *Conservationist*
%Friends of Earth Foundation, 124 Spear St, San Francisco, CA 94105

Brown Heritage, Doris *Track Athlete*
%Seattle Pacific College, Athletic Dept, Seattle, WA 98119

Brown, Bailey *Judge*
%Federal Bldg, 167 N Main, Memphis, TN 38103

Brown, Bill *Football Player*
4208 W 100th St, Bloomington, MN 55431

Brown, Blair *Actress*
434 W 20th St, #3, New York, NY 10011

Brown, Bo *Cartoonist*
218 Wyncote Rd, Jenkintown, PA 19046

Brown, Bob *Football Player*
1200 Lakeshore Ave, Oakland, CA 94606

Brown, Bobby *Singer, Dancer, Songwriter*
%MCA Records, 1755 Broadway, New York, NY 10019

Brown, Bryan *Actor*
%Creative Artists Agency, 9830 Wilshire Blvd, Beverly Hills, CA 90212

Brown, Charles L *Businessman*
%American Telephone & Telegraph Co, 550 Madison Ave, New York, NY 10022

Brown, Charlie *Football Player*
%Washington Redskins, Dulles Airport, PO Box 17247, Washington, DC 20041

Brown, Chris *Baseball Player*
%San Francisco Giants, Candlestick Park, San Francisco, CA 94124

Brown, Clarence J, Jr *Representative, OH*
%Commerce Department, 14th St NW, Washington, DC 20230

Brown, Curtis L, Jr *Astronaut*
%NASA, Johnson Space Ctr, Houston, TX 77058

Brown, Dale *Basketball Coach*
%Louisiana State University, Athletic Dept, Baton Rouge, LA 70894

Brown, Dave *Football Player*
%Green Bay Packers, 1265 Lombardi Ave, Green Bay, WI 54303

Brown, David *Movie Producer*
%Zanuck/Brown Co, 200 W 57th St, New York, NY 10019

Brown, Eddie *Football Player*
%Cincinncati Bengals, 200 Riverfront Stadium, Cincinnati, OH 44114

Brown, Edmund G (Jerry), Jr *Governor, CA*
%California Democratic Party, 329 Bryant St, #3-C, San Francisco, CA 94107

Brown, Edmund G (Pat) *Governor, CA*
2040 Ave of Stars, #C-208, Los Angeles, CA 90067

Brown, Ellis L *Businessman*
%Petrolite Corp, 100 N Broadway, St Louis, MO 63102

Brown, Faith *Actress*
%Million Dollar Music Co, 12 Praed Mews, London W2 1QY, England

Brown, Georg Stanford *Actor*
2934 1/2 Beverly Glen Cir, #404, Los Angeles, CA 90077

Brown, George C, Jr *Football Player*
1662 E Main St, #421, El Cajon, CA 92021

Brown, George E, Jr *Representative, CA*
%House of Representatives, Washington, DC 20515

Brown, George L *Financier*
%First National Bank of Boston, 100 Federal St, Boston, MA 02110

Brown, George Mackay *Writer*
3 Mayburn Ct, Stromness, Orkey, Scotland

Brown, Hank *Senator, CO*
2311 16th St, #306, Greeley, CO 80632

Brown, Harold *Secretary, Defense*
%Johns Hopkins University, International Studies School, Washington, DC 20036

Brown, Helen Gurley *Editor, Writer*
%Cosmopolitan Magazine, 224 W 57th St, New York, NY 10019

Brown, Herbert C *Nobel Chemistry Laureate*
1840 Garden St, West Lafayette, IN 47906

Brown, Himan *Director*
221 W 26th St, New York, NY 10001

Brown, Hubie *Basketball Coach*
6 Cobblewood Rd, Livingston, NJ 07039

Brown, J Carter *Businessman*
%Commission on Fine Arts, 708 Jackson Pl NW, Washington, DC 20006

Brown, James *Singer*
%Polydor Records, 3800 W Alameda Ave, Burbank, CA 91505

Brown, James *Sportscaster*
%CBS-TV, Sports Dept, 51 W 52nd St, New York, NY 10019

Brown, James L *Actor*
20543 Tiara St, Woodland Hills, CA 91367

Brown, Jerome *Football Player*
%Philadelphia Eagles, Veterans Stadium, Philadelphia, PA 19148

Brown, Jesse *Association Official*
%Disabled American Veterans, 807 Maine Ave SW, Washington, DC 20024

Brown, Jim *Football Player, Actor*
1851 Sunset Plaza Dr, Los Angeles, CA 90069

Brown, Jim Ed *Singer*
4308 Kenilwood Dr, Nashville, TN 37204

Brown, John M *Businessman*
%National Fuel Gas Co, 30 Rockefeller Plz, New York, NY 10112

Brown, John R *Judge*
%US Court of Appeals, 515 Rusk Ave, Houston, TX 77002

Brown, John Y, Jr *Governor, KY*
Cave Hill Pl, Lexington, KY 40544

Brown, Julie *Actress, Comedienne*
%"Downtown Julie Brown" Show, MTV, 1515 Broadway, New York, NY 10036

Brown, Kenneth J *Labor Leader*
Graphic Communications International Union, 1900 "L" St NW, Washington, DC 20036

Brown, L Dean *Diplomat*
3030 Cambridge Pl, Washington, DC 20007

Brown, Larry *Basketball Coach*
%Los Angeles Clippers, Sports Arena, 3939 S Figeroa St, Los Angeles, CA 90037

B

Brown – Brown

Brown, Larry *Football Player*
%Pittsburgh Steelers, Three Rivers Stadium, Pittsburgh, PA 15212

Brown, Les *Orchestra Leader*
603 Ocean Ave, #5-S, Santa Monica, CA 90405

Brown, Leslie A *Transportation Economist*
34 Fields E, Champaign, IL 61820

Brown, Lester R *Ecologist*
%Worldwatch Institute, 1776 Massachusetts Ave NW, Washington, DC 20036

Brown, Lew *Actor*
%Atkins Assoc, 303 S Crescent Heights Blvd, Los Angeles, CA 90024

Brown, Mark N *Astronaut*
%NASA, Johnson Space Ctr, Houston, TX 77058

Brown, Michael J *Businessman*
%Comdisco Inc, 6400 Shafer Ct, Rosemont, IL 60018

Brown, Michael S *Nobel Medicine Laureate*
5719 Redwood Ln, Dallas, TX 75209

Brown, Mike *Football Executive*
%Cleveland Browns Cleveland Stadium, Cleveland, OH 44114

Brown, Olivia *Actress*
5856 College Ave, #139, Oakland, CA 94618

Brown, Owsley, II *Businessman*
%Brown-Forman Inc, PO Box 1080, Louisville, KY 40201

Brown, Peter *Actor*
3408 The Strand, Manhattan Beach, CA 90266

Brown, Philip *Actor*
%Century Artists, 9744 Wilshire Blvd, #308, Beverly Hills, CA 90212

Brown, R Manning, Jr *Businessman*
%New York Life Insurance, 51 Madison Ave, New York, NY 10010

Brown, Ray *Jazz Bassist*
PO Box 845, Concord, CA 94522

Brown, Raymond (Tay) *Football Player*
450 N Rossmore Ave, #502, Los Angeles, CA 90004

Brown, Rita Mae *Writer, Social Activist*
%Julian Bach Agency, 747 3rd Ave, New York, NY 10017

Brown, Robert McAfee *Religious Leader*
2090 Columbia Ave, Palo Alto, CA 94306

Brown, Roger *Basketball Player*
%Evansville Thunder, 510 S Green River Rd, Evansville, IN 47715

Brown, Roger W *Social Psychologist*
100 Memorial Dr, Cambridge, MA 02142

Brown, Ron *Track Athlete, Football Player*
%Los Angeles Rams, 2327 W Lincoln Ave, Anaheim, CA 92801

Brown, Ron H *Government Official*
%Democratic National Committee, 430 S Capitol St SE, Washington, DC 20003

Brown, Ronald H *Publisher*
%New England Journal of Medicine, 1440 Main St, Waltham, MA 02554

Brown, Roosevelt *Football Player*
153 Van Buskirk Ave, Teaneck, NJ 07666

Brown, Stephen L *Businessman*
%John Hancock Mutual Life Insurance, PO Box 111, Boston, MA 02117

Brown, Tim *Football Player*
%Los Angeles Raiders, 332 Center St, El Segundo, CA 90245

Brown, Tina *Editor*
%Vanity Fair Magazine, 350 Madison Ave, New York, NY 10017

Brown, Tom *Football Player*
%Pemberton Houston Willoughby, Bentall Ctr 4, Vancouver BC, Canada

Brown, Tracy *Ballerina*
%Royal Ballet, Convent Garden, London WL2E 7Q4, England

Brown, Vanessa *Actress*
14340 Mulholland Dr, Los Angeles, CA 90024

Brown, W L Lyons, Jr *Businessman*
%Brown-Forman Inc, PO Box 1080, Louisville, KY 40201

Brown, Willard *Baseball Player*
2217 Breckenridge, Houston, TX 77026

Brown, William L *Financier*
%Bank of Boston Corp, 100 Federal St, Boston, MA 02110

Brown, Willie *Football Player*
%California State University Long Beach, Athletic Dept, Long Beach, CA 90840

Browne, Katherine *Actress*
%Leonard Grainger, 9903 Kip Dr, Beverly Hills, CA 90210

Browne, Leslie *Ballerina*
%American Ballet Theatre, 890 Broadway, New York, NY 10003

Browne, Roscoe Lee *Actor*
3531 Wonderview Dr, Los Angeles, CA 90068

Browne, Secor D *Aviation Engineer, Government Official*
2101 "L" St NW, #207, Washington, DC 20037

Brownell, Herbert *Attorney General*
%Lord Day Lord, 25 Broadway, New York, NY 10004

Browner, Joey *Football Player*
%Minnesota Vikings, 9520 Viking Dr, Eden Prairie, MN 55344

Browner, Keith *Football Player*
%San Diego Chargers, 9449 Friars Rd, San Diego, CA 92120

Browner, Ross *Football Player*
%Los Angeles Rams, 2327 W Lincoln Blvd, Anaheim, CA 92801

Browning, Edmond L *Religious Leader*
%Episcopal Church, Box 6885, San Antonio, TX 78209

Browning, James R *Judge*
%US Court of Appeals, Court Bldg, San Francisco, CA 94101

Browning, John *Concert Pianist*
%Columbia Artists Mgmt Inc, 165 W 57th St, New York, NY 10019

Browning, Kurt *Figure Skater*
%Royal Glenora Club, 11160 River Valley Rd, Edmonton ON T5J 2G7, Canada

Browning, L L, Jr *Businessman*
%Emerson Electric Co, 8000 W Florissant Ave, St Louis, MO 63136

Browning, Tom *Baseball Player*
5312 Vanderbilt Rd, Mt Juliet, TN 37122

Brownmiller, Susan *Feminist Leader*
61 Jane St, New York, NY 10014

Brownstein, Philip N *Government Official*
550 "N" St NW, Washington, DC 20024

Broyles, Frank *Football Coach, Sportscaster*
%University of Arkansas, Broyles Athletic Complex, Fayetteville, AR 72701

Broyles, William D, Jr *Journalist*
PO Box 1569, Austin, TX 78767

Brubeck, Dave *Jazz Pianist*
221 Millstone Rd, Wilton, CT 06897

Brubeck, William H *Government Official*
7 Linden St, Cambridge, MA 02138

Bruce, Aundray *Football Player*
%Atlanta Falcons, Suwanee Rd, Suwanee, GA 30174

Bruce, Carol *Actress*
1361 N Laurel Ave, Los Angeles, CA 90046

Bruce, Earle *Football Coach*
%Colorado State University, Athletic Dept, Fort Collins, CO 80523

Bruce, Harry J *Businessman*
%Illinois Central Gulf Railroad Co, 233 N Michigan Ave, Chicago, IL 60601

Bruce, Jack *Singer (Cream), Bassist*
%MEB, 412 Pleasant Valley Way, East Orange, NJ 07052

Bruce, James E *Businessman*
%Idaho Power Co, 1220 Idaho St, Boise, ID 83707

Bruce, Robert J *Businessman*
%Southwestern Life Insurance, 8150 N Central Expy, Dallas, TX 75206

Bruce, Robert V *Historian*
Evans Rd, RFD, Durham, NH 03824

Bruce, Terry L *Representative, IL*
%House of Representatives, Washington, DC 20515

Brueckner, Keith A *Physicist*
7723 Ludington Pl, La Jolla, CA 92037

Brugger, Ernst *President, Switzerland*
8625 Gossau ZH, Switzerland

Bruggink, Eric G *Judge*
%US Claims Court, 717 Madison Pl NW, Washington, DC 20005

B

Bruhl – Bucha

Bruhl, Heidi *Actress*
Oberer Seeweg 13-B, D-8130 Starnberg, Germany

Brumback, Charles T *Publisher*
%Tribune Co, 435 N Michigan Ave, Chicago, IL 60611

Brumel, Valeryi *Track Athlete*
%Olympic Committee, Loujnetzkaya Nab 8, Moscow, Russia

Brumley, Jon *Businessman*
%Southland Royalty Co, 200 InterFirst Tower, Forth Worth, TX 76102

Brunansky, Tom *Baseball Player*
1319 S Hillward Ave, West Covina, CA 91791

Brundage, Howard D *Publisher*
Ely's Ferry Rd, Lyme, CT 06371

Brundtland, Gro Harlem *Prime Minister, Norway*
Det Norske Arbeiderparti, Youngstorget 2V, 0181 Oslo 1, Norway

Brunet, Andre Joly *Figure Skater*
423 Pearl St, Boyne City, MI 49712

Brunetti, Melvin *Judge*
%US Court of Appeals, US Courthouse, 300 Booth St, Reno, NV 89509

Brunhart, Hans *Chief of Government, Liechtenstein*
%Government Palace, 9490 Vaduz, Liechtenstein

Brunner, J Terrance *Association Executive*
%Better Government Assn, 230 N Michigan Ave, Chicago, IL 60601

Brunner, Jerome *Psychologist, Educator*
%New School for Social Research, 65 5th Ave, New York, NY 10003

Brusati, Franco *Movie Director*
%Tourism & Education Ministry, Via Della Ferrarella, 00184 Rome, Italy

Bruskin, Grisha *Artist*
%William Struve, Struve Gallery, 309 W Superior, Chicago, IL 60610

Brustein, Robert *Educator, Theater Producer, Critic*
%Loeb Drama Centre, 64 Brattle St, Cambridge, MA 02138

Bruynes, Cees *Businessman*
%North American Philips Corp, 100 E 42nd St, New York, NY 10017

Bry, Ellen *Actress*
%Harris & Goldberg Agency, 1999 Ave of Stars, #2850, Los Angeles, CA 90067

Bryan, Anthony J A *Businessman*
%Copperweld Corp, 2 Oliver Plz, Pittsburgh, PA 15222

Bryan, John H, Jr *Businessman*
%Sara Lee Corp, 3 First National Plz, Chicago, IL 60602

Bryan, Richard H *Governor/Senator, NV*
606 Mountain St, Carson City, NV 89710

Bryan, Rick *Football Player*
%Atlanta Falcons, Suwanne Rd, Suwanee, GA 30174

Bryan, Wright *Journalist*
100 Wyatt Ave, PO Box 470, Clemson, SC 29633

Bryant, Douglas W *Librarian*
PO Box 463, Cambridge, MA 02238

Bryant, Farris *Governor, FL*
PO Box 2918, Jacksonville, FL 32203

Bryant, John *Representative, TX*
%House of Representatives, Washington, DC 20515

Bryant, Joshua *Actor*
%Century Artists, 9744 Wilshire Blvd, #308, Beverly Hills, CA 90212

Bryant, Kelvin *Football Player*
%Washington Redskins, Box 17247, Dulles Airport, Washington, DC 20041

Bryce, Graham C *Financier*
%Orbanco Financial Services Corp, 1001 SW Fifth Ave, Portland, OR 97204

Brymer, Jack *Concert Clarinettist*
Underwood, Ballards Farm Rd, South Croydon, Surrey, England

Brzezinski, Zbigniew *Government Official, Educator*
Center for Strategic/International Studies, 1800 "K" St NW, Washington, DC 20006

Buatta, Mario *Interior Designer*
120 E 80th St, New York, NY 10021

Bubb, Harry G *Businessman*
%Pacific Mutual Life Insurance, 700 Newport Center Dr, Newport Beach, CA 92660

Bucha, Paul W *Vietnam War Army Hero (CMH)*
Foot of the Chapel Ave, Jersey City, NJ 07305

Buchanan, C Jackson *Businessman*
%Lance Inc, 8600 South Blvd, Charlotte, NC 28210
Buchanan, Edna *Journalist*
%Miami Herald, 1 Herald Plz, Miami, FL 33101
Buchanan, James M *Nobel Economics Laureate*
%George Mason University, Ctr for Study of Public Choice, Fairfax, VA 22030
Buchanan, John M *Biochemist*
56 Meriam St, Lexington, MA 02173
Buchanan, Junious (Buck) *Football Player*
%Pro Football Hall of Fame, 2121 George Halas Dr NW, Canton, OH 44708
Buchanan, Patrick J *Columnist, Government Official*
1017 Savile Ln, McLean, VA 22101
Buchanan, Peter T *Financier*
%First Boston Inc, Park Avenue Plz, New York, NY 10055
Buchen, Philip W *Attorney, Government Official*
800 25th Ave NW, Washington, DC 20037
Bucher, Lloyd *Navy Hero*
11296 Rostrata Hill, Poway, CA 92064
Buchholz, Horst *Actor*
6068 Lenzer Heibe, Switzerland
Buchi, George H *Chemist*
%Massachusetts Institute of Technology, Chemistry Dept, Cambridge, MA 02139
Buchli, James F *Astronaut*
%NASA, Johnson Space Ctr, Houston, TX 77058
Buchwald, Art *Columnist*
2000 Pennsylvania Ave NW, Washington, DC 20006
Buck, Jack *Sportscaster*
%KMOX-TV, Sports Dept, 1 Memorial Dr, St Louis, MO 63102
Buck, Jason *Football Player*
%Washington Redskins, Dulles Airport, Box 17247, Washington, DC 20041
Buck, Robert *Museum Director*
%Brooklyn Museum, 188 Eastern Pkwy, Brooklyn, NY 11238
Buckingham, Lindsey *Musician*
%Michael Brokaw Mgmt, 3389 Camino de la Cumbre, Sherman Oaks, CA 91423
Bucklew, Neil S *Educator*
%West Virginia University, President's Office, Morgantown, WV 26505
Buckley, Betty *Actress*
530 West End Ave, New York, NY 10024
Buckley, James L *Judge*
%US Court of Appeals, 3rd & Constitution Ave NW, Washington, DC 20001
Buckley, Richard *Conductor*
1776 Broadway, #504, New York, NY 10019
Buckley, Robert J *Businessman*
RD 1, Scaife Rd, Sewickley, PA 15143
Buckley, William F, Jr *Commentator, Editor*
%National Review Magazine, 150 E 35th St, New York, NY 10016
Buckner, Bill *Baseball Player*
3 McDonald Cir, Andover, MA 01810
Buckner, Fred L *Businessman*
%Hercules Inc, Hercules Plz, Wilmington, DE 19894
Buckner, Quinn *Basketball Player; Sportscaster*
%Data Line, 885 S Village Oaks Dr, Covina, CA 91724
Buckson, David P *Governor, DE*
110 N Main St, Camden, DE 19934
Bucy, J Fred *Businessman*
%Texas Instruments Inc, 13500 N Central Expy, Dallas, TX 75265
Bucyk, John *Hockey Player*
%Boston Bruins, 150 Causeway St, Boston, MA 02114
Buczkowski, Bob *Football Player*
%Los Angeles Raiders, 332 Center St, El Segundo, CA 90245
Budd Pieterse, Zola *Track Athlete*
General Delivery, Bloemfontein, South Africa
Budd, Edward H *Businessman*
%Travelers Corp, 1 Tower Sq, Hartford, CT 06115
Budd, Harold *Composer, Poet*
%Opal/Warner Bros Records, 6834 Camrose Dr, Los Angeles, CA 90068

B

Budd – Bumbry

Budd, Julie — *Actress*
%Herb Bernstein Mgmt, 180 West End Ave, New York, NY 10023

Budig, Gene A — *Educator*
%University of Kansas, Chancellor's Office, Lawrence, KS 66045

Bueche, Wendell F — *Businessman*
%Allis-Chalmers Corp, 1205 S 70th St, West Allis, WI 53214

Bueno, Maria — *Tennis Player*
Rua Consolagao 3414, #10, 1001 Edificio Augustus, Sao Paulo, Brazil

Buerger, Martin Julian — *Mineralogist, Crystallographer*
Weston Rd, Lincoln, MA 01773

Buffet, Bernard — *Artist*
%Galerie Maurice Garnier, 6 Ave Matignon, 75008 Paris, France

Buffett, Jimmy — *Singer*
%Front Line Mgmt, 345 N Maple Dr, #235, Beverly Hills, CA 90210

Buffett, Warren E — *Businessman*
%Berkshire Hathaway Inc, 1440 Kiewit Plz, Omaha, NE 68131

Buffkins, Archie Lee — *Performing Arts Administrator*
%Kennedy Ctr, Executive Suite, Washington, DC 20566

Buffone, Doug — *Football Player*
Brian Acres, Rural Valley, PA 16249

Buffum, William B — *Diplomat*
%US Delegation, United Nations, New York, NY 10017

Bufkin, I David — *Businessman*
%Texas Eastern Corp, 1221 McKinley St, Houston, TX 77010

Bufman, Zev — *Theater Producer*
1466 Broadway, New York, NY 10036

Bugel, Joe — *Football Coach*
%Phoenix Cardinals, PO Box 888, Phoenix, AZ 85001

Bugliosi, Vincent T — *Attorney, Writer*
9911 W Pico Blvd, #300, Los Angeles, CA 90035

Buhl, Bob — *Baseball Player*
146 Orange Blossom Ln SW, Winter Haven, FL 33880

Bujold, Genevieve — *Actress*
1849 Sawtelle Blvd, #500, Los Angeles, CA 90025

Buktenica, Raymond — *Actor*
11873 Rochester Ave, Los Angeles, CA 90025

Bulifant, Joyce — *Actress*
%Irv Schechter Co, 9300 Wilshire Blvd, #410, Beverly Hills, CA 90212

Bulkeley, John D — *WW II Navy Hero (CMH); Admiral*
10706 Lovain Ave, Silver Springs, MD 20901

Bull, John S — *Astronaut*
1674 Alexander Ct, Los Altos, CA 94024

Bull, Richard — *Actor*
%MEW Inc, 151 N San Vicente Blvd, Beverly Hills, CA 90211

Bullen, Voy M — *Religious Leader*
%Church of God, 1207 Willow Brook, Huntsville, AL 35802

Bullins, Ed — *Writer*
425 Lafayette St, New York, NY 10003

Bullitt, John C — *Attorney, Government Official*
%Shearman Sterling, 53 Wall St, New York, NY 10005

Bullock, J Richard — *Businessman*
%Wyman-Gordon Co, 105 Madison St, Worcester, MA 01613

Bullock, Jm J — *Actor*
6210 Temple Hill Dr, Los Angeles, CA 90069

Bullock, Theodore H — *Biologist, Educator*
3258 Caminito Ameca, La Jolla, CA 92037

Bulovic, Bozdar — *Businessman*
%Wm Wrigley Jr Co, 410 N Michigan Ave, Chicago, IL 60611

Bulzacchelli, John — *Businessman*
%Wickes Companies, 3340 Ocean Park Blvd, Santa Monica, CA 90405

Bumbeck, David — *Artist*
Drew Ln, RD 3, Middlebury, VT 05753

Bumbry, Al — *Baseball Player*
28 Tremblant Ct, Lutherville, MO 21093

Bumbry, Grace — *Opera Singer*
%Columbia Artists Mgmt Inc, 165 W 57th St, New York, NY 10019

Bumpers, Dale L *Senator/Governor, AR*
PO Box 98, Charleston, AR 72933

Bund, Karlheinz *Businessman*
%Ruhrkohle, Rellinghauser Str 1, 4300 Essen 1, Germany

Bundschuh, George A W *Businessman*
%New York Life Insurance, 51 Madison Ave, New York, NY 10010

Bundy, Brooke *Actress*
833 N Martel Ave, Los Angeles, CA 90046

Bundy, McGeorge *Government Official, Educator*
%New York University, History Dept, New York, NY 10003

Bundy, William P *Government Official, Editor*
58 E 68th St, New York, NY 10021

Bunetta, Bill *Bowler*
1176 E San Bruno, Fresno, CA 93710

Bunge, Bettina *Tennis Player*
%Women's International Tennis Assn, 2665 S Bayshore Dr, Miami, FL 33133

Bunker, Wally *Baseball Player*
502 1st St, Langley, WA 98260

Bunnell, David *Editor, Publisher*
%PCW Communications, 555 DeHaro, San Francisco, CA 94107

Bunning, Jim *Representative, KY; Baseball Player*
%House of Representatives, Washington, DC 20015

Bunting, George L, Jr *Businessman*
%Noxell Corp, 11050 York Rd, Cockeysville, MD 21030

Bunting, James W *Educator*
211 Lakeshore Dr, Milledgeville, GA 31061

Bunting, John R *Financier*
%First Pennsylvania Corp, 1500 Market St, Philadelphia, PA 19101

Bunting, John R, Jr *Financier*
%Tri-County Savings & Loan, Camden, NJ 31061

Buntrock, Dean L *Businessman*
%Waste Management Inc, 3003 Butterfield Rd, Oak Brook, IL 60521

Burba, Edwin H, Jr *Army General*
CinC, Forces Command, Ft McPherson, GA 30330

Burbidge, Margaret P *Astronomer*
%University of California, Astrophysics Ctr, 9500 Gilman Dr, La Jolla, CA 92093

Burchhardt, Helmuth *Businessman*
%Eschweiler Bergwerks-Verein, 5120 Herzogenrath, Germany

Burchill, Thomas F (Tony) *Radio Executive*
%RKO General, 1440 Broadway, New York, NY 10018

Burchuladze, Paata *Opera Singer*
%Metropolitan Opera Assn, Lincoln Center Plz, New York, NY 10023

Burden, John W, III *Businessman*
%Federated Department Stores, 7 W 7th St, Cincinnati, OH 45202

Burden, William A M *Diplomat, Financier*
820 5th Ave, New York, NY 10021

Burdette, Lou *Baseball Player*
2019 Beveva Rd, Sarasota, FL 34232

Burdge, Jeffrey J *Businessman*
%Harsco Corp, PO Box 8888, Camp Hill, PA 17011

Burdick, Quentin N *Senator, ND*
1110 S 9th St, Fargo, ND 58103

Burenga, Kenneth L *Businessman*
%Dow Jones Co, 200 Liberty St, New York, NY 10281

Burger, Warren *Supreme Court Chief Justice*
%US Supreme Court, 1 1st St NW, Washington, DC 20543

Burgess, Anthony *Writer*
44 Rue Grimaldi, Monte Carlo, Monaco

Burgess, Neil *Electrical Engineer*
8425 Kugler Mill Rd, Cincinnati, OH 45243

Burgess, Robert K *Businessman*
%Pulte Home Corp, 6400 Farmington Rd, West Bloomfield, MI 48033

Burgess, William H *Financier*
550 Palisades Dr, Palm Springs, CA 92262

Burghoff, Gary *Actor*
%Robert Crystal, 146 S Spaulding Dr, Beverly Hills, CA 90212

B

Burgin – Burnet

Burgin, C David *Editor*
%Dallas Times Herald, Herald Sq, Dallas, TX 75202

Burgin, Robert A *Businessman*
%Leaseway Transportation Corp, 3700 Park East Dr, Beachwood, OH 44122

Burguieres, Philip *Businessman*
%Cameron Iron Works, 13013 Northwest Fwy, Houston, TX 77040

Burhle, Dietrich *Financier*
%Union Bank of Switzerland, Hofwiesenstr 135, 8021 Zurich, Switzerland

Burk, Henry *Businessman*
%Dun & Bradstreet Corp, 299 Park Ave, New York, NY 10171

Burke Hederman, Lynn *Swimmer*
26 White Oak Tree Rd, Laurel Hollow, NY 11791

Burke, Arleigh A *Navy Admiral*
%The Virginian, 9229 Arlington Blvd, #323, Fairfax, VA 22031

Burke, Bernard F *Physicist, Astrophysicist*
10 Bloomfield St, Lexington, MA 02173

Burke, Chris *Actor*
%Abrams Artists, 9200 Sunset Blvd, #625, Los Angeles, CA 90069

Burke, Daniel B *Businessman*
%Capital Cities Communications, 24 E 51st St, New York, NY 10022

Burke, Delta *Actress*
PO Box 411295, Los Angeles, CA 90041

Burke, Jack, Jr *Golfer*
%Champions Golf Club, 13722 Champions Dr, Houston, TX 77069

Burke, James *Commentator*
Henley House, Terrace Barnes, London SW13 0NP, England

Burke, James E *Businessman*
%Partnership for a Drug Free America, 666 3rd Ave, New York, NY 10017

Burke, John F *Surgeon, Educator*
216 Prospect St, Belmont, MA 02178

Burke, Kenneth *Writer*
RD 2, Box 293, Andover, NJ 07821

Burke, Lloyd L *Korean War Army Hero (CMH)*
9170 Lakeview Dr, Foley, AL 36535

Burke, Paul *Actor*
6310 San Vicente Blvd, #407, Los Angeles, CA 90048

Burke, Ray A *Businessman*
%Unocal Corp, 1201 W 5th St, Los Angeles, CA 90051

Burke, Yvonne Brathwaite *Representative, CA*
%Jones Day Reavis Pogue, 355 S Grand Ave, Los Angeles, CA 90071

Burket, Harriet *Editor*
700 John Ringling Blvd, Sarasota, FL 34236

Burkhalter, Edward A, Jr *Navy Admiral*
%Navy Department, Pentagon, Washington, DC 20350

Burkhardt, Hans *Artist*
1914 Jewett Dr, Los Angeles, CA 90046

Burkhardt, Lisa *Sportscaster*
%Madison Square Garden Network, 4 Pennsylvania Plz, New York, NY 10001

Burki, Fred A *Labor Leader*
%United Retail Workers Union, 9865 W Roosevelt Rd, Westchester, IL 60153

Burkitt, Denis P *Surgeon*
Hartwell Cottage, Wells Rd, Bisley, Glos GL6 VAG, England

Burks, Arthur W *Applied Mathematician, Philosopher*
3445 Vintage Valley Rd, Ann Arbor, MI 48105

Burleson, Ira L *Businessman*
%Torchmark Corp, 2001 3rd Ave S, Birminham, AL 35233

Burleson, Rick *Baseball Player*
270 E Mira Verde Dr, La Habra Heights, CA 90631

Burleson, Tom *Basketball Player*
%General Delivery, Newland, NC 28657

Burlingame, John F *Businessman*
45 Hancock Ln, Darien, CT 06820

Burnes, Karen *Commentator*
%CBS-TV, News Dept, 51 W 52nd St, New York, NY 10019

Burnet, Frank Macfarlane *Nobel Medicine Laureate*
48 Monomeath Ave, Canterbury, Vic 3126, Australia

Burnett, Carol *Actress, Comedienne*
%Kalola, 500 S Buena Vista St, Burbank, CA 91521

Burnett, Howard J *Educator*
%Washington & Jefferson College, President's Office, Washington, PA 15301

Burnett, James E *Government Official*
%Transportation Safety Board, 800 Independence SW, Washington, DC 20594

Burnett, Robert A *Publisher*
%Meredith Corp, 1716 Locust St, Des Moines, IA 50336

Burney, Leroy E *Physician*
%Milbank Memorial Fund, 40 Wall St, New York, NY 10005

Burnham, Duane L *Businessman*
%Abbott Laboratories, Abbott Park, North Chicago, IL 60064

Burnham, I W, II *Businessman*
%Drexel Burnham Lambert Inc, 60 Broad St, New York, NY 10004

Burnison, Chantal S *Businesswoman*
%Chantal Pharmaceutical Corp, 12400 Wilshire Blvd, Los Angeles, CA 90024

Burnley, James H, IV *Secretary, Transportation*
%Department of Transportation, 400 7th St SW, Washington, DC 20590

Burns, Arthur E *Government Official, Economist*
400 Massachusetts Ave NW, Washington, DC 20016

Burns, Catherine *Actress*
%STE Representation, 9301 Wilshire Blvd, #312, Beverly Hills, CA 90210

Burns, Conrad *Governor, Senator MT*
%US Senate, Washington, DC 20510

Burns, Eric *Television Entertainer*
%"Arts & Entertainment Revue" Show, 402 E 76th St, New York, NY 10021

Burns, George *Actor, Comedian*
720 N Maple Dr, Beverly Hills, CA 90210

Burns, James MacGregor *Political Scientist, Historian*
High Mowing Bee Hill, Williamstown, MA 01267

Burns, Jere *Actor*
%Harris & Goldberg Agency, 1999 Ave of Stars, #2850, Los Angeles, CA 90067

Burns, M Anthony *Businessman*
%Ryder System Inc, 3600 NW 82nd Ave, Miami, FL 33166

Burns, Norman *Economist*
3813 N 37th Ave, Arlington, VA 22207

Burns, Pat *Hockey Coach*
%Montreal Canadiens, 2313 St Catherine St W, Montreal PQ H3H 1N2, Canada

Burns, Ward *Businessman*
%J P Stevens Co, 1185 Ave of Americas, New York, NY 10036

Burns, William G *Businessman*
%NYNEX Corp, 335 Madison Ave, New York, NY 10017

Burnside, Waldo H *Businessman*
%Carter Hawley Hale Stores, 444 S Flower St, Los Angeles, CA 90071

Burr, Raymond *Actor*
PO Box 678, Geyserville, CA 95441

Burrell, J Earl *Businessman*
%PPG Industries, 1 PPG Pl, Pittsburgh, PA 15272

Burrell, Kenny *Jazz Guitarist, Composer*
%Helen Keane Artists, 49 E 96th St, New York, NY 10028

Burris, Robert H *Biochemist*
%University of Wisconsin, Biochemistry Dept, Madison, WI 53706

Burroughs, Jeff *Baseball Player*
6155 Laguna Ct, Long Beach, CA 90803

Burroughs, Robert P *Pension Funds Designer*
1280 Union St, Manchester, NH 03104

Burroughs, William *Writer*
PO Box 147, Lawrence, KS 66044

Burrows, Eva *Religious Leader*
%Salvation Army International, 101 Queen Victoria St, London EC4, England

Burrows, Stephen *Fashion Designer*
10 W 57th St, New York, NY 10019

Burrud, Bill *Movie Producer*
17045 S Pacific St, Sunset Beach, CA 90742

Bursch, Daniel W *Astronaut*
%NASA, Johnson Space Center, Houston, TX 77058

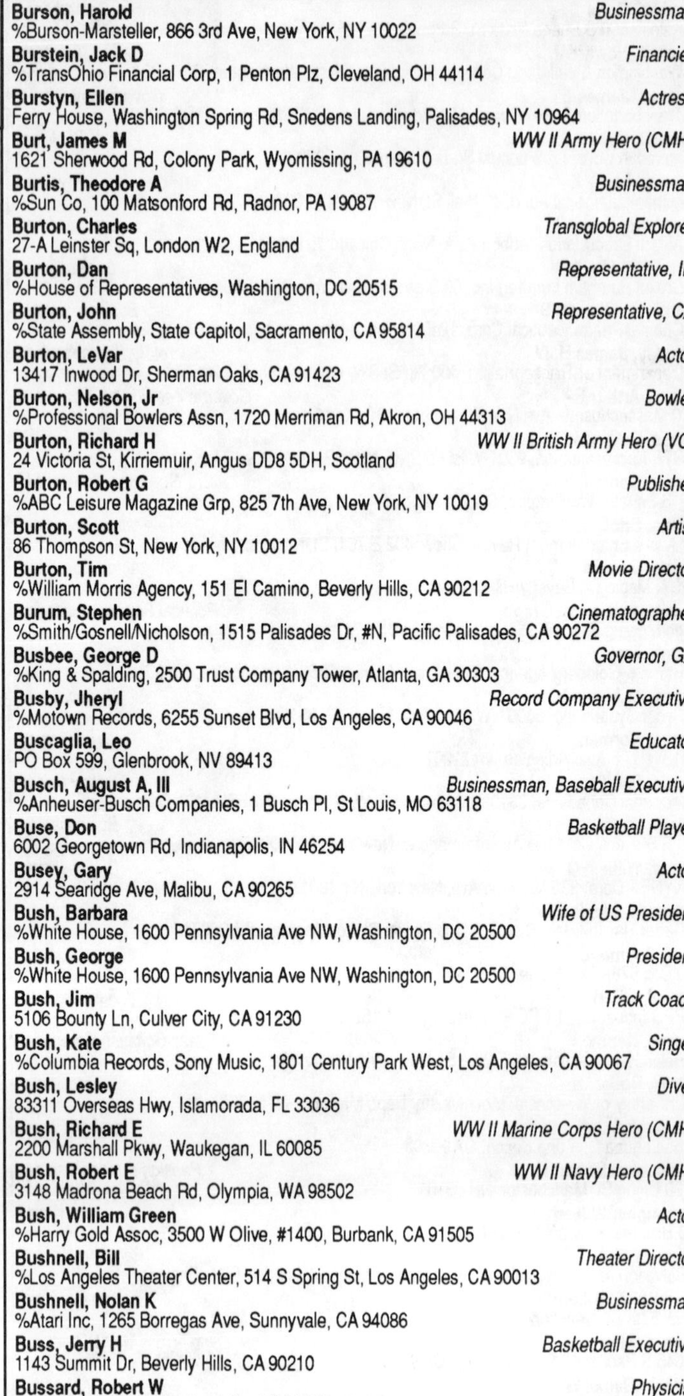

Burson, Harold *Businessman*
%Burson-Marsteller, 866 3rd Ave, New York, NY 10022

Burstein, Jack D *Financier*
%TransOhio Financial Corp, 1 Penton Plz, Cleveland, OH 44114

Burstyn, Ellen *Actress*
Ferry House, Washington Spring Rd, Snedens Landing, Palisades, NY 10964

Burt, James M *WW II Army Hero (CMH)*
1621 Sherwood Rd, Colony Park, Wyomissing, PA 19610

Burtis, Theodore A *Businessman*
%Sun Co, 100 Matsonford Rd, Radnor, PA 19087

Burton, Charles *Transglobal Explorer*
27-A Leinster Sq, London W2, England

Burton, Dan *Representative, IN*
%House of Representatives, Washington, DC 20515

Burton, John *Representative, CA*
%State Assembly, State Capitol, Sacramento, CA 95814

Burton, LeVar *Actor*
13417 Inwood Dr, Sherman Oaks, CA 91423

Burton, Nelson, Jr *Bowler*
%Professional Bowlers Assn, 1720 Merriman Rd, Akron, OH 44313

Burton, Richard H *WW II British Army Hero (VC)*
24 Victoria St, Kirriemuir, Angus DD8 5DH, Scotland

Burton, Robert G *Publisher*
%ABC Leisure Magazine Grp, 825 7th Ave, New York, NY 10019

Burton, Scott *Artist*
86 Thompson St, New York, NY 10012

Burton, Tim *Movie Director*
%William Morris Agency, 151 El Camino, Beverly Hills, CA 90212

Burum, Stephen *Cinematographer*
%Smith/Gosnell/Nicholson, 1515 Palisades Dr, #N, Pacific Palisades, CA 90272

Busbee, George D *Governor, GA*
%King & Spalding, 2500 Trust Company Tower, Atlanta, GA 30303

Busby, Jheryl *Record Company Executive*
%Motown Records, 6255 Sunset Blvd, Los Angeles, CA 90046

Buscaglia, Leo *Educator*
PO Box 599, Glenbrook, NV 89413

Busch, August A, III *Businessman, Baseball Executive*
%Anheuser-Busch Companies, 1 Busch Pl, St Louis, MO 63118

Buse, Don *Basketball Player*
6002 Georgetown Rd, Indianapolis, IN 46254

Busey, Gary *Actor*
2914 Searidge Ave, Malibu, CA 90265

Bush, Barbara *Wife of US President*
%White House, 1600 Pennsylvania Ave NW, Washington, DC 20500

Bush, George *President*
%White House, 1600 Pennsylvania Ave NW, Washington, DC 20500

Bush, Jim *Track Coach*
5106 Bounty Ln, Culver City, CA 91230

Bush, Kate *Singer*
%Columbia Records, Sony Music, 1801 Century Park West, Los Angeles, CA 90067

Bush, Lesley *Diver*
83311 Overseas Hwy, Islamorada, FL 33036

Bush, Richard E *WW II Marine Corps Hero (CMH)*
2200 Marshall Pkwy, Waukegan, IL 60085

Bush, Robert E *WW II Navy Hero (CMH)*
3148 Madrona Beach Rd, Olympia, WA 98502

Bush, William Green *Actor*
%Harry Gold Assoc, 3500 W Olive, #1400, Burbank, CA 91505

Bushnell, Bill *Theater Director*
%Los Angeles Theater Center, 514 S Spring St, Los Angeles, CA 90013

Bushnell, Nolan K *Businessman*
%Atari Inc, 1265 Borregas Ave, Sunnyvale, CA 94086

Buss, Jerry H *Basketball Executive*
1143 Summit Dr, Beverly Hills, CA 90210

Bussard, Robert W *Physicist*
11077 Torrey Pines Rd, La Jolla, CA 92037

Bussell, Darcey *Ballerina*
%Royal Ballet, Convent Garden, London WL2E 7Q4, England
Bustamente, Albert G *Representative, TX*
%House of Representatives, Washington, DC 20515
Buster, John E *Obstetrician*
%Harbor-UCLA Medical Ctr, 1000 W Carson St, Torrance, CA 90509
Buster, William F *Businessman*
%NCR Corp, 1700 S Patterson Blvd, Dayton, OH 45479
Butcher, Susan *Dog Sled Racer*
%Trail Breaker Kennel, 1 Eureka, Manley, AK 99756
Butenandt, Adolf *Nobel Chemistry Laureate*
Marsopstrasse 5, 8 Munich 60, Germany
Buthelezi, Chief Mangosuthu G *Government Official, Kwazulu*
Private Bag X-01, Ulundi 3838, Kwazulu, South Africa
Butkus, Dick *Football Player, Actor*
%William Morris Agency, 151 El Camino, Beverly Hills, CA 90212
Butler, Bill *Cinematographer*
%Smith/Gosnell/Nicholson, 1515 Palisades Dr, #N, Pacific Palisades, CA 90272
Butler, George L *Air Force General*
Commander in Chief, Strategic Air Command, Offutt Air Force Base, NE 68113
Butler, Jerry *Football Player*
%Butler Mechanical Inc, 63 Zoar Valley Rd, Springville, NY 14141
Butler, Manley C *Representative, VA*
845 Orchard Rd SW, Roanoke, VA 24014
Butler, Michael *Financier, Producer*
Natoma, Oak Brook, IL 60521
Butler, Richard A *Government Official, England*
Spencers, Great Yeldham, Essex CO9 4JG, England
Butler, Robert *Television Director*
650 Club View Dr, Los Angeles, CA 90024
Butler, Robert N *Gerontologist*
%Mt Sinai Medical Ctr, Geriatrics Dept, New York, NY 10029
Butler, Roy *Businessman*
%Noble Affiliates, 330 Neustadt Plz, Ardmore, OK 73401
Butler, Samuel *Attorney*
%Cravath Swain Moore, 1 Chase Manhattan Plz, New York, NY 10005
Butsavage, Bernard *Labor Leader*
%Molders & Allied Workers Union, 1225 E McMillan St, Cincinnati, OH 45206
Butt, Charles C *Businessman*
%H E Butt Grocery Co, PO Box 9216, Corpus Christi, TX 78408
Butterfield, Alexander P *Government Official*
2171 Ridge Dr, Los Angeles, CA 90049
Butterfield, Jack *Hockey Executive*
%American Hockey League, 218 Memorial Ave, West Springfield, MA 01089
Buttner, Jean B *Businesswoman*
%Value Line Inc, 711 3rd Ave, New York, NY 10017
Button, Richard T *Figure Skater, Television Producer*
%Candid Productions, 250 W 57th St, #818, New York, NY 10107
Buttons, Red *Actor*
778 Tortuoso Way, Los Angeles, CA 90077
Butts, William L *Businessman*
%Towle Manufacturing Co, 144 Addison St, Boston, MA 02128
Butz, Earl *Secretary, Agriculture*
312 Jefferson Dr, West Lafayette, IN 47906
Butzner, John D, Jr *Judge*
PO Box 2188, Richmond, VA 23217
Buyoya, Pierre *President, Burundi*
%President's Office, Bujumbura, Burundi
Buzzi, Ruth *Comedienne*
%Artists Group, 1930 Century Park West, #403, Los Angeles, CA 90067
Byars, Keith *Football Player*
%Philadelphia Eagles, Veterans Stadium, Philadelphia, PA 19148
Bychkov, Semyon *Conductor*
%Buffalo Philharmonic, 71 Symphony Cir, Buffalo, NY 14222
Bykovsky, Valeri F *Cosmonaut*
141 160 Svyosdny Gorodok, Moskovskoi Oblasti, Potchta Kosmonavtov, Russia

B

Byner – Bywater

Byner, Earnest *Football Player*
%Washington Redskins, PO Box 17247, Dulles Airport, Washington, DC 20041

Byner, John *Actor*
5863 Ramirez Canyon Rd, Malibu, CA 90265

Bynoe, Peter *Basketball Executive*
%Denver Nuggets, 1635 Clay St, Denver, CO 80204

Bynum, William *Businessman*
%Carrier Corp, Carrier Pkwy, Syracuse, NY 13202

Byrd, Benjamin F, Jr *Physician*
2122 West End Ave, Nashville, TN 37203

Byrd, Charlie *Jazz Guitarist*
PO Box 1515, New York, NY 10023

Byrd, Gill *Football Player*
%San Diego Chargers, PO Box 20666, San Diego, CA 92120

Byrd, Harry F, Jr *Senator, VA*
%General Delivery, Winchester, VA 22601

Byrd, Robert C *Senator, WV*
%US Senate, Washington, DC 20510

Byrket, Robert E *Businessman*
%Dana Corp, 4500 Dorr St, Toledo, OH 43615

Byrne, Brendan T *Governor, NJ*
%Carella Byrne Bain Gilfillan Rhodes, Gateway 1, Newark, NJ 07102

Byrne, David *Musician*
%Overland, 1775 Broadway, New York, NY 10019

Byrne, John *Cartoonist (Superman)*
%DC Comics, 355 Lexington Ave, New York, NY 10017

Byrne, John M *Businessman*
%Fireman's Fund Corp, 1600 Los Gamos Rd, San Rafael, CA 94903

Byrne, John V *Educator*
%Oregon State University, President's Office, Corvallis, OR 97331

Byrne, Patrick P *Businessman*
%Ford Espana, Paseo de la Castellana 135, Madrid 16, Spain

Byrne, Tommy *Baseball Player*
442 Pineview Ave, Wake Forest, NC 27587

Byrnes, Edd *Actor*
%Stone Manners Agency, 9113 Sunset Blvd, Los Angeles, CA 90069

Byrom, Fletcher L *Businessman*
%Koppers Co, Koppers Bldg, Pittsburgh, PA 15219

Byron, Beverly B *Representative, MD*
306 Grove Blvd, Frederick, MD 21701

Byron, Jeffrey *Actor*
%J Michael Bloom Ltd, 9200 Sunset Blvd, #710, Los Angeles, CA 90069

Byron, Kathleen *Actress*
PO Box 130, Hove, East Sussex BN3 6QU, England

Byrum, John *Movie Director*
7435 Woodrow Wilson Dr, Los Angeles, CA 90046

Bywater, William H *Labor Leader*
%International Electronic Workers, 1126 16th St NW, Washington, DC 20036

Caan, James *Actor*
10266 Chrysanthemum Ln, Los Angeles, CA 90077

Caballe, Montserrat *Opera Singer*
%Columbia Artists Mgmt Inc, 165 W 57th St, New York, NY 10019

Cabana, Robert D *Astronaut*
%NASA, Johnson Space Ctr, Houston, TX 77058

Cabot, Louis W *Businessman*
%Cabot Corp, 125 High St, Boston, MA 02110

Cabot, Paul C *Financier*
%First National Bank, 225 Franklin St, Boston, MA 02110

Cacoyannis, Michael *Movie, Theatre Director*
15 Mouson St, Athens 401, Greece

Caddell, Patrick H *Pollster*
%Cambridge Research Inc, 1625 "I" St NW, Washington, DC 20006

Cadell, Elizabeth *Writer*
%Hodder & Stoughton, Mill Rd, Dunton Green, Kent TN13 2YA, England

Cadigan, Dave *Football Player*
83 Baldwin Ave, Point Lookout, NY 11569

Cadmus, Paul *Artist, Etcher*
PO Box 1255, Weston, CT 06883

Cady, Frank *Actor*
%Greenvine Agency, 110 E 9th St, #C-1005, Los Angeles, CA 90079

Caen, Herb *Columnist, Writer*
%San Francisco Chronicle, 901 Mission St, San Francisco, CA 94103

Caesar, Irving *Lyricist*
%Irvin Caesar Music Corp, 850 7th Ave, New York, NY 10019

Caesar, Sid *Comedian*
1910 Loma Vista Dr, Beverly Hills, CA 90210

Cafego, George *Football Player*
10121 El Pinar, Knoxville, TN 37922

Caffrey, Stephen *Actor*
%Triad Artists, 10100 Santa Monica Blvd, #1600, Los Angeles, CA 90067

Cage, John *Composer*
101 W 18th St, New York, NY 10011

Cage, Michael *Basketball Player*
%Seattle SuperSonics, 190 Queen Ann Ave N, Seattle, WA 98109

Cage, Nicolas *Actor*
%International Creative Mgmt, 8899 Beverly Blvd, Los Angeles, CA 90048

Cahill, James *Actor*
400 W 43rd St, #11-G, New York, NY 10036

Cahill, William T *Governor/Senator, NJ*
%Cahill Wilinski Cahill, 25 Chestnut St, Haddonfield, NJ 08033

Cahn, Sammy *Lyricist*
704 N Canon Dr, Beverly Hills, CA 90210

Cahouet, Frank V *Financier*
%Mellon Bank Corp, 1 Mellon Bank Ctr, Pittsburgh, PA 15258

Cain, Paul W *Businessman*
%Mesa Limited Partnership, 1 Mesa Sq, Amarillo, TX 79189

Cain, Stanley A *Ecologist, Botanist*
109 Oak Knoll Dr, Santa Cruz, CA 95060

Caine, Michael *Actor*
Rectory Farm House, Northstoke, Oxfordshire, England

Cairncross, Alexander K *Government Official, England*
14 Staverton Rd, Oxford, England

Cairns, Hugh J F *Molecular Biologist*
%Harvard University, Public Health School, Microbiology Dept, Boston, MA 02115

Cairns, Theodore L *Chemist*
PO Box 3941, Greenville, DE 19807

Calcavecchi, Mark *Golfer*
%Professional Golfers Assn, PO Box 109601, Palm Beach Gardens, FL 33410

Calder, A William *Businessman*
%Joy Manufacturing Co, 301 Grant St, Pittsburgh, PA 15219

Calder, Iain *Editor*
%National Enquirer, 600 SE Coast Ave, Lantana, FL 33464

Calder, Nigel *Writer*
8 The Chase, Furnace Green, Crawley, West Sussex RH10 6HW, England

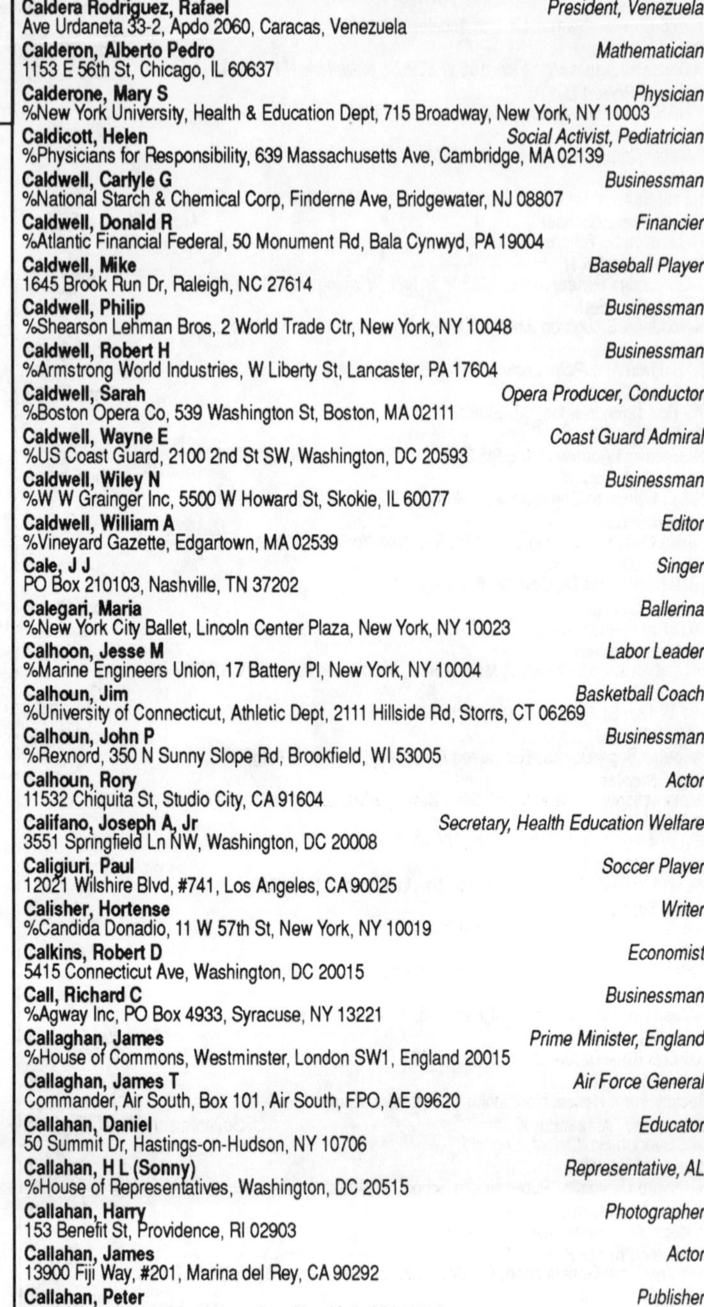

Caldera Rodriguez, Rafael — *President, Venezuela*
Ave Urdaneta 33-2, Apdo 2060, Caracas, Venezuela

Calderon, Alberto Pedro — *Mathematician*
1153 E 56th St, Chicago, IL 60637

Calderone, Mary S — *Physician*
%New York University, Health & Education Dept, 715 Broadway, New York, NY 10003

Caldicott, Helen — *Social Activist, Pediatrician*
%Physicians for Responsibility, 639 Massachusetts Ave, Cambridge, MA 02139

Caldwell, Carlyle G — *Businessman*
%National Starch & Chemical Corp, Finderne Ave, Bridgewater, NJ 08807

Caldwell, Donald R — *Financier*
%Atlantic Financial Federal, 50 Monument Rd, Bala Cynwyd, PA 19004

Caldwell, Mike — *Baseball Player*
1645 Brook Run Dr, Raleigh, NC 27614

Caldwell, Philip — *Businessman*
%Shearson Lehman Bros, 2 World Trade Ctr, New York, NY 10048

Caldwell, Robert H — *Businessman*
%Armstrong World Industries, W Liberty St, Lancaster, PA 17604

Caldwell, Sarah — *Opera Producer, Conductor*
%Boston Opera Co, 539 Washington St, Boston, MA 02111

Caldwell, Wayne E — *Coast Guard Admiral*
%US Coast Guard, 2100 2nd St SW, Washington, DC 20593

Caldwell, Wiley N — *Businessman*
%W W Grainger Inc, 5500 W Howard St, Skokie, IL 60077

Caldwell, William A — *Editor*
%Vineyard Gazette, Edgartown, MA 02539

Cale, J J — *Singer*
PO Box 210103, Nashville, TN 37202

Calegari, Maria — *Ballerina*
%New York City Ballet, Lincoln Center Plaza, New York, NY 10023

Calhoon, Jesse M — *Labor Leader*
%Marine Engineers Union, 17 Battery Pl, New York, NY 10004

Calhoun, Jim — *Basketball Coach*
%University of Connecticut, Athletic Dept, 2111 Hillside Rd, Storrs, CT 06269

Calhoun, John P — *Businessman*
%Rexnord, 350 N Sunny Slope Rd, Brookfield, WI 53005

Calhoun, Rory — *Actor*
11532 Chiquita St, Studio City, CA 91604

Califano, Joseph A, Jr — *Secretary, Health Education Welfare*
3551 Springfield Ln NW, Washington, DC 20008

Caligiuri, Paul — *Soccer Player*
12021 Wilshire Blvd, #741, Los Angeles, CA 90025

Calisher, Hortense — *Writer*
%Candida Donadio, 11 W 57th St, New York, NY 10019

Calkins, Robert D — *Economist*
5415 Connecticut Ave, Washington, DC 20015

Call, Richard C — *Businessman*
%Agway Inc, PO Box 4933, Syracuse, NY 13221

Callaghan, James — *Prime Minister, England*
%House of Commons, Westminster, London SW1, England 20015

Callaghan, James T — *Air Force General*
Commander, Air South, Box 101, Air South, FPO, AE 09620

Callahan, Daniel — *Educator*
50 Summit Dr, Hastings-on-Hudson, NY 10706

Callahan, H L (Sonny) — *Representative, AL*
%House of Representatives, Washington, DC 20515

Callahan, Harry — *Photographer*
153 Benefit St, Providence, RI 02903

Callahan, James — *Actor*
13900 Fiji Way, #201, Marina del Rey, CA 90292

Callahan, Peter — *Publisher*
%US Magazine, 215 Lexington Ave, New York, NY 10016

Callan, K — *Actress*
4957 Matilija Ave, Sherman Oaks, CA 91423

Callan, Michael — *Actor*
%Irv Schechter Co, 9300 Wilshire Blvd, #410, Beverly Hills, CA 90212

Callander, Robert J *Financier*
%Chemical Banking Corp, 277 Park Ave, New York, NY 10172
Callaway, Ely R, Jr *Businessman*
%Callaway Vineyard & Winery, 32720 Rancho California Rd, Temecula, CA 92390
Callaway, Howard H *Government Official*
PO Box 528, Crested Butte, CO 81224
Callaway, Paul Smith *Concert Organist*
%Washington Cathedral, Mount St Alban, Washington, DC 20016
Callaway, Thomas *Actor*
%Artists Agency, 10000 Santa Monica Blvd, #305, Los Angeles, CA 90067
Callen Jones, Gloria *Swimmer*
1508 Chafton Rd, Charleston, WV 25314
Calligaris, Novella *Swimmer*
Via Cassiaano 1199, 00123 Rome, Italy
Calloway, Cab *Jazz Band Leader*
1040 Knollwood Rd, White Plains, NY 10603
Calloway, D Wayne *Businessman*
%PepsiCo Inc, Anderson Hill Rd, Purchase, NY 10577
Calman, Robert F *Businessman*
%IU International Corp, 1500 Walnut St, Philadelphia, PA 19102
Calne, Roy Y *Surgeon*
Addenbrooke's Hospital, Surgery Dept, Hills Rd, Cambridge CB2 2QQ, England
Calugas, Jose, Sr *WW II Army Hero (CMH)*
2807 N Bristol, Tacoma, WA 98407
Calvani, Terry *Government Official*
%Federal Trade Commission, Pennsylvania & 6th NW, Washington, DC 20580
Calverly, Ernie *Basketball Player*
36 Hillside Rd, Wakefield, RI 02879
Calvert, James F *Navy Officer, Writer*
900 Long Ridge Rd, Stamford, CT 06902
Calvert, Phyllis *Actress*
Argyll Lodge, Towersey, Thames, Oxon, England
Calvet, Corinne *Actress*
%Pacific Plaza Towers, 1431 Ocean Ave, #109, Santa Monica, CA 90401
Calvet, Jacques *Businessman*
75 Ave de la Grande Armee, 75116 Paris, France
Calvin, John *Actor*
1794 Washington Way, Venice, CA 90292
Calvin, Mack *Basketball Player, Coach*
%Los Angeles Clippers, Sports Arena, 3939 S Figueroa St, Los Angeles, CA 90037
Calvin, Melvin *Nobel Chemistry Laureate*
2683 Buena Vista, Berkeley, CA 94708
Calvo Sotelo Bustelo, Leopoldo *Premier, Spain*
%Las Cortes Generales, Madrid, Spain
Calvo, Paul M *Governor, GU*
%Governor's Office, Capitol Bldg, Agana, GU 96910
Camacho, Hector *Boxer*
%Marty Cohen, 5151 Collins Ave, #522, Miami Beach, FL 33140
Camara, Helder P *Religious Leader*
Ruo do Giriquiti 48, Recife, Pernambuco, Brazil
Camdessus, Michel *Financier*
%International Monetary Fund, 700 19th St NW, Washington, DC 20431
Cameron, Colin Campbell *Businessman*
PO Box 187, Kahului, HI 96732
Cameron, Dean *Actor*
Barrett Benson McCartt Weston, 9320 Wilshire Blvd, #301, Beverly Hills, CA 90212
Cameron, Glenn *Football Player*
%Gunster Yoakley Criser Stewart, 777 S Flagler Dr, West Palm Beach, FL 33402
Cameron, James *Movie Director*
%Lightstorm Entertainment, 3100 Damon Way, Burbank, CA 91505
Cameron, Joanna *Actress*
PO Box 1400, Pebble Beach, CA 93953
Cameron, Kenneth D *Astronaut*
%NASA, Johnson Space Ctr, Houston, TX 77058
Cameron, Kirk *Actor*
4425 Lakeside Dr, Burbank, CA 91505

C

Cameron, Michelle *Synchronized Swimmer*
Box 2, Site 1-SS-3, Calgary AL T3C 3N9, Canada
Camilli, Doug *Baseball Player*
872 Oriole Dr SE, Winter Haven, FL 33880
Camm, John S *Businessman*
%Dickinson Robinson Grp, 1 Sutcliffe St, Bristol BS99 7QY, England
Camp, Colleen *Actress*
12359 Emelita St, North Hollywood, CA 91607
Camp, Dave *Representative, MI*
%House of Representatives, Washington, DC 20515
Camp, John *Journalist*
%St Paul Pioneer Press & Dispatch, 55 E 4th St, St Paul, MN 55101
Campaigne, Jameson Gilbert *Journalist*
370 Orwell Ln, Encinitas, CA 92024
Campanella, Joseph *Actor*
4647 Arcola Ave, North Hollywood, CA 91602
Campanella, Joseph J *Businessman*
%Singer Co, 8 Stamford Forum, Stamford, CT 06904
Campanella, Roy *Baseball Player*
6213 Capistrano Ave, Woodland Hills, CA 91367
Campaneris, Bert *Baseball Player*
PO Box 8232, Scottsdale, AZ 85252
Campbell of Airds, Lorne M *WW II British Army Hero (VC)*
95 Trinity Rd, Edinburgh EH5 3JX, Scotland
Campbell, Allan McCulloch *Biologist*
947 Mears Ct, Stanford, CA 94305
Campbell, Ben Nighthorse *Representative, CO*
%House of Representatives, Washington, DC 20515
Campbell, Bill *Baseball Player*
133 S Hale St, Palatine, IL 60067
Campbell, Carroll A, Jr *Governor, SC*
%Governor's Office, State House, Columbia, SC 29201
Campbell, Cheryl *Actress*
%Hope & Lyne, 5 Milner Pl, London N1 1TN, England
Campbell, Earl *Football Player*
%University of Texas, Men's Athletic Dept, PO Box 7399, Austin, TX 78713
Campbell, Glen *Singer*
10351 Santa Monica Blvd, #300, Los Angeles, CA 90025
Campbell, Hugh D *Navy Admiral, Attorney*
%Judge Advocate General's Office, 200 Stovall St, Alexandria, VA 22332
Campbell, J Jeffrey *Businessman*
%Pillsbury Co, 200 S 6th St, Minneapolis, MN 55402
Campbell, Jack M *Governor, NM*
110 N Guadalupe St, #1, Santa Fe, NM 87501
Campbell, James Arthur *Baseball Executive*
%Detroit Tigers, Tiger Stadium, Detroit, MI 48216
Campbell, John *Harness Racing Driver*
%John D Campbell Stable, 823 Allison Dr, River Vale, NJ 07676
Campbell, John *Educator*
%Oklahoma State University, President's Office, Stillwater, OK 74078
Campbell, Levin H *Judge*
%US Court of Appeals, McCormack Federal Bldg, Boston, MA 02109
Campbell, Marion *Publisher*
%Atlantic Monthly Co, 8 Arlington St, Boston, MA 02116
Campbell, Milton *Track Athlete*
1132 St Marks Pl, Plainfield, NJ 07062
Campbell, Patrick J *Labor Leader*
%Carpenters & Joiners Union, 101 Constitution Ave NW, Washington, DC 20001
Campbell, Robert E *Businessman*
%Johnson & Johnson, 1 Johnson & Johnson Plz, New Brunswick, NJ 08933
Campbell, Robert H *Businessman*
%Sun Co, 100 Matsonford Rd, Radnor, PA 19087
Campbell, Robert K *Businessman*
%Pennsylvania Power & Light Co, 2 N 9th St, Allentown, PA 18101
Campbell, Thomas D *Religious Leader*
%Cumberland Presbyterian Church, 1978 Union Ave, Memphis, TN 38104

Campbell, Tony *Basketball Player*
%Minnesota Timberwolves, 500 City Pl, 730 Hennepin Ave, Minneapolis, MN 55403

Campbell, Wallace M *Financier*
%Northeast Savings, 147 Charter Oak Ave, Hartford, CT 06106

Campeau, Robert *Businessman*
%Federated/Allied Stores Corp, 1114 Ave of Americas, New York, NY 10036

Campion, Robert T *Businessman*
%Lear Siegler Inc, 2850 Ocean Park Blvd, Santa Monica, CA 90405

Camras, Marvin *Engineer, Inventor*
560 Lincoln Ave, Glencoe, IL 60022

Canadeo, Tony *Football Player*
1746 Carriage Ct, Green Bay, WI 54304

Canary, David *Actor*
98 West End Ave, #1-B, New York, NY 10025

Canavan, Bernard *Businessman*
%American Home Products Corp, 685 3rd Ave, New York, NY 10017

Canby, Vincent *Movie Critic*
215 W 88th St, New York, NY 10024

Canby, William C, Jr *Judge*
%US Court of Appeals, US Courthouse, 230 N 1st Ave, Phoenix, AZ 85025

Candela, Felix *Engineer, Architect*
PO Box 356, Bronxville, NY 10708

Candy, John *Comedian, Actor*
%Agency for Performing Arts, 9000 Sunset Blvd, #1200, Los Angeles, CA 90069

Canetti, Elias *Nobel Literature Laureate*
%Farrar Straus & Giroux, 19 Union Sq W, New York, NY 10003

Canfield, William N *Editorial Cartoonist*
143 Wayside Rd, Tinton Falls, NJ 07724

Cann, Howard G *Basketball Coach*
342 S Buckhout St, Irvington, NY 10533

Cannell, Stephen J *Televison Producer*
%Stephen J Cannell Productions, 7083 Hollywood Blvd, Los Angeles, CA 90028

Canning, Fred F *Businessman*
%Walgreen Co, 200 Wilmot Rd, Deerfield, IL 60015

Cannon, Charles N *Businessman*
%Fluor Corp, 3333 Michelson Dr, Irvine, CA 92730

Cannon, Dyan *Actress*
1355 Beverly Estates Dr, Beverly Hills, CA 90210

Cannon, Freddy *Singer*
%Cannon Productions, 18641 Cassandra St, Tarzana, CA 91356

Cannon, Howard W *Senator, NV*
6300 Evermay Dr, McLean, VA 22101

Cannon, J D *Actor*
%Schiffman Ekman Morrison Marx, 156 5th Ave, New York, NY 10010

Cannon, Katherine *Actress*
%Gores/Fields Agency, 10100 Santa Monica Blvd, #700, Los Angeles, CA 90067

Cannon, Robert H, Jr *Guidance Engineer*
%Stanford University, Aeronautics & Astronautics Dept, Stanford, CA 94305

Canova, Diana *Actress*
%The Agency, 10351 Santa Monica Blvd, #211, Los Angeles, CA 90025

Canseco, Jose *Baseball Player*
4525 Sheridan Ave, Miami Beach, FL 33140

Cantahede, Plinio *Businessman*
%Siderugica Macional, Ave Treze de Maio 13, 20 000 Rio de Janeiro, Brazil

Cantalupo, James R *Businessman*
%McDonald's International, McDonald's Plz, Oak Brook, IL 60521

Cantinflas *Comedian*
Atletas 2, Mexico City 21 DF, Mexico

Canton, Mark *Movie Executive*
%Columbia Pictures, Columbia Plz, Burbank, CA 91505

Cantone, Vic *Editorial Cartoonist*
%Daily News, 220 E 42nd St, New York, NY 10017

Cantrell, Lana *Singer*
300 E 71st St, New York, NY 10021

Capa, Cornell *Photographer*
275 5th Ave, New York, NY 10028

C

Capalbo – Carcani

Capalbo, Carmen *Theatre Producer, Director*
%Edward Carpenter, 254 W 73rd St, New York, NY 10023

Cape, Ronald E *Businessman*
%Cetus Corp, 600 Bancroft Way, Berkeley, CA 94710

Capecchi, Mario R *Biologist*
%University of Utah, Biology Dept, Salt Lake City, UT 84112

Capellupo, John P *Businessman*
%Douglas Aircraft Co, 3855 Lakewood Blvd, Long Beach, CA 90846

Capen, Richard G *Publisher*
%Miami Herald, 1 Herald Plaza, Miami, FL 33101

Caperton, W Gaston, III *Governor, WV*
%Governor's Office, State Capitol, Charleston, WV 25305

Capice, Philip *Television Producer*
1359 Miller Dr, Los Angeles, CA 90069

Capilla, Joaquin *Diver*
Torres de Mixcoac, Lomas de Plateros, Mexico 19 DF, Mexico

Caplan, Frieda *Businesswoman*
%Frieda's Finset, PO Box 58488, Los Angeles, CA 90058

Caplin, Mortimer M *Government Official*
4536 29th St NW, Washington, DC 20008

Capobianco, Tito *Opera Director*
PO Box 988, San Diego, CA 92112

Caponigro, Paul *Photographer*
Rt 3, Box 96-D, Santa Fe, NM 87501

Caporali, Renso *Businessman*
%Grumman Corp, 1111 Stewart Ave, Bethpage, NY 11714

Cappelletti, Gino *Football Player*
%WBZ-Radio, 1170 Soldiers Field Rd, Brighton, MA 02134

Cappelletti, John *Football Player*
28791 Brant Ln, Laguna Niguel, CA 92677

Capps, Thomas E *Businessman*
%Dominion Resources, 1 James River Plz, Richmond, VA 23261

Capps, Walter H *Humanist*
%University of California, Religious Dept, Santa Barbara, CA 93106

Cappy, Joseph E *Businessman*
%American Motors Corp, 27777 Franklin Rd, Southfield, MI 48034

Capra, Buzz *Baseball Player*
7112 Riverside Dr, Berwyn, IL 60402

Capriati, Jennifer *Tennis Player*
%Palmer Academy, 100 Saddlebrook Way, Wesley Chapel, FL 33543

Caprio, Giuseppe Cardinal *Religious Leader*
%Office of Patrimony of Holy See, 00120 Vatican City, Rome, Italy

Captain Beefheart (Don Van Vliet) *Musician*
PO Box 1897, San Francisco, CA 94101

Capucill, Terese *Dancer*
%Martha Graham Contemporary Dance Ctr, 316 E 63rd St, New York, NY 10021

Cara, Irene *Singer*
8033 Sunset Blvd, #735, Los Angeles, CA 90046

Caras, Roger *Writer*
46 Fenmarsh Rd, East Hampton, NY 11937

Caray, Harry *Sportscaster*
%Chicago White Sox, Comiskey Park, Chicago, IL 60616

Caray, Skip *Sportscaster*
%Turner Broadcasting System, 1050 Techwood Dr NW, Atlanta, GA 30348

Carazo Odio, Rodrigo *President, Costa Rica; Educator*
%UN University for Peace, Rector's Office, Ciudad Colon, Costa Rica

Carbajal, Michael *Boxer*
914 E Filmore St, Phoenix, AZ 85006

Carberry, John Cardinal *Religious Leader*
4445 Lindell Blvd, St Louis, MO 63108

Carbine, Patricia *Editor, Publisher*
%Ms Magazine, 370 Lexington Ave, New York, NY 10017

Carbonneau, Guy *Hockey Player*
%Montreal Canadiens, 2313 St Catherine W, Montreal PQ H3H 1N2, Canada

Carcani, Adil *Premier, Albania*
%Prime Minister's Office, Council of Ministers, Tirana, Albania

Card, Andrew H, Jr *Secretary, Transportation*
%Department of Transportation, 400 7th St SW, Washington, DC 20590

Cardamone, Richard J *Judge*
%US Court of Appeals, 10 Broad St, Utica, NY 13503

Cardiff, Jack *Cinematographer*
%Smith, 10 Wyndham Pl, London W1, England

Cardin, Benjamin L *Representative, MD*
%House of Representatives, Washington, DC 20515

Cardin, Pierre *Fashion Designer*
59 Rue Du Faubourg-Saint-Honore, 75008 Paris, France

Cardwell, John James *Businessman*
%Consolidated Foods Corp, 135 S La Salle St, Chicago, IL 60603

Caretto-Brown, Patty *Swimmer*
16079 Mesquite Cir, Santa Ana, CA 92708

Carew, Rod *Baseball Player*
5144 E Crescent Dr, Anaheim, CA 92807

Carey, George *Archbishop, Canterbury*
%Lambeth Palace, London SE1 9JU, England

Carey, Harry, Jr *Actor*
14159 Dickens St, #303, Sherman Oaks, CA 91423

Carey, Hugh L *Governor, NY*
9 Prospect Pl W, Brooklyn, NY 11215

Carey, MacDonald *Actor*
1543 Benedict Canyon, Beverly Hills, CA 90210

Carey, Mariah *Singer*
%Columbia Records, Sony Music, 1801 Century Park West, Los Angeles, CA 90067

Carey, Raymond B, Jr *Marine Corps General*
%Marine Corps Headquarters, Pentagon, Washington, DC 20380

Carey, Richard E *Marine Corps General*
%Marine Corps Headquarters, Pentagon, Washington, DC 20380

Carey, Ron *Actor*
419 N Larchmont Ave, Los Angeles, CA 90004

Carey, Ron *Labor Official*
%International Teamsters Brotherhood, 25 Louisiana Ave NW, Washington, DC 20001

Carey, William D *Publisher*
%Science Magazine, 1333 "H" St NW, 11th Floor, Washington, DC 20005

Carey, William H *Religious Leader*
%National Gay Pentecostal Alliance, PO Box 1391, Schenectady, NY 12301

Cargo, David E *Governor, NM*
Sego Ranch, Star Route, Box 460, Corrales, NM 87408

Carideo, Frank *Football Player*
1 Fairway Dr, PO Box 771, Gulf Hills, MS 39564

Carillo, Mary *Sportscaster*
%CBS-Sports, 51 W 52nd St, New York, NY 10019

Cariou, Len *Actor*
%STE Representation, 9301 Wilshire Blvd, Beverly Hills, CA 90210

Carl Gustaf XVI *King, Sweden*
%Royal Palace, Stockholm, Sweden

Carl Philip Edmund Bertil *Prince, Sweden*
%Royal Palace, Stockholm, Sweden

Carle, Frankie *Musician*
PO Box 7415, Mesa, AZ 85216

Carlesimo, P J *Basketball Coach*
%Seton Hall University, Athletic Dept, South Orange, NJ 07079

Carley, John B *Businessman*
%Albertson's Inc, 250 Parkcenter Blvd, Boise, ID 83726

Carlile, Forbes *Swimming Coach*
16 Cross St, Ryde NSW 2112, Australia

Carlin, George *Comedian*
%Carlin Productions, 901 Bringham Ave, Los Angeles, CA 90049

Carlin, John *Governor, KS*
3226 Skyline Pkwy, Topeka, KS 66614

Carlin, Lynn *Actress*
%David Shapira Assoc, 15301 Ventura Blvd, #345, Sherman Oaks, CA 91403

Carlin, Paul N *Government Official*
%US Postal Service, 475 L'Enfant Plz, Washington, DC 20260

C

Carlin – Caroline

Carlin, Thomas R *Publisher*
%St Paul Pioneer Press, 55 E 4th St, St Paul, MN 55101

Carlino, Lewis John *Movie Director*
991 Oakmont Dr, Los Angeles, CA 90049

Carlisle, Belinda *Singer*
1843 Benedict Canyon Dr, Beverly Hills, CA 90210

Carlisle, Dwight L, Jr *Businessman*
%Russell Corp, PO Box 272, Alexander City, AL 35010

Carlisle, Kitty *Singer*
32 E 64th St, New York, NY 10021

Carlough, Edward J *Labor Leader*
%Sheet Metal Workers Assn, 1750 New York Ave NW, Washington, DC 20006

Carlson, Arne *Governor, MN*
%Governor's Office, State Capitol Bldg, #130, Minneapolis, MN 55155

Carlson, Curtis *Businessman*
%Carlson Companies, 12715-B State Hwy 55, Minneapolis, MN 55441

Carlson, D H E *Publisher*
%The Spectator, 44 Frid St, Hamilton ON L8N 3G3, Canada

Carlson, G Raymond *Religious Leader*
%Assemblies of God, 1445 Boonville Ave, Springfield, MO 65802

Carlson, Jack *Association Executive*
%American Assn of Retired Persons, 1901 "K" St NW, Washington, DC 20049

Carlton, Steve *Baseball Player*
90 Balsam, Oldsmar, FL 33557

Carlyle, Joan *Opera Singer*
Griffin, Ruthin Clwyd, North Wales, British Isles

Carlyle, Randy *Hockey Player*
%Pittsburgh Penguins, Civic Arena, Pittsburgh, PA 15219

Carman, Gregory W *Judge; Representative, NY*
%US Court of International Trade, 1 Federal Plz, New York, NY 10007

Carmen, Eric *Singer*
%Carmer/Daryl, PO Box 461483, Los Angeles, CA 90046

Carne, Judy *Comedienne*
Carne Lodge, Chapel Brampton, Northants, England

Carne, Marcel *Movie Director*
16 Rue De l'Abbaye, 75006 Paris, France

Carnegie, Roderick *Businessman*
%CRA Ltd, 55 Collins St, 27th Fl, Melbourne 3001, Australia

Carner, JoAnne *Golfer*
%Ladies Professional Golf Assn, 2570 Volusia Ave, #B, Daytona Beach, FL 32114

Carnes, Kim *Singer*
3231 Barry Ave, Los Angeles, CA 90066

Carnesecca, Lou *Basketball Coach*
%St John's University, Athletic Dept, Jamaica, NY 11439

Carnevale, Ben L *Basketball Coach*
113 W Kingswood Dr, Williamsburg, VA 23185

Carney, Art *Actor*
143 Kingfisher Ln, Westbrook, CT 06498

Carney, Dennis J *Businessman*
4536 Brownsville Rd, Pittsburgh, PA 15236

Carney, William *Representative, NY*
7 Garvey Dr, Hauppauge, NY 11787

Carnovsky, Morris *Actor, Movie Director*
%University of Bridgeport, Theatre Arts Dept, Bridgeport, CT 06601

Carnoy, Martin *Economist*
%Stanford University, Economic Studies Ctr, Stanford, CA 94305

Carns, Michael P C *Air Force General*
Vice Chief of Staff, Hq USAF, Washington, DC 20330

Caro, Anthony *Sculptor*
111 Frognal, Hampstead, London NW3, England

Caro, Robert A *Writer*
%International Creative Mgmt, 40 W 57th St, New York, NY 10019

Caroline *Princess, Monaco*
%Palace de Monaco, 98015 Monte Carlo 518, Monaco

Caroline, J C *Football Player*
2501 Stanford, Champaign, IL 61820

C

Caron, Leslie *Actress*
6 Rue De Bellechaisse, 75007 Paris, France

Carothers, Robert L *Educator*
%University of Rhode Island, President's Office, Kingston, RI 02881

Carpenter, Ben H *Financier*
%Southland Financial Corp, 5215 N O'Connor Blvd, Irving, TX 75039

Carpenter, Bob *Hockey Player*
%Boston Bruins, 150 Causeway, Boston, MA 02114

Carpenter, Carleton *Actor*
RD 2, Warwick, NY 10990

Carpenter, David R *Businessman*
%Transamerica Life Insurance, 1150 S Olive St, Los Angeles, CA 90015

Carpenter, Edmund M *Businessman*
%General Signal Corp, High Ridge Park, Stamford, CT 06904

Carpenter, John H *Movie Director*
%Jennings Levy Co, 8383 Wilshire Blvd, #840, Beverly Hills, CA 90211

Carpenter, John M *Opera Singer*
%Maurel Enterprises, 225 W 34th St, #1012, New York, NY 10001

Carpenter, John W, III *Financier*
%Southland Financial Corp, 5215 N O'Connor Blvd, Irving, TX 75039

Carpenter, M Scott *Astronaut*
PO Box 3161, Vail, CO 81695

Carpenter, Mary-Chapin *Singer*
%CBS Records, 51 W 52nd St, New York, NY 10019

Carpenter, Michael *Businessman*
%Kidder Peabody Co, 10 Hanover Sq, New York, NY 10005

Carpenter, Richard *Musician, Songwriter*
8341 Lubec Ave, Downey, CA 90241

Carpenter, Teresa *Journalist*
%Village Voice, 842 Broadway, New York, NY 10003

Carpenter, Thomas G *Educator*
%Memphis State University, President's Office, Memphis, TN 38152

Carpenter, William S, Jr *Army General, Hero, Football Player*
Commanding General, CFA/DCG/EUSA, APO, AP 96258

Carper, Thomas R *Representative, DE*
%House of Representatives, Washington, DC 20515

Carpino, Francesco Cardinal *Religious Leader*
Piazza S Calisto 16, 00153 Rome, Italy

Carr, Antoine *Basketball Player*
%San Antonio Spurs, 600 E Market St, San Antonio, TX 78205

Carr, Bob *Representative, MI*
%House of Representatives, Washington, DC 20515

Carr, Darlene *Actress*
%Artists Group, 1930 Century Park West, #403, Los Angeles, CA 90067

Carr, Fred *Businessman*
%First Executive Corp, 11444 W Olympic Blvd, Los Angeles, CA 90064

Carr, Gerald P (Jerry) *Astronaut*
PO Box 919, Huntsville, AR 72740

Carr, Jane *Actress*
%Susan Smith Assoc, 121 N San Vicente Blvd, Beverly Hills, CA 90211

Carr, Kenneth Monroe *Navy Admiral*
%Navy Department, Pentagon, Washington, DC 20350

Carr, M L *Basketball Player*
20 Walnut Pl, Wellesley Hills, MA 02181

Carr, Michael *Publisher*
%National Lampoon, 155 6th Ave, New York, NY 10003

Carr, Paul *Actor*
%H David Moss Assoc, 8019 1/2 Melrose Ave, #3, Los Angeles, CA 90046

Carr, Philippa *Writer*
%G P Putnam's Sons, 200 Madison Ave, New York, NY 10166

Carr, Robert C *Businessman*
%Montgomery Ward & Co, 535 W Chicago Ave, Chicago, IL 60607

Carr, Vikki *Singer*
2289 Betty Ln, Beverly Hills, CA 90210

Carradine, David *Actor*
3222 Benda Dr, Los Angeles, CA 90068

C

Carradine – Carter

Carradine, Keith *Actor*
%William Morris Agency, 151 El Camino, Beverly Hills, CA 90212

Carradine, Robert *Actor*
7640 Mulholland Dr, Los Angeles, CA 90046

Carrera, Barbara *Actress*
15430 Milldale Dr, Los Angeles, CA 90077

Carreras, Jose *Opera Singer*
%Opera Caballe, Via Augusta 59, Barcelona, Spain

Carrere, Tia *Actress*
%Artists Agency, 10000 Santa Monica Blvd, #305, Los Angeles, CA 90067

Carrier, George Francis *Applied Mathematician*
Rice Spring Ln, Wayland, MA 01778

Carrier, Mark *Football Player*
%Chicago Bears, 250 N Washington, Lake Forest, IL 60045

Carriere, Jean *Writer*
Les Broussanes, Domessargues, 30350 Ledignan, France

Carrington, Peter A R *Government Official, England*
Manor House, Bledlow nr Aylesbury, Bucks HP17 9PE, England

Carroll, Charles O *Football Player*
%Carroll Rindal Kennedy Schuck, 1200 Westlake N, Seattle, WA 98109

Carroll, Daniel Thuering *Businessman*
%Hoover Universal Inc, 825 Victors Way, Ann Arbor, MI 48106

Carroll, Diahann *Singer*
9108 Alanda Pl, Beverly Hills, CA 90210

Carroll, Earl W *Labor Official*
%United Garment Workers of America, 4207 Lebanon Rd, Hermitage, TN 37076

Carroll, Joe Barry *Basketball Player*
%Denver Nuggets, 1635 Clay St, Denver, CO 80204

Carroll, John S *Editor*
%Baltimore Sun, 501 N Calvert St, Baltimore, MD 21278

Carroll, Julian M *Governor, KY*
Scruggs Ln, Frankfort, KY 40601

Carroll, Lester *Cartoonist (Our Boarding House)*
21100 Beachwood Dr, Rocky River, OH 44116

Carroll, Loren K *Businessman*
%Smith International Inc, 4490 Von Karman Ave, Newport Beach, CA 92660

Carroll, Pat *Actress*
8635 Wonderland Park Ave, Los Angeles, CA 90046

Carroll, Wallace E *Businessman*
%Katy Industries, 853 Dundee Ave, Elgin, IL 60120

Carruthers, Garrey E *Governor, NM*
%Governor's Office, State Capitol, Santa Fe, NM 87503

Carruthers, James H (Red) *Skier*
8 Malone Ave, Garnerville, NY 10923

Carruthers, Kitty *Figure Skater*
%Dorothy Hamill's Winter Wonderland, IMG, 1 Erieview Plz, Cleveland, OH 44114

Carruthers, Peter *Figure Skater*
%Dorothy Hamill's Winter Wonderland, IMG, 1 Erieview Plz, Cleveland, OH 44114

Carruthers, Robert *Electrical Engineer*
Norman Cottage, 32 Norman Ave, Abingdon, Oxon OX14 2HJ, England

Carson, Edward M *Financier*
%First Interstate Bancorp, 707 Wilshire Blvd, Los Angeles, CA 90017

Carson, Harry *Football Player*
%New York Giants, Giants Stadium, East Rutherford, NJ 07073

Carson, Jimmy *Hockey Player*
%Detroit Red Wings, 600 Civic Center Dr, Detroit, MI 48226

Carson, Johnny *Entertainer*
%Carson Tonight Inc, 3000 W Alameda Ave, Burbank, CA 91523

Carson, Willie *Thoroughbred Racing Jockey*
West Ilsey Near Newbury, Berks, England

Carstens, Karl *President, West Germany*
Dechant-Kreiten-Strs 43, 5309 Meckenheim, Germany

Carter, Anthony *Football Player*
%Minnesota Vikings, 9520 Viking Dr, Eden Prairie, MN 55344

Carter, Arthur L *Publisher*
%Nation Magazine, 72 5th Ave, New York, NY 10011

Carter, Benny *Jazz Alto Saxophonist*
8321 Skyline Dr, Los Angeles, CA 90046
Carter, Betty *Singer*
%Kurland, 173 Brighton Ave, Boston, MA 02134
Carter, Cris *Football Player*
%Philadelphia Eagles, Veterans Stadium, Philadelphia, PA 19148
Carter, Dexter *Football Player*
%San Francisco 49ers, 4949 Centennial Blvd, Santa Clara, CA 95054
Carter, Dixie *Actress*
618 S Lucerne Blvd, Los Angeles, CA 90005
Carter, Don *Bowler*
13600 SW 88th St, Miami, FL 33186
Carter, Donald *Basketball Executive*
%Dallas Mavericks, Reunion Arena, 777 Sports St, Dallas, TX 75207
Carter, Donald *Financier*
%The Carter Organization, 116 John, New York, NY 10038
Carter, Duane (Pancho) *Auto Racing Driver*
32 Forest, Brownsburg, IN 46112
Carter, Edward W *Businessman*
%Carter Hawley Hale Stores, 444 S Flower St, Los Angeles, CA 90071
Carter, Elliott *Composer*
Mead St, Waccabuc, NY 10597
Carter, G Emmett Cardinal *Religious Leader*
%Archdiocese of Toronto, 355 Church St, Toronto ON M5B 1Z8, Canada
Carter, Gary *Baseball Player*
15 Huntly Dr, Palm Beach Gardens, FL 33418
Carter, Herbert Edmund *Biochemist, Educator*
2401 Cerrada de Promesa, Tucson, AZ 85718
Carter, Hodding, III *Government Official*
214 N Columbus, Alexandria, VA 22314
Carter, Jack *Comedian*
%Nigro Karlin Segal, 10100 Santa Monica Blvd, #2460, Los Angeles, CA 90067
Carter, Jimmy (James Earl, Jr) *President, United States*
%Carter Presidential Ctr, 1 Copenhill, Atlanta, GA 30307
Carter, Joe *Baseball Player*
1800 NE 51st St, Oklahoma City, OK 73111
Carter, John Mack *Editor*
%Good Housekeeping, 959 8th Ave, New York, NY 10019
Carter, Joseph R *Businessman*
%Wyman-Gordon Co, 105 Madison St, Worcester, MA 01613
Carter, Lynda *Actress*
9200 Harrington Dr, Potomac, MD 20854
Carter, Lynne *Actress*
%Lew Sherrell Agency, 1354 Los Robles, Palm Springs, CA 92262
Carter, Michael *Football Player*
%San Francisco 49ers, 4949 Centennial Blvd, Santa Clara, CA 95054
Carter, Nell *Singer, Actress*
%Triad Artists, 10100 Santa Monica Blvd, #1600, Los Angeles, CA 90067
Carter, Ralph *Actor*
104-60 Queens Blvd, #10, Forest Hills, NY 11375
Carter, Rosalynn *Wife of US President*
1 Woodland Dr, Plains, GA 31780
Carter, Rubin *Football Player*
%Denver Broncos, 13655 E Dove Valley Pkwy, Englewood, CO 80112
Carter, Russell *Football Player*
%New York Jets, 598 Madison Ave, New York, NY 10022
Carter, Terry *Actor*
1280 21st St NW, #909, Washington, DC 20036
Carter, Thomas S *Businessman*
%Kansas City Southern Industries, 114 W 11th St, Kansas City, MO 64105
Carter, Tim Lee *Representative, KY*
701 N Main St, Tompkinsville, KY 42167
Carteri, Rosana *Opera Singer*
%Angel Records, 1370 Ave of Americas, New York, NY 10019
Cartier-Bresson, Henri *Photographer*
%Magnum Photos, 2 Rue des Grards-Augustin, 75006 Paris, France

C

Cartland - Cash

Cartland, Barbara *Writer*
Camfield Pl, Hatfield, Herts AL9 6JE, England

Cartledge, Raymond E *Businessman*
%Union Camp Corp, 1600 Valley Rd, Wayne, NJ 07470

Cartwright, Angela *Actress*
4330 Backman St, North Hollywood, CA 91602

Cartwright, Bill *Basketball Player*
%Chicago Bulls, 980 N Michigan Ave, Chicago, IL 60611

Cartwright, Lynn *Actress*
%Dietrich Agency, 10850 Riverside Dr, North Hollywood, CA 91602

Cartwright, Veronica *Actress*
%McLean Assoc, 12725 Ventura Blvd, #H, Studio City, CA 91604

Carty, Rico *Baseball Player*
5 Ens Enriquillo, San Pedro de Macoris, Dominican Republic

Caruso, Anthony *Actor*
1706 Mandeville Ln, Los Angeles, CA 90049

Caruth, William Walter, Jr *Businessman*
5803 Greenville Ave, Dallas, TX 75206

Carvel, Elbert N *Governor, DE*
Clayton Ave, Laurel, DE 19956

Carver, Martin G *Businessman*
%Bandag Inc, Bandag Ctr, Mucatine, IA 52761

Carver, Randall *Actor*
%MEW Inc, 8489 W 3rd St, #1105, Los Angeles, CA 90048

Carvey, Dana *Comedian*
9200 Sunset Blvd, #428, LA 90069

Cary, Frank T *Businessman*
%International Business Machines Corp, Old Orchard Rd, Armonk, NY 10504

Cary, W Sterling *Religious Leader*
302 S Grant St, Hinsdale, IL 60521

Casablancas, John *Model Agency Executive*
%Elite Model Mgmt, 111 E 22nd St, 2nd Floor, New York, NY 10010

Casals, Rosemary *Tennis Player*
%Sportswoman Inc, 85 Filbert Ave, Sausalito, CA 94965

Casanova, Len *Football Coach*
2611 Windsor Cir W, Eugene, OR 97405

Casares, Maria *Actress*
8 Rue Asseline, 75014 Paris, France

Casaroli, Agostino Cardinal *Religious Leader*
%Office of Secretary of State, 00120 Vatican City, Rome, Italy

Casbarian, John *Architect*
%Taft Architects, 807 Peden St, Houston, TX 77006

Case, Everett Needham *Historian*
Van Hornesville, Hirkimer County, NY 13475

Case, Scott *Football Player*
%Atlanta Falcons, Suwanee Rd, Suwanee, GA 30174

Casey, Albert V *Businessman, Government Official*
%Resolution Trust Corp, 801 17th St NW, Washington, DC 20434

Casey, Bernie *Actor, Football Player*
6145 Flight Ave, Los Angeles, CA 90056

Casey, Charles F *Businessman*
%Dorsey Corp, PO Box 6339, Chattanooga, TN 37401

Casey, E Paul *Businessman*
%Ex-Cell-O Corp, 2855 Coolidge Rd, Troy, MI 48084

Casey, Joe D *Law Enforcement Official*
%Police Department, 200 James Robertson Pkwy, Nashville, TN 37201

Casey, John *Writer*
%University of Virginia, English Dept, Charlottesville, VA 22903

Casey, Robert P *Governor, PA*
%Governor's Office, Main State Capitol Bldg, Harrisburg, PA 17120

Cash, Johnny *Singer*
711 Summerfield Dr, Hendersonville, TN 37075

Cash, June Carter *Singer*
711 Summerfield Dr, Hendersonville, TN 37075

Cash, Pat *Tennis Player*
281 Clarence St, Sydney NSW 2000, Australia

Cash, Rosalind *Actress*
%John Sekura/A Talent Agency, 7469 Melrose Ave, Los Angeles, CA 90046

Cash, Rosanne *Singer*
1016 17th Ave, #4, Nashville, TN 37212

Cash, Tommy *Singer*
50 Music Sq E, #806, Nashville, TN 37203

Cashin, Bonnie *Fashion Designer*
866 United Nations Plz, New York, NY 10017

Casillas, Tony *Football Player*
%Dallas Cowboys, 1 Cowboys Pkwy, Irving, TX 75063

Caslavska, Vera *Gymnast*
SVS Sparta Prague, Korunovacni 29, Prague 7, Czechoslovakia

Casoria, Giuseppe Cardinal *Religious Leader*
Via Pancrazio Pfeiffer 10, 00193 Rome, Italy

Casper, Billy *Golfer*
PO Box 71, Springville, UT 84663

Casper, John H *Astronaut*
%NASA, Johnson Space Ctr, Houston, TX 77058

Caspersen, Finn M W *Financier*
%Beneficial Corp, 1100 Carr Rd, Wilmington, DE 19899

Caspersson, Tobjorn *Biochemist, Cancer Specialist*
Emanuel Birkes Vag 2, S-144 00 Ronninge, Sweden

Cass, Peggy *Actress*
%William Morris Agency, 151 El Camino, Beverly Hills, CA 90212

Cassady, Howard (Hopalong) *Football Player*
PO Box 2940, Tampa, FL 33601

Cassel, Jean-Pierre *Actor*
%International Creative Mgmt, 388/396 Oxford St, London W1, England

Cassel, Seymour *Actor*
2800 Neilson Way, #1610, Santa Monica, CA 90405

Cassel, Walter *Opera Singer*
%Indiana University, Music School, Bloomington, IN 47401

Cassell, Ollan *Sports Executive*
%Athletics Congress, PO Box 120, Indianapolis, IN 46206

Cassidy, David *Actor, Singer*
%Harris Goldberg Agency, 1999 Ave of Stars, Los Angeles, CA 90067

Cassidy, Edward Cardinal *Religious Leader*
%Pontifical Council for Christian Unity, Vatican City, 00120 Rome, Italy

Cassidy, Joanna *Actress*
12427 Sunset Blvd, Los Angeles, CA 90049

Cassidy, Patrick *Actor*
701 N Oakhurst Dr, Beverly Hills, CA 90210

Cassidy, Ryan *Actor*
701 N Oakhurst Dr, Beverly Hills, CA 90210

Cassidy, Shaun *Actor*
%International Creative Mgmt, 8899 Beverly Blvd, Los Angeles, CA 90048

Cassilly, Richard *Opera Singer*
%Robert Lombardo Assoc, 30 W 60th St, New York, NY 10023

Cassini, Oleg *Fashion Designer*
3 W 57th St, New York, NY 10019

Castanada, Jorge *Government Official, Mexico*
Fuego N 990 Pedregal, Mexico City DF, Mexico

Castaneda, Carlos *Writer, Anthropologist*
%Simon & Schuster Inc, 1230 Ave of Americas, New York, NY 10020

Casteen, John T, III *Educator*
%University of Virginia, President's Office, Charlottesville, VA 22906

Castel, Nico *Opera Singer*
%Metropolitan Opera Assn, Lincoln Ctr, New York, NY 10023

Castelli, Leo *Art Dealer*
420 W Broadway, New York, NY 10012

Castille, Jeremiah *Football Player*
%Denver Broncos, 13655 E Dove Valley Pkwy, Englewood, CO 80112

Castillo Lara, Rosalio Jose Cardinal *Religious Leader*
Patrimony of Holy See, Vatican City, Rome, Italy

Castle, John K *Financier*
775 Park Ave, New York, NY 10021

C

Castle, Michael N *Governor, DE*
%Governor's Office, Legislative Hall, Legislative Ave, Dover, DE 19901

Castleman, Riva *Museum Curator*
%Museum of Modern Art, 11 W 53rd St, New York, NY 10019

Castren, Fredrik *Businessman*
%Kymmene-Stromberg Corp, POB 300, 00131 Helsinki, Finland

Castro Ruz, Fidel *President, Cuba*
Palacio del Gobierno, Havana, Cuba

Castro Ruz, Raul *Prime Minister, Cuba*
%First Vice President's Office, Havana, Cuba

Castro, Emilio *Religious Leader*
%World Council of Churches, 475 Riverside Dr, New York, NY 10115

Castro, Raul H *Governor, AZ*
1433 E Thomas St, Phoenix, AZ 85014

Catacosinos, William J *Businessman*
%Long Island Lighting Co, 175 E Old Country Rd, Hicksville, NY 11801

Catalano, Eduardo F *Architect*
44 Gronzier Rd, Cambridge, MA 02138

Catalona, William J *Urologist (Prostrate Cancer Blood Test)*
%Washington University School of Medicine, Urology Div, St Louis, MO 63110

Cates, Gilbert *Movie Director*
%Gil Cates Productions, 10920 Wilshire Blvd, #600, Los Angeles, CA 90024

Cates, Phoebe *Actress*
%InterTalent Agency, 131 S Rodeo Dr, #300, Beverly Hills, CA 90212

Catledge, Terry *Basketball Player*
%Orlando Magic, Box 76, 1 Dupont Cir, Orlando, FL 32802

Catlett, Mary Jo *Actress*
4357 Farmdale Ave, North Hollywood, CA 91604

Catlin, Tom *Football Player, Coach*
%Seattle Seahawks, 5305 Lake Washington Blvd, Kirkland, WA 98033

Cattani, Richard J *Publisher*
%Christian Science Monitor, 1 Norway St, Boston, MA 02115

Cattell, Christine *Actress*
%Epstein Wyckoff Assoc, 280 S Beverly Dr, #400, Beverly Hills, CA 90212

Catto, Henry E, Jr *Diplomat*
7718 Georgetown Pike, McLean, VA 22101

Cattrall, Kim *Actress*
616 Lorna Ln, Los Angeles, CA 90049

Caulfield, Lore *Fashion Designer*
2228 Cotner, Los Angeles, CA 90024

Caulfield, Maxwell *Actor*
%Triad Artists, 10100 Santa Monica Blvd, Los Angeles, CA 90067

Caulkins, Tracy *Swimmer*
213 Ocella, Nashville, TN 37209

Causley, Charles S *Poet*
2 Cyprus Well, Launceston, Cornwall PL15 8BT, England

Cauthen, Steve *Thoroughbred Racing Jockey*
%Barry Hills, Lambourne, England

Cavaco Silva, Anibal *Prime Minister, Portugal*
%Prime Minister's Office, Lisbon, Portugal

Cavaiani, Jon R *Vietnam War Army Hero (CMH)*
616 "D" St, Davis, CA 95616

Cavallini, Paul *Hockey Player*
%St Louis Blues, 5700 Oakland Ave, St Louis, MO 63110

Cavanaugh, James H *Government Official*
%White House, 1600 Pennsylvania Ave NW, Washington, DC 20500

Cavaretta, Phil *Baseball Player*
2206 Portside Passage, Palm Harbor, FL 33563

Cavazos, Lauro F *Secretary, Education*
%Department of Education, 400 Maryland Ave SW, Washington, DC 20202

Cave, L W R *Businessman*
%Australian Consolidated Industries, 555 Bourke St, Melbourne, Australia

Cave, Roy *Editor*
%Time Inc, Rockefeller Ctr, New York, NY 10020

Cavett, Dick *Entertainer*
109 E 79th St, #2-C, New York, NY 10021

Cavezza, Carmen J *Army General*
Commanding General, I Corps & Fort Lewis, Fort Lewis, WA 98433

Cawthorn, Robert E *Businessman*
%Rorer Grp, 500 Virginia Dr, Fort Washington, PA 19034

Cayne, James E *Financier*
%Bear Stearns Co, 55 Water St, New York, NY 10041

Cayton, Roy S *Businessman*
%Overnite Transportation Co, 1000 Semmes Ave, Richmond, VA 23224

Cazenove, Christopher *Actor*
%Chatto & Linnit, Prince of Wales Theatre, Coventry, London WC2, England

Cazier, Stanford *Educator*
%Utah State University, President's Office, Logan, UT 84322

Ce, Marco Cardinal *Religious Leader*
Divine Worship & Sacraments, Clergy, Vatican City, Rome, Italy

Ceccato, Aldo *Conductor*
Chaunt da Crusch, 7524 Zuoz, Switzerland

Cece, Joseph W *Publisher*
%TV Guide Magazine, 100 Matsonville Rd, Radnor, PA 19088

Cech, Thomas R *Nobel Chemistry Laureate*
%University of Colorado, Chemistry & Biochemistry Dept, Boulder, CO 80309

Cedeno, Cesar *Baseball Player*
9919 Sage Downe, Houston, TX 77034

Cela, Camilio Jose *Nobel Literature Laureate*
La Bonanova, Palma de Mallorca, Spain

Celebrezze, Anthony J *Secretary, Health Education Welfare*
25043 Westwood Rd, Westlake, OH 44145

Celibidache, Sergiu *Conductor, Composer*
%Munich Philharmonic, Rindermarkt 3-4, 8000 Munich 2, Germany

Celio, Nello *President, Switzerland*
Via Ronchi 13, Lugano, Switzerland

Celler, Emanuel *Representative, NY*
9 Prospect Park, West Brooklyn, NY 11215

Cenker, Robert J *Astronaut*
%RCA-Astro-Electronics, PO Box 800, Princeton, NJ 08540

Cennamo, Ralph *Labor Leader*
%Leather Plastics & Novelty Workers Union, 265 W 14th St, New York, NY 10011

Cepeda, Orlando *Baseball Player*
3 Sommer Ridge Dr, #156, Roseville, CA 95678

Cerezo Arevalo, Vinicio *President, Guatemala*
%President's Office, Guatemala City, Guatemala

Cerjan, Paul G *Army General*
Deputy Commander In Chief, US Army Europe & 7th Army, APO, AE 09014

Cernan, Eugene A *Astronaut*
%Cernan Energy Corp, 900 Town & Country Ln, #300, Houston, TX 77024

Cernik, Oldrich *Prime Minister, Czechoslovakia*
%Investment Development Committee, Slezskay, Prague 2, Czechoslovakia

Cerrone, Rick *Baseball Player*
63 Eisenhower, Cresskill, NJ 07626

Cervenka, Exene *Singer*
%Rhino Records, 2225 Colorado Ave, Santa Monica, CA 90404

Cervi, Al *Basketball Player*
177 Dunrovin Ln, Rochester, NY 14618

Cetlinski, Matt *Swimmer*
4290 Mediterranean Rd, Lake Worth, FL 33461

Cey, Ron *Baseball Player*
22714 Creole Rd, Woodland Hills, CA 91364

Cha Hak Koo *Businessman*
%Lucky Ltd, 537 Namdaemunro 5-Ga, Jungku, Seoul, South Korea

Chaban-Delmas, Jacques M P *Prime Minister, France*
Marie de Bordeaux, 33000 Bordeaux, France

Chabot, Herbert L *Judge*
%US Tax Court, 400 2nd St NW, Washington, DC 20217

Chabrol, Claude *Movie Director, Producer*
15 Quai Conti, 75006 Paris, France

Chadli, Bendjedid *President, Algeria*
%President's Office, El Mouradia, Algiers, Algeria

C

Chadnois, Lynn *Football Player*
2048 Walden Ct, Flint, MI 48504

Chadwick, Bill *Hockey Referee*
22 Rugby Rd, Westbury, NY 11590

Chadwick, Florence *Channel Swimmer*
814 Armada Terr, San Diego, CA 92106

Chadwick, Gloria C *Skier*
%US Olympic Training Ctr, Northern Michigan University, Marquette, MI 49855

Chadwick, June *Actress*
%Ambrosio/Mortimer Assoc, 301 N Canon Dr, #305, Beverly Hills, CA 90210

Chadwick, Lynn *Sculptor*
Lypiatt Park, Stroud, Glos, England

Chadwick, Wallace L *Construction Engineer*
1133 Lorain Rd, San Marino, CA 91108

Chafee, John H *Senator/Governor, RI*
Ives Rd, Warwick, RI 02818

Chafetz, Sidney *Artist*
%Ohio State University, Art Dept, Columbus, OH 43210

Chaffee, Suzy *Skier*
5106 Woodwind Ln, Anaheim, CA 92807

Chailly, Riccardo *Conductor*
%London Records, 810 7th Ave, New York, NY 10019

Chakiris, George *Actor*
1010 N Palm Ave, Los Angeles, CA 90069

Chalfin, W Loren *Businessman*
%Countrymark Inc, 35 E Chestnut St, Columbus, OH 43216

Chalker, Durwood *Businessman*
%Central & South West Corp, 2121 San Jacinto St, Dallas, TX 75266

Chalsty, John S *Financier*
%Donaldson Lufkin Jenrette Inc, 140 Broadway, New York, NY 10005

Chamberlain, Charles E *Representative, MI*
1747 Pennsylvania Ave NW, Washington, DC 20006

Chamberlain, David M *Businessman*
%Shaklee Corp, 444 Market St, San Francisco, CA 94111

Chamberlain, John A *Sculptor*
%Ten Coconut Inc, 1315 10th St, Sarasota, FL 34236

Chamberlain, Joseph W *Astronomer*
%Rice University, Space Physics & Astronomy Dept, Houston, TX 77001

Chamberlain, Owen *Nobel Physics Laureate*
%University of California, Physics Dept, Berkeley, CA 94720

Chamberlain, Wilt *Basketball Player*
15216 Antelo Pl, Los Angeles, CA 90024

Chamberlin, John S *Businessman*
182 Fairway Dr, Princeton, NJ 08540

Chambers, Anne Cox *Businesswoman*
%Cox Enterprises, 1400 Lake Hearn Dr NE, Atlanta, GA 30319

Chambers, Dave *Hockey Coach*
%Quebec Nordiques, 2205 Ave du Colisee, Quebec PQ G1L 4W7, Canada

Chambers, Herb *Businessman*
%A-Copy Inc, 47 Eastern Blvd, Glastonbury, CT 06033

Chambers, Paul *Businessman*
1-A Frognal Grdns, Hampstead, London NW3, England

Chambers, Raymond *Businessman*
%Wesray Corp, 330 South St, Morristown, NJ 07960

Chambers, Richard H *Judge*
%US Court of Appeals, 55 E Broadway, Tucson, AZ 85701

Chambers, Tom *Basketball Player*
%Phoenix Suns, 2910 N Central, Phoenix, AZ 85012

Chambliss, Chris *Baseball Player*
140 Prospect St, #11-N, Hackensack, NJ 07601

Chamorro, Violeta Barrios de *President, Nicaragua*
%Casa Presidencial, Managua, Nicaragua

Champion, Marge *Dancer, Actress*
Prospect Hill, PO Box 248, Stockbridge, MA 01262

Champlin, Charles *Movie Critic*
2169 Linda Flora Dr, Los Angeles, CA 90024

Chan Sy *Premier, Kampuchea*
%Premier's Office, Phnom-Penh, People's Republic of Kampuchea

Chan, Julius *Prime Minister, Papua New Guinea*
PO Box 717, Rabaul, Papua New Guinea

Chance, Britton *Biophysicist, Educator*
4014 Pine St, Philadelphia, PA 19104

Chance, Dean *Baseball Player*
9505 W Smithville Western, Wooster, OH 44691

Chancellor, John *Commentator*
%NBC-TV, News Dept, 30 Rockefeller Plz, New York, NY 10020

Chand, Lokendra Bahadur *Prime Minister, Nepal*
%Prime Minister's Office, Katmandu, Nepal

Chandler, Alice *Educator*
%State University of New York, President's Office, New Paltz, NY 12561

Chandler, Colby H *Businessman*
%Eastman Kodak Co, 343 State St, Rochester, NY 14650

Chandler, Don *Football Player*
6501 S Fulton Ave, Tulsa, OK 74136

Chandler, Dorothy *Philanthropist*
455 S Lorraine Blvd, Los Angeles, CA 90020

Chandler, Jennifer *Diver*
9095 N Oracle, #2204, Oro Valley, AZ 85704

Chandler, John H *Educator*
%Scripps College, President's Office, Claremont, CA 91711

Chandler, John W *Educator*
%Williams College, President's Office, Williamstown, MA 01267

Chandler, Otis *Publisher*
%Times Mirror Co, Times Mirror Sq, Los Angeles, CA 90053

Chandler, Robert *Television News Executive*
65 E 76th St, New York, NY 10021

Chandler, Rod *Representative, WA*
%House of Representatives, Washington, DC 20515

Chandler, Wallace L *Businessman*
%Universal Leaf Tobacco Co, Hamilton & Broad, Richmond, VA 23230

Chandler, Wes *Football Player*
%San Francisco 49ers, 4949 Centennial Blvd, Santa Clara, CA 95054

Chandola, Walter *Photographer*
%General Delivery, Annandale, NJ 08801

Chandrasekhar, Subrahmanyan *Nobel Physics Laureate*
%Astrophysics & Space Research Lab, 933 E 56th St, Chicago, IL 60637

Chaney, Don *Basketball Player, Coach*
%Houston Rockets, Summit, Greenway Plaza, #10, Houston, TX 77046

Chaney, John *Basketball Coach*
%Temple University, Athletic Dept, Philadelphia, PA 19122

Chaney, William R *Businessman*
%Tiffany Co, 727 5th Ave, New York, NY 10022

Chang, Michael *Tennis Player*
1025 N Holt Dr, Placentia, CA 92670

Chang-Diaz, Franklin R *Astronaut*
%NASA, Johnson Space Ctr, Houston, TX 77058

Channing, Carol *Actress, Singer*
9301 Flicker Way, Los Angeles, CA 90069

Channing, Stockard *Actress*
1155 Park Ave, New York, NY 10128

Chapin, Dwight L *Publisher, Government Official*
%Success Unlimited Magazine, 401 N Wabash Ave, Chicago, IL 60611

Chapin, Roy D, Jr *Businessman*
%American Motors Corp, 27777 Franklin Rd, Southfield, MI 48034

Chapin, Schuyler G *Opera Executive*
901 Lexington Ave, New York, NY 10021

Chaplin, Geraldine *Actress*
6 Rue Asseline, 75015 Paris, France

Chaplin, Lita Gray *Actress*
8440 Fountain Ave, #302, Los Angeles, CA 90028

Chapman, Alvah H, Jr *Publisher*
%Knight-Ridder Inc, 1 Herald Plz, Miami, FL 33101

Chapman, Bruce K *Government Official*
4109 17th St NW, Washington, DC 20011

Chapman, Charles J *Businessman*
%Del Monte Corp, 1 Market Plz, San Francisco, CA 94119

Chapman, E T *WW II British Army Hero*
%Victoria Cross Society, Old Admiralty Bldg, London SW1A 2BE, England

Chapman, James C *Businessman*
%Outboard Marine Corp, 100 Sea-Horse Dr, Waukegan, IL 60085

Chapman, Jim *Representative, TX*
%House of Representatives, Washington, DC 20515

Chapman, Lonny *Actor*
3973 Goodland Ave, Studio City, CA 91604

Chapman, Michael *Movie Director, Cinematographer*
%Gersh Agency, 232 N Canon Dr, Beverly Hills, CA 90212

Chapman, Morris M *Religious Leader*
%Southern Baptist Convention, 5452 Grannywhite Pike, Brentwood, TN 37027

Chapman, Rex *Basketball Player*
%Charlotte Hornets, 2 First Union Center, #2600, Charlotte, NC 28202

Chapman, Robert F *Judge*
%US Court of Appeals, Federal Courthouse, PO Box 7097, Columbia, SC 29202

Chapman, Samuel *Football Player*
11 Andrew Dr, #39, Tiburon, CA 94920

Chapman, Tracy *Singer*
506 Santa Monica Blvd, #506, Santa Monica, CA 90401

Chappell, Fred *Poet*
305 Kensington Rd, Greensboro, NC 27403

Chappuis, Bob *Football Player*
315 Covington Lake Dr, Fort Wayne, IN 46804

Charette, William R (Doc) *Korean War Navy Hero (CMH)*
5237 Limberlost Dr, Lake Wales, FL 33853

Chargaff, Erwin *Biochemist, Educator*
350 Central Park West, New York, NY 10025

Charisse, Cyd *Actress, Dancer*
%Burton Moss Agency, 113 N San Vicente Blvd, #202, Beverly Hills, CA 90211

Charles *Prince of Wales, England*
Kensington Palace, London W8, England

Charles, Bob *Golfer*
%International Management Grp, 1 Erieview Plz, Cleveland, OH 44114

Charles, Eugenia *Prime Minister, Dominica*
%Government House, Roseau, Dominica

Charles, Nick *Sportscaster*
%Cable News Network, Sports Dept, 1 CNN Ctr, PO Box 105366, Atlanta, GA 30348

Charles, Ray *Singer*
%Ray Charles Enterprises, 2107 W Washington Blvd, #200, Los Angeles, CA 90018

Charlesworth, James H *Theologian*
%Princeton Theological Seminary, Theology Dept, Princeton, NJ 08540

Charlton, Bobby *Soccer Player*
Garthollerton, Cleford Rd, Ollerton near Knutsford, Cheshire, England

Charlupski, Allen *Businessman*
%Thorn Apple Valley Inc, 18700 W Ten Mile Rd, Southfield, MI 48075

Charmoli, Tony *Choreographer, Director*
1271 Sunset Plaza Dr, Los Angeles, CA 90069

Charnin, Martin *Theatre Producer, Director, Lyricist*
%Bean One Ltd, 850 7th Ave, New York, NY 10019

Charo *Entertainer*
1801 Lexington Rd, Beverly Hills, CA 90210

Charpie, Robert A *Businessman*
%Cabot Corp, 125 High St, Boston, MA 02110

Charteris, Leslie *Writer*
Levett, 8 Southampton Row, London WC1, England

Chartoff, Melanie *Actress*
%Abrams-Rubaloff Lawrence, 8075 W 3rd St, #303, Los Angeles, CA 90048

Chartoff, Robert *Entertainment Executive*
%Chartoff Productions, 1250 6th St, #201, Santa Monica, CA 90401

Charyk, Joseph V *Businessman*
5126 Tilden St NW, Washington, DC 20016

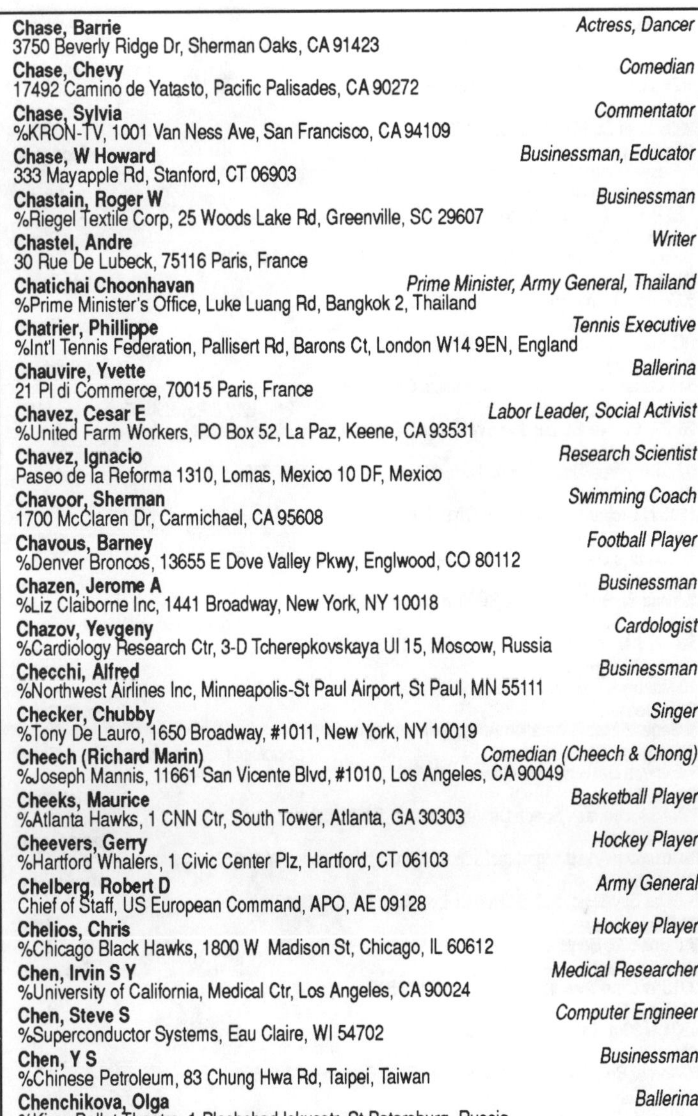

Chase, Barrie *Actress, Dancer*
3750 Beverly Ridge Dr, Sherman Oaks, CA 91423

Chase, Chevy *Comedian*
17492 Camino de Yatasto, Pacific Palisades, CA 90272

Chase, Sylvia *Commentator*
%KRON-TV, 1001 Van Ness Ave, San Francisco, CA 94109

Chase, W Howard *Businessman, Educator*
333 Mayapple Rd, Stanford, CT 06903

Chastain, Roger W *Businessman*
%Riegel Textile Corp, 25 Woods Lake Rd, Greenville, SC 29607

Chastel, Andre *Writer*
30 Rue De Lubeck, 75116 Paris, France

Chatichai Choonhavan *Prime Minister, Army General, Thailand*
%Prime Minister's Office, Luke Luang Rd, Bangkok 2, Thailand

Chatrier, Phillippe *Tennis Executive*
%Int'l Tennis Federation, Pallisert Rd, Barons Ct, London W14 9EN, England

Chauvire, Yvette *Ballerina*
21 Pl di Commerce, 70015 Paris, France

Chavez, Cesar E *Labor Leader, Social Activist*
%United Farm Workers, PO Box 52, La Paz, Keene, CA 93531

Chavez, Ignacio *Research Scientist*
Paseo de la Reforma 1310, Lomas, Mexico 10 DF, Mexico

Chavoor, Sherman *Swimming Coach*
1700 McClaren Dr, Carmichael, CA 95608

Chavous, Barney *Football Player*
%Denver Broncos, 13655 E Dove Valley Pkwy, Englwood, CO 80112

Chazen, Jerome A *Businessman*
%Liz Claiborne Inc, 1441 Broadway, New York, NY 10018

Chazov, Yevgeny *Cardologist*
%Cardiology Research Ctr, 3-D Tcherepkovskaya Ul 15, Moscow, Russia

Checchi, Alfred *Businessman*
%Northwest Airlines Inc, Minneapolis-St Paul Airport, St Paul, MN 55111

Checker, Chubby *Singer*
%Tony De Lauro, 1650 Broadway, #1011, New York, NY 10019

Cheech (Richard Marin) *Comedian (Cheech & Chong)*
%Joseph Mannis, 11661 San Vicente Blvd, #1010, Los Angeles, CA 90049

Cheeks, Maurice *Basketball Player*
%Atlanta Hawks, 1 CNN Ctr, South Tower, Atlanta, GA 30303

Cheevers, Gerry *Hockey Player*
%Hartford Whalers, 1 Civic Center Plz, Hartford, CT 06103

Chelberg, Robert D *Army General*
Chief of Staff, US European Command, APO, AE 09128

Chelios, Chris *Hockey Player*
%Chicago Black Hawks, 1800 W Madison St, Chicago, IL 60612

Chen, Irvin S Y *Medical Researcher*
%University of California, Medical Ctr, Los Angeles, CA 90024

Chen, Steve S *Computer Engineer*
%Superconductor Systems, Eau Claire, WI 54702

Chen, Y S *Businessman*
%Chinese Petroleum, 83 Chung Hwa Rd, Taipei, Taiwan

Chenchikova, Olga *Ballerina*
%Kirov Ballet Theatre, 1 Ploshchad Iskusstr, St Petersburg, Russia

Chenery, Hollis Burnley *Economist*
5 Hemlock Dr, Cambridge, MA 02138

Cheney, Richard B *Secretary, Defense*
%Department of Defense, Pentagon, Washington, DC 20301

Chennault, Anna *Businesswoman, Writer*
Watergate East, 2510 Virginia Ave NW, #1404, Washington, DC 20005

Cher *Actress, Singer*
%Creative Artists Agency, 9830 Wilshire Blvd, Beverly Hills, CA 90212

Chereau, Patrice *Movie, Opera, Theater Director*
%Nanterre-Amandiers, 7 Ave Pablo Picasso, 9200 Nanterre, France

Cherenkov, Pavel A *Nobel Physics Laureate*
%Lebedev Physics Institute, Leninsky Prospekt 53, Moscow, Russia

Cherkassky, Shura *Concert Pianist*
%Shaw Concerts, 1900 Broadway, 2nd Fl, New York, NY 10023

C

Chermayeff, Peter *Architect*
%Cambridge Seven Assoc, 1050 Massachusetts Ave, Cambridge, MA 02138

Chermayeff, Serge *Architect, Artist*
%Design Arts, Box "NN", Wellfleet, MA 02667

Chern, Shiing-Shen *Mathematician*
8336 Kent Ct, El Cerrito, CA 94530

Cherne, Leo *Economist*
%Research Institute of America, 90 5th Ave, New York, NY 10011

Cherrill, Virginia *Actress*
160 Pomar Ave, Montecito, CA 93108

Cherry, Deron *Football Player*
%Kansas City Chiefs, 1 Arrowhead Dr, Kansas City, MO 64129

Cherry, Don S *Hockey Coach*
%Boston Bruins, 150 Causeway St, Boston, MA 02114

Cherry, Neneh *Singer*
PO Box 1622, London NW10 5TF, England

Chertok, Jack *Movie Producer*
515 Ocean Ave, #305, Santa Monica, CA 90402

Cheshire, G Leonard *WW II Royal Air Force Hero (VC)*
26-29 Maunsel St, London SW1P 2QN, England

Cheshire, Maxine *Columnist*
%Los Angeles Times, Times Mirror Sq, Los Angeles, CA 90053

Chester, Colby *Actor*
1245 N Orchard Dr, Burbank, CA 91506

Chestnutt, Jane *Editor*
%Woman's Day Magazine, 1515 Broadway, New York, NY 10036

Chevalier, Samuel F *Financier*
%Irving Bank Corp, 1 Wall St, New York, NY 10005

Chevrier, Lionel *Government Official, Canada*
500 Pl d'Armes, #1200, Montreal PQ H2Y 2W4, Canada

Chew, Geoffrey F *Physicist*
10 Maybeck Twin Dr, Berkeley, CA 94708

Chi Haotian *General, China*
%General Staff, Liberation Army, Beijing, China

Chiang-Kai Shek, Madame *Sociologist; Government Official, China*
%General Delivery, Lattingtown, NY 11101

Chiao, Leroy *Astronaut*
%NASA, Johnson Space Center, Houston, TX 77058

Chiara, Maria *Opera Singer*
%Columbia Artists Mgmt Inc, 165 W 57th St, New York, NY 10019

Chiat, Jay *Art Director*
%Chiat/Day/Mojo, 517 S Olive St, Los Angeles, CA 90013

Chicago, Judy *Artist*
PO Box 834, Benicia, CA 94570

Chihara, Paul *Composer*
3815 W Olive Ave, #202, Burbank, CA 91505

Chihuly, Dale *Artist*
4301 N 33rd, Tacoma, WA 98407

Child, Jane *Singer*
%Warner Bros Records, 3300 Warner Blvd, Burbank, CA 91505

Child, Julia *Food Expert, Writer*
%WGBH, 125 Western Ave, Boston, MA 02134

Childers, Ernest *WW II Army Hero (CMH)*
13415 S 308 East Ave, Cowetta, OK 74429

Childress, Ray *Football Player*
%Houston Oilers, PO Box 1516, Houston, TX 77251

Childs, David M *Architect*
%Skidmore Owings Merrill, 220 E 42nd St, New York, NY 10017

Childs, Toni *Singer*
%MFC Management, 1830 S Robertson Blvd, #102, Los Angeles, CA 90035

Chiles, H Eddie *Businessman, Baseball Executive*
%Western Co of North America, 6000 Western Pl, Fort Worth, TX 76107

Chiles, Henry G, Jr *Navy Admiral*
Commander, Submarine Force Atlantic, Norfolk, VA 23511

Chiles, Lawton M *Senator, Governor, FL*
%Governor's Office, State Capitol Bldg, Tallahassee, FL 32399

Chiles, Linden *Actor*
2521 Skyline Dr, Topanga, CA 90290
Chiles, Lois *Actress*
644 San Lorenzo, Santa Monica, CA 90402
Chillida Juantegui, Eduardo *Sculptor*
Villa Paz, Alto de Maracruz, San Sebastian, Spain
Chilstrom, Herbert W *Religious Leader*
%Evangelical Lutheran Church, 8765 W Higgins Rd, Chicago, IL 60631
Chilton, J E R, III *Businessman*
%Chilton Corp, 12606 Greenville Ave, Dallas, TX 75243
Chilton, Kevin P *Astronaut*
%NASA, Johnson Space Ctr, Houston, TX 77058
Chiluba, Frederick *President, Zambia*
%President's Office, State House, PO Box 135, Lusaka, Zambia
Chino, Tetsuo *Businessman*
%Honda Motor Co Ltd, 1-1 2-chome, Minami-Aoyama, Minatoku, Tokyo, Japan
Chirac, Jacques R *Prime Minister, France*
110 Rue du Bac, 75007 Paris, France
Chisholm, Shirley *Representative, NY*
48 Crestwood Ln, Williamsville, NY 14221
Chisholm-Carillo, Linda *Volleyball Player*
%Women's Pro Volleyball Assn, 13101 Washington Blvd, Los Angeles, CA 90066
Chissano, Joaquim *President, Mozambique*
%President's Office, Avenida Julius Nyerere, Maputo, Mozambique
Chivers, Warren *Skier*
%Vermont Academy, Saxtons River, WI 05154
Chizova, Nadezhda *Track Athlete*
%Olympic Committee, Luzhnetzkaya Nab 8, Moscow, Russia
Cho, Paul *Evangelist*
%Full Gospel Central Church, Yoido Plz, Seoul, South Korea
Choate, Clyde L *WW II Army Hero (CMH)*
Rt 1, Anna, IL 62906
Chodorow, Marvin *Physicist, Educator*
809 San Francisco Terr, Stanford, CA 94305
Chomsky, Marvin J *Television Director*
4707 Ocean Front Walk, Venice, CA 90291
Chomsky, Noam *Linguist*
15 Suzanne Rd, Lexington, MA 02173
Chorzempa, Daniel Walter *Concert Pianist, Composer*
Grosse Budengasse 11, 5000 Cologne 1, Germany
Chou, Harry H S *Businessman*
%Wang Laboratories, 1 Industrial Ave, Lowell, MA 01851
Choy, Herbert Y C *Judge*
300 Ala Moana Blvd, #C-328, PO Box 50127, Honolulu, HI 96850
Chretien, Jean *Government Official, Canada*
%Lang Michener Lash Johnson, 50 O'Connor St, Ottawa ON K1P GL2, Canada
Chretien, Jean-Loup *Spatinaute, France*
%CNES, 18 Ave Edouard-Belin, 31055 Toulouse Cedex, France
Christensen, Todd *Football Player, Sportscaster*
%Management Team, 9507 Santa Monica Blvd, #304, Beverly Hills, CA 90210
Christian, Shirley *Journalist*
%Miami Herald, 1 Herald Plz, Miami, FL 33101
Christian-Jacque *Movie Director, Screenwriter*
42 Bis Rue de Paris, 92100 Boulognw-Billancourt, France
Christians, F Wilhelm *Financier*
%Konigsallee 45-47, 4000 Dusseldorf, Germany
Christie, H Frederick *Businessman*
%Southern California Edison Co, 2244 Walnut Grove Ave, Rosemead, CA 91770
Christie, Julie *Actress, Model*
23 Linden Grdns, London W3, England
Christine, Virginia *Actress*
12348 Rochedale Ln, Los Angeles, CA 90049
Christo *Sculptor*
48 Howard St, New York, NY 10013
Christoff, Boris *Opera Singer*
Via Bertolini 1, Rome, Italy

C

Christoffersen – Cizik

Christoffersen, Jon M *Financier*
%Visa USA, PO Box 26673, San Francisco, CA 94126

Christopher, Bishop *Religious Leader*
%Serbian Orthodox Church, St Sava Monastery, Box 519, Libertyville, IL 60048

Christopher, Dennis *Actor*
%Lantz Office, 4104 Farmdale Ave, Studio City, CA 91604

Christopher, Jordan *Actor*
%STE Representation, 9301 Wilshire Blvd, #312, Beverly Hills, CA 90210

Christopher, Warren M *Attorney, Government Official*
%O'Melveny & Myers, 611 W 6th St, Los Angeles, CA 90017

Christopher, William *Actor*
PO Box 50690, Pasadena, CA 91105

Christopherson, Weston R *Businessman*
%Northern Trust Corp, 50 S LaSalle St, Chicago, IL 60603

Christy, James *Astronomer*
1720 W Niona Pl, Tucson, AZ 85704

Christy, John Gilray *Businessman*
%IU International Corp, 1500 Walnut St, Philadelphia, PA 19102

Christy, Robert F *Physicist*
1230 Arden Rd, Pasadena, CA 91106

Chrysostom, Bishop *Religious Leader*
%Serbian Orthodox Church, St Sava Monastery, Box 519, Libertyville, IL 60048

Chryssa *Sculptor*
565 Broadway, Soho, New York, NY 10012

Chu, Paul C W *Physicist*
%University of Houston, Center for Superconductivity, Houston, TX 77204

Chubb, Percy, III *Businessman*
%Chubb Corp, 15 Mountain View Rd, Warren, NJ 07061

Chung, Connie *Commentator*
%CBS-TV, News Dept, 524 W 57th St, New York, NY 10019

Chung, Kyung-Wha *Concert Violinist*
%Harrison/Parrott Ltd, 12 Penzance Pl, London W11 4PA, England

Chung, Myung Whun *Concert Pianist, Conductor*
%Opera-Bastille, 120 Ave du Lyon, 75011 Paris, France

Church, Alonzo *Philosopher, Mathematician*
%University of California, Philosophy Dept, Los Angeles, CA 90024

Church, Sam *Labor Leader*
%United Mine Workers of America, 900 15th St NW, Washington, DC 20005

Churchill, Caryl *Playwright*
%M Ramsey, 14-A Goodwin Ct, St Martin's Ln, London WC2N 4LL, England

Chute, Marchette *Writer*
450 E 63rd St, New York, NY 10021

Chwast, Seymour *Artist*
%Push Pin Grp, 215 Park Ave S, New York, NY 10003

Ciampi, Joe *Basketball Coach*
%Auburn University, Athletic Dept, Auburn, AL 36831

Cianciolo, August M *Army General*
Military Deputy, OASA, Director Army Acquisition Corps, Washington, DC 20310

Ciappi, Mario Luigi Cardinal *Religious Leader*
Via di Porto Angelica, #63, 00193 Rome, Italy

Ciccolini, Aldo *Concert Pianist*
%IMG Artists, 22 E 71st St, New York, NY 10001

Cimino, Leonardo *Actor*
%Triad Artists, 10100 Santa Monica Blvd, #1600, Los Angeles, CA 90067

Cimino, Michael *Movie Director*
%Collins Productions, 7120 Hayvenhurst Ave, #108, Van Nuys, CA 91406

Cioffi, Charles *Actor*
Glover Ave, Norwalk, CT 06850

Cisler, Walker Lee *Engineer*
1071 Devonshire Rd, Grosse Point, MI 48230

Cisneros, Henry *Mayor, Association Executive*
%National Civic League, 1601 Grant St, #250, Denver, CO 80203

Civiletti, Benjamin R *Attorney General*
%Mercantile Bank & Trust Bldg, #1800, 2 Hopkins Plz, Baltimore, MD 21201

Cizik, Robert *Businessman*
%Cooper Industries, 1001 Fannin St, Houston, TX 77002

Claiborne Ortenberg, Liz *Fashion Designer*
%Liz Claiborne Inc, 1441 Broadway, New York, NY 10018

Claiborne, Craig *Journalist, Food Expert*
15 Clamshell Ave, East Hampton, NY 11937

Clampett, Bobby *Golfer*
PO Box 5155, 2615 Kildaire Farm Rd, Cary, NC 27512

Clampitt, Amy *Poet*
%Random House, 201 E 50th St, New York, NY 10022

Clancy, Edward Bede Cardinal *Religious Leader*
St Mary's Cathedral, Sydney, NSW 2000, Australia

Clancy, Tom *Writer*
%G P Putnam's Sons, 200 Madison Ave, New York, NY 10016

Clapp, Charles E, II *Judge*
%US Tax Court, 400 2nd St NW, Washington, DC 20217

Clapp, Joseph M *Businessman*
%Roadway Services Inc, 1077 Gorge Blvd, Akron, OH 44309

Clapp, Norton *Businessman*
PO Box 99, Medina, WA 98039

Clapper, James R, Jr *Air Force General*
Director, Defense Intelligence Agency, Washington, DC 20304

Clapton, Eric *Singer, Guitarist*
67 Brook St, London W1, England

Clare, David R *Businessman*
%Johnson & Johnson, 1 Johnson & Johnson Plz, New Brunswick, NJ 08933

Clark, Bernard F *Businessman*
%Mitchell Energy & Development Corp, 2001 Timberloch Pl, Woodlands, TX 77380

Clark, Burton R *Sociologist*
201 Ocean Ave, Santa Monica, CA 90402

Clark, Candy *Actress*
2276 Century Hill, Los Angeles, CA 90067

Clark, Charles *Judge*
%US Court of Appeals, US Courthouse, 245 E Capitol St, Jackson, MS 39201

Clark, Charles *Financier*
%Georgia Federal Bank, 20 Marietta St NW, Atlanta, GA 30303

Clark, Dane *Actor*
1680 Old Oak Rd, Los Angeles, CA 90049

Clark, Dick *Entertainer, Television Producer*
%Dick Clark Productions, 3003 W Olive Ave, Burbank, CA 91505

Clark, Dick C *Senator, IA*
4424 Edmunds St NW, Washington, DC 20007

Clark, Donald C *Businessman*
%Household International, 2700 Sanders Rd, Prospect Heights, IL 60070

Clark, Dwight *Football Player*
%San Francisco 49ers, 4949 Centennial Blvd, Santa Clara, CA 95054

Clark, E H, Jr *Businessman*
%Baker International Corp, 500 City Pkwy W, Orange, CA 92668

Clark, Earl *Businessman*
%Occidental Life Insurance, 1150 S Olive St, Los Angeles, CA 90015

Clark, Earl *Diver*
1145 NE 126th St, #4, North Miami, FL 33161

Clark, Eugenie *Zoologist*
7817 Hampden Ln, Bethesda, MD 20742

Clark, Gary *Football Player*
%Washington Redskins, Box 17247, Dulles Airport, Washington, DC 20041

Clark, Howard L *Businessman*
PO Box 513, Riverview Rd, Hobe Sound, FL 33455

Clark, J Daniel *Businessman*
%C & J Clark Ltd, 40 High St, Somerset, England

Clark, J Desmond *Anthropologist*
1941 Yosemite Rd, Berkeley, CA 94707

Clark, J E (Bud) *Mayor*
%Mayor's Office, City Hall, 1220 SW 5th Ave, Portland, OR 97204

Clark, Jack *Baseball Player*
4478 Deer Ridge Rd, Danville, CA 94526

Clark, James M *Educator*
%State University of New York, President's Office, Cortland, NY 13045

Clark, Joe *Prime Minister, Canada*
Stornoway, 541 Acacia Ave, Ottawa ON, Canada

Clark, Joe *Educator*
366 S Ridgewood Rd, South Orange, NJ 07079

Clark, John *Businessman*
%Plessey Co, Vicarage Ln, Ilford, Essex IG1 4AQ, England

Clark, Kenneth B *Psychologist, Educator*
%Kenneth B Clark Assoc, 615 Broadway, Hastings-on-Hudson, NY 10706

Clark, Mary Higgins *Writer*
%Simon & Schuster, 1230 Ave of Americas, New York, NY 10020

Clark, Matt *Actor*
%Paul Kohner Inc, 9169 Sunset Blvd, Los Angeles, CA 90069

Clark, Peter B *Publisher*
49150 Della Robbia Ln, Palm Desert, CA 92260

Clark, Petula *Singer*
PO Box 498, Quakertown, PA 18951

Clark, Ramsey *Attorney General*
113 University Pl, New York, NY 10003

Clark, Robert A *Businessman*
Munstead Wood, Godalming, Surrey, England

Clark, Robert C *Artist*
PO Box 597, Cambria, CA 93428

Clark, Roy *Singer*
%Jim Halsey Co, 1800 Forrest Blvd, Tulsa, OK 74114

Clark, Steve *Swimmer*
29 Upper Martling Rd, San Anselmo, CA 94960

Clark, Susan *Actress*
%Sutton Barth Vennari, 145 S Fairfax Ave, Los Angeles, CA 90036

Clark, Thomas A *Judge*
%US Court of Appeals, 56 Forsyth St NW, Atlanta, GA 30303

Clark, Will *Baseball Player*
6526 Virgilian St, New Orleans, LA 70126

Clark, William J *Businessman*
%Massachusetts Mutual Life Insurance, 1295 State St, Springfield, MA 01111

Clark, William P *Secretary, Interior*
201 N Figueroa St, Los Angeles, CA 90012

Clark, Worley H, Jr *Businessman*
%Nalco Chemical Co, 2901 Butterfield Rd, Oak Brook, IL 60521

Clarke, Angela *Actress*
%Gores/Fields Agency, 10100 Santa Monica Blvd, #700, Los Angeles, CA 90067

Clarke, Arthur C *Writer, Underwater Explorer*
Leslie's House, 25 Barnes Pl, Colombo 7, Sri Lanka

Clarke, Bobby *Hockey Player, Executive*
%Minnesota North Stars, 7901 S Cedar Ave S, Bloomington, MN 55425

Clarke, Brian Patrick *Actor*
5 Toluca Estates Dr, North Hollywood, CA 91602

Clarke, Cyril A *Physician, Geneticist*
High Close, Thorsway, Caldy, Cheshire, England

Clarke, David H *Businessman*
%Hanson Industries, 100 Wood Ave S, Iselin, NJ 08830

Clarke, Gilmore D *Landscape Architect*
480 Park Ave, New York, NY 10022

Clarke, J Brian *Businessman*
%Coleco Industries, 999 Quaker Ln S, West Hartford, CT 06110

Clarke, John *Actor*
%"Days of Our Lives" Show, KNBC-TV, 3000 W Alameda Ave, Burbank, CA 91523

Clarke, Mae *Actress*
%Motion Picture-TV Country House, 23388 Mulholland Dr, Woodland Hills, CA 91364

Clarke, Martha *Dancer, Choreographer*
%Sheldon Soffer Mgmt, 130 W 56th St, New York, NY 10019

Clarke, Richard A *Businessman*
%Pacific Gas & Electric Co, 77 Beale St, San Francisco, CA 94106

Clarke, Robert B *Businessman*
%Grolier Inc, Sherman Tpke, Danbury, CT 06916

Clarke, Ron *Track Athlete*
1 Bay St, Brighton Vic 3186, Australia

Clarke, Stanley *Jazz Bassist, Composer*
8817 Rangley Ave, Los Angeles, CA 90048

Clarkson, Lana *Actress*
%L A Talent, 8335 Sunset Blvd, Los Angeles, CA 90069

Claus George Willem Otto Frederik Geert *Prince, Netherlands*
%Huis ten Bosch, The Hague, Netherlands

Clausen, A W (Tom) *Financier*
%BankAmerica Corp, Bank of America Ctr, San Francisco, CA 94104

Clauser, Francis H *Aeronautical Engineer, Educator*
4072 Chevy Chase, Flintridge, CA 91011

Clavel, Bernard *Writer*
Chemin du Cret 10, 1110 Monges, Switzerland 20433

Clavell, James *Writer*
%JC Enterprises, 200 W 57th St, #1007, New York, NY 10019

Clay, John W, Sr *Financier*
%Third National Bank, 201 4th Ave N, Nashville, TN 37219

Clay, Orson C *Businessman*
%American National Insurance, 1 Moody Plz, Galveston, TX 77550

Clay, William L *Representative, MO*
%House of Representatives, Washington, DC 20515

Clayborn, Raymond *Football Player*
%Cleveland Browns, Cleveland Stadium, Cleveland, OH 44114

Clayburgh, Jill *Actress*
225 McLain St, Mt Kisco, NY 10549

Clayman, Ralph V *Surgeon*
%Barnes Hospital, Surgery Dept, 416 S Kingshighway Blvd, St Louis, MO 63110

Clayton, Jack *Movie Director*
9018 Elevado Ave, Los Angeles, CA 90069

Clayton, Robert N *Chemist, Educator*
5201 S Cornell Ave, Chicago, IL 60615

Claytor, Robert B *Businessman*
%Norfolk Southern Corp, 1 Commerce Pl, Norfolk, VA 23510

Claytor, W Graham, Jr *Government Official*
2912 "N" St NW, Washington, DC 20007

Clayworth, June *Actress*
1641 S Veteran Ave, Los Angeles, CA 90024

Cleary, Beverly *Writer*
%William Morrow Co, 105 Madison Ave, New York, NY 10016

Cleary, James W *Educator*
%California State University, President's Office, Northridge, CA 91330

Cleary, Russell G *Businessman*
%G Heileman Brewing Co, 100 Harborview Plz, La Crosse, WI 54601

Cleave, Mary L *Astronaut*
%NASA, Johnson Space Ctr, Houston, TX 77058

Cleaver, Vera *Writer*
600 E Lake Elbert Dr, Winter Haven, FL 33881

Cleland, Max *Government Official*
%Secretary of State, 214 StateCapitol Bldg, Atlanta, GA 30334

Clemens, Roger *Baseball Player*
1818 Brookchester, Katy, TX 77450

Clement, John *Businessman*
%Unigate, Unigate House, Western Ave, London W3 0SH, England

Clement, Rene *Movie Director*
91 Ave Henri Martin, 75016 Paris, France

Clements, George L *Businessman*
PO Box 866, Carefree, AZ 85331

Clements, William P, Jr *Governor, TX*
%Governor's Office, State Capitol, Austin, TX 78711

Clements, Woodrow W *Businessman*
%Dr Pepper Co, 5523 E Mockingbird Ln, Dallas, TX 75265

Clendenin, John L *Businessman*
%BellSouth Corp, 675 W Peachtree St NE, Atlanta, GA 30375

Clennon, David *Actor*
%Susan Smith Assoc, 121 N San Vicente Blvd, Beverly Hills, CA 90211

Clerico, Christian *Restauranteur*
%Lido-Normandie, 116 Bis Ave des Champs Elysees, 75008 Paris, France

Clervoy, Jean-Francois *Spatinaut, France*
%CNES, 18 Ave Edouard Belin, F-31055 Toulouse Cedex, France

Cleveland, Harlan *Diplomat, Educator*
5720 Camelback Dr, Edina, MN 55436

Cleveland, James C *Representative, NH*
%Cleveland Waters & Bass, New London, NH 03257

Cleveland, Odessa *Actress*
6058 Fair Ave, Woodland Hills, CA 91364

Cleveland, Patience *Actress*
21321 Providencia St, Woodland Hills, CA 91364

Clevenger, Raymond C, III *Judge*
%US Court of Appeals, 717 Madison Pl NW, Washington, DC 20439

Clexton, Edward W, Jr *Navy Admiral*
Deputy CINC, US Naval Forces Europe, Box 2, FPO, New York, NY 09510

Cliburn, Van *Concert Pianist*
455 Wilder Pl, Shreveport, LA 71104

Cliff, Jimmy *Singer*
%GTI, 1700 Broadway, 10th Fl, New York, NY 10019

Clifford, Clark M *Secretary, Defense*
%Clifford & Warnke, 815 Connecticut Ave NW, Washington, DC 20006

Clifford, Michael R *Astronaut*
%NASA, Johnson Space Center, Houston, TX 77058

Clifford, Thomas J *Educator*
%University of North Dakota, President's Office, Grand Forks, ND 58202

Cline, Martin J *Physician, Educator*
%University of California, Health Science Ctr, Los Angeles, CA 90024

Cline, Robert S *Businessman*
%Airborne Freight Corp, 3101 Western Ave, Seattle, WA 98121

Clinger, Debra *Actress*
4415 Auckland Ave, North Hollywood, CA 91602

Clinger, William F, Jr *Representative, PA*
%House of Representatives, Washington, DC 20515

Clinton, Bill *Governor, AR*
1800 Center St, Little Rock, AR 72206

Clohessy, Robert *Actor*
%Agency for Performing Arts, 9000 Sunset Blvd, #1200, Los Angeles, CA 90069

Cloninger, Tony *Baseball Player*
RR 2, Box 381-A, Iron Station, NC 28080

Clooney, Rosemary *Singer*
1019 N Roxbury Dr, Beverly Hills, CA 90210

Clore, Alan E *Businessman*
%Gulf Resources & Chemical Corp, 1100 Milam Bldg, Houston, TX 77002

Close, Chuck *Artist*
271 Central Park West, New York, NY 10024

Close, Glenn *Actress*
888 7th Ave, #1800, New York, NY 10019

Clotworthy, Bob *Diver*
11221 Cameo Ave NE, Albuquerque, NM 87111

Clotworthy, Robert *Actor*
%Fred Amsel Assoc, 6310 San Vicente Blvd, #407, Los Angeles, CA 90048

Cloud, Jack *Football Player*
805 Janice Dr, Annapolis, MD 21403

Clough, Charles E *Businessman*
%Nashua Corp, 44 Franklin St, Nashua, NH 03061

Clough, Charles M *Businessman*
%Wyle Laboratories, 128 Maryland St, El Segundo, CA 90245

Clow, Lee *Businessman*
%Chiat/Day/Mojo, 517 S Olive St, Los Angeles, CA 90013

Clower, Jerry *Comedian, Writer*
%Top Billing, PO Box 121089, Nashville, TN 37212

Clyne, Patricia *Fashion Designer*
353 W 39th St, New York, NY 10018

Coachman Davis, Alice *Track Athlete*
515 Louis Ave, Albany, GA 30117

Coase, Ronald H *Nobel Economics Laureate*
1111 E 60th St, Chicago, IL 60637

Coates, Phyllis *Actress*
PO Box 3664, Carmel, CA 93921

Coats, Daniel R *Senator, IN*
%US Senate, Washington, DC 20510

Coats, Michael L *Astronaut*
%NASA, Johnson Space Ctr, Houston, TX 77058

Coats, William D *Businessman*
%Coats Patons, 155 St Vincent St, Glasgow G2 5PA, England

Coatsworth, Elizabeth *Writer*
Chimney Farm, Nobleboro, ME 04555

Cobb, Henry N *Architect*
%Harvard University, School of Architecture, Cambridge, MA 02138

Cobb, Miles A *Financier*
%Bell National Corp, 400 S El Camino Real, San Mateo, CA 94402

Coble, Howard *Representative, NC*
%House of Representatives, Washington, DC 20515

Coblentz, Stanton A *Writer*
200 Glenwood Cir, #D-3, Monterey, CA 93940

Cobos, Jesus Lopez *Conductor*
%Cincinnati Symphony, 1241 Elm St, Cincinnati, OH 45210

Coburn, James *Actor*
3930 Hollyline Ave, Sherman Oaks, CA 91403

Coca, Imogene *Comedienne*
200 E 66th St, #1803-D, New York, NY 10021

Cochereau, Pierre *Concert Organist*
15 Bis Des Ursins, 75004 Paris, France

Cochran, Barbara Ann *Skier*
RFD 4, Box 2510, Montpelier, VT 05602

Cochran, Brad *Football Player*
%Los Angeles Raiders, 332 Center St, El Segundo, CA 90245

Cochran, Hank *Songwriter*
PO Box 120537, Nashville, TN 37212

Cochran, John *Commentator*
%NBC-TV, News Dept, 4001 Nebraska Ave NW, Washington, DC 20016

Cochran, Thad *Senator, MS*
%US Senate, Washington, DC 20510

Cochrane, Harwood *Businessman*
%Overnite Transportation Co, 1000 Semmes Ave, Richmond, VA 23224

Cocker, Joe *Singer*
%Capitol Records, 1750 N Vine St, Los Angeles, CA 90028

Cockerell, Christopher *Engineer, Hovercraft Inventor*
16 Prospect Pl, Hythe, Southampton, Hants SO4 6AU, England

Cockrell, Kenneth D *Astronaut*
%NASA, Johnson Space Center, Houston, TX 77058

Cockrell, Lila *Mayor*
%Mayor's Office, City Hall, Military Plaza, San Antonio, TX 78205

Cockroft, Don *Football Player*
%North Coast Energy, 5311 Northfield Rd, Bedford Heights, OH 44146

Code, Arthur D *Astronomer*
%WUPPE Project, University of Wisconsin, Astronomy Dept, Madison, WI 53706

Cody, Iron Eyes *Actor*
2013 Griffith Park Blvd, Los Angeles, CA 90039

Coe, George *Actor*
%Gersh Agency, 232 N Canon Dr, Beverly Hills, CA 90210

Coe, Sebastian *Track Athlete*
%Sports Council, 16 Upper Woburn Pl, London WC1H 0QP England

Coelho, Susie *Actress*
26525 Josel Dr, Canyon Country, CA 91350

Coen, Ethan *Movie Director, Screenwriter*
%United Talent, 9560 Wilshire Blvd, #500, Beverly Hills, CA 90210

Coen, Joel *Movie Director, Screenwriter*
%United Talent, 9560 Wilshire Blvd, #500, Beverly Hills, CA 90210

Coetzee, Gerrie *Boxer*
Bolesburg Township, South Africa

Coetzee, J M *Writer*
PO Box 92, Rondebosch, Cape Province 7700, South Africa

C

Cofer, Mike *Football Player*
%Detroit Lions, Silverdome, 1200 Featherstone Rd, Pontiac, MI 48057

Coffey, John L *Judge*
%US Court of Appeals, US Courthouse, 517 E Wisconsin Ave, Milwaukee, WI 53202

Coffey, Paul *Hockey Player*
%Pittsburgh Penguins, Civic Arena, Pittsburgh, PA 15219

Coffey, Shelby, III *Editor*
%Los Angeles Times, Times Mirror Sq, Los Angeles, CA 90053

Coffin, David L *Businessman*
%Dexter Corp, 1 Elm St, Windsor Locks, CT 06906

Coffin, Frank M *Judge; Representative, ME*
%US Court of Appeals, 156 Federal St, Portland, ME 04112

Coffin, Tad *Equestrian Rider*
%General Delivery, Strafford, VT 05072

Coffin, Tristam *Writer*
%Washington Spectator, PO Box 70023, Washington, DC 20088

Coffin, William Sloane, Jr *Social Activist, Religious Leader*
%SANE/Freeze, 55 Van Dyke Ave, Hartford, CT 06106

Coffman, Stanley K, Jr *Educator*
%State University of New York, English Dept, Albany, NY 12203

Cogan, Kevin *Auto Racing Driver*
%CART, 390 Enterprise Ct, Bloomfield Hills, MI 48013

Coggan of Canterbury, Baron *Religious Leader*
Kingshead House, Sissinghurst, Cranbrook, Kent TN17 2JE, England

Coggeshall, Peter C *Businessman*
%Sonoco Products Co, N 2nd St, Hartsville, SC 29550

Coghlan, Eamon *Track Athlete*
%International Management Grp, 1 Erieview Plz, Cleveland, OH 44114

Cohane, Tim *Sportswriter*
203 School St, Watertown, MA 02179

Coheleach, Guy *Artist*
%Pandion Art, PO Box 96, Bernardsville, NJ 07924

Cohen, Aaron *Space Administrator*
%Director's Office, NASA, Johnson Space Center, Houston, TX 77058

Cohen, Alexander H *Movie Producer*
%Shubert Theatre, 225 W 44th St, New York, NY 10036

Cohen, Israel *Businessman*
%Giant Food Co, 6300 Sheriff Rd, Landover, MD 20785

Cohen, Joel E *Educator*
%Rockefeller University, Populations Dept, New York, NY 10021

Cohen, Joseph *Television Executive*
%Hughes Television Network, 4 Penn Plz, New York, NY 10001

Cohen, Leonard *Businessman*
%National Medical Enterprises, 2700 Colorado Ave, Santa Monica, CA 90404

Cohen, Leonard N *Poet, Songwriter*
%Associated Talent International, 888 7th Ave, New York, NY 10106

Cohen, Mary Ann *Judge*
%US Tax Court, 400 2nd St NW, Washington, DC 20217

Cohen, Morris *Metallurgist, Materials Scientist*
491 Puritan Rd, Swampscott, MA 01907

Cohen, Philip P *Physiological Chemist*
1117 Oak Way, Madison, WI 53706

Cohen, Robert A *Publisher*
250 5th Ave, New York, NY 10001

Cohen, Seymour S *Biochemist*
106 Quaker Path, Stonybrook, NY 11790

Cohen, Sheldon S *Government Official*
5518 Trent St, Chevy Chase, MD 20015

Cohen, Stanley *Nobel Medicine Laureate*
%Vanderbilt University Medical Ctr, 1161 21st Ave, Nashville, TN 37232

Cohen, Stanley N *Geneticist*
%Stanford University Medical Ctr, Genetics Dept, Stanford, CA 94305

Cohen, William S *Senator, ME*
%US Senate, Washington, DC 20510

Cohn, Alvin W *Businessman*
%Staley Continental Inc, 1701 Golf Rd, Rolling Meadows, IL 60008

C

Cohn, Marc *Singer*
115 Central Park West, New York, NY 10023
Cohn, Mildred *Biochemist, Biophysicist*
747 Clarendon Rd, Narbeth, PA 19104
Cohn, Mindy *Actress*
%Light Co, 901 Bringham Ave, Los Angeles, CA 90049
Cohn, Robert H *Businessman*
%Staley Continental Inc, 1701 Golf Rd, Rolling Meadows, IL 60008
Coker, Charles W, Jr *Businessman*
%Sonoco Products Co, N 2nd St, Hartsville, SC 29550
Colalillo, Mike *WW II Army Hero (CMH)*
577 Riley Rd, Duluth, MN 55803
Colalucci, Gianluigi *Art Restorer*
%Office of Restoration, Vatican City, Rome, Italy
Colangelo, Jerry *Basketball Executive*
%Phoenix Suns, PO Box 1369, Phoenix, AZ 85001
Colbert, Claudette *Actress*
Bellerive, St Peter, Barbados, West Indies
Colbert, Edwin H *Vertebrate Palaeontologist*
%Museum of Northern Arizona, Rt 4, Box 720, Flagstaff, AZ 86001
Colbert, Lester L *Businessman*
3401 Gulf Shore Blvd N, Naples, FL 33940
Colbert, Lewis *Football Player*
%Kansas City Chiefs, 1 Arrowhead Dr, Kansas City, MO 64129
Colbert, Robert *Actor*
%First Artists Agency, 1000 Riverside Dr, #6, Toluca Lake, CA 91602
Colborn, Jim *Baseball Player*
2932 Solimar Beach Dr, Ventura, CA 93001
Colby, William E *Government Official*
%Reid & Priest, 1111 19th St NW, Washington, DC 20036
Cole, Artemas *Cartoonist*
PO Box 1057, Alta Loma, CA 91701
Cole, Dennis *Actor*
%Rickey Barr Agency, PO Box 69590, Los Angeles, CA 90069
Cole, Eunice *Labor Leader*
%American Nurses Assn, 2420 Pershing Rd, Kansas City, MO 64108
Cole, Gary *Actor*
%International Creative Mgmt, 8899 Beverly Blvd, Los Angeles, CA 90048
Cole, Kenneth S *Biophysicist*
2404 Loring St, San Diego, CA 92109
Cole, Natalie *Singer*
%Elektra Records, 9229 Sunset Blvd, #718, Los Angeles, CA 90069
Cole, Olivia *Actress*
%Century Artists, 9744 Wilshire Blvd, #308, Beverly Hills, CA 90212
Cole, Thomas, Jr *Educator*
%Clark College, President's Office, Atlanta, GA 30314
Cole, Tina *Actress*
%WFA, 2126 Cahuenga Blvd, Los Angeles, CA 90068
Coleman, Cy *Composer*
%Cy Coleman Enterprises, 161 W 54th St, New York, NY 10019
Coleman, Dabney *Actor*
715 Napoli Dr, Pacific Palisades, CA 90272
Coleman, Daniel J *Publisher*
%Popular Mechanics Magazine, 224 W 57th St, New York, NY 10019
Coleman, Derrick *Basketball Player*
%New Jersey Nets, Meadowlands Arena, East Rutherford, NJ 07073
Coleman, Don *Football Player*
424 McPherson, Lansing, MI 48915
Coleman, E Thomas *Representative, MO*
%House of Representatives, Washington, DC 20515
Coleman, Elizabeth *Educator*
%Bennington College, President's Office, Bennington, VT 05201
Coleman, Gary *Actor*
%Burton Moss Agency, 113 N San Vicente Blvd, #202, Beverly Hills, CA 90211
Coleman, George *Jazz Saxophonist*
63 E 9th St, New York, NY 10003

C

Coleman – Collins

Coleman, Jack *Actor*
%Harris & Goldberg Agency, 1999 Ave of Stars, #2850, Los Angeles, CA 90067

Coleman, James S *Sociologist*
University of Chicago, Sociology Dept, 1126 E 59th St, Chicago, IL 60637

Coleman, Lester E *Businessman*
%Lubrizol Corp, 29400 Lakeland Blvd, Wickliffe, OH 44092

Coleman, Lewis W *Financier*
%BankAmerica Corp, Bank of America Ctr, San Francisco, CA 94104

Coleman, Ornette *Jazz Saxophonist, Composer*
%Joyce Agency, 435 E 79th St, New York, NY 10021

Coleman, Ronald *Representative, TX*
%House of Representatives, Washington, DC 20515

Coleman, Vince *Baseball Player*
1864 Hermitage, Imperial, MO 63052

Coleman, William T, Jr *Secretary, Transportation*
%O'Melveny & Myers, 1800 "M" St NW, Washington, DC 20036

Coles, Robert *Psychiatrist*
75 Mount Auburn St, Cambridge, MA 02138

Colescott, Warrington *Artist*
Rt 1, Hollandale, WI 53544

Coley, John Ford *Singer, Songwriter*
%Twin Trumpets Productions, 10100 Santa Monica Blvd, Los Angeles, CA 90067

Colgrass, Michael Charles *Composer*
583 Palmerston Ave, Toronto ON M6G 2P6, Canada

Colin, Oswaldo Roberto *Financier*
%Banco do Brasil, Bancario Sul-Lote 23, Edificio Sede III-19 Andar, Brazil

Colker, James *Businessman*
%Contraves Goerz Corp, 632 Ft Duquesne Blvd, Pittsburgh, PA 15222

Coll, Steve *Journalist*
%Washington Post, 1150 15th St NW, Washington, DC 20071

Collado, Emilio Gabriel *Government Official, Businessman*
Mill River Rd, Oyster Bay, NY 11771

Collard, Jean-Philippe *Concert Pianist*
Boite Postal 210, 75426 Paris Cedex 09, France

Colledge, Cecilia *Figure Skater*
18 Groveland St, Auburndale, MA 02166

Collen, Desire *Medical Researcher*
%University of Leuven, Leuven, Belgium

Collette, Buddy *Jazz Musician*
900 S Sierra Bonita Ave, Los Angeles, CA 90036

Colley, Ed *Cartoonist (Suburban Cowgirls)*
%Tribune Media Services, 64 E Concord St, Orlando, FL 32801

Collier, Abram T *Businessman*
%New England Mutual Life Insurance, 501 Boylston St, Boston, MA 02117

Collins, Barbara-Rose *Representative, MI*
%House of Representatives, Washington, DC 20515

Collins, Bud *Sportscaster*
%NBC-TV, Sports Dept, 30 Rockefeller Plz, New York, NY 10020

Collins, Cardiss R *Representative, IL*
%House of Representatives, Washington, DC 20515

Collins, David E *Businessman*
%Johnson & Johnson, 1 Johnson & Johnson Plz, New Brunswick, NJ 08933

Collins, Eileen M *Astronaut*
%NASA, Johnson Space Center, Houston, TX 77058

Collins, Gary *Actor*
2751 Hutton Dr, Beverly Hills, CA 90210

Collins, Gary *Football Player*
PO Box 455, Palmyra, PA 17078

Collins, Jack *Actor*
%Contemporary Artists, 132 Lasky Dr, #B, Beverly Hills, CA 90212

Collins, Jackie *Writer*
710 N Foothill Rd, Beverly Hills, CA 90210

Collins, Joan *Actress*
1196 Cabrillo Dr, Beverly Hills, CA 90210

Collins, John W *Businessman*
%Clorox Co, 1221 Broadway, Oakland, CA 94612

Collins, Judy *Singer*
%Rocky Mountain Productions, PO Box 1296, Cathedral Station, New York, NY 10025

Collins, Larry *Writer*
%Simon & Schuster, 1230 Ave of Americas, New York, NY 10020

Collins, Martha Layne *Governor, KY*
PO Box 11890, Lexington, KY 40578

Collins, Marva *Educator*
%Westside Preparatory School, 4146 W Chicago Ave, Chicago, IL 60651

Collins, Michael *Astronaut*
%Michael Collins Assoc, 4206 48th Pl NW, Washington, DC 20016

Collins, Pat *Hypnotist*
524 W 57th St, New York, NY 10019

Collins, Patrick *Actor*
%Schiffman Eckman Morrison Marx, 156 5th Ave, New York, NY 10016

Collins, Paul J *Financier*
%Citicorp, 399 Park Ave, New York, NY 10013

Collins, Phil *Singer*
%Atlantic Records, 75 Rockefeller Plz, New York, NY 10019

Collins, Samuel C *Mechanical Engineer, Cryogenist*
12322 Riverview Rd, Oxon Hill, MD 20022

Collins, Stephen *Actor*
PO Box 95, Fitchville, CT 06334

Collins, William F *Businessman*
%Revere Copper & Brass Inc, 605 3rd Ave, New York, NY 10158

Collinson, John T *Businessman*
%CSX Corp, 901 E Cary St, Richmond, VA 23219

Collor de Mello, Fernando *President, Brazil*
Palacio du Planakti, Praca dos Tres Poderos, 70.150 Brasilia DF, Brazil

Colodny, Edwin I *Businessman*
%USAir Grp, 2345 Crystal Dr, Arlington, VA 22227

Colombo, Emilio *Prime Minister, Italy*
Via Aurelia 239, Rome, Italy

Colombo, Giovanni Cardinal *Religious Leader*
Palazzo Arcivescovile, Piazza Fontana 2, Milan, Italy

Colomby, Scott *Actor*
%Borinstein Oreck Bogart, 8271 Melrose Ave, #110, Los Angeles, CA 90046

Colson, Charles W *Watergate Figure*
%Prison Fellowship, PO Box 40562, Washington, DC 20016

Colson, William L *Businessman*
%Ocean Drilling & Exploration Co, 1600 Canal St, New Orleans, LA 70161

Colt, Marshall *Actor*
%William Morris Agency, 151 El Camino, Beverly Hills, CA 90212

Colter, Jessie *Singer*
1117 17th Ave S, Nashville, TN 37212

Coltrane, Robby *Actor*
%Caroline Dawson Assoc, 47 Courtfield Rd, London SW7 4DB, England

Colville, Alex *Artist*
408 Main St, Wolfville NS B0P 1XP, Canada

Colvin, Jack *Actor*
%Century Artists, 9744 Wilshire Blvd, #308, Beverly Hills, CA 90212

Colvin, John O *Judge*
%US Tax Court, 400 2nd St NW, Washington, DC 20217

Colwell, John A *Association Executive*
%American Diabetes Assn, 1660 Duke St, Alexandria, VA 22314

Combes, Willard W *Editorial Cartoonist*
1266 Oakridge Dr, Cleveland, OH 44121

Combest, Larry *Representative, TX*
%House of Representatives, Washington, DC 20515

Combs, T Neal *Businessman*
%Fruehauf Corp, 10900 Harper Ave, Detroit, MI 48213

Comden, Betty *Lyricist, Writer*
117 E 95th St, New York, NY 10028

Comer, Anjanette *Actress*
%Dade/Rosen/Schultz Agency, 11846 Ventura Blvd, #100, Studio City, CA 91403

Comfort, Alex *Writer, Medical Biologist*
683 Oak Grove Dr, Santa Barbara, CA 93158

Comissiona, Sergiu *Conductor*
%Houston Symphony, 615 Louisiana St, Houston, TX 77002

Commager, Henry Steele *Historian*
405 S Pleasant St, Amherst, MA 01002

Commes, Thomas A *Businessman*
%Sherwin-Williams Co, 101 Prospect Ave NW, Cleveland, OH 44115

Commoner, Barry *Plant Physiologist*
%Queens College, Biology of Natural Systems Ctr, Flushing, NY 11367

Como, Perry *Singer*
%Roncom Productions, 305 Northern Blvd, #3-A, Great Neck, NY 11021

Compaore, Blaise *President, Burkina Faso*
%President's Office, Ouagadougou, Burkina Faso

Compton, Ann Woodruff *Commentator*
%ABC-TV, News Dept, 1717 DeSales St NW, Washington, DC 20036

Compton, Forrest *Actor*
%Cunningham Escott Dipene, 919 3rd Ave, New York, NY 10022

Compton, John G M *Prime Minister, St Lucia*
%Prime Minister's Office, Castries, St Lucia

Compton, Joyce *Actress*
4124 Davana Rd, Sherman Oaks, CA 91403

Compton, Ronald E *Businessman*
%Aetna Life & Casualty, 151 Farmington Ave, Hartford, CT 06156

Compton, Walter Ames *Businessman*
%Miles Laboratories, 1127 Myrtle St, Elkhart, IN 46515

Comroe, Julius H, Jr *Physiologist*
555 Laurent Rd, Hillsborough, CA 94010

Conable, Barber B, Jr *Financier; Representative, NY*
10532 Alexander Rd, Alexander, NY 14005

Conant, Herbert D *Businessman*
%Turner Corp, 633 3rd Ave, New York, NY 10017

Conant, Kenneth John *Archaeologist*
3 Carlton Village, #T-105, Bedford, MA 01730

Conaton, Michael *Educator*
%Xavier University, President's Office, Cincinnati, OH 45207

Conaway, Jeff *Actor*
%Agency for Performing Arts, 9000 Sunset Blvd, #1200, Los Angeles, CA 90069

Conaway, John B *Air Force General*
Chief, National Guard Bureau, Washington, DC 20310

Concepion, Davey *Baseball Player*
Urb Los Caobos Botalon 5-D, 5-Piso-Maracay, Venezuela

Condit, Gary A *Representative, CA*
%House of Representatives, Washington, DC 20515

Condon, Richard T *Writer*
3436 Ashbury, Dallas, TX 75205

Cone Vanderbush, Carin *Swimmer*
116-B Washington Rd, West Point, NY 10996

Cone, David *Baseball Player*
3612 Birchwood Dr, Kansas City, MO 64137

Conerly, Charles A *Football Player*
1045 Lynn Dr, Clarkesdale, MS 38614

Conforti, Gino *Actor*
%Cunningham-Escott-Dipene, 261 S Robertson Blvd, Beverly Hills, CA 90211

Conger, Harry M *Businessman*
%Homestake Mining Co, 650 California St, San Francisco, CA 94108

Conklin, George T, Jr *Businessman*
%Guardian Life Insurance, 201 Park Ave, New York, NY 10003

Conlan, Shane *Football Player*
PO Box 413, Frewsburg, NY 14738

Conley, Clare *Editor*
%Outdoor Life Magazine, 2 Park Ave, New York, NY 10016

Conley, Joe *Actor*
10332 Christine Pl, Chatsworth, CA 91311

Conlon, James *Conductor*
%Columbia Artists Mgmt Inc, 165 W 57th St, New York, NY 10019

Conn, Billy *Boxer*
544 Gettysburg St, Pittsburgh, PA 15206

Conn, Jerome W *Medical Researcher*
Admiralty Point, 2369 Gulf Shore Blvd N, Naples, FL 33940
Connally, John B, Jr *Secretary, Treasury; Governor, TX*
PO Box 2557, Houston, TX 72252
Connell, John MacFarlane *Businessman*
%Distillers Co, 12 Torphechen St, Edinburgh EH3 8YT, Scotland
Connelly, Jennifer *Actress*
2637 Ellendale Pl, #16, Los Angeles, CA 90007
Conner, Bart *Gymnast*
PO Box 1013, Norman, OK 73030
Conner, Bruce *Artist*
45 Sussex St, San Francisco, CA 94131
Conner, Dennis *Yachtsman*
2225 Hancock St, #B, San Diego, CA 92110
Conner, Finnis F *Businessman*
%Conner Peripherals, 3081 Zanker Rd, San Jose, CA 95134
Connery, Sean *Actor*
Casa Malibu, Fuente del Rodeo, Noeva Anda Lucia, Malaga, Spain
Connery, Vincent L *Labor Leader*
%National Treasury Employees Union, 1730 "K" St NW, Washington, DC 20006
Connick, Harry, Jr *Pianist*
298 Mulberry St, New York, NY 10012
Connick, Robert E *Chemist*
50 Marguerita Rd, Berkeley, CA 94707
Conniff, Cal *Skier*
157 Pleasantview Ave, Longmeadow, MA 01106
Conniff, Ray *Conductor, Composer*
2154 Hercules Dr, Los Angeles, CA 90046
Connolly, Billy *Actor*
%"Head of the Class" Show, NBC-TV, 4000 Warner Blvd, Burbank, CA 91522
Connolly, David I *Businessman*
%Albertson's Inc, 250 Parkchester Blvd, Boise, ID 83726
Connolly, Eugene B *Businessman*
%USG Corp, 101 S Wacker Dr, Chicago, IL 60606
Connolly, Harold *Track Athlete*
%Santa Monica High School, 601 Pico Blvd, Santa Monica, CA 90405
Connolly, Norma *Actress*
%Agency for Performing Arts, 9000 Sunset Blvd, #1200, Los Angeles, CA 90069
Connolly, Olga *Track Athlete*
11027 Ocean Dr, Culver City, CA 90230
Connor, George *Football Player*
235 E Walton Pl, #5, Chicago, IL 60611
Connor, James P *WW II Army Hero*
6 Ritchie Dr, Bear, DE 19701
Connor, John T *Secretary, Commerce*
1328 Lake Worth Ln, Lost Tree Village, North Palm Beach, FL 33408
Connor, Joseph E *Businessman*
%Price Waterhouse World, 1251 Ave of Americas, New York, NY 10020
Connor, Ralph *Chemist*
9866 Highwood Ct, Sun City, AZ 85373
Connor, Richard L *Publisher*
%Fort Worth Star-Telegram, 400 W 7th St, Fort Worth, TX 76101
Connors, Chuck *Actor*
Star Rt 3-4400, Box 73, Tehachapi, CA 93561
Connors, Jimmy *Tennis Player*
200 S Refugio Rd, Santa Ynez, CA 93406
Connors, Mike *Actor*
4810 Louise Ave, Encino, CA 91316
Conombo, Joseph Issoufou *Prime Minister, Upper Volta*
%Prime Minister's Office, Ouagadougou, Upper Volta
Conover, C Todd *Government Official*
%Edgar Dunn Conover, 1 Market Plz, San Francisco, CA 94111
Conrad, Charles, Jr *Astronaut*
19411 Merion Cir, Huntington Beach, CA 92648
Conrad, John H *Astronaut*
%Hughes Aircraft Space & Communications Grp, Box 92919, Los Angeles, CA 90009

Conrad, Kent *Senator, ND*
%US Senate, Washington, DC 20510
Conrad, Paul *Editorial Cartoonist*
28649 Crestridge Rd, Palos Verdes, CA 90274
Conrad, Robert *Actor*
21355 Pacific Coast Hwy, #200, Malibu, CA 90265
Conrad, William *Actor*
4031 Longridge Ave, Sherman Oaks, CA 91403
Conradt, Judy *Basketball Coach*
%University of Texas, Athletic Dept, Austin, TX 78712
Conroy, Pat *Writer*
%Houghton Mifflin Co, 52 Vanderbilt Ave, New York, NY 10017
Considine, Frank W *Businessman*
%National Can Corp, 8101 Higgins Rd, Chicago, IL 60631
Considine, Tim *Actor*
10328 Viretta Ln, Los Angeles, CA 90077
Constable, George *Editor*
%Time-Life Books, Rockefeller Ctr, New York, NY 10020
Constantine XII *King, Greece*
4 Linnell Dr, Hampstead Way, London NW11, England
Conte, James W *Businessman*
%Community Psychiatric Centers, 2130 E 4th St, Santa Ana, CA 92705
Conte, John *Actor*
75600 Beryl Dr, Indian Wells, CA 92260
Conte, Lansana *President, Guinea*
%President's Office, Conakry, Guinea
Conti, Bill *Composer*
%Bart-Milander Assoc, 4146 Lankershim Blvd, #300, North Hollywood, CA 91602
Conti, Tom *Actor*
%Plant & Froggatt, 4 Windmill St, London W1, England
Contie, Leroy J, Jr *Judge*
%US Court of Appeals, Federal Bldg, 2 S Main St, Akron, OH 44308
Converse-Roberts, William *Actor*
%Triad Artists, 10100 Santa Monica Blvd, #1600, Los Angeles, CA 90067
Conway, Gary *Actor*
2035 Mandeville Canyon Rd, Los Angeles, CA 90049
Conway, Jill K *Historian*
125 Canton Ave, Milton, MA 02186
Conway, Joseph G *Financier*
%NBD Bancorp, 611 Woodward Ave, Detroit, MI 48226
Conway, Stephen J *Financier*
%S J Conway Co, 122 E 55th St, New York, NY 10022
Conway, Tim *Actor*
425 S Beverly Dr, Beverly Hills, CA 91316
Conyers, John, Jr *Representative, MI*
%House of Representatives, Washington, DC 20515
Conzen, W H *Businessman*
%Schering-Plough Corp, 1 Giralda Farms, Madison, NJ 07940
Coobar, Abdulmegid *Prime Minister, Libya*
Asadu El-Furat St 29, Garden City, Tripoli, Libya
Cooder, Ry *Guitarist, Composer*
%Warner Bros Records, 3300 Warner Blvd, Burbank, CA 91505
Coody, Charles *Golfer*
%Professional Golfers Assn, PO Box 109601, Palm Beach Gardens, FL 33410
Cook, Barbara *Actress, Singer*
%Columbia Records, 51 W 52nd St, New York, NY 10019
Cook, Bobby Lee *Attorney*
Riverside Dr, Summerville, GA 30747
Cook, Carole *Comedienne*
8829 Ashcroft, Los Angeles, CA 90048
Cook, Chauncey W W *Businessman*
1116 Challenger St, Lakeway, Austin, TX 78734
Cook, David S *Financier*
%Buckeye Financial Corp, 36 E Gay St, Columbus, OH 43215
Cook, Don *Golfer*
%Professional Golfers Assn, PO Box 109601, Palm Beach Gardens, FL 33410

Cook, Donald C *Businessman*
%Lazard Freres Co, 1 Rockefeller Plz, New York, NY 10020

Cook, Elisha, Jr *Actor*
PO Box 335, Bishop, CA 93514

Cook, Fielder *Television Producer, Director*
%New York Athletic Club, 180 Central Park South, New York, NY 10019

Cook, Frederick H *Businessman*
%Purolator Courier Corp, 131 Morristown Rd, Basking Ridge, NJ 07920

Cook, G Bradford *Stock Exchange Executive*
Woman Lake, Longville, MN 56655

Cook, J Michael *Businessman*
%Deloitte & Touche, 1114 Ave of Americas, New York, NY 10036

Cook, Jane Bancroft *Businesswoman*
%Dow Jones & Co, 22 Cortlandt St, New York, NY 10007

Cook, Jeff *Singer (Alabama)*
%Dale Morris Assoc, 818 19th Ave S, Nashville, TN 37203

Cook, John *Golfer*
1111 Tahquitz E, #121, Palm Springs, CA 92262

Cook, Lodwrick M *Businessman*
%Atlantic Richfield Co, 515 S Flower St, Los Angeles, CA 90071

Cook, Paul M *Businessman*
%Raychem Corp, 300 Constitution Dr, Menlo Park, CA 94025

Cook, Peter *Comedian*
24 Perrine Walk, London NW3, England

Cook, Robert E *Businessman*
%Roper Corp, 1905 W Court St, Kankakee, IL 60901

Cook, Robin *Writer*
%Jonathan Clowes Ltd, 22 Prince Albert Rd, London NW1 7ST, England

Cook, Stanton R *Publisher*
%Tribune Co, 435 N Michigan Ave, Chicago, IL 60611

Cooke, Alistair *Writer, Commentator*
1150 5th Ave, New York, NY 10128

Cooke, Jack Kent *Football Executive*
%Washington Redskins, Box 17247, Dulles Airport, Washington, DC 20041

Cooke, James *Businessman*
Cedarbrook Hill Apartments, Wyncote, PA 19095

Cooke, Janis *Journalist*
%Washington Post, 1150 15th St NW, Washington, DC 20071

Cooke, Lee *Mayor*
%Mayor's Office, City Hall, PO Box 1088, Austin, TX 78767

Cooke, M Todd *Financier*
%Meritor Financial Grp, 1212 Market St, Philadelphia, PA 19107

Cooke, Peter *Financier*
Heathside, Fulmer Way, Gerrards Cross, Bucks, England

Cooks, Johnie *Football Player*
%Cleveland Browns Cleveland Stadium, Cleveland, OH 44114

Cooksey, Dave *Religious Leader*
%Brethren Church, 524 College Ave, Ashland, OH 44805

Cookson, Catherine *Writer*
Bristol Lodge, Langley on Tyne, Northumberland, England

Cookson, John R *Businessman*
%Lever Brothers Co, 390 Park Ave, New York, NY 10022

Cooley, Denton A *Surgeon*
%Texas Heart Institution, 6720 Bertner, Houston, TX 77030

Coolidge, Charles H *WW II Army Hero (CMH)*
1054 Balmoral Dr, Signal Mountain, TN 37377

Coolidge, Harold J *Conservationist*
38 Standley St, Beverly, MA 01915

Coolidge, Martha *Movie Director*
%Kaufman & Bernstein, 1900 Ave of Stars, #2201, Los Angeles, CA 90067

Coolidge, Rita *Singer*
9454 Wilshire Blvd, #206, Beverly Hills, CA 90212

Coombs, Philip H *Economist*
River Rd, Essex, CT 06426

Coon, Carleton S *Anthropologist*
207 Concord St, Gloucester, MA 01930

C

Cooney - Copeland

Cooney, Joan Ganz *Educator, Television Executive*
%Children's TV Workshop, 1 Lincoln Plz, New York, NY 10023

Cooney, Thomas M *Businessman*
%Gibson Greetings Inc, 2100 Section Rd, Cincinnati, OH 45237

Cooper, Alexander *Architect*
%Cooper Robertson & Partners, 311 W 43rd St, New York, NY 10036

Cooper, Alice *Singer, Songwriter*
4135 E Keim Dr, Paradise Valley, AZ 85253

Cooper, Arthur *Editor*
%Gentlemen's Quarterly Magazine, 350 Madison Ave, New York, NY 10017

Cooper, Cecil *Baseball Player*
1431 Misty Bend, Katy, TX 77450

Cooper, Charles Arthur *Economist*
360 N Wilton Rd, New Canaan, CT 06840

Cooper, Charles G *Marine Corps General*
%Marine Corps Headquarters, Washington, DC 20380

Cooper, Christin *Skier*
%General Delivery, Sun Valley, ID 83353

Cooper, Cortz *Religious Leader*
%Presbyterian Church in America, 1852 Century Pl, Atlanta, GA 30345

Cooper, Frederick E *Businessman*
%Flowers Industries, PO Box 1338, Thomasville, GA 31799

Cooper, Hal *Television Director*
2651 Hutton Dr, Beverly Hills, CA 90210

Cooper, Harry *Golfer*
7 Verne Pl, Hartsdale, NY 10530

Cooper, Jackie *Movie Director, Actor*
9621 Royalton Dr, Beverly Hills, CA 90210

Cooper, Jeanne *Actress*
%J Carter Gibson Agency, 9000 Sunset Blvd, #801, Los Angeles, CA 90069

Cooper, Jim *Representative, TN*
%House of Representatives, Washington, DC 20515

Cooper, John *Football Coach*
%Ohio State University, Athletic Dept, Columbus, OH 43210

Cooper, L Gordon, Jr *Astronaut*
5011 Woodley, Encino, CA 91436

Cooper, Leon N *Nobel Physics Laureate*
49 Intervale Rd, Providence, RI 02906

Cooper, Lester I *Television Producer*
45 S Moringside Dr, Westport, CT 06880

Cooper, Michael *Basketball Player, Executive*
%Los Angeles Lakers, Great Western Forum, 3900 W Manchester, Inglewood, CA 90306

Cooper, Ron *Artist*
1310 Main St, Venice, CA 90291

Cooper, Theodore *Businessman*
%Upjohn Co, 7000 Portage Rd, Kalamazoo, MI 49001

Cooper, Wayne *Artist*
126 W 1025 S, Kouts, IN 46347

Cooper, Wayne *Basketball Player*
%Portland Trail Blazers, 700 NE Multnomah St, Portland, OR 97237

Cooper, Wilma Lee *Singer*
%Cooper Enterprises, PO Box 873, Brentwood, TN 37027

Coor, Lattie F *Educator*
%Arizona State University, President's Office, Tempe, AZ 85287

Coors, Jeffrey H *Businessman*
%Adolph Coors Co, 1221 Ford, Golden, CO 80401

Coors, Joseph *Businessman*
%Adolph Coors Co, 1221 Ford, Golden, CO 80401

Coors, William K *Businessman*
%Adolph Coors Co, 1221 Ford, Golden, CO 80401

Cope, Derrike *Auto Racing Driver*
%Bob Whitcomb Racing, 9201 Garrison Rd, Charlotte, NC 28208

Copeland, Al *Powerboat Racing Driver, Businessman*
%Popeye's Famous Fried Chicken, 1333 S Clearview Pkwy, Jefferson, LA 70121

Copeland, Joan *Actress*
%Triad Artists, 10100 Santa Monica Blvd, #1600, Los Angeles, CA 90067

Copeland, Kenneth *Evangelist*
%Kenneth Copeland Ministries, PO Box 961010, Fort Worth, TX 76161

Copeland, Lila *Artist*
31 W 9th St, New York, NY 10011

Copley, Helen K *Publisher*
7776 Ivanhoe Ave, La Jolla, CA 92037

Copperfield, David *Illusionist*
11777 San Vicente Blvd, #601, Los Angeles, CA 90049

Coppola, Francis Ford *Movie Director*
%Zoetrope Studios, 916 Kearny St, San Francisco, CA 94133

Corbally, John E *Educator*
2209 S Vine, Urbana, IL 61801

Corbett, Glenn *Actor*
%Dade/Rosen/Schultz Agency, 11846 Ventura Blvd, #100, Studio City, CA 91403

Corbett, Gretchen *Actress*
%Harry Gold Assoc, 3500 W Olive Ave, #1400, Burbank, CA 91505

Corbett, Mike *Rock Climber*
PO Box 917, Yosemite National Park, CA 95389

Corbett, Ronnie *Comedian*
57 Great Cumberland Pl, London W1H 7LJ, England

Corbin, Barry *Actor*
%Writers & Artists Agency, 11726 San Vicente Blvd, #300, Los Angeles, CA 90049

Corbin, Tyrone *Basketball Player*
%Utah Jazz, 5 Triad Center, Salt Lake City, UT 84180

Corbus, William *Football Player*
1100 Union St, #1100, San Francisco, CA 94109

Corby, Ellen *Actress*
9024 Harratt St, Los Angeles, CA 90069

Corcoran, Kevin *Actor*
8617 Balcom Ave, Northridge, CA 91325

Corcoran, Tom *Representative, IL*
RFD 2, Ottawa, IL 61350

Cord, Alex *Actor*
%Stone Manners Agency, 9113 Sunset Blvd, Los Angeles, CA 90069

Corday, Barbara *Entertainment Executive*
%Columbia Pictures Television, Columbia Plz N, #410, Burbank, CA 91505

Cordeiro, Joseph Cardinal *Religious Leader*
St Patrick's Cathedral, Karachi 3, Pakistan

Cordell, Joe B *Businessman*
%Jim Walter Corp, 1500 N Dale Mabry Hwy, Tampa, FL 33607

Cordero, Angel *Thoroughbred Racing Jockey*
%New York Racing Assn, PO Box 90, Jamaica, NY 11417

Cordes, Edward J *Businessman*
%Ralston Purina Co, Checkerboard Sq, St Louis, MO 63164

Corea, Chick *Jazz Pianist, Composer*
2635 Griffith Park Blvd, Los Angeles, CA 90039

Corelli, Franco *Opera Singer*
%S A Gorlinsky Ltd, 35 Dover St, London W1X 4NJ, England

Corey, Elias James *Nobel Chemistry Laureate*
20 Avon Hill St, Cambridge, MA 02140

Corey, Jeff *Actor*
29445 Bluewater Rd, Malibu, CA 90265

Corey, Professor Irwin *Comedian*
58 Nassau Dr, Great Neck, NY 11022

Corfield, Kenneth *Businessman*
%Standard Telephone & Cables, 190 Strand, London WC2B 1DU, England

Corkle, Francesa *Ballerina*
%Pittsburgh Ballet Theatre, 244 Blvd of Allies, Pittsburgh, PA 15222

Corley, Al *Actor*
%Triad Artists, 10100 Santa Monica Blvd, #1600, Los Angeles, CA 90067

Corley, Pat *Actor*
%Agency for Performing Arts, 9000 Sunset Blvd, #1200, Los Angeles, CA 90069

Cormack, Allan MacLeod *Nobel Medicine Laureate*
18 Harrison St, Winchester, MA 08190

Corman, Avery *Writer*
%International Creative Mgmt, 40 W 57th St, New York, NY 10019

C

Corman, Roger *Movie Director, Producer*
2501 La Mesa Dr, Pacific Palisades, CA 90402

Corn, Alfred *Poet*
1806 Yale Station, New Haven, CT 06520

Corneille (Cornelius Van Beverloo) *Artist*
%Society of Independent Artists, Cours la Reine, 75008 Paris, France

Cornelius, Don *Television Producer*
12685 Mulholland Dr, Beverly Hills, CA 90210

Cornelius, Helen *Singer, Songwriter*
PO Box 121321, Nashville, TN 37212

Cornelius, William E *Businessman*
%Union Electric Co, 1901 Gratiot St, St Louis, MO 63103

Cornell, Don *Singer*
PO Box C, River Edge, NJ 07661

Cornell, Harry M, Jr *Businessman*
%Leggett & Platt Inc, 1 Leggett Rd, Carthage, MO 64836

Cornell, John P *Businessman*
%Columbia Gas System, 20 Montchanin Rd, Wilmington, DE 19807

Cornell, Lydia *Actress*
142 S Bedford Dr, Beverly Hills, CA 90212

Cornelsen, Rufus *Religious Leader*
415 S Chester Rd, Swarthmore, PA 19102

Corness, Colin R *Businessman*
%Redland, Redland House, Reigate, Surrey RH2 0SJ, England

Cornfeld, Bernard *Businessman*
%Better Living Enterprises, 1100 Carolyn Way, Beverly Hills, CA 90210

Cornforth, John W *Nobel Chemistry Laureate*
Saxon Down, Cuilfail, Lewes, East Sussex BN7 2BE, England

Corns, Johnnie H *Army General*
Commanding General, US Army Pacific, Fort Shafter, HI 96858

Cornthwaite, Robert *Actor*
11656 Jacaranda Ave, Hesperia, CA 92345

Corr, D Joseph *Businessman*
%Continental Airlines, LA International Airport, Los Angeles, CA 90009

Corrada Del Rio, Baltasar *Representative, PR*
%House of Representatives, Washington, DC 20515

Correa, Charles M *Architect*
Sonmarg, Napean Sea Rd, Bombay 40006, India

Corrick, Ann Marjorie *Journalist*
3050 Dover Dr, #56, Santa Cruz, CA 95065

Corrigan, Douglas (Wrong Way) *Aviator*
2828 N Flower, Santa Ana, CA 92706

Corrigan, E Gerald *Government Official, Financier*
%Federal Reserve Bank of New York, 33 Liberty St, New York, NY 10005

Corrigan, Mairead *Nobel Peace Laureate*
%Peace People Community, 224 Lisburn Rd, Belfast BT9 6GE, North Ireland

Corrigan, Wilfred J *Businessman*
%LSI Logic, 1551 McCarthy Blvd, Milpitas, CA 95035

Corripio Ahumada, Ernesto Cardinal *Religious Leader*
Apartado Postal 24-433, Mexico 7 DF, Mexico

Corrock-Luby, Susie *Skier*
PO Box 424, Edwards, CO 81632

Corry, Charles A *Businessman*
%USX Corp, 600 Grant St, Pittsburgh, PA 15230

Corry, Lawrence L *Businessman*
%Amagamated Sugar Co, First Security Bank Bldg, Ogden, UT 84401

Corsaro, Frank A *Theater, Opera Director*
33 Riverside Dr, New York, NY 10023

Corson, Dale R *Physicist, Educator*
122 Northview Rd, Ithaca, NY 14850

Corson, Fred P *Religious Leader*
Cornwall Manor, Cornwall, PA 17016

Corson, Shayne *Hockey Player*
%Montreal Canadiens, 2313 St Catherine St W, Montreal PQ H3H 1N2, Canada

Corson, Thomas H *Businessman*
%Coachman Industries, 601 E Beardsley Ave, Elkhart, IN 46515

Cortese, Joseph *Actor*
%Artists Agency, 10100 Santa Monica Blvd, #305, Los Angeles, CA 90067
Cortese, Valentina *Actress*
Piazza S Erasnio 9, 20121 Milan, Italy
Cortright, Edgar M, Jr *Aerospace Engineer*
9701 Calvin St, Northridge, CA 91324
Corwin, Norman *Writer*
1840 Fairburn Ave, #302, Los Angeles, CA 90025
Coryell, Larry *Musician*
%International Creative Mgmt, 8899 Beverly Blvd, Los Angeles, CA 90048
Corzine, Dave *Basketball Player*
%Orlando Magic, Box 76, 1 Dupont Cir, Orlando, FL 60611
Cosby, Bill *Comedian, Actor*
1500 Sorrento Dr, Pacific Palisades, CA 90272
Cosell, Howard *Sportscaster*
150 E 69th St, New York, NY 10021
Cosgrave, Liam *Prime Minister, Ireland*
Beachpark, Templeogue County, Dublin, Ireland
Coslet, Bruce *Football Coach*
%New York Jets, 598 Madison Ave, New York, NY 10022
Coss, Kenneth L *Labor Leader*
%United Rubber Cork Linoleum Plastics Workers, 87 S High St, Akron, OH 44308
Cossiga, Francesco *President, Italy*
%President's Office, Rome, Italy
Cossotto, Fiorenza *Opera Singer*
%Columbia Artists Mgmt Inc, 165 W 57th St, New York, NY 10019
Costa, Manuel Pinto da *Prime Minister, Sao Tome and Principe*
%Prime Minister's Office, Sao Tome, Sao Tome & Principe
Costa, Mary *Opera Singer*
1182 Market St, #418, San Francisco, CA 94102
Costa-Gavras, Contantin *Movie Director*
%Artmedia, 10 Ave George V, 75008 Paris, France
Costanza, Margaret (Midge) *Government Official*
4518 Agnes Ave, Studio City, CA 91607
Costanzo, Henry J *Financier*
414 N Lee St, Alexandria, VA 22314
Costas, Bob *Sportscaster*
%NBC-Sports, 30 Rockefeller Plz, New York, NY 10020
Costello, Billy *Boxer*
15 Laura Dr, New Paultz, NY 12561
Costello, Elvis *Singer*
%Associated Talent International, 888 7th Ave, New York, NY 10106
Costello, John D *Coast Guard Admiral*
%Coast Guard Headquarters Pacific, Coast Guard Island, Alameda, CA 94501
Costello, Larry *Basketball Player, Coach*
%Utica College, Athletic Dept, Utica, NY 13502
Costello, Mariclare *Actress*
%Twentieth Century Artists, 3800 Barham Blvd, Los Angeles, CA 90068
Coster, Nicolas *Actor*
%STE Representation, 9301 Wilshire Blvd, #312, Beverly Hills, CA 90210
Costie Burke, Candy *Synchronized Swimmer*
5732 NE 190th, Seattle, WA 98155
Costle, Douglas M *Government Official, Educator*
%Harvard University, Public Health School, Cambridge, MA 02138
Costner, Kevin *Actor*
%Creative Artists Agency, 9830 Wilshire Blvd, Beverly Hills, CA 90212
Cotchett, Joseph W *Attorney*
840 Malcolm Rd, Burlingame, CA 94010
Cotlow, Lewis Nathaniel *Explorer*
132 Lakeshore Dr, North Palm Beach, FL 33408
Cotrubas, Ileana *Opera Singer*
%Royal Opera House, Covent Grdn, London WC2, England
Cotsworth, Stats *Actor*
360 E 55th St, New York, NY 10022
Cottee, Kay *Sailor*
%Showcase Productions, 113 Willoughby Rd, Crows Nest NSW 2065, Australia

Cotten, Joseph *Actor*
1993 Mesa Dr, Palm Springs, CA 92264

Cotting, James C *Businessman*
%International Harvester Co, 401 N Michigan Ave, Chicago, IL 60611

Cotton, Frank A *Chemist*
Twaycliffe Ranch, Rt 2, Box 230, Bryan, TX 77801

Cotton, James *Singer*
3204 N Wilton Ave, Chicago, IL 60657

Cotton, Marcus *Football Player*
%Seattle Seahawks, 11220 NE 53rd St, Kirkland, WA 98033

Cottrell, Donald P *Educator*
6671 Olentangy River Rd, Worthington, OH 43085

Cottrell, Ralph *Relgious Leader*
%Baptist Missionary Assn, PO Box 1203, Van, TX 75790

Couch, John C *Businessman*
%Alexander & Baldwin Inc, 822 Bishop St, Honolulu, HI 96801

Couch, John N *Botanist*
1109 Caroll Woods, Chapel Hills, NC 27514

Couch, Richard S *Test Pilot*
%B-2 Stealth Bomber Program, USAF Plant 42, Edwards Air Force Base, CA 93523

Coughlan, Robert *Writer, Journalist*
Madison St, Sag Harbor, NY 11963

Coughlin, Bernard J *Educator*
%Gonzaga University, President's Office, Spokane, WA 99258

Coughlin, Lawrence *Representative, PA*
%House of Representatives, Washington, DC 20515

Coulson, William L *Financier*
%Home Federal Savings & Loan, 707 Broadway, San Diego, CA 92101

Coulter, Arthur E *Hockey Player*
10600 SW 128th St, Miami, FL 33176

Counsilman, James E *Swimming Coach*
3806 Cameron Ave, Bloomington, IN 47401

Couples, Fred *Golfer*
13198 Forest Hill Blvd, West Palm Beach, FL 33414

Couric, Katie *Commentator*
%NBC-TV, News Dept, 30 Rockefeller Plz, New York, NY 10020

Courier, Jim *Tennis Player*
%Assn of Tennis Professionals, 200 Tournament Players Rd, Ponte Vedra, FL 32082

Courlouris, George *Actor*
Chestnut Cottage, Vale of Heath, Hampstead, London NW3, England

Cournoyer, Yvan *Hockey Player*
%Brasserie 12, 625 32nd St, Lachine PQ H8T 3G6, Canada

Courreges, Andre *Fashion Designer*
27 Rue Delabordere, 92 Neuilly-Sur-Seine, France

Court, Hazel *Actress*
%Taylor, 1111 San Vicente Blvd, Santa Monica, CA 90402

Courtenay, Margaret *Actress*
16 Brookfield Rd, London W4, England

Courtenay, Tom *Actor*
%International Creative Mgmt, 388/396 Oxford St, London W1, England

Courter, James A *Representative, NJ*
19 Reese Ave, Hackettstown, NJ 07840

Courtney, Jacqueline *Actress*
%ABC-TV, 1330 Ave of Americas, New York, NY 10019

Courtney, Tom *Track Athlete*
Pink House Rd, Sewickley Heights, PA 15143

Cousin, Philip R *Religious Leader*
%National Council of Churches, 475 Riverside Dr, New York, NY 10115

Cousins, Ralph W *Navy Admiral*
Leconfield House, Curzon St, London W1Y 8JR, England

Cousins, Robin *Figure Skater*
%Blue Jay Ice Castle, 27307 Hwy 189, Blue Jay, CA 92317

Cousteau, Jacques-Yves *Oceanographer*
Musee Oceanografique, Ave Saint-Martin, Monaco-Ville MC, Monaco

Cousteau, Jean-Michel *Oceanographer*
%Cousteau Society, 930 W 21st St, Norfolk, VA 23517

Cousy, Bob *Basketball Player*
459 Salisbury St, Worcester, MA 01609

Couve de Murville, Maurice *Prime Minister, France*
44 Rue Du Bac, 75007 Paris, France

Cover, Franklin *Actor*
%Writers & Artists Agency, 11726 San Vicente Blvd, #300, Los Angeles, CA 90049

Coverly, Dave *Editorial Cartoonist*
%Bloomington Herald-Times, 1900 S Walnut, Bloomington, IN 47402

Covert, Jimbo *Football Player*
%Chicago Bears, 250 N Washington Rd, Lake Forest, IL 60045

Covey, Richard O *Astronaut*
%NASA, Johnson Space Ctr, Houston, TX 77058

Cowan, Warren *Businessman*
%Rodgers & Cowan, 10000 Santa Monica Blvd, #400, Los Angeles, CA 90067

Cowen, Donna *Actress, Dancer*
340 S Ocean Blvd, Palm Beach, FL 33480

Cowen, Robert E *Judge*
%US Court of Appeals, 402 E State St, Trenton, NJ 08608

Cowen, Wilson *Judge*
%US Court of Appeals, 717 Madison Pl NW, Washington, DC 20439

Cowens, Al *Baseball Player*
5723 Keniston Ave, Los Angeles, CA 90043

Cowens, Dave *Basketball Player*
Dave Cowens Basketball School, 433 Grove St, Needham, MA 02192

Cowhill, William Joseph *Navy Admiral*
1336 Elsinore Ave, McLean, VA 22102

Cowley, William M *Hockey Player*
75 Sunnyside St, Ottawa ON, Canada

Cowper, Steve *Governor, AK*
%Governor's Office, State Capitol, Juneau, AK 99811

Cox, Allan V *Geophysicist*
%Stanford University, Earth Sciences School, Stanford, CA 94305

Cox, Archibald *Attorney, Government Official*
%Harvard University, School of Law, Cambridge, MA 02138

Cox, Charles C *Government Official*
%Securities & Exchange Commission, 450 5th St NW, Washington, DC 20549

Cox, Christopher *Representative, CA*
%House of Representatives, Washington, DC 20515

Cox, Courteney *Actress*
88156 Appian Way, Los Angeles, CA 90046

Cox, Danny *Baseball Manager*
306 Feagin Mill Rd, Warner Robbins, GA 31093

Cox, Edwin L, Jr *Businessman*
%Swift Independent Corp, 115 W Jackson Blvd, Chicago, IL 60604

Cox, Emmett R *Judge*
%US Court of Appeals, 113 St Joseph St, Mobile, AL 36602

Cox, G David *Religious Leader*
%Church of God, Box 2420, Anderson, IN 46018

Cox, Harvey G, Jr *Educator, Theologian*
%Harvard University, Divinity School, Cambridge, MA 02140

Cox, John W *Navy Admiral, Physician*
%Surgeon General's Office, Navy Department, Washington, DC 20372

Cox, John W, Jr *Representative, IL*
%House of Representatives, Washington, DC 20515

Cox, Lester L *Businessman*
%Ozark Holdings Inc, Lambert Field, St Louis, MO 63145

Cox, Lynne *Distance Swimmer*
%Advanced Sport Research, 4141 Ball Rd, #142, Cypress, CA 90630

Cox, Mark *Tennis Player*
The Oaks, Ashtead Woods Rd, Astead, Surrey KT21 2ER, England

Cox, Ronny *Actor*
%International Creative Mgmt, 8899 Beverly Blvd, Los Angeles, CA 90048

Coyer, Frank P, Jr *Businessman*
%Fruehauf Corp, 10900 Harper Ave, Detroit, MI 48213

Coyne, William J *Representative, PA*
%House of Representatives, Washington, DC 20515

C

Coyote – Crane

Coyote, Peter *Actor*
%International Creative Mgmt, 8899 Beverly Blvd, Los Angeles, CA 90048

Cozad, James W *Businessman*
%Whitman Corp, 111 E Wacker, Chicago, IL 60601

Cozzarelli, Nicholas *Biologist*
%University of California, Biology Dept, Berkeley, CA 94720

Crable, Bob *Football Player*
%New York Jets, 598 Madison Ave, New York, NY 10022

Craddock, Billy (Crash) *Singer*
3198 Royal Ln, #205, Dallas, TX 75229

Craft, Christine *Commentator*
%KRBK-TV, News Dept, 500 Media Pl, Sacramento, CA 95815

Craft, Clarence B *WW II Army Hero (CMH)*
902 W 12th St, Fayetteville, AR 72701

Craft, Robert *Conductor*
%Alfred Knopf, 201 E 50th St, New York, NY 10022

Cragun, Richard *Ballet Dancer*
%Stuttgart Ballet, Stuttgart, Germany

Craig, Eugene W *Editorial Cartoonist*
73 E Kramer St Canal, Winchester, OH 43110

Craig, George N *Governor, IN*
524 N Meridian St, Brazil, IN 47834

Craig, Helen *Actress*
%Beal, 205 W 54th St, New York, NY 10019

Craig, Jenny *Nutritionist*
445 Marine View Dr, #300, Del Mar, CA 92014

Craig, Jim *Hockey Player*
36 N Main St, North Easton, MA 02156

Craig, Larry E *Senator, ID*
%General Delivery, Midvale, ID 83645

Craig, Roger *Football Player*
2453 Canora Ave, Alpine, CA 92331

Craig, Roger L *Baseball Player, Manager*
26658 San Felipe Ave, Warner Springs, GA 92086

Craig, Yvonne *Actress*
1221 Ocean Ave, #202, Santa Monica, CA 90401

Craighead, Frank C, Jr *Ecologist*
%Craighead Environmental Research Institute, Box 156, Moose, WY 83012

Crain, Jeanne *Actress*
354 Hilgard Ave, Los Angeles, CA 90024

Crain, Keith E *Publisher*
%Crain Communications, 1400 Woodbridge Ave, Detroit, MI 48207

Crain, Rance *Publisher*
%Crain Communications, 740 N Rush St, Chicago, IL 60611

Cram, Donald J *Nobel Chemistry Laureate*
1250 Roscomare Rd, Los Angeles, CA 90024

Cram, Steve *Track Athlete*
%General Delivery, Jarrow, England

Cramer, Bud *Representative, AL*
%House of Representatives, Washington, DC 20515

Cramer, Floyd *Pianist*
110 Glancy St, #201, Goodlettsville, TN 37072

Cramer, Grant *Actor*
%Harry Gold Assoc, 3500 W Olive Ave, #1400, Burbank, CA 91505

Cramer, Richard Ben *Journalist*
%Philadelphia Inquirer, 400 N Broad St, Philadelphia, PA 19101

Crampton, Bruce *Golfer*
7107 Spanky Branch Dr, Dallas, TX 75248

Crandall, Del *Baseball Player*
25 Rock Cliff Pl, Pomona, CA 91766

Crandall, Robert L *Businessman*
%AMR Corp, PO Box 619616, Dallas-Fort Worth Airport, TX 75261

Crane, Daniel B *Representative, IL*
%House of Representatives, Washington, DC 20515

Crane, Edward J *Businessman*
%Ozark Holdings Inc, Lambert Field, St Louis, MO 63145

Crane, Horace Richard *Physicist*
830 Avon Rd, Ann Arbor, MI 48104

Crane, Irving *Pocket Billiards Player*
270 Yarmouth Rd, Rochester, NY 14610

Crane, Keith *Businessman*
%Colgate-Palmolive Co, 300 Park Ave, New York, NY 10022

Crane, L Stanley *Businessman*
%Consolidated Rail Corp, 6 Penn Center Plz, Philadelphia, PA 19104

Crane, Les *Radio Entertainer*
424 S Rexford Dr, Beverly Hills, CA 90212

Crane, Philip M *Representative, IL*
307 Manawa Trl, Mount Prospect, IL 60056

Cranston, Alan *Senator, CA*
2024 Camden Ave, Los Angeles, CA 90025

Craven, Wes *Movie Director*
%Wes Craven Films, 10000 W Washington Blvd, #3011, Culver City, CA 90232

Crawford, Bruce *Opera Official*
%Metropolitan Opera Assn, Lincoln Center Plz, New York, NY 10023

Crawford, Bryce, Jr *Chemist*
1545 Branston St, St Paul, MN 55108

Crawford, Cindy *Model*
%Elite Model Mgmt, 111 E 22nd St, New York, NY 10010

Crawford, Frederick C *Businessman*
PO Box 17036, Cleveland, OH 44117

Crawford, John *Actor*
%Twentieth Century Artists, 3518 W Cahuenga Blvd, Los Angeles, CA 90068

Crawford, Michael *Actor*
%Chatto & Linnit Ltd, Globe Theatre, Shaftesbury Ave, London W1, England

Crawford, Shag (Henry C) *Baseball Umpire*
1530 Virginia Ave, Havertown, PA 19083

Crawford, William A *Diplomat*
4402 Boxwood Rd, Bethesda, MD 20816

Crawford, William J *WW II Army Hero (CMH)*
Box 4, Palmer Lake, CO 80133

Crawley, John B *Publisher*
%Outdoor Life Magazine, 380 Madison Ave, New York, NY 10017

Craxi, Bettino *Prime Minister, Italy*
Via Foppo 5, 20144 Milan, Italy

Cray, Robert *Singer*
%Rosebud Agency, PO Box 170429, San Francisco, CA 94117

Cray, Seymour R *Computer Engineer*
%Cray Computer Co, 1110 Bayfield Dr, Colorado Springs, CO 80906

Creach, Pappa John *Violinist*
%Sy'kian, 1122 S La Jolla Ave, Los Angeles, CA 90035

Crean, John C *Businessman*
%Fleetwood Enterprises, 3125 Myers St, Riverside, CA 92523

Crecine, John P *Educator*
%Georgia Institute of Technology, President's Office, Atlanta, GA 30602

Creedon, John J *Businessman*
%Metropolitan Life Insurance, 1 Madison Ave, New York, NY 10010

Creekmur, Lou *Football Player*
%Ryder Truck Rental Inc, 3600 NW 82nd Ave, Miami, FL 33166

Creeley, Robert W *Writer*
Back Cottage 2, 388 Summer St, Buffalo, NY 14213

Creighton, J D *Publisher*
%Toronto Sun, 333 King St E, Toronto ON M5A 3X5, Canada

Creighton, John O *Astronaut*
%NASA, Johnson Space Ctr, Houston, TX 77058

Creighton, John W, Jr *Businessman*
%Weyerhaeuser Co, 33663 32nd Ave S, Tacoma, WA 98003

Crenna, Richard *Actor*
3941 Valley Meadow Rd, Encino, CA 91436

Crenshaw, Ben *Golfer*
%US Golf Assn, Liberty Corners Rd, Far Hills, NJ 07931

Crenshaw, Gordon L *Businessman*
%Universal Leaf Tobacco Co, Hamilton & Broad, Richmond, VA 23230

C

Creson – Cronenberg

Creson, William T *Businessman*
%Crown Zellerbach Corp, 1 Bush St, San Francisco, CA 94104

Crespin, Regine *Opera Singer*
%Michel Glotz, 141 Blvd Saint-Michel, 75005 Paris, France

Creswell, Isaiah T *Educator*
910 17th Ave N, Nashville, TN 37208

Crewdson, John M *Journalist*
%Chicago Tribune, 435 N Michigan Ave, Chicago, IL 60611

Crewe, Albert V *Physicist*
63 Old Creek Rd, Palos Park, IL 60464

Crews, David *Psychobiologist*
%University of Texas, Zoology Dept, Austin, TX 78712

Crews, Harry *Writer*
1800 NW 8th Ave, Gainesville, FL 32601

Crews, John R *WW II Army Hero (CMH)*
1324 SW 54th St, Oklahoma City, OK 73119

Crews, Phillip *Chemist*
%University of California, Chemistry Dept, Santa Cruz, CA 99504

Crichton, Charles *Actor*
%Max Naughton Lowe, 200 Fulham Rd, London SW10 9PN, England

Crichton, Michael *Writer*
2210 Wilshire Blvd, #433, Santa Monica, CA 90403

Crick, Francis H C *Nobel Chemistry Laureate*
1792 Colgate Dr, La Jolla, CA 92037

Crier, Catherine *Commentator*
%Cable News Network, News Dept, 1 CNN Center, PO Box 105366, Atlanta, GA 30348

Crim, Jack C *Businessman*
%Talley Industries, 2702 N 44th St, Phoenix, AZ 85008

Crimmins, Alfred S *Businessman*
%Collins & Aikman Corp, 210 Madison Ave, New York, NY 10016

Crimmins, Bobby *Basketball Coach*
%Georgia Insititute of Technology, Athletic Dept, Atlanta, GA 30332

Crinkley, Richmond *Television, Theater Producer*
59 W 71st St, New York, NY 10023

Crippen, Robert L *Astronaut*
%NASA Headquarters, Code M, Washington, DC 20249

Criqui, Don *Sportscaster*
%NBC-TV, Sports Dept, 30 Rockefeller Plz, New York, NY 10020

Criss, Peter *Singer*
%Aucoin, 645 Madison Ave, New York, NY 10022

Crist, George B *Marine Corps General*
%CBS-TV, News Dept, 51 W 52nd St, New York, NY 10019

Crist, Judith *Journalist*
180 Riverside Dr, New York, NY 10024

Cristal, Linda *Actress*
9129 Hazen Dr, Beverly Hills, CA 90210

Cristiani, Alfredo *President, El Salvador*
%President's Office, Casa Presidencial, San Salvador, El Salvador

Cristofer, Michael *Playwright*
%William Morris Agency, 1350 Ave of Americas, New York, NY 10019

Cristol, Stanley J *Chemist*
2918 3rd St, Boulder, CO 80302

Critchfield, Charles L *Physicist*
391 El Conejo, Los Alamos, NM 87544

Critchfield, Richard P *Writer, Journalist*
%Peggy Trimble, Washington Star, 225 Virginia Ave SE, Washington, DC 20061

Crockett, Bruce L *Businessman*
%Communications Satellite Corp, 950 L'Enfant Plz SW, Washington, DC 20024

Cromwell, James *Actor*
%Century Artists, 9744 Wilshire Blvd, #308, Beverly Hills, CA 90212

Cromwell, Nolan *Football Player, Coach*
%Green Bay Packers, 1265 Lombardi Ave, Green Bay, WI 54307

Cronbach, Lee J *Educator, Psychologist*
16 Laburnum, Atherton, CA 94025

Cronenberg, David *Movie Director*
%David Cronenberg Productions, 217 Avenue Rd, Toronton ON M5R 2J3, Canada

Cronenweth, Jordan *Cinematographer*
2276 S Beverly Glen Blvd, #306, Los Angeles, CA 90064

Croner, Richard *Businessman*
%Agway Inc, PO Box 4933, Syracuse, NY 13221

Cronin, Gilbert F *Businessman*
%Transamerica Life Insurance, 1150 S Olive, Los Angeles, CA 90015

Cronin, James A, III *Businessman*
%Tiger International, 1888 Century Park East, Los Angeles, CA 90067

Cronin, James W *Nobel Physics Laureate*
1445 E 56th St, Chicago, IL 60637

Cronin, Paul William *Representative, MA*
8 Punchard Ave, Andover, MA 01810

Cronk, William F, III *Businessman*
%Dreyer's Grand Ice Cream, 5929 College Ave, Oakland, CA 94618

Cronkite, Kathy *Actress*
%DMI, 250 W 57th St, New York, NY 10107

Cronkite, Walter *Commentator*
519 E 84th St, New York, NY 10028

Cronym, Hume *Actor*
%Martha Luttrell, 8898 Beverly Blvd, Los Angeles, CA 90048

Crook, Edward *Boxer*
4512 Moline Ave, Columbus, GA 92629

Croom, John H *Businessman*
%Columbia Gas System, 20 Montchanin Rd, Wilmington, DE 19807

Cropper, William A *Businessman*
%Houston Industries, 611 Walker Ave, Houston, TX 77002

Crosbie, John *Political Leader, Canada*
PO Box 9192, Station B, St John's ND A1A 2X9, Canada

Crosby, Bob *Orchestra Leader*
939 Coast Blvd, La Jolla, CA 90237

Crosby, Cathy Lee *Actress*
10488 Eastborne Ave, #308, Los Angeles, CA 90024

Crosby, Gordon E, Jr *Businessman*
%USLife Corp, 125 Maiden Ln, New York, NY 10038

Crosby, James M *Businessman*
%Resorts International, 915 NE 125th St, North Miami, FL 33161

Crosby, John O *Conductor*
%Santa Fe Opera, PO Box 2408, Santa Fe, NM 87504

Crosby, Kathryn *Actress*
400 S Burnside Ave, #12-H, Los Angeles, CA 90036

Crosby, Mary *Actress*
2875 S Barrymore Dr, Malibu, CA 90265

Crosby, Norm *Comedian*
%Shefrin Co, PO Box 48559, Los Angeles, CA 90048

Crosby, Phil *Actor*
21801 Providencia St, Woodland Hills, CA 91364

Crosby, Philip B *Management Consultant*
1711 Barcelona Way, Winter Park, FL 32789

Crosetti, Frank *Baseball Player*
65 W Monterey Ave, Stockton, CA 95204

Cross, Amanda (Carolyn Heilbrun) *Writer*
%Columbia University, English Dept, New York, NY 10027

Cross, Ben *Actor*
29 Burlington Grdns, London W4, England

Cross, Burton *Governor, ME*
934 Riverside Dr, Augusta, ME 04330

Cross, Christopher *Singer*
%Reprise Records, Warner Bros, 75 Rockefeller Plz, New York, NY 10019

Cross, Randy *Football Player, Sportscaster*
%CBS-TV, Sports Dept, 51 W 52nd St, New York, NY 10019

Cross, Richard Eugene *Businessman*
%American Motors Corp, 400 Renaissance Ctr, #1900, Detroit, MI 48243

Crossen, Frank M *Businessman*
%Centex Corp, 4600 RepublicBank Tower, Dallas, TX 75201

Crossfield, Scott *Test Pilot*
12100 Thoroughbred Rd, Herndon, VA 22071

Crouch, Helen B *Educator*
%Literacy Volunteers of America, 404 Oak St, Syracuse, NY 13203

Crouch, Paul *Evangelist*
%Trinity Broadcasting Network, PO Box A, Santa Ana, CA 92711

Crough, Daniel F *Businessman*
%Colonial Penn Grp, 5 Penn Center Plz, Philadelphia, PA 19181

Crouse, Lindsay *Actress*
%Marion Rosenberg, 8428 Melrose Pl, #C, Los Angeles, CA 90069

Crow, Harlan R *Businessman*
%Trammel Crow Co, 2001 Bryan St, Dallas, TX 75201

Crow, James F *Geneticist*
24 Glenway, Madison, WI 53706

Crow, John David *Football Player, Coach*
%Texas A&M University, Athletic Dept, College Station, TX 77843

Crow, Marvin B *Businessman*
%J P Stevens & Co, 1185 Ave of Americas, New York, NY 10036

Crow, Trammell *Businessman*
%Trammell Crow Co, 2001 Ross Ave, #3500, Dallas, TX 75201

Crowe, Jack *Football Coach*
%University of Arkansas, Broyles Athletic Complex, Fayetteville, AR 72701

Crowe, William J, Jr *Navy Admiral*
%University of Oklahoma, Political Science Dept, Norman, OK 73069

Crowell, Rodney *Singer, Songwriter*
PO Box 120576, Nashville, TN 37212

Crowley, Joseph N *Educator*
%University of Nevada, President's Office, Reno, NV 89557

Crowley, Mart *Playwright*
8955 Beverly Blvd, Los Angeles, CA 90048

Crowley, Pat *Actress*
%Light Co, 901 Bringham Ave, Los Angeles, CA 90049

Crown, David Allan *Criminologist*
3103 Jessie Ct, Fairfax, VA 22030

Crown, Lester *Businessman*
%Henry Crown & Co, 300 W Washington St, Chicago, IL 60606

Crowson, Richard *Editorial Cartoonist*
%Wichita Eagle-Beacon, 825 E Douglas, Wichita, KS 67202

Cruickshank, John A *WW II Royal Air Force Hero (VC)*
34 Frogston Rd W, Edinburgh EH10 7AJ, Scotland

Cruikshank, Thomas H *Businessman*
%Halliburton Co, 2600 Southland Ctr, Dallas, TX 75201

Cruise, Tom *Actor*
%Creative Artists Agency, 9830 Wilshire Blvd, Beverly Hills, CA 90212

Crull, Tim F *Businessman*
%Carnation Co, 5045 Wilshire Blvd, Los Angeles, CA 90036

Crum, Denny *Basketball Coach*
%University of Louisville, Athletic Dept, Louisville, KY 40292

Crumb, George *Composer*
240 Kirk Ln, Media, PA 19063

Crumb, Robert *Cartoonist (Keep on Trucking)*
8 Russell St, Winters, CA 95694

Crumley, James R, Jr *Religious Leader*
%Lutheran Church, 231 Madison Ave, New York, NY 10016

Crumpacker, Shephard J, Jr *Representative, IN; Judge*
1925 Ribourde Dr, South Bend, IN 46628

Crutcher, Lawrence M *Publisher*
%Book-of-the-Month Club, Rockefeller Ctr, New York, NY 10020

Crutchfield, Edward E, Jr *Financier*
%First Union National Bank, Jefferson-First Union Tower, Charlotte, NC 28288

Crutchfield, Jimmy *Baseball Player*
3420 Cottage Grove Ave, Chicago, IL 60616

Crutsinger, Robert K *Businessman*
%Wetterau Inc, 8920 Pershall Rd, Hazelwood, MO 63042

Crutzen, Paul *Chemist*
%Mainz Institute, Mainz, Germany

Cruz, Celia *Singer*
PO Box P-11007, Cambria Heights, NY 11411

Cruz, Jose *Baseball Player*
B-15 Jardines Lafayette, Arroyo, PR 00615
Cruz-Romo, Gilda *Opera Singer*
397 Warwick Ave, Teaneck, NJ 07666
Cryer, Jon *Actor*
%United Talent, 9560 Wilshire Blvd, #500, Beverly Hills, CA 90212
Crysel, James W *Army General*
Commanding General, 2nd US Army, Fort Gillem, GA 30050
Crystal, Ronald G *Molecular Biologist (Cystic Fibrosis)*
%National Heart Lung Blood Institute, 9000 Rockville Pike, Bethesda, MD 20892
Csikszentmihalyi, Mihaly *Psychologist*
%University of Chicago, Psychology Dept, Chicago, IL 60637
Csonka, Larry *Football Player*
37256 Hunter Camp Rd, Lisbon, OH 44128
Ctvrtlik, Bob *Volleyball Player*
%US Volleyball Assn, 1750 E Boulder, Colorado Springs, CO 80909
Cuccinello, Tony *Baseball Player*
3610 Beach Dr, Tampa, FL 33609
Cuckney, John G *Financier*
%Brooke Bond Grp, 45 Berkeley St, London EC4R 1DH, England
Cudahy, Richard D *Judge*
%US Court of Appeals, 219 S Dearborn St, Chicago, IL 60604
Cuellar, Mike *Baseball Player*
PO Box 50016, Levittown, PR 00950
Cuevas, Jose Luis *Artist*
Galeana 1049, San Angel Inn, Mexico 20 DF, Mexico
Cuff, Ward *Football Player*
16611 NE 26th, Bellevue, WA 98004
Culbertson, Frank L, Jr *Astronaut*
%NASA, Johnson Space Ctr, Houston, TX 77058
Culkin, Macaulay *Actor*
%International Creative Mgmt, 8899 Beverly Blvd, Los Angeles, CA 90048
Cullberg, Brigit *Choreographer*
Svenska Rikst eatern, Rasundavagen 150, 171 30 Solna, Sweden
Cullen, Brett *Actor*
PO Box 5617, Beverly Hills, CA 90210
Cullinane, John J *Businessman*
%Cullinet Software Inc, 400 Blue Hill Dr, Westwood, MA 02090
Cullman, Edgar M *Businessman*
%Culbro Corp, 387 Park Ave S, New York, NY 10016
Cullman, Hugh *Businessman*
%Philip Morris Companies, 120 Park Ave, New York, NY 10017
Cullman, Joseph F, III *Businessman*
%Philip Morris Companies, 120 Park Ave, New York, NY 10017
Cullum, John *Actor, Singer*
%International Creative Mgmt, 40 W 57th St, New York, NY 10019
Cullum, Leo *Cartoonist*
2945 Valmere Dr, Malibu, CA 90265
Cullum, Mark *Editorial Cartoonist*
%Birmingham News, Editorial Department, PO Box 2553, Birmingham, AL 35202
Culp, Robert *Actor*
%Agency for Performing Arts, 9000 Sunset Blvd, #1200, Los Angeles, CA 90069
Culver, David M *Businessman*
%Alcan Aluminium Ltd, 1 Pl Ville Marie, Montreal PQ H3C 3H2, Canada
Culver, John C *Senator, IA*
%Arent Fox Kintner Plotkin Kahn, 1050 Connecticut Ave NW, Washington, DC 20036
Culverhouse, Hugh F *Football Executive*
4765 Ortega Blvd, Jacksonville, FL 32210
Cummings, Constance *Actress*
68 Old Church St, London SW3 6EP, England
Cummings, Quinn *Actress*
%Pietragallo Agency, 11755 Thunderbird Ave, Northridge, CA 91326
Cummings, Ralph W *Agriculturist*
812 Rosemont Ave, Raleigh, NC 27607
Cummings, Richard H *Financier*
%NBD Bancorp, 611 Woodward Ave, Detroit, MI 48226

C

Cummings – Curry

Cummings, Terry *Basketball Player*
%San Antonio Spurs, 600 E Market, San Antonio, TX 78205

Cummings, Tilden *Financier*
1025 Hill Rd, Winnetka, IL 60093

Cummings, Walter J *Judge*
%US Court of Appeals, 219 S Dearborn St, Chicago, IL 60604

Cundry, Dean *Cinematographer*
%Smith/Gosnell/Nicholson, 1515 Palisades Dr, #N, Pacific Palisades, CA 90272

Cunniff, John *Hockey Coach*
%New Jersey Devils, Meadowlands Arena, East Rutherford, NJ 07073

Cunningham, Glen *Track Athlete*
8 Rosewood, Conway, AR 72032

Cunningham, Harry B *Businessman*
210 Lowell Ct, Bloomfield Hills, MI 48013

Cunningham, John *Test Pilot*
Canley, Kinsbourne Green, Harpenden, Herts, England

Cunningham, John *Actor*
%Gage Group, 9255 Sunset Blvd, #515, Los Angeles, CA 90069

Cunningham, John F *Businessman*
%Wang Laboratories, 1 Industrial Ave, Lowell, MA 01851

Cunningham, Merce *Choreographer*
463 West St, New York, NY 10014

Cunningham, R Walter *Astronaut*
%Alcorn Ventures, 520 Post Oak Blvd, #130, Houston, TX 77027

Cunningham, Randall *Football Player*
%Philadelphia Eagles, Veterans Stadium, Philadelphia, PA 19148

Cunningham, Randy (Duke) *Representative, CA*
%House of Representatives, Washington, DC 20515

Cunningham, Sean S *Movie Director, Producer*
155 Long Lots Rd, Westport, CT 06880

Cunningham, Thomas P *Exchange Executive*
%Chicago Board of Trade, 141 W Jackson Blvd, Chicago, IL 60604

Cunningham, William *Educator*
%University of Texas, President's Office, Austin, TX 78712

Cuomo, Mario M *Governor, NY*
%Governor's Office, State Capitol, Albany, NY 12224

Curb, Mike *Record Producer*
1820 Carla Ridge, Beverly Hills, CA 90210

Curcio, John B *Businessman*
%Mack Trucks Inc, 2100 Mack Blvd, Allentown, PA 18105

Cureton, Thomas K *Swimming Contributor*
501 E Washington, Urbana, IL 61801

Curler, Howard J *Businessman*
%Bemis Co, 800 Northstar Ctr, Minneapolis, MN 55402

Curley, John J *Publisher*
%Gannett Co, 1100 Wilson Blvd, Arlington, VA 22209

Curley, Thomas *Publisher*
%USA Today, 1000 Wilson Blvd, Arlington, VA 22209

Curnin, Thomas F *Attorney*
%Cahill Gordon Reindel, 80 Pine St, New York, NY 10005

Curran, Charles E *Theologian*
%Cornell University, English Dept, Rockefeller Hall, Ithaca, NY 14853

Curran, Frank L *Mayor*
4901 Randall St, San Diego, CA 92109

Currey, Francis S *WW II Army Hero (CMH)*
106 Pinopolis Cir, Bonneau, SC 29431

Currie, Louise *Actress*
1317 Delresto Dr, Beverly Hills, CA 90210

Currie, Malcolm R *Businessman*
%Hughes Aircraft Co, 2000 El Segundo Blvd, El Segundo, CA 90245

Currie, Sondra *Actress*
3951 Longridge Ave, Sherman Oaks, CA 91423

Curry, Anne *Actress*
%Stone Manners Agency, 9113 Sunset Blvd, Los Angeles, CA 90069

Curry, Bill *Football Player, Coach*
%University of Kentucky, Athletic Dept, Lexington, KY 40506

Curry, John *Figure Skater, Ice Choreographer*
%Kirk Singer, 1841 Broadway, New York, NY 10023

Curry, Tim *Singer*
%Cameron-Haywood Co, 3 Lord Napier Pl, London W6, England

Curti, Merle *Historian*
110 S Henry St, Madison, WI 53703

Curtin, David *Journalist*
%Colorado Springs Gazette Telegraph, 30 S Prospect, Colorado Springs, CO 80901

Curtin, David Yarrow *Chemist*
3 Montclair Rd, Urbana, IL 61801

Curtin, Jane *Actress*
%Writers & Artists Agency, 11726 San Vicente Blvd, #300, Los Angeles, CA 90049

Curtin, John J, Jr *Attorney*
%Bingham Dana Gould, 100 Federal St, 35th Fl, Boston, MA 02110

Curtin, Phyllis *Opera Singer*
%Boston University, School for the Arts, Boston, MA 02215

Curtin, Valerie *Actress*
%Creative Artists Agency, 9830 Wilshire Blvd, Beverly Hills, CA 90212

Curtis Cuneo, Ann *Swimmer*
35 Golden Hinde Blvd, San Rafael, CA 94901

Curtis, Carl T *Senator, NE*
6613 31st Pl, Washington, DC 20015

Curtis, Ellwood F *Businessman*
4005 7th Ave, Moline, IL 61265

Curtis, Jamie Lee *Actress*
1242 S Camden Dr, Los Angeles, CA 90035

Curtis, Keene *Actor*
6363 Ivarene Ave, Los Angeles, CA 90068

Curtis, Kenneth M *Governor, ME; Diplomat*
1154 Shore Rd, Cape Elizabeth, ME 04107

Curtis, Tony *Actor*
11831 Folkstone Lane, Los Angeles, CA 90077

Curtis, V O *Businessman*
%Denny's Inc, 14256 E Firestone Blvd, La Mirada, CA 90637

Cusack, Cyril *Actor*
Cwain Ghaoin, Br Sorrento, Deilginis County, Dublin, Ireland

Cusack, Joan *Actress*
%International Creative Mgmt, 40 W 57th St, New York, NY 10019

Cusack, John *Actor*
%Geddes Agency, 8457 Melrose Pl, #200, Los Angeles, CA 90069

Cusack, Sinead *Actress*
%Hutton, 200 Fulham Rd, London SW10, England

Cushing, Peter *Actor*
Seasalter, Whitstable, Kent, England

Cussler, Clive *Writer*
7731 W 72nd Pl, Arvada, CO 80002

Cutler, Lloyd N *Government Official*
5215 Chamberlin Ave, Chevy Chase, MD 20015

Cutler, Roden *WW II Australian Army Hero (VC)*
22 Ginahgulla RD, Bellevue Hill NSW 2023, Australia

Cutler, Walter L *Diplomat*
%Department of State, 2201 "C" St NW, Washington, DC 20520

Cutter, Kiki *Skier*
PO Box 1317, Carbondale, CO 81623

Cutter, Lise *Actress*
%Harris & Goldberg Agency, 1999 Ave of Stars, #2850, Los Angeles, CA 90067

Cutter, Slade *Football Player*
11510 Whisper Breeze, San Antonio, TX 78230

Cypher, Jon *Actor*
4458 Matilja Ave, Sherman Oaks, CA 91423

Cyr, Conrad K *Judge*
%US Court of Appeals, PO Box 635, Bangor, ME 04501

Czarnecki, Gerald M *Financier*
%First Southern Federal Savings, 851 S Beltline Hwy, Mobile, AL 36606

Czyz, Bobby *Boxer*
15 Garry Pl, Wanaque, NJ 07465

D

D'Abo – Daland

D'Abo, Maryam *Actress*
%Metropolitan Talent Agency, 9320 Wilshire Blvd, #300, Beverly Hills, CA 90212

D'Abo, Olivia *Actress*
%Special Artists Agency, 335 N Maple Dr, #360, Beverly Hills, CA 90210

D'Amato, Alfonse M *Senator, NY*
%US Senate, Washington, DC 20510

D'Amato, Anthony S *Businessman*
%Borden Inc, 277 Park Ave, New York, NY 10172

D'Amboise, Jacques *Dancer, Choreographer*
%National Dance Institute, 599 Broadway, 11th Floor, New York, NY 10012

D'Ambrosio, Dominick *Labor Leader*
%Allied Industrial Workers Union, 3520 W Oklahoma Ave, Milwaukee, WI 53215

D'Amours, Norman E *Representative, NH*
922 Elm St, Manchester, NH 03101

D'Angelo, Beverly *Actress*
%Keith Addis Assoc, 8444 Wilshire Blvd, #500, Beverly Hills, CA 90211

D'Angio, Giulio J *Radiation Therapist*
%Children's Hospital, 34th & Civic Center Blvd, Philadelphia, PA 19104

D'Antoni, Philip *Movie, Television Producer*
90 Cairnsmuir Ln, New York, NY 10956

D'Arbanville, Patti *Actress*
%Harris & Goldberg Agency, 1999 Ave of Stars, #2850, Los Angeles, CA 90067

D'Arcy, Alex *Actor*
1310 Olive, #1, Los Angeles, CA 90069

D'Aubuisson, Roberto *Government Official, El Salvador*
%Constitution Assembly, San Salvador, El Salvador

D'Eath, Tom *Boat Racing Driver*
7773 Farnsworth, Fair Haven, MI 48023

D'Oriola, Christian *Fencer*
Valdebanne, Rt de Generac, 30 Nimes, France

Da Costa, Manuel P *Prime Minister, Sao Tome & Principe*
%Prime Minister's Office, Sao Tome, Sao Tome & Principe

Daane, James D *Government Official, Financier*
%Commerce Union Bank, 1 Commerce Pl, Nashville, TN 37205

Dabney, Virginius *Writer, Editor*
14 Tapoan Rd, Richmond, VA 23226

Dafoe, Willem *Actor*
33 Wooster St, #200, New York, NY 10013

Daggett, Tim *Gymnast*
%Victor Randazza, 53 Harmon St, Long Beach, NY 11561

Dahanayake, Wijeyananda *Prime Minister, Ceylon*
225 Richmond Hill Rd, Galle, Sri Lanka

Dahl, Arlene *Actress*
%Dahlmark Productions, PO Box 116, Sparkill, NY 10976

Dahl, Charles R *Businessman*
1170 Sacramento St, San Francisco, CA 94108

Dahl, Robert A *Political Scientist*
17 Cooper Rd, North Haven, CT 06473

Dahlbeck, Eva *Actress*
22 Rue Carqueron, CH 1220 Avanchet, Switzerland

Dahlberg, A W *Businessman*
%Southern Co, 64 Perimeter Cir E, Atlanta, GA 30346

Dahlgren, Edward C *WW II Army Hero (CMH)*
Box 26, Mars Hill, ME 04758

Dahlsten, Gunnar *Businessman*
%Swedish Match, PO Box 16100, 103 22, Stockholm, Sweden

Dailey, Peter H *Diplomat*
%Department of State, 2201 "C" St NW, Washington, DC 20520

Daily, Bill *Actor*
%Agency for Performing Arts, 9200 Sunset Blvd, #1200, Los Angeles, CA 90069

Daily, E G *Singer*
%A&M Records, 1416 N La Brea Ave, Los Angeles, CA 90028

Dalai Lama, The *Religious Leader; Nobel Peace Laureate*
Thekchen Choeling, McLeod Ganj 176219, Dharamsal, Himachal Pradesh, India

Daland, Peter *Diving Coach*
1963 Elmsbury Rd, Westlake Village, Thousand Oaks, CA 91360

Dale, Bruce *Photographer*
%National Geographic Magazine, 17th & "M" St NW, Washington, DC 20036

Dale, Carroll *Football Player*
109 Southwood Ln, Bristol, TN 37620

Dale, Charles *Labor Leader*
%Newspaper Guild, 8611 2nd Ave, Silver Spring, MD 20910

Dale, Francis L *Publisher, Businessman*
5604 Bridher Ct, Missoula, MT 59803

Dale, Jim *Actor*
26 Pembridge Villas, London W11, England

Dale, William B *Economist, Government Official*
6008 Landon Ln, Bethesda, MD 20817

Daler, Jiri *Cyclist*
Jiraskova 43, 601 00 Brno, Czechoslovakia

Dalessandro, Peter J *WW II Army Hero (CMH)*
199 Old Niskyna Rd, Latham, NY 12410

Daley, Richard M *Mayor*
%Mayor's Office, City Hall, 121 N LaSalle St, Chicago, IL 60602

Dalis, Irene *Opera Singer*
1635 Mulberry Ln, San Jose, CA 95125

Dalla Chiesa, Romeo *Financier*
%Banco di Roma, Via del Corso 307, Rome, Italy

Dalle, Francois *Businessman*
%L'Oreal, 14 Rue Royale, 75008 Paris, France

Dallenbach, Wally *Auto Racing Executive*
%CART, 390 Enterprise Ct, Bloomfield Hills, MI 48013

Dalrymple, Jean *Theatre Producer*
150 W 55th St, New York, NY 10019

Dalton, Jack *Librarian*
%Columbia University, Library Service School, New York, NY 10027

Dalton, Lacy J *Singer*
%Ten Ten Mgmt, 1010 16th Ave S, Nashville, TN 37212

Dalton, Timothy *Actor*
15 Golden Sq, #315, London W1, England

Daltrey, Roger *Musician*
%Warner Bros Records, 3300 Warner Blvd, Burbank, CA 91510

Daly, Chuck *Basketball Coach*
%Detroit Pistons, Palace, 1 Championship Dr, Auburn Hills, MI 48057

Daly, Edward J *Businessman*
%World Airways, Oakland International Airport, Oakland, CA 94314

Daly, John F *Businessman*
%Johnson Controls, 5757 N Green Bay Ave, Milwaukee, WI 53201

Daly, Joseph R *Businessman*
%Doyle Dane Bernbach International, 437 Madison Ave, New York, NY 10022

Daly, Michael J *WW II Army Hero (CMH)*
228 Main St, Southport, CT 06490

Daly, Robert A *Entertainment Executive*
%Warner Bros Inc, 4000 Warner Blvd, Burbank, CA 91522

Daly, Tyne *Actress*
%Camden ITG Agency, 822 S Robertson Blvd, #200, Los Angeles, CA 90035

Dam, Kenneth W *Government Official*
%Department of State, 2201 "C" St NW, Washington, DC 20520

Damiani, Damiano *Movie Director*
Via Delle Terme Deciane 2, Rome, Italy

Dammeyer, Rod F *Businessman*
%Itel Corp, 1 Embarcadero Ctr, San Francisco, CA 94111

Damon, Mark *Actor*
%Joseph Heldfond Rix, 1717 N Highland Ave, #414, Los Angeles, CA 90028

Damon, Roger C *Financier*
172 Beacon St, Boston, MA 02116

Damon, Stuart *Actor*
367 N Van Ness Ave, Los Angeles, CA 90004

Damone, Vic *Singer*
9108 Alanda Pl, Beverly Hills, CA 90210

Damsel, Richard A *Businessman*
%Leaseway Transportation Corp, 3700 Park East Dr, Beachwood, OH 44122

D

Damson – Danneels

Damson, Barrie M *Businessman*
%Damson Oil Corp, 366 Madison Ave, New York, NY 10017

Dana, Bill *Comedian*
PO Box 1792, Santa Monica, CA 90406

Dana, Bill *Test Pilot*
%Ames Research Center, DFRF, PO Box 273, Edwards AFB, CA 93523

Dana, Justin *Actor*
13111 Ventura Blvd, #102, Studio City, CA 91604

Danby, Gordon *Superconducting Magnet Engineer*
%Brookhaven National Laboratory, Upton, NY 11973

Dance, Bill *Fisherman*
%ESPN-TV, Sports Dept, ESPN Plz, Bristol, CT 06010

Dance, Charles *Actor*
%Caroline Dawson Assoc, 47 Courtfield Rd, #20, London SW7 4DB, England

Dancer, Stanley *Harness Racing Driver*
PO Box 428, Archertown Rd, New Egypt, NJ 08533

Dandridge, Ray *Baseball Player*
PO Box 1139, Palm Bay, FL 32906

Danenberg, Emil Charles *Educator*
154 Forest St, Oberlin, OH 44074

Danforth, John C *Senator, MO*
Rt 1, Box 91, Newburg, MO 65550

Danforth, William H *Educator*
%Washington University, President's Office, St Louis, MO 63130

Dangerfield, George *Writer*
883 Toro Canyon Rd, Santa Barbara, CA 93108

Dangerfield, Rodney *Comedian*
520 E 77th St, New York, NY 10023

Daniel, Beth *Golfer*
%Ladies Professional Golf Assn, 2570 Volusia Ave, #B, Daytona Beach, FL 32114

Daniel, Clifton, Jr *Journalist*
830 Park Ave, New York, NY 10028

Daniel, Margaret Truman *Writer*
830 Park Ave, New York, NY 10028

Daniel, Richard N *Businessman*
%Handy & Harman, 850 3rd Ave, New York, NY 10022

Daniel, Robert W, Jr *Representative, VA*
Brandon Plantation, Spring Grove, VA 23881

Daniell, Averell E *Football Player*
1150 Bower Hill Rd, #712-A, Pittsburgh, PA 15243

Daniell, Martin H, Jr *Coast Guard Admiral*
Vice Commandant, US Coast Guard, 2100 2nd St SW, Washington, DC 20593

Daniell, Robert F *Businessman*
%United Technologies Corp, United Technologies Bldg, Hartford, CT 06101

Daniels, Charlie *Singer, Songwriter*
Box 882, Mt Joliet, TN 37122

Daniels, Cheryl *Bowler*
18660 San Juan, Detroit, MI 48221

Daniels, Faith *Commentator*
%NBC-TV, 30 Rockefeller Plz, New York, NY 10112

Daniels, John H *Businessman*
2472 Parkview Dr, Hamel, MN 55340

Daniels, Mel *Basketball Player*
Circle M Ranch, RR 3, Box 420-A, Sheridan, IN 46069

Daniels, William *Actor*
%Artists Agency, 10000 Santa Monica Blvd, #305, Los Angeles, CA 90067

Danielsen, Egil *Track Athlete*
Storhamar, 2300 Hamar, Norway

Daniloff, Nicholas *Journalist*
PO Box 892, Chester, VT 05143

Danilova, Alexandra *Ballet Dancer, Choreographer*
100 W 57th St, New York, NY 10019

Dankworth, John *Jazz Pianist, Composer*
Old Rectory, Wavendon, Milton Kenyes MK17 8LT, England

Danneels, Godfried Cardinal *Religious Leader*
Aartsbisdom, Wollemarkt 15, B-2800 Mechelen, Belgium

Dannemeyer, William E *Representative, CA*
%House of Representatives, Washington, DC 20515
Dannemiller, John C *Businessman*
%Leaseway Transportation Corp, 3700 Park East Dr, Beachwood, OH 44122
Danner, Blythe *Actress*
304 21st St, Santa Monica, CA 90402
Danning, Harry *Baseball Player*
212 Fox Chapel Ct, Valparaiso, IN 46304
Danning, Sybil *Actress*
8578 Walnut Dr, Los Angeles, CA 90004
Dano, Royal *Actor*
517 20th St, Santa Monica, CA 90402
Danova, Cesare *Actor*
%Burton Moss Agency, 113 N San Vicente Blvd, #202, Beverly Hills, CA 90211
Danson, Ted *Actor*
%Creative Artists Agency, 9830 Wilshire Blvd, Beverly Hills, CA 90212
Dantas, Carl E *Businessman*
%Compugraphic Corp, 200 Ballardvale St, Wilmington, MA 01887
Dante, Joe *Movie Director*
%Gersh Agency, 232 N Canon Dr, Beverly Hills, CA 90210
Dantine, Nikki *Actress*
707 N Palm Dr, Beverly Hills, CA 90210
Danton, J Periam *Librarian*
%University of California, Library Studies School, Berkeley, CA 94720
Dantzig, George B *Computer Scientist*
821 Tolman Dr, Stanford, CA 94305
Danza, Tony *Actor*
19722 Trull Brook Dr, Tarzana, CA 91356
Danzig, Frederick P *Editor*
%Advertising Age, 220 E 42nd St, New York, NY 10017
Daphnis, Nassos *Artist*
362 W Broadway, New York, NY 10013
Darboven, Hanne *Artist*
Am Burgberg 26, 21 Hamburg 90, Germany
Darby, Kim *Actress*
%Susan Smith Assoc, 121 N San Vicente Blvd, Beverly Hills, CA 90211
Darby, William Jefferson *Nutritionist*
Rt 2, Box 218, Thompson Station, TN 37179
Darden, George *Representative, GA*
%House of Representatives, Washington, DC 20515
Darden, Severn *Actor*
3220 Laurel Canyon Blvd, Studio City, CA 91604
Darion, Joe *Librettist, Lyricist*
Pinnacle Rd, Lynne, NH 03768
Dark, Alvin *Baseball Player, Manager*
103 Cranberry Way, Easley, SC 29640
Darling, Jennifer *Actress*
%Schiowitz Halpern Inc, 291 S La Cienega Blvd, Beverly Hills, CA 90211
Darling, L Gordon *Businessman*
Broken Hill Proprietary Co, 140 William, Melbourne, Vic 3000, Australia
Darling, Ron *Baseball Player*
19 Woodland St, Millbury, MA 01527
Darlington, Cyril Dean *Cytologist, Geneticist*
%Botany School, Oxford, England
Darman, Richard G *Government Official*
%Office of Management & Budget, Executive Office Bldg, Washington, DC 20503
Darmojuwono, Justine Cardinal *Religious Leader*
Jalan Kamfer Raya 49, Semarang, Selatan, Java, Indonesia
Darnall, Robert J *Businessman*
%Inland Steel Co, 30 W Monroe St, Chicago, IL 60603
Darnton, John *Journalist*
%New York Times, 229 W 43rd St, New York, NY 10036
Darragh, John K *Businessman*
%Standard Register Co, 626 Albany St, Dayton, OH 45408
Darren, James *Singer, Actor*
PO Box 1088, Beverly Hills, CA 90213

D

Darrieux – Davidson

Darrieux, Danielle *Actress*
3 Quai Malaivais, 75006 Paris, France

Darrow, Henry *Actor*
%Paul Kohner Inc, 9169 Sunset Blvd, Los Angeles, CA 90069

Dascalescu, Constantin *Prime Minister, Romania*
%Prime Minister's Office, Bucharest, Romania

Daschle, Thomas A *Senator, SD*
%US Senate, Washington, DC 20510

Dash, Samuel *Attorney, Watergate Committee Counsel*
110 Newlands St, Chevy Chase, MD 20015

Dassin, Jules *Movie Director*
Anagnostopoulou 25, Athens, Greece

Dater, Judy *Photographer*
PO Box 709, San Anselmo, CA 94960

Daub, Hal *Representative, NE*
%House of Representatives, Washington, DC 20515

Daube, David *Attorney, Educator*
%University of California, Law School, Berkeley, CA 94720

Dauben, William G *Chemist*
20 Eagle Hill, Berkeley, CA 94707

Daugherty, Brad *Basketball Player*
%Cleveland Cavaliers, 2923 Statesboro Rd, Richfield, OH 44286

Dausset, Jean *Nobel Medicine Laureate*
9 Rue de Villersexel, 75007 Paris, France

Davalos, Richard *Actor*
1958 Vestal Ave, Los Angeles, CA 90026

Davenport, David *Educator*
%Pepperdine University, President's Office, Malibu, CA 90265

Davenport, Nigel *Actor*
%Leading Artists, 60 St James St, London SW1, England

Davenport, Willie *Track Athlete*
4876 Campbell Dr, Baton Rouge, LA 70807

Davey, John *Actor*
%Barskin Agency, 120 S Victory Blvd, Burbank, CA 91501

Davi, Robert *Actor*
%Agency for Performing Arts, 9000 Sunset Blvd, #1200, Los Angeles, CA 90069

Daviau, Allen *Cinematographer*
2249 Bronson Hill Dr, Los Angeles, CA 90069

David, Edward E, Jr *Underwater Sound Engineer*
%Exxon Research & Engineering Co, PO Box 101, Florham Park, NJ 07932

David, Hal *Lyricist*
5253 Lankershim Blvd, North Hollywood, CA 91601

David, Mack *Songwriter*
1575 Toledo Cir, Palm Springs, CA 92262

David-Weill, Michel A *Financier*
%Lazard Freres & Co, 1 Rockfeller Plz, New York, NY 10020

Davidovich, Bella *Concert Pianist*
%Jacques Leiser, Dorchester Towers, 155 W 68th St, New York, NY 10023

Davidovich, Lolita *Actress*
%International Creative Mgmt, 8899 Beverly Blvd, Los Angeles, CA 90048

Davidovsky, Mario *Composer*
490 West End Ave, New York, NY 10024

Davidsen, Arthur F *Astronomer*
Johns Hopkins University, Astrophysical Sciences Ctr, Baltimore, MD 21218

Davidson, Alfred E *International Attorney*
5 Rue de la Manutention, 75116 Paris, France

Davidson, Ben *Football Player*
447 Aldwych Rd, El Cajon, CA 92020

Davidson, Bruce *Equestrian Rider*
Chesterland, Box 453, Unionville, PA 19375

Davidson, Eileen *Actress*
%Hugh Roberts, 6363 Wilshire Blvd, Los Angeles, CA 90068

Davidson, George A, Jr *Businessman*
%Consolidated Natural Gas Co, 4 Gateway Ctr, Pittsburgh, PA 15222

Davidson, Gordon *Theatrical Producer, Director*
%Center Theatre Grp, 135 N Grand Ave, Los Angeles, CA 90012

Davidson, John *Singer*
28260 Rey de Copas Ln, Malibu, CA 90265
Davidson, Norman R *Molecular Biologist*
318 E Laurel Ave, Sierra Madre, CA 91024
Davidson, Ralph P *Publisher*
%Time Inc, Rockefeller Ctr, New York, NY 10020
Davidson, Thomas M *Businessman*
%Arrow Electronics Inc, 767 5th Ave, New York, NY 10153
Davidson, William *Businessman*
%Guardian Industries, 43043 W Nine Mile Rd, Northville, MI 48167
Davies, Gail *Singer*
246 Cherokee Rd, Nashville, TN 37205
Davies, John *Swimmer*
520 Madeline Dr, Pasadena, CA 91105
Davies, Laura *Golfer*
%Ladies Professional Golf Assn, 2570 Volusia Ave, #B, Daytona Beach, FL 32114
Davies, Michael J *Editor, Publisher*
%Baltimore Sun, 501 N Calvert St, Baltimore, MD 21278
Davies, Peter *Biochemist*
%Albert Einstein College of Medicine, Biochemisty Dept, Bronx, NY 10461
Davies, Peter Maxwell *Composer*
%Judy Arnold, 50 Hogarth Rd, London SW5, England
Davies, Richard Townsend *Diplomat*
3511 Leland St, Chevy Chase, MD 20815
Davies, Robertson *Writer*
%Massey College, 4 Devonshire Pl, Toronto ON M5S 2E1, Canada
Davignon, Etienne *Government Official; Businessman*
12 Ave Des Fleurs, Brussels, Belgium
Davis, A Dano *Businessman*
%Winn-Dixie Stores, 5050 Edgewood Ct, Jacksonville, FL 32203
Davis, Al *Football Executive*
%Los Angeles Raiders, 332 Center St, El Segundo, CA 90245
Davis, Andrew *Conductor*
%Toronto Symphony, 60 Simcoe St, Toronto ON M5J 2H5, Canada
Davis, Angela *Political Activist, Educator*
%Random House, 201 E 50th St, New York, NY 10022
Davis, Ann B *Actress*
1427 Reaves Rd, Ambridge, PA 15003
Davis, Anthony *Football Player*
%Service One Corp, 21032 Devonshire St, #215, Chatsworth, CA 91311
Davis, Anthony *Jazz Pianist, Composer*
%American International Artists, 575 E 89th St, New York, NY 10128
Davis, Artemus D *Businessman*
%Winn-Dixie Stores, 5050 Edgewood Ct, Jacksonville, FL 32203
Davis, Bernard D *Microbiologist*
23 Clairemont Rd, Belmont, MA 02178
Davis, Bobby (Robert T, Jr) *Football Player*
PO Box 1509, Shelby, NC 28150
Davis, Carl *Composer*
99 Church Rd, Barnes, London SW13 9HL, England
Davis, Clarissa *Basketball Player*
%University of Texas, Women's Intercollegiate Athletics Dept, Austin, TX 78712
Davis, Clifton *Actor*
%Sharr Enterprises, 9145 Sunset Blvd, Los Angeles, CA 90069
Davis, Clive *Record Producer*
%Arista Records, 6 W 57th St, New York, NY 10019
Davis, Colin *Conductor*
%Royal Opera House, Covent Gdn, Bow St, London WC2, England
Davis, David *Bowler*
%DeStasio, 710 Shore Rd, Spring Lake Heights, NJ 07762
Davis, Donald C *Navy Admiral*
%Commander-in-Chief's Office, Pacific Fleet, Pearl Harbor, HI 96860
Davis, Donald W *Businessman*
%Stanley Works, 1000 Stanley Dr, New Britain, CT 06050
Davis, Eric *Baseball Player*
6606 Denver Ave, #1, Los Angeles, CA 90044

D

Davis – Davis

Davis, Geena *Actress*
8225 Hollywood Blvd, Los Angeles, CA 90069

Davis, George H *Educator*
%University of Vermont, President's Office, Burlington, VT 05405

Davis, Glenn E *Baseball Player*
%Houston Astros, PO Box 288, Astrodome, Houston, TX 77001

Davis, Glenn H *Track Athlete*
801 Robinson Ave, Barberton, OH 44203

Davis, Glenn W *Football Player*
3508 Woodcliffe Rd, Sherman Oaks, CA 91403

Davis, H Roy *Financier*
%First Federal Savings & Loan, 301 College St, Greenville, SC 29602

Davis, J Morton *Financier*
%D H Blair & Co, 44 Wall St, New York, NY 10005

Davis, Jack *Representative, IL*
%House of Representatives, Washington, DC 20515

Davis, Jack *Businessman*
%Dataproducts, 6200 Canoga Ave, Woodland Hills, CA 91365

Davis, Jackie *Actor*
1160 Wilshire Blvd, Los Angeles, CA 90024

Davis, Jacob E *Businessman*
5685 Kugler Mill Rd, Cincinnati, OH 45236

Davis, James B *Air Force General*
Chief of Staff, SHAPE, APO, AE 09705

Davis, James E *Businessman*
%Winn-Dixie Stores, 5050 Edgewood Ct, Jacksonville, FL 32203

Davis, James L *Businessman*
%H H Robertson Co, 2 Gateway Ctr, Pittsburgh, PA 15222

Davis, Jim *Cartoonist (Garfield)*
%United Feature Syndicate, 200 Park Ave, New York, NY 10166

Davis, Jimmie *Governor, LA; Singer*
1331 Lakeridge Dr, Baton Rouge, LA 70802

Davis, Joe E *Businessman*
%BMC Industries, 100 American National Bank Bldg, St Paul, MN 55101

Davis, John K *Marine Corps General*
%Marine Corps Headquarters, Washington, DC 20380

Davis, Johnny *Basketball Player*
%Atlanta Hawks, 100 Techwood Dr NW, Atlanta, GA 30303

Davis, Josie *Actress*
%Cristopher Nassif Assoc, 1801 Ave of Stars, #1250, Los Angeles, CA 90067

Davis, Judy *Actress*
%International Creative Mgmt, 8899 Beverly Blvd, Los Angeles, CA 90048

Davis, Kenneth *Football Player*
%Green Bay Packers, 1265 Lombardi Ave, Green Bay, WI 54303

Davis, L Edward *Religious Leader*
%Evangelical Presbyterian Church, 26049 Five Mile Rd, Detroit, MI 48239

Davis, Mac *Singer, Songwriter*
759 Nimes Rd, Los Angeles, CA 90024

Davis, Mark *Microbiologist*
%Stanford University, Medical Ctr, Stanford, CA 94305

Davis, Mark *Baseball Player*
1820 Reading Blvd, Wyomissing, PA 19610

Davis, Martin S *Businessman*
%Paramount Communications, 1 Paramount Communications Plz, New York, NY 10023

Davis, Marvin *Businessman*
%Davis Co, Fox Plz, 2121 Ave of Stars, Los Angeles, CA 90067

Davis, N Jan *Astronaut*
%NASA, Johnson Space Ctr, Houston, TX 77058

Davis, Nathanael V *Businessman*
%Alcan Alumninium, 1 Pl Ville Marie, Montreal PQ H3C 3H2, Canada

Davis, Nathaniel *Diplomat*
%Department of State, 2201 "C" St NW, Washington, DC 20520

Davis, Ossie *Actor*
%Emmalyn II Productions, PO Box 1318, New Rochelle, NY 10802

Davis, Phyllis *Actress*
%Gage Group, 9255 Sunset Blvd, #515, Los Angeles, CA 90069

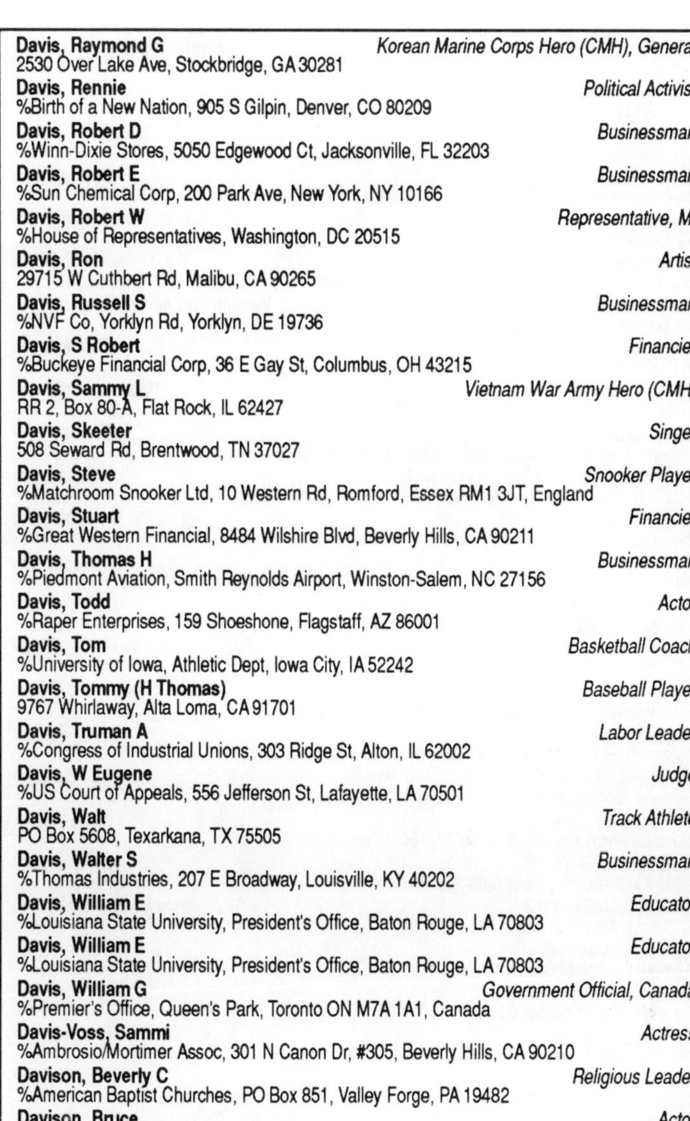

Davis, Raymond G *Korean Marine Corps Hero (CMH), General*
2530 Over Lake Ave, Stockbridge, GA 30281

Davis, Rennie *Political Activist*
%Birth of a New Nation, 905 S Gilpin, Denver, CO 80209

Davis, Robert D *Businessman*
%Winn-Dixie Stores, 5050 Edgewood Ct, Jacksonville, FL 32203

Davis, Robert E *Businessman*
%Sun Chemical Corp, 200 Park Ave, New York, NY 10166

Davis, Robert W *Representative, MI*
%House of Representatives, Washington, DC 20515

Davis, Ron *Artist*
29715 W Cuthbert Rd, Malibu, CA 90265

Davis, Russell S *Businessman*
%NVF Co, Yorklyn Rd, Yorklyn, DE 19736

Davis, S Robert *Financier*
%Buckeye Financial Corp, 36 E Gay St, Columbus, OH 43215

Davis, Sammy L *Vietnam War Army Hero (CMH)*
RR 2, Box 80-A, Flat Rock, IL 62427

Davis, Skeeter *Singer*
508 Seward Rd, Brentwood, TN 37027

Davis, Steve *Snooker Player*
%Matchroom Snooker Ltd, 10 Western Rd, Romford, Essex RM1 3JT, England

Davis, Stuart *Financier*
%Great Western Financial, 8484 Wilshire Blvd, Beverly Hills, CA 90211

Davis, Thomas H *Businessman*
%Piedmont Aviation, Smith Reynolds Airport, Winston-Salem, NC 27156

Davis, Todd *Actor*
%Raper Enterprises, 159 Shoeshone, Flagstaff, AZ 86001

Davis, Tom *Basketball Coach*
%University of Iowa, Athletic Dept, Iowa City, IA 52242

Davis, Tommy (H Thomas) *Baseball Player*
9767 Whirlaway, Alta Loma, CA 91701

Davis, Truman A *Labor Leader*
%Congress of Industrial Unions, 303 Ridge St, Alton, IL 62002

Davis, W Eugene *Judge*
%US Court of Appeals, 556 Jefferson St, Lafayette, LA 70501

Davis, Walt *Track Athlete*
PO Box 5608, Texarkana, TX 75505

Davis, Walter S *Businessman*
%Thomas Industries, 207 E Broadway, Louisville, KY 40202

Davis, William E *Educator*
%Louisiana State University, President's Office, Baton Rouge, LA 70803

Davis, William E *Educator*
%Louisiana State University, President's Office, Baton Rouge, LA 70803

Davis, William G *Government Official, Canada*
%Premier's Office, Queen's Park, Toronto ON M7A 1A1, Canada

Davis-Voss, Sammi *Actress*
%Ambrosio/Mortimer Assoc, 301 N Canon Dr, #305, Beverly Hills, CA 90210

Davison, Beverly C *Religious Leader*
%American Baptist Churches, PO Box 851, Valley Forge, PA 19482

Davison, Bruce *Actor*
PO Box 57593, Sherman Oaks, CA 91703

Davison, Fred C *Educator*
570 Prince Ave, Athens, GA 30601

Dawber, Pam *Actress*
%Pony Productions, Columbia Plz, Burbank, CA 91505

Dawes, Joseph *Cartoonist*
20 Church Ct, Closter, NJ 07624

Dawkins, Johnny *Basketball Player*
%San Antonio Spurs, Hemisfair Arena, PO Box 530, San Antonio, TX 78292

Dawkins, Peter M *Football Player, Businessman*
178 Rumson Rd, Rumson, NJ 07760

Dawson, Andre *Baseball Player*
10301 SW 144th St, Miami, FL 33176

Dawson, Buck *Swimming Executive*
%Swimming Hall of Fame, 1 Hall of Fame Dr, Fort Lauderdale, FL 33316

D

Dawson, Lenny *Football Player, Sportscaster*
%KNBC-TV, 1049 Central Ave, Kansas City, MO 64105

Dawson, Richard *Actor*
1117 Angelo Dr, Beverly Hills, CA 90210

Day, Bill *Editorial Cartoonist*
%Detroit Free Press, 321 W Lafayette Blvd, Detroit, MI 48231

Day, Castle N *Businessman*
%American Bakeries Co, 100 Park Ave, New York, NY 10017

Day, Chon *Cartoonist (Brother Sebastian)*
22 Cross St, Westerly, RI 02891

Day, Doris *Actress, Singer*
%Doris Day Pet Foundation, PO Box 8509, Universal City, CA 91608

Day, George E (Bud) *Vietnam War Air Force Hero (CMH)*
23 Bayshore Dr, Shalimar, FL 32579

Day, Guy *Businessman*
%Chiat/Day/Mojo, 517 S Olive St, Los Angeles, CA 90013

Day, J Edward *Postmaster General*
5804 Brookside Dr, Chevy Chase, MD 20015

Day, J Graham *Businessman*
%Dome Petroleum, 800 Sixth Ave SW, Calgary AB T2P ON1, Canada

Day, Larraine *Actress*
10313 Lauriston Ave, Los Angeles, CA 90025

Day, Robin *Journalist*
%BBC Studios, Lime Grove, London W12, England

Day, Stanley R *Businessman*
%Champion Home Builders Co, 5573 E North St, Dryden, MI 48428

Day, Thomas B *Educator*
%San Diego State University, President's Office, San Diego, CA 92182

Dayne, Taylor *Singer*
PO Box 476, Rockville Centre, NY 11571

Days, Drews S, 3rd *Government Official*
%Yale University, Law School, New Haven, CT 06520

Dayton, June *Actress*
%Abrams-Rubaloff Lawrence, 8075 W 3rd St, #303, Los Angeles, CA 90048

De Bakey, Michael E *Surgeon*
%Baylor College of Medicine, 1200 Moursund Ave, Houston, TX 77030

De Benedetti, Carlo *Businessman*
%Ing C Olivetti Co, Via G Jervis 77, 10015 Ivrea/Turin, Italy

De Benning, Burr *Actor*
4235 Kingfisher Rd, Calabasas, CA 91302

De Blanc, Jefferson J *WW II Marine Corps Hero (CMH)*
321 St Martin St, St Martinville, LA 70582

De Blasis, Celeste *Writer*
Kemper Campbell Ranch, #9, Victorville, CA 92392

De Borchgrave, Arnaud *Editor*
%Insight Magazine, 3600 New York Ave NE, Washington, DC 20002

De Branges, Louis *Mathematician*
%Purdue University, Mathematics Dept, West Lafayette, IN 47907

De Brignac, Guy *Businessman*
%Lesieur, 122 Ave General Leclerc, 92103 Boulogne-Billancourt, France

De Camilli, Pietro *Biologist*
%Yale University, School of Medicine, Cell Biology Dept, New Haven, CT 06512

De Carlo, Yvonne *Actress*
%Ruth Webb Enterprises, 7500 Devista Dr, Los Angeles, CA 90046

De Castro, Edson D *Businessman*
%Data General Corp, 4400 Computer Dr, Westboro, MA 01580

De Concini, Dennis *Senator, AZ*
%US Senate, Washington, DC 20510

De Cordova, Frederick *Movie, Television Producer, Director*
1875 Carla Ridge, Beverly Hills, CA 90210

De Duve, Christian R *Nobel Medicine Laureate*
80 Central Park West, New York, NY 10023

De Escondrillas, Jose Maria *Businessman*
%Union Explosivos Rio Tinto, Paseo de la Castellellana 20, Madrid, Spain

De Frank, Vincent *Conductor*
%Memphis Symphony, 3100 Walnut Grove Rd, Memphis, TN 38111

De Gaspe, Philippe *Publisher*
%Canadian Living Magazine, 50 Holly St, Toronto ON M4S 3B3, Canada
De Gennes, Pierre-Gilles *Nobel Physics Laureate*
%College of Physics & Chemistry, 10 Rue Vauquelin, 75005 Paris, France
De Ghetto, Kenneth A *Businessman*
%Foster Wheeler Corp, 110 S Orange Ave, Livingston, NJ 07039
De Givenchy, Hubert *Fashion Designer*
3 Ave George V, 75008 Paris, France
De Grandpre, A J *Businessman*
%Northern Telecom Ltd, 1600 Dorchester Blvd W, Montreal PQ H3H 1R1, Canada
De Grazia, Ettore Ted *Artist*
6300 N Swan, Tucson, AZ 85718
De Grazia, Sebastian *Writer*
%Princeton University Press, PO Box 190, Princeton, NJ 08544
De Grey, Roger *Educator*
%Royal Academy of Art, 124 Kennington Park Rd, London SW11, England
De Guire, Frank C *Businessman*
%Pabst Brewing Co, 917 Junea Ave, Milwaukee, WI 53201
De Hartog, Jan *Writer*
%Harper & Row, 10 E 53rd St, New York, NY 10022
De Haven, Gloria *Actress*
%Gage Group, 9255 Sunset Blvd, #515, Los Angeles, CA 90069
De Havilland, Olivia *Actress*
3 Rue Benouville, 75016 Paris, France
De Hoffmann, Frederic *Research Scientist*
9736 La Jolla Farms Rd, La Jolla, CA 92037
De Johnette, Jack *Jazz Drummer*
Silver Hollow Rd, Willow, NY 11201
De Kieweit, Cornelis W *Historian*
22 Berkeley St, Rochester, NY 14607
De Klerk, Frederik W *President, South Africa*
%President's Office, Union Bldgs, Prvt Bag X-1000, Pretoria, South Africa
De Klert, Albert *Concert Organist*
Crayenesterlaan 22, Haarlem, Netherlands
De Kooning, Willem *Artist*
Woodbine Dr, The Springs, East Hampton, NY 11973
De Kruif, Robert M *Financier*
%H F Ahmanson & Co, 3731 Wilshire Blvd, Los Angeles, CA 90010
De La Cruz, Rosie *Model*
%Next Model Mgmt, 115 E 57th St, #1540, New York, NY 10022
De la Espriella, Ricardo *President, Panama*
%President's Office, Panama City, Panama
De La Garza, E(kika) *Representative, TX*
%House of Representatives, Washington, DC 20515
De Lancey, William J *Businessman*
2952 Kingsley Rd, Shaker Heights, OH 44120
De Larrocha, Alicia *Concert Pianist*
%Herbert H Breslin Inc, 119 W 57th St, #1505, New York, NY 10019
De Laurentiis, Dino *Movie Producer*
%De Laurentiis Entertainment Grp, 8670 Wilshire Blvd, Beverly Hills, CA 90211
De Lauro, Rosa L *Representative, CT*
%House of Representatives, Washington, DC 20515
De Leeuw, Ton *Composer*
Costeruslaan 4, Hilversum, Netherlands
De Los Angeles, Victoria *Opera Singer*
%E Magrini, Paseo de Gracia, 87-7-D Barcelona, Spain
De Lue, Donald *Sculptor*
82 Highland Ave, Leonardo, NJ 07737
De Madariaga, Antonio *Businessman*
%Petronor, Plaza de Carlos VII, Bilbao, Spain
De Maiziere, Lothar *Prime Minister, East Germany*
%Prime Minister's Office, Protokoll, Klosterstr 47, Berlin, Germany
De Marco, Jean *Sculptor*
Cervaro 03044, Prov-Frosinore, Italy
De Ment, Jack *Research Chemist*
%Oregon Health Care Ctr, 11325 NE Weidler St, #44, Portland, OR 97220

D

De Merchant, Paul *Religious Leader*
%Missionary Church, 3901 S Wayne Ave, Ft Wayne, IN 46516

De Meuse, Donald H *Businessman*
%Fort Howard Paper Co, 1919 S Broadway, Green Bay, WI 54304

De Mille, Agnes *Choreographer*
25 E 9th St, New York, NY 10003

De Mille, Katherine *Actress*
%Morg, 10780 Santa Monica Blvd, #280, Los Angeles, CA 90025

De Mita, Ciriaco *Prime Minister, Italy*
%Prime Minister's Office, Chamber of Deputies, Rome, Italy

De Montebello, Philippe *Museum Executive*
%Metropolitan Museum of Art, 82nd St & 5th Ave, New York, NY 10028

De Oliveira, Joao *Track Athlete*
%Olympic Committee, Rua de Assembleia 10-32, 20011 Rio de Janeiro, Brazil

De Paiva, James *Actor*
%"One Life to Live" Show, ABC-TV, 1330 Ave of Americas, New York, NY 10019

De Peyer, Gervase *Concert Clarinetist, Conductor*
16 Langford Pl, St John's Wood, London NW8, England

De Preist, James *Conductor*
142 West End Ave, #3-U, New York, NY 10023

De Rita, Curly Joe *Comedian*
10611 Moorpark Ave, North Hollywood, CA 91601

De Tomaso, Alejandro *Businessman*
%De Tomaso Modena, Canalgrande Hotel, Modena, Italy

De Valois, Ninette *Choreographer*
%Royal Ballet School, 153 Talgarth Rd, London W14, England

De Vaucouleurs, Gerard H *Astronomer*
%University of Texas, Astronomy Dept, Austin, TX 78712

De Vicenzo, Roberto *Golfer*
%Noni Lann, 5025 Veloz Ave, Tarzana, CA 91356

De Villenejane, Bernard *Businessman*
%Imetal, Tour Monparnesse, 33 Ave du Maine, 75755 Paris Cedex 15, France

De Vries, Peter *Writer*
170 Cross Hwy, Westport, CT 06880

De Vries, Rimmer *Economist*
Hill & Dale Rd, RFD 3, Lebanon, NJ 08833

De Waart, Edo *Conductor*
Essenlaan 68, Rotterdam 3016, Netherlands

De Weck, Philippe *Financier*
%Union Bank of Switzerland, Hofwiesenstrasse 135, 8021 Zurich, Switzerland

De Weldon, Felix *Sculptor*
219 Randolph Pl NE, Washington, DC 20002

De Windt, E Mandell *Businessman*
%Eaton Corp, Eaton Ctr, 1111 Superior Ave, Cleveland, OH 44114

De Witt, Joyce *Actress*
%Lantz Office, 4101 Framdale Ave, Studio City, CA 91604

De Young, Cliff *Actor*
%International Creative Mgmt, 8899 Beverly Blvd, Los Angeles, CA 90048

Deacon, Richard *Sculptor*
%Margarete Roeder Gallery, 545 Broadway, New York, NY 10012

Deacon, Terrence *Neuroanatomist*
%Harvard University, Neuroanatomy Dept, Cambridge, MA 02138

Dean, Charles H *Government Official*
%Tennessee Valley Authority, TVA Towers, Knoxville, TN 37902

Dean, Eddie *Singer, Actor*
32161 Sailview Ln, Westlake Village, CA 91360

Dean, Everett S *Basketball Coach*
Rt 1, Box 101, Orleans, IN 47452

Dean, Hollis R *Businessman*
%Houston Industries, 611 Walker Ave, Houston, TX 77002

Dean, Howard *Governor, VT*
%Governor's Office, Pavilion Office Bldg, Montpelier, VT 05609

Dean, Howard M *Businessman*
%Dean Foods Co, 3600 N River Rd, Franklin Park, IL 60131

Dean, James F *Businessman*
%Exxon Corp, 1251 Ave of Americas, New York, NY 10020

Dean, Jimmy *Singer*
%Tom Jennings Assoc, 28035 Dorothy Dr, #210-A, Agoura, CA 91301
Dean, John G *Diplomat*
%Department of State, 2201 "C" St NW, Washington, DC 20520
Dean, John W *Watergate Figure*
9496 Rembert Ln, Beverly Hills, CA 90210
Dean, Laura *Choreographer, Composer*
%Dean Dance & Music Foundation, 15 W 17th St, New York, NY 10011
Dean, R Hal *Businessman*
%Ralston Purina Co, Checkerboard Sq, St Louis, MO 63164
Dearden, James *Movie Director*
%International Creative Mgmt, 8899 Beverly Blvd, Los Angeles, CA 90048
Dearden, William E C *Businessman*
%Hershey Foods Corp, 100 Mansion Rd E, Hershey, PA 17033
Dearie, Blossom *Singer*
%The Ballroom, 253 W 28th St, New York, NY 10001
Dearth, Robert A *Businessman*
%Circle K Corp, 7th St & McDowell, Phoenix, AZ 85006
Deas, Justin *Actor*
%Gores/Fields Agency, 10100 Santa Monica Blvd, #700, Los Angeles, CA 90067
DeBarge, El *Singer*
%Motown Records, 6255 Sunset Blvd, Los Angeles, CA 90028
DeBartolo, Edward J, Jr *Football Executive*
%Edward J DeBartolo Corp, 7620 Market St, Youngstown, OH 44513
DeBell, Kristine *Actress, Model*
%Twentieth Century Artists, 3800 Barham Blvd, Los Angeles, CA 90068
DeBerg, Steve *Football Player*
%Kansas City Chiefs, 1 Arrowhead Dr, Kansas City, MO 64129
DeBold, Adolfo J *Medical Researcher*
%Ottawa Civic Hospital, 1053 Carling Ave, Ottawa ON K1Y 4E9, Canada
Debre, Michel *Prime Minister, France*
20 Rue Jacob, 75006 Paris, France
Debreu, Gerald *Nobel Economics Laureate*
267 Gravatt Dr, Berkeley, CA 94705
DeBusschere, Dave *Basketball Player*
90 3rd St, Garden City, NY 11530
Deby, Idriss *President, Chad*
%Office of Chief Executive, N'Djamena, Chad
DeCamp, Rosemary *Actress*
317 Camino de Los Colinas, Redondo Beach, CA 90277
DeCarlo, Yvonne *Actress*
PO Box 374, Los Olivos, CA 93441
DeCastella, Robert *Track Athlete*
%Australian Institute of Sport, PO Box 176, Belconnen ACT 2616, Australia
Decines, Doug *Baseball Player*
2 Lessburg Ct, Newport Beach, CA 92660
Decio, Arthur J *Businessman*
%Skyline Corp, 2520 By-Pass Rd, Elkhart, IN 46515
Decker Slaney, Mary *Track Athlete*
2923 Flintlock St, Eugene, OR 97402
DeConcini, John C *Labor Leader*
%Bakery Confectionery & Tobacco Union, 10401 Connecticut, Kensington, MD 20895
DeCoster, Roger *Motorcycle Racing Rider*
%MC Sports, 1919 Torrance Blvd, Torrance, CA 90501
Decourtray, Albert Cardinal *Religious Leader*
Archeveche de Lyon, 1 Place de Fourviere, 69321 Lyon Cedex 05, France
DeCrane, Alfred C, Jr *Businessman*
%Texaco Inc, 2000 Westchester Ave, White Plains, NY 10650
Decter, Midge *Writer*
120 E 81st St, New York, NY 10028
Dedeaux, Rod *Baseball Coach*
1430 S Eastman Ave, Los Angeles, CA 90023
Dedini, Eldon *Cartoonist*
PO Box 1630, Monterey, CA 93940
Dee, Frances *Actress*
Rt 3, Box 375, Camarillo, CA 93010

D

Dee – DeLay

Dee, Robert F *Businessman*
%SmithKline Beckman Corp, 1 Franklin Plz, Philadelphia, PA 19101

Dee, Ruby *Actress*
PO Box 1318, New Rochelle, NY 10802

Dee, Sandra *Actress*
%Morgan & Martindale, 10780 Santa Monica Blvd, #280, Los Angeles, CA 90025

Deeb, Gary *Television Critic*
%Chicago Sun-Times, 401 N Wabash Ave, Chicago, IL 60611

Deependra Bir Bikram Shah Dev *Crown Prince, Nepal*
%Narayanhity Royal Palace, Kathmandu, Nepal

Dees, Bowen Causey *Science Administrator*
%Franklin Institute, 20th & Benjamin Franklin Pkwy, Philadelphia, PA 19103

Dees, Rick *Actor*
19580 Wells Dr, Tarzana, CA 91356

Deffeyes, Robert J *Businessman*
%Carlisle Corp, 1600 Columbia Plz, Cincinnati, OH 45202

DeFigueiredo, Rui J P *Computer Engineer*
%University of California, Intelligent Sensors/Systems Lab, Irvine, CA 92717

DeFleur, Lois B *Educator*
%State University of New York, President's Office, Binghamton, NY 13902

Deford, Frank *Sportswriter*
%Newsweek Magazine, 444 Madison Ave, New York, NY 10022

DeFore, Don *Actor*
2496 Mandeville Ln, Los Angeles, CA 90049

DeForest, Roy *Artist*
PO Box 47, Port Costa, CA 94569

DeFranco, Buddy *Musician*
%WAI, 660 Madison Ave, New York, NY 10021

DeFrantz, Anita *Sports Executive*
%U S Olympic Committee, 1750 E Boulder St, Colorado Springs, CO 80909

DeFries, C E *Labor Leader*
%Marine Engineer Beneficial Assn, 444 N Capitol St NW, Washington, DC 20001

Degener, Richard *Diver*
2737 S Kihei Rd, Kihei, HI 96753

DeHaan, Richard W *Religious Leader*
3000 Kraft Ave SE, Grand Rapids, MI 49508

Dehmelt, Hans G *Nobel Physics Laureate*
1600 43rd Ave E, Seattle, WA 98112

Deighton, Len *Writer*
Fairymount, Blackrock, Dundalk, County Louth, Ireland

Deihl, Richard H *Financier*
%H F Ahmanson Co, 3731 Wilshire Blvd, Los Angeles, CA 90010

Deisenhofer, Johann *Nobel Chemistry Laureate*
%Howard Hughes Medical Institute, 5323 Harry Hines Blvd, Dallas, TX 75235

Del Monaco, Mario *Opera Singer*
%Metropolitan Opera Assn, Lincoln Ctr, New York, NY 10023

Del Portillo, Alvaro *Religious Leader*
%Opus Dei, Viale Bruno Buozzi 73, 00197 Rome, Italy

Del Rio, Jack *Football Player*
%Dallas Cowboys, 1 Cowboys Pkwy, Irving, TX 75063

Del Tredici, David *Composer*
463 West St, #G-121, New York, NY 10014

DeLamielleure, Joe *Football Player*
149 Medaris Dr, Charlotte, NC 28211

Delaney, Kim *Actress*
%William Morris Agency, 151 El Camino, Beverly Hills, CA 90212

Delaney, Shelagh *Playwright*
%Tess Sayle, 11 Jubilee Pl, London SW3 3TE, England

Delano, Robert B *Association Executive*
%American Farm Bureau Federation, 225 Touhy Ave, Park Ridge, IL 60068

Delany, Dana *Actress*
%International Creative Mgmt, 8899 Beverly Blvd, Los Angeles, CA 90048

DeLap, Tony *Artist*
225 Jasmine St, Corona del Mar, CA 92625

DeLay, Tom *Representative, TX*
%House of Representatives, Washington, DC 20515

Deleeuw, Dianne *Figure Skater*
%Ice Follies, 3201 New Mexico Ave NW, Washington, DC 20016

Delfont, Bernard *Impressario, Movie Executive*
%Trusthouse Forte Leisure Ltd, 17 Golden Sq, London W1R 3AG, England

Delgado, Pedro *Cyclist*
%General Delivery, Segovia, Spain

DeLillo, Don *Writer*
%Wallace & Sheil, 177 E 70th St, New York, NY 10021

Dell'Olio, Louis *Fashion Designer*
%Anne Klein & Co, 205 W 39th St, New York, NY 10018

Dell, Donald L *Tennis Player, Attorney*
%ProServ Inc, 888 17th St NW, #1200, Washington, DC 20006

Della Casa-Debeljevic, Lisa *Opera Singer*
Schloss Gottlieben, Thurgau, Switzerland 10504

Della Femina, Jerry *Businessman*
625 Madison Ave, New York, NY 10022

Della Malva, Joseph *Actor*
%William Morris Agency, 151 El Camino, Beverly Hills, CA 90212

Dello Joio, Norman *Composer*
PO Box 154, Hampton, NY 11937

Dellums, Ronald V *Representative, CA*
%House of Representatives, Washington, DC 20515

Delmotte, Louis *Financier*
%Kredietbank, Arenbergstraat 7, 1000 Brussels, Belgium

Delo, Ken *Actor*
%Bush & Ross Talents, 4942 Vineland Ave, North Hollywood, CA 91601

Delon, Alain *Actor*
%Adel Productions, 4 Rue Chambiges, 75008 Paris, France

Deloria, Vine (Victor), Jr *Indian Rights Activist*
%CSERA, University of Colorado, Campus Box 339, Boulder, CO 80309

Delorme, Jean Henri *Businessman*
%Liquid Air Corp, 1 Embarcadero Ctr, San Francisco, CA 94111

Delruelle, Gerard *Businessman*
%Cockerille Sambre, 1 Ave A Greiner, 4100 Seraing, Belgium

Delugg, Milton *Musician*
2740 Claray Dr, Los Angeles, CA 90024

DeLuise, Dom *Comedian*
1186 Corsica Dr, Pacific Palisades, CA 90272

DeLuise, Peter *Actor*
%William Morris Agency, 151 El Camino, Beverly Hills, CA 90212

Delvaux, Paul *Artist*
42 Kabouterweg, 8670 St Idesbald, Belgium

Delvecchio, Alex *Hockey Player*
%Detroit Red Wings, 600 Civic Center Dr, Detroit, MI 48226

Demarchelier, Patrick *Photographer*
162 W 21st St, New York, NY 10011

Demarest, Arthur A *Archeologist*
%Vanderbilt University, Anthropology Dept, Nashville, TN 37235

Demars, Bruce *Navy Admiral*
Director, Naval Nuclear Propulsion, Navy Department, Washington, DC 20362

Demers, Jacques *Hockey Coach*
%Detroit Red Wings, 600 Civic Center Dr, Detroit, MI 48226

Demetriadis, Phokion *Editorial Cartoonist*
3rd September St 174, Athens, Greece

Demeure de Lespaul, Adolphe *Businessman*
%Petrofina, Rue de la Loi 33, 1040 Brussels, Belgium

Demin, Lev *Cosmonaut*
141 160 Svyosdny Gorodok, Moskovskoi Oblasti, Potchta Kosmonavtov, Russia

Deming, W Edwards *Management Expert*
4924 Butterworth Pl NW, Washington, DC 20016

Demirel, Suleiman *President, Turkey*
Adalet Partisi, Ankara, Turkey

Demme, Jonathan *Movie Director*
1355 Miller Pl, Los Angeles, CA 90069

Demos, George J *Businessman*
%General Signal Corp, High Ridge Park, Stamford, CT 06904

D

Demos – Dennis

Demos, John *Businessman*
%Super Food Services, Kettering Box 2323, Dayton, OH 45429

Dempsey, Jerry E *Businessman*
%Waste Management Inc, 3003 Butterfield Rd, Oak Brook, IL 60521

Dempsey, John C *Businessman*
%Greif Bros Corp, 621 Pennsylvania Ave, Delaware, OH 43015

Dempsey, Patrick *Actor*
431 Lincoln Blvd, Santa Monica, CA 90402

Dempsey, Rick *Baseball Player*
5641 Mason Ave, Woodland Hills, CA 91364

Dempsey, William H *Association Executive*
%Assn of American Railroads, 1920 "L" St NW, Washington, DC 20036

Dempster, Carol *Actress*
5815 La Jolla Mesa Dr, La Jolla, CA 92037

Demske, James M *Educator*
%Canisius College, President's Office, Buffalo, NY 14208

Demus, Joerg *Concert Pianist*
%LYRA, Doblinger Hauptstrasse 77-A/10, 1190 Vienna, Austria

DeMuth, Laurence W, Jr *Businessman*
%US West Inc, 7800 E Orchard Rd, Englewood, CO 80111

Demuth, Richard H *Attorney, Financier*
5404 Bradley Blvd, Bethesda, MD 20814

Den Hartog, Jacob Pieter *Engineer*
Barnes Hill Rd, Concord, MA 01742

Den Herder, Vern *Football Player*
%General Delivery, Sioux Center, IA 51250

Den Ouden, Willy *Swimmer*
Goudsewagenstraat 23-B, Rotterdam, Holland

Den Tagayasu *Choreographer*
%Ondekoza, Koda Performing Arts Co, Sado Island, Japan

Denard, Michael *Ballet Dancer*
%Paris Opera Ballet, Pl de l'Opera, 75009 Paris, France

Dench, Judi *Actress*
%Leading Artists, 60 St James St, London SW1, England

Denenberg, Herbert S *Educator, Government Official*
PO Box 146, Wynnewood, PA 19096

Denes, Agnes C *Artist*
595 Broadway, New York, NY 10012

Deneuve, Catherine *Actress*
76 Rue Bonaparte, 75016 Paris, France

Deng Xiaoping *Chairman, Chinese Communist Party*
%Communist Party Central Committee, Beijing, China

Denham, Maurice *Actor*
44 Brunswick Gardens, #2, London W8, England

DeNiro, Robert *Actor*
%Tribeca Productions, Tribeca Film Center, 375 Greenwich St, New York, NY 10013

Denison, Anthony John *Actor*
%InterTalent Agency, 131 S Rodeo Dr, #300, Beverly Hills, CA 90212

Denison, Edward F *Economist*
Cottage 846, Sherwood Forest, MD 21405

Denker, Henry *Playwright*
241 Central Park West, New York, NY 10024

Denlea, Leo E, Jr *Businessman*
%Farmers Grp, 4680 Wilshire Blvd, Los Angeles, CA 90010

Dennehy, Brian *Actor*
%Susan Smith Assoc, 121 N San Vicente Blvd, Beverly Hills, CA 90211

Denney, Kathleen *Actress*
%Susan Nathe Assoc, 8281 Melrose Ave, #200, Los Angeles, CA 90046

Denning of Whitechurch, Baron *Judge*
The Lawn, Whitechurch, Hants, England

Denning, Richard *Actor*
%Lew Deuser Agency, 449 S Beverly Dr, Beverly Hills, CA 90212

Dennis, Dean R *Businessman*
%Robertshaw Controls Co, 1701 Byrd Ave, Richmond, VA 23261

Dennis, Richard *Financier*
%C&D Commodities, 4 World Trade Ctr, New York, NY 10047

Dennis, Sandy *Actress*
93 N Sylvan Rd, Westport, CT 06880

Dennison, Rachel *Actress*
%Katz-Gallin-Morey, 9255 Sunset Blvd, Los Angeles, CA 90069

Denny, J William *Businessman*
%Nashville Gas Co, 814 Church St, Nashville, TN 37203

Densen-Gerber, Judianne *Psychiatrist, Social Activist*
%Odyssey Resources Inc, 817 Fairfield Ave, Bridgeport, CT 06604

Dent, Bucky *Baseball Player*
5540 E Coach House Cir, Boca Raton, FL 33432

Dent, Frederick B *Secretary, Commerce*
19 Montgomery Dr, Spartanburg, SC 29302

Dent, Richard *Football Player*
%Chicago Bears, 250 N Washington Rd, Lake Forest, IL 60045

Denton, Jeremiah A, Jr *Senator, AL*
Rt 1, Box 305, Theodore, AL 36582

DeNunzio, Ralph D *Financier*
%Kidder Peabody Co, 10 Hanover Sq, New York, NY 10005

Denver, Bob *Actor*
6010 W Cheyenne Ave, #615, Las Vegas, NV 89108

Denver, John *Singer, Songwriter*
PO Box 1587, Aspen, CO 81612

DeOre, Bill *Editorial Cartoonist*
%Dallas Morning News, Communications Ctr, Dallas, TX 75265

Depardieu, Gerald *Actor*
4 Pl de la Chapale, Bougival, France

Depp, Johnny *Actor*
%International Creative Mgmt, 8899 Beverly Blvd, Los Angeles, CA 90048

DePree, Hugh D *Businessman*
%Herman Miller Inc, 8500 Byron Rd, Zeeland, MI 49464

DePree, Max O *Businessman*
%Herman Miller Inc, 8500 Byron Rd, Zeeland, MI 49464

Dequae, Andre *Financier*
%Banque Bruxelles Lambert, 24 Ave Marnix, 1050 Brussels, Belgium

Dercum, Max *Skier*
PO Box 189, Dillon, CO 80435

Derek, Bo *Actress*
3625 Roblar, Santa Ynez, CA 93460

Derek, John *Actor*
3625 Roblar, Santa Ynez, CA 93460

Dern, Bruce *Actor*
23430 Malibu Colony Rd, Malibu, CA 90265

Dern, Laura *Actress*
%InterTalent Agency, 131 S Rodeo Dr, #300, Beverly Hills, CA 90212

Dernesch, Helga *Opera Singer*
Hauptstrasse 56, 3400 Weidling, Austria

DeRoburt, Hammer *President, Nauru*
%President's Office, Yaren, Nauru

DeRogatis, Al *Football Player*
%Prudential Life Insurance, Prudential Plz, Newark, NJ 07101

Derosier, Michael *Drummer (Heart)*
219 N 1st Ave N, #333, Seattle, WA 98109

DeRover, Jolanda *Swimmer*
%Olympic Committee, Surinamestraat 33, 2514 La Harve, Netherlands

Derow, Peter A *Publisher*
Old Roaring Brook Rd, Chappaqua, NY 10514

Derr, Kenneth T *Businessman*
%Chevron Corp, 225 Bush St, San Francisco, CA 94104

Derr, Richard *Actor*
8965 Cynthia St, West Hollywood, CA 90069

Derrick, Butler C, Jr *Representative, SC*
Stonehenge Rd, Edgefield, SC 29824

Derricks, Cleavant *Actor*
%Susan Smith Assoc, 121 N San Vicente, Beverly Hills, CA 90211

Dershowitz, Alan M *Attorney, Educator*
%Harvard University, Law School, Cambridge, MA 02138

D

Derveloy – DeVos

Derveloy, Christian *Businessman*
%Prouvost, 149 Rue d'Oran, 59061 Roubaix Cedex 1, France

Derwinski, Edward J *Secretary, Veterans Affairs*
%Department of Veterans Affairs, 810 Vermont Ave NW, Washington, DC 20420

Desai, Shri Morarji Ranchhodji *Prime Minister, India*
Oceana, Marine Dr, Bombay, India

DeSailly, Jean *Actor*
53 Quai des Grands Augustins, 75006 Paris, France

Deschanel, Caleb *Movie Director, Cinematographer*
575 Tahquitz Pl, Pacific Palisades. CA 90272

Deschanel, Mary Jo *Actress*
844 Chautauqua Blvd, Pacific Palisades, CA 90272

DeShannon, Jackie *Singer*
%Stone Manners Agency, 9113 Sunset Blvd, Los Angeles, CA 90069

Deshays, Claudie *Spatinaut, France*
%Hopital Cochin, Rhumatologie Dept, 75000 Paris, France

Desiderio, Robert *Actor*
3960 Laurel Canyon Blvd, #280, Studio City, CA 91604

DeSimone, Livio D *Businessman*
%Minnesota Mining & Manufacturing Co, 3-M Ctr, St Paul, MN 55144

Desio, Ardito *Explorer, Geologist*
Viale Maino 14, 20129 Milan, Italy

Deskur, Andrzej Maria Cardial *Religious Leader*
Council for Social Communications, Vatican City, Rome, Italy

Desny, Ivan *Actor*
Casa al Sole, 6612 CH-Ascona-Collina, Switzerland

Dethier, Vincent Gaston *Biologist*
%University of Massachusetts, Zoology Dept, Amherst, MA 01003

Detmar, Ty *Football Player*
%Brigham Young University, Athletic Dept, Provo, UT 84602

Detweiler, Robert *Educator*
%California State University, President's Office, Dominguez Hills, CA 90747

Detwiler, Peter M *Financier*
%E F Hutton Grp, 1 Battery Park Plz, New York, NY 10004

Deukmejian, George *Governor, CA*
%Sidley & Austin, 633 W 5th St, #3500, Los Angeles, CA 90071

Deutekom, Cristina *Opera Singer*
Lancasterdreef 41, Dronten 8251 T G, Holland

Deutsch, Patti *Actress*
%Barry Freed Co, 9255 Sunset Blvd, Los Angeles, CA 90069

Devan Nair, Chandra Veetil *President, Singapore*
%Istana, Singapore 0922, Singapore

Devaney, Bob *Football Coach*
%University of Nebraska, Athletic Dept, Lincoln, NE 68588

DeVarona, Donna *Swimmer, Sportscaster*
30 Lincoln Plz, #1300, New York, NY 10023

Devenow, Chester *Businessman*
%Sheller-Globe Corp, 1505 Jefferson Ave, Toldeo, OH 43624

Deville, Michel *Movie Director*
36 Rue Reinhardt, 92100 Boulogne, France

Devine, Dan *Football Coach*
%Sun Angel Foundation, 3800 N Central Ave, #D-3, Phoenix, AZ 85012

DeVita, Vincent T, Jr *Oncologist*
%Memorial Sloan Kettering Cancer Ctr, 1275 York Ave, New York, NY 10021

DeVito, Mathias J *Businessman*
%Rouse Co, Rouse Bldg, Columbia, MD 21044

Devitt, James E *Businessman*
%Mutual Life Insurance, 1740 Broadway, New York, NY 10019

Devitt, John *Swimmer*
46 Beacon Ave, Beacon Hill NSW 2100, Australia

Devlin, Bruce *Golfer*
2907 Pine Lake Trl, Houston, TX 77068

Devlin, John *Actor*
825 N Crescent Heights Blvd, Los Angeles, CA 90046

DeVos, Richard M *Businessman*
%Amway Corp, 7575 E Fulton Rd, Ada, MI 49355

DeVries, William C *Surgeon*
%Humana Inc, 1800 First National Tower, Louisville, KY 40202
Dewar, Jane E *Editor*
%Legion Magazine, 359 Kent St, #504, Ottawa ON K2P 0R6, Canada
Dewar, Marion *Mayor*
869 Rex Ave, Ottawa ON, Canada
Dewar, Michael J S *Chemist*
6808 Mesa Dr, Austin, TX 78731
Dewar, Robert E *Businessman*
%K Mart Corp, 3100 W Big Beaver Rd, Troy, MI 48084
Dewey, Duane E *Korean War Marine Corps Hero (CMH)*
Rt 1, Box 494, Irons, MI 49644
Dewey, L William, Jr *Businessman*
%Briggs & Stratton Corp, 12301 W Wirth St, Wauwatosa, WI 53222
DeWilde, Edy *Museum Director*
%Stedelijk Museum, Amsterdam, Netherlands
DeWine, Michael *Representative, OH*
%House of Representatives, Washington, DC 20515
Dey, Susan *Actress*
9542 Cherokee Ln, Beverly Hills, CA 90210
Di Beligiojoso, Lodovico B *Architect*
%Studio Architetti BBPR, 2 Via Dei Chiostri, Milan, Italy
Di Mucci, Dion *Singer*
19301 Ventura Blvd, #205, Tarzana, CA 91356
Di Paolo, Nicholas P *Businessman*
%Manhattan Industries Inc, 1155 Ave of Americas, New York, NY 10036
Di Preta, Tony *Cartoonist (Rex Morgan, MD; Joe Palooka)*
%North America Syndicate, 200 Park Ave, New York, NY 10166
Di Sant'Angelo, Giorgio *Fashion Designer*
20 W 57th St, New York, NY 10019
Di Stefano, Giuseppe *Opera Singer*
Via Palatino 10, 20148 Milan, Italy
Di Suvero, Mark *Sculptor*
%Richard Bellamy, 333 Park Ave S, New York, NY 10010
Di Tolla, Alfred W *Labor Leader*
%Threatical/Stage/Movie Machine Operators, 1515 Broadway, New York, NY 10036
Dials, Lou *Baseball Player*
12311 Chandler Blvd, #9, North Hollywood, CA 91607
Diamandis, Peter G *Publisher*
%Diamandis Communications, 1515 Broadway, New York, NY 10036
Diamond, David L *Composer*
249 Edgerton St, Rochester, NY 14607
Diamond, Michael *Singer (Beastie Boys)*
%Beastie Boys, Rush Productions, 1133 Broadway, New York, NY 10010
Diamond, Neil *Singer, Songwriter*
161 S Mapleton Dr, Los Angeles, CA 90048
Diamond, Seymour *Physician*
%Diamond Headache Clinic, 5252 N Western Ave, Chicago, IL 60625
Diamond, William *Financier*
3315 Garfield St NW, Washington, DC 20008
Diamont, Don *Actor*
%Craig Agency, 8485 Melrose Pl, Los Angeles, CA 90069
Diana *Princess, Wales*
Highgrove House, Doughton, Tetbury, Glos 8TG GL8, England
Diaz Alvarez, Juan Antonio *Businessman*
%SEAT, Paseo de la Castellana 278, Madrid 16, Spain
Diaz-Verson, Salvador, Jr *Businessman*
%American Family Corp, 1932 Wynnton Rd, Columbus, GA 31999
DiBiaggio, John *Educator*
%Michigan State University, President's Office, East Lansing, MI 48824
Dibiasi, Klaus *Diver*
Via Baiamonti 4, Rome, Italy
DiBona, Richard T *Businessman*
%M/A-Com Inc, 7 New England Executive Park, Burlington, MA 01803
DiCarlo, Dominick L *Judge*
%US Court of International Trade, 1 Federal Plz, New York, NY 10007

D

DiCenzo, George *Actor*
RD 1, Box 728, Stone Hollow Farm, Pipersville, PA 18947

Dichter, Mischa *Concert Pianist*
%International Creative Mgmt Artists, 40 W 57th St, New York, NY 10019

Dick, Douglas *Actor*
604 Gretna Green Way, Los Angeles, CA 90049

Dicke, Robert H *Physicist*
321 Prospect Ave, Princeton, NJ 08540

Dickens, Jimmy *Singer*
5010 W Concord, Brentwood, TN 37027

Dicker, Richard *Businessman*
%Penn Central Corp, 500 W Putnam Ave, Greenwich, CT 06836

Dickerson, Eric *Football Player*
%Indianapolis Colts, 7001 W 56th St, Indianapolis, IN 46254

Dickey, Bill *Baseball Player*
5817 S Country Club Blvd, Little Rock, AR 72207

Dickey, Charles D, Jr *Businessman*
%Scott Paper Co, Scott Plz, Philadelphia, PA 19113

Dickey, James *Writer*
4620 Lelia's Ct, Columbia, SC 29206

Dickey, Lynn *Football Player*
8100 Parkhill, Lenexa, KS 66215

Dickey, Robert W *Businessman*
%Paccar Inc, 777 106th Ave NE, Bellevue, WA 98004

Dickey, Robert, III *Businessman*
%Dravo Corp, 1 Oliver Plz, Pittsburgh, PA 15222

Dickey, William D *Businessman*
%Cyclops Corp, 650 Washington Rd, Pittsburgh, PA 15228

Dickinson, Angie *Actress*
9580 Lime Orchard Rd, Beverly Hills, CA 90210

Dickinson, Judy *Golfer*
%Ladies Professional Golf Assn, 2570 Volusia Ave, #B, Daytona Beach, FL 32114

Dickinson, William L *Representative, AL*
%House of Representatives, Washington, DC 20515

Dickman, James B *Photographer*
%Dallas Times-Herald, Herald Sq, Dallas, TX 75202

Dicks, Norman D *Representative, WA*
%House of Representatives, Washington, DC 20515

Dickson, Chris *Yachtsman*
%International Management Grp, 1 Erieview Plz, Cleveland, OH 44114

Dickson, Clarence *Law Enforcement Official*
%Police Department, Metro Justice, 1351 NW 12th St, Miami, FL 33125

Diebenkorn, Richard *Artist*
334 Amalfi Dr, Santa Monica, CA 90402

Diebold, John *Businessman*
%Diebold Grp, 475 Park Ave, New York, NY 10016

Dieckamp, Herman *Businessman*
%General Public Utilities Corp, 100 Interpace Pkwy, Parsippany, NJ 07054

Diefenbacker, John G *Prime Minister, Canada*
115 Lansdowne Rd, Ottawa ON, Canada

Diehl, Digby *Journalist*
788 S Lake Ave, Pasadena, CA 91106

Dierdof, Dan *Football Player, Sportscaster*
%ABC-TV, Sports Dept, 1330 Ave of Americas, New York, NY 10019

Dierker, Larry *Baseball Player*
8318 N Tahoe, Houston, TX 77040

Dietrich, Bill *Journalist*
%Seattle Times, Fairview Ave N & John St, Seattle, WA 98111

Dietrich, Dena *Actress*
4006 Madelia Ave, Sherman Oaks, CA 91403

Dietrich, Marlene *Actress*
12 Ave Montaigne, 75008 Paris, France

Diffrient, Niels *Industrial Designer*
%General Delivery, Ridgefield, CT 06877

DiGenova, Joseph E *Attorney*
%US Attorney's Office, Washington, DC 20001

D

DiGirolamo – Dionne

DiGirolamo, Joseph — *Businessman*
%CTS Corp, 905 N West Blvd, Elkhart, IN 46514

DiGregorio, Ernie — *Basketball Player*
60 Chestnut Ave, Narragansett, RI 02882

Dilenschneider, Robert L — *Businessman*
%Hill & Knowlton Inc, 633 3rd Ave, New York, NY 10017

Dill, Guy — *Artist*
819 Milwood Ave, Venice, CA 90291

Dill, Laddie John — *Artist*
1625 Electric Ave, Venice, CA 90291

Dillard, Annie — *Writer*
%Blanch Gregory, 2 Tudor Pl, New York, NY 10017

Dillard, Harrison — *Track Athlete*
3842 E 147th St, Cleveland, OH 44128

Dille, Earl K — *Businessman*
%Union Electric Co, 1901 Gratiot St, St Louis, MO 63103

Diller, Barry — *Entertainment Executive*
1940 Coldwater Canyon Dr, Beverly Hills, CA 90210

Diller, Phyllis — *Comedienne*
163 S Rockingham Rd, Los Angeles, CA 90049

Dillman, Bradford — *Actor*
770 Hot Springs Rd, Santa Barbara, CA 93103

Dillon, C Douglas — *Secretary, Treasury*
1270 Ave of Americas, #2300, New York, NY 10020

Dillon, Gary G — *Businessman*
%Household Manufacturing, 2700 Sanders Rd, Prospect Heights, IL 60070

Dillon, George C — *Businessman*
%Manville Corp, Ken-Caryl Ranch, Denver, CO 80217

Dillon, John R — *Businessman*
%Cox Enterprises, 1400 Lake Hearn Dr NE, Atlanta, GA 30319

Dillon, Matt — *Actor*
%Vic Ramos, 49 W 9th St, New York, NY 10011

Dillon, Melinda — *Actress*
%STE Representation, 9301 Wilshire Blvd, #312, Beverly Hills, CA 90210

Dillon, Ray E, Jr — *Businessman*
%Kroger Co, 1014 Vine St, Cincinnati, OH 45202

Dillon, Richard W — *Businessman*
%Kroger Co, 1014 Vine St, Cincinnati, OH 45202

DiMaggio, Dom — *Baseball Player*
162 Point Rd, Marion, MA 02738

DiMaggio, Joe — *Baseball Player*
2150 Beach St, San Francisco, CA 94123

Dimbleby, David — *Journalist, Commentator*
14 King St, Richmond, Surrey TW9 1NF, England

Dine, James — *Artist*
%Pace Gallery, 32 E 57th St, New York, NY 10022

Dineen, Bill — *Hockey Coach*
%Philadelphia Flyers, Pattison Pl, Philadelphia, PA 19148

Dineen, Kevin — *Hockey Player*
%Hartford Whalers, 1 Civic Center Plz, Hartford, CT 06103

Dingell, John D, Jr — *Representative, MI*
%House of Representatives, Washington, DC 20515

Dingman, Michael D — *Businessman*
%Henley Grp, 11255 N Tory Pines Rd, La Jolla, CA 92037

Dinitz, Simcha — *Government Official, Israel*
40 Nayot, Jerusalem, Israel

Dinitz, Simon — *Educator*
298 N Cassidy St, Columbus, OH 43209

Dinkins, David N — *Mayor*
%Mayor's Office, Gracie Mansion, New York, NY 10007

Dioguardi, Joseph — *Representative, NY*
%House of Representatives, Washington, DC 20515

Dion, Philip J — *Businessman*
%Del E Webb Corp, 3800 N Central Ave, Phoenix, AZ 85012

Dionne, Joseph L — *Publisher*
%McGraw-Hill Inc, 1221 Ave of Americas, New York, NY 10020

D

Dionne, Marcel *Hockey Player*
30 Empty Saddle, Rolling Hills, CA 90274

Diouf, Abdou *President, Senegal*
%President's Office, Dakar, Senegal

DiPaolo, Domeric *Labor Leader*
%Leather Goods Plastic Novelty Workers Union, 265 W 14th St, New York, NY 10011

Dipertuan *Sultan & Yang, Brunei Darussalam*
%Suntan & Yang's Residence, Bandar Seri Begawan, Brunei Darussalam

DiPrete, Edward D *Governor, RI*
555 Wilbur Ave, Cranston, RI 02920

DiSalle, Michael V *Governor, OH; Government Official*
Watergate East, #1014-N, 2510 Virginia Ave NW, Washington, DC 20037

Disbrow, Richard E *Businessman*
%American Electric Power Co, 1 Riverside Plz, Columbus, OH 43215

Disch, Thomas M *Writer*
%Karpfinger Agency, 500 5th Ave, New York, NY 10110

Dischinger, Terry *Basketball Player*
3943 SW Douglas Way, Lake Oswego, OR 97034

Dishy, Bob *Actor*
20 E 9th St, New York, NY 10003

Disney, Anthea *Editor*
%TV Guide Magazine, 100 Matsonville Rd, Radnor, PA 19088

Disney, Roy E *Entertainment Executive*
%Shamrock Broadcasting Co, 4444 Lakeside Dr, Burbank, CA 91510

Distal, Sacha *Singer*
3 Quai Malaquais, 75006 Paris, France

Ditka, Mike *Football Player, Coach*
%Chicago Bears, 250 N Washington Rd, Lake Forest, IL 60045

Ditz, Nancy *Track Athlete*
524 Moore Rd, Woodside, CA 94069

Divac, Vlade *Basketball Player*
%Los Angeles Lakers, Great Western Forum, 3939 Manchester, Inglewood, CA 90306

Divine, Harold S *Businessman*
%Rapid-American Corp, 888 7th Ave, New York, NY 10106

DiVlio, Albert J *Educator*
%Marquette University, President's Office, Milwaukee, WI 53233

Diwakar, R R *Writer*
%Sri Arvind Krupa, 233 Sadashiv Nagar, Bangalore 560006, Karnataka, India

Dix, Drew D *Vietnam War Army Hero (CMH)*
%Tundra Air, General Delivery, Manley Hot Springs, AK 99756

Dixon, Alan J *Senator, IL*
7606 Foley Dr, Belleville, IL 62223

Dixon, Becky *Sportscaster*
%ABC-TV, Sports Dept, 1330 Ave of Americas, New York, NY 10019

Dixon, Donna *Actress*
%Edrick/Rich Mgmt, 8955 Norma Pl, Los Angeles, CA 90069

Dixon, Frank J *Pathologist, Immunologist*
2355 Avenida de la Playa, La Jolla, CA 92037

Dixon, George F, Jr *Businessman*
%Carlisle Corp, 1600 Columbia Plz, Cincinnati, OH 45202

Dixon, George H *Financier*
%First Bank System, 1200 First Bank Pl E, Minneapolis, MN 55402

Dixon, Hanford *Football Player*
%San Francisco 49ers, 4949 Centennial Blvd, Santa Clara, CA 95054

Dixon, Ivan *Actor*
3432 N Marengo Ave, Altadena, CA 91001

Dixon, Jeane *Psychic, Columnist*
%James L Dixon & Co, 1225 Connecticut Ave NW, Washington, DC 20036

Dixon, John W *Businessman*
%E-Systems Inc, 6250 LBJ Fwy, Dallas, TX 75266

Dixon, Julian C *Representative, CA*
%House of Representatives, Washington, DC 20515

Dixon, Kenneth H M *Businessman*
%Rowntree Mackintosh, York YO1 1XY, England

Dixon, Kent *Financier*
%Northeast Savings, 147 Charter Oak Ave, Hartford, CT 06106

Dixon, Mead *Businessman*
%Harrah's Casino, 219 N Center St, Reno, NV 89501

Dixon, Randy *Football Player*
%University of Pittsburgh, Athletic Dept, Pittsburgh, PA 15260

Dixon, Robert W *Businessman*
%Harvey Hubbell Inc, 584 Derby Milford Rd, Orange, NJ 06477

Dixon, Rod *Track Athlete*
1010 Doyce Ave, #9, Menlo Park, CA 94025

Dixon, Sharon Pratt *Mayor, Washington*
%Mayor's Office, District Bldg, 14th & "E" NW, Washington, DC 20004

Djerassi, Carl *Chemist*
%Stanford University, Chemistry Dept, Stanford, CA 94305

Djian, Philippe *Writer*
%Weidenfeld & Nicolson, 10 E 53rd St, New York, NY 10022

Djilas, Milovan *Government Official, Yugoslavia; Writer*
%Harcourt Brace & Jovanovich, 757 3rd Ave, New York, NY 10017

Djuranovic, Veselin *President, Yugoslavia*
%Federal Executive Council, Bul Lenjina 2, 11075 Novi Belgrad, Yugoslavia

Do Moi *Prime Minister, Vietnam*
%Chairman's Office, Council of Ministers, Hanoi, Vietnam

Do Nascimento, Alexandre Cardinal *Religious Leader*
Arcebispado, CP 87, Luanda, Angola

Doan, Charles A *Physician*
4935 Oletangy Blvd, Columbus, OH 43214

Doan, Herbert D *Businessman*
3801 Valley Dr, Midland, MI 48640

Doar, John *Attorney*
9 E 63rd St, New York, NY 10021

Dobbin, Edmund J *Educator*
%Villanova University, President's Office, Villanova, PA 19085

Dobbs, Glenn *Football Player*
7436 S Winston Pl, Tulsa, OK 74136

Dobbs, Mattiwilda *Opera Singer*
1101 S Arlington Ridge Rd, Arlington, VA 22202

Dobey, James K *Financier*
%Wells Fargo Co, 420 Montgomery St, San Francisco, CA 94163

Dobkin, Lawrence *Movie Director, Actor*
1787 Old Ranch Rd, Los Angeles, CA 90049

Dobler, Conrad *Football Player*
%KCMO-Radio, 508 Westport Rd, Kansas City, MO 64111

Dobson, James C *Religious Leader*
%Focus on the Family, 801 Corporate Ctr, Pomona, CA 91768

Dobson, Kevin *Actor*
11930 Iredell St, Studio City, CA 91604

Dobson, Tamara *Actress*
1880 Century Park East, #819, Los Angeles, CA 90067

Doby, Larry *Baseball Player*
Nishuane Rd, #45, Montclair, NJ 07042

Dockson, Robert R *Financier*
%CalFed Inc, 5670 Wilshire Blvd, Los Angeles, CA 90036

Dockstader, Frederick J *Museum Director*
165 W 66th St, New York, NY 10023

Doctorow, E L *Novelist*
170 Broadview Ave, New Rochelle, NY 10804

Dodd, Carl H *Korean War Army Hero (CMH)*
RR 4, Box 269, Corbin, KY 40701

Dodd, Christopher J *Senator, CT*
%US Senate, Washington, DC 20510

Dodd, Edwin D *Businessman*
%Owens-Illinois Inc, 1 SeaGate, Toledo, OH 43666

Dodd, Lamar *Artist*
%University of Georgia, Art Dept, Athens, GA 30602

Dodd, Patty *Volleyball Player*
%Danskin Inc, 111 W 40th St, 18th Fl, New York, NY 10018

Dodge, Brooks *Skier*
Box "C", Jackson, NH 03846

Dodge, John Vilas *Editor*
%Encyclopedia Brittanica, 3851 N Mission Hills Rd, Northbrook, IL 60062
Dodson, Jack *Actor*
%Twentieth Century Artists, 3800 Barham Blvd, Los Angeles, CA 90068
Doering, William von Eggers *Chemist*
53 Francis Ave, Cambridge, MA 02138
Doerr, Bobby *Baseball Player*
33705 Illamo-Agness Rd, Agness, OR 97406
Doerr, Harriet *Writer*
%Viking Penguin Press, 40 W 23rd St, New York, NY 10010
Doerr, Howard P *Businessman*
%US West Inc, 7800 E Orchard Rd, Englewood, CO 80111
Doherty, Ken *Track Coach*
347 Michigan Ave, Swarthmore, PA 19081
Doherty, Shannen *Actress*
%Larry Thompson Organization, 345 N Maple Dr, #183, Beverly Hills, CA 90210
Doi, Takao *Astronaut, Japan*
%NSDA, 2-4-1 Hamamatsucho, Minatoku, Tokyo 105, Japan
Dolan, Beverly Franklin *Businessman*
%Textron Inc, 40 Westminster St, Providence, RI 02903
Dolan, Thomas I *Businessman*
%A O Smith Corp, 11270 W Park Pl, Milwaukee, WI 53224
Dolby, David C *Vietnam War Army Hero (CMH)*
Pekiomen Ave, PO Box 218, Oaks, PA 19456
Dolby, Ray *Inventor, Sound Engineer*
%Dolby Laboratories, 100 Potrero Ave, San Francisco, CA 94103
Dolby, Thomas *Singer*
%Capitol Records, 1750 N Vine St, Los Angeles, CA 90028
Dolci, Danilo *Writer, Social Worker*
Centro Iniziative Studi, Largo Scalia 5, 90047, Partinico/Palermo, Italy
Dole, Elizabeth H *Secretary, Health-Human Services; Labor*
%Watergate South, #112, 2510 Virginia Ave NW, Washington, DC 20037
Dole, Robert J *Senator, KS*
%Watergate South, #112, 2510 Virginia Ave NW, Washington, DC 20037
Dole, Vincent P *Medical Researcher*
%Rockefeller University, 1230 York Ave, New York, NY 10021
Doleman, Chris *Football Player*
%Minnesota Vikings, 9520 Viking Dr, Eden Prairie, MN 55344
Dolenz, Mickey *Actor, Musician*
2921 W Alameda Ave, Burbank, CA 91505
Dolive, Earl *Businessman*
%Genuine Parts Co, 2999 Circle 75 Pkwy, Atlanta, GA 30339
Doll, Richard *Epidemiologist*
12 Rawlinson Rd, Oxford, England
Dollar, Linda *Volleyball Coach*
%Southwest Missouri State University, Athletic Dept, Springfield, MO 65804
Dollfus, Audouin *Astronomer, Physicist*
%Observatoire de Paris, 5 Place Jules Janssen, 92195 Meudon, France
Dolson, Charles H *Businessman*
660 W Conway Dr NW, Atlanta, GA 30327
Dombasle, Arielle *Actress*
%Paul Kohner Inc, 9169 Sunset Blvd, Los Angeles, CA 90069
Dombrowski, Jim *Football Player*
%New Orleans Saints, 6928 Saints Dr, Metairie, LA 70003
Domenici, Pete V *Senator, NM*
11110 Stephalee Ln, Rockville, MD 20852
Domingo, Placido *Opera Singer*
%Eric Semon Assoc, 111 W 57th St, New York, NY 10019
Dominick, Peter H *Senator, CO*
5050 E Quincy St, Englewood, CO 80110
Domino, Fats (Antoine) *Singer*
5525 Marais St, New Orleans, LA 70117
Domnanovich, Joe *Football Player*
4949 Nottingham Ln, Birmingham, AL 35223
Donahue, Elinor *Actress*
4525 Lemp Ave, North Hollywood, CA 91602

Donahue, Kenneth *Museum Director*
245 S Westgate, Los Angeles, CA 90049

Donahue, Phil *Entertainer*
%Phil Donahue Show, NBC-TV, 3000 W Alameda Ave, Burbank, CA 91532

Donahue, Richard K *Businessman*
%Nike Inc, 3900 SW Murray Blvd, Beaverton, OR 97005

Donahue, Terry *Football Coach*
%University of California, Athletic Dept, Los Angeles, CA 90024

Donahue, Thomas M *Atmospheric Scientist*
1781 Arlington Blvd, Ann Arbor, MI 48104

Donahue, Thomas R *Labor Leader*
%American Federation of Labor, 815 16th St NW, Washington, DC 20006

Donald, David H *Historian*
PO Box 158, Lincoln Rd, Lincoln Center, MA 01773

Donaldson, Edward M *Test Pilot*
3 Fair Oak Ct, Tower Close, Alverstoke, Gosport PO12 2TV, England

Donaldson, James *Basketball Player*
%Dallas Mavericks, Reunion Arena, 777 Sports St, Dallas, TX 75207

Donaldson, Ray *Football Player*
%Indianapolis Colts, 7001 W 56th St, Indianapolis, IN 46254

Donaldson, Robert H *Educator*
%University of Tulsa, President's Office, Tulsa, OK 74104

Donaldson, Roger *Movie Director*
%Creative Artists Agency, 9830 Wilshire Blvd, Beverly Hills, CA 90212

Donaldson, Sam *Commentator*
%ABC-TV, News Dept, 1717 DeSales St NW, Washington, DC 20036

Donaldson, Simon K *Mathematician*
%Oxford University, Mathematics Dept, Oxford, England

Donaldson, William H *Financier*
%New York Stock Exchange, 11 Wall St, New York, NY 10005

Donat, Peter *Actor*
PO Box 5617, Beverly Hills, CA 90210

Donath, Helen *Opera Singer*
Bergstrasse 5, 3002 Wedemark 1, Germany

Donen, Stanley *Movie Director*
300 Stone Canyon Rd, Los Angeles, CA 90077

Donis, Peter P *Businessman*
%Caterpillar Co, 100 NE Adams St, Peoria, IL 61629

Donkova, Yordanka *Track Athlete*
%Olympic Committee, Rue Anghel Kantchev 4, 1000 Sofia, Bulgaria

Donlan, Yolande *Actress*
11 Mellina Pl, London NW8, England

Donleavy, J P *Writer*
Levington Park, Mullingar, County Westmeath, Ireland

Donley, Edward *Businessman*
326 N 27th St, Allentown, PA 18104

Donlon, Roger H C *Vietnam War Army Hero (CMH)*
2101 Wilson Ave, Leavenworth, KS 66048

Donlon, William J *Businessman*
%Niagara Mohawk Power Corp, 300 Erie Blvd W, Syracuse, NY 13202

Donne, D L *Businessman*
%Dalgety, 19 Hanover Sq, London W1R 9DA, England

Donnell, James C, II *Businessman*
839 S Main St, Findlay, OH 45840

Donnelly, Brian J *Representative, MA*
%House of Representatives, Washington, DC 20515

Donner, Clive *Movie Director*
1466 N Kings Rd, Los Angeles, CA 90069

Donner, Jorn *Movie Director*
Pohjoisranta 12, SF-00170 Helsinki 17, Finland

Donner, Richard *Movie Director*
%Richard Donner Prod, Warner Bros, 4000 Warner Blvd, Bldg 102, Burbank, CA 91522

Donovan (Leitch) *Singer, Songwriter*
PO Box 472, London SW7 2QB, England

Donovan, Alan B *Educator*
%State University of New York, President's Office, Oneonta, NY 13820

D

Donovan – Douaihy

Donovan, Art *Football Player*
1512 Jeffers Rd, Baltimore, MD 21204

Donovan, Dick *Baseball Player*
61 Deep Run Rd, Cohasset, MA 02025

Donovan, Francis R *Navy Admiral*
Commander, Military Sealift Command, Navy Department, Washington, DC 20398

Donovan, Jason *Singer*
%Atlantic Records, 75 Rockefeller Plz, New York, NY 10019

Donovan, Raymond J *Secretary, Labor*
%Department of Labor, 200 Constitution Ave NW, Washington, DC 20210

Donovan, Thomas F *Financier*
%Marine Midland Banks, 1 Marine Midland Ctr, Buffalo, NY 14240

Doob, Joseph L *Mathematician*
%University of Illinois, Mathematics Dept, Urbana, IL 61801

Doob, Leonard W *Psychologist*
%Yale University, Psychology Dept, New Haven, CT 06520

Doohan, James *Actor*
PO Box 1100, Burbank, CA 91507

Dooley, Calvin *Representative, CA*
%House of Representatives, Washington, DC 20515

Dooley, Vince *Football Coach*
%University of Georgia, Athletic Dept, Athens, GA 30602

Doolittle, James H *WW II Army Air Corps Hero (CMH), General*
PO Box 566, Pebble Beach, CA 93935

Doolittle, John T *Representative, CA*
%House of Representatives, Washington, DC 20515

Doran, Ann *Actress*
1610 N Orange Grove Ave, Los Angeles, CA 90046

Dorazio *Artist*
%Marlborough Galleria d'Arte, Rome, Italy

Dorfman, Henry *Businessman*
%Thorn Apple Valley Inc, 18700 W Ten Mile Rd, Southfield, MI 48075

Dorfman, Joel *Businessman*
%Thorn Apple Valley Inc, 18700 W Ten Mile Rd, Southfield, MI 48075

Dorgan, Byron L *Representative, ND*
%House of Representatives, Washington, DC 20515

Dorio, Gabriella *Track Athlete*
%Federation of Light Athletics, Viale Tiaiano 70, 00196 Rome, Italy

Dorman, Gerald D *Physician*
2365 Village Ln, Orient, NY 11957

Dorn, William Jennings Bryan *Representative, SC*
RFD 1, Greenwood, SC 29646

Dornan, Robert K *Representative, CA*
%House of Representatives, Washington, DC 20515

Dorsey, Bob R *Businessman*
5151 San Felipe St, #1380, Houston, TX 77056

Dorsey, Eric *Football Player*
%New York Giants, Giants Stadium, East Rutherford, NJ 07073

Dorso, Betty McLauchlen *Model*
444 N Camden Dr, Beverly Hills, CA 90210

Dortort, David *Movie Producer*
133 Udine Way, Los Angeles, CA 90024

Dos Santos, Jose Eduardo *President, Angola*
%President's Office, Luanda, Angola

Doss, Desmond T *WW II Army Medical Corps Hero (CMH)*
Rt 2, Box 307, Rising Fawn, GA 30738

Doss, Reggie *Football Player*
%Los Angeles Rams, 2327 W Lincoln Ave, Anaheim, CA 92801

Dotrice, Roy *Actor*
%Hutton, 200 Fulham Rd, London SW10, England

Dotson, Richard *Baseball Player*
4240 Palomino Cir, Reno, NV 89509

Doty, Paul M *Biochemist*
%Harvard University, John F Kennedy School of Government, Cambridge, MA 02138

Douaihy, Saliba *Artist*
Vining Rd, Windham, NY 12496

Douce, William C *Businessman*
2666 Cherokee Hills Dr, Bartlesville, OK 74003

Doucette, John *Actor*
PO Box 252, Cabazon, CA 92230

Dougherty, Charles J *Businessman*
%Union Electric Co, 1901 Gratiot St, St Louis, MO 63103

Dougherty, Joseph P *Broadcast Executive*
%Capital Cities Communications, 24 E 51st St, New York, NY 10022

Dougherty, William A, Jr *Navy Admiral*
Deputy CINC, US Space Command, Peterson Air Force Base, CO 80914

Douglas, Barry *Concert Pianist*
%Thea Dispeker, 59 E 54th St, New York, NY 10022

Douglas, Cathleen *Lawyer, Conservationist*
815 Connecticut Ave NW, Washington, DC 20006

Douglas, Donald W, Jr *Businessman*
707 Brooktree Rd, Pacific Palisades, CA 90272

Douglas, Donna *Actress*
PO Box 49455, Los Angeles, CA 90049

Douglas, Gordon *Movie Director*
%Ryder Stilwell Inc, 5900 Wilshire Blvd, #1100, Los Angeles, CA 90036

Douglas, James (Buster) *Boxer*
%Stephen D Enz, 2400 Corporate Exchange Dr, Columbus, OH 43229

Douglas, Kenneth J *Businessman*
%Dean Foods Co, 3600 N River Rd, Franklin Park, IL 60131

Douglas, Kirk *Actor*
805 N Rexford Dr, Beverly Hills, CA 90210

Douglas, Michael *Movie Producer, Director, Actor*
936 Hot Springs Rd, Montecito, CA 93108

Douglas, Paul W *Businessman*
%Pittston Co, 1 Pickwick Plz, Greenwich, CT 06830

Douglas, Robert R *Financier*
%Chase Manhattan Corp, 1 Chase Manhattan Plz, New York, NY 10081

Douglas, Sherman *Basketball Player*
%Boston Celtics, 151 Merrimac St, Boston, MA 02114

Douglass, Bobby *Football Player*
%Lettuce Entertain You Enterprises, 5419 N Sheridan Rd, Chicago, IL 60040

Douglass, Robyn *Actress*
10 Canterbury Ct, Wilmette, IL 60091

Doull, Adrian M *Businessman*
%Inspiration Resources Corp, 250 Park Ave, New York, NY 10177

Dourif, Brad *Actor*
%Edrick Mgmt, 8955 Norma Pl, Los Angeles, CA 90069

Dourlet, Ernest F *Businessman*
%Dayco Corp, 333 W 1st St, Dayton, OH 45402

Dove, Billie *Actress*
%Thunderbird Country Club, 70612 Highway 111, Rancho Mirage, CA 92270

Dove, Grant A *Businessman*
%Microelectronics & Computer Technology, 3500 Balcones Club Dr, Austin, TX 78731

Dove, Rita *Poet*
%Arizona State University, English Dept, Tempe, AZ 85287

Dow, Tony *Actor*
1731 Gunnison Trl, Topanga, CA 90290

Dowdle, James C *Broadcast Executive*
%Tribune Broadcasting Co, 435 N Michigan Ave, Chicago, IL 60611

Dowdle, Walter R *Microbiologist*
1708 Mason Mill Rd, Atlanta, GA 30329

Dowdy, Wayne *Representative, MS*
%House of Representatives, Washington, DC 20515

Dowell, Anthony *Ballet Dancer*
%Royal Ballet, Convent Gdn, London WL2E 7QA, England

Dowie, Mark *Editor*
%Mother Jones Magazine, 625 3rd St, San Francisco, CA 94107

Dowiyogo, Bernard *President, Nauru*
%Parliament House, Nauru, Central Pacific 94107

Dowler, Boyd *Football Player*
2303 S Lila Ln, Tampa, FL 33629

D

Dowling – Drake

Dowling, Doris *Actress*
9026 Elevado Ave, Los Angeles, CA 90069

Dowling, James H *Businessman*
%Burson-Marsteller, 866 3rd Ave, New York, NY 10022

Dowling, John *Businessman*
%Cushman & Wakefield Inc, 1166 Ave of Americas, New York, NY 10036

Down, Lesley-Anne *Actress*
6509 Wandermere Rd, Malibu, CA 93105

Down, Sarah *Cartoonist (Betsey's Buddies)*
%Playboy Magazine, 919 N Michigan Ave, Chicago, IL 60611

Downer, Joseph P *Businessman*
%Atlantic Richfield Co, 515 S Flower St, Los Angeles, CA 90071

Downes, Edward *Music Historian*
1 W 72nd St, New York, NY 10023

Downes, Ralph *Concert Organist*
%The Oratory, London SW7, England

Downey, James *Educator*
58 Waterloo Rd, Fredericton NB E3B 1Y9, Canada

Downey, Morton, Jr *Entertainer*
%The Agency, 10351 Santa Monica Blvd, #211, Los Angeles, CA 90025

Downey, Robert *Movie Director*
8497 Crescent Dr, Los Angeles, CA 90046

Downey, Robert, Jr *Actor*
1494 N Kings Rd, Los Angeles, CA 90069

Downey, Thomas J *Representative, NY*
155 Cedar St, Amityville, NY 11701

Downing, Al *Baseball Player*
2800 Neilson Way, #412, Santa Monica, CA 90405

Downing, Brian *Baseball Player*
4861 Silver Spurs, Yorba Linda, CA 92686

Downing, Thomas N *Representative, VA*
27 Indigo Dam Rd, Newport Beach, VA 23606

Downing, Wayne A *General, Army*
Commanding General, US Army Special Operations Cmd, Fort Bragg, NC 28307

Downs, Hugh *Journalist*
PO Box 1132, Carefree, AZ 85331

Doyle, David *Actor*
4731 Noeline Ave, Encino, CA 91436

Doyle, Larry *Cartoonist (Pogo)*
%Los Angeles Times Syndicate, Times Mirror Sq, Los Angeles, CA 90053

Dozier, Lamont *Singer*
4175 Stansbury Ave, Sherman Oaks, CA 91423

Drabek, Doug *Baseball Player*
1803 Travis, Victoria, TX 77901

Drabowsky, Moe *Baseball Player*
530 Audubon Pl, Highland Park, IL 60035

Dragon, Daryl *Musician (Captain & Tennille)*
%Triad Artists, 10100 Santa Monica Blvd, #1600, Los Angeles, CA 90067

Dragon, William, Jr *Businessman*
%Genesco Inc, Genesco Park, Nashville, TN 37202

Dragone, Allan R *Businessman*
%Celanese Corp, 1211 Ave of Americas, New York, NY 10036

Dragoti, Stan *Movie Director*
755 Stadella Rd, Los Angeles, CA 90077

Drai, Victor *Movie Producer*
1201 Delresto Dr, Beverly Hills, CA 90210

Drake, Carl R *Businessman*
%BMC Industries, 1100 American National Bank Bldg, St Paul, MN 55101

Drake, Frances *Actress*
1511 Summit Ridge Dr, Beverly Hills, CA 90210

Drake, Frank D *Astronomer*
%National Astronomy & Ionosphere Ctr, Cornell University, Ithaca, NY 14853

Drake, Fred O, Jr *Businessman*
%Mobile Home Industries, 1309 Thomasville Rd, Tallahassee, FL 32303

Drake, Harrington *Businessman*
%Dun & Bradstreet, 299 Park Ave, New York, NY 10017

Drake, Juel D *Labor Leader*
%Iron Workers Union, 1750 New York Ave NW, Washington, DC 20006

Drake, Larry *Actor*
602 1/2 Belmont Ave, Los Angeles, CA 90026

Drake, Stanley A *Cartoonist (Juliet Jones, Blondie)*
46 Post Rd E, Westport, CT 06880

Drapeau, Jean *Mayor*
5700 Des Plaines Ave, Montreal PQ H1T 2X1, Canada

Draper, E Linn *Businessman*
%Gulf States Utilities Co, 350 Pine St, Beaumont, TX 77701

Dravecky, Dave *Baseball Player*
806 Park Harbour Dr, Boardman, OH 44512

Draves, Vickie *Diver*
5732 Geyser Ave, Tarzana, CA 91356

Dreesen, Tom *Comedian*
5155 Costello Ave, Sherman Oaks, CA 91403

Dreier, David T *Representative, CA*
%House of Representatives, Washington, DC 20515

Drell, Sidney D *Physicist*
570 Alvarado Row, Stanford, CA 94305

Drendel, Frank M *Businessman*
%M/A-Com Inc, 7 New England Executive Park, Burlington, MA 01803

Drennen, William M *Judge*
%US Tax Court, 400 2nd St NW, Washington, DC 20217

Drew, Elizabeth A *Journalist*
%Doubleday & Co, 245 Park Ave, New York, NY 10017

Drexel, Walter A *Businessman*
%Burlington Northern Inc, 999 3rd Ave, Seattle, WA 98104

Drexler, Austin J *Museum Director*
%Museum of Modern Art, 11 W 53rd St, New York, NY 10019

Drexler, Clyde *Basketball Player*
%Portland Trail Blazers, 700 NE Multnomah St, Portland, OR 97232

Drexler, Millard S *Businessman*
%The Gap Inc, 900 Cherry Ave, San Bruno, CA 94066

Dreyfus, Lee S *Governor, WI*
3159 Madison St, Brookshire, WI 53188

Dreyfuss, Richard *Actor*
2809 Nicholas Canyon Rd, Los Angeles, CA 90046

Drick, John E *Financier*
1039 Miami Rd, Wilmette, IL 60091

Drickamer, Harry G *Chemical Engineer*
304 E Pennsylvania St, Urbana, IL 61801

Driedger, Florence *Religious Leader*
%General Conference Mennonite Church, 722 Main St, Newton, KS 67114

Driesell, Charles (Lefty) *Basketball Coach*
%James Madison University, Athletic Dept, Harrisonburg, VA 22807

Driessen, Dan *Baseball Player*
PO Box 1001, Hilton Head Island, SC 29928

Driggs, Don C *Financier*
%Western Savings & Loan, 3443 N Central Ave, Phoenix, AZ 85012

Driggs, Douglas H *Financier*
%Western Savings & Loan, 3443 N Central Ave, Phoenix, AZ 85012

Driggs, Gary *Financier*
%Western Savings & Loan, 3443 N Central Ave, Phoenix, AZ 85012

Driggs, John D *Financier*
%Western Savings & Loan, 3443 N Central Ave, Phoenix, AZ 85012

Drinan, Robert F *Representative, MA*
%Georgetown University, Law School, Washington, DC 20001

Driscoll, John G *Educator*
%Iona College, President's Office, New Rochelle, NY 10801

Drivas, Robert *Actor*
376 Bleecker St, New York, NY 10014

Driver, William J *Government Official*
215 W Columbia St, Falls Church, VA 22046

Drobney, Jaroslav *Tennis Player*
23 Kenilworth Ct, Lower Richmond Rd, London SW15 1EW, England

Drogheda, Earl of *Publisher*
Parkside House, Englefield Green, Surrey SW1, England

Dropo, Walt *Baseball Player*
7 Grant Rd, Marblehead, MA 01945

Drowley, Jesse R *WW II Army Hero (CMH)*
523 E Wabash, Spokane, WA 99207

Dru, Joanne *Actress*
1455 Carla Ridge Dr, Beverly Hills, CA 90210

Drucker, Daniel C *Engineer*
%University of Illinois, Engineering Dept, Urbana, IL 61801

Drucker, Mort *Cartoonist (Ort)*
%Mad Magazine, 485 Madison Ave, New York, NY 10022

Drucker, Peter F *Educator, Management Consultant, Writer*
636 Wellesley Dr, Claremont, CA 91711

Druckman, Jacob *Composer*
%Yale University, Music School, New Haven, CT 06520

Drummond, Gerard K *Businessman*
%NERCO Inc, 111 SW Columbia, Portland, OR 97201

Drummond, Roscoe *Columnist*
6637 MacLean Dr, Olde Dominion Sq, McLean, VA 22101

Drury, Allen *Writer*
PO Box 647, Tiburon, CA 94920

Drury, James *Actor*
12755 Mill Ridge, #622, Cypress, TX 77429

Drut, Guy *Track Athlete*
9 Rue Ernest-Cresson, 75014 Paris, France

Dryer, Fred *Actor, Football Player*
PO Box 932, Maywood, NJ 07607

Dryke, Matt *Skeet Marksman*
4702 Davis Ave S, #2-B-102,Renton, WA 98055

Drysdale, Cliff *Tennis Player*
%Landfall, 1801-F Eastwood Rd, Wilmington, NC 28405

Drysdale, Don *Baseball Player, Sportscaster*
1488 Rutherford Dr, Pasadena, CA 91103

Du Bain, Myron *Businessman*
%Amfac Inc, 3333 California St, San Francisco, CA 94118

Du Bois, Ja'Net *Actress*
405 W Ivy St, #204, Glendale, CA 91204

Du Bridge, Lee A *Physicist, Educator*
1730 Homet Rd, Pasadena, CA 91106

Du Pont, Edmond *Businessman*
PO Box 137, Montchanin, DE 19807

Du Pont, Pierre S, IV *Governor, DE*
%Richards Layton Finger, PO Box 551, Wilmington, DE 19899

Dubbie, Curtis *Religious Leader*
%Church of Brethren, 1451 Dundee Ave, Elgin, IL 60120

Dubcek, Alexander *Government Official, Czechoslovakia*
%Chairman's Office, Parliament, Prague, Czechoslovakia

Duberstein, Kenneth M *Government Official*
%White House, 1600 Pennsylvania Ave NW, Washington, DC 20500

Dubinbaum, Gail *Opera Singer*
%Metropolitan Opera Assn, Lincoln Ctr, New York, NY 10023

Duchin, Peter *Jazz Pianist*
400 Madison Ave, New York, NY 10017

DuCille, Michel *Photographer*
%Miami Herald, 1 Herald Plz, Miami, FL 33101

Duckworth, Kevin *Basketball Player*
%Portland Trail Blazers, 700 NE Multnomah St, Portland, OR 97232

Dudinskyaya, Natalia *Ballerina, Ballet Director*
2 Gogol St, #13, St Petersburg 191065, Russia

Dudley, Bill *Football Player*
3801 Sheringham Pl, Lynchburg, VA 24503

Dudley, Jaquelin *Microbiologist*
%University of Texas, Microbiology Dept, Austin, TX 78712

Dudley, Paul H, Jr *Businessman*
%Consolidated Natural Gas Co, 4 Gateway Ctr, Pittsburgh, PA 15222

Dudley, Rick *Hockey Coach*
%Buffalo Sabres, Memorial Auditorium, Buffalo, NY 14202

Duenkel Fuldner, Virginia *Swimmer*
707 Eisenhower, Monett, MO 65708

Duerson, Dave *Football Player*
%Chicago Bears, 250 N Washington Rd, Lake Forest, IL 60045

Duesenberry, James S *Economist*
25 Fairmont St, Belmont, MA 02178

Duff, John *Sculptor*
5 Doyers St, New York, NY 10013

Duffey, Joseph B *Educator*
%American University, President's Office, Washington, DC 20016

Duffy, Brian *Astronaut*
%NASA, Johnson Space Ctr, Houston, TX 77058

Duffy, Brian *Editorial Cartoonist*
%Des Moines Register, PO Box 957, Des Moines, IA 50304

Duffy, Helen *Actress*
%Jack Scagnetti Agency, 5330 Lankershim Blvd, North Hollywood, CA 91601

Duffy, James E *Television Executive*
%ABC-TV Network, 1330 Ave of Americas, New York, NY 10019

Duffy, John *Composer*
%Meet the Composer, 2112 Broadway, New York, NY 10023

Duffy, Julia *Actress*
%Gores/Fields Agency, 10100 Santa Monica Blvd, #700, Los Angeles, CA 90067

Duffy, Patrick *Actor*
%Montana Power Inc, 10000 Washington Blvd, #411, Culver City, CA 90232

Dufour, Val *Actor*
40 W 22nd St, New York, NY 10010

Dugan, Alan *Poet*
Box 97, Truro, MA 02666

Dugan, Dennis *Actor*
2072 1/2 N Commonwealth Ave, Los Angeles, CA 90027

Dugan, Michael J *Air Force General*
Box 19611, Alexandria, VA 22320

Duguay, Ron *Hockey Player*
%Los Angeles Kings, Great Western Forum, 3900 Manchester, Inglewood, CA 90306

Duhe, John M, Jr *Judge*
%US Court of Appeals, 556 Jefferson St, Lafayette, LA 70501

Dukakis, Kitty *Wife, Presidential Candidate*
85 Perry St, Brookline, MA 02146

Dukakis, Michael S *Governor, MA*
85 Perry St, Brookline, MA 02146

Dukakis, Olympia *Actress*
%Whole Theatre Co, 22 Valley Rd, Montclair, NJ 07042

Duke, A W, Jr *Businessman*
%Overnite Transportation Co, 1000 Semmes Ave, Richmond, VA 23224

Duke, Angier Biddle *Diplomat, Foundation Executive*
435 E 52nd St, New York, NY 10022

Duke, Charles M, Jr *Astronaut*
280 Lakeview, New Braunfels, TX 78130

Duke, Paul *Commentator*
%PBS-TV, 475 L'Enfant Plz SW, Washington, DC 20024

Dukes, David *Actor*
%International Creative Mgmt, 8899 Beverly Blvd, Los Angeles, CA 90048

Dulbecco, Renato *Nobel Medicine Laureate*
7525 Hillside Dr, La Jolla, CA 92307

Dullea, Keir *Actor*
6 Dogwood Ln, Westport, CT 06880

Dulles, Avery R *Theologian*
%Catholic University, Theology Dept, Washington, DC 20064

Dulo, Jane *Actress*
904 Hilldale Ave, #2, Los Angeles, CA 90069

Dumars, Joe *Basketball Player*
%Detroit Pistons, Palace, 1 Championship Dr, Auburn Hills, MI 48057

Dumas, Charlie *Track Athlete*
10709 8th Ave, Inglewood, CA 90303

D

Dumas – Dunn

Dumas, Georges *Financier*
%Credit Industriel & Commercial, 66 Rue de Victoire, 75009 Paris, France

Dunant, Yves *Businessman*
%Sandoz Ltd, Postfach, CH-4002 Basel, Switzerland

Dunaway, Faye *Actress*
15147 Mulholland Dr, Los Angeles, CA 90077

Dunbar, Bonnie J *Astronaut*
%NASA, Johnson Space Ctr, Houston, TX 77058

Duncan, Angus *Actor*
%Tom Jennings Assoc, 28035 Dorothy Dr, #210, Agoura, CA 91301

Duncan, C A, Jr *Financier*
%Farm & Home Savings, 221 W Cherry, Nevada, MO 64772

Duncan, Charles K *Navy Admiral*
813 1st St, Coronado, CA 92118

Duncan, Charles W, Jr *Secretary, Energy*
9 Briarwood Ct, Houston, TX 77019

Duncan, David Douglas *Photojournalist*
Castellaras Mouans-Sartoux 06370, France

Duncan, George *Radio Executive*
%Metromedia Inc, 1 Harmon Pl, Secaucus, NJ 07094

Duncan, John C *Businessman*
%Cyprus Minerals Co, 7200 S Alton Way, Englewood, CO 80155

Duncan, Sandy *Actress*
8743 Ashcroft, Los Angeles, CA 90048

Duncan, William *Businessman*
%Rolls-Royce Ltd, 65 Buckingham Gate, London SW1E 6AT, England

Dundee, Earl of *Government Official, England*
Birkhill, Cupar, Fife, Scotland

Dunderstadt, James *Educator*
%University of Michigan, President's Office, Ann Arbor, MI 48109

Dunham, Katherine *Dancer, Choreographer*
%Performing Arts Training Ctr, 226 N Main, St Louis, MO 62201

Dunham, Russell E *WW II Army Hero (CMH)*
328 Lindenwood, Alton, IL 62002

Duning, George W *Composer*
PO Box 190, Borrego Springs, CA 92004

Dunlap, Leonard D *Businessman*
%Fuller Brush Co, 28000 Rockcreek Pkwy, Kansas City, MO 64117

Dunlap, Robert H *WW II Marine Corps Hero (CMH)*
615 N 6th St, Monmouth, IL 61462

Dunleavy, Mike *Basketball Player, Coach*
%Los Angeles Lakers, Great Western Forum, 3900 W Manchester, Inglewood, CA 90306

Dunlop, John T *Secretary, Labor*
509 Pleasant St, Belmont, MA 02178

Dunlop, Richard G *Businessman*
%American Stores Co, 709 E South Temple, Salt Lake City, UT 84102

Dunlop, Robert G *Businessman*
%Sun Co, 100 Matsonford Rd, Radnor, PA 19087

Dunn, Gregory *Publisher*
%Redbook Magazine, 224 W 57th St, New York, NY 10019

Dunn, Halbert L *Statistician*
3637 Edelmar Terr, Rossmoor Silver Spring, MD 20906

Dunn, Holly *Singer*
%Friends of Holly, PO Box 726, Temple, TX 76503

Dunn, James Joseph *Publisher*
%Forbes Magazine, 60 5th Ave, New York, NY 10011

Dunn, Mary Maples *Educator*
%Smith College, President's Office, Northampton, MA 01063

Dunn, Mignon *Opera Singer*
%Columbia Artists Mgmt, 165 W 57th St, New York, NY 10019

Dunn, Oscar L *Businessman*
%Zurn Industries, 1 Zurn Pl, Erie, PA 16505

Dunn, Stepen L *Religious Leader*
%Churches of God General Conference, 7176 Glenmeadow Dr, Frederick, MD 21701

Dunn, T R *Basketball Player*
1014 19th SW, Birmingham, AL 35211

Dunn, William G *Publisher*
%US News & World Report Magazine, 2400 "N" St NW, Washington, DC 20037

Dunn, William L *Publisher*
%Information Services Grp, Dow Jones Co, 22 Cortlandt St, New York, NY 10007

Dunn, Winfield C *Governor, TN*
40 Concord Park E, Nashville, TN 37205

Dunne, Dominick *Writer*
%Vanity Fair Magazine, 350 Madison Ave, New York, NY 10017

Dunne, Griffin *Actor*
40 W 12th St, New York, NY 10011

Dunne, John Gregory *Writer*
%International Creative Mgmt, 40 W 57th St, New York, NY 10019

Dunnigan, Frank J *Publisher*
%Prentice-Hall Inc, 2050 Center Ave, Ft Lee, NJ 07024

Dunnigan, T Kevin *Businessman*
%Thomas & Betts Corp, 920 Rt 202, Raritan, NJ 08869

Dunphy, Jerry *Commentator*
%KHJ-TV, 5515 Melrose Ave, Los Angeles, CA 90038

Dunphy, Paul J *Businessman*
%Towle Manufacturing Co, 144 Addison St, Boston, MA 02128

Dunphy, T J Dermot *Businessman*
%Sealed Air Corp, Park 80 Plz E, Saddle Brook, NJ 07662

Dupard, Reggie *Football Player*
%New England Patriots, Sullivan Stadium, Foxboro, MA 02035

Duque, Carlos *Government Official, Panama*
%Nationalist Liberation Coalition, Panama City, Panama

Duques, Ric *Businessman*
%Automatic Data Processing, 1 ADP Blvd, Roseland, NJ 07068

Duran, Roberto *Boxer*
Box 157, Arena Colon, Panama City, Panama

Durang, Christopher *Playwright*
%Helen Merrill, 361 W 17th St, New York, NY 10011

Duras, Marguerite *Writer, Movie Director*
5 Rue St Benoit, 75006 Paris, France

Durbin, Mike *Bowler*
%Professional Bowlers Assn, 1720 Merriman Rd, Akron, OH 44313

Durbin, Richard J *Representative, IL*
%House of Representatives, Washington, DC 20515

Durbridge, Francis *Writer*
4 Fairacres, Roehampton Ln, London SW15 5LX, England

Durden, Allen *Football Player*
%Detroit Lions, Silverdome, 1200 Featherstone Rd, Pontiac, MI 48057

Durenberger, David F *Senator, MO*
7732 Canal Ct, McLean, VA 22101

Durham, G Robert *Businessman*
%Phelps Dodge Corp, 300 Park Ave, New York, NY 10022

Durham, Kenneth *Businessman*
%Unilever, Unilever House, Blackfriars EC4P 4BQ, England

Durkin, John A *Senator, NH*
%Perito Duerk Carlson Pinco, 1140 Connecticut NW, Washington, DC 20036

Durning, Charles *Actor*
%Gores/Fields Agency, 10100 Santa Monica Blvd, #700, Los Angeles, CA 90067

Durr Browning, Francoise *Tennis Player*
195 Rue de Lourmel, 75015 Paris, France

Durrance, Richard *Skier*
PO Box 290, Aspen, CO 81612

Durrance, Samuel T *Astronaut*
%Johns Hopkins University, Astrophysical Sciences Ctr, Baltimore, MD 21218

Durrell, Gerald *Naturalist, Writer*
%Jersey Zoo Park, "Les Augres Manor", Trinity, Jersey, Channel Islands

Durslag, Mel *Sportswriter*
523 Dalehurst Ave, Los Angeles, CA 90024

Dury, Ian *Singer*
%Associated Talent International, 888 7th Ave, New York, NY 10019

Dusay, Marj *Actress*
%Artists Group, 1930 Century Park West, #403, Los Angeles, CA 90067

Dusenberry, Ann *Actress*
%Agency for Performing Arts, 9000 Sunset Blvd, #1200, Los Angeles, CA 90069

Dussault, Nancy *Actress*
12211 Iredell St, North Hollywood, CA 91604

Dusto, Fred R *Businessman*
%Harvey Hubbell Inc, 584 Derby Milford Rd, Orange, CT 06477

Dutoit, Charles *Conductor*
%Montreal Symphony, 200 Blvd de Maisonneuve, Montreal PQ H2X 1Y9, Canada

Dutt, James L *Businessman*
%Beatrice Foods Co, 2 LaSalle St, Chicago, IL 60602

Duva, Lou *Boxing Promoter*
%Main Events, 2 Andrews Dr, West Paterson, NJ 07424

Duval, Daniel W *Businessman*
%Midland-Ross Corp, 20600 Chagrin Blvd, Cleveland, OH 44122

Duval, Leon-Etienne Cardinal *Religious Leader*
%Archbishop's House, 13 Rue Khelifa-Boukhalfa, Algiers, Algeria

Duval, William A *Labor Leader*
%Painters & Allied Trades Union, 1750 New York Ave NW, Washington, DC 20006

Duvall, Jed *Commentator*
%ABC-TV, News Dept, 1717 De Sales St NW, Washington, DC 20036

Duvall, Robert *Actor*
257 W 86th St, New York, NY 10024

Duvall, Sammy *Water Skier*
PO Box 871, Windermere, FL 32786

Duvall-Hero, Camille *Water Skier*
PO Box 871, Windermere, FL 32786

Duvignaud, Jean *Writer*
28 Rue Saint-Leonard, 1700 La Rochelle, France

Duvillard, Henri *Skier*
Le Mont d'Arbois, 74120 Megere, France

Duwez, Pol E *Applied Physicist*
1535 Oakdale St, Pasadena, CA 91106

Dwinell, Lane *Governor, NH*
94 Bank St, Lebanon, NH 03766

Dworsky, Dan *Football Player*
%Daniel L Dworsky Assoc, 2029 Century Park East, Los Angeles, CA 90067

Dwyer, Bernard J *Representative, NJ*
%House of Representatives, Washington, DC 20515

Dye, Pat *Football Coach*
%Auburn University, Athletic Dept, PO Box 351, Auburn, AL 36831

Dyer, David W *Judge*
PO Box 012319, Miami, FL 33101

Dykstra, John *Artist, Animator, Cinematographer*
%Apogee Productions, 6842 Valjean Ave, Van Nuys, CA 91406

Dykstra, Len *Baseball Player*
908 Rashford Dr, Placentia, CA 92670

Dylan, Bob *Singer, Songwriter*
%Lookout Mgmt, 9120 Sunset Blvd, Los Angeles, CA 90069

Dymally, Mervyn M *Representative, CA*
%House of Representatives, Washington, DC 20515

Dysart, Richard *Actor*
%Writers & Artists Agency, 11726 San Vicente Blvd, #300, Los Angeles, CA 90049

Dyson, Brian G *Businessman*
%Coca-Cola USA, 310 North Ave NW, Atlanta, GA 30313

Dyson, Freeman J *Physicist*
105 Battle Road Cir, Princeton, NJ 08540

Dystel, Oscar *Publisher*
Purchase Hill Dr, The Springs, Purchase, NY 10577

Dzau, Victor *Medical Researcher*
%Stanford University Hospital, Cardiovascular Medicine Div, Stanford, CA 94305

Dzeliwe *Queen Regent, Swaziland*
%Royal Palace, Mbabane, Swaziland

Dzhanibekov, Vladimir *Cosmonaut*
141 160 Svyosdny Gorodok, Moskovskoi Oblasti, Potchta Kosmonavtov, Russia

Dzunda, George *Actor*
%William Morris Agency, 151 El Camino, Beverly Hills, CA 90212

Eads, Ora Wilbert *Religious Leader*
%Christian Congregation, 804 W Hemlock St, LaFollette, TN 37766

Eagle, Harry *Cell Biologist*
370 Orienta Ave, Mamaroneck, NY 10543

Eagleburger, Lawrence S *Government Official*
4522 N 4th Rd, Arlington, VA 22203

Eagleson, Alan *Labor Leader*
%NHL Players Assn, 37 Maitland St, Toronto ON M4Y 1CB, Canada

Eagleton, Thomas F *Senator, MO*
%Thompson & Mitchell, 1 Mercantile Ctr, St Louis, MO 63101

Eakin, Thomas C *Businessman*
2729 Shelley Rd, Shaker Heights, OH 44122

Eamer, Richard K *Businessman*
%National Medical Enterprises, 2700 Colorado Ave, Santa Monica, CA 90404

Eanes, Antonio dos Santos Ramalho *President, Portugal*
%Palacio de Belem, Lisbon 3, Portugal

Earl, Anthony S *Governor, WI*
806 Huron Hill, Madison, WI 53711

Earle, Eyvind *Artist*
2900 Santa Lucia Ave, Carmel-by-the-Sea, CA 93923

Earle, Steve *Singer, Songwriter*
%UNI Records, MCA, 70 Universal City Plz, Universal City, CA 91608

Earle, Sylvia A *Oceanographer*
National Oceanic/Atmospheric Admin, 14th & Constitution NW, Washington, DC 20230

Early, Joseph D *Representative, MA*
34 Mechanic St, Worcester, MA 01608

Earnhardt, Dale *Auto Racing Driver*
PO Box 647, Oakboro, NC 28129

Easterbrook, Frank H *Judge*
%US Court of Appeals, 219 S Dearborn St, Chicago, IL 60604

Eastman, Benjamin *Track Athlete*
RFD, Rt 2, Hotchkiss, CO 81419

Eastman, Dean E *Physicist*
806 Pines Bridge Rd, Ossining, NY 10562

Eastman, John *Attorney*
%Eastman & Eastman, 39 W 54th St, New York, NY 10019

Eastman, John R *Businessman*
%Sheller-Globe Corp, 1505 Jefferson Ave, Toledo, OH 43624

Easton, Bill *Track Coach*
1024 Mississippi St, Lawrence, KS 66044

Easton, Robert *Actor*
1000 S Pasadena Ave, Pasadena, CA 91105

Easton, Sheena *Singer*
%Wasserman, 5954 Wilkinson Ave, North Hollywood, CA 91607

Eastwood, Clint *Actor*
%Malpaso Productions, 4000 Warner Blvd, #16, Burbank, CA 91522

Easum, Donald B *Diplomat*
%African-American Institute, 833 United Nations Plz, New York, NY 10017

Eaton, John *Composer*
4585 N Hartstrait Rd, Bloomington, IN 47401

Eaton, Lewis S *Financier*
%Guarantee Financial Corp, 1177 Fulton Mall, Fresno, CA 93721

Eaton, Mark *Basketball Player*
%Utah Jazz, 5 Triad Ctr, Salt Lake City, UT 84180

Eaton, Shirley *Actress*
2 Bucks Ave, Oxney, Herts, England

Eban, Abba *Government Official, Israel*
%Beit Berl Research Centre, Doar Beit Berl, Kfar Saba 44905, Israel

Ebb, Fred *Lyricist, Libretist*
146 Central Park West, #14-D, New York, NY 10023

Ebel, David M *Judge*
%US Court of Appeals, US Courthouse, 1929 Stout St, Denver, CO 80294

Eberhard, Wolfram *Sociologist*
22479 Golf Club Dr, Twain Harte, CA 95383

Eberhart, Richard *Poet*
5 Webster Terr, Hanover, NH 03755

E

Eberle, William D *Government Official*
Masconomo St, Manchester, MA 01944
Ebersol, Dick *Television Executive*
%NBC-Sports, 30 Rockefeller Plz, New York, NY 10112
Ebert, James D *Embryologist*
2101 Connecticut Ave NW, Washington, DC 20008
Ebert, Leonard T *Financier*
%Philadelphia Saving Fund Society, 1212 Market St, Philadelphia, PA 19107
Ebert, Roger *Movie Critic*
509 W Dickens, Chicago, IL 60614
Ebright, George W *Businessman*
%SmithKline Beckman Corp, 1 Franklin Plz, Philadelphia, PA 19101
Ebsen, Bonnie *Actress*
PO Box 356, Agoura, CA 91301
Ebsen, Buddy *Actor*
530 S Bay Front, Newport Beach, CA 92662
Eccles of Chute, Viscount *Government Official, England*
Dean Farm, Chute Near Andover, Hants, England
Eccles, John Carew *Nobel Medicine Laureate*
Ca'a la Gra', CH 6611 Contra, Ticino, Switzerland
Ecclestone, Bernie *Auto Racing Executive*
%Formula One, 8 Rue de La Concorde, 70008E Paris, France
Ecevit, Bulent *Prime Minister, Turkey*
Or-An Sehri 69/5, Ankara, Turkey
Echeverria Alvarez, Luis *President, Mexico*
%Mexican Embassy, 1 Beagle St, Red Hill, Canberra ACT 2603, Australia
Eckardt, Carl R *Businessman*
%GAF Corp, 1361 Alps Rd, Wayne, NJ 07470
Eckart, Dennis E *Representative, OH*
26111 Chagrin Blvd, Beachwood, OH 44122
Eckerd, Jack *Businessman*
%Jack Eckerd Corp, 8333 Bryan Dairy Rd, Largo, FL 33543
Eckersley, Dennis *Baseball Player*
747 Statler Office Tower, Cleveland, OH 44115
Eckert, J Presper, Jr *Computer Engineer*
PO Box 500, Blue Bell, PA 19422
Eckman, John W *Businessman*
%Rorer Grp, 500 Virginia Dr, Fort Washington, PA 19034
Eckrich, Donald P *Businessman*
%Central Soya Co, 1300 Fort Wayne National Bank Bldg, Fort Wayne, IN 46802
Eckstine, Billy *Singer*
1118 15th St, #4, Santa Monica, CA 90403
Eco, Umberto *Writer, Educator*
%University of Bologna, Literature Dept, Bologna, Italy
Edberg, Stefan *Tennis Player*
Spinnaregatan 6, 59300 Vastervik, Sweden
Eddy, Duane *Singer, Songwriter*
PO Box 10771, Zephyr Cove, NV 89448
Edel, Leon *Writer, Educator*
%University of Hawaii, English Dept, Honolulu, HI 96822
Edelin, Kenneth C *Physician*
720 Harrison Ave, Boston, MA 02118
Edelman, Asher *Financier*
%Plaza Securities, 717 5th Ave, New York, NY 10022
Edelman, Asher B *Businessman*
%Datapoint Corp, 9725 Datapoint Dr, San Antonio, TX 78284
Edelman, Gerald M *Nobel Medicine Laureate*
35 E 85th St, New York, NY 10028
Edelman, Marian Wright *Association Executive*
%Children's Defense Fund, 122 "C" St NW, Washington, DC 20001
Edelmann, Otto *Opera Singer*
Breitenfurterstrasse 547, Wein-Kalksburg 1238, Austria
Edelstein, Jean *Artist*
48 Brooks Ave, Venice, CA 90291
Eden, Barbara *Actress*
%Triad Artists, 10100 Santa Monica Blvd, #1600, Los Angeles, CA 90067

Eder, Richard *Literary Critic*
%Los Angeles Times, Times Mirror Sq, Los Angeles, CA 90053

Ederle Reichenback, Gertrude *Channel Swimmer*
4465 SW 37th Ave, Fort Lauderdale, FL 33312

Edgar, Jim *Governor, IL*
%Governor's Office, State House, #207, Springfield, IL 62706

Edgar, Robert W *Representative, PA*
221 S Sproul Rd, Broomall, PA 19008

Edge, Julie *Actress*
56 Suffolk Rd, London SW13, England

Edgell, Robert L *Publisher*
%Edgell Communications, 7500 Old Oak Blvd, Cleveland, OH 44130

Edler, Inge G *Cardiologist*
%University Hospital, Cardiology Dept, Lund, Sweden

Edley, Christopher F *Association Director*
%United Negro College Fund, 500 E 62nd St, New York, NY 10021

Edlund, Richard *Cinematographer*
%Boss Film Corp, 13335 Maxella, Marina del Rey, CA 90292

Edmiston, Mark H *Publisher*
%TVSM Inc, 475 5th Ave, New York, NY 10017

Edmonds, Walter D *Writer*
27 River St, Concord, MA 01742

Edmondson, J L *Judge*
%US Court of Appeals, 56 Forsyth St NW, Atlanta, GA 30303

Edney, Leon A *Navy Admiral*
Commander in Chief, US Atlantic Command, Norfolk, VA 23511

Edsall, John T *Biological Chemist*
985 Memorial Dr, Cambridge, MA 02138

Edwardes, Michael O *Businessman*
BL PLC, 35-38 Portland Sq, London W1H 0HQ, England

Edwards, Bill *Football Coach*
%Wittenberg University, Athletic Dept, Springfield, OH 45501

Edwards, Blake *Movie Director, Producer*
%Blake Edwards Entertainment, 9336 W Washington Blvd, Culver City, CA 90230

Edwards, Charles C *Physician*
Keeney Park, 10666 N Torrey Pines Rd, La Jolla, CA 92307

Edwards, Charles C, Jr *Publisher*
%Des Moines Register & Tribune, 715 Locust St, Des Moines, IA 50304

Edwards, Chet *Representative, TX*
%House of Representatives, Washington, DC 20515

Edwards, Danny *Golfer*
%Royal Grip Inc, 9525 E Double Tree Ranch Rd, #110, Scottsdale, AZ 85258

Edwards, Don *Representative, CA*
%House of Representatives, Washington, DC 20515

Edwards, Edwin W *Governor, LA*
10566 Airline Hwy, Baton Rouge, LA 70816

Edwards, George *Radio Executive*
%National Black Network, 1350 Ave of Americas, New York, NY 10019

Edwards, George C, Jr *Judge*
%US Courthouse, 5th & Walnut Sts, Cincinnati, OH 45202

Edwards, Gordon *Businessman*
74 Winding Ln, Greenwich, CT 06830

Edwards, H B *Businessman*
%Arco Pipe Line Co, Arco Bldg, Independence, KS 67301

Edwards, Harry *Educator, Social Activist*
%University of California, Sociology Dept, Berkeley, CA 94720

Edwards, Harry T *Judge*
%US Court of Appeals, 3rd & Constitution NW, Washington, DC 20001

Edwards, Jack *Representative, AL*
5628 Newington Ct, Bethesda, MD 20816

Edwards, James *Basketball Player*
%Los Angeles Clippers, Sports Arena, 3939 S Figueroa St, Los Angeles, CA 90037

Edwards, James B *Secretary, Energy*
100 Venning St, Mount Pleasant, SC 29464

Edwards, Jimmy *Actor*
Atheralis Farm, Fletching, Uckfield, E Sussex TN22 3TD, England

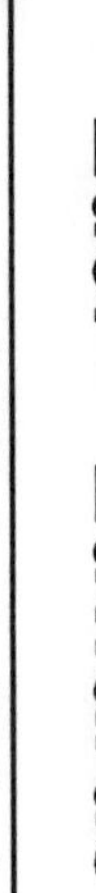

Edwards, LaVell *Football Coach*
%Brigham Young University, Athletic Dept, Provo, UT 84602
Edwards, Lena F *Physician*
821 Woodland Dr, Lakewood, NJ 08701
Edwards, Marvin H (Mickey) *Representative, OK*
%House of Representatives, Washington, DC 20515
Edwards, Ralph *Entertainer*
1717 N Highland Ave, #1018, Los Angeles, CA 90028
Edwards, Robert G *Physiologist (Test Tube Baby)*
Duck End Farm, Dry Drayton, Cambridge, England
Edwards, Robert J *Editor*
%Sunday Mirror, 33 Holborn, London EC1P 1DG, England
Edwards, Sherman *Composer, Lyricist*
N Beverwyck Rd, Boonton Manor, NJ 07005
Edwards, Stephanie *Actress*
8075 W 3rd St, #303, Los Angeles, CA 90048
Edwards, Teresa *Basketball Player*
Teresa Edwards Dr, Cairo, GA 31728
Edwards, Vince *Actor*
4267 Marina City Dr, #60, Marina del Rey, CA 90292
Edwards, W Donald *Representative, CA*
1625 The Alameda, San Jose, CA 95126
Edwards, William H *Businessman*
%Hilton Hotels Corp, 9336 Santa Monica Blvd, Beverly Hills, CA 90210
Edwards, William R *Businessman*
%Revco D S Inc, 1925 Enterprise Pkwy, Twinsburg, OH 44087
Efi, Taisi Tupuola Tufuga *Prime Minister, Western Samoa*
%Prime Minister's Office, Apia, Western Samoa
Egal, Mohamed Ibrahim *Prime Minister, Somalia*
PO Box 120, Mogadishu, Somalia
Egan, Peter *Actor*
%Fraser & Dunlop Ltd, 91 Regent St, London W1, England
Egawa, Shiro *Financier*
%Nippon Credit Bank, 13-10 Kudankita, Chiyodaku, Tokyo 103, Japan
Egeberg, Roger O *Physician, Government Official*
4039 North Bldg, 330 Independence St SW, Washington, DC 20201
Eggar, Samantha *Actress*
%Craig Agency, 8485 Melrose Pl, #E, Los Angeles, CA 90069
Egger, R L (Roger), Jr *Government Official*
1801 "K" St NW, Washington, DC 20006
Eggers, Melvin A *Educator*
%Syracuse University, President's Office, Syracuse, NY 13244
Eggert, Nicole *Actress*
%Irv Schechter Co, 9300 Wilshire Blvd, Beverly Hills, CA 90067
Eggert, Robert J *Economist*
Schnebly Hill Rd, PO Box 1569, Sedona, AZ 86336
Eggleton, Arthur C *Mayor*
%Mayor's Office, City Hall, Toronto ON M5H 2N2, Canada
Eguchi, Tomonaru *Businessman*
%Daihatsu Motor Co, 1-1 Daihatsucho, Ikeda City 563, Japan
Ehlers, Walter D *WW II Army Hero (CMH)*
8382 Valley View, Buena Park, CA 90620
Ehlers, Walter G *Businessman*
%TIAA-CREF, 730 3rd Ave, New York, NY 10017
Ehmann, Frank A *Businessman*
%American Hospital Supply Corp, 1 American Plz, Evanston, IL 60201
Ehrlich, Paul R *Population Biologist*
%Stanford University, Biological Sciences Dept, Stanford, CA 94305
Ehrlich, S Paul, Jr *Physician*
%Georgetown School of Medicine, 37th & "O", Washington, DC 20057
Ehrlich, Thomas *Educator*
%Indiana University, President's Office, Bloomington, IN 47405
Ehrlichman, John D *Government Official*
PO Box 5559, Santa Fe, NM 87502
Ehrling, Sixten *Conductor*
%Park Ten, 10 W 66th St, New York, NY 10023

Eichenberg, Fritz *Artist*
142 Oakwood Dr, Peace Dale, RI 02883

Eickhoff, Gottfred *Artist*
Frederiksholms Kanal 28-c, Copenhagen, Denmark

Eigen, Manfred *Nobel Chemistry Laureate*
Max Planck Institute, Am Fassburg, 3400 Gottingen-Nikolausberg, Germany

Eikenberry, Jill *Actress*
2183 Mandeville Canyon, Los Angeles, CA 90049

Eilbacher, Lisa *Actress*
2949 Deep Canyon, Beverly Hills, CA 90201

Eilenberg, Samuel *Mathematician*
%Columbia University, Mathematics Dept, New York, NY 10027

Einbender, Alvin H *Financier*
%Bear Stearns Co, 55 Water St, New York, NY 10041

Einem, Gottfried von *Composer*
1/2/5 Nikolaigasse, Vienna A1010, Austria

Einhorn, Eddie *Baseball Executive*
%Chicago White Sox, Comiskey Park, 333 W 35th St, Chicago, IL 60616

Einstein, Bob *Actor*
%International Creative Mgmt, 8899 Beverly Blvd, Los Angeles, CA 90048

Eisen, Herman N *Immunologist*
9 Homestead St, Waban, MA 02168

Eisenberg, Kenneth S *Restoration Expert*
1000 Connecticut Ave NW, Washington, DC 20036

Eisenberg, Lee *Editor*
%Esquire Magazine, 1790 Broadway, New York, NY 10019

Eisenhardt, Roy *Baseball Executive*
%Oakland A's, Oakland Coliseum, Oakland, CA 94621

Eisenhower, Milton S *Educator*
3900 N Charles St, #1102, Baltimore, MD 21218

Eisenman, Peter *Architect*
%Eisenman Architects, 40 W 25th St, New York, NY 10010

Eisenmann, Ike *Actor*
%Gage Group, 9229 Sunset Blvd, #515, Los Angeles, CA 90069

Eisenstaedt, Alfred *Photographer*
%Time Inc, Time-Life Bldg, #2850, New York, NY 10020

Eisner, Michael D *Entertainment Executive*
%Walt Disney Productions, 500 S Buena Vista St, Burbank, CA 91521

Eisner, Thomas *Biologist*
%Cornell University, Biological Sciences Dept, Ithaca, NY 14853

Eisner, Will *Cartoonist (The Spirit)*
51 Winslow Rd, White Plains, NY 10606

Eiszner, James R *Businessman*
%CPC International, International Plz, Englewood Cliffs, NJ 07632

Eitan, Raphael *Army General, Israel*
%Tsomet Party, Knesset, Tel-Aviv, Israel

Eizenstat, Stuart E *Government Official*
1110 Vermont Ave NW, Washington, DC 20005

Ekandem, Dominic Cardinal *Religious Leader*
%Cardinal's House, Library Ave, Ikot Ekpene, Cross River State, Nigeria

Ekland, Britt *Actress*
1744 N Doheny Dr, Los Angeles, CA 90069

Eklund, Coy G *Businessman*
%Equitable Life Assurance Society, 787 7th Ave, New York, NY 10019

Eklund, Sigvard *Nuclear Physicist*
Krapfenwaldgasse 48, 1190 Vienna, Austria

Ekstrom, Norris K *Businessman*
%Becor Western Inc, PO Box 56, South Milwaukee, WI 53172

Elam, Jack *Actor*
PO Box 5718, Santa Barbara, CA 93108

Elberson, Robert E *Businessman*
%Sara Lee Corp, 3 First National Plz, Chicago, IL 60602

Elcar, Dana *Actor*
%Artists Agency, 10000 Santa Monica Blvd, #305, Los Angeles, CA 90067

Elder, Lee *Golfer*
%Lee Elder Enterprises, 1725 "K" St NW, #1201, Washington, DC 20006

Elder, R P *Businessman*
%Southwest Forest Industries, 6225 N 24th St, Phoenix, AZ 85016

Elder, Will *Cartoonist (Little Annie Fanny)*
143 Booth Ave, Englewood, NJ 07631

Eldredge, Todd *Figure Skater*
Rancho Pensaquitos Blvd, #89-12728, San Diego, CA 92129

Elegant, Robert *Writer*
Manor House, Middle Green nr Langley, Bucks SL3 6BS, England

Eleniak, Erika *Actress*
%Kenneth Schwartz Mgmt, 11300 W Olympic Blvd, #610, Los Angeles, CA 90064

Elewonibi, Mohammed (Moe) *Football Player*
%Washington Redskins, Dulles Airport, Box 17247, Washington, DC 20041

Elfman, Danny *Singer, Composer*
%Oingo Bongo Secret Society, PO Box 10815, Beverly Hills, CA 90213

Elg, Taina *Actress*
%Michael Hartig Agency, 114 E 28th St, New York, NY 10016

Elias, Eddie *Bowling Executive*
%Professional Bowlers Assn, 1720 Merriman Rd, Akron, OH 44313

Elias, Rosalind *Opera Singer*
%Columbia Artists Mgmt Inc, 165 W 57th St, New York, NY 10019

Elicker, Paul H *Businessman*
%SCM Corp, 299 Park Ave, New York, NY 10171

Eliel, Ernest L *Chemist*
725 Kenmore Rd, Chapel Hill, NC 27514

Elion, Gertrude B *Nobel Medicine Laureate*
1 Banbury Ln, Chapel Hill, NC 27514

Elisha, Walter Y *Businessman*
%Springs Industries, 205 N White St, Fort Hill, SC 29715

Elizabeth *Queen Mother, England*
Clarence House, London SW1, England

Elizabeth II *Queen, England*
%Buckingham Palace, London SW1, England

Elizondo, Hector *Actor*
5040 Noble Ave, Sherman Oaks, CA 91401

Elkes, Joel *Physician*
%McMaster Medical Ctr, Psychiatry Dept, Hamilton ON, Canada

Elkes, Terrence A *Businessman*
%Viacom International, 1211 Ave of Americas, New York, NY 10036

Elkins, Hillard *Theater Producer*
1335 N Doheny Dr, Los Angeles, CA 90069

Elkins, J A, Jr *Financier*
%First City Bancorp of Texas, 1001 Fannin St, #400, Houston, TX 77002

Ellard, Henry *Football Player*
%Los Angeles Rams, 2327 W Lincoln Ave, Anaheim, CA 92801

Ellena, Jack *Football Player*
%Mountain Meadow Ranch, PO Box 610, Susanville, CA 96130

Ellenstein, Robert *Actor*
5215 Sepulveda Blvd, #23-F, Culver City, CA 90230

Eller, Carl *Football Player*
%National Football League, 410 Park Ave, New York, NY 10022

Ellerbee, Linda *Commentator*
%ABC-TV, 7 W 66th St, New York, NY 10023

Elliman, Yvonne *Singer*
%Alive Enterprises, 8600 Melrose Ave, Los Angeles, CA 90069

Ellinghaus, William M *Businessman*
%New York Stock Exchange, 11 Wall St, New York, NY 10005

Elliot, Jane *Actress*
%Judy Schoen Assoc, 606 N Larchmont Blvd, #309, Los Angeles, CA 90004

Elliot, Win *Sportscaster*
14 October Pl, Weston, CT 06883

Elliott, Bill *Auto Racing Driver*
%General Delivery, Dawsonville, GA 30534

Elliott, Bob *Comedian (Bob & Ray)*
%Goulding Elliott Greybar Productions, 420 Lexington Ave, New York, NY 10017

Elliott, Chalmers (Bump) *Football Player, Coach*
%University of Iowa, Athletic Dept, Iowa City, IA 52242

Elliott, Denholm *Actor*
75 Albert St, Regents Park, London NW1, England

Elliott, Herb *Track Athlete*
40 Porteous Rd, Sorrento WA, Australia

Elliott, John, Jr *Businessman*
2 E 48th St, New York, NY 10017

Elliott, Osborn *Journalist*
%Columbia University, Journalism Bldg, New York, NY 10027

Elliott, Robert M *Businessman*
%Levitz Furniture Co, 1317 NW 167th St, Miami, FL 33169

Elliott, Ross *Actor*
%Joshua Gray Assoc, 6736 Laurel Canyon, #306, North Hollywood, CA 91601

Elliott, Sam *Actor*
33050 Pacific Coast Hwy, Malibu, CA 90265

Elliott, Sean *Basketball Player*
%San Antonio Spurs, 600 E Market St, San Antonio, TX 78205

Ellis, Albert *Clinical Psychologist*
45 E 65th St, New York, NY 10021

Ellis, Alton *Singer*
27 McConnell House, Deeley Rd, London SW8, England

Ellis, Clarence *Football Player*
PO Box 95247, Atlanta, GA 30347

Ellis, Dale *Basketball Player*
%Milwaukee Bucks, 901 N 4th St, Milwaukee, WI 53203

Ellis, Elmer *Historian*
107 W Brandon Rd, Columbia, MO 65201

Ellis, Gilbert R *Businessman*
%Household International, 2700 Sanders Rd, Prospect Heights, IL 60070

Ellis, Herb *Jazz Guitarist*
%Lambros, 1136 Pinemont Pl, #3-B, Annapolis, MD 21403

Ellis, Howard S *Economist*
936 Cragmont Ave, Berkeley, CA 94708

Ellis, John Tracy *Religious Leader, Historian*
%Little Sisters of the Poor Home, 4200 Harewood Rd NE, Washington, DC 20017

Ellis, Kathy *Swimmer*
3024 Woodshore, Carmel, IN 46032

Ellis, Mary *Actress*
%Chase Manhattan Bank, Woolgate House, Coleman St, London EC2, England

Ellis, Patrick *Educator*
%LaSalle University, President's Office, Philadelphia, PA 19141

Ellis, Sam *Baseball Player*
6111 Whiteway, Temple Terrace, FL 33617

Ellison, Harlan *Writer*
3484 Coy Dr, Sherman Oaks, CA 91423

Ellison, Jerome *Writer, Editor*
43 Wallingford Rd, Cheshire, CT 06410

Ellison, Pervis *Basketball Player*
%Washington Bullets, Capital Centre, Landover, MD 20785

Ellison, Ralph *Writer*
730 Riverside Dr, New York, NY 10031

Ellroy, James *Writer*
%Mysterious Press, 129 W 56th St, New York, NY 10019

Ellsberg, Daniel *Political Activist*
90 Norwood Ave, Kensington, CA 94707

Ellsworth, Dick *Baseball Player*
1099 W Morris, Fresno, CA 93705

Ellsworth, Ralph E *Librarian*
860 Willowbrook Rd, Boulder, CO 80302

Elwood, Paul M, Jr *Physician*
5655 Christmas Lake Pt, Excelsior, MN 55331

Elsaesser, Robert J *Businessman*
%Hoover Co, 101 Maple St E, North Canton, OH 44720

Elsna, Hebe *Writer*
%Curtis Brown Ltd, 1 Cravel Hill, London W2 3EP, England

Elstrom, N K *Businessman*
%Bucyrus-Erie Co, PO Box 56, South Milwaukee, WI 53172

Elton - Endacott

Elton, Charles S *Zoologist*
61 Park Town, Oxford OX2 6SL, England

Elvin, Violetta *Ballerina*
Marina di Equa, 80066 Seiano, Bay of Naples, Italy

Elvira (Cassandra Peterson) *Entertainer*
%Panacea Entertainment, 2705 Glendower Ave, Los Angeles, CA 90027

Elway, John *Football Player*
%Denver Broncos, 13655 E Dove Valley Pkwy, Englewood, CO 80112

Ely, Joe *Singer, Songwriter*
PO Box 160668, Austin, TX 78716

Ely, Joseph B, II *Businessman*
%Fieldcrest Mills, 326 E Stadium Dr, Eden, NC 27288

Ely, Ron *Actor*
%William Morris Agency, 151 El Camino, Beverly Hills, CA 90212

Elytis, Odysseus *Nobel Literature Laureate*
23 Skoufa St, Athens, Greece

Emanuels, Severinus D *Prime Minister, Suriname*
98 Wassenaarse Weg, 2596 CZ The Hague, Netherlands

Emberg, Kelly *Actress, Model*
%Artists Agency, 10000 Santa Monica Blvd, Los Angeles, CA 90067

Embry, Wayne *Basketball Player, Executive*
%Cleveland Cavaliers, 2923 Statesboro Rd, Richfield, OH 44286

Emeleus, Harry J *Chemist*
149 Shelford Rd, Trumpington, Cambridge CB2 2ND, England

Emeneau, Murray B *Linguist*
909 San Benito Rd, Berkeley, CA 94707

Emerson, Alice F *Educator*
%Wheaton College, President's Office, Norton, MA 02766

Emerson, David F *Navy Admiral*
1777 Chelwood Cir, Charleston, SC 29407

Emerson, Grover (Ox) *Football Player*
1700 Pearce Rd, Austin, TX 78730

Emerson, J Martin *Labor Leader*
%American Federation of Musicians, 1501 Broadway, New York, NY 10036

Emerson, Roy *Tennis Player*
2221 Alta Vista Dr, Newport Beach, CA 92660

Emerson, William *Representative, MO*
Rt 6, Box 80, DeSoto, MO 63020

Emerson, William R *Librarian*
%F D Roosevelt Library & Museum, Old Albany Post Rd, Hyde Park, NY 12538

Emery, John *Bobsled Athlete*
2001 Union St, San Francisco, CA 94123

Emery, John C, Jr *Businessman*
%Emery Air Freight Corp, Old Danbury Rd, Wilton, CT 06897

Emery, Kenneth O *Oceanographer*
74 Ransom Rd, Falmouth, MA 02540

Emery, O D *Religious Leader*
%Wesleyan Church, PO Box 50434, Indianapolis, IN 46250

Emmanuel *Singer*
%RCA/Mexico Records, 6363 Sunset Blvd, #437, Los Angeles, CA 90028

Emmerton, Bill *Marathon Runner*
615 Ocean Ave, Santa Monica, CA 90402

Emmett, Paul H *Chemist*
23 Da Vinci, Lake Oswego, OR 97034

Emmons, Howard W *Mechanical Engineer*
233 Concord Rd, Sudbury, MA 01776

Empain, Edouard-Jean *Businessman*
%Empain-Schneider Grp, Plz Athenee Hotel, Ave Montaigne, Paris, France

Empson, William *Writer*
Studio House, 1 Hampstead Hill Gdns, London NW3, England

Emtman, Steve *Football Player*
%University of Washington, Athletic Dept, Seattle, WA 98195

Enberg, Dick *Sportscaster*
%NBC-Sports, 30 Rockefeller Plz, New York, NY 10020

Endacott, Paul *Basketball Player*
916 Cherokee Ave, Bartlesville, OK 74003

Endara, Guillermo *President, Panama*
%President's Office, Panama City 1, Panama

Ende, Michael *Writer*
Blumenstr 36, 7000 Stuttgart 1, Germany

Endeley, E M L *Premier, South Cameroons*
PO Box 5, Buea, Southwest Province, South Cameroons

Enders, Thomas O *Economist*
%Department of State, 2201 "C" St NW, Washington, DC 20520

Endrich, Louise *Writer*
PO Box 70, Cornish Flat, NH 03746

Engebrecht, Richard E *Businessman*
%Univar Corp, 1600 Norton Bldg, Seattle, WA 98104

Engel, Albert E *Geologist*
%University of California, Scripps Institute, La Jolla, CA 92093

Engel, Albert J *Judge*
%US Court of Appeals, Federal Bldg, 110 Michigan Ave NW, Grand Rapids, MI 49503

Engel, Georgia *Actress*
350 W 57th St, #10-E, New York, NY 10019

Engelberger, Joseph F *Robotics Engineer*
%Transition Research Corp, 15 Durant Ave, Bethel, CT 06801

Engelhardt, Thomas A *Editorial Cartoonist*
%St Louis Post-Dispatch, 900 N Tucker Blvd, St Louis, MO 63101

Engen, Alf *Skier*
%Alta Ski Lifts, Alta, UT 84092

Engen, Corey *Skier*
PO Box 774, McCall, ID 83638

Engen, Donald D *Government Official*
809 Duke St, Alexandria, VA 22314

Engen, Richard A *Businessman*
%Minnesota Mutual Life Insurance, 400 N Robert St, St Paul, MN 55101

Engen, Sverre *Skier*
9058 Green Hills Dr, Sandy, UT 84092

England, Anthony W *Astronaut, Geophysicist*
%University of Michigan, Electrical Engineering Dept, Ann Arbor, MI 48109

Englander, Harold R *Dental Researcher*
11502 Whisper Bluff, San Antonio, TX 78230

Engle, Joe H *Astronaut, Air Force General*
PO Box 58386, Houston, TX 77258

Englehart, Bob *Editorial Cartoonist*
%Hartford Courant, 280 Broad St, Hartford, CT 06115

Engler, John *Governor, MI*
%Governor's Office, State Capitol Bldg, 2nd Fl, Lansing, MI 48913

English, Alex *Basketball Player*
201 Wood Duck Rd, Columbia, SC 29206

English, Glenn *Representative, OK*
%House of Representatives, Washington, DC 20515

Englund, Robert *Actor*
2451 Horseshoe Canyon Rd, Los Angeles, CA 90046

Engman, Lewis A *Association Executive*
%Pharmaceutical Manufacturers Assn, 1155 15th St NW, Washington, DC 20005

Engstrom, Ted W *Association Executive*
%World Vision, 919 W Huntington Dr, Arcadia, CA 91016

Enloe, Ted *Financier*
%Lomas & Nettleton Financial Corp, 2001 Bryan Tower, Dallas, TX 75201

Ennis, Del *Baseball Player*
712 Woodside Rd, Jenkintown, PA 19046

Eno, Brian *Composer, Musician*
%Opal Records, 330 Harrow Rd, London W9 2HP, England

Enrico, Roger A *Businessman*
%PepsiCo Inc, Anderson Hill Rd, Flushing, NY 10577

Enright, Dennis J *Writer, Educator*
35-A Viewfield Rd, London SW18 5JD, England

Enright, Jim *Basketball Referee*
7731 N Sheridan Rd, Chicago, IL 60626

Enrique y Tarancon, Vicente Cardinal *Religious Leader*
Palacio Arzobispal, S Justo 2, Madrid 12, Spain

Enters – Eriksson

Enters, Angna *Mime, Artist*
35 W 57th St, New York, NY 10019
Entremont, Philippe *Conductor, Concert Pianist*
14 Rue D'Alger, 75001 Paris, France
Enzensberger, Hans M *Poet, Writer*
%Suhrkamp Verlag, Fach 2446, Frankfurt/Main, Germany
Ephron, Nora *Writer*
%Janklow & Nesbit Assoc, 598 Madison Ave, New York, NY 10022
Epley, Marion J, Jr *Businessman*
356 Worth Ave, Palm Beach, FL 33480
Epstein, Daniel *Poet, Dramatist*
%Viking Press, 625 Madison Ave, New York, NY 10022
Epstein, Jason *Editor*
%Random House, 201 E 58th St, New York, NY 10022
Epstein, Joseph *Writer, Educator*
522 Church St, Evanston, IL 60201
Epstein, Sidney *Businessman*
%Allied Van Lines, 2120 S 25th St, Broadview, IL 60153
Erb, Donald *Composer*
6733 Leameadow, Dallas, TX 75248
Erb, Richard D *Government Official*
%International Monetary Fund, 700 19th St NW, Washington, DC 20431
Erbe, Norman *Governor, IA*
328 Greene, Boone, IA 50036
Erburu, Robert F *Publisher*
%Times Mirror Co, Times Mirror Sq, Los Angeles, CA 90053
Erdelyi, Miklos *Conductor*
Tetenyi Ut 7-A, 1115 Budapest, Hungary
Erdman, Paul E *Writer*
1817 Lytton Springs Rd, Healdsburg, CA 95448
Erdman, Richard *Actor*
5655 Greenbush Ave, Van Nuys, CA 91401
Erdreich, Ben *Representative, AL*
4326 Kennesaw, Birmingham, AL 35213
Erdrich, Louise *Writer*
%Henry Holt Co, 115 W 18th St, New York, NY 10011
Erediauwa, Omo N'Edo Uku-Akpolokpolo *Oba, Benin*
%Royal Palace, Box 1, Benin City, Benin
Erhard, Werner *est Founder*
1945 Franklin St, San Francisco, CA 94109
Erhardt, Warren R *Publisher*
455 Wakefield Dr, Metchen, NJ 08840
Erhart, Charles H, Jr *Businessman*
%W R Grace Co, 1114 Ave of Americas, New York, NY 10036
Erickson, Arthur C *Architect*
2412 Laurel St, Vancouver BC V5Z 3T2, Canada
Erickson, Craig *Football Player*
%University of Miami, Athletic Dept, PO Box 248167, Coral Gables, FL 33124
Erickson, Don *Editor*
%Esquire Magazine, 304 W 44th St, New York, NY 10019
Erickson, Robert *Composer*
%University of California, Music Dept, La Jolla, CA 92093
Erickson, Steve *Writer*
%Poseidon Press, 1230 Ave of Americas, New York, NY 10020
Ericson, John *Actor*
%Henderson/Hogan Agency, 247 S Beverly Dr, #102, Beverly Hills, CA 90210
Ericson, Leif *Actor*
18202 W Wakecrest Dr, Malibu, CA 90265
Eriksen, Stein *Skier*
%General Delivery, Park City, UT 84060
Erikson, Erik H *Psychoanalyst*
1705 Centro West, Tiburon, CA 94920
Erikson, Raymond *Medical Researcher*
%Harvard University Medical School, 25 Shattuck St, Boston, MA 02115
Eriksson, Per Olof *Businessman*
%Sandvik AB Grp, 811 81 Sandviken, Sweden

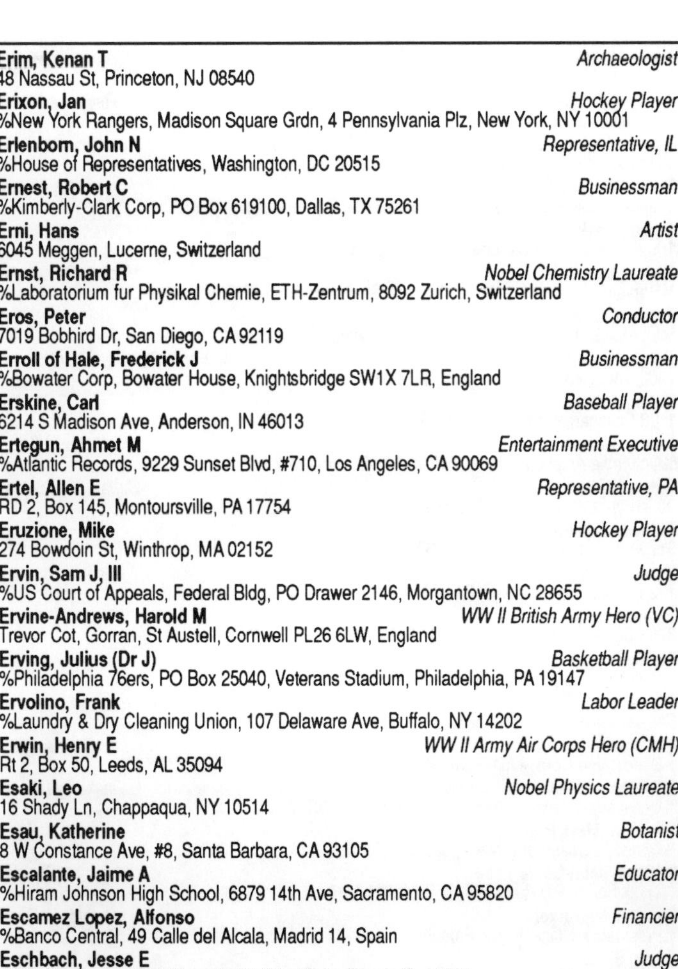

Erim, Kenan T — *Archaeologist*
48 Nassau St, Princeton, NJ 08540

Erixon, Jan — *Hockey Player*
%New York Rangers, Madison Square Grdn, 4 Pennsylvania Plz, New York, NY 10001

Erlenborn, John N — *Representative, IL*
%House of Representatives, Washington, DC 20515

Ernest, Robert C — *Businessman*
%Kimberly-Clark Corp, PO Box 619100, Dallas, TX 75261

Erni, Hans — *Artist*
6045 Meggen, Lucerne, Switzerland

Ernst, Richard R — *Nobel Chemistry Laureate*
%Laboratorium fur Physikal Chemie, ETH-Zentrum, 8092 Zurich, Switzerland

Eros, Peter — *Conductor*
7019 Bobhird Dr, San Diego, CA 92119

Erroll of Hale, Frederick J — *Businessman*
%Bowater Corp, Bowater House, Knightsbridge SW1X 7LR, England

Erskine, Carl — *Baseball Player*
6214 S Madison Ave, Anderson, IN 46013

Ertegun, Ahmet M — *Entertainment Executive*
%Atlantic Records, 9229 Sunset Blvd, #710, Los Angeles, CA 90069

Ertel, Allen E — *Representative, PA*
RD 2, Box 145, Montoursville, PA 17754

Eruzione, Mike — *Hockey Player*
274 Bowdoin St, Winthrop, MA 02152

Ervin, Sam J, III — *Judge*
%US Court of Appeals, Federal Bldg, PO Drawer 2146, Morgantown, NC 28655

Ervine-Andrews, Harold M — *WW II British Army Hero (VC)*
Trevor Cot, Gorran, St Austell, Cornwell PL26 6LW, England

Erving, Julius (Dr J) — *Basketball Player*
%Philadelphia 76ers, PO Box 25040, Veterans Stadium, Philadelphia, PA 19147

Ervolino, Frank — *Labor Leader*
%Laundry & Dry Cleaning Union, 107 Delaware Ave, Buffalo, NY 14202

Erwin, Henry E — *WW II Army Air Corps Hero (CMH)*
Rt 2, Box 50, Leeds, AL 35094

Esaki, Leo — *Nobel Physics Laureate*
16 Shady Ln, Chappaqua, NY 10514

Esau, Katherine — *Botanist*
8 W Constance Ave, #8, Santa Barbara, CA 93105

Escalante, Jaime A — *Educator*
%Hiram Johnson High School, 6879 14th Ave, Sacramento, CA 95820

Escamez Lopez, Alfonso — *Financier*
%Banco Central, 49 Calle del Alcala, Madrid 14, Spain

Eschbach, Jesse E — *Judge*
%US Courthouse, 701 Clematis St, West Palm Beach, FL 33401

Eschenbach, Christoph — *Conductor*
Maspalomas, Monte Leon 760625, Gran Canaria, Spain

Eshleman, Clayton — *Poet, Educator*
%Black Sparrow Press, Box 3993, Santa Barbara, CA 93105

Eshleman, Edwin D — *Representative, PA*
2173 West Ridge Dr, Lancaster, PA 17603

Eshleman, J Richard — *Financier*
%Landmark Savings Assn, 335 5th Ave, Pittsburgh, PA 15222

Esiason, Boomer — *Football Player*
%Cincinnati Bengals, 200 Riverfront Stadium, Cincinnati, OH 45202

Esmond, Carl — *Actor*
576 Tigertail Rd, Los Angeles, CA 90049

Esperian, Kallen — *Opera Singer*
%Herbert Breslin Inc, 119 W 57th St, #1505, New York, NY 10019

Espey, John — *Writer*
PO Box 107, Topanga, CA 90290

Esposito, Frank — *Bowling Executive*
200 Rt 17, Paramus, NJ 07652

Esposito, Phil — *Hockey Player, Executive*
%Tampa Bay Lightning, Mack Center, 501 E Kennedy Blvd, Tampa, FL 33602

Esposito, Tony — *Hockey Player, Executive*
%Pittsburgh Penguins, Civic Arena, Pittsburgh, PA 15219

Espy, Michael *Representative, MS*
%House of Representatives, Washington, DC 20515

Espy, R H Edwin *Religious Leader*
475 Riverside Dr, New York, NY 10027

Esquivel, Manuel *Prime Minister, Belize*
%Prime Minister's Office, Belize City, Belize

Esrey, William T *Businessman*
%United Telecommunications, 2330 Johnson Dr, Westwood, KS 66205

Essex, David *Singer*
109 Eastbourne Mews, London W2, England

Essex, Myron E *Medical Researcher*
%Harvard Medical School, 25 Shattuck St, Boston, MA 02115

Estefan, Gloria *Singer*
%Estefan Enterprises, 6205 SW 40th St, Miami, FL 33155

Estes, Howell M, Jr *Air Force General, Businessman*
7603 Shadywood Rd, Bethesda, MD 20817

Estes, James *Cartoonist*
1103 Callahan, Amarillo, TX 79106

Estes, Simon *Opera Singer*
%Columbia Artists Mgmt Inc, 165 W 57th St, New York, NY 10019

Estes, William K *Behavioral Scientist*
95 Irving St, Cambridge, MA 02138

Estevez, Emilio *Actor*
31709 Sea Level Dr, Malibu, CA 90265

Estevez, Luis *Fashion Designer*
122 E 7th St, Los Angeles, CA 90014

Estrada, Erik *Actor*
3768 Eureka, North Hollywood, CA 91604

Etchegaray, Roger Cardinal *Religious Leader*
4 Pl du Colonel Edon, 13007 Marseille, France

Etherington, Edwin D *Stock Exchange Executive*
Bassett Creek Trl, Hobe Sound, FL 33455

Ethington, James W *Businessman*
%Sundstrand Corp, 4751 Harrison Ave, Rockford, IL 61125

Ethridge, Kamie *Basketball Player*
%University of Texas, Athletic Dept, Austin, TX 78712

Ethridge, Mark F, III *Editor*
%Charlotte Observer & News, 600 S Tryon St, Charlotte, NC 28202

Etienne, Jean-Louis *Explorer*
%Think South, PO Box 4097, St Paul, MN 55104

Etpison, Ngiratkel *President, Palau*
%President's Office, Koror, Palau

Etrog, Sorel *Artist*
PO Box 5943, Terminal A, Toronto ON M5W 1P3, Canada

Etsel, Ed *Marksman*
%University of Virginia, Athletic Dept, Charlottesville, VA 22906

Etzioni, Amitai *Sociologist*
7110 Arran Pl, Bethesda, MD 20817

Eubanks, Bob *Entertainer*
23801 Calabasas Rd, #2050, Calabasas, CA 91302

Eulich, John *Businessman*
%Vantage Co, 2525 Stemmons Fwy, Dallas, TX 75207

Eure, Wesley *Actor*
PO Box 69405, Los Angeles, CA 90069

Evangelista, Linda *Model*
%Elite Model Mgmt, 111 E 22nd St, New York, NY 10010

Evans, Anthony M *Educator*
%California State University, President's Office, San Bernardino, CA 92407

Evans, Billy Lee *Representative, GA*
1337 Pinetree Rd, McLean, VA 22101

Evans, Britt *Financier*
%Homestead Financial Corp, 1777 Murchison Dr, Burlingame, CA 94010

Evans, Dale *Actress*
15650 Seneca Rd, Victorville, CA 92392

Evans, Daniel J *Senator/Governor, WA*
%Station KIRO-TV, 2807 3rd Ave, #C, Seattle, WA 98111

Evans, Darrell 31918 Foxfield Dr, Westlake Village, CA 91361	*Baseball Player*
Evans, Dennis E %First Bank System, 1200 First Bank Pl E, Minneapolis, MN 55402	*Financier*
Evans, Dick %Miami Herald, Herald Plz, Miami, FL 33101	*Bowling Writer*
Evans, Earl A, Jr 12 E Scott St, Chicago, IL 60610	*Biochemist*
Evans, Edward P %Macmillan Inc, 866 3rd Ave, New York, NY 10022	*Publisher*
Evans, Edward Parker %H K Porter Co, 300 Park Ave, New York, NY 10022	*Businessman*
Evans, Evans 101 Malibu Colony Rd, Malibu, CA 90265	*Actress*
Evans, Frank E 610 "A" St SE, Washington, DC 20003	*Representative, CO*
Evans, Geraint 17 Highcliffe, 32 Albermarle Rd, Beckenham, Kent, England	*Opera Singer*
Evans, Greg 660 Elm Tree Ln, San Marcos, CA 92069	*Cartoonist (Luann)*
Evans, Harold J 2939 Mulkey St, Corvallis, OR 97330	*Plant Physiologist*
Evans, Harold M %Random House, 201 E 50th St, New York, NY 10022	*Editor*
Evans, Heloise PO Box 32000, San Antonio, TX 78216	*Columnist*
Evans, James H %Union Pacific Corp, 345 Park Ave, New York, NY 10022	*Businessman*
Evans, Janet 424 Brower, Placentia, CA 92670	*Swimmer*
Evans, John B %Murdoch Magazines, 755 2nd Ave, New York, NY 10017	*Publisher*
Evans, John J %Manufacturers Hanover Corp, 270 Park Ave, New York, NY 10017	*Financier*
Evans, John R %Rockefeller Foundation, 1133 Ave of Americas, New York, NY 10036	*Educator, Foundation Executive*
Evans, John V %D L Evans Bank, 397 N Overland, Burley, ID 83318	*Governor, ID*
Evans, Lane %House of Representatives, Washington, DC 20515	*Representative, IL*
Evans, Linda 601 N Faring Rd, Los Angeles, CA 90077	*Actress*
Evans, Loren K %Arvin Industries, 1531 13th St, Columbus, IN 47201	*Businessman*
Evans, Michael PO Box 581, Van Nuys, CA 91408	*Actor*
Evans, Ray R 5632 Pembroke Ln, Shawnee Mission, KS 66208	*Football Player*
Evans, Richard %Madison Square Garden, 4 Pennsylvania Plz, New York, NY 10001	*Sports Executive*
Evans, Robert 1052 Woodlawn, Beverly Hills, CA 90210	*Movie Producer*
Evans, Robert S %Crane Co, 757 3rd Ave, New York, NY 10017	*Businessman*
Evans, Ronald M %Salk Institute for Biological Studies, Biology Dept, La Jolla, CA 92093	*Biologist*
Evans, Rowland, Jr 3125 "O" St NW, Washington, DC 20006	*Columnist*
Evans, Russell W Walnut Tree, Roehampton Gate, London SW15, England	*Movie Producer*
Evans, Thomas B, Jr 1111 Brandon Ln, Washington, DE 19807	*Representative, DE*
Evans, Thomas M %Crane Co, 300 Park Ave, New York, NY 10022	*Businessman*
Evans, Troy 260 E Mountain View St, Long Beach, CA 90805	*Actor*

Evans, Walker *Truck, Off-Road Racing Driver*
%Walker Evans Racing, 6192 Magnolia, Riverside, CA 92506

Evenson, Kim *Actress*
7627 Norton Ave, #4, Los Angeles, CA 90046

Everett, Chad *Actor*
19901 Northridge Rd, Chatsworth, CA 91311

Everett, Danny *Track Athlete*
%Santa Monica Track Club, 1801 Ocean Park Ave, #112, Santa Monica, CA 91607

Everett, Jim *Football Player*
%Los Angeles Rams, 2327 W Lincoln Ave, Anaheim, CA 92801

Everett, Marje *Thoroughbred Racing Executive*
%Hollywood Park Race Track, 1050 S Prairie Ave, Inglewood, CA 90301

Everhard, Nancy *Actress*
%Abrams Artists, 9200 Sunset Blvd, #625, Los Angeles, CA 90069

Everhart, Angie *Model*
%Elite Model Mgmt, 111 E 22nd St, New York, NY 10010

Everingham, Lyle J *Businessman*
%Kroger Co, 1014 Vine St, Cincinnati, OH 45202

Everly, Phil *Singer (Everly Brothers)*
10414 Camarillo St, North Hollywood, CA 91602

Evers, Charles *Civil Rights Activist*
1072 Lunch St, Jackson, MS 39203

Evers, Jason *Actor*
%Sekura A Talent Agency, 1680 N Vine St, #1003, Los Angeles, CA 90028

Eversley, Frederick *Sculptor*
1110 W Washington Blvd, Venice, CA 90291

Everson, Cory *Body Builder*
%Sampson & Delilah, 7324 Reseda Blvd, #208, Reseda, CA 91335

Evert, Chris *Tennis Player*
500 NE 25th St, Wilton Manors, FL 33305

Evigan, Greg *Actor, Singer*
6030 Graciosa Dr, Los Angeles, CA 90068

Evren, Kenan *President, Turkey*
%President's Office, Ankara, Turkey

Evron, Ephraim *Government Official, Israel*
%Ministry of Foreign Affairs, Tel-Aviv, Israel

Ewart, Gavin *Poet*
57 Kenilworth Ct, Lower Richmond Rd, London SW15 1EN, England

Ewbank, Weeb (Wilbur C) *Football Coach*
7 Patrick Dr, Oxford, OH 45056

Ewell, Barney *Track Athlete*
55 Green St, Lancaster, PA 17602

Ewell, Tom *Actor*
53 Aspen Way, Rolling Hills Estates, CA 90274

Ewen, David *Musician, Author*
Century Village, Preston A-18, Boca Raton, FL 33434

Ewing, Maria *Opera Singer*
33 Bramerton St, London SW3, England

Ewing, Patrick *Basketball Player*
%New York Knicks, Madison Square Grdn, 4 Pennsylvania Plz, New York, NY 10001

Exley, Charles E, Jr *Businessman*
%NCR Corp, 1700 S Patterson Blvd, Dayton, OH 45479

Exley, Frederick *Writer*
%International Creative Mgmt, 40 W 57th St, New York, NY 10019

Exon, J James *Governor/Senator, NE*
1615 Brent Blvd, Lincoln, NE 68520

Exum, Glenn *Musician, Mountaineer*
XM Chalet 95, Ranch Moose, WY 83012

Eyadema, Gnassingbe *President, Togo*
%President's Office, Lome, Togo

Eyes, Raymond *Publisher*
%McCall's Magazine, 230 Park Ave, New York, NY 10169

Eysenck, Hans J *Psychologist*
58 Ruskin Park House, Champion Hill, London SE5 8TH, England

Eytchison, Ronald M *Navy Admiral*
Vice Director, Strategic Target Planning Staff, Offutt Air Force Base, NE 68113

Fabares, Shelley PO Box 6010, Sherman Oaks, CA 91413	*Actress*
Faber, Sandra %Lick Observatory, Mt Hamilton, San Jose, CA 95140	*Astronomer*
Fabian (Forte) %Contemporary Artists, 132 Lasky Dr, Beverly Hills, CA 90212	*Singer*
Fabian, John M %Anser, Space Systems Dept, 1215 Jefferson Davis Hwy, #800, Arlington, VA 22202	*Astronaut*
Fabiani, Dante C 15 North Ave, Westport, CT 06880	*Businessman*
Fabiola Mora y Aragon, Dona %Royal Palace, Brussels, Belgium	*Queen, Belgium*
Fabius, Laurent 15 Pl du Pantheon, 75005 Paris, France	*Premier, France*
Fabray, Nanette 14360 Sunset Blvd, Pacific Palisades, CA 90272	*Singer*
Fabulous Moolah %TitanSports, 1055 Summer St, Stamford, CT 06905	*Wrestler*
Face, Elroy 608 Della Dr, #5-F, North Versailles, PA 15137	*Baseball Player*
Fadeyechev, Aleksei %State Academic Bolshoi Theatre, 1 Ploschad Sverdlova, Moscow, Russia	*Ballet Dancer*
Fadeyechev, Nicolai %State Academic Bolshoi Theatre, 1 Ploschad Sverdlova, Moscow, Russia	*Ballet Dancer*
Fadiman, Clifton Beach Home 13, S S Plantation, PO Box 459, Captiva, FL 33924	*Writer*
Fagan, Clifford B 36 W Franklin St, Crystal Lake, IL 60014	*Basketball Executive*
Fagan, John J %International Teamsters Brotherhood, 25 Louisiana Ave NW, Washington, DC 20001	*Labor Leader*
Fagan, Kevin PO Box 2582, Mission Viejo, CA 92690	*Cartoonist*
Fagan, Seymour %Columbia Savings & Loan, 8840 Wilshire Blvd, Beverly Hills, CA 90211	*Financier*
Fagen, Donald 24109 Malibu Rd, Malibu, CA 90265	*Singer*
Fagerbakke, Bill %Writers & Artists Agency, 11726 San Vicente Blvd, #300, Los Angeles, CA 90049	*Actor*
Fagerholm, Karl-August Temppelik 15, Helsinki, Finland	*Prime Minister, Finland*
Faget, Maxime %Space Industries, 711 Bay Area Blvd, Houston, TX 77058	*Space Scientist*
Fagg, George C %US Court of Appeals, US Courthouse, East 1st & Walnut St, Des Moines, IA 50309	*Judge*
Faggs Starr, Mae 10152 Shady Ln, Cincinnati, OH 45215	*Track Athlete*
Fagin, David K %Homestake Mining Co, 650 California St, San Francisco, CA 94108	*Businessman*
Fahd Ibn Abdul Aziz Royal Palace, Riyadh, Saudi Arabia	*King, Saudi Arabia*
Fahey, Jeff %William Morris Agency, 151 El Camino, Beverly Hills, CA 90212	*Actor*
Fahn, Stanley %Columbia University, Neurology Dept, 710 W 168th St, New York, NY 10032	*Neurologist*
Fahrenkopf, Frank J, Jr %Republican National Committee, 310 1st St SE, Washington, DC 20003	*Political Leader*
Fahringer, John %Peggy Schaefer Agency, 10850 Riverside Dr, #505, North Hollywood, CA 91602	*Actor*
Fahrney, Delmer Stater 10245 Vivera Dr, La Mesa, CA 92041	*Navy Admiral, Missile Expert*
Fain, Ferris PO Box 2000, Vacaville, CA 95696	*Baseball Player*
Fairbairn, Bruce %Century Artists, 9744 Wilshire Blvd, #308, Beverly Hills, CA 90212	*Actor*
Fairbanks, Jerry PO Box 50553, Santa Barbara, CA 93150	*Movie Director, Producer*

Fairchild - Farenthold

Fairchild, Morgan *Actress*
3480 Blair Dr, Los Angeles, CA 90068

Fairchild, S M *Businessman*
%Sohio Pipe Line Co, Midland Bldg, Cleveland, OH 44115

Fairchild, Thomas E *Judge*
%US Courthouse, 219 S Dearborn St, Chicago, IL 60604

Fairchild, W G *Labor Leader*
%Railway Carmen Division (BRC Division TCU), 4929 Main St, Kansas City, MO 64112

Faison, Earl *Football Player*
2430 Cardinal Rd, #21, San Diego, CA 92123

Faithfull, Marianne *Singer*
Yew Tree Cottage, Aldridge, Berks, England

Falahee, James B *Businessman*
%Consumers Power Co, 212 W Michigan Ave, Jackson, MI 49201

Falck, Hildegard *Track Athlete*
%Olympic Committee, Postfach 710130, 6000 Frankfurt-am-Main, Germany

Falco, Louis *Dancer, Choreographer*
131 W 24th St, New York, NY 10011

Faldo, Nick *Golfer*
%Professional Golfers Assn, PO Box 109601, Palm Beach Gardens, FL 33410

Falk, Isidore S *Medical Economist*
472 Whitney Ave, New Haven, CT 06511

Falk, Lee H *Cartoonist (Mandrake, Phantom)*
PO Box Z, Truro, MA 02666

Falk, Paul *Figure Skater*
Sybelstr 21, 4000 Dusseldorf, Germany

Falk, Peter *Actor*
1004 N Roxbury Dr, Beverly Hills, CA 90210

Falk, Randall M *Religious Leader*
%Temple, 5015 Harding Rd, Nashville, TN 37205

Falk, Ria *Figure Skater*
Sybelstr 21, 4000 Dusseldorf, Germany

Falkenburg McCrary, Jinx *Model, Actress*
10 Shelter Rock Rd, Manhasset, NY 11030

Falkenburg, Robert *Tennis Player*
259 St Pierre Rd, Los Angeles, CA 90024

Falkenstein, Claire *Artist*
719 Ocean Front Walk, Venice, CA 90291

Falkner, Keith *Singer*
Low Cottages, Ilketshall St Margaraet, Bungay, Suffolk, England

Falldin, Thorbjorn *Prime Minister, Sweden*
As, 870 16 Ramvik, Sweden

Fallon, Walter A *Businessman*
35 Edgewater Ln, Irondequoit, NY 14617

Fallows, James B *Editor*
%Atlantic Monthly Magazine, 745 Boylston St, Boston, MA 02116

Faltings, Gerd *Mathematician*
%Princeton University, Mathematics Dept, Princeton, NJ 08544

Faltskog, Agnetha *Singer (ABBA)*
%ABBA, PO Box 26072, 100 41 Stockholm, Sweden

Faludi, Susan C *Journalist*
%Wall Street Journal, 200 Liberty St, New York, NY 10281

Falvo, Anthony J, Jr *Businessman*
%USG Corp, 101 S Wacker Dr, Chicago, IL 60606

Falwell, Jerry *Religious Leader*
%Moral Majority Inc, PO Box 190, Forest, VA 24551

Fanfani, Amintore *Prime Minister, Italy*
Piazza Madama 1, 00186, Rome, Italy

Fang Lizhi *Astrophysicist; Political Activist*
%Institute of Astronomy, Cambridge University, Cambridge, England

Fannin, Paul J *Senator, AZ*
599 Orange Blossom Ln, Phoenix, AZ 85018

Faracy, Stephanie *Actress*
5000 Lankershim Blvd, #12, North Hollywood, CA 91601

Farenthold, Frances T *Women's Activist, Educator*
3303 Main St, #332, Houston, TX 77002

Farentino, Debrah *Actress*
%Gersh Agency, 232 N Canon Dr, Beverly Hills, CA 90210

Farentino, James *Actor*
%William Morris Agency, 151 El Camino, Beverly Hills, CA 90212

Fargis, Joe *Equestrian Rider*
%Sandron, PO Box 1675, Petersburg, VA 23805

Fargo, Donna *Singer*
PO Box 15385, Nashville, TN 37215

Faricy, William T *Association Executive*
4914 Glenbrook Rd NW, Washington, DC 20016

Farina, Battista (Pinin) *Industrial Designer*
%Pinitarina SpA, Via Lesna 78, 10095 Grugliasco (Turin) Italy

Farina, David *Religious Leader*
%General Council, Christian Church, Box 141-A, RD 1, Transfer, PA 16154

Farina, Dennis *Actor*
%Geddes Agency, 8457 Melrose Pl, #200, Los Angeles, CA 90069

Faris, Mohammed *Cosmonaut, Syria*
141 160 Svyosdny Gorodok, Moskovskoi Oblasti, Potchta Kosmonavtov, Russia

Farkas, Bertalan *Cosmonaut, Hungary*
A Magyar Nepkoztarsasag Urhajosa, Pf 251885, Budapest, Hungary

Farley, Carole *Opera, Concert Singer*
270 Riverside Dr, New York, NY 10025

Farley, Edward A *Financier*
%Manufacturers Hanover Trust, 270 Park Ave, New York, NY 10017

Farley, F J *Businessman*
%Black & Decker Manufacturing Co, 701 E Joppa Rd, Towson, MD 21204

Farley, James D *Financier*
%Citicorp, 399 Park Ave, New York, NY 10043

Farley, Joseph M *Businessman*
%Alabama Power Co, 600 N 18th St, Birmingham, AL 35203

Farley, William F *Businessman*
%Farley Industries, 233 S Wacker Dr, Chicago, IL 60606

Farman, Richard D *Businessman*
%Southern California Gas Co, 810 S Flower St, Los Angeles, CA 90017

Farmer, Art *Jazz Musician*
%Helen Keane Artists, 49 E 96th St, New York, NY 10128

Farmer, James L *Civil Rights Activist*
3805 Guinea Station Rd, Fredericksburg, VA 22401

Farner, Donald S *Zoo Physiologist*
%University of Washington, Zoology Dept, Seattle, WA 98195

Farnsworth, Richard *Actor*
3219 Ellington Dr, Los Angeles, CA 90068

Farquhar, Robert W *Rocket Scientist*
%Johns Hopkins University, Applied Physics Laboratory, Laurel, MD 20723

Farquhar, Robin H *Educator*
%University of Winnipeg, President's Office, Winnipeg MB R3M 3P6, Canada

Farr, Jaime *Actor*
%Agency for Performing Arts, 9000 Sunset Blvd, #1200, Los Angeles, CA 90069

Farrar, Frank L *Governor, SD*
203 9th Ave, Britton, SD 57430

Farreley, Alexander *Governor, VI*
%Governor's Office, Government Offices, Charlotte Amalie, VI 00801

Farrell, David C *Businessman*
%May Department Stores, 611 Olive St, St Louis, MO 63101

Farrell, Eileen *Opera Singer*
72 Louis St, Staten Island, NY 10304

Farrell, George T *Financier*
%Mellon Bank Corp, 1 Mellon Bank Ctr, Pittsbrugh, PA 15258

Farrell, Jeff *Swimmer*
2405 Capri, Wichita, KS 67207

Farrell, Joseph C *Businessman*
%Pittston Co, 1 Pickwick Plz, Greenwich, CT 06830

Farrell, Mike *Actor*
%MJ&E Productions, PO Box 5961, Sherman Oaks, CA 91413

Farrell, Sean *Football Player*
%New England Patriots, Sullivan Stadium, Foxboro, MA 02035

Farrell – Faye

Farrell, Suzanne *Ballet Dancer*
%New York City Ballet, Lincoln Center Plz, New York, NY 10023

Farrimond, Richard A *Astronaut, England*
%Defense Ministry, 98 High Holburn, London WC1V 6LL, England 77058

Farrington, Jerry *Businessman*
%Texas Utilities Co, 2001 Bryan Tower, Dallas, TX 75201

Farris, Jerome *Judge*
%US Court of Appeals, US Courthouse, 1010 5th Ave, Seattle, WA 98104

Farris, Joseph *Cartoonist*
PO Box 4203, New York, NY 10017

Farrow, Mia *Actress*
135 Central Park West, New York, NY 10023

Fasanella, Ralph *Artist*
15 Chester St, Ardskey, NY 10502

Fascell, Dante B *Representative, FL*
6300 SW 99th Terr, Miami, FL 33156

Fasi, Frank *Mayor*
2054 Makiki St, Honolulu, HI 96822

Fass, Peter J *Businessman*
%Reichhold Chemicals Inc, 525 N Broadway, White Plains, NY 10603

Fassbaender, Brigitte *Opera Singer*
%Jennifer Selby, Ittisstrasse 57, 8000 Munich 82, Germany

Fassi, Carlo *Figure Skating Coach*
%Broadmoor World Arena Club, Colorado Springs, CO 80901

Fast, Howard *Writer*
1401 Laurel Way, Beverly Hills, CA 90210

Faubus, Orval E *Governor, AR*
PO Box 488, Little Rock, AR 72203

Fauci, Anthony *Immunologist*
%National Institute of Allergy & Infectious Diseases, Bethesda, MD 20014

Faulkner, John *Organic Chemist*
%Scripps Institution of Oceanography, La Jolla, CA 92093

Fauntroy, Walter E *Representative, DC*
%House of Representatives, Washington, DC 20515

Faure, Hubert *Businessman*
960 5th Ave, New York, NY 10021

Faurot, Donald B *Football Coach*
%Missouri Senior Golf Assn, 108 Burnam, Columbia, MO 65201

Fauroux, Roger *Businessman*
%Saint-Gobain-Pony-a-Mousson, 54 Ave Hoche, 75365 Paris Cedex 08, France

Faust, Gerry *Football Coach*
%University of Akron, Athletic Dept, Akron, OH 44325

Faustino, David *Actor*
%Booh Schut Agency, 11350 Ventura Blvd, #206, Studio City, CA 91604

Fauvet, Jacques *Editor*
5 Rue Louis-Boilly, 70016 Paris, France

Favier, Jean-Jacques *Spatinaut, France*
%CENG, 53 Ave des Martyrs, 38041 Grenoble Cedex, France

Fawcett, Don W *Anatomist*
%Harvard Medical School, Anatomy Dept, 25 Shattuck St, Boston, MA 02115

Fawcett, Farrah *Actress, Model*
3130 Antelo Rd, Los Angeles, CA 90077

Fawcett, S L *Research Physicist*
2820 Margate Rd, Columbus, OH 43221

Fawell, Harris W *Representative, IL*
%House of Representatives, Washington, DC 20515

Fay, David *Golf Executive*
%U S Golf Assn, Liberty Corner Rd, Far Hills, NJ 07931

Fay, Peter T *Judge*
%US Court of Appeals, Courthouse Bldg, 300 NE 1st St, Miami, FL 33132

Fay, Ronald P *Businessman*
%Wendy's International, 4288 W Dublin Granville Rd, Dublin, OH 43017

Fay, William M *Judge*
%US Tax Court, 400 2nd St NW, Washington, DC 20217

Faye, Alice *Actress*
49400 John F Kennedy Trl, Palm Springs, CA 92260

Faye, Herbie *Actor*
1501 Kenneth Rd, Glendale, CA 91201

Fazio, Buzz *Bowler*
%Professional Bowlers Assn, 1720 Merriman Rd, Akron, OH 44313

Fazio, Vic *Representative, CA*
%House of Representatives, Washington, DC 20515

Fears, Tom *Football Player*
27642 Rosedale Dr, San Juan Capistrano, CA 92675

Feather, Leonard *Jazz Critic*
13833 Riverside Dr, Sherman Oaks, CA 91423

Featherston, C Moxley *Judge*
%US Tax Court, 400 2nd St NW, Washington, DC 20217

Feck, Luke M *Editor*
%Columbus Dispatch, 34 S 3rd St, Columbus, OH 43216

Fedoseyev, Vladimir I *Conductor*
%Bolshoi Theater, Ploshchad Sverdlova, Moscow, Russia

Feeney, Charles S *Baseball Executive*
%San Diego Padres, PO Box 2000, San Diego, CA 92120

Fehr, Donald *Labor Leader*
%Major League Baseball Players Assn, 1370 Ave of Americas, New York, NY 10019

Feiffer, Jules *Cartoonist*
325 West End Ave, New York, NY 10023

Feigenbaum, Armand V *Management Consultant*
%General Systems Co, Park Sq, 43 East St, Pittsfield, MA 01201

Feigenbaum, Edward A *Computer Scientist*
1017 Cathcart Way, Stanford, CA 94305

Feigenbaum, Mitchell J *Physicist*
%Cornell University, Physics Dept, Ithaca, NY 14853

Feighan, Edward F *Representative, OH*
%House of Representatives, Washington, DC 20515

Fein, Bernard *Businessman*
%United Industrial Corp, 18 E 48th St, New York, NY 10017

Feinberg, Wilfred *Judge*
%US Court of Appeals, US Courthouse, Foley Sq, New York, NY 10007

Feininger, Andreas *Photographer*
5 E 22nd St, #26-R, New York, NY 10010

Feinstein, Dianne *Mayor, San Francisco*
909 Montgomery St, San Francisco, CA 94133

Feld, Eliot *Dancer, Choreographer*
%Feld Ballet, 890 Broadway, New York, NY 10003

Feld, Fritz *Actor*
12348 Rochedale Ln, Los Angeles, CA 90049

Feld, Kenneth *Entertainment Executive*
%Ringling Bros-Barnum Bailey, L'Enfant Station Plz, #266, Washington, DC 20026

Feldberg, Stanley H *Businessman*
%Zayre Corp, 770 Cochituate Rd, Framingham, MA 01701

Feldberg, Sumner L *Businessman*
%Zayre Corp, 770 Cochituate Rd, Framingham, MA 01701

Feldenkrais, Moshe *Psychologist*
University of Tel-Aviv, Tel-Aviv, Israel 01701

Felder, Raoul Lionel *Attorney*
437 Madison Ave, New York, NY 10022

Feldman, Bella *Artist*
12 Summit Ln, Berkeley, CA 94708

Feldman, Marty *Comedian, Director*
%Shapiro-West Agency, 141 El Camino Dr, Beverly Hills, CA 90212

Feldman, Myer *Government Official*
%Ginsburg & Feldman, 1700 Pennsylvania Ave NW, Washington, DC 20006

Feldon, Barbara *Model, Actress*
%Creative Artists Agency, 9830 Wilshire Blvd, Beverly Hills, CA 90212

Feldshuh, Tovah *Actress*
110 Riverside Dr, #16-F, New York, NY 10024

Feldstein, Martin S *Government Official*
147 Clifton St, Belmont, MA 02178

Felici, Pericle Cardinal *Religious Leader*
Via Pfeiffer 10, 10093 Rome, Italy

F

Feliciano – Ferguson

Feliciano, Jose *Singer*
17871 Santiago Blvd, #206, Villa Park, CA 92667

Felipe *Crown Prince, Spain*
%Palacio de la Zarzuela, Madrid, Spain

Felke, Petra *Track Athlete*
%SC Motor Jena, Wollnitzevstr 42, 6900 Jena PF 177, Germany

Felker, Clay *Editor*
322 E 57th St, New York, NY 10024

Fell, Norman *Actor*
%Burton Moss Agency, 113 N San Vicente Blvd, #202, Beverly Hills, CA 90211

Feller, Bob *Baseball Player*
PO Box 157, Gates Mill, OH 44040

Felley, Donald L *Businessman*
%Rohm & Haas Co, Independence Mall W, Philadelphia, PA 19105

Fellini, Federico *Movie Director*
Via Margutta 110, 00187 Rome, Italy

Fellner, William J *Economist*
131 Edgehill Rd, New Haven, CT 06511

Fellows, Edith *Actress*
2016 1/2 N Vista del Mar, Los Angeles, CA 90068

Felt, Irving *Businessman*
800 5th Ave, New York, NY 10021

Felton, Norman *Movie, Television Producer*
%Arena Productions, 22146 Pacific Coast Hwy, Malibu, CA 90265

Feltsman, Vladimir *Concert Pianist*
%Columbia Artists Mgmt Inc, 165 W 57th St, New York, NY 10019

Femia, John *Singer*
1650 Broadway, #714, New York, NY 10019

Fencik, Gary *Football Player*
%Chicago Bears, 250 N Washington Rd, Lake Forest, IL 60045

Fender, Freddy *Singer*
PO Box 4003, Beverly Hills, CA 90213

Fenical, William *Organic Chemist*
%Scripps Institution of Oceanography, La Jolla, CA 92093

Fenimore, Bob *Football Player*
1214 Fairway Dr, Stillwater, OK 74074

Fenley, Molissa *Dancer, Choreographer*
%Molissa Fenley Dancers, PO Box 450, Prince Street Station, New York, NY 10012

Fenn, Sherilyn *Actress*
%Prima Artists, 933 N La Brea Ave, #200, Los Angeles, CA 90038

Fenneman, George *Entertainer*
13214 Moorpark St, #206, Sherman Oaks, CA 91423

Fenoglio, William R *Businessman*
%Barnes Grp, 123 Main St, Bristol, CT 06010

Fenswick, J Henry *Editor*
%Modern Maturity Magazine, 3200 E Carson St, Lakewood, CA 90712

Feoktistov, Konstantin P *Cosmonaut*
141 160 Svyosdny Gorodok, Moskovskoi Oblasti, Potchta Kosmonavtov, Russia

Ferden, Bruce *Conductor*
%Colbert Artists, 111 W 57th St, New York, NY 10019

Ferguson Cullum, Cathy *Swimmer*
9212 Wilhelm Cir, Huntington Beach, CA 92648

Ferguson, Charles A *Editor*
%New Orleans Times-Picayune, 3800 Howard Ave, New Orleans, LA 70140

Ferguson, Clarence C, Jr *Diplomat, Lawyer*
%Harvard University, Law School, Cambridge, MA 02138

Ferguson, Frances D *Educator*
%Vassar College, President's College, Poughkeepsie, NY 12601

Ferguson, Francis E *Businessman*
817 W Autumn Path Ln, Milwaukee, WI 53217

Ferguson, Frederick E *Vietnam War Army Hero (CMH)*
106 E Stellar Pkwy, Chandler, AZ 85226

Ferguson, Glenn W *Educator, Government Official*
Wagner Rd, Shelter Harbour, RI 02891

Ferguson, Jack H *Businessman*
%Dominion Resources Inc, 1 James River Plz, Richmond, VA 23261

F

Ferguson, James L *Businessman*
%Philip Morris Companies, 120 Park Ave, New York, NY 10017
Ferguson, Maynard *Jazz Trumpteer*
PO Box 716, Ojai, CA 93023
Ferguson, Robert R, III *Businessman*
%Continental Airlines, 2929 Allen Pkwy, Houston, TX 77019
Ferguson, Ronald E *Businessman*
%General Re Corp, Financial Ctr, Stamford, CT 06904
Ferguson, Thomas R, Jr *Air Force General*
Comdr, Aeronautical Systems Division, Wright-Patterson Air Force Base, OH 45433
Ferguson, Tom *Rodeo Rider*
%General Delivery, Miami, OK 74355
Ferguson, Warren J *Judge*
%Federal Bldg, 34 Civic Center Plz, Santa Ana, CA 92701
Fergusson, Francis *Writer*
PO Box 143, Kingston, NJ 98528
Ferland, E James *Businessman*
%Public Service Enterprise Group Inc, 80 Park Plz, Newark, NJ 07101
Ferlinghetti, Lawrence *Writer*
%City Lights Booksellers, 261 Columbus Ave, San Francisco, CA 94133
Fernandez Maldonado, Jorge *Prime Minister, Peru*
%Prime Minister's Office, Lima, Peru
Fernandez, Ferdinand F *Judge*
%US Court of Appeals, 127 S Grand Ave, Pasadena, CA 91109
Fernandez, Juan R *Educator*
%University of Puerto Rico, President's Office, Rio Piedras, PR 00931
Fernandez, Mario F *Artist*
13188 Cardinal Creek Rd, Eden Prairie, MN 55346
Fernandez, Mary Joe *Tennis Player*
%Women's Tennis Assn, 133 1st St NE, St Petersburg, FL 33701
Fernandez, Sid *Baseball Player*
748 Kalanipuu St, Honolulu, HI 96825
Ferragamo, Vince *Football Player*
6715 Horseshoe Rd, Orange, CA 92669
Ferrante, Jack *Football Player*
552 Andrew Rd, Springfield, PA 19064
Ferrara, Arthur V *Businessman*
%Guardian Life Insurance Co, 201 Park Ave, New York, NY 10003
Ferrare, Cristina *Model, Entertainer*
%Triad Artists, 10100 Santa Monica Blvd, #1600, Los Angeles, CA 90067
Ferrari, Michael *Educator*
%Drake University, President's Office, Des Moines, IA 50311
Ferraro, Geraldine A *Representative, NY*
22 Deerdene Rd, Forest Hills, NY 11375
Ferraro, John *Football Player*
641 N Wilcox Ave, Los Angeles, CA 90004
Ferrazzi, Ferruccio *Artist*
Piazza delle Muse, Via GG Porro 27, 00197 Rome, Italy
Ferre, Gianfranco *Fashion Designer*
%House of Dior, 30 Ave Montaigne, 75008 Paris, France
Ferre, Maurice A *Mayor*
2501 Bicknell Ave, #802, Miami, FL 33133
Ferrell, Conchata *Actress*
1347 N Seward St, Los Angeles, CA 90028
Ferrell, Rick *Baseball Player*
2199 Golfview, #203, Troy, MI 48084
Ferrer, Lupita *Actress*
861 Stone Canyon Rd, Los Angeles, CA 90024
Ferrer, Mel *Actor*
6590 Camino Caretta, Carpinteria, CA 93013
Ferrer, Miguel *Actor*
%William Morris Agency, 151 El Camino, Beverly Hills, CA 90212
Ferrigno, Lou *Actor*
PO Box 1671, Santa Monica, CA 90406
Ferriss, David (Boo) *Baseball Player*
510 Robinson Dr, Cleveland, MS 38732

Ferry, Bryan *Singer, Songwriter*
%EG Mgmt, 63-A Kings Rd, London SW3 4NT, England

Ferry, Danny *Basketball Player*
%Cleveland Cavaliers, 2923 Statesboro Rd, Richfield, OH 44286

Ferry, John Douglass *Chemist*
137 N Prospect Ave, Madison, WI 53705

Ferry, Richard *Businessman*
%Korn/Ferry International, 1800 Ave of Stars, Los Angeles, CA 90067

Fery, John B *Businessman*
%Boise Cascade Corp, 1 Jefferson Sq, Boise, ID 83728

Festinger, Leon *Psychologist*
37 W 12th St, New York, NY 10011

Fetterman, John H, Jr *Navy Admiral*
Chief Naval Education/Training, Naval Air Station, Pensacola, FL 32508

Feuer, Cy *Theatrical, Movie Producer*
630 Park Ave, New York, NY 10021

Feuer, Seymour S *Businessman*
%Ex-Cell-O Corp, 2855 Coolidge, Troy, MI 48084

Feuillere, Edwige *Actress*
19 Rue Eugene Manuel, 75016 Paris, France

Feulner, Edwin J, Jr *Foundation Executive*
%Heritage Foundation, 513 "C" St NE, Washington, DC 20002

Fey, E C *Businessman*
%Pinkenton's Inc, 100 Church St, New York, NY 10007

Fiaccavento, Carrado *Businessman*
%EFIM, Via XXIV Maggio 43/45, 00187 Rome, Italy

Fibingerova, Helena *Track Athlete*
Jeremenkova 5, Ostrava 700 00, Czechoslovakia

Fichtel, Anja *Fencer*
%Florettfectterin des Fecht, Tauberbischofsheim 1, Germany

Fichter, John L *Businessman*
%Anderson Clayton Co, 1100 Louisiana, #3800, Houston, TX 77002

Fickling, William A, Jr *Businessman*
%Charter Medical Corp, 577 Mulberry St, Macon, GA 31298

Fidrych, Mark *Baseball Player*
260 West St, Northboro, MA 01532

Fiedler, John *Actor*
%International Creative Mgmt, 8899 Beverly Blvd, Los Angeles, CA 90048

Fiedler, Leslie A *Writer, Critic*
154 Morris Ave, Buffalo, NY 14214

Field, George B *Theoretical Astrophysicist*
60 Garden St, Cambridge, MA 02138

Field, Sally *Actress*
8436 W 3rd St, #650, Los Angeles, CA 90048

Fielder, Cecil *Baseball Player*
%Detroit Tigers, Tiger Stadium, 2121 Trumbull Ave, Detroit, MI 48216

Fields, Debbi *Businesswoman*
%Mrs Fields Cookies, 333 Main, Park City, UT 84060

Fields, Harold T, Jr *Army General*
Deputy Commander in Chief, US Pacific Command, Camp H M Smith, HI 96858

Fields, Jack M *Representative, TX*
3022 S Houston Ave, Humble, TX 77338

Fields, Kim *Actress*
%All Talent Agency, 2437 E Washington Blvd, Pasadena, CA 91104

Fiennes, Ranulph *Transglobal Explorer*
Robins, Lodsworth, Petworth, West Sussex, England

Fierstein, Harvey *Playwright, Actor*
%William Morris Agency, 1350 Ave of Americas, New York, NY 10019

Figgie, Harry E, Jr *Businessman*
%Figgie International Holdings Inc, 4420 Sherwin Rd, Willoughby, OH 44094

Figini, Luigi *Architect*
Via Perone di S Martino 8, Milan, Italy

Figini, Michela *Skier*
CH-6799 Prato-Leventina, Switzerland

Figueiredo, Joao Baptista de *President, Brazil*
Av Prefeito Mendes de Moraes 1400/802, S Conrado, Rio de Janeiro, Brazil

Filarski, Myron *Financier*
%TransOhio Financial Corp, 1 Penton Plz, Cleveland, OH 44114

Filchock, Frank *Football Player*
1725 SW Fernwood Dr, Lake Oswego, OR 97034

Filer, John H *Businessman*
%Aetna Life & Casualty Co, 151 Framington Ave, Hartford, CT 06115

Filipchenko, Anatoly N *Cosmonaut*
141 160 Svyosdny Gorodok, Moskovskoi Oblasti, Potchta Kosmonavtov, Russia

Filippini, Carlos *Businessman*
%Union Explosivos Rio Tinto, Paseo de la Castellellana 20, Madrid, Spain

Fill, Dennis C *Businessman*
%Bristol-Myers Squibb Corp, PO Box 4000, Princeton, NJ 08540

Filmus, Tully *Artist*
17 Stuart St, Great Neck, NY 11023

Finch, Charles B *Businessman*
%Allegheny Power System, 320 Park Ave, New York, NY 10022

Finch, Harold B, Jr *Businessman*
%Nash Finch Co, 3381 Gorham Ave, St Louis Park, MN 55426

Finch, Jon *Actor*
Neasrader, 135 New King's Rd, London SW6 4SL, England

Finch, Larry *Basketball Player, Coach*
%Memphis State University, Athletic Dept, Memphis, TN 38152

Finch, Robert H *Secretary, Health Education & Welfare*
1106 Las Reindas, Pasadena, CA 91107

Finch, William G H *Radio Engineer, Inventor*
3025 Moringside Blvd, Port St Lucie, FL 33452

Findley, Paul *Representative, IL*
115 W Jefferson St, Pittsfield, IL 62363

Fine, Travis *Actor*
%Vaughn D Hart, 200 N Robertson Blvd, Beverly Hills, CA 90211

Fingers, Rollie *Baseball Player*
11582 Avenida Sirvita, San Diego, CA 92128

Fini, Leonor *Artist*
8 Rue de la Vrilliere, 75001 Paris, France

Fink, Donald E *Editor*
%Aviation Week Magazine, 1221 Ave of Americas, New York, NY 10020

Finkelstein, Edward S *Businessman*
%R H Macy Co, 151 W 34th St, New York, NY 10001

Finks, Jim *Football Executive*
%New Orleans Saints, 6928 Saints Dr, Metairie, LA 70003

Finland, Maxwell *Physician*
%Boston City Hospital, Boston, MA 02118

Finlay, Frank *Actor*
55 Park Ln, London W1, London, England

Finley, Charles O *Baseball Executive*
%Charles O Finley Insurance, 151 N Michigan Ave, Chicago, IL 60605

Finley, James D *Businessman*
%J P Stevens Co, 1185 Ave of Americas, New York, NY 10036

Finley, Karen *Conceptual Artist*
%Kitchen Center for Video-Music-Dance, 512 W 9th, New York, NY 10011

Finley, Murray H *Labor Leader*
%Clothing & Textile Workers Union, 15 Union Sq, New York, NY 10003

Finn, Chester E, Jr *Educator*
%Educational Excellence Network, 1112 16th St NW, #500, Washington, DC 20036

Finnane, Dan *Basketball Executive*
%Golden State Warriors, Oakland Coliseum, Oakland, CA 94621

Finnbogagottir, Vigdis *President, Iceland*
%President's Office, Reykjavik, Iceland

Finnegan, John R *Editor*
%St Paul Pioneer Press Dispatch, 345 Cedar St, St Paul, MN 55101

Finneran Rittenhouse, Sharon *Swimmer*
212 Harbor Dr, Santa Cruz, CA 95062

Finneran, John G *Navy Admiral*
5600 Beam Ct, Bethesda, MD 20817

Finney, Albert *Actor*
39 Seymour Walk, London SW10, England

Finney, Allison *Golfer*
72-750-A Cactus Ct, Palm Desert, CA 92260

Finney, Joan *Governor, KS*
%Governor's Office, State Capitol, 2nd Fl, Topeka, KS 66612

Finney, Ross Lee *Composer*
2015 Geddes, Ann Arbor, MI 48104

Finster, Howard *Artist*
Rt 2, Box 106-A, Summerville, GA 30747

Finsterwald, Dow *Golfer*
%Broadmoor Golf Club, 1 Lake Cir, Colorado Springs, CO 80906

Fiona *Actress*
%Camden ITG, 822 S Robertson Blvd, #200, Los Angeles, CA 90035

Fiore, Bill *Actor*
10 E 44th St, #700, New York, NY 10017

Fiorillo, Elisa *Singer*
%Chrysalis Records, 9255 Sunset Blvd, Los Angeles, CA 90069

Firby, Howard *Swimmer*
1445 Pendrell St, #501, Vancouver BC V6G 1S3, Canada

Fireman, Paul *Businessman*
%Reebok International, 150 Royal St, Canton, MA 02021

Firestone, Leonard K *Businessman*
515 S Flower St, #4470, Los Angeles, CA 90071

Firestone, Raymond C *Businessman*
Lauray Farms, Bath, OH 44210

Firestone, Roy *Sportscaster*
%Seizen/Wallach Productions, 257 Rodeo Dr, Beverly Hills, CA 90212

Firkusny, Rudolf *Concert Pianist*
%General Delivery, Staatsburg, NY 12580

Firth, Peter *Actor*
%Plant & Froggatt, Julian House, 4 Windmill St, London W1, England

Fischbach, Bert *Financier*
%Westdeutsche Landesbank Girozentrale, 4000 Duesseldorf, Germany

Fischbach, Ephraim *Physicist*
120 Pathway Ln, Lafayette, IN 47906

Fischer, Annie *Concert Pianist*
Szent Istvan Park 14, 1137 Budapest XIII, Hungary

Fischer, Bill (Moose) *Football Player*
1909 Prairie, Ishpeming, MI 49849

Fischer, Bobby (Robert J) *Chess Player*
%US Chess Federation, 186 Rt 9-W, New Windsor, NY 12550

Fischer, Ernst Otto *Nobel Chemistry Laureate*
Sohnckestrasse 16, 8 Munich 71, Germany

Fischer, Eugene H *Air Force General*
Inspector General, Hq USAF, Washington, DC 20330

Fischer, Gottfried B *Publisher*
PO Box 237, Old Greenwich, CT 06807

Fischer, Michael *Association Executive*
%Sierra Club, 730 Polk St, San Francisco, CA 94109

Fischer-Dieskau, Dietrich *Opera, Concert Singer*
Lindenallee 22, 1 Berlin 19, Germany

Fischl, Eric *Artist*
%Mary Boone Gallery, 417 W Broadway, New York, NY 10012

Fish, Hamilton, Jr *Representative, NY*
%House of Representatives, Washington, DC 20015

Fish, Henry E *Businessman*
%American Sterlizer Co, 2222 W Grandview Blvd, Erie, PA 16512

Fish, Lawrence K *Financier*
%Bank of New England, 28 State St, Boston, MA 02109

Fisher, Anna L *Astronaut*
%NASA, Johnson Space Ctr, Houston, TX 77058

Fisher, Bernard *Physician*
5636 Aylesboro Ave, Pittsburgh, PA 15217

Fisher, Carrie *Actress*
9555 Oak Pass Rd, Beverly Hills, CA 90210

Fisher, Charles T, III *Financier*
%NDB Bancorp, 611 Woodward Ave, Detroit, MI 48226

Fisher, E A (Bud) *Bowling Executive*
%Professional Bowlers Assn, 1720 Merriman Rd, Akron, OH 44313

Fisher, Eddie *Singer*
%Charles Rapp Enterprises, 1650 Broadway, New York, NY 10019

Fisher, Eddie G *Baseball Player*
408 Cardinal Cir S, Altus, OK 73521

Fisher, George M C *Businessman*
%Motorola Inc, 1303 E Algonquin Rd, Schaumburg, IL 60196

Fisher, Herbert E *Businessman*
%Kaneb Services, 1 Sugar Creek Pl, Sugar Land, TX 77478

Fisher, Joseph L *Representative, VA*
%Wilderness Society, 1901 Pennsylvania Ave NW, Washington, DC 20006

Fisher, Jules *Lighting Designer*
%Jules Fisher Enterprises, 126 5th Ave, New York, NY 10011

Fisher, M F K *Writer*
13935 Sonoma Hwy, Glen Ellen, CA 95442

Fisher, Max M *Businessman*
2210 Fisher Bldg, Detroit, MI 48202

Fisher, Richard Y *Businessman*
%Farm House Foods Corp, 777 E Wisconsin Ave, Milwaukee, WI 53202

Fisher, Roger *Guitarist (Heart)*
219 1st Ave N, #333, Seattle, WA 98109

Fisher, Steve *Basketball Coach*
%University of Michigan, Crisler Arena, 1000 S State St, Ann Arbor, MI 48109

Fisher, Wayne H *Businessman*
%Lucky Stores, 6300 Clark Ave, Dublin, CA 94566

Fisher, William F *Astronaut*
%NASA, Johnson Space Ctr, Houston, TX 77058

Fisherman, William S *Businessman*
%ARA Services, Independence Sq W, Philadelphia, PA 19106

Fishko, Sol *Labor Leader*
%Printing & Communications Union, 1730 Rhode Island, Washington, DC 20036

Fisk, Carlton *Baseball Player*
16612 Catawba Rd, Lockport, IL 60441

Fisk, James B *Physicist*
Lees Hill Rd, Basking Ridge, NJ 60441

Fistoulari, Anatole *Conductor*
65 Redington Rd, London NW3, England

Fitch, Bill *Basketball Coach*
%New Jersey Nets, Meadowlands Arena, East Rutherford, NJ 07073

Fitch, Val L *Nobel Physics Laureate*
292 Hartley Ave, Princeton, NJ 08540

Fitch, William H *Marine Corps General*
%Marine Corps Headquarters, Washington, DC 20380

Fites, Donald *Businessman*
%Caterpillar Inc, 100 NE Adams St, Peoria, IL 61629

Fithian, Floyd *Representative, IN*
%House of Representatives, Washington, DC 20515

Fittipaldi, Emerson *Auto Racing Driver*
%Fittipaldi USA, Venetia Town Residences, 1717 N Bayshore Dr, Miami, FL 33132

Fitz, Raymond L *Educator*
%University of Dayton, President's Office, Dayton, OH 45469

Fitzgerald, A Ernest *Government Efficiency Advocate*
%Air Force Management Systems, Pentagon, Washington, DC 20330

Fitzgerald, Ella *Singer*
%Franklyn Agency, 1010 Hammond St, #312, Los Angeles, CA 90069

FitzGerald, Frances *Writer*
%Simon & Schuster, 1230 Ave of Americas, New York, NY 10020

FitzGerald, Garret *Prime Minister, Ireland*
%Dail Eireann, Leinster House, Kildare St, Dublin 2, Ireland

Fitzgerald, Geraldine *Actress*
50 E 79th St, New York, NY 10019

Fitzgerald, Jack *Actor*
%Gerritsen International, 8721 Sunset Blvd, #103, Los Angeles, CA 90069

Fitzgerald, Jim *Basketball Executive*
%Golden State Warriors, Oakland Coliseum, Oakland, CA 94621

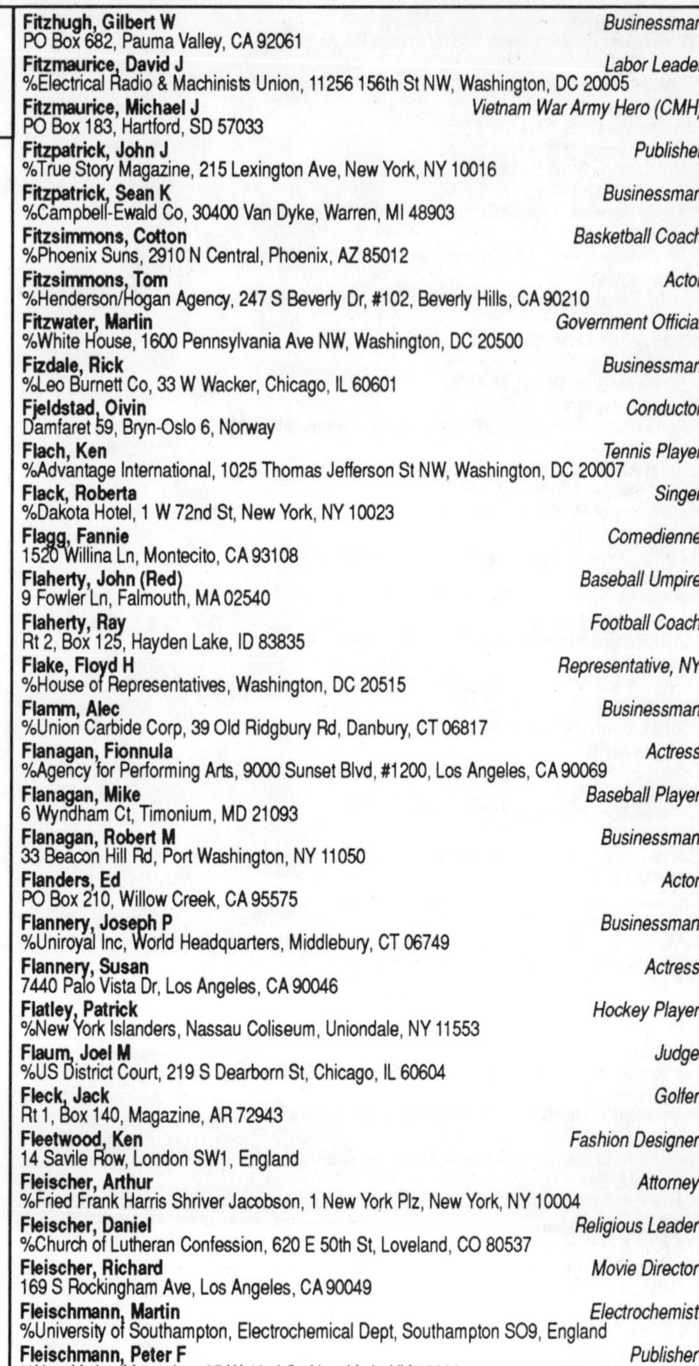

F

Fitzhugh, Gilbert W *Businessman*
PO Box 682, Pauma Valley, CA 92061

Fitzmaurice, David J *Labor Leader*
%Electrical Radio & Machinists Union, 11256 156th St NW, Washington, DC 20005

Fitzmaurice, Michael J *Vietnam War Army Hero (CMH)*
PO Box 183, Hartford, SD 57033

Fitzpatrick, John J *Publisher*
%True Story Magazine, 215 Lexington Ave, New York, NY 10016

Fitzpatrick, Sean K *Businessman*
%Campbell-Ewald Co, 30400 Van Dyke, Warren, MI 48903

Fitzsimmons, Cotton *Basketball Coach*
%Phoenix Suns, 2910 N Central, Phoenix, AZ 85012

Fitzsimmons, Tom *Actor*
%Henderson/Hogan Agency, 247 S Beverly Dr, #102, Beverly Hills, CA 90210

Fitzwater, Marlin *Government Official*
%White House, 1600 Pennsylvania Ave NW, Washington, DC 20500

Fizdale, Rick *Businessman*
%Leo Burnett Co, 33 W Wacker, Chicago, IL 60601

Fjeldstad, Oivin *Conductor*
Damfaret 59, Bryn-Oslo 6, Norway

Flach, Ken *Tennis Player*
%Advantage International, 1025 Thomas Jefferson St NW, Washington, DC 20007

Flack, Roberta *Singer*
%Dakota Hotel, 1 W 72nd St, New York, NY 10023

Flagg, Fannie *Comedienne*
1520 Willina Ln, Montecito, CA 93108

Flaherty, John (Red) *Baseball Umpire*
9 Fowler Ln, Falmouth, MA 02540

Flaherty, Ray *Football Coach*
Rt 2, Box 125, Hayden Lake, ID 83835

Flake, Floyd H *Representative, NY*
%House of Representatives, Washington, DC 20515

Flamm, Alec *Businessman*
%Union Carbide Corp, 39 Old Ridgbury Rd, Danbury, CT 06817

Flanagan, Fionnula *Actress*
%Agency for Performing Arts, 9000 Sunset Blvd, #1200, Los Angeles, CA 90069

Flanagan, Mike *Baseball Player*
6 Wyndham Ct, Timonium, MD 21093

Flanagan, Robert M *Businessman*
33 Beacon Hill Rd, Port Washington, NY 11050

Flanders, Ed *Actor*
PO Box 210, Willow Creek, CA 95575

Flannery, Joseph P *Businessman*
%Uniroyal Inc, World Headquarters, Middlebury, CT 06749

Flannery, Susan *Actress*
7440 Palo Vista Dr, Los Angeles, CA 90046

Flatley, Patrick *Hockey Player*
%New York Islanders, Nassau Coliseum, Uniondale, NY 11553

Flaum, Joel M *Judge*
%US District Court, 219 S Dearborn St, Chicago, IL 60604

Fleck, Jack *Golfer*
Rt 1, Box 140, Magazine, AR 72943

Fleetwood, Ken *Fashion Designer*
14 Savile Row, London SW1, England

Fleischer, Arthur *Attorney*
%Fried Frank Harris Shriver Jacobson, 1 New York Plz, New York, NY 10004

Fleischer, Daniel *Religious Leader*
%Church of Lutheran Confession, 620 E 50th St, Loveland, CO 80537

Fleischer, Richard *Movie Director*
169 S Rockingham Ave, Los Angeles, CA 90049

Fleischmann, Martin *Electrochemist*
%University of Southampton, Electrochemical Dept, Southampton SO9, England

Fleischmann, Peter F *Publisher*
%New Yorker Magazine, 25 W 43rd St, New York, NY 10036

Fleisher, Leon *Concert Pianist, Conductor*
20 Merrymount Rd, Baltimore, MD 21210

Fleishman, Joel L *Educator, Lawyer*
205 Wood Cir, Chapel Hill, NC 27514
Fleming Jenkins, Peggy *Figure Skater*
1223 N Sweetzer St, Los Angeles, CA 90069
Fleming, Douglas G *Businessman*
16817 Tonkel Rd, Leo, IN 46765
Fleming, James P *Vietnam War Air Force Hero (CMH)*
USAF-CAP NELR/CC, Bldg 2401, McGuire Air Force Base, NJ 08641
Fleming, John M *Businessman*
%Vauxhall Motors, Kimpton Rd, Luton, Beds LU2 0SY, England
Fleming, John V *Educator*
39 University Pl, Princeton, NJ 08540
Fleming, Mac A *Labor Leader*
%Maintenance of Way Employees Brotherhood, 12050 Woodward Ave, Detroit, MI 48203
Fleming, Ned N *Businessman*
%Fleming Companies, 6301 Waterford Blvd, Oklahoma City, OK 73126
Fleming, Peter F, Jr *Attorney*
%Curtis Mallet-Prevost Colt Mosle, 100 Wall St, New York, NY 10005
Fleming, Rhonda *Actress*
2129 Century Woods Way, Los Angeles, CA 90067
Fleming, Richard C D *Urban Developer*
%Downtown Denver Inc, Guaranty Bank Bldg, #704, Denver, CO 80202
Fleming, Robben W *Educator*
2108 Vinewood Ave, Ann Arbor, MI 48104
Fleming, Sam M *Financier*
%Third National Bank, 201 4th Ave N, Nashville, TN 37219
Fleming, Vern *Basketball Player*
%Indiana Pacers, 2 W Washington St, Indianapolis, IN 46204
Flemming, Arthur S *Secretary, Health Education & Welfare*
%Commission on Civil Rights, 1121 Vermont Ave NW, Washington, DC 20425
Flemming, Bill (William N) *Sportscaster*
%ABC-TV, Sports Dept, 77 W 66th St, New York, NY 10023
Fletcher, Arthur *Government Official*
%Commission on Civil Rights, 1121 Vermont Ave NW, Washington, DC 20425
Fletcher, Betty B *Judge*
%US Court of Appeals, US Courthouse, 1010 5th Ave, Seattle, WA 98104
Fletcher, Charles M *Physician, Research Scientist*
2 Coastguard Cottages, Newtown PO30 4PA, England
Fletcher, Kim *Financier*
%Home Federal Savings & Loan, 707 Broadway, San Diego, CA 92101
Fletcher, Louise *Actress*
1520 Camden Ave, #105, Los Angeles, CA 90025
Fletcher, Martin *Commentator*
%NBC-TV, News Dept, 4001 Nebraska Ave NW, Washington, DC 20016
Fletcher, Philip B *Businessman*
%ConAgra Inc, 1 Central Park Plz, Omaha, NE 68102
Flexner, James T *Writer*
530 E 86th St, New York, NY 10028
Flindt, Flemming *Ballet Dancer, Choreographer*
Christiansholms Parkv 24, 2930 Klampenborg, Denmark
Flippo, Ronnie G *Representative, AL*
114 Lance Ln, Florence, AL 35630
Flom, Joseph H *Attorney*
%Skadden Arps Slate Meagher Flom, 919 3rd Ave, New York, NY 10022
Flood, Ann *Actress*
19 W 44th St, #1500, New York, NY 10036
Flood, Curt *Baseball Player*
4139 Cloverdale Ave, Los Angeles, CA 90008
Flood, F G *Businessman*
%BPB Industries, Langley Park House, Uxbridge Rd, Lough SL3 6DU, England
Flood, Frank J *Businessman*
%Wolverine World Wide Inc, 9341 Courtland Dr, Rockford, MI 49351
Flor, Claus Peter *Conductor*
%Mariedl Anders Artists, 535 El Camino Del Mar, San Francisco, CA 94121
Florek, Dann *Actor*
%J Michael Bloom Ltd, 9200 Sunset Blvd, #710, Los Angeles, CA 90069

F

Floren – Fock

Floren, Myron *Accordionist*
Benson East, #B-10, Jenkintown, PA 19046

Florence, Leonard *Businessman*
%Towle Manufacturing Co, 144 Addison St, Boston, MA 02128

Flores, Patrick F *Religious Leader*
%Archbishop's Residence, 2600 Woodlawn Ave, San Antonio, TX 78228

Flores, Tom *Football Player, Coach, Executive*
%Seattle Seahawks, 11220 NE 53rd St, Seattle, WA 98033

Florio, James J *Governor; Representative, NJ*
%Governor's Office, State House, Trenton, NJ 08625

Florio, Steven T *Publisher*
%New Yorker Magazine, 25 W 43rd St, New York, NY 10036

Flory, Med *Actor*
6044 Ensign Ave, North Hollywood, CA 91606

Flournoy, Craig *Journalist*
%Dallas News, Communications Ctr, Dallas, TX 75265

Flower, John A *Educator*
%Cleveland State University, President's Office, Cleveland, OH 44115

Flower, Joseph R *Religious Leader*
%Assemblies of God, 1445 Boonville Ave, Springfield, MO 65802

Flowers, Langdon S *Businessman*
%Flowers Industries, PO Box 1338, Thomasville, GA 31799

Flowers, William H, Jr *Businessman*
%Flowers Industries, PO Box 1338, Thomasville, GA 31799

Floyd, Carlisle *Composer*
4491 Yoakum Blvd, Houston, TX 77006

Floyd, Eric (Sleepy) *Basketball Player*
%Houston Rockets, Summit, Greenway Plaza, #10, Houston, TX 77046

Floyd, Ray *Golfer*
%International Management Grp, 1 Erieview Plz, #1300, Cleveland, OH 44114

Fluckey, Eugene B *WW II Navy Hero (CMH); Admiral*
1016 Sandpiper Ln, Annapolis, MD 21403

Fluegel, Darlanne *Actress*
%Harris & Goldberg Agency, 1999 Ave of Stars, #2850, Los Angeles, CA 90067

Fluno, Jere D *Businessman*
%W W Grainger Inc, 5500 W Howard St, Skokie, IL 60077

Flutie, Doug *Football Player*
21 Spring Valley Rd, Natick, MA 01760

Flynn, Barbara *Actress*
%Markham & Froggatt, Julian House, 4 Windmill St, London W1, England

Flynn, Raymond L *Mayor*
%Mayor's Office, City Hall, 1 City Hall Sq, Boston, MA 02201

Flynn, Richard J *Businessman*
%Norton Co, 120 Front St, Worcester, MA 01608

Flynn, William J *Businessman*
%Mutual of America, 666 5th Ave, New York, NY 10103

Flynn, William S *Army General*
Commanding General, 21st Theater Army Area Command, USA Europe, APO, AE 09263

Flynne, Robert L *Businessman*
%Smith International, 4490 Von Karman Ave, Newport Beach, CA 92660

Flynt, John James, Jr *Representative, GA*
115 N 6th St, Griffin, GA 30224

Flynt, Larry *Publisher*
%Hustler Magazine, 9171 Wilshire Blvd, #300, Beverly Hills, CA 90210

Fo, Dario *Writer*
%Pietro Sciotto, Via Alessandria 4, 20144 Milan, Italy

Foa, Joseph V *Aeronautical Engineer*
3404 Thornapple St, Chevy Chase, MD 20815

Foale, C Michael *Astronaut*
%NASA, Johnson Space Ctr, Houston, TX 77058

Fobes, John E *Diplomat*
739 Gimghoul Rd, Chapel Hill, NC 27514

Foch, Nina *Actress*
PO Box 1884, Beverly Hills, CA 90213

Fock, Jeno *Prime Minister, Hungary*
%Communist Central Committee, Szechenyirakpart 19, Budapest V, Hungary

Fodor, Eugene N *Concert Violinist*
22314 N Turkey Creek Rd, Morrison, CO 80465

Foeger, Luggi *Skier*
%Christopher C Foeger, 230 S Balsamina Way, Portola Valley, CA 94028

Foelber, Charles H *Businessman*
%USF&G Corp, 100 Light St, Baltimore, MD 21202

Foell, Earl W *Editor*
%Christian Science Monitor, 1 Norway St, Boston, MA 02115

Fogarty, William M *Navy Admiral*
Commander, Joint Task Force Middle East, FPO, New York, NY 09501

Fogelberg, Dan *Singer, Songwriter*
PO Box 824, Pagosa Springs, CO 81147

Fogelman, Ronald R *Air Force General*
Commander, 7th Air Force, APO, AP 96278

Fogerty, John *Singer*
%Warner Bros Records, 3300 Warner Blvd, Burbank, CA 91505

Foggs, Edward L *Religious Leader*
%Church of God, Box 2420, Anderson, IN 46018

Foglietta, Thomas M *Representative, PA*
%House of Representatives, Washington, DC 20515

Foldes, Andor *Concert Pianist*
8704 Herrliberg Near Zurich, Switzerland

Foley, Bill *Photojournalist*
%Time Magazine, 1271 Ave of Americas, New York, NY 10020

Foley, Robert F *Vietnam War Army Hero (CMH), General*
Asst Div Cdr, 2nd Infantry Division, EUSA, Korea, Unit 15041, APO, AP 96224

Foley, Sylvester R, Jr *Navy Admiral*
%Navy Department, Pentagon, Washington, DC 20350

Foley, Thomas S *Representative, WA; Speaker*
1228 E 29th Ave, Spokane, WA 99202

Foligno, Mike *Hockey Player*
%Buffalo Sabres, Memorial Auditorium, Buffalo, NY 14202

Folkenberg, Robert S *Religious Leader*
%Seventh-Day Adventists, 12501 Old Columbia Pike, Silver Spring, MD 20904

Folkers, Karl *Chemist*
6406 Mesa Dr, Austin, TX 78731

Follett, Ken *Writer*
PO Box 708, London SW10 0DH, England

Folley, Clyde H *Businessman*
%Ingersoll-Rand Co, 200 Chestnut Ridge Rd, Woodcliff Lake, NJ 07675

Follows, Megan *Actress*
%Susan Smith Assoc, 121 N San Vicente Blvd, Beverly Hills, CA 90211

Folon, Jean-Michel *Artist*
Burcy, 77890 Beaumont-du-Gatinais, France

Folsom, Robert S *Mayor*
%Mayor's Office, City Hall, Dallas, TX 75201

Folsome, Claire *Microbiologist*
%University of Hawaii, Microbiology Dept, Honolulu, HI 96822

Fomon, Robert M *Businessman*
%E F Hutton Grp, 1 Battery Park Plz, New York, NY 10004

Fonda, Jane *Actress*
%Fonda Films, PO Box 1198, Santa Monica, CA 90406

Fonda, Peter *Actor*
%Pando Co, RR 38, Box 2024, Livingston, MT 59047

Fong, Hiram *Senator, HI*
1102 Alewa Dr, Honolulu, HI 96817

Fong, Kam *Actress*
9430 W Washington Blvd, #5, ulver City, CA 90230

Fonrodona Sala, Jaime *Businessman*
%Petroliber, Juan Bravo 3-B, Madrid 6, Spain

Fontaine, Frank *Singer*
%Suffolk Marketing, 475 5th Ave, New York, NY 10017

Fontaine, Joan *Actress*
PO Box 222600, Carmel, CA 93922

Fontaine, Richard H *Financier*
%T Rowe Price Capital Appreciation Fund, 100 E Pratt St, Baltimore, MD 21202

Fontes, Wayne *Football Coach*
%Detroit Lions, Silverdome, 1200 Featherstone Rd, Pontiac, MI 48342

Fonville, Charles *Track Athlete*
2427 Glynn Ct, Detroit, MI 48206

Foot, Michael *Government Official, England*
%House of Commons, Westminister, London SW1, England

Foote, Edward T, II *Educator*
%University of Miami, President's Office, Coral Gables, FL 33124

Foote, Emerson *Businessman*
Gypsy Trl, Carmel, NY 10512

Foote, H Robert B *WW II British Army Hero (VC), General*
Furzefield, West Chiltington, Pulborough, West Sussex RH20 2QY, England

Foote, Horton *Playwright*
95 Horatio St, #322, New York, NY 10014

Foote, Robert T *Businessman*
%Universal Foods Corp, 433 E Michigan St, Milwaukee, WI 53202

Foote, Shelby *Writer*
542 East Pkwy S, Memphis, TN 38104

Foray, June *Actress*
22745 Erwin St, Woodland Hills, CA 91367

Forbes, Bryan *Movie Director, Screenwriter*
Bookshop, Virginia Water, Surrey, England

Forbes, Malcolm S (Steve), Jr *Publisher*
%Forbes Magazine, 60 5th Ave, New York, NY 10011

Forbes, Murray *Financier*
%Howard Savings Bank, 768 Broad St, Newark, NJ 07101

Force, John *Auto Racing Driver*
%John Force Racing, 23253 E La Palma Ave, Yorba Linda, CA 92687

Ford, Alan *Swimmer*
1821 Ivy Ln, Midland, MI 48640

Ford, Betty *Wife of US President*
40365 Sand Dune Rd, Rancho Mirage, CA 92270

Ford, Chris *Basketball Player, Coach*
%Boston Celtics, 151 Merrimac St, Boston, MA 02114

Ford, Doug *Golfer*
4701 Oak Terr, Lake Worth, FL 33463

Ford, Eileen O *Model Agency Executive*
%Ford Model Agency, 344 E 59th St, New York, NY 10022

Ford, Faith *Actress*
%William Morris Agency, 151 El Camino, Beverly Hills, CA 90212

Ford, Gerald R *President, United States*
40365 Sand Dune Rd, Rancho Mirage, CA 92270

Ford, Gerard W *Model Agency Executive*
%Ford Model Agency, 344 E 59th St, New York, NY 10022

Ford, Glenn *Actor*
911 Oxford Way, Beverly Hills, CA 90210

Ford, Harold E *Representative, TN*
%House of Representatives, Washington, DC 20515

Ford, Harrison *Actor*
655 MacCullock Dr, Los Angeles, CA 90049

Ford, Jesse Hill *Writer*
500 Plantation Ct, Nashville, TN 37221

Ford, Larry C *Gynecologic Oncologist*
%University of California, Medical School, Los Angeles, CA 90024

Ford, Louis Henry *Religious Leader*
%Church of God in Christ, 272 S Main St, Memphis, TN 38101

Ford, Morgan *Judge*
Casa Del Sur Apts, 655 Tourmaline St, San Diego, CA 92109

Ford, Ruth *Actress*
%Dakota Hotel, 1 W 72nd St, New York, NY 10023

Ford, T Mitchell *Businessman*
%Emhart Corp, 426 Colt Hwy, Farmington, CT 06032

Ford, Wendell H *Governor/Senator, KY*
4974 Sentinel Dr, #2, Bethesda, MD 20816

Ford, Whitey (Edward C) *Baseball Player*
38 Schoolhouse Ln, Lake Success, NY 11020

Ford, William C *Businessman*
%Ford Motor Co, American Rd, Dearborn, MI 48121

Ford, William D *Representative, MI*
%House of Representatives, Washington, DC 20515

Ford, William F *Financier*
%First Nationwide Financial Corp, 700 Market St, San Francisco, CA 94102

Fordice, Kirk *Governor, MS*
%Governor's Office, State Capitol, PO Box 139, Jackson, MS 39212

Foreman, Carol *Government Official*
5408 Trent St, Chevy Chase, MD 20015

Foreman, George *Boxer*
7639 Pine Oak Dr, Humble, TX 77397

Foret, Mickey *Businessman*
%Continental Air Lines, LA International Airport, Los Angeles, CA 90009

Forget, Guy *Tennis Player*
%Societe IMG, 20 Rue Dusrenoy, 75116 Paris, France

Forker, Lee R *Businessman*
%Quaker State Oil Refining Corp, 255 Elm St, Oil City, PA 16301

Forlani, Arnaldo *Prime Minister, Italy*
Piazzale Schumann 15, Rome, Italy

Forman, Milos *Movie Director*
Hampshire House, 150 Central Park South, New York, NY 10019

Forman, Tom *Cartoonist (Motley's Crew)*
%Tribune Media Services, 34 E Concord St, Orlando, FL 32801

Formia, Osvaldo *Harness Racing Trainer*
6501 Winfield Blvd, #A-10, Margate, FL 33063

Fornell, Gordon E *Air Force General*
Commander, Electronic Systems Division, Hanscom Air Force Base, MA 01731

Forrest, Frederic *Actor*
%Camden ITG Agency, 822 S Robertson Blvd, #200, Los Angeles, CA 90035

Forrest, Sally *Actress*
1125 Angelo Dr, Beverly Hills, CA 90210

Forrest, Steve *Actor*
10620 Wilkins Ave, #3, Los Angeles, CA 90024

Forrester, James *Medical Researcher*
%Cedars-Sinai Medical Center, 8700 Beverly Blvd, Los Angeles, CA 90048

Forrester, Jay W *Computer Engineer, Educator*
%Massachusetts Institute of Technology, Management School, Cambridge, MA 02139

Forrester, Maureen *Concert Singer*
26 Edmond Ave, Toronto ON M4V 1H3, Canada

Forsch, Bob *Baseball Player*
428 Hickory Glen Ln, St Louis, MO 63141

Forsch, Ken *Baseball Player*
7445 Stone Creek Ln, Anaheim, CA 92807

Forsell, Arne *Businessman*
%Atlas Copco MCT AB, S-104 84 Stockholm, Sweden

Forslund, Constance *Actress*
%Ambrosio/Mortimer Assoc, 301 N Canon Dr, #305, Beverly Hills, CA 90210

Forsse, Ken *Businessman (Teddy Ruxpin)*
%Alchemy II, 9207 Eton Ave, Chatsworth, CA 91311

Forster, A W *Businessman*
%Esso UK, Esso House, Victoria St, London SW1E 5JW, England

Forster, Robert *Actor*
8550 Holloway Dr, #402, Los Angeles, CA 90069

Forstmann, Theodore *Financier*
%Forstmann Little & Co, 767 5th Ave, New York, NY 10153

Forsyth, Bill *Movie Director*
%Lake Films, 20 Winton Dr, Glasgow G12, Scotland

Forsyth, Rosemary *Actress*
18663 Ventura Blvd, Tarzana, CA 91356

Forsythe, Henderson *Actor*
204 Elm St, Tenafly, NJ 07670

Forsythe, John *Actor*
14215 Sunset Blvd, Pacific Palisades, CA 90272

Fort, Edward B *Educator*
%North Carolina A&T University, Chancellor's Office, Greensboro, NC 27411

Fort, John F *Businessman*
%Tyco Laboratories, Tyco Park, Exeter, NH 03833
Fort-Brescia, Bernardo *Architect*
%Arquitectonica International, 2151 LaJeuen Rd, Coral Gables, FL 33134
Forte, Chet *Television Director, Basketball Player*
3 Glenwood Dr, Saddle River, NJ 07458
Fortess, Karl E *Artist*
311 Plochmann Ln, Woodstock, NY 12498
Fortier, Claude *Physiologist*
1014 De Grenoble, Ste-Foy, Quebec PQ G1V 2Z9, Canada
Fortmann, Daniel J *Football Player*
111 S Orange Grove Blvd, #309, Pasadena, CA 91105
Fosbury, Dick *Track Athlete*
General Delivery, Ketchum, ID 83340
Fosco, Angelo *Labor Leader*
%Laborers International Union, 905 16th St NW, Washington, DC 20006
Foss, Joseph *WW II Marine Hero (CMH); Governor, SD*
PO Box 566, Scottsdale, AZ 85252
Foss, Lukas *Composer, Conductor*
17 E 96th St, New York, NY 10028
Fossen, Steve *Bassist (Heart)*
219 1st Ave N, #333, Seattle, WA 98109
Foster, Bill *Basketball Coach*
%Virginia Polytechnic Institute, Athletic Dept, Blacksburg, VA 24061
Foster, Bob *Boxer*
%Bernalillo County Sheriff Dept, 401 Marquette Ave, Albuquerque, NM 87102
Foster, Brendan *Track Athlete*
3 Ivy Ln, Low Fell, Gateshead, Tyne & Wear, England
Foster, George *Baseball Player*
Box 11098, Greenwich, CT 06830
Foster, Greg *Track Athlete*
PO Box 21053, Long Beach, CA 90801
Foster, Harold (Bud) *Basketball Player*
2214 Hollister Ave, Madison, WI 53705
Foster, Jodie *Actress*
%International Creative Mgmt, 8899 Beverly Blvd, Los Angeles, CA 90048
Foster, John S, Jr *Physicist*
23555 Euclid Ave, Cleveland, OH 44117
Foster, Kenneth C *Businessman*
%Prudential Insurance Co, Prudential Plz, Newark, NJ 07101
Foster, Lawrence *Conductor*
%International Creative Mgmt, 40 W 57th St, New York, NY 10019
Foster, Meg *Actress*
%STE Representation, 9301 Wilshire Blvd, #312, Beverly Hills, CA 90210
Foster, Norman R *Architect*
%Foster Associates, 178-182 Great Portland St, London W1N 5TB, England
Foster, Roy *Football Player*
%San Francisco 49ers, 4949 Centennial Blvd, Santa Clara, CA 95054
Foster, Todd *Boxer*
2222 Westerland, #100, Houston, TX 77063
Foster, William C *Government Official*
3304 "R" St NW, Washington, DC 20007
Foster, William E (Bill) *Basketball Coach*
%University of South Carolina, Athletic Dept, Columbia, SC 29208
Fouche, Jacobus J *President, South Africa*
9 De Jongh St, Strand 7140, South Africa
Foulkes, Llyn *Artist*
6010 Eucalyptus Ln, Los Angeles, CA 90806
Fountain, L H *Representative, NC*
%General Delivery, Tarboro, NC 27886
Fountain, Pete *Jazz Clarinetist*
%As Was, 2 Poydras St, New Orleans, LA 70140
Foussianes, Basil G *Religious Leader*
%Greek Orthodox Archdiocese, 8-10 E 79th St, New York, NY 10021
Fouts, Dan *Football Player, Sportscaster*
%CBS-TV, Sports Dept, 51 W 52nd St, New York, NY 10019

Fowden, Leslie *Plant Chemist*
%Rothamsted Experimental Station, Harpenden, Herts, England

Fowler, Henry H *Secretary, Treasury*
200 E 66th St, New York, NY 10021

Fowler, Mark S *Government Official*
%Latham & Watkins, 1333 New Hampshire Ave NW, Washington, DC 20036

Fowler, Robert E, Jr *Businessman*
%Rubbermaid Inc, 1147 Akron Rd, Wooster, OH 44691

Fowler, W Wyche, Jr *Senator, GA*
US Senate, Washington, DC 20510

Fowler, William A *Nobel Physics Laureate*
%California Institute of Technology, Kellogg Laboratory, Pasadena, CA 91125

Fowles, John *Writer*
%Anthony Sheil Assoc, 45 Doughty St, London WC1N 2LF, England

Fox, Allen *Tennis Player, Coach*
%Pepperdine University, Athletic Dept, Malibu, CA 90265

Fox, Bernard *Actor*
%Joshua Gray Assoc, 6736 Laurel Canyon Blvd, North Hollywood, CA 91601

Fox, Bertrand *Economist*
12 Hayes Ave, Lexington, MA 02173

Fox, Carol *Opera Producer*
%Chicago Lyric Opera, 20 N Wacker St, Chicago, IL 60606

Fox, Charles *Composer, Conductor*
6671 Sunset Blvd, #1574, Los Angeles, CA 90028

Fox, Edward *Actor*
25 Maida Ave, London W2, England

Fox, Edward A *Businessman*
%Student Loan Marketing Assn, 1050 Thomas Jefferson St, Washington, DC 20007

Fox, J Carter *Businessman*
%Chesapeake Corp, PO Box 311, West Point, VA 23181

Fox, James *Actor*
3 Spencer Park Rd, London SW18, England

Fox, Marye Anne *Organic Chemist*
%University of Texas, Chemistry Dept, Austin, TX 78712

Fox, Michael J *Actor*
3960 Laurel Canyon Blvd, Studio City, CA 91604

Fox, Robert P *Businessman*
%American Hoist & Derrick Co, 63 S Robert St, St Paul, MN 55107

Fox, Samantha *Singer*
11 Mount Pleasant Villas, London 4HH, England

Fox, Sheldon *Architect*
%Kohn Pedersen Fox Assoc, 111 W 57th St, New York, NY 10019

Fox, Wesley L *Vietnam War Marine Corps Hero (CMH)*
OCS MCCOC, Development & Education Command, Quantico, VA 22134

Foxworth, Robert *Actor*
1230 Benedict Canyon Dr, Beverly Hills, CA 90210

Foy, Eddie, III *Actor*
13332 McCormick, Van Nuys, CA 91401

Foy, Lewis W *Businessman*
Elms, Saucon Valley Rd, RD 4, Bethlehem, PA 18015

Foyt, A J *Auto Racing Driver*
6415 Toledo, Houston, TX 77008

Fradon, Dana *Cartoonist*
RFD 2, Brushy Hill Rd, Newtown, CT 06470

Fraenkel, Gottfried S *Entomologist*
606 W Oregon, Urbana, IL 61801

Fraenkel-Conrat, Heinz *Research Biochemist*
870 Grizzly Peak Blvd, Berkeley, CA 94708

Fraker, William A *Cinematographer*
%Gersh Agency, 232 N Canon Dr, Beverly Hills, CA 90210

Frakes, Jonathan *Actor*
%Gores/Fields Agency, 10100 Santa Monica Blvd, #700, Los Angeles, CA 90067

Fraley, John L *Businessman*
%Carolina Freight Corp, North Carolina Hwy 150 E, Cherryville, NC 28021

Fralic, Bill *Football Player*
%Atlanta Falcons, Suwanee Rd, Suwanee, GA 30174

F

Frame – Frank

Frame, Clarence G %Tosco Corp, 2401 Colorado Ave, Santa Monica, CA 90406	*Financier*
Frame, Janet 276 Glenfield Rd, Auckland 10, New Zealand	*Writer*
Frampton, Peter %Hit & Run Music, 81-83 Walton St, London SW3 2HR, England	*Singer*
Franca, Celia 250 Clemow Ave, Ottawa ON K1S 2B6, Canada	*Ballerina, Choreographer*
France, Bill, Jr %NASCAR, 1801 Volusia Blvd, Daytona Beach, FL 32015	*Auto Racing Executive*
Franciosa, Tony 567 Tigertail Rd, Los Angeles, CA 90024	*Actor*
Francis, Anne PO Box 5417, Santa Barbara, CA 93103	*Actress*
Francis, Arlene 112 Central Park South, New York, NY 10019	*Actress*
Francis, Clarence (Bevo) %General Delivery, Salineville, OH 43945	*Basketball Player*
Francis, Connie 11 Pompton Ave, Verona, NJ 07044	*Singer*
Francis, Dick Penny Chase, Blewbury, Didcot OX11 9NH, England	*Writer*
Francis, Emile %Hartford Whalers, 1 Civic Center Plz, Hartford, CT 06103	*Hockey Coach, Executive*
Francis, Fred %NBC-TV, News Dept, 4001 Nebraska Ave NW, Washington, DC 20016	*Commentator*
Francis, Genie 5062 Calvin Ave, Tarzana, CA 91356	*Actress*
Francis, Harrison (Sam) 2850 S Chambery, Springfield, MO 65804	*Football Player*
Francis, James %Cincinnati Bengals, 200 Riverfront Stadium, Cincinnati, OH 45202	*Football Player*
Francis, James D %Charter Oil Co, 1 Charter Plz, Jacksonville, FL 32202	*Businessman*
Francis, Richard H %Pan American Corp, 200 Park Ave, New York,, NY 10166	*Businessman*
Francis, Ron %Hartford Whalers, 1 Civic Center Plz, Hartford, CT 06103	*Hockey Player*
Francis, Sam 345 W Channel Rd, Santa Monica, CA 90402	*Artist*
Francisco, George J %Fireman & Oilers Union, 1100 Circle 75 Pkwy, Atlanta, GA 30339	*Labor Leader*
Franck, George H 1628 22nd St, Rock Island, IL 61201	*Football Player*
Franco, Abel %LaRocca Entertainment, 3800 Barham Blvd, Los Angeles, CA 90068	*Actor*
Franco, Edmund J 826 3rd St, Secaucus, NJ 07094	*Football Player*
Franco, John %Capital Holding Corp, 680 Fourth Ave, Louisville, KY 40232	*Businessman*
Franco, John 54 Bay 46th St, Brooklyn, NY 11214	*Baseball Player*
Franco, Julio CF 16 B Libre Ing Cons, San Pedro de Macoris, Dominican Republic	*Baseball Player*
Francois, Jean %Lafarge Corp, 12700 Park Central Pl, Dallas, TX 75251	*Businessman*
Francois-Poncet, Jean A 6 Blvd Suchet, 75116 Paris, France	*Financier; Government Official, France*
Franjieh, Suleiman %President's Office, Beirut, Lebanon	*President, Lebanon*
Frank, Barney 114 Floral St, Newton, MA 02161	*Representative, MA*
Frank, Charles %Century Artists, 9744 Wilshire Blvd, #308, Beverly Hills, CA 90212	*Actor*
Frank, Clinton E 28 Bridlewood Rd, Northbrook, IL 60062	*Football Player*

Frank, F Charles *Physicist*
Orchard Cottage, Grove Rd, Coombe Dingle, Bristol BS9 2RL, England

Frank, Gerold *Writer*
%William Morris Agency, 1350 Ave of Americas, New York, NY 10019

Frank, Jerome D *Psychiatrist, Educator*
603 W University Pkwy, Baltimore, MD 21210

Frank, Joe *Radio Personality*
%KCRW-FM, 1900 Pico Blvd, Santa Monica, CA 90405

Frank, Neil L *Meteorologist*
%National Hurricane Ctr, 1320 S Dixie, Miami, FL 33146

Frank, Reuven *Television Producer*
%NBC-TV, 30 Rockefeller Plz, New York, NY 10020

Franke, W A *Businessman*
%Southwest Forest Industries, 6225 N 24th St, Phoenix, AZ 85016

Frankel, Max *Editor*
%New York Times, 229 W 43rd St, New York, NY 10036

Franken, Steve *Actor*
3704 Whitespeak Dr, Sherman Oaks, CA 91403

Frankenheimer, John *Movie Director*
101 Malibu Colony Rd, Malibu, CA 90265

Frankenthaler, Helen *Artist*
173 E 94th St, New York, NY 10028

Frankfurt, Stephen O *Businessman*
%Young & Rubicam, 285 Madison Ave, New York, NY 10028

Frankl, Peter *Concert Pianist*
5 Gresham Gdns, London NW11 8NX, England

Frankl, Viktor E *Psychiatrist, Writer*
Mariannengasse 1, Vienna 1090, Austria

Franklin, Aretha *Singer*
PO Box 12137, Birmingham, MI 48012

Franklin, Barbara Hackman *Secretary, Commerce*
%Department of Commerce, 14th St & Commerce Ave NW, Washington, DC 20230

Franklin, Bonnie *Actress*
15745 Royal Oak Rd, Encino, CA 91436

Franklin, J L, Jr *Businessman*
%Bassett Furniture Industries, PO Box 626, Bassett, VA 24055

Franklin, John H *Writer, Educator*
208 Pineview Rd, Durham, NC 27707

Franklin, Jon D *Journalist*
%University of Maryland, College of Journalism, College Park, MD 20742

Franklin, Pamela *Actress*
1280 Sunset Plaza Dr, Los Angeles, CA 90069

Franklin, Tony *Football Player*
%New England Patriots, Sullivan Stadium, Foxboro, MA 02035

Franklin, William H *Businessman*
4444 Knoxville St, Peoria, IL 61614

Franklyn, Sabina *Actress*
%Michael Ladkin, 2-A Warwick Pl N, London SW1V 1QW, England

Franks of Headington, Baron *Government Official, England*
Blackhall Farm, Garford Rd, Oxford OX2 6UU, England

Franks, Gary A *Representative, CT*
%House of Representatives, Washington, DC 20515

Frankston, Robert M *Computer Software Designer (VisiCalc)*
%Slate Corp, 15035 N 73rd St, Scottsdale, AZ 85260

Frann, Mary *Actress*
2790 Hutton Dr, Beverly Hills, CA 90210

Fransioli, Thomas A *Artist*
55 Dodges Row, Wenham, MA 01984

Frantz, Lou *Bowling Executive*
%Pro-Bowl Inc, 200 Kirkwood, Abilene, TX 79603

Franz, Dennis *Actor*
11805 Bellagio Rd, Los Angeles, CA 90049

Franz, Frederick W *Religious Leader*
%Jehovah's Witnesses, 25 Columbia Heights, Brooklyn, NY 11201

Franz, Frederick W *Religious Leader*
%Jehovah's Witnesses, 25 Columbia Heights, Brooklyn, NY 11201

F

Franz – Frederick

Franz, Rod *Football Player*
1448 Engberg Ct, Carmichael, CA 95608

Franzen, Jonathan *Writer*
%Farrar Straus Giroux, 19 Union Sq W, New York, NY 10003

Franzen, Ulrich J *Architect*
975 Park Ave, New York, NY 10028

Frasca, Robert *Architect*
%Zimmer Gunsul Frasca, 320 SW Oak, #500, Portland, OR 97204

Frasconi, Antonio *Artist*
26 Dock Rd, South Norwalk, CT 06854

Fraser Ware, Dawn *Swimmer*
87 Birchgrove Rd, Balmain NSW, Australia

Fraser, Antonio *Writer*
%Curtis Brown, 162-168 Regent St, London W1, England

Fraser, David W *Educator*
%Swarthmore College, President's Office, Swarthmore, PA 19081

Fraser, Donald M *Mayor; Representative, MN*
%Mayor's Office, City Hall, Minneapolis, MN 55415

Fraser, Douglas *Labor Leader*
%United Auto Workers, 8000 E Jefferson Ave, Detroit, MI 48214

Fraser, Gretchen *Skier*
PO Box 1335, Sun Valley, ID 83353

Fraser, Ian E *WW II British Royal Navy Hero (VC)*
Innisfallen, 47 Warren Dr, Wallasey, Merseyside, England

Fraser, Malcolm *Prime Minister, Australia*
%Parliament House, Canberra ACT, Australia

Fraser, Neale *Tennis Player*
%International Tennis Hall of Fame, 194 Bellevue Ave, Newport, RI 02840

Fratello, Mike *Basketball Coach, Sportscaster*
%NBC-TV, Sports Dept, 30 Rockefeller Plz, New York, NY 10020

Fratianne, Linda *Figure Skater*
18214 Septo St, Northridge, CA 91324

Frawley, David A *Businessman*
%Petro-Lewis Corp, 717 17th St, Denver, CO 80201

Frawley, Patrick *Businessman*
%Frawley Corp, 1901 Ave of Stars, Los Angeles, CA 90067

Frayn, Michael *Writer*
%Elaine Green Ltd, 31 Newington Glen, London N16 9PU, England

Frazee, John P, Jr *Businessman*
%Centel Corp, 5725 NE River Rd, Chicago, IL 60631

Frazee, Rowland C *Financier*
%Royal Bank of Canada, 1 Pl Ville Marie, Montreal PQ H3B 4A7, Canada

Frazer, Liz *Actress*
42/43 Grafton House, 2/3 Golden Sq, London W1, England

Frazetta, Frank *Artist*
%Ballantine Books, 201 E 50th St, New York, NY 10022

Frazier, Dallas *Singer, Songwriter*
Rt 5, Box 133, Longhollow Pike, Gallatin, TN 37066

Frazier, Ian *Writer*
%Farrar Straus & Giroux, 19 Union Sq W, New York, NY 10003

Frazier, Joe *Boxer*
2917 N Broad St, Philadelphia, PA 19132

Frazier, Owsley B *Businessman*
%Brown-Forman Inc, PO Box 1080, Louisville, KY 40201

Frazier, Walt *Basketball Player*
675 Flamingo Dr SW, Atlanta, GA 30311

Frears, Stephen *Movie Director*
93 Talbot Rd, London W2, England

Freberg, Stan *Comedian*
%Capitol Records, 1750 N Vine St, Los Angeles, CA 90028

Freccia, Massimo *Conductor*
25 Eaton Sq, London SW1, England

Frederick, Robert R *Businessman*
%RCA Corp, 30 Rockefeller Plz, New York, NY 10020

Frederick, Sherman R *Editor*
%Las Vegas Review-Journal, 1111 W Bonanza Rd, Las Vegas, NV 89106

Fredericks, Fred *Cartoonist (Mandrake the Magician)*
Bridge Rd, Box 475, Eastham, MA 02642

Frederik Andre Henrik Christian *Prince, Denmark*
%Amalienborg Palace, Copenhagen, Denmark

Fredkin, Ed *Computer Engineer*
%Reliable Water Co, 35 Dunham Rd, Billerica, MA 01821

Fredriksson, Gert *Canoeist*
Bruunsgat 13, 61122 Nykoping, Sweden

Freed, Bert *Actor*
418 N Bowling Green, Los Angeles, CA 90049

Freed, Curt *Neurobiologist*
%University of Colorado Health Sciences Center, 4200 E 9th Ave, Denver, CO 80262

Freed, Dean W *Businessman*
%EG&G Inc, 45 William St, Wellesley, MA 02181

Freedman, Gerald A *Theatre, Opera Director*
%Theatre Julliard School, Lincoln Ctr, New York, NY 10023

Freedman, James O *Educator*
%Dartmouth College, President's Office, Hanover, NH 03755

Freedman, Michael H *Mathematician*
%University of California, Mathematics Dept, La Jolla, CA 92093

Freedman, Sandra W *Mayor*
%Mayor's Office, Municipal Bldg, 306 E Jackson, Tampa, FL 33602

Freehan, Bill *Baseball Player*
4248 Sunningdale, Bloomfield Hills, MI 48103

Freeman, Gaylord A, Jr *Financier*
White Thorn Rd, Wayne, IL 60184

Freeman, J E *Actor*
%Judy Schoen Assoc, 606 N Larchmont Blvd, Los Angeles, CA 90004

Freeman, James O *Educator*
%Dartmouth College, President's Office, Hanover, NH 03755

Freeman, Joe B, Jr *Businessman*
7509 Spring Meadow Ln, Dallas, TX 75042

Freeman, Kathleen *Actress*
6247 Orion Ave, Van Nuys, CA 91411

Freeman, Mona *Actress*
608 N Alpine Dr, Beverly Hills, CA 90210

Freeman, Morgan *Actor*
%Triad Artists, 10100 Santa Monica Blvd, #1600, Los Angeles, CA 90067

Freeman, Orville L *Secretary, Agriculture*
%Business International Corp, 1 Dag Hammarskjold Plz, New York, NY 10017

Freeman, Ron *Track Athlete*
61-63 Myrtle Ave, North Plainfield, NJ 07060

Freeman, Sandi *Commentator*
%Cable News Network, 2133 Wisconsin Ave NW, Washington, DC 20007

Fregosi, Jim *Baseball Player, Manager*
5730 Midnight Pass Rd, #408-B, Sarasota, FL 34242

Freilicher, Jane *Artist*
%Fishbach Gallery, 24 W 57th St, New York, NY 10019

Freire, Paolo *Educator*
%World Council of Churches, Geneva, Switzerland

Freitag, Merle *General, Army*
Comptroller, US Army, OSA, Washington, DC 20310

Freleng, Fritz *Cartoonist (Pink Panther)*
1058 S Alfred St, Los Angeles, CA 90035

Frelich, Phyllis *Actress*
139 Spring St, New York, NY 10012

Freling, Fritz *Animator*
1543 W Olympic Blvd, #534, Los Angeles, CA 90015

Frelinghuysen, Peter H B *Representative, NJ*
Sand Spring Ln, Morristown, NJ 07960

Fremaux, Louis J F *Conductor*
25 Edencroft, Wheeleys Rd, Birmingham B15 2LW, England

French, Charles S *Plant Biologist*
11970 Rhus Ridge Rd, Los Altos Hills, CA 94022

French, Leigh *Actress*
%Commercials Unlimited, 7461 Beverly Blvd, #400, Los Angeles, CA 90036

F

French – Friedman

French, Marilyn *Writer*
%Simon & Schuster, 1230 Ave of Americas, New York, NY 10020

Freni, Mirella *Opera Singer*
%John Coast Concerts, 1 Park Close, London SW1, England 91602

Frens, Arthur J *Businessman*
%Gerber Products Co, 445 State St, Fremont, MI 49412

Fresno Lorrain, Juan Cardinal *Religious Leader*
Erasmo Escala 1822, Santiago 30-D, Chile

Freud, Lucian *Artist*
%Anthony d'Offay, 9 Dering St, London W1, England

Freudenberg, Dieter *Businessman*
%Freudenberg & Co, Postfach 1369, 6940 Weinheim, Germany

Freund, Miriam Kottler *Religious Leader*
515 S Lexington Pkwy S, St Paul, MN 55116

Frew, James E *Businessman*
%Stone Container Corp, 360 N Michigan Ave, Chicago, IL 60601

Frewer, Matt *Actor*
%Abrams Artists, 9200 Sunset Blvd, #625, Los Angeles, CA 90069

Frey, Donald N *Businessman*
%Bell & Howell Co, 5215 Old Orchard Rd, Skokie, IL 60077

Frey, Howard H *Businessman*
%Westmoreland Coal Co, 2500 Fidelity Bldg, Philadelphia, PA 19109

Frey, Jim *Baseball Manager*
1805 Reuter Rd, Timonium, MD 21093

Fribourg, Michel *Businessman*
%Continental Grain Co, 277 Park Ave, New York, NY 10172

Frick, Gottlob *Opera Singer*
Eichelberg-Haus Waldfrieden, 7531 Olbronn-Durrn, Germany

Fricke, Janie *Singer*
PO Box 798, Lancaster, TX 75146

Fricke, Richard I *Businessman*
%National Life Insurance, National Life Dr, Montpelier, VT 05604

Fricker, Peter R *Composer*
5423 Throne Ct, Santa Barbara, CA 93111

Friday, Nancy *Writer*
%Simon & Schuster, 1230 Ave of Americas, New York, NY 10022

Fridell, Squire *Actor*
%J Michael Bloom Ltd, 9200 Sunset Blvd, #710, Los Angeles, CA 90069

Friderichs, Hans *Businessman*
%AEG-Telefunken, Theodor-Stern-Kai 1, Frankfurt-am-Main, Germany

Fridh, Gertrude *Actress*
%Svenska Filminstitutet, Kungsgatan 48, Stockholm C, Sweden

Fried, Josef *Organic Chemist*
5717 S Kenwood Ave, Chicago, IL 60637

Friedan, Betty *Feminist Activist*
%University of Southern California, Women & Men Inst, Los Angeles, CA 90089

Frieder, Bill *Basketball Coach*
%Arizona State University, Athletic Dept, Tempe, AZ 85287

Friedheim, Jerry W *Newspaper Executive*
%American Newspaper Publishers Assn, 11600 Sunrise Rd, Reston, VA 22091

Friedkin, William *Movie Director*
668 Perugia Way, Los Angeles, CA 90077

Friedlander, Lee *Artist, Photographer*
44 S Mountain Rd, New City, NY 10956

Friedman, Bruce Jay *Writer*
430 E 63rd St, #12-H, New York, NY 10021

Friedman, Daniel M *Judge*
%US Court of Appeals, 717 Madison Pl NW, Washington, DC 20439

Friedman, Emanuel A *Medical Educator, Obstetrician*
%Beth-Israel Hospital, 330 Brookline Ave, Boston, MA 02215

Friedman, Herbert *Physicist*
2643 N Upshur St, Arlington, VA 22207

Friedman, Irving S *Economist*
6620 Fernwood Ct, Bethesda, MD 20817

Friedman, Jerome I *Nobel Physics Laureate*
75 Greenough Cir, Brookline, MA 02146

Friedman, Meyer *Cardiologist*
160 San Carlos Ave, Sausalito, CA 94120
Friedman, Milton *Nobel Economics Laureate*
%Hoover Institution, Stanford University, Stanford, CA 94305
Friedman, Thomas L *Journalist*
%New York Times, 229 W 43rd St, New York, NY 10036
Friel, Brian *Writer*
Ardmore, Muff, Lifford, County Donegal, Ireland
Friend, Bob *Baseball Player*
4 Salem Cir, Fox Chapel, PA 15238
Friend, Richard H *Chemist*
%Chemistry Dept, Cavendish Laboratory, Cambridge, England
Friendly, Fred W *Journalist*
4614 Fieldston Rd, Riverdale, NY 10471
Friese, George R *Businessman*
%SCOA Industries, 15 Dan Rd, Canton, MA 02021
Frigon, Henry F *Businessman*
%Batus Inc, 2000 Citizens Plz, Louisville, KY 40202
Frimout, Dirk *Astronaut, Belgium*
%ESTEC, Postbus 2999, 2200 AG Noordwijk, Netherlands
Frink, Elisabeth *Sculptor*
Csaky, Woolland House, Woolland Near Blandford, Dorset DT11 0EP, England
Frisbee, Don C *Businessman*
%PacifiCorp, 851 SW 6th Ave, Portland, OR 97204
Frische, Carl Alfred *Businessman, Physicist*
6642 Praying Monk Rd, Scottsdale, AZ 85253
Frist, Thomas F *Businessman*
%Hospital Corp of America, 1 Park Plz, Nashville, TN 37203
Frist, Thomas F, Jr *Businessman*
%Hospital Corp of America, 1 Park Plz, Nashville, TN 37203
Fristedt, Hans *Businessman*
%Esselte Business Systems, 71 Clinton Rd, Garden City, NY 11530
Fritz, Harold A *Vietnam War Army Hero (CMH)*
168 Logan Loop, Fort Sheridan, IL 60037
Fritz, Jack W *Businessman*
%John Blair Co, 1290 Ave of Americas, New York, NY 10104
Froebel, Henry E *Businessman*
%Frank B Hall Co, 549 Pleasantville Rd, Briarcliff Manor, NY 10510
Froehlich, Harold V *Representative, WI*
1008 E Marnie Ln, Appleton, WI 54911
Froehlke, Robert F *Businessman*
%Equitable Life Assurance Society, 787 7th Ave, New York, NY 10019
Froemming, Bruce *Baseball Umpire*
5045 Elk Ct, Milwaukee, WI 53223
Frohnmayer, John E *Government Official*
%National Endowment for the Arts, 1100 Pennsylvania Ave NW, Washington, DC 20506
Froines, John *Social Activist, Educator*
%University of California, School of Public Health, Los Angeles, CA 90024
Frommelt, Paul *Skier*
%Liechtenstein Ski Federation, Vaduz, Liechtenstein
Fromstein, Milton B *Businessman*
%Manpower Inc, 5301 N Ironwood Rd, Milwaukee, WI 53217
Fromstein, Mitchell S *Businessman*
%Parker Pen Co, 1 Parker Pl, Janesville, WI 53545
Frondel, Clifford *Mineralogist*
20 Beatrice Cir, Belmont, MA 02178
Frondizi, Arturo *President, Argentina*
Luis Maris Campos 665, Buenos Aires, Argentina
Fronius, Hans *Artist*
Guggenberggasse 18, 2380 Perchtoldadorf bei Vienna, Austria
Fronterhouse, Gerald W *Financier*
%First RepublicBank, 1800 First RepublicBank Bldg, Dallas, TX 75201
Frontiere, Georgia *Football Executive*
%Los Angeles Rams, 2327 W Lincoln Ave, Anaheim, CA 92801
Frost, David *Entertainer*
46 Egerton Crescent, London SW3, England

Frost, David *Golfer*
%Professional Golfers Assn, PO Box 109601, Palm Beach Gardens, FL 33410

Frost, J Martin *Representative, TX*
%House of Representatives, Washington, DC 20515

Fruedek, Jacques *Physicist*
2 Rue Jean-Francois Gerbillion, 70006 Paris, France

Fruh, Eugen *Artist*
Romergasse 9, 8001 Zurich, Switzerland

Fruhbeck de Burgos, Rafael *Conductor*
Reyes Magos 20, Madrid 7, Spain

Fruit, Chuck *Businessman*
Anheuser-Busch Companies, Media/Sports Marketing, 1 Busch Pl, St Louis, MO 63118

Frutig, Ed *Football Player*
811 Mohawk, Dearborn, MI 48214

Fruton, Joseph Stewart *Biochemist*
123 York St, New Haven, CT 06511

Fry Irvin, Shirley *Tennis Player*
1970 Asylum Ave, West Hartford, CT 06117

Fry, Arthur L *Inventor (Post-its)*
%Minnesota Mining & Manufacturing Co, 3-M Center, Bldg 230-2S, St Paul, MN 55144

Fry, Christopher *Writer*
Toft, East Dean Near Chichester, Sussex, England

Fry, E Maxwell *Architect*
West Lodge, Cotherstone, Barnard Castle, County Durham DL1Z 9PF, England

Fry, Hayden *Football Coach*
%University of Iowa, Athletic Dept, Iowa City, IA 52242

Fry, Thornton C *Mathematician*
500 Mohawk Dr, Boulder, CO 80303

Fryar, Irving *Football Player*
%New England Patriots, Sullivan Stadium, Foxboro, MA 02035

Frye, Northrop *Educator*
127 Clifton Rd, Toronto ON M4T 2G5, Canada

Frye, Richard N *Orientalist*
86 Beech St, Belmont, MA 02178

Ftorek, Robbie *Hockey Coach*
%Quebec Nordiques, 2205 Ave du Colisee, Quebec PQ G1L 4W7, Canada

Fu, T H *Businessman*
%China Steel Corp, 1 Chung Kang Rd, Hsiao Kang, Kaohsiung, Taiwan

Fuchs, Ann Sutherland *Publisher*
%Vogue Magazine, 350 Madison Ave, New York, NY 10017

Fuchs, Fritz *Obstetrician*
1130 Park Ave, New York, NY 10028

Fuchs, Joseph *Publisher*
%Mademoiselle Magazine, 350 Madison Ave, New York, NY 10017

Fuchs, Vivian E *Explorer, Geologist*
78 Barton Rd, Cambridge, England

Fudge, Alan *Actor*
%Writers & Artists Agency, 11726 San Vicente Blvd, #300, Los Angeles, CA 90049

Fuente, David *Businessman*
%Sherwin-Williams Co, 101 Prospect Ave NW, Cleveland, OH 44115

Fuente, Luis *Ballet Dancer*
98 Rue Lepic, 75018 Paris, France

Fuentealba, Victor W *Labor Leader*
%American Federation of Musicians, 1500 Broadway, New York, NY 10036

Fugard, Athol *Writer*
PO Box 5090, Walmer, Port Elizabeth, South Africa

Fuhr, Grant *Hockey Player*
%Toronto Maple Leafs, 60 Carlton St, Toronto ON M5B 1L1, Canada

Fuhrman, Robert A *Businessman*
%Lockheed Corp, 4500 Park Granada Blvd, Calabasas, CA 91399

Fujimori, Alberto *President, Peru*
%President's Office, Lima, Peru

Fujimori, Masamichi *Businessman*
%Sumitomo Metal Mining Co, 5-11-3 Shimbashi, Minatoku, Tokyo 105, Japan

Fujimori, Tetsuo *Financier*
%Daialchi Kangyo Bank, 1-5 Uchisaiwaicho, Chiyodaku, Tokyo 100, Japan

Fujimoto, Shun *Businessman*
%Toyota Automobile Body Co, 100 Kanayama, Kariya City 448, Japan

Fujinuma, Mototoshi *Businessman*
%Sekisui Chemical Co, 2-4-4 Nishi-Tenma, Kitaku, Osaka 530, Japan

Fujisaki, Akira *Businessman*
%Sumitomo Metal Mining Co, 5-11-3 Shimbashi, Minatoku, Tokyo 105, Japan

Fujisawa, Tomokichiro *Businessman*
%Fujisawa Pharmaceutical Co, 4-3 Doshomachi, Higashiku, Osaka 541, Japan

Fujita, Hiroyuki *Microbiotics Engineer*
%University of Tokyo, Institute of Industrial Science, Tokyo 106, Japan

Fujiyoshi, Tsuguhide *Businessman*
%Toray Industries, 2-2 Nihonbashi-Muromachi, Chuoku, Tokyo 103, Japan

Fukuda, Takeo *Prime Minister, Japan*
4-20-3 Nozawa, Setagayaku, Tokyo, Japan

Fukui, Kenichi *Nobel Chemistry Laureate*
Fundamental Chemistry Inst, 34-4 Takano-Nishihiraki-cho, Kyoto 606, Japan

Fukuma, Seikan *Religious Leader*
%Buddhist Churches of America, 1710 Octavia St, San Francisco, CA 94109

Fulbright, J William *Senator, AR*
%Hogan & Hartson, 815 Connecticut Ave NW, Washington, DC 20006

Fulford, Millie Hughes *Astronaut*
%NASA, Johnson Space Ctr, Houston, TX 77058

Fulghum, Robert *Religious Leader, Writer*
219 1st Ave N, Box 369, Seattle, WA 98109

Fuller, Charles *Writer*
%William Morris Agency, 1350 Ave of Americas, New York, NY 10019

Fuller, E Keith *Journalist*
%Associated Press, 50 Rockefeller Plz, New York, NY 10020

Fuller, Edmund *Literary Critic, Writer*
%Wall Street Journal, Editorial Dept, 22 Cortlandt St, New York, NY 10007

Fuller, H Laurance *Businessman*
%Amoco Corp, 200 E Randolph Dr, Chicago, IL 60601

Fuller, Jack *Journalist*
%Chicago Tribune, 435 N Michigan, Chicago, IL 60611

Fuller, John S *Financier*
%Valley Federal Savings & Loan, 6842 Van Nuys Blvd, Van Nuys, CA 91405

Fuller, Kathryn *Association Official*
%World Wildlife Fund, 1250 24th St NW, Washington, DC 20037

Fuller, Lance *Actor*
%Dale Garrick Agency, 8831 Sunset Blvd, #402, Los Angeles, CA 90069

Fuller, Robert *Actor*
10620 Landale St, #28, Toluca Lake, CA 91602

Fuller, Sam *Movie Director*
7628 Woodrow Wilson Dr, Los Angeles, CA 90046

Fullerton, C Gordon *Astronaut*
%NASA DFRF/ODF, PO Box 273, Edwards Air Force Base, CA 93523

Fullerton, Fiona *Actress*
%London Mgmt, 235/241 Regent St, London W1A 2JI, England

Fullerton, Gail *Educator*
%San Jose State University, President's Office, San Jose, CA 95192

Fullmer, Gene *Boxer*
9250 S 2200 Ave, Riverton, UT 84065

Fullwood, Brent *Football Player*
%Green Bay Packers, 1265 Lombardi Ave, Green Bay, WI 54303

Fulton, Eileen *Actress*
%"As the World Turns" Show, CBS-TV, 524 W 57nd St, New York, NY 10019

Fulton, Paul *Businessman*
%Sara Lee Corp, 3 First National Plz, Chicago, IL 60602

Fulton, Robert D *Governor, IA*
141 Hillcrest Rd, Waterloo, IA 50701

Fung King Hey *Financier*
%Sun Hug Kai Bank, Hong Kong, British Colony

Funicello, Annette *Actress*
16202 Sandy Ln, Encino, CA 91316

Funk, Leonard A, Jr *WW II Army Hero (CMH)*
1100 Hartman St, McKeesport, PA 15132

F

Funk, Paul E *Army General*
Vice Director, J-3, The Joint Staff, Pentagon, Washington, DC 20301

Funston, G Keith *Stock Exchange Executive*
Vineyard Ln, Greenwich, CT 06830

Funt, Allen *Comedian, Television Producer*
2359 Nichols Canyon, Los Angeles, CA 90068

Fuoss, Raymond M *Chemist*
68 N Lake Dr, Hamden, CT 05517

Fuqua, J B *Businessman*
%Fuqua Industries, 4900 Georgia-Pacific Ctr, Atlanta, GA 30303

Furakawa, Susumu *Financier*
%Daiwa Bank, 2-21 Bingomachi, Higashiku, Osaka 541, Japan

Furcolo, Foster *Governor, MA; Judge*
%US Court House, Post Office Sq, Boston, MA 02109

Furlanetto, Ferrucio *Opera Singer*
%Metropolitan Opera Assn, Lincoln Center Plz, New York, NY 10023

Furlaud, Richard M *Businessman*
%Bristol-Myers Squibb Corp, PO Box 4000, Princeton, NJ 08540

Furness, Betty *Journalist, Consumer Advocate*
%NBC-TV, News Dept, 30 Rockefeller Plz, New York, NY 10020

Furniss, Bruce *Swimmer*
13902 Sandustead Rd, Santa Ana, CA 92705

Furrer, Reinhold *Astronaut, West Germany*
%DFVLR, Linder Hole, 5000 Kohn 90, Germany

Furst, Stephen *Actor*
%Harry Gold Assoc, 3500 W Olive, #1400, Burbank, CA 91505

Furth, Alan C *Businessman*
%Santa Fe Southern Pacific Corp, 224 S Michigan Ave, Chicago, IL 60604

Furth, George *Actor, Playwright*
%Artists Agency, 10000 Santa Monica Blvd, #305, Los Angeles, CA 90067

Furth, Warren Wolfgang *International Official*
13 Rt de Presinge, 1241 Puplinge, Geneva, Switzerland

Furuhashi, Hironshin *Swimmer*
3-9-11 Nozawa, Setagayaku, Tokyo, Japan

Furukawa, Masaru *Swimmer*
5-5-12 Shinohara Honmachi, Nadaku, Kobe, Japan

Furuta, Norimasa *Businessman*
%Mazda Motor Corp, 3-1 Shinchi, Fuchucho, Akigun, Hiroshima 730-91, Japan

Fussell, Paul *Writer, Educator*
2 Nassau St, Princeton, NJ 08540

Futey, Bohdan A *Judge*
%US Claims Court, 717 Madison Pl NW, Washington, DC 20005

Futia, Leo R *Businessman*
%Guardian Life Insurance, 201 Park Ave, New York, NY 10003

Futter, Ellen V *Educator*
%Barnard College, President's Office, New York, NY 10027

Fylstra, Daniel *Computer Software Designer*
%Visicorp, 2895 Zanken Rd, San Jose, CA 95134

Gabariel, Roman *Football Player*
%Raleigh-Durham Skyhawks, 3226 Spring Forest Rd, Raleigh, NC 27604

Gabet, Sharon *Actress*
222 E 44th St, New York, NY 10017

Gable, Dan *Wrestler, Coach*
%University of Iowa, Athletic Dept, Iowa City, IA 52242

Gabor, Eva *Actress*
100 Delfern Dr, Los Angeles, CA 90024

Gabor, Zsa Zsa *Actress*
1001 Bel Air Rd, Los Angeles, CA 90077

Gabriel, Charles A *Air Force General*
%Hicks Assoc, 1710 Goodridge Dr, #1300, McLean, VA 22101

Gabriel, John *Actor*
130 W 42nd St, #1804, New York, NY 10036

Gabriel, Peter *Singer*
%Gailforce Mgmt, 81-83 Walton St, London SW3 2HP, England

Gabriel, Ralph H *Historian*
484 Whitney Ave, New Haven, CT 06511

Gaddafi, Mu'ammar Mohammad al- *President, Libya*
%President's Office, Tripoli, Libya

Gaddis, William *Writer*
%Candida Donadio Agency, 231 W 22nd St, New York, NY 10011

Gade, Marvin F *Businessman*
%Kimberly-Clark Corp, PO Box 619100, Dallas, TX 75261

Gadzhiev, Raul S O *Composer*
%Azerbaizhan State Popular Orchestra, Baku, Azerbaizhan,

Gaetano, Cortesi *Businessman*
%Alfa Romeo SpA, Via Gattemelata 45, 20149 Milan, Italy 48217

Gaffney, F Andrew *Astronaut*
%Division of Cardiology, H8 122, 5323 Harry Hines Blvd, Dallas, TX 75235

Gaffney, Thomas F *Businessman*
%Guardian Industries Corp, 43043 W Nine Mile Rd, Northville, MI 48167

Gage, Nicholas *Columnist*
37 Nelson St, North Grafton, MA 01536

Gagnebin, Albert P *Businessman*
143 Grange Ave, Fair Haven, NJ 07701

Gagnon, Edouard Cardinal *Religious Leader*
%Pontifical Family Council, Palazzo S Calisto, 00120 Vatican City, Italy

Gago, Jenny *Actress*
%Paul Kohner Inc, 9169 Sunset Blvd, Los Angeles, CA 90069

Gahan, James T *Financier*
%Prudential-Bache Securities, 100 Gold St, New York, NY 10292

Gail, Max *Actor*
29451 Bluewater Rd, Malibu, CA 90265

Gaillard, Bob *Basketball Coach*
50 Bonnie Brae Dr, Novato, CA 94947

Gain, Bob *Football Player*
11 Nokomis Dr, Willoughby, OH 44094

Gaines, Boyd *Actor*
%J Michael Bloom Ltd, 9200 Sunset Blvd, #710, Los Angeles, CA 90069

Gaines, Clarence *Basketball Coach*
%Basketball Hall of Fame, PO Box 179, Springfield, MA 01101

Gaines, Ernest J *Writer*
128 Buena Vista, Lafayette, LA 70503

Gaines, James R *Editor, Publisher*
%Time Warner Inc, Life Magazine, Rockefeller Ctr, New York, NY 10020

Gaines, John R *Thoroughbred Racing Breeder*
%Gainesway Farm, 3750 Paris Pike, Lexington, KY 40511

Gaines, William *Journalist*
%Chicago Tribune, 435 N Michigan Ave, Chicago, IL 60611

Gainey, Bob *Hockey Player, Coach*
%Minnesota North Stars, 7901 Cedar Ave S, Bloomington, MN 55420

Gaither, Alonzo (Jake) *Football Coach*
212 Young St, Tallahassee, FL 32301

Gaither, Bill *Gospel Songwriter*
%Gaither Music Co, PO Box 737, Alexandria, IN 46001

G

Gajdusek – Gallo

Gajdusek, D Carleton — *Nobel Medicine Laureate*
4 Laurel Pkwy, Chevy Chase, MD 20015

Gaje Ghale — *WW II Indian Army Hero (VC)*
Alexendre Lines, Almora 26301 UP, India

Galambos, Robert — *Neuroscientist*
8826 La Jolla Scenic Dr, La Jolla, CA 92037

Galan, Augie — *Baseball Player*
1345 Nob Hill, Pinole, CA 94564

Galanos, James — *Fashion Designer*
2254 S Sepulveda Blvd, Los Angeles, CA 90064

Galarraga, Andres — *Baseball Player*
%Montreal Expos, PO Box 500, Station M, Montreal PQ H1V 3P2, Canada

Galati, Frank J — *Stage, Opera Director*
993 Maple St, Evanston, IL 60202

Galbraith, Evan G — *Diplomat, Financier*
%Morgan Stanley Grp, 1251 Ave of Americas, New York, NY 10020

Galbraith, John Kenneth — *Government Official, Economist*
30 Francis Ave, Cambridge, MA 02138

Galbreath, Tony — *Football Player*
%New York Giants, Giants Stadium, East Rutherford, NJ 07073

Galdikas, Birute — *Anthropologist*
%Camp Leakey, Tanjung Puting Reserve, Borneo, Indonesia

Gale, Lauren (Laddie) — *Basketball Player*
Hound Dog Rd, Gold Beach, OR 97444

Gale, Robert P — *Medical Researcher*
2316 Donella Cir, Bel Air, CA 90077

Galef, Andrew G — *Businessman*
%Warnaco Inc, 359 Lafayette St, Bridgeport, CT 06601

Galella, Ron — *Photographer*
17 Glover Ave, Yonkers, NY 10704

Galen, Louis J — *Financier*
%Golden West Financial Corp, 1970 Broadway, Oakland, CA 94612

Galer, Robert E — *WW II Marine Corps Hero (CMH), General*
3310 Fairmount, #8-A, Dallas, TX 75201

Gall, Joseph G — *Biologist*
81 North Lake Dr, Hamden, CT 06517

Gallagher, Helen — *Singer, Actress*
260 West End Ave, New York, NY 10023

Gallagher, John — *Religious Leader*
%Advent Christian Church, PO Box 23152, Charlotte, NC 28212

Gallagher, Megan — *Actress*
%Susan Smith Assoc, 121 N San Vicente Blvd, Beverly Hills, CA 90211

Gallagher, Peter — *Actor*
%Davian Littlefield, 1619 Broadway, New York, NY 10019

Galland, Adolf — *Army General, Germany*
Gotenstrasse 157 Am Hockreg, 5300 Bonn-Bad Godesberg, Germany

Gallant, Mavis — *Writer*
14 Rue Jean Ferrandi, 75006 Paris, France

Gallarneau, Hugh — *Football Player*
2216 Maple Dr, Northbrook, IL 60062

Gallatin, Harry — *Basketball Player*
2010 Madison Ave, Edwardsville, IL 62025

Gallegly, Elton — *Representative, CA*
%House of Representatives, Washington, DC 20515

Galley, Garry — *Hockey Player*
%Los Angeles Kings, Great Western Forum, 3900 W Manchester, Inglewood, CA 90306

Galligan, Thomas J, Jr — *Businessman*
%Boston Edison Co, 800 Boylston St, Boston, MA 02199

Gallison, Joseph — *Actor*
%Allen Goldstein Assoc, 5015 Lemona Ave, Sherman Oaks, CA 91423

Gallo, Bill — *Cartoonist*
1 Mayflower Dr, Yonkers, NY 10710

Gallo, Dean A — *Representative, NJ*
%House of Representatives, Washington, DC 20515

Gallo, Ernest — *Businessman*
%Gallo Vineyards, 600 Yosemite Blvd, Modesto, CA 95354

Gallo, Frank *Sculptor*
%University of Illinois, Art Dept, Urbana, IL 61801

Gallo, Julio *Businessman*
%Gallo Vineyards, 600 Yosemite Blvd, Modesto, CA 95354

Gallo, Lew *Movie Director*
915 N Beverly Dr, Beverly Hills, CA 90210

Gallo, Robert C *Research Scientist*
%National Institutes of Health, Bldg 37, Bethesda, MD 20892

Galloway, Don *Actor*
13001 Blairwood Dr, North Hollywood, CA 91604

Gallup, George H, II *Statistician, Pollster*
53 Bank St, Princeton, NJ 08540

Galotti, Donna *Publisher*
%Ladies Home Journal, 641 Lexington Ave, New York, NY 10022

Galtieri, Leopold *President, Argentina*
Campo de Mayo, Buenos Aires, Argentina

Galvin, James *Poet*
%University of Iowa, Writers' Workshop, Iowa City, IA 52242

Galvin, John R *Army General*
Supreme Allied Command, Europe/CINCUSEUCOM, APO, New York, NY 09055

Galvin, Robert W *Businessman*
%Motorola Inc, 1303 E Algonquin Rd, Schaumberg, IL 60196

Galway, James *Concert Flutist*
%London Artists, 73 Baker St, London W1M 1AH, England

Gam, Rita *Actress*
%Ambrosio/Mortimer Assoc, 301 N Canon Dr, #305, Beverly Hills, CA 90210

Gamba, Piero *Conductor*
%Winnipeg Symphony Orchestra, 555 Main St, Winnipeg MB R3B 1C3, Canada

Gambill, Malcolm W *Businessman*
%Harsco Corp, PO Box 8888, Camp Hill, PA 17011

Gamble, Donald P, Jr *Businessman*
%Pacific Gamble Robinson Co, 10829 NE 68th St, Kirkland, WA 98033

Gamble, Douglas S *Businessman*
%Pacific Gamble Robinson Co, 10829 NE 68th St, Kirkland, WA 98033

Gamble, Ed *Editorial Cartoonist*
%Florida Times-Union, 1 Riverside Ave, Jacksonville, FL 32202

Gambrell, David H *Senator, GA*
3820 Castlegate Dr NW, Atlanta, GA 30327

Gambril, Don *Swimming Coach*
%University of Alabama, Athletic Dept, University, AL 35486

Ganju Lama *WW II Indian Army Hero (VC)*
Shangderpa House, 34 Singtam Ravangla Rd, PO Ravangla, South Sikkim, India

Gant, Harry *Auto Racing Driver*
PO Box 1258, Mooresville, NC 28115

Gantin, Bernardin Cardinal *Religious Leader*
Piazzi S Calisto 16, 00153 Rome, Italy

Gantz, Wilbur H *Businessman*
%Baxter Travenol Laboratories, 1 Baxter Pkwy, Deerfield, IL 60015

Garagiola, Joe *Sportscaster, Baseball Player*
6221 E Huntress Dr, Paradise Valley, AZ 85253

Garas, Kaz *Actor*
%Atkins Assoc, 303 S Crescent Heights Blvd, Los Angeles, CA 90048

Garber, Gene *Baseball Player*
771 Stonemill Dr, Elizabethtown, PA 17022

Garber, Harry D *Businessman*
%Equitable Life Assurance Society, 787 7th Ave, New York, NY 10019

Garci, Jose Luis *Movie Director*
%Direccion General del Libro, Paseo de la Castellana 109, Madrid 16, Spain

Garcia Marquez, Gabriel *Nobel Literature Laureate*
%Carmen Balceusy Agency Literario, Calle Urgel 241, Barcelona, Spain

Garcia Meza, Luis *President, Bolivia*
%General Delivery, Sucre, Bolivia

Garcia Perez, Alan *President, Peru*
%Palcio del Gobierno, Lima, Peru

Garcia, Andy *Actor*
%STE Representation, 9301 Wilshire Blvd, #700, Beverly Hills, CA 90210

G

Garcia – Garner

Garcia, Jerry *Guitarist, Composer*
PO Box 323, Forest Knoll, CA 97933

Garcia, Manuel *Businessman*
%NCR Corp, 1700 S Patterson Blvd, Dayton, OH 45479

Garcia, Robert *Representative, NY*
%Prison Fellowship Ministries, PO Box 40562, Washington, DC 20016

Gardelli, Lamberto *Conductor*
%Allied Artists, 42 Montpelier Sq, London SW7 1J2, England

Gardenia, Vincent *Actor*
888 7th Ave, #2500, New York, NY 10106

Gardiner of Kittisford, Gerald *Barrister*
%Mote End, Nan Clark's Ln, Mill Hill, London NW7 4HH, England

Gardiner, John Eliot *Conductor*
Gore Farm, Ashmore, Salisbury, Wilts, England

Gardiner, Robert K A *United Nations Official, Ghana*
%Ministry of Finance & Economic Planning, Accra, Ghana

Gardner, Bill *Baseball Manager*
35 Dayton Rd, Waterford, CT 06385

Gardner, Booth *Governor, WA*
%Governor's Office, Legislative Bldg, Olympia, WA 98504

Gardner, Dale A *Astronaut*
TRW Sig, Senior Systems Engineering, 1555 N Newport, Colorado Springs, CO 80916

Gardner, David P *Educator*
%University of California System, President's Office, Berkeley, CA 77058

Gardner, Gayle *Sportscaster*
%NBC-Sports, 30 Rockefeller Plz, New York, NY 10112

Gardner, Guy S *Astronaut*
%NASA, Johnson Space Ctr, Houston, TX 77058

Gardner, Jack (James H) *Basketball Coach*
2486 Michigan Ave, Salt Lake City, UT 84108

Gardner, John W *Secretary, Health Education Welfare*
2030 "M" St NW, #600, Washington, DC 20036

Gardner, Philip J *WW II British Army Hero (VC)*
Wakehurst, 19 Princes Cr, Hove, Sussex BN3 4GS, England

Gardner, Randy *Figure Skater*
4640 Glencove Ave, #6, Marina del Rey, CA 90292

Gardner, Richard N *Diplomat*
1150 5th Ave, New York, NY 10028

Gare, Danny *Hockey Player*
%Edmonton Oilers, Northlands Coliseum, Edmonton AL T5B 4M9, Canada

Garfield, Brian W *Writer*
PO Box 376, Alpine, NJ 07620

Garfield, David C *Businessman*
%Ingersoll-Rand Co, 200 Chestnut Ridge Rd, Woodcliffe Lakes, NJ 07675

Garfunkel, Art *Singer*
9 E 79th St, New York, NY 10021

Garland, Beverly *Actress*
%Beverly Garland Hotels, 4222 Vineland Ave, North Hollywood, CA 91602

Garland, George D *Geophysicist*
1 Forest Glen Crescent, Toronto On 12, Canada

Garlits, Dan (Big Daddy) *Drag Racing Driver*
%Garlits Racing Museum, 13700 SW 16th Ave, Ocala, FL 32676

Garn, Jake *Senator, UT; Astronaut*
%US Senate, Washington, DC 20510

Garneau, Marc *Astronaut, Canada*
%National Research Council, Montreal Rd, Ottawa ON K1A 0R6, Canada

Garner, Columbus G *Businessman*
1320 Devereux Dr, Dayton, OH 45419

Garner, James *Actor*
33 Oakmont Dr, Los Angeles, CA 90049

Garner, Phil *Baseball Player*
2451 Lake Village Dr, Kingwood, TX 77339

Garner, Richard K *Businessman*
%National Medical Enterprises, 11620 Wilshire Blvd, Los Angeles, CA 90025

Garner, Wendell R *Psychologist*
48 Yowago Ave, Branford, CT 06405

Garner, William S *Editorial Cartoonist*
%Memphis Commercial Appeal, 495-501 Union Ave, Memphis, TN 38101

Garnett, David *Writer*
Le Verger de Charry, 46 Montcuq, France

Garnie, Joe *Dog Sled Racer*
%General Delivery, Manley, AK 99077

Garr, Ralph *Baseball Player*
7819 Chaseway Dr, Missouri City, TX 77459

Garr, Terri *Actress*
%Creative Artists Agency, 9830 Wilshire Blvd, Beverly Hills, CA 90212

Garrahy, J Joseph *Governor, RI*
200 Kingstown Rd, Narragansett, RI 02882

Garrels, Robert M *Geologist*
%South Florida University, Marine Science Dept, St Petersburg, FL 33701

Garrett, Betty *Actress*
3231 Oakdell Rd, Studio City, CA 91604

Garrett, David C, Jr *Businessman*
%Delta Air Lines, Hartsfield International Airport, Atlanta, GA 30320

Garrett, George *Writer*
PO Box 264, York Harbor, ME 03911

Garrett, H Lawrence, III *Government Official*
%Secretary's Office, Department of Navy, Pentagon, Washington, DC 20350

Garrett, Leif *Actor*
11524 Amanda Dr, Studio City, CA 91404

Garrett, Lila *Movie Producer*
1356 Laurel Way, Beverly Hills, CA 90210

Garrett, Mike *Football Player*
%University of Southern California, Heritage Hall, Los Angeles, CA 90089

Garrett, Pat *Songwriter*
%Dutch Kitchen, RD 1, Bethel, PA 19507

Garrett, Robert *Financier*
%Security Capital Corp, 1290 Ave of Americas, New York, NY 10104

Garrett, Wilbur E *Editor*
%National Geographic Magazine, 17th & "M" Sts, Washington, DC 20036

Garrett, William E *Photographer*
209 Seneca Rd, Great Falls, VA 22066

Garriott, Owen K *Astronaut*
%Teledyne Brown Engineering, MS-52, 300 Sparkman Dr, Huntsville, AL 35807

Garrison, U Edwin *Businessman*
%Morton Thiokel Inc, 110 N Wacker Dr, Chicago, IL 60606

Garrison, Zina *Tennis Player*
9417 Denbury Way, Houston, TX 77025

Garrone, Gabriel Marie Cardinal *Religious Leader*
Largo del Colonato 3, 00193 Rome, Italy

Garrow, David J *Political Scientist*
%City College of New York, Political Science Dept, New York, NY 10031

Garrum, Larry *Hockey Player*
987 Pleasant St, Framingham, MA 01701

Garson, Greer *Actress*
3525 Turtle Creek Rd, Dallas, TX 75219

Garth, Leonard I *Judge*
%US Court of Appeals, US Courthouse, Newark, NJ 07101

Gartner, Michael G *Television Executive*
%NBC News, 30 Rockefeller Plz, New York, NY 10020

Gartner, Mike *Hockey Player*
%New York Rangers, Madison Square Grdn, 4 Pennsylvania Plz, New York, NY 10001

Garver, Kathy *Actress*
%Atkins Assoc, 303 S Crescent Heights Blvd, Los Angeles, CA 90048

Garvey, Ned *Baseball Player*
PO Box 114, Ney, OH 42549

Garvey, Steve *Baseball Player*
13162 Caminito Point Del Mar, Del Mar, CA 92014

Garvin, Clifton C, Jr *Businessman*
%Exxon Corp, 1251 Ave of Americas, New York, NY 10020

Garwin, Richard L *Physicist*
%IBM Corp, Watson Research Ctr, PO Box 218, Yorktown Heights, NY 10598

G

Garwood – Gavin

Garwood, William L *Judge*
%US Court of Appeals, 200 W 8th St, Austin, TX 78701

Gary, Cleveland *Football Player*
%Los Angeles Rams, 2327 W Lincoln Blvd, Anaheim, CA 92801

Gary, James F *Businessman*
%Pacific Resources Inc, PO Box 3379, Honolulu, HI 96842

Gary, Lorraine *Actress*
1158 Tower Dr, Beverly Hills, CA 90210

Garza Sada, Bernardo *Businessman*
%Grupo Industrial Alfa, Ave de Los Angeles 325 Ote, Monterey NL, Mexico

Garza, Reynaldo G *Judge*
%US Temporary Emergency Court of Appeals, PO Box 1129, Brownsville, TX 78522

Gasparro, Frank *Sculptor*
216 Westwood Park Dr, Havertown, PA 19083

Gass, William *Philosopher*
6304 Westminster Pl, St Louis, MO 63130

Gassman, Vittorio *Actor*
Guiseppe Prosa, Via San Dominico, 2 Bis Rome, Italy

Gastineau, Mark *Football Player*
1000 Fulton Ave, Hempstead, NY 11550

Gaston, Cito *Baseball Player, Manager*
1421 Glen Burnie Rd, Mississauga ON L5G 3C7, Canada

Gaston, William W *Businessman*
%Gold Kist Inc, 244 Perimeter Center Pkwy NE, Atlanta, GA 30301

Gately, George *Cartoonist (Heathcliff)*
%Tribune Media Services, 64 E Concord St, Orlando, FL 32801

Gates, Charles C *Businessman*
%Gates Learjet Corp, 1255 E Aero Park Blvd, Tucson, AZ 85734

Gates, Daryl F *Law Enforcement Official*
%Los Angeles Police Dept, PO Box 30158, Los Angeles, CA 90030

Gates, Henry L, Jr *Educator*
%Yale University, English Dept, New Haven, CT 06520

Gates, Marshall De M, Jr *Chemist*
41 West Brook Rd, Pittsburgh, PA 14534

Gates, Robert M *Government Official*
%Central Intelligence Agency, Washington, DC 20505

Gates, William H, III *Businessman*
%Microsoft Corp, 1 Microsoft Way, Redmond, WA 98052

Gathercole, Terry *Swimmer*
PO Box 36, Forestville NSW 2087, Australia

Gatlin, Larry *Singer*
%Gatlin Enterprises, 7003 Chadwick Dr, #360, Brentwood, TN 37027

Gatski, Frank *Football Player*
PO Box 677, Grafton, WV 26354

Gaudiani, Claire *Educator*
%Connecticut College, President's Office, New London, CT 06320

Gaudion, Donald A *Businessman*
%Sybron Corp, 1100 Midtown Tower, Rochester, NY 14604

Gaul, Gilbert M *Journalist*
%Philadelphia Inquirer, 400 N Broad St, Philadelphia, PA 19101

Gault, Stanley C *Businessman*
%Rubbermaid Inc, 1147 Akron Rd, Wooster, OH 44691

Gault, William Campbell *Writer*
482 Vaquero Ln, Santa Barbara, CA 93111

Gault, Willie *Football Player*
%Travis Clark Mgmt, 5700 Wilshire Blvd, #575, Los Angeles, CA 90036

Gautier, Dick *Actor*
11333 Moorpark St, #59, North Hollywood, CA 91602

Gavazzeni, Gianandrea *Conductor*
Via Porta Dipinta 5, Bergamo, Italy

Gaventa, John P *Political Scientist, Social Activist*
%Highlander Research & Education Ctr, New Market, TN 37820

Gavin, James J, Jr *Businessman*
%Borg-Warner Corp, 200 S Michigan Ave, Chicago, IL 60604

Gavin, John *Diplomat, Actor*
2415 Century Hill, Los Angeles, CA 90069

Gavin, Joseph G, Jr *Businessman*
%Grumman Corp, 1111 Stewart Ave, Bethpage, NY 11714
Gaviria, Cesar *President, Colombia*
%President's Office, Palacio de Narino, Correra 8, Bogota DE, Colombia
Gavitt, Dave *Basketball Executive*
%Boston Celtics, 151 Merrimac St, Boston, MA 02114
Gavrilov, Andrei *Concert Pianist*
%Harold Holt Ltd, 31 Sinclair Rd, London W14 ON5, England
Gay, Peter J *Historian*
105 Blue Trl, Hamden, CT 06518
Gaydos, Joseph M *Representative, PA*
3000 Valley Ridge Rd, McKeesport, PA 15133
Gayle, Crystal *Singer*
51 Music Sq E, Nashville, TN 37203
Gayle, Jackie *Comedian*
13109 Chandler Blvd, Van Nuys, CA 91401
Gaylor, Noel *Navy Admiral*
%East-West Accords Committee, 227 Massachuesetts NW, Washington, DC 20002
Gaylord, Edson Ingersoll *Businessman*
%Ingersoll Milling Machine Co, 707 Fulton St, Rockford, IL 61101
Gaylord, Edward L *Broadcast Executive, Publisher*
%Gaylord Broadcasting Co, PO Box 25125, Oklahoma City, OK 73125
Gaylord, Mitch *Gymnast*
%Craig Agency, 8485 Melrose Pl, #E, Los Angeles, CA 90069
Gaynes, George *Actor*
3344 Campanil Dr, Santa Barbara, CA 93109
Gaynor, Gloria *Singer*
%Malcolm Field Agency, Longford Ave, Southall, Middlesex UB1 3QT, England
Gaynor, Mitzi *Actress, Dancer*
610 N Arden Dr, Beverly Hills, CA 90210
Gayoom, Maumoon Abdul *President, Maldives*
%President's Office, Male, Maldives
Gazzara, Ben *Actor*
%Agency for Performing Arts, 888 7th Ave, New York, NY 10106
Gearhart, Marvin *Businessman*
%Gearhart Industries, PO Box 1936, Fort Worth, TX 76101
Geary, Anthony *Actor*
7010 Pacific View Dr, Los Angeles, CA 90068
Geary, Cynthia *Actress*
%William Felber Assoc, 2126 Cahuenga Blvd, Los Angeles, CA 90068
Gebel-Williams, Gunther *Circus Animal Trainer*
%Ringling Bros Barnum & Bailey, 320 New Mexico Ave NE, Washington, DC 20016
Geckle, Jerome W *Businessman*
%PHH Grp, 11333 McCormick Rd, Hunt Valley, MD 21301
Gedda, Nicolai *Opera Singer*
%Lies Askonas, 19-A Air St, London W2, England
Geddes, Jane *Golfer*
150 SE 25th Rd,, #6-A, Miami, FL 33129
Gee, E Gordon *Educator*
%Ohio State University, President's Office, Columbus, OH 43210
Gee, James D *Religious Leader*
%Pentecostal Church of God, 4901 Pennsylvania, Joplin, MO 64802
Gee, Thomas G *Judge*
%US Court of Appeals, 515 Rusk Ave, Houston, TX 77002
Geer, Ellen *Actress*
%Dade/Rosen/Schultz Agency, 11846 Ventura Blvd, #100, Studio City, CA 91604
Geeson, Judy *Actress*
%Abrams Artists, 9200 Sunset Blvd, #625, Los Angeles, CA 90069
Geffen, David *Movie, Music Producer*
%Geffen Records, 9126 Sunset Blvd, Los Angeles, CA 90069
Gehringer, Charlie *Baseball Player*
32301 Lahser Rd, Birmingham, MI 48010
Gehrke, Hans, Jr *Financier*
%First Federal of Michigan, 1001 Woodward Ave, Detroit, MI 48226
Gehry, Frank O *Architect*
15208 Cloverfield Blvd, Santa Monica, CA 90404

G

Geiberger – George

Geiberger, Al *Golfer*
700 Mesa Dr, Solvang, CA 93463

Geier, James A D *Businessman*
%Cincinnati Milacron Inc, 4701 Marburg Ave, Cincinnati, OH 45209

Geier, Philip H, Jr *Businessman*
%Interpublic Group of Companies, 1271 Ave of Americas, New York, NY 10020

Geiger, Keith *Labor Leader*
%National Education Assn, 1201 16th St NW, Washington, DC 20036

Geiger, Roy S *Marine Corps General*
%Marine Corps Headquarters, Washington, DC 20380

Geis, Bernard *Publisher*
1385 York Ave, New York, NY 10021

Gejdenson, Samuel *Representative, CT*
%House of Representatives, Washington, DC 20515

Gekas, George W *Representative, PA*
%House of Representatives, Washington, DC 20515

Gelb, Bruce S *Businessman*
%Bristol-Myers Squibb Co, 345 Park Ave, New York, NY 10154

Gelb, Ignace Jay *Linguist*
%University of Chicago, Oriental Institute, Chicago, IL 60637

Gelb, Richard L *Businessman*
%Bristol-Meyers Squibb Co, 345 Park Ave, New York, NY 10154

Gelber, Jack *Writer*
215 Marlborough Rd, Brooklyn, NY 11226

Geldof, Bob *Singer*
Davington Priory, Faversham, Kent, England

Gelin, Daniel *Actor*
92 Blvd Murat, 75016 Paris, France

Gell-Mann, Murray *Nobel Physics Laureate*
%California Institute of Technology, Physics Laboratory, Pasadena, CA 91125

Gelles, Richard J *Sociologist*
%University of Rhode Island, Sociology Dept, Kingston, RI 02881

Gellhorn, Martha *Writer*
%Douglas Rae Mgmt, 28 Charing Cross Rd, London WC2H 0DB, England

Gelman, Larry *Actor*
%BDP Assoc, 10637 Burbank Blvd, North Hollywood, CA 91601

Gemar, Charles D *Astronaut*
%NASA, Johnson Space Ctr, Houston, TX 77058

Gendron, Edward C *Businessman*
%Midland-Ross Corp, 20600 Chagrin Blvd, Cleveland, OH 44122

Gendron, George *Editor*
%Inc Magazine, 38 Commercial Wharf, Boston, MA 02110

Geneen, Harold S *Businessman*
320 Park Ave, New York, NY 10022

Gennaro, Peter *Choreographer*
115 Central Park West, New York, NY 10024

Genscher, Hans-Dietrich *Government Official, West Germany*
Auswartiges Amt, Adenauerallee 99-103, 5300 Bonn, Germany

Gentry, Bobbie *Singer*
11595 Bellagio Rd, Los Angeles, CA 90049

Gentry, Grant C *Businessman*
%Pantry Pride Inc, Fort Lauderdale, FL 90210

Gentry, Teddy *Singer (Alabama)*
%Dale Morris Assoc, 818 19th Ave S, Nashville, TN 37203

Geoffrin, Bernie (Boom Boom) *Hockey Player*
307 Willowglenn, Marietta, GA 30067

George, Jeff *Football Player*
%Indianapolis Colts, 7001 W 56th St, Indianapolis, IN 46254

George, Lynda Day *Actress*
10310 Riverside Dr, #104, Toluca Lake, CA 91602

George, Susan *Actress*
%Commercials Unlimited, 7461 Beverly Blvd, #400, Los Angeles, CA 90036

George, Tony *Motor Sports Executive*
%Indianapolis Motor Speedway, 4790 W 16th St, Speedway, IN 46224

George, W H Krome *Businessman*
%Aluminum Co of America, 1501 Alcoa Bldg, Pittsburgh, PA 15219

George, Wally *Entertainer*
PO Box 787, Los Angeles, CA 90028

George-Brown, Phyllis *Commentator*
Cave Hill Pl, Lexington, KY 40544

Georges, John A *Businessman*
%International Paper Co, 77 W 45th St, New York, NY 10036

Georgije, Bishop *Religious Leader*
%Serbian Orthodox Church, St Sava Monastery, Box 519, Libertyville, IL 60048

Georgine *Princess, Liechtenstein*
Schloss Vaduz, Principality of Liechtenstein

Gephardt, Richard A *Representative, MO*
4121 Fairview St, St Louis, MO 63116

Gerard, Gil *Actor*
%Artists Agency, 10000 Santa Monica Blvd, #305, Los Angeles, CA 90067

Gerardo (Mejia) *Singer*
20912 Delphine Dr, Walnut, CA 91789

Gerber, Fritz *Businessman*
%Roche Hoffmann LA, Grenzacherstrasse 124, 4002 Basel, Switzerland

Gerber, Joel *Judge*
%US Tax Court, 400 2nd St NW, Washington, DC 20217

Gerberding, William P *Educator*
%University of Washington, President's Office, Seattle, WA 98195

Gerbner, George *Social Scientist*
%University of Pennsylvania, Communications School, Philadelphia, PA 19104

Gere, Richard *Actor*
%International Creative Mgmt, 8899 Beverly Blvd, Los Angeles, CA 90048

Geren, Pete *Representative, TX*
%House of Representatives, Washington, DC 20515

Gerety, Tom, Jr *Educator*
%Trinity College, President's Office, Hartford, CT 06106

Gerevich, Aladar *Fencer*
Attila Ut 39, 1013 Budapest, Hungary

Gergen, David R *Editor*
%US News & World Report Magazine, 2400 "N" St NW, Washington, DC 20037

Geri, Joe *Football Player*
140 Chalfont Dr, Athens, GA 30603

Gerken, Walter B *Businessman*
%Pacific Mutual Life Insurance, 700 Newport Center Dr, Newport Beach, CA 92660

Gerlach, Gary *Publisher*
%Des Moines Register & Tribune, 715 Locust St, Des Moines, IA 50304

Gerlach, John B *Businessman*
%Lancaster Colony Corp, 37 W Broad St, Columbus, OH 43215

Gerlach, John J *Businessman*
%Lancaster Colony Corp, 37 W Broad St, Columbus, OH 43215

Germane, Geoffrey J *Mechanical Engineer*
%Brigham Young University, Mechanical Engineering Dept, Provo, UT 84602

Gerner, Robert *Behavioral Psychiatrist*
%University of California, Neuropsychiatric Institute, Los Angeles, CA 90024

Gerogian, Theodore *Religious Leader*
%Orthodox Presbyterian Church, 7401 Old York Rd, Philadelphia, PA 19126

Geronimo, Cesar *Baseball Player*
Tefada Flo, #46, Santo Domingo, Dominican Republic

Gerring, Cathy *Golfer*
%Ladies Professional Golf Assn, 2570 Volusia Ave, #B, Daytona Beach, FL 32114

Gerry, Elbridge T *Businessman*
%Union Pacific Corp, 345 Park Ave, New York, NY 10154

Gerstacker, Carl A *Businessman*
PO Box 226, Midland, MI 48640

Gerstein, Hilda Kirschbaum *Businesswoman*
%Petrie Stores Corp, 70 Enterprise Ave, Secaucus, NJ 07094

Gerstenberg, Richard C *Businessman*
80 Cranbrook Rd, Bloomfield Hills, MI 48013

Gerstner, Louis V, Jr *Businessman*
%RJR Nabisco Inc, Reynolds Blvd, Winston-Salem, NC 27102

Gerstner, William C *Businessman*
%Illinois Power Co, 500 S 27th St, Decatur, IL 62525

Gerth, Donald R — *Educator*
%California State University, President's Office, Sacramento, CA 95819

Gertz, Jami — *Actress*
%International Creative Mgmt, 8899 Beverly Blvd, Los Angeles, CA 90048

Gerwick, Ben Clifford, Jr — *Construction Engineer*
5874 Margarido Dr, Oakland, CA 94618

Gestring Redlick, Marjorie — *Diver*
1254 San Reymundo Rd, Hillsborough, CA 94010

Getaneh, Anna — *Model*
%Ford Model Agency, 344 E 59th St, New York, NY 10022

Getty, Estelle — *Actress*
%Green/Siegel Assoc, 1140 Alta Loma Terr, #105, Los Angeles, CA 90068

Getty, Gordon P — *Financier*
%J Paul Getty Museum, 17985 Pacific Coast Hwy, Malibu, CA 90265

Gettys, Thomas S — *Representative, SC*
PO Box 707, Rock Hill, SC 29730

Getz, John — *Actor*
%Gersh Agency, 232 N Canon Dr, Beverly Hills, CA 90210

Geyer, George — *Artist*
%Karl Bornstein Gallery, 1662 12th St, Santa Monica, CA 90404

Geyer, Georgie Anne — *Columnist*
%The Plaza, 800 25th St NW, Washington, DC 90037

Ghani, Abdul Aziz Abdel — *Prime Minister, Yemen Arab Republic*
%Prime Minister's Office, Sana'a, Yemen Arab Republic

Ghiardi, John F L — *Economist, Government Official*
12 Park Overlook Ct, Bethesda, MD 20034

Ghiarov, Nicolai — *Opera Singer*
%John Coast Concerts, 1 Park Close, London SW1, England

Ghiglia, Oscar — *Concert Guitarist*
BP 1795, Papeete, Tahiti, French Polynesia

Ghostley, Alice — *Actress*
3800 Reklaw Dr, Studio City, CA 91604

Giacco, Alexander F — *Businessman*
%Himont Inc, Hercules Plz, Wilmington, DE 19894

Giacconi, Riccardo — *Astrophysicist*
4205 Underwood Rd, Baltimore, MD 21218

Giacomin, Ed — *Hockey Player*
%New York Rangers, Madison Square Grdn, 4 Pennsylvania Plz, New York, NY 10001

Giaever, Ivar — *Nobel Physics Laureate*
2080 Van Antwerp Rd, Schenectady, NY 12309

Giambalvo, Louis — *Actor*
%Judy Schoen Assoc, 606 N Larchmont Blvd,, Los Angeles, CA 90004

Gianacakes, Peter J — *Businessman*
%Research-Cottrell Inc, PO Box 1500, Somerville, NJ 08876

Giannini, Giancarlo — *Actor*
Via Mercalli 46, 100197 Rome, Italy

Gianulias, Nikki — *Bowler*
%Ladies Pro Bowlers Tour, 7171 Cherryvale Blvd, Rockford, IL 61112

Giardello, Joey — *Boxer*
1214 Severn Ave, Cherry Hill, NJ 08002

Gibb, Barry — *Singer (Bee Gees), Songwriter*
%Borman Sternberg, 9220 Sunset Blvd, #320, Los Angeles, CA 90069

Gibb, Cynthia — *Actress*
%William Morris Agency, 151 El Camino, Beverly Hills, CA 90212

Gibb, Maurice — *Singer (Bee Gees), Songwriter*
%Borman Sternberg, 9220 Sunset Blvd, #320, Los Angeles, CA 90069

Gibb, Richard D — *Educator*
%University of Idaho, President's Office, Moscow, ID 83843

Gibb, Robin — *Singer (Bee Gees), Songwriter*
%Borman Sternberg, 9220 Sunset Blvd, #320, Los Angeles, CA 90069

Gibb, Walter F — *Test Pilot*
Bennelong House, 55 Nacquarrie St, Sydney NSW 2000, Australia

Gibberd, Frederick — *Architect*
The House, Marsh Ln, Old Harlow, Essex CM17 0NA, England

Gibbons, Edward F — *Businessman*
%F W Woolworth Co, 233 Broadway, New York, NY 10007

Gibbons, Leeza *Entertainer*
%"Entertainment Tonight" Show, 5555 Melrose Ave, Los Angeles, CA 90038

Gibbons, Sam M *Representative, FL*
%House of Representatives, Washington, DC 20515

Gibbs, Gary *Football Coach*
%University of Oklahoma, Athletic Dept, 180 W Brooks, Norman, OK 73019

Gibbs, Georgia *Singer*
%Frank Gervasi, 965 5th Ave, New York, NY 10021

Gibbs, Joe *Football Coach*
%Washington Redskins, Box 17247, Dulles Airport, Washington, DC 20041

Gibbs, Lawrence *Government Official*
%Internal Revenue Service, 1111 Constitution Ave NW, Washington, DC 20224

Gibbs, Marla *Actress*
2323 W Martin Luther King Blvd, Los Angeles, CA 90008

Gibbs, Patt *Labor Leader*
%Flight Attendants Assn, 1625 Massachusetts Ave NW, Washington, DC 20036

Gibbs, Terri *Singer*
414 Gibbs Cir, Grovetown, GA 30813

Gibbs, Timothy *Actor*
%David Shapira Assoc, 15301 Ventura Blvd, #345, Sherman Oaks, CA 91403

Giblin, E Burke *Businessman*
%Warner-Lambert Co, 201 Tabor Rd, Morris Plains, NJ 07950

Giblin, Edward J *Businessman*
%Ex-Cell-O Corp, 2855 Coolidge Rd, Troy, MI 48084

Gibran, Kahlil *Sculptor*
160 W Canton St, Boston, MA 02118

Gibron, Abe *Football Coach*
%Seattle Seahawks, 11220 NE 53rd St, Kirkland, WA 98033

Gibson Darbeu, Althea *Tennis Player*
PO Box 768, East Orange, NJ 07019

Gibson, Alexander D *Conductor*
15 Cleveden Gdns, Glasgow G12 0PU, Scotland

Gibson, Bob *Baseball Player*
215 Belleview Rd S, Belleview, NE 68005

Gibson, Charles *Commentator*
%ABC-TV, 1330 Ave of Americas, New York, NY 10019

Gibson, Debbie *Singer*
1684 Sterling Ave, Merrick, NY 11566

Gibson, Don *Singer*
PO Box 50474, Nashville, TN 37205

Gibson, Edward G *Astronaut*
%Booz Allen Hamilton, 4330 East West Hwy, Bethesda, MD 20814

Gibson, Eleanor Jack *Psychologist*
111 Oakhill Rd, Ithaca, NY 14850

Gibson, Everett K, Jr *Space Scientist*
1015 Trowbridge Dr, Houston, TX 77062

Gibson, Floyd R *Judge*
%US Courthouse, 811 Grand Ave, Kansas City, MO 64106

Gibson, Henry *Actor*
26740 Latigo Shore Dr, Malibu, CA 90265

Gibson, John R *Judge*
%US Court of Appeals, US Courthouse, 811 Grand Ave, Kansas City, MO 64106

Gibson, Kirk *Baseball Player*
1082 Oak Pointe Dr, Pontiac, MI 48054

Gibson, Mel *Actor*
72 Queen St, Woolhomra NSW, Australia

Gibson, Quentin H *Biochemist*
98 Dodge Rd, Ithaca, NY 14850

Gibson, Reginald W *Judge*
%US Claims Court, 717 Madison Pl NW, Washington, DC 20005

Gibson, Robert E *Financier*
%Valley Federal Savings & Loan, 6842 Van Nuys Blvd, Van Nuys, CA 91405

Gibson, Robert L *Astronaut*
%NASA, Johnson Space Ctr, Houston, TX 77058

Gibson, William *Writer*
%General Delivery, Stockbridge, MA 01262

Gideon, Miriam *Composer*
410 Central Park West, New York, NY 10025

Gideon, Raynold *Actor, Writer*
3524 Multiview Dr, Los Angeles, CA 90068

Gidwitz, Gerald S *Businessman*
%Helene Curtis Industries, 325 N Wells St, Chicago, IL 60610

Gidwitz, Joseph L *Businessman*
%Helene Curtis Industries, 325 N Wells St, Chicago, IL 60610

Gidwitz, Ronald J *Businessman*
%Helene Curtis Industries, 325 N Wells St, Chicago, IL 60610

Giel, Paul *Football Player, Administrator*
13400 McGintz Rd, Minneapolis, MN 55343

Gielen, Michael A *Conductor, Composer*
%Cincinnati Symphony, 1241 Elm St, Cincinnati, OH 45210

Gielgud, John *Actor*
South Pavilion, Wotton Underwood, Aylesbury Bucks HP18 0SB, England

Gienow, Herbert *Businessman*
%Klockner-Werke, Klocknerstr 29, 4100 Duisburg, Germany

Gierek, Edward *Premier, Poland*
Polska Zjednoczona Partia Robotnicza, Nowy Swiat 6, 00-497 Warsaw, Poland

Giesen, Richard A *Publisher*
%RCM Investments, 30 N LaSalle St, #1720, Chicago, IL 60602

Gifford, Charles K *Financier*
%Bank of Boston Corp, 100 Federal St, Boston, MA 02110

Gifford, Frank *Football Player, Sportscaster*
%ABC-TV, Sports Dept, 47 W 66th St, New York, NY 10023

Gifford, Nelson S *Businessman*
%Dennison Manufacturing Co, 300 Howard St, Framingham, MA 01701

Gilbert, Brad *Tennis Player*
%ProServ Inc, 888 17th St NW, #1200, Washington, DC 20006

Gilbert, Felix *Historian*
266 Mercer Rd, Princeton, NJ 08540

Gilbert, Lewis *Movie Director*
C House, 99 Aidwych, London WC2 BJY, England

Gilbert, Richard W *Publisher*
%Des Moines Register & Tribune, 715 Locust St, Des Moines, IA 50304

Gilbert, Ronnie *Singer*
%Abbe Alice Artist Mgmt, 425 E 58th St, #4-H, New York, NY 10022

Gilbert, S Parker *Financier*
%Morgan Stanley Co, 1251 Ave of Americas, New York, NY 10020

Gilbert-Brinkman, Melissa *Actress*
%Raymond Katz Enterprises, 9255 Sunset Blvd, #1115, Los Angeles, CA 90069

Gilbride, John T *Businessman*
%Todd Shipyards Corp, 1 State Street Plz, New York, NY 10004

Gilchrest, Wayne T *Representative, MD*
%House of Representatives, Washington, DC 20515

Gilchrist, Paul R *Religious Leader*
%Presbyterian Church in America, 1862 Century Pl, Atlanta, GA 30345

Gilder, George *Writer, Economist*
%General Delivery, Tyringham, MA 01264

Giles, Nancy *Actress*
%Cunningham-Escott-Dipene Assoc, 261 S Robertson Blvd, Beverly Hills, CA 90211

Giles, Warren C *Baseball Executive*
%Philadelphia Phillies, Veterans Stadium, Philadelphia, PA 19148

Giles, William H *Editor*
667 College Hill Dr, Baton Rouge, LA 70808

Giletti, Alain *Figure Skater*
103 Pl de L'Eglise, 74400 Chamonix, France

Gilfillan, G W *Businessman*
%Morrison Knudsen Corp, Morrison Knudsen Plz, Boise, ID 83707

Gill, Brendan *Writer*
%New Yorker Magazine, 25 W 43rd St, New York, NY 10036

Gill, Daniel E *Businessman*
%Bausch & Lomb Inc, 1 Lincoln First Sq, Rochester, NY 14601

Gill, George N *Publisher*
%Louisville Courier-Journal & Times, 525 W Broadway, Louisville, KY 40202

Gill, Howard R, Jr *Publisher*
%Golf Digest/Tennis Magazine, 495 Westport Ave, Norwalk, CT 06856
Gill, Janis *Singer*
%CBS Records, 51 W 52nd St, New York, NY 10019
Gill, Robert B *Businessman*
%J C Penney Co, 1301 Ave of Americas, New York, NY 10019
Gill, William A, Jr *Labor Leader*
%Flight Engineers Assn, 905 16th St NW, Washington, DC 20006
Gilles, Genevieve *Actress*
%Dakota Hotel, 1 W 72nd St, New York, NY 10023
Gillespie, Alexander J, Jr *Businessman*
%ASARCO Inc, 180 Maiden Ln, New York, NY 10028
Gillespie, Dizzy *Jazz Trumpeteer, Composer*
477 N Woodland St, Englewood, NJ 07631
Gillespie, Gwain H *Businessman*
%RJR Nabisco Inc, Reynolds Blvd, Winston-Salem, NC 27102
Gillet, Andre *Businessman*
%International Multifoods Corp, PO Box 2942, Minneapolis, MN 55402
Gillett, George *Publisher*
%Gillett Group, 4400 Harding Rd, Nashville, TN 37265
Gillette, Anita *Actress*
%Artists Agency, 10000 Santa Monica Blvd, #305, Los Angeles, CA 90067
Gilley, Mickey *Singer*
%Gilley's Enterprises, PO Box 1242, Pasadena, TX 77501
Gilliam, Armon *Basketball Player*
%Philadelphia 76ers, PO Box 25040, Philadelphia, PA 19147
Gilliam, Terry *Animator, Actor, Writer (Monty Python)*
%Creative Artists Agency, 9830 Wilshire Blvd, Beverly Hills, CA 90212
Gilliand, Merle E *Financier*
300 Fox Chapel Rd, #518, Pittsburgh, PA 15238
Gilliatt, Neal *Businessman*
%Interpublic Group of Co, 1271 Ave of Americas, New York, NY 10020
Gilliatt, Penelope *Writer*
31 Chester Sq, London SW1W 9HT, England
Gilligan, John G *Governor, OH*
%University of Notre Dame, Law School, Notre Dame, IN 46556
Gilliland, Richard *Actor*
%David Shapira Assoc, 15301 Ventura Blvd, #345, Sherman Oaks, CA 91403
Gillman, Sid *Football Coach*
2968 Playa Rd, Carlsbad, CA 92009
Gilman, Benjamin A *Representative, NY*
PO Box 358, Middletown, NY 10940
Gilman, Dorothy *Writer*
7 Fox Ct, #410, Portland, ME 04101
Gilman, Henry *Chemist*
3221 Oakland St, Ames, IA 50010
Gilmartin, John A *Businessman*
%Millipore Corp, 80 Ashby Rd, Bedford, MA 01730
Gilmore, Clarence P *Editor*
201 W 70th St, New York, NY 10023
Gilmore, Robert E *Businessman*
%Caterpillar Tractor Co, 100 NE Adams St, Peoria, IL 61629
Gilmour, Doug *Hockey Player*
%Calgary Flames, PO Box 1540, Calgary AB T2P 3B9, Canada
Gilpatric, Roswell L *Government Official*
3 E 77th St, New York, NY 10021
Gilroy, Frank *Writer*
9255 Sunset Blvd, #1122, Los Angeles, CA 90069
Gilruth, Robert R *Aerospace Engineer*
5128 Park Ave, Dickinson, TX 77539
Gimbel, Bruce A *Businessman*
435 E 52nd St, New York, NY 10022
Gimbel, Norman *Songwriter*
1172 Centinela Ave, Santa Monica, CA 90403
Gimeno, Andres *Tennis Player*
Paseo de la Bonanova 38, Barcelona 6, Spain

G

Gingrich, Newton L *Representative, GA*
%House of Representatives, Washington, DC 20515

Ginn, Robert M *Businessman*
%Centerior Energy Corp, 6200 Oak Tree Blvd, Independence, OH 44101

Ginn, Sam L *Businessman*
%Pacific Telesis Grp, 140 New Montgomery St, San Francisco, CA 94105

Ginsberg, Allen *Poet*
PO Box 582, Stuyvesant Station, New York, NY 10009

Ginsburg, Douglas H *Judge*
%US Court of Appeals, 3rd & Constitution NW, Washington, DC 20001

Ginsburg, Ruth Bader *Judge*
%US Court of Appeals, 3rd & Constitution NW, Washington, DC 20001

Ginty, Robert *Actor*
%Stone Manners Agency, 9113 Sunset Blvd, Los Angeles, CA 90069

Ginzberg, Eli *Economist*
845 West End Ave, New York, NY 10025

Ginzburg, Ralph *Publisher*
251 W 57th St, New York, NY 10019

Ginzton, Edward L *Electrical Engineer, Businessman*
%Varian Assoc, 611 Hansen Way, Palo Alto, CA 94303

Giordano, Michele Cardinal *Religious Leader*
Largo Donnaregina 22, 80138 Naples, Italy

Giordano, Richard *Businessman*
%BOC Group, Hammersmith House, London W6, England

Giordano, Salvatore, Jr *Businessman*
%Fedders Corp, Woodbridge Ave, Edison, NJ 08817

Giovanni, Nikki E *Poet*
%Eugene Winick, 5 W 45th St, New York, NY 10022

Giraldi, Bob *Movie Director*
%Director's Guild, 110 W 57th St, New York, NY 10019

Girard, S A *Businessman*
%Kaiser Steel Corp, PO Box 5050, Fontana, CA 92335

Girardelli, Marc *Skier*
%Olympic Committee, 7 Ave Victor-Hugo, 1750 Luxembourg

Giri, Tulsi *Prime Minister, Nepal*
Jawakpurdham, District Dhanuka, Nepal 10019

Giri, Varahagiri Venkata *President, India*
Girija, 1 Third Block, Jayanagar, Bangalore 56011, India

Giroux, Robert *Publisher*
%Farrar Straus & Giroux, 19 Union Sq W, New York, NY 10003

Giscard d'Estaing, Valery *President, France*
Varvasse, Chanonat (Puy de Dome), France

Gish, Annabeth *Actress*
%Triad Artists, 10100 Santa Monica Blvd, Los Angeles, CA 90067

Gish, Lillian *Actress*
430 E 57th St, New York, NY 10022

Githens, Thomas F *Financier*
%Security Capital Corp, 1290 Ave of Americas, New York, NY 10104

Gitner, Gerald L *Businessman*
%Texas Air Corp, 333 Clay St, #4040, Houston, TX 77002

Gittis, Howard *Businessman*
%Revlon Group Inc, 767 5th Ave, New York, NY 10153

Giuggio, John P *Businessman*
%Affilated Publications, 135 Morrissey Blvd, Boston, MA 02107

Giuliani, Rudolph W *Attorney*
%Anderson Kill Olick Oshinsky, 666 3rd Ave, 10th Fl, New York, NY 10017

Giulini, Carlo Maria *Conductor*
%General Delivery, Bolzano, Italy

Giuranna, Bruno *Concert Violist*
Via Misurina 71, 00135 Rome, Italy

Givens, Robin *Actress*
8818 Thrasher Ave, Los Angeles, CA 90069

Gjertsen, Doug *Swimmer*
%University of Texas, Athletic Dept, Austin, TX 78712

Gladstone, William L *Businessman*
%Arthur Young Co, 277 Park Ave, New York, NY 10172

Glamack, George *Basketball Player*
50 Pleasant Way, Rochester, NY 14622
Glamann, Kristoff *Businessman*
%United Breweries, Vesterfaelledvej 100, 1799 Copenhagen, Denmark
Glanville, Jerry *Football Coach*
%Atlanta Falcons, Suwanee Rd, Suwanee, GA 30174
Glaser, Daniel *Sociologist*
901 S Ogden Dr, Los Angeles, CA 90036
Glaser, Donald A *Nobel Physics Laureate*
%University of California, Molecular Biology Laboratory, Berkeley, CA 94720
Glaser, Milton *Graphic Artist*
207 E 32nd St, New York, NY 10016
Glaser, Paul Michael *Actor*
317 Georgina Ave, Santa Monica, CA 90402
Glaser, Robert L *Television Executive*
%RKO General, 1440 Broadway, New York, NY 10018
Glashow, Sheldon Lee *Nobel Physics Laureate*
30 Prescott St, Brookline, MA 02146
Glaspie, April *Diplomat*
Foreign Service Lounge, Main State Bldg, #1252, State Dept, Washington, DC 20520
Glass, Bill *Football Player*
%Bill Glass Evangelistic Assn, PO Box 356, Dallas, TX 75221
Glass, Bradley G *Financier*
%Buckeye Financial Corp, 36 E Gay St, Columbus, OH 43215
Glass, David D *Businessman*
%Wal-Mart Stores, 702 SW 8th St, Bentonville, AK 72712
Glass, H Bentley *Biologist*
PO Box 65, East Setankey, NY 11733
Glass, Philip *Composer*
231 2nd Ave, New York, NY 10003
Glass, Ron *Actor*
%David Shapira Assoc, 15301 Ventura Blvd, #345, Sherman Oaks, CA 91403
Glasser, Ira *Attorney, Legal Activist*
%American Civil Liberties Union, 132 W 43rd St, New York, NY 10036
Glasser, James J *Businessman*
%GATX Corp, 120 S Riverside Plz, Chicago, IL 60606
Glasser, William *Psychiatrist*
11633 San Vicente Blvd, Los Angeles, CA 90049
Glavin, Denis Joseph *Labor Leader*
%Electrical Radio & Machine Workers Union, 11 E 1st St, New York, NY 10022
Glavin, William F *Businessman*
%Xerox Corp, 1600 Summer St, Stanford, CT 06904
Glavine, Tom *Baseball Player*
23905 Hitching Post Rd, Sonora, CA 95370
Glazer, Nathan *Sociologist*
%Harvard University, Education School, Cambridge, MA 02138
Glazkov, Yuri *Cosmonaut*
141 160 Svyosdny Gorodok, Moskovskoi Oblasti, Potchta Kosmonavtov, Russia
Gleacher, Eric J *Financier*
%Morgan Stanley Co, 1251 Ave of Americas, New York, NY 10020
Gleason, Alfred M *Businessman*
%PacifiCorp, 851 SW 6th Ave, Portland, OR 97204
Gleason, Andrew M *Mathematician*
110 Larchwood Dr, Cambridge, MA 02138
Gleason, Joanna *Actress*
%International Creative Mgmt, 8899 Beverly Blvd, Los Angeles, CA 90048
Gleason, Paul *Actor*
%Harris & Goldberg Agency, 1999 Ave of Stars, #2850, Los Angeles, CA 90067
Gleason, Thomas D *Businessman*
%Wolverine World Wide Inc, 9341 Courtland Dr, Rockford, IL 49351
Gledhill, Arthur E *Businessman*
%Stanley Works, 1000 Stanley Dr, New Britain, CT 06050
Glemp, Jozef Cardinal *Religious Leader*
Sekretariat Prymasa, Kolski, Ul Miodowa 17, 00-246 Warsaw, Poland
Glenn, John H, Jr *Senator, OH; Astronaut*
1000 Urlin Ave, Columbus, OH 43212

Glenn, Scott *Actor*
PO Box 1018, Ketchum, ID 83340

Glenn, Wayne E *Labor Leader*
%United Paperworkers Int'l Union, 3340 Perimeter Hill Dr, Nashville, TN 37202

Glennan, Robert E *Educator*
%Emporia State University, President's Office, Emporia, KS 66801

Glennan, T Keith *Government Official, Space Administrator*
11400 Washington Plz W, #903, Reston, VA 22090

Glenville, Peter *Theater Director, Actor*
%Aaron R Frosch, 300 Central Park West, New York, NY 10024

Gless, Sharon *Actress*
106 Pocono Pk, Wilkes-Barre, PA 18702

Glickman, Dan *Representative, KS*
%House of Representatives, Washington, DC 20515

Glimm, James G *Mathematician*
%Rockefeller University, Mathematics Dept, New York, NY 10021

Glitman, Maynard W *Diplomat*
%General Delivery, Jeffersonville, VT 05464

Globus, Yoram *Movie Producer*
%Cannon Films, 6464 Sunset Blvd, #1150, Los Angeles, CA 90028

Glossop, Peter *Opera Singer*
End Cottage, 7 Gate Close, Hawkchurch nr Axminster, Devon, England

Glover, Brian *Actor*
%DeWolfe, Manfield House, 376/378 The Strand, London WC2R OLR, England

Glover, Danny *Actor*
%Carrie Productions, PO Box 590237, San Francisco, CA 94159

Glover, John *Actpr*
2517 Micheltorena St, Los Angeles, CA 90039

Glover, Richard *Football Player*
5097 Eppling Ln, San Jose, CA 95111

Gluck, Henry *Businessman*
%Caesars World Inc, 1801 Century Park East, #2600, Los Angeles, CA 90067

Gluck, Jeffrey *Publisher*
%St Louis Globe-Democrat, 710 N Tucker Blvd, St Louis, MO 06310

Gluck, Louis *Physician*
%University of California, Medical School, La Jolla, CA 92093

Glucksman, Lewis L *Financier*
%Lehman Brothers Kuhn Loeb, 55 Water St, New York, NY 10041

Glynn, Carlin *Actress*
1165 5th Ave, New York, NY 10029

Gminski, Mike *Basketball Player*
%Charlotte Hornets, 2 First Union Center, #2600, Charlotte, NC 28282

Goalby, Bob *Golfer*
5950 Town Hall Rd, Belleville, IL 62223

Gochberg, Thomas J *Financier*
%Security Capital Corp, 1290 Ave of Americas, New York, NY 10104

Godard, Jean-Luc *Movie Director*
%Sonimage, 99 Rue du Roule, 92200 Neuilly, France

Godbold, John C *Judge*
PO Box 1589, Montgomery, AL 36102

Goddard, David R *Biologist*
738-A I Walcott Dr, Philadelphia, PA 19118

Goddard, John *Explorer*
4224 Beulah Dr, La Canada, CA 91011

Goddard, Samuel P, Jr *Governor, AZ*
4724 E Camelback Canyon Dr, Phoenix, AZ 85018

Godfree McKane, Kathleen *Tennis Player*
55 York Ave, East Sheen, London SW1 4LQ, England

Godfrey, Paul V *Publisher*
%Toronto Sun, 333 King St E, Toronto ON M5A 3X5, Canada

Godunov, Alexander *Ballet Dancer*
%Harris & Goldberg Agency, 1999 Ave of Stars, #2850, Los Angeles, CA 90067

Godwin, Gail *Writer*
%Paul R Reynolds Inc, 12 E 41st St, New York, NY 10017

Godwin, Linda M *Astronaut*
%NASA, Johnson Space Ctr, Houston, TX 77058

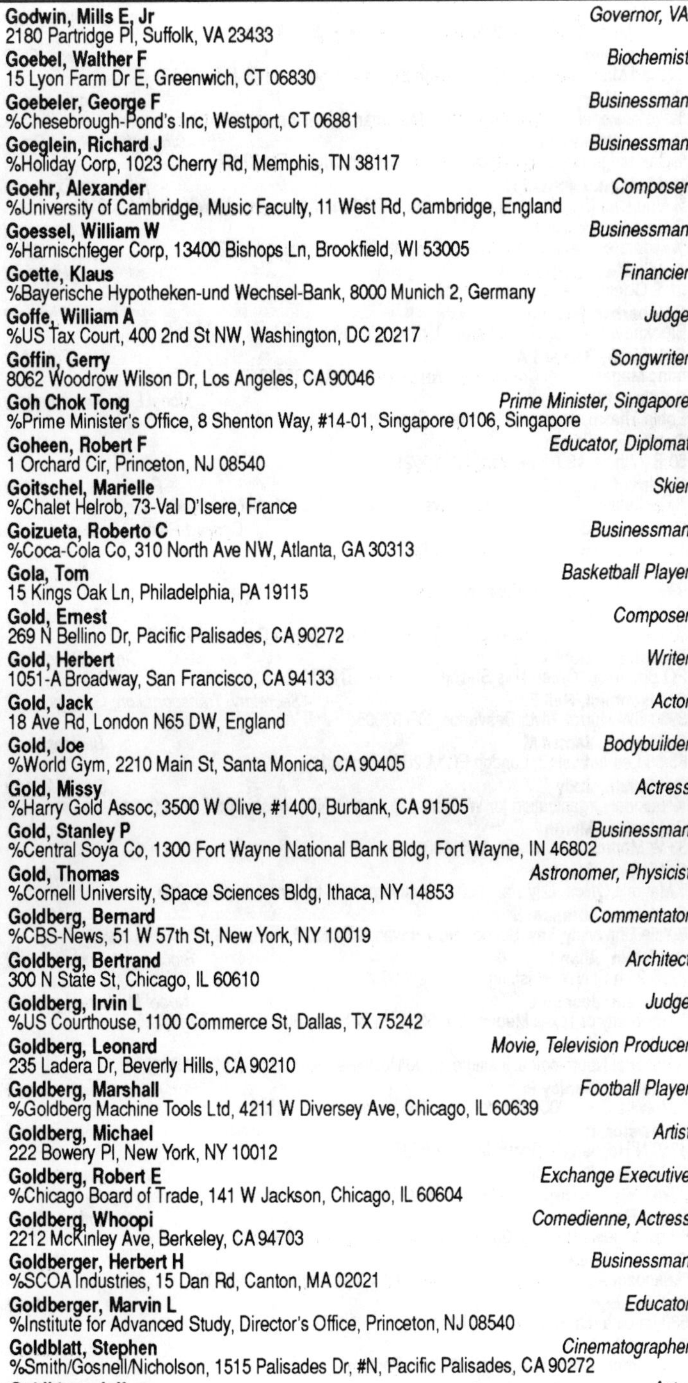

Godwin, Mills E, Jr — *Governor, VA*
2180 Partridge Pl, Suffolk, VA 23433

Goebel, Walther F — *Biochemist*
15 Lyon Farm Dr E, Greenwich, CT 06830

Goebeler, George F — *Businessman*
%Chesebrough-Pond's Inc, Westport, CT 06881

Goeglein, Richard J — *Businessman*
%Holiday Corp, 1023 Cherry Rd, Memphis, TN 38117

Goehr, Alexander — *Composer*
%University of Cambridge, Music Faculty, 11 West Rd, Cambridge, England

Goessel, William W — *Businessman*
%Harnischfeger Corp, 13400 Bishops Ln, Brookfield, WI 53005

Goette, Klaus — *Financier*
%Bayerische Hypotheken-und Wechsel-Bank, 8000 Munich 2, Germany

Goffe, William A — *Judge*
%US Tax Court, 400 2nd St NW, Washington, DC 20217

Goffin, Gerry — *Songwriter*
8062 Woodrow Wilson Dr, Los Angeles, CA 90046

Goh Chok Tong — *Prime Minister, Singapore*
%Prime Minister's Office, 8 Shenton Way, #14-01, Singapore 0106, Singapore

Goheen, Robert F — *Educator, Diplomat*
1 Orchard Cir, Princeton, NJ 08540

Goitschel, Marielle — *Skier*
%Chalet Helrob, 73-Val D'Isere, France

Goizueta, Roberto C — *Businessman*
%Coca-Cola Co, 310 North Ave NW, Atlanta, GA 30313

Gola, Tom — *Basketball Player*
15 Kings Oak Ln, Philadelphia, PA 19115

Gold, Ernest — *Composer*
269 N Bellino Dr, Pacific Palisades, CA 90272

Gold, Herbert — *Writer*
1051-A Broadway, San Francisco, CA 94133

Gold, Jack — *Actor*
18 Ave Rd, London N65 DW, England

Gold, Joe — *Bodybuilder*
%World Gym, 2210 Main St, Santa Monica, CA 90405

Gold, Missy — *Actress*
%Harry Gold Assoc, 3500 W Olive, #1400, Burbank, CA 91505

Gold, Stanley P — *Businessman*
%Central Soya Co, 1300 Fort Wayne National Bank Bldg, Fort Wayne, IN 46802

Gold, Thomas — *Astronomer, Physicist*
%Cornell University, Space Sciences Bldg, Ithaca, NY 14853

Goldberg, Bernard — *Commentator*
%CBS-News, 51 W 57th St, New York, NY 10019

Goldberg, Bertrand — *Architect*
300 N State St, Chicago, IL 60610

Goldberg, Irvin L — *Judge*
%US Courthouse, 1100 Commerce St, Dallas, TX 75242

Goldberg, Leonard — *Movie, Television Producer*
235 Ladera Dr, Beverly Hills, CA 90210

Goldberg, Marshall — *Football Player*
%Goldberg Machine Tools Ltd, 4211 W Diversey Ave, Chicago, IL 60639

Goldberg, Michael — *Artist*
222 Bowery Pl, New York, NY 10012

Goldberg, Robert E — *Exchange Executive*
%Chicago Board of Trade, 141 W Jackson, Chicago, IL 60604

Goldberg, Whoopi — *Comedienne, Actress*
2212 McKinley Ave, Berkeley, CA 94703

Goldberger, Herbert H — *Businessman*
%SCOA Industries, 15 Dan Rd, Canton, MA 02021

Goldberger, Marvin L — *Educator*
%Institute for Advanced Study, Director's Office, Princeton, NJ 08540

Goldblatt, Stephen — *Cinematographer*
%Smith/Gosnell/Nicholson, 1515 Palisades Dr, #N, Pacific Palisades, CA 90272

Goldblum, Jeff — *Actor*
%International Creative Mgmt, 8899 Beverly Blvd, Los Angeles, CA 90048

Goldblum – Gomes

Goldblum, Stanley *Businessman*
%Pele Medi-Corp, 9460 Wilshire Blvd, Beverly Hills, CA 90210

Golden, Diana *Skier*
%Sharf Marketing Grp, 822 Boylston St, #203, Chestnut Hill, MA 02167

Golden, Harry *Bowling Executive*
%Professional Bowlers Assn, 1720 Merriman Rd, Akron, OH 44313

Golden, William Lee *Singer (Oak Ridge Boys)*
%Oak Ridge Boys, 329 Rockland Rd, Hendersonville, TN 37075

Goldenson, Leonard H *Television Executive*
%American Broadcasting Companies, 1330 Ave of Americas, New York, NY 10019

Goldfeder, Howard *Businessman*
%Federated Department Stores, 7 W 7th St, Cincinnati, OH 45202

Goldharber, Gertrude S *Physicist*
91 S Gillette Ave, Bayport, NY 11705

Goldharber, Maurice *Physicist*
Brookhaven National Laboratory, Upton, NY 11973

Goldhirsh, Bernard A *Publisher*
%Inc Magazine, 38 Commercial Wharf, Boston, MA 02110

Golding, William *Nobel Literature Laureate*
Ebble Thatch, Bowerchalke, Wilts, England

Goldman, William *Writer*
50 E 77th St, #30, New York, NY 10021

Goldmark, Peter C, Jr *Foundation Executive*
%Rockefeller Foundation, 1133 Ave of Americas, New York, NY 10036

Goldovsky, Boris *Concert Pianist, Opera Educator*
183 Clinton Rd, Brookline, MA 02146

Goldreich, Peter *Astronomer*
999 San Pasqual, #7, Pasadena, CA 91106

Goldrich, Jona *Businessman*
%Goldrich & Kest Industries, 5150 Overland Ave, Culver City, CA 90230

Goldsboro, Bobby *Singer, Songwriter*
PO Box 6706, Green Hills Station, Nashville, TN 37215

Goldschmidt, Neil E *Secretary, Transportation; Governor, OR*
3900 SW Murray Blvd, Beaverton, OR 97005

Goldsmith, James M *Businessman*
65-68 Leadenhall St, London EC3A 2BA, England

Goldsmith, Judy *Social Activist*
%National Organization for Women, 425 13th St NW, Washington, DC 20004

Goldsmith, Myron *Architect*
33 W Monroe St, Chicago, IL 60603

Goldsmith, Stephen *Mayor*
%Mayor's Office, City Hall, 200 E Washington St, Indianapolis, IN 46204

Goldstein, Abraham S *Attorney*
%Yale University, Law School, New Haven, CT 06520

Goldstein, Allan L *Biochemist, Immunologist*
2795 28th St NW, Washington, DC 20008

Goldstein, Joseph L *Nobel Medicine Laureate*
%University of Texas Medical Ctr, 5324 Harry Hines Blvd, Dallas, TX 75235

Goldstein, Murray *Physician*
%National Neurological Institute, 9000 Rockville Pike, Bethesda, MD 20205

Goldstein, Stanley P *Businessman*
%Melville Corp, 3000 Westchester Ave, Harrison, NY 10528

Goldwater, Barry *Senator, AZ*
6250 N Hoghan Dr, Scottsdale, AZ 85253

Goldwater, Barry, Jr *Representative, CA*
23241 Ventura Blvd, Woodland Hills, CA 91364

Golic, Bob *Football Player*
%Los Angeles Raiders, 332 Center St, El Segundo, CA 90245

Golonka, Arlene *Actress*
%Sanders Agency, 8831 Sunset Blvd, #304, Los Angeles, CA 90069

Golub, Leon *Artist*
530 La Guardia Pl, New York, NY 10012

Gombrich, Ernst *Art Historian*
19 Briardale Gdns, London NW3 7PN, England

Gomes, Francisco da Costa *President, Portugal*
Ave Dos Eva 121-9-C, Lisbon, Portugal

Gomez, Alain *Businessman*
%Thomson Grp, 173 Blvd Haussmann, 75369 Paris Cedex 08, France
Gomez, Ruben *Baseball Player*
T2-8 Iquaza Park Gdns, Rio Piedra, PR 00928
Gomi, Akira *Financier*
%Hokkaido-Takushoku Bank, 3-7 Odorinishi, Chuoku, Sapporo 060, Japan
Gomory, Ralph E *Mathematician, Foundation Executive*
260 Douglas Rd, Chappaqua, NY 10514
Goncalves, Vascos dos Santos *Prime Minister, Portugal*
Ave Estados Unidos da America 86, 5 Esq, 1700 Lison, Portugal
Gonick, Larry *Cartoonist*
247 Missouri St, San Francisco, CA 94107
Gonshaw, Francesca *Actress*
%Greg Mellard, 12 D'Arblay St, #200, London W1V 3FP, England
Gonzales, Dalmacio *Opera Singer*
%Metropolitan Opera Assn, Lincoln Ctr, New York, NY 10023
Gonzalez Marquez, Felipe *Prime Minister, Spain*
%Prime Minister's Office, Madrid, Spain
Gonzalez Martin, Marcelo Cardinal *Religious Leader*
Arco de Palacio 1, Toledo, Spain
Gonzalez, Henry B *Representative, TX*
%House of Representatives, Washington, DC 20515
Gooch, Gerald *Artist*
%Hansen Fuller Gallery, 228 Grant Ave, San Francisco, CA 94108
Good, David I *Financier*
%United First Federal Savings & Loan, 1390 Main St, Sarasota, FL 33577
Good, Hugh W *Religious Leader*
%Primitive Advent Christian Church, 395 Frame Rd, Elkview, WV 25071
Good, Robert A *Physician*
%All Children's Hospital, 801 6th St S, St Petersburg, FL 33701
Goodacre, Jill *Model*
%Elite Model Mgmt, 111 E 22nd St, New York, NY 10010
Goodall, Caroline *Actress*
%James Sharkey, 15 Golden Sq, #300, London W1RV 3AG, England
Goodall, Jane *Ethnologist, Primatologist*
%Jane Goodall Institute, PO Box 26846, Tucson, AZ 85726
Goode, David R *Businessman*
%Norfolk Southern Corp, 1 Commerce Pl, Norfolk, VA 23510
Goode, Joe *Artist*
1645 Electric Ave, Venice, CA 90291
Goode, Richard *Concert Pianist*
%Byers Schwalk Assoc, 1 5th Ave, New York, NY 10011
Goodell, Brian *Swimmer*
2 Via Caballo, Rancho San Margaret, CA 92688
Gooden, Dwight *Baseball Player*
6755 30th St S, St Petersburg, FL 33712
Goodenough, Ward H *Antropologist*
204 Fox Ln, Wallingford, PA 19086
Goodes, Melvin R *Businessman*
%Warner-Lambert Co, 201 Tabor Rd, Morris Plains, NJ 07950
Goodeve, Charles P *Physical Chemist*
38 Middleway, London NW11, England
Goodeve, Grant *Actor*
%Joan Green Mgmt, 9200 Sunset Blvd, #931, Los Angeles, CA 90069
Goodfellow, Peter N *Geneticist*
Imperial Cancer Research Fund, Lincoln Inn Fields, London WC2A 3PX,England
Goodfriend, Lynda *Actress*
%Light Co, 901 Bringham Ave, Los Angeles, CA 90049
Goodlad, John I *Educator*
%University of California, Education School, Los Angeles, CA 90024
Goodling, William F *Representative, PA*
%House of Representatives, Washington, DC 20515
Goodman, Alfred *Composer*
Clemens Krauss Strasse 22, 8 Munich 60, Germany
Goodman, Corey *Neurobiologist*
%Stanford University Medical Ctr, Neurobiology Dept, Stanford, CA 94305

G

Goodman – Gordon

Goodman, Dody *Comedienne*
%Ruth Webb Enterprises, 7500 Devista Dr, Los Angeles, CA 90046

Goodman, Ellen *Columnist*
%Boston Globe, 135 Morrissey Blvd, Boston, MA 02107

Goodman, Julian *Broadcast Executive*
%National Broadcasting Co, 30 Rockefeller Plz, New York, NY 10020

Goodman, Linda *Writer*
%Mannu United, 137 Hayden St, Cripple Creek, CO 80813

Goodman, Oscar *Attorney*
520 S 4th, Las Vegas, NV 89101

Goodreault, Gene *Football Player*
95 Colby St, Bradford, MA 01830

Goodrich, Alton C *Businessman*
%Southland Royalty Co, 200 InterFirst Tower, Fort Worth, TX 76102

Goodrich, Gail *Basketball Player*
601 26th St, Santa Monica, CA 90402

Goodrich, Henry C *Businessman*
%Sonat Inc, First National-Southern Natural Bldg, Birmingham, AL 35203

Goodrich, Theodocia *Actress*
%Booh Schut Agency, 11350 Ventura Blvd, #206, Studio City, CA 91604

Goodson, Mark *Televison Producer*
375 Park Ave, New York, NY 10022

Goodwin, Alfred T *Judge*
%US Court of Appeals, 125 S Grand Ave, Pasadena, CA 91109

Goodwin, Charles (Tod) *Football Player*
102 Stahl, New Castle, PA 19720

Goodwin, Dan *Climber (Sears Tower)*
%Goodwin Enterprises, Box 3209, Benician Meadows, San Rafael, CA 94912

Goodwin, Doris Kearns *Writer*
%General Delivery, Concord, MA 01742

Goodwin, Michael *Actor*
%Susan Smith Assoc, 121 N San Vicente Blvd, Beverly Hills, CA 90211

Goodwin, Ron *Composer, Conductor*
Black Nest Cottage, Hockford Ln, Br Com, Reading RG7 4RP, England

Gookin, R Burt *Businessman*
Park Mansions, 5023 Frew Ave, Pittsburgh, PA 15213

Gorbatko, Viktor V *Cosmonaut*
141 160 Svyosdny Gorodok, Moskovskoi Oblasti, Potchta Kosmonavtov, Russia

Gorbunovs, Anatolijs *Chairman, Latvia*
%Supreme Council, Riga, Latvia

Gordimer, Nadine *Nobel Literature Laureate*
7 Frere Rd, Parktown, Johannesburg, South Africa

Gordin, Sidney *Artist*
903 Camilia St, Berkeley, CA 94710

Gordon, Bart *Representative, TN*
%House of Representatives, Washington, DC 20515

Gordon, Cyrus H *Orientalist*
130 Dean Rd, Brookline, MA 02146

Gordon, Don *Actor*
%First Artists Agency, 1000 Riverside Dr, Toluca Lake, CA 91602

Gordon, Ellen *Businesswoman*
%Tootsie Roll Industries, 7401 S Cicero Ave, Chicago, IL 60629

Gordon, Gale *Actor*
Tub Canyon Farm, Box 126, Borrego Springs, CA 92004

Gordon, Gerald *Actor*
%Lichtman Co, 12456 Ventura Blvd, #1, Studio City, CA 91604

Gordon, Hannah *Actress*
%Hutton Mgmt, 200 Fulham Rd, London SW10 9PN, England

Gordon, Larry *Entertainment Executive*
%20th Century Fox Films, 10201 W Pico Blvd, Los Angeles, CA 90035

Gordon, Leo *Actor*
9977 Wornom Ave, Sunland, CA 91040

Gordon, Lincoln *Economist, Diplomat*
3069 University Terr NW, Washington, DC 20016

Gordon, Mark *Actor*
10 E 44th St, #700, New York, NY 10017

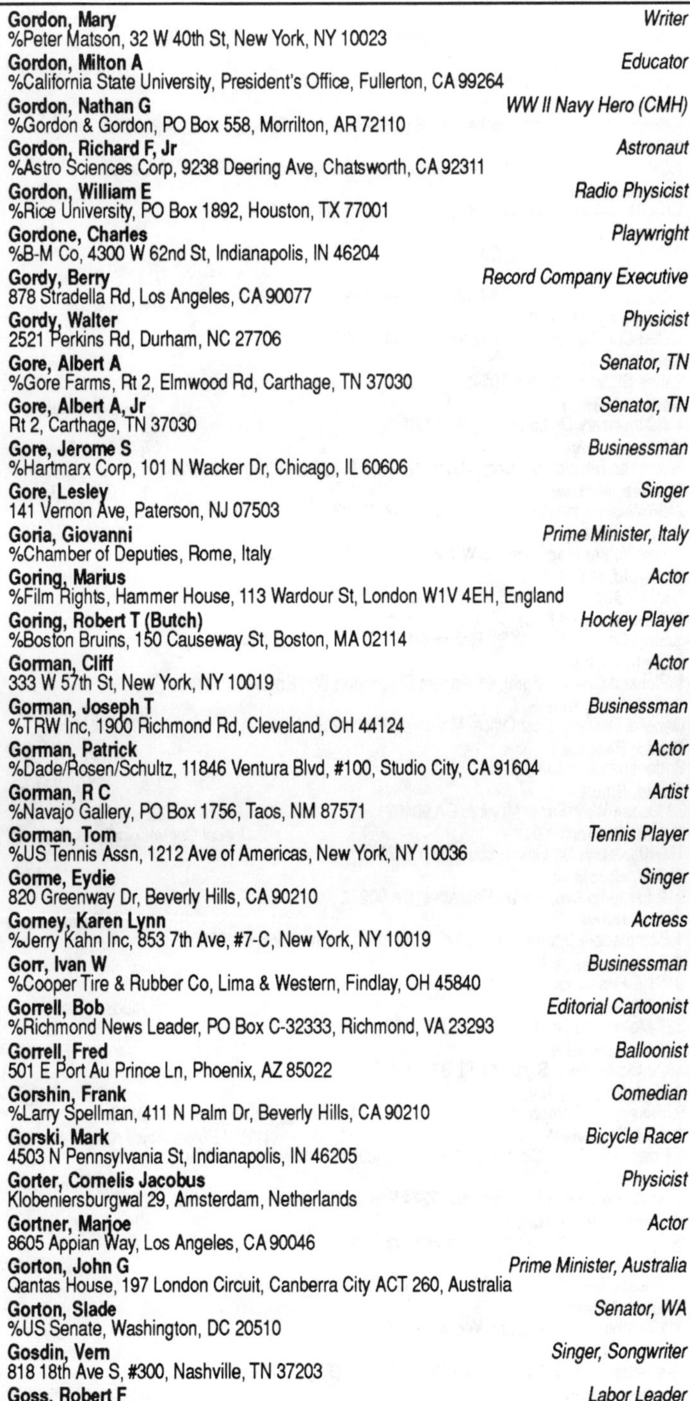

Gordon, Mary — *Writer*
%Peter Matson, 32 W 40th St, New York, NY 10023

Gordon, Milton A — *Educator*
%California State University, President's Office, Fullerton, CA 99264

Gordon, Nathan G — *WW II Navy Hero (CMH)*
%Gordon & Gordon, PO Box 558, Morrilton, AR 72110

Gordon, Richard F, Jr — *Astronaut*
%Astro Sciences Corp, 9238 Deering Ave, Chatsworth, CA 92311

Gordon, William E — *Radio Physicist*
%Rice University, PO Box 1892, Houston, TX 77001

Gordone, Charles — *Playwright*
%B-M Co, 4300 W 62nd St, Indianapolis, IN 46204

Gordy, Berry — *Record Company Executive*
878 Stradella Rd, Los Angeles, CA 90077

Gordy, Walter — *Physicist*
2521 Perkins Rd, Durham, NC 27706

Gore, Albert A — *Senator, TN*
%Gore Farms, Rt 2, Elmwood Rd, Carthage, TN 37030

Gore, Albert A, Jr — *Senator, TN*
Rt 2, Carthage, TN 37030

Gore, Jerome S — *Businessman*
%Hartmarx Corp, 101 N Wacker Dr, Chicago, IL 60606

Gore, Lesley — *Singer*
141 Vernon Ave, Paterson, NJ 07503

Goria, Giovanni — *Prime Minister, Italy*
%Chamber of Deputies, Rome, Italy

Goring, Marius — *Actor*
%Film Rights, Hammer House, 113 Wardour St, London W1V 4EH, England

Goring, Robert T (Butch) — *Hockey Player*
%Boston Bruins, 150 Causeway St, Boston, MA 02114

Gorman, Cliff — *Actor*
333 W 57th St, New York, NY 10019

Gorman, Joseph T — *Businessman*
%TRW Inc, 1900 Richmond Rd, Cleveland, OH 44124

Gorman, Patrick — *Actor*
%Dade/Rosen/Schultz, 11846 Ventura Blvd, #100, Studio City, CA 91604

Gorman, R C — *Artist*
%Navajo Gallery, PO Box 1756, Taos, NM 87571

Gorman, Tom — *Tennis Player*
%US Tennis Assn, 1212 Ave of Americas, New York, NY 10036

Gorme, Eydie — *Singer*
820 Greenway Dr, Beverly Hills, CA 90210

Gorney, Karen Lynn — *Actress*
%Jerry Kahn Inc, 853 7th Ave, #7-C, New York, NY 10019

Gorr, Ivan W — *Businessman*
%Cooper Tire & Rubber Co, Lima & Western, Findlay, OH 45840

Gorrell, Bob — *Editorial Cartoonist*
%Richmond News Leader, PO Box C-32333, Richmond, VA 23293

Gorrell, Fred — *Balloonist*
501 E Port Au Prince Ln, Phoenix, AZ 85022

Gorshin, Frank — *Comedian*
%Larry Spellman, 411 N Palm Dr, Beverly Hills, CA 90210

Gorski, Mark — *Bicycle Racer*
4503 N Pennsylvania St, Indianapolis, IN 46205

Gorter, Cornelis Jacobus — *Physicist*
Klobeniersburgwal 29, Amsterdam, Netherlands

Gortner, Marjoe — *Actor*
8605 Appian Way, Los Angeles, CA 90046

Gorton, John G — *Prime Minister, Australia*
Qantas House, 197 London Circuit, Canberra City ACT 260, Australia

Gorton, Slade — *Senator, WA*
%US Senate, Washington, DC 20510

Gosdin, Vern — *Singer, Songwriter*
818 18th Ave S, #300, Nashville, TN 37203

Goss, Robert F — *Labor Leader*
%Oil Chemical & Atomic International, 1636 Champa St, Denver, CO 80202

Gossage, Richard M (Goose) *Baseball Player*
10565 Viacha Way, San Diego, CA 92124

Gossage, Thomas L *Businessman*
%Hercules Inc, Hercules Plz, Wilmington, DE 19894

Gosselaar, Mark-Paul *Actor*
%Cunningham-Escott-Dipene, 261 S Robertson Blvd, Beverly Hills, CA 90211

Gosselin, Mario *Hockey Player*
%Quebec Nordiques, 2205 Ave du Colisee, Charlesbourg PQ G1L 4W7, Canada

Gossett, Bruce *Football Player*
%KXRX, Sports Dept, 1420 Koll Cir, San Jose, CA 95112

Gossett, Louis, Jr *Actor*
5916 Bonsall Dr, Malibu, CA 90265

Gossett, Milt *Businessman*
%Compton Advertising, 767 5th Ave, New York, NY 10022

Gossick Crockatt, Sue *Diver*
13768 Christian Barrett Dr, Moorpark, CA 93021

Gott, Rodney C *Businessman*
Sarles St, Mt Kisco, NY 10549

Gottfried, Brian *Tennis Player*
4030 Inverrary Dr, Lauderhill, FL 33319

Gottlieb, Jerry *Television Executive*
%Lorimar-Telepictures Corp, 3970 Overland Ave, Culver City, CA 90203

Gottlieb, Michael *Movie Director*
2436 Washington Ave, Santa Monica, CA 90403

Gottlieb, Robert A *Editor, Publisher*
%New Yorker Magazine, 25 W 43rd St, New York, NY 10036

Gottwald, Bruce C *Businessman*
%Ethyl Corp, 330 S 4th St, Richmond, VA 23217

Gottwald, Floyd D, Jr *Businessman*
%Ethyl Corp, 330 S 4th St, Richmond, VA 23217

Gough, Michael *Actor*
%Plunkett Greene Mgmt, 91 Regent St, London W1, England

Gould Innes, Shane *Swimmer*
General Delivery, Post Office, Margaret River 6285, Australia

Gould, Beatrice B *Editor*
Bedensbrook, Hopewell, NJ 08525

Gould, Elliott *Actor*
78 Ocean Way, Santa Monica, CA 90402

Gould, Gordon *Optical Communications Physicist*
15940 Luanne Dr, Gaithersburg, MD 20760

Gould, Harold *Actor*
912 El Medio Ave, Pacific Palisades, CA 90272

Gould, Irving *Businessman*
%Commodore International, 3330 Scott Blvd, Santa Clara, CA 95050

Gould, Laurence M *Geologist*
9451 E Rosewood, Tucson, AZ 85710

Gould, Morton *Composer, Conductor*
327 Melbourne Rd, Great Neck, NY 11021

Gould, Samuel B *Educator*
4822 Ocean Blvd, Sarasota, FL 33581

Gould, Stephen Jay *Paleontologist*
%Museum of Comparative Zoology, Harvard University, Cambridge, MA 02138

Gould, Thomas W *WW II British Royal Navy Hero (VC)*
6 Howlands, Orton Gold Hay, Peterborough, Cambridgeshire, England

Gould, William R *Businessman*
%Southern California Edison Co, 2244 Walnut Grove Ave, Rosemead, CA 91770

Gouled Aptidon, Hassan *President, Djibouti*
%President's Office, Djibouti, Republic of Djibouti

Goulet, Michel *Hockey Player*
%Chicago Blackhawks, 1800 W Madison St, Chicago, IL 60612

Goulet, Robert *Singer*
3110 Monte Rosa Ave, Las Vegas, NV 89120

Goulet, Victor N *Financier*
%Imperial Corp of America, 401 W "A" St, San Diego, CA 92101

Goulian, Mehran *Physician, Biochemist*
8433 Prestwick Dr, La Jolla, CA 92037

Gourad Hamadou, Barkad *Prime Minister, Djibouti*
%Prime Minister's Office, Djibouti, Republic of Djibouti

Gousseland, Pierre *Businessman*
%PaineWebber Grp, 1285 Ave of Americas, New York, NY 10019

Gouyon, Paul Cardinal *Religious Leader*
Archeveche, 3 Contour de la Motte, 35042 Rennes Cedex, France

Gowdy, Curt *Sportscaster*
9 Pierce Rd, Wellesley Hills, MA 02181

Gowon, Yakub *President, Nigeria*
%University of Warwick, Politics Dept, Coventry CV4 7AL, England

Grabar, Pierre *President, Switzerland*
%Social-Democratic Party, Postfach 4084, 3001 Berne, Switzerland

Grabe, Ronald J *Astronaut*
%NASA, Johnson Space Ctr, Houston, TX 77058

Graber, Bill *Track Athlete*
1136 N Columbia Ave, Ontario, CA 91764

Grabois, Neil R *Educator*
%Colgate University, President's Office, Hamilton, NY 13346

Grabowski, Jim *Football Player*
308 Briarwood Ln, Palantine, IL 60067

Grace, J Peter *Businessman*
%W R Grace & Co, 1114 Ave of Americas, New York, NY 10036

Grace, William E *Businessman*
6001 Indian Creek Ct, Fort Worth, TX 76107

Gracey, James S *Coast Guard Admiral*
%Coast Guard Headquarters, 2100 2nd St SW, Washington, DC 20593

Grad, Harold *Mathematician*
248 Overlook Rd, New Rochelle, NY 10804

Graddy, Sam *Track Athlete, Football Player*
%Los Angeles Raiders, 332 Center St, El Segundo, CA 90245

Grade of Elstree, Lew *Television Executive*
Embassy House, 3 Audley Sq, London W1Y 5DR, England

Grade, Jeffery T *Businessman*
%Harnischfeger Corp, 13400 Bishops Ln, Brookfield, WI 53005

Gradishar, Randy *Football Player*
%Denver Broncos, 13655 E Dove Valley Pkwy, Englewood, CO 80112

Gradison, Willis D, Jr *Representative, OH*
2200 Victory Pkwy, Cincinnati, OH 45206

Grady, Don *Actor*
3575 Cahuenga Blvd W, #320, Los Angeles, CA 90068

Grady, James T *Labor Leader*
%International Teamsters Brotherhood, 25 Louisiana Ave NW, Washington, DC 20001

Grady, Wayne *Golfer*
8619 French Oak Dr, Orlando, FL 32811

Graf, Carl N *Businessman*
%W R Grace & Co, 1114 Ave of Americas, New York, NY 10036

Graf, Steffi *Tennis Player*
Normannenstrasse 14, 6831 Bruhl, Germany

Graff, George S *Businessman*
%McDonnell Douglas Corp, PO Box 516, St Louis, MO 63166

Graffman, Gary *Concert Pianist*
PO Box 30, Tenafly, NJ 07670

Grafton, Sue *Writer*
PO Box 41447, Santa Barbara, CA 93140

Graham, Alex *Cartoonist (Fred Basset)*
%Tribune Media Services, 34 E Concord St, Orlando, FL 32801

Graham, Billy (William F) *Evangelist*
1300 Harmon Pl, Minneapolis, MN 55403

Graham, David *Golfer*
5531 Bent Green Dr, Dallas, TX 75248

Graham, Donald E *Publisher*
%Washington Post Co, 1150 15th St NW, Washington, DC 20071

Graham, Donald Martin *Financier*
2247 Orrington Ave, Evanston, IL 60201

Graham, Hugh J, Jr *Financier*
%AmeriWest Financial Corp, 6400 Uptown Blvd NE, Albuquerque, NM 87110

G

Graham – Grant

Graham, James A *Businessman*
%Sheller-Globe Corp, 1505 Jefferson Ave, Toledo, OH 43624

Graham, Jorie *Poet*
%University of Iowa, Writers' Workshop, Iowa City, IA 55242

Graham, Katharine M *Publisher*
%Washington Post Co, 1150 15th St NW, Washington, DC 20071

Graham, Lou *Golfer*
%Professional Golfers Assn, PO Box 109601, Palm Beach Gardens, FL 33410

Graham, Otto *Football Player, Coach*
2241 Beneva Terr, Sarasota, FL 33582

Graham, Patricia A *Educator*
%Harvard University, Education School, Cambridge, MA 02138

Graham, Robert *Sculptor*
69 Windward Ave, Marina del Rey, CA 90292

Graham, Thomas C *Businessman*
%USX Corp, 600 Grant St, Pittsburgh, PA 15230

Graham, Virginia *Commentator*
%Ruth Webb Enterprises, 7500 Devista Dr, Los Angeles, CA 90046

Graham, William B *Businessman*
%Baxter Travenol Laboratories, 1 Baxter Pkwy, Deerfield, IL 60015

Graham, William E, Jr *Businessman*
%Carolina Power & Light Co, 411 Fayetteville St, Raleigh, NC 27602

Graham, William R *Government Official*
%NASA, 400 Maryland Ave SW, Washington, DC 20546

Grainger, David W *Businessman*
%W W Grainger Inc, 5500 W Howard St, Skokie, IL 60077

Gralish, Tom *Photographer*
%Philadelphia Inquirer, 400 N Broad St, Philadelphia, PA 19101

Gralla, Lawrence *Publisher*
%Gralla Publications, 1515 Broadway, New York, NY 10036

Gralla, Milton *Publisher*
%Gralla Publications, 1515 Broadway, New York, NY 10036

Gramley, Lyle E *Financier*
%Federal Reserve System, 20th & Constitution NW, Washington, DC 20551

Gramm, Phil *Senator, TX*
%US Senate, Washington, DC 20510

Gramm, Wendy L *Government Official*
%Commodity Futures Trading Commission, 2033 "K" St NW, Washington, DC 20581

Grammer, Kathy *Actress*
%Artists Agency, 10000 Santa Monica Blvd, #305, Los Angeles, CA 90067

Grammer, Kelsey *Actor*
%Artists Agency, 10000 Santa Monica Blvd, #305, Los Angeles, CA 90067

Granatelli, Andy *Auto Racing Builder*
%TuneUp Masters, 21031 Ventura Blvd, Woodland Hills, CA 91364

Grandy, Fred *Representative, IA; Actor*
508 Pierce St, Sioux City, IA 51101

Granger, Farley *Actor*
18 W 72nd St, #25-D, New York, NY 10023

Granger, Stewart *Actor*
17331 Tramanto Dr, #1, Pacific Palisades, CA 90272

Granger, William W, Jr *Businessman*
%Beatrice Companies, 2 N La Salle St, Chicago, IL 60602

Granit, Ragnar A *Nobel Medicine Laureate*
14 Eriksbergsgatan, 11430 Stockholm, Sweden

Granlund, Paul T *Sculptor*
%Adolphus College, Art Dept, St Peter, MN 56082

Grant, Amy *Singer*
Riverston Farm, Moran Rd, Franklin, TN 37064

Grant, B Donald *Television Executive*
%CBS Entertainment, 51 W 52nd St, New York, NY 10019

Grant, Boyd *Basketball Coach*
%Colorado State University, Athletic Dept, Fort Collins, CO 80523

Grant, Gogi *Singer*
1709 Ambassador Ave, Beverly Hills, CA 90210

Grant, Horace *Basketball Player*
%Chicago Bulls, 980 N Michigan Ave, Chicago, IL 60611

Grant, James P *Government Official*
%UNICEF, 866 United Nations Plz, #A-6004, New York, NY 10004

Grant, Jim (Mudcat) *Baseball Player*
1020 S Dunsmuir, Los Angeles, CA 90019

Grant, Toni *Radio Psychologist*
1289 Sunset Plaza Dr, Los Angeles, CA 90069

Grant, Verne E *Biologist*
2811 Frescoe Dr, Austin, TX 78731

Grantham, Don L *Businessman*
201 N Green Bay Rd, Lake Forrest, IL 60045

Granville, Keith *Businessman*
Speedbird, 1837 Chateux-D'Oex, Switzerland

Granville, Maurice F *Businessman*
%Texaco Inc, 2000 Westchester Ave, White Plains, NY 10650

Granz, Norman *Record Producer*
%Pablo Records, 451 N Canon Dr, Beverly Hills, CA 90210

Granzow, Paul H *Businessman*
%Standard Register Co, 626 Albany St, Dayton, OH 45408

Grappelli, Stephane *Jazz Violinist*
87 Rue de Dunkerque, 75009 Paris, France

Grass, Gunter *Writer*
Niedstrasse 13, 1 Berlin 41, Germany

Grassle, Karen *Actress*
%Century Artists, 9744 Wilshire Blvd, #308, Beverly Hills, CA 90212

Grassley, Charles E *Senator, IA*
RR 1, New Hartford, IA 50660

Grasso, Richard A *Stock Exchange Executive*
%New York Stock Exchange, 11 Wall St, New York, NY 10005

Grau, Shirley Ann *Writer*
%Brandt & Brandt, 1501 Broadway, New York, NY 10036

Graubard, Seymour *Businessman*
%Gulf Resources & Chemical Corp, 1100 Milam Bldg, Houston, TX 77002

Graubard, Stephen R *Educator, Historian, Editor*
83 Whits End Rd, Concord, MA 02138

Gravel, Mike *Senator, AK*
%Mike Gravel Resource Analysts, 201 E 3rd Ave, Anchorage, AK 99501

Graveline, Duane E *Astronaut*
%Health Maintenance Ctr, PO Box 35, Winooski, VT 05404

Graves, Denyce *Opera Singer*
%Metropolitan Opera Assn, Lincoln City Plz, New York, NY 10023

Graves, Earl G *Publisher*
%Black-Enterprise Magazine, 130 5th Ave, New York, NY 10011

Graves, Harold N, Jr *Journalist, Government Official*
4816 Grantham Ave, Chevy Chase, MD 20015

Graves, Howard D *Army General*
%US Military Academy, Superintendent's Office, West Point, NY 10996

Graves, Michael *Architect*
341 Nasssau St, Princeton, NJ 08540

Graves, Morris *Artist*
%Willard Gallery, 29 E 72nd St, New York, NY 10021

Graves, Nancy *Artist*
69 Wooster St, New York, NY 10012

Graves, Peter *Actor*
415 N Crescent Dr, #210, Beverly Hills, CA 90210

Gray, Alfred M, Jr *Marine Corps General*
%Commandant's Office, US Marine Corps, Washington, DC 20380

Gray, Barry *Commentator*
425 E 58th St, New York, NY 10022

Gray, Charles *Actor*
%London Mgmt, 235/241 Regent St, London W1A 2JI, England

Gray, Coleen *Actress*
1432 N Kenwood St, Burbank, CA 91505

Gray, Dulcie *Actress*
Shardeloes, Amersham, Bucks, England

Gray, Edwin J *Financier*
%Chase Federal Savings & Loan, 7300 Kendall Dr, Miami, FL 33156

G

Gray, Erin *Model, Actress*
%Hissong Co, 1438 N Gower St, Courtyard #41, Los Angeles, CA 90028

Gray, Gordon Cardinal *Religious Leader*
Hermitage, Whitehouse Loan, Edinburgh EH9 1BB, Scotland

Gray, Hannah H *Educator*
%University of Chicago, President's Office, Chicago, IL 60637

Gray, Harry B *Chemist*
1415 E California Blvd, Pasadena, CA 91106

Gray, Henry H *Businessman*
%Revco D S Inc, 1925 Enterprise Pkwy, Twinsburg, OH 44087

Gray, J Douglas *Businessman*
%Swift Independent Corp, 115 W Jackson Blvd, Chicago, IL 60604

Gray, Jerry *Football Player*
%Los Angeles Rams, 2327 W Lincoln Ave, Anaheim, CA 92801

Gray, John B *Businessman*
%Dennison Manufacturing Co, 300 Howard St, Framingham, MA 01701

Gray, John D *Businessman*
%Tektronix Inc, PO Box 500, Beaverton, OR 97077

Gray, Ken *Representative, IL*
%House of Representatives, Washington, DC 20515

Gray, Ken *Football Player*
%Right Guard International, Rt 7, Box 212, Llano, TX 78643

Gray, L Patrick, III *Director, FBI*
PO Box 1591, New London, CT 06320

Gray, Linda *Actress*
PO Box 5064, Sherman Oaks, CA 91403

Gray, Mel *Football Player*
%Detroit Lions, 1200 Featherstone Rd, Pontiac, MI 48057

Gray, Pete *Baseball Player*
203 Phillips St, Nanticoke, PA 18634

Gray, Robert *Government Official*
%Gray & Co, 3020 "K" St NW, Washington, DC 20007

Gray, Simon *Writer*
%Judy Daish Assoc, 83 Eastbourne Mews, London W2 6LQ, England

Gray, William H, III *Association Leader, Representative, PA*
%United Negro College Fund, 500 E 62nd St, New York, NY 10021

Graysmith, Robert *Editorial Cartoonist*
%San Francisco Chronicle, 901 Mission St, San Francisco, CA 94119

Grayson, C Jackson, Jr *Government Official, Educator*
123 N Post Oak Ln, Houston, TX 77024

Grayson, Kathryn *Singer, Actress*
2009 La Mesa Dr, Santa Monica, CA 90402

Grazzola, Kenneth E *Publisher*
%Aviation Week Magazine, 1221 Ave of Americas, New York, NY 10020

Grebstein, Sheldon N *Educator*
%State University of New York, President's Office, Purchase, NY 10577

Grechko, Georgi *Cosmonaut*
141 160 Svyosdny Gorodok, Moskovskoi Oblasti, Potchta Kosmonavtov, Russia

Greco, Emilio *Sculptor*
Viale Cortina d'Ampezzo 132, 00135 Rome, Italy

Greco, Jose *Dancer, Choreographer*
224 W 49th St, New York, NY 10019

Greeley, Andrew M *Writer, Sociologist*
6030 S Ellis Ave, Chicago, IL 60637

Green, A C *Basketball Player*
%Los Angeles Lakers, Great Western Forum, 3900 W Manchester, Inglewood, CA 90306

Green, Adolph *Lyricist*
211 Central Park West, New York, NY 10024

Green, Al *Singer, Clergyman*
PO Box 456, Memphis, TN 38053

Green, Alvar J *Businessman*
%Autodesk Inc, 2320 Marinship Way, Sausalito, CA 94965

Green, Dallas *Baseball Manager*
RR 1, Box 227-A, West Grove, PA 19390

Green, Darrell *Football Player*
%Washington Redskins, Dulles Airport, Box 17247, Washington, DC 20041

Green, David E *Chemist*
5339 Brody Dr, Madison, WI 53705
Green, Dennis *Football Coach*
%Minnesota Vikings, 9520 Viking Dr, Eden Prairie, MN 55344
Green, Eric *Football Player*
%Pittsburgh Steelers, Three Rivers Stadium, Pittsburgh, PA 15212
Green, Gaston *Football Player*
%Denver Broncos, 13655 E Dove Valley Pkwy, Englewood, CO 80112
Green, Gerald *Writer*
%Scott Meredith Agency, 845 3rd Ave, New York, NY 10022
Green, Hamilton *Prime Minister, Guyana*
%Prime Minister's Office, Georgetown, Guyana
Green, Howard *Medical Researcher*
%Harvard Medical School, Physiology & Biophysics Dept, Boston, MA 02115
Green, Hubert *Golfer*
PO Box 28030, Panama City, FL 32411
Green, Hugh *Football Player*
%Miami Dolphins, 2269 NW 199th St, Miami, FL 33056
Green, Jacob *Football Player*
%Seattle Seahawks, 11220 NE 53rd St, Kirkland, WA 98033
Green, John R, Jr *Businessman*
%Magic Chef Inc, 740 King Edward Ave SE, Cleveland, TN 37311
Green, Julien *Novelist*
%Academie Francaise, 23 Quai de Conti, Paris, France
Green, Kate *Writer*
%Delacorte Press, 666 5th Ave, New York, NY 10103
Green, Lucinda *Equestrian Rider*
Appleshaw House, Andover, Hants, England
Green, Marshall *Diplomat*
5063 Millwood Ln NW, Washington, DC 20016
Green, Maurice Spurgeon *Editor*
Hermitage, Twyford House, Hants, England
Green, Mike *Football Player*
%San Diego Chargers, 9449 Friars Rd, San Diego, CA 92108
Green, Paul *Writer*
Old Lystra Rd, Chapel Hill, NC 27514
Green, Peter J F *Businessman*
%Lloyd's of London, Lime St, London EC3M 7HL, England
Green, Rick *Hockey Player*
%Montreal Canadiens, 2313 St Catherine St W, Montreal PQ H3H 1N2, Canada
Green, Rickey *Basketball Player*
%Charlotte Hornets, 2 First Union Ctr, #2600, Charlotte, NC 28202
Green, Robert L *Businessman*
%Community Psychiatric Centers, 2130 E 4th St, Santa Ana, CA 92705
Green, S William *Representative, NY*
755 Park Ave, New York, NY 10021
Green, Sidney *Basketball Player*
%Orlando Magic, Box 76, 1 Dupont Cir, Orlando, FL 32802
Greenberg, Alan C *Financier*
%Bear Sterns Co, 55 Water St, New York, NY 10041
Greenberg, Arnold C *Businessman*
%Coleco Industries, 999 Quaker Ln S, West Hartford, CT 06110
Greenberg, Carl *Journalist*
6001 Canterbury Dr, Culver City, CA 90230
Greenberg, Frank S *Businessman*
%Burlington Industries, 3330 W Friendly Ave, Greensboro, NC 27410
Greenberg, Joseph H *Anthropologist*
860 Mayfield St, Stanford, CA 94305
Greenberg, Leonard *Businessman*
%Coleco Industries, 999 Quaker Ln S, West Hartford, CT 06110
Greenberg, Maurice R *Businessman*
%American International Grp, 70 Pine St, New York, NY 10270
Greenberg, Morton I *Judge*
%US Court of Appeals, 402 E State St, Trenton, NJ 08608
Greenburg, Dan *Writer*
323 E 50th St, New York, NY 10022

G

Greenburg – Greer

Greenburg, Paul *Journalist*
2406 W 39th St, Pine Bluff, AR 71601

Greenbush, Rachel Lindsay *Actress*
%Harry Gold Assoc, 3500 W Olive Ave, #1400, Burbank, CA 91505

Greenbush, Sidney Robin *Actress*
%Harry Gold Assoc, 3500 W Olive Ave, #1400, Burbank, CA 91505

Greene Raine, Nancy *Skier*
%Nancy Greene Hotel, Whistler/Blackcomb BC, Canada

Greene, (Mean) Joe *Football Player, Coach*
%Miami Dolphins, Robbie Stadium, 2269 NW 199th St, Miami, FL 33056

Greene, Balcomb *Artist*
2 Sutton Pl S, New York, NY 10022

Greene, Harold H *Judge*
%US District Court, 3rd & Constitution NW, Washington, DC 20001

Greene, Jack P *Historian*
1010 Bellemore Rd, Baltimore, MD 21210

Greene, Kevin *Football Player*
%Los Angeles Rams, 2327 W Lincoln Ave, Anaheim, CA 92801

Greene, Michele *Actress*
%Gores/Fields Agency, 10100 Santa Monica Blvd, #700, Los Angeles, CA 90069

Greene, Raleigh W (Lee), III *Financier*
%Florida Federal Savings & Loan, PO Box 1509, St Petersburg, FL 33731

Greene, Raleigh W, Jr *Financier*
%Florida Federal Savings & Loan, PO Box 1509, St Petersburg, FL 33731

Greene, Robert B (Bob), Jr *Columnist*
%Chicago Tribune, 435 N Michigan Ave, Chicago, IL 60611

Greene, Shecky *Comedian*
1220 Shadow Ln, Las Vegas, NV 89102

Greenewalt, Crawford H *Businessman*
%General Delivery, Greenville, DE 19807

Greenfield, James Lloyd *Journalist*
850 Park Ave, New York, NY 10021

Greenfield, Meg *Journalist*
3318 "R" St NW, Washington, DC 20007

Greenlee, John A *Educator*
50 Oak Hill Ln, South Pasadena, CA 91030

Greenspan, Alan *Economist, Government Official*
%Federal Reserve Board, 20th & Constitution NW, Washington, DC 20551

Greenspan, Bud *Producer, Director*
252 E 61st St, New York, NY 10021

Greenstein, Jesse L *Astronomer*
2057 San Pasqual St, Pasadena, CA 91107

Greenwald, Gerald *Businessman*
%UAL Inc, 1200 Algonquin Rd, Elk Grove Township, IL 60007

Greenwald, Joseph A *Economist, Diplomat*
Town House, 8-5-25 Asaka, Minatoku, Tokyo 107, Japan

Greenwald, Milton *Paleontologist*
%Museum of Paleontology, University of California, Berkeley, CA 94720

Greenwell, Mike *Baseball Player*
954 E Hyacinth St, North Fort Myers, FL 33903

Greenwood, Bruce *Actor*
%Agency for Performing Arts, 9000 Sunset Blvd, #1200, Los Angeles, CA 90069

Greenwood, David *Basketball Player*
%Chicago Bulls, 980 N Michigan Ave, Chicago, IL 60611

Greenwood, Joan *Actress*
27 Slaidburn St, Chelsea, London SW10, England

Greenwood, Lee *Singer*
1111 16th Ave S, #200, Nashville, TN 37212

Greer, Dabbs *Actor*
%Dade/Rosen/Schultz, 11846 Ventura Blvd, #100, Studio City, CA 91604

Greer, Germaine *Writer, Feminist*
%University of Tulsa, English Dept, 600 S College Ave, Tulsa, OK 74104

Greer, Gordon G *Editor*
%Better Homes & Gardens Magazine, 1716 Locust St, Des Moines, IA 50336

Greer, Hal *Basketball Player*
460 Hidden River Rd, Narbeth, PA 19072

Greer, Jane *Actress*
966 Moraga Dr, Los Angeles, CA 90049

Gregg, Forrest *Football Player, Coach, Administrator*
%Southern Methodist University, Athletic Dept, Dallas, TX 75275

Gregg, Hugh *Governor, NH*
RFD 5, Gregg Rd, Nashua, NH 03062

Gregg, Judd A *Governor, NH*
%Governor's Office, State House, Concord, NH 03301

Gregg, Stephen R *WW II Army Hero (CMH)*
130 Lexington Ave, Bayonne, NJ 07002

Gregoire, Paul Cardinal *Religious Leader*
%Archbishopric, 2000 Rue Sherbrooke Quest, Montreal PQ H3H 1G4, Canada

Gregorian, Vartan *Educator*
%Brown University, President's Office, Providence, RI 02912

Gregorio, Rose *Actress*
%Paul Kohner Inc, 9169 Sunset Blvd, Los Angeles, CA 90069

Gregory, Bettina *Commentator*
%ABC-TV, News Dept, 1717 DeSales St NW, Washington, DC 20036

Gregory, Cynthia *Ballet Dancer*
%American Ballet Theatre, 890 Broadway, New York, NY 10003

Gregory, Dick *Comedian*
PO Box 3270, Plymouth, MA 02361

Gregory, Frederick D *Astronaut*
%NASA, Johnson Space Ctr, Houston, TX 77058

Gregory, Horace V *Writer, Poet*
Palisades, Rockland County, NY 10964

Gregory, Irving *Businessman*
%Deloitte & Touche, 1633 Broadway, New York, NY 10019

Gregory, James *Actor*
55 Cathedral Rock Dr, #33, Sedona, AZ 86336

Gregory, Marion F *Businessman*
%Snap-on Tools Corp, 2801 80th St, Kenosha, WI 53141

Gregory, Paul *Movie Producer*
PO Box 38, Palm Springs, CA 92262

Gregory, Richard *Religious Leader*
%Independent Fundamental Churches, 2684 Meadow Ridge Dr, Byron Center, MI 49315

Gregory, Robert E, Jr *Businessman*
%VF Corp, 1047 N Park Rd, Wyomissing, PA 19610

Gregory, Vincent L, Jr *Businessman*
%Rohm & Haas Co, Independence Mall W, Philadelphia, PA 19105

Gregory, William G *Astronaut*
%NASA, Johnson Space Center, Houston, TX 77058

Gregory, William H *Editor*
%Aviation Week Magazine, 1221 Ave of Americas, New York, NY 10020

Grehl, Michael *Editor*
%Memphis Commerical Appeal, 495 Union Ave, Memphis, TN 38101

Greindl, Josef *Opera, Concert Singer*
Kuchelstrasse 1-A, 8000 Munich 70, Germany

Greist, Kim *Actress*
%Creative Artists Agency, 9830 Wilshire Blvd, Beverly Hills, CA 90212

Grengel, Fred L *Businessman*
%Johnson Controls Inc, 5757 N Green Bay Ave, Milwaukee, WI 53201

Grentz, Theresa *Basketball Coach*
%Rutgers University, Athletic Dept, PO Box 1149, East Brunswick, NJ 08854

Gretzky, Wayne *Hockey Player*
14135 Beresford Dr, Beverly Hills, CA 90210

Grey, Aida *Fashion Expert*
%Aida Grey Salon, 9459 Wilshire Blvd, Beverly Hills, CA 90212

Grey, Beryl *Ballerina*
Fernhill, Priory Rd, Forest Row, East Sussex RH18 55E, England

Grey, Jennifer *Actress*
%Susan Smith Assoc, 121 N San Vicente Blvd, Beverly Hills, CA 90211

Grey, Joel *Actor*
1 W 67th St, New York, NY 10023

Grey, Linda *Publisher*
%Bantam Books, 666 5th Ave, New York, NY 10103

G

Grey – Griffith

Grey, Virginia *Actress*
15101 Magnolia Blvd, #54, Sherman Oaks, CA 91403

Grich, Bobby *Baseball Player*
206 Prospect Ave, Long Beach, CA 90803

Griem, Helmut *Actor*
Holbeinstrasse 4, 8000 Munich 80, Germany

Grier, J A D *Businessman*
%Cincinnati Milacron Inc, 4701 Marbury Ave, Cincinnati, OH 45209

Grier, Pam *Actress*
%Agency for Performing Arts, 9000 Sunset Blvd, #1200, Los Angeles, CA 90069

Grier, Rosey *Football Player, Actor*
%Rosey Grier's AYC, 1977 S Vermont Ave, #200, Los Angeles, CA 90007

Griese, Bob *Football Player, Sportscaster*
3250 Mary St, Miami, FL 33133

Griesemer, John *Government Official*
%US Postal Service, 475 L'Enfant Plaza West SW, Washington, DC 20260

Grieve, Pierson M *Businessman*
%Economics Laboratory, Osborn Bldg, St Paul, MN 55102

Griffen, Gerald D *Aeronautical Engineer*
%NASA, Johnson Space Ctr, Houston, TX 77058

Griffey, Ken *Baseball Player*
3942 Mack Rd, #9, Fairfield, OH 45014

Griffin, Archie *Football Player*
2389 Brookwood, Columbus, OH 43209

Griffin, Brian C *Businessman*
%Petroleum Investments, 1410-50 Penn Pl, Oklahoma City, OK 73118

Griffin, Charles D *Navy Admiral*
4610 Dexter St NW, Washington, DC 20007

Griffin, Donald R *Biologist*
471 Walnut Ln, Princeton, NJ 08540

Griffin, James Bennett *Anthropologist*
360 Evergreen Pl, Ann Arbor, MI 48104

Griffin, James D *Mayor*
%Mayor's Office, City Hall, 65 Niagara Sq, Buffalo, NY 14202

Griffin, Merv *Entertainer*
1541 N Vine St, Los Angeles, CA 90028

Griffin, Robert P *Senator, MI*
%Miller Canfield Paddock Stone, Grandview Plz, Traverse City, MI 49684

Griffin, Stephen J *Businessman*
%Gillette Co, Prudential Tower Bldg, Boston, MA 02199

Griffin, W L Hadley *Businessman*
%Brown Grp, 8400 Maryland Ave, St Louis, MO 63105

Griffith Joyner, Florence *Track Athlete*
%Gordon Baskin Assoc, 11444 W Olympic Blvd, 10th Fl, Los Angeles, CA 90064

Griffith, Andy *Actor*
%Richard Link Assoc, 4445 Cartwright, #305, North Hollywood, CA 91602

Griffith, Darrell *Basketball Player*
%Utah Jazz, Salt Palace, 100 SW Temple, Salt Lake City, UT 84101

Griffith, Ed *Actor*
9255 Sunset Blvd, #510, Los Angeles, CA 90069

Griffith, Ernest S *Political Scientist*
1941 Parkside Dr NW, Washington, DC 20012

Griffith, Frank W *Businessman*
%Iowa Public Service Co, PO Box 778, Sioux City, IA 51102

Griffith, James *Actor*
PO Box 2151, Avila Beach, CA 93424

Griffith, Melanie *Actress*
%Elliot Mintz, 2934 Beverly Glen Cir, #412, Bel Air, CA 90077

Griffith, Nanci *Singer*
%Vector Mgmt, 1500 17th Ave S, Nashville, TN 37212

Griffith, Ronald H *General, Army*
Inspector General's Office, OSA, Washington, DC 20310

Griffith, Thomas *Editor*
25 East End Ave, New York, NY 10028

Griffith, Tom W *Labor Leader*
%Rural Letter Carriers Assn, 1448 Duke St, #100, Alexandria, VA 22314

Griffiths, Edgar H %RCA Corp, 30 Rockefeller Plz, New York, NY 10020	*Businessman*
Grigorovich, Yuri N %State Academic Bolshoi Theatre, 1 Ploshchad Sverdlova, Moscow, Russia	*Ballet Master*
Grigson, Geoffrey Broad Town Farm, Broad Town Near Swindon, Wilts, England	*Poet*
Grim, Bob 7118 Cody, Overland Park, KS 66203	*Baseball Player*
Grimes, Tammy %Gage Group, 9255 Santa Monica Blvd, #515, Los Angeles, CA 90069	*Actress, Singer*
Grimm, Russ %Washington Redskins, Dulles Airport, Box 17247, Washington, DC 20041	*Football Player*
Grimsley, Ross 39 Judges Ln, Towson, MD 21204	*Baseball Player*
Grimwade, Andrew S %Australian Consolidated Industries, 555 Bourke St, Melbourne, Australia	*Businessman*
Grinham Rawley, Judy 103 Green Ln, Northwood, Middx HA6 1AP, England	*Swimmer*
Grinnell, Alan D %University of California, Physiology Dept, Los Angeles, CA 90024	*Physiologist*
Grinstead, Eugene A %Director's Office, Defense Logistics Agency, Alexandria, VA 22314	*Navy Admiral*
Grinstead, Stanley %Grand Metropolitan, 11-12 Hanover Sq, London W1A 1DP, England	*Businessman*
Grinville, Patrick Academie Goncourt, 38 Rue du Faubourg Saint Jacques, 75014 Paris, France	*Writer*
Grisanti, Eugene P %International Flavors & Fragrances, 521 W 57th St, New York, NY 10019	*Businessman*
Grishin, Evgenii %Committee of Physical Culture, Skatertny p 4, Moscow, Russia	*Speed Skater*
Grishin, Viktor V %Moscow City Committee, 6 Staraya Ploshchad, Moscow, Russia	*Government Official, USSR*
Grist, Reri %Columbia Artists Mgmt, 165 W 57th St, New York, NY 10019	*Opera Singer*
Griswold, Erwin N 3900 Watson Pl NW, Washington, DC 20016	*Attorney*
Grizzard, George 400 E 54th St, New York, NY 10022	*Actor*
Groat, Dick 320 Beech St, Pittsburgh, PA 15218	*Baseball, Basketball Player*
Grodin, Charles 965 5th Ave, New York, NY 10021	*Actor*
Groebli, Werner (Mr Frick) Box 7886, Incline Village, NV 89450	*Ice Skater*
Groener, Harry %Susan Smith Assoc, 121 N San Vicente Blvd, Beverly Hills, CA 90211	*Actor*
Groening, Matt %Acme Features Syndicate, 2219 Main St, #E, Santa Monica, CA 90405	*Cartoonist (Life in Hell, Simpsons)*
Groer, Hans Hermann Cardinal Erzbischofliches, Wollzeile 2, 1010 Vienna, Austria	*Religious Leader*
Grogan, Steve %New England Patriots, Sullivan Stadium, Foxboro, MA 02035	*Football Player*
Grohman, Robert T %Levi Strauss Co, 2 Embarcadero Ctr, San Francisco, CA 94106	*Businessman*
Gron, Andre %Le Journal de Montreal, 155 Quest Port Royal, Montreal PQ H3L 2B1, Canada	*Publisher*
Grondal, Benedikt %Embassy of Iceland, Kommendorsgatan 35, Stockholm 114 58, Sweden	*Prime Minister, Iceland*
Gronouski, John A 1204 Castle Hill, Austin, TX 78703	*Postmaster General*
Groom, Sam %Irv Schechter Co, 9300 Wilshire Blvd, #410, Beverly Hills, CA 90212	*Actor*
Grooms, Red 186 Grand St, New York, NY 10013	*Artist*
Groothaerdt, Jacques %Societe Generale de Banque, 3 Rue Montagne du Paris, Brussels, Belgium	*Financier*

Gropp, Louis Oliver *Editor*
140 Riverside Dr, #6-G, New York, NY 10024

Grosbard, Ulu *Movie Director*
29 W 10th St, New York, NY 10011

Grosfeld, James *Businessman*
%Pulte Home Corp, 6400 Framington Rd, West Bloomfield, MI 48033

Gross, Ludwik *Physician*
%Veterans Administration Hospital, 130 W Kingsbridge Rd, Bronx, NY 10468

Gross, Michael *Swimmer*
Paul-Ehrlich-Strasse 6, 6000 Frankfurt 70, Germany

Gross, Robert A *Physicist*
14 Sunnyside Way, New Rochelle, NY 10804

Gross, Terry *Commentator*
%WHYY-FM, Independence Mall W, Philadelphia, PA 19104

Gross, William N *Businessman*
%Paccar Inc, 777 106th Ave NE, Bellevue, WA 98004

Grossfeld, Stanley *Photographer*
%Boston Globe, 135 Morrissey Blvd, Boston, MA 02107

Grossinger, Paul *Businessman*
%Grossinger Hotel, Grossinger, NY 12734

Grossman, Andrew C *Businessman*
%Gelco Corp, 1 Gelco Dr, Eden Prairie, MN 55344

Grossman, Lawrence K *Television Executive*
%PBS, 475 L'Enfant Plz NW, Washington, DC 20024

Grossman, N Bud *Businessman*
%Gelco Corp, 1 Gelco Dr, Eden Prairie, MN 55344

Grossman, R Earl *Businessman*
%National Cooperative Refinery Assn, 2000 S Main St, McPherson, KS 67460

Grossman, Robert *Illustrator*
19 Crosby St, New York, NY 10013

Grosvenor, Gilbert M *Publisher*
%National Geographic Society, 17th & "M" NW, Washington, DC 20036

Grotowski, Jerzy *Theatre Director*
%Teatr Laboratorium, Rynek Ratusz 27, 50-101 Wroclaw, Poland

Grove, Andrew S *Businessman*
%Intel Corp, 3065 Bowers Ave, Santa Clara, CA 95051

Grove, Ernest L, Jr *Businessman*
%Detroit Edison Co, 2000 2nd Ave, Detroit, MI 48226

Groves, Charles *Conductor*
12 Camden Sq, London NW1 9UY, England

Groves, Raymond J *Businessman*
%Ernst & Young, 2000 National City Ctr, Cleveland, OH 44114

Groves, Wallace *Businessman*
PO Box 5, Freeport, Grand Bahamas, Bahamas

Groza, Alex *Basketball Player*
6418 Camino Corto, San Diego, CA 92120

Groza, Lou *Football Player*
5287 Parkway Dr, Berea, OH 44017

Grubb, Louis Edward *Businessman*
Laurel Ln, Durham, NH 03824

Grubbs, Gary *Actor*
%Fields Talent Agency, 3325 Wilshire Blvd, #749, Los Angeles, CA 90010

Grubman, Allen *Attorney*
%Grubman Indursky Schindler, 575 Madison Ave, New York, NY 10022

Gruenbeck, Max *Businessman*
%Zahnradfabik Friedrichshafen, PO Box 2520, Friedrichshafen, Germany

Grum, Clifford J *Businessman*
%Temple-Inland Inc, 303 S Temple Dr, Diboll, TX 75941

Grumme, Fred J *Businessman*
%Mayflower Corp, 9998 N Michigan Rd, Carmel, IN 46032

Grummer, Elisabeth *Opera Singer*
%Staatliche Hochschule fur Musik & Darnstellende Kunst, Berlin, Germany

Grundfest, Joseph *Government Official*
%Stanford University, Law School, Stanford, CA 94305

Grundhofer, Jerry A *Financier*
%Security Pacific National Bank, 333 S Hope St, Los Angeles, CA 90071

Grune, George V *Publisher*
%Reader's Digest Assn, Pleasantville, NY 10570
Grunewald, Herbert *Businessman*
%Bayer, 5090 Leverkusen, Germany
Grunwald, Ernest *Chemist*
%Brandeis University, Chemistry Dept, Waltham, MA 02154
Grunwald, Henry A *Editor, Diplomat*
50 E 72nd St, New York, NY 10021
Grushin, Pyotr D *Aviation Engineer*
%Academy of Sciences, 14 Lenisky Prospekt, Moscow, Russia
Grusin, Dave *Composer*
%GRP Records, 555 W 57th St, New York, NY 10019
Gruson, Sydney *Publisher*
%New York Times, 229 W 43rd St, New York, NY 10036
Grutman, N Roy *Attorney*
%Grutman Miller Greenspoon Hendler, 505 Park Ave, New York, NY 10022
Grzelecki, Frank E *Businessman*
%Beatrice Companies, 2 N LaSalle St, Chicago, IL 60602
Guarascio, Phil *Businessman*
%General Motors, Advertising Dept, 3044 W Grand Blvd, Detroit, MI 48202
Guardino, Harry *Actor*
%Mimi Weber Mgmt, 9738 Arby Dr, Beverly Hills, CA 90210
Guare, John *Playwright*
%Konecky Burovic, 1 Dag Hammarskjold Plz, New York, NY 10017
Guarini, Frank J *Representative, NJ*
610 Newark Ave, Jersey City, NJ 07306
Guarneri String Quartet *Concert Music Group*
%Harry Beall Mgmt, 119 W 57th St, New York, NY 10019
Guarrera, Frank *Concert, Opera Singer*
4514 Latona Ave NE, Seattle, WA 98105
Gubarev, Alexei *Cosmonaut*
141 160 Svyosdny Gorodok, Moskovskoi Oblasti, Potchta Kosmonavtov, Russia
Guber, Peter *Movie Producer*
%Columbia Pictures, 10202 W Washington Blvd, Culver City, CA 90230
Gubicza, Mark *Baseball Player*
593 Monastery Ave, Philadelphia, PA 19128
Gubser, Charles S *Representative, CA*
395 Tam O'Shanter Way, Monument, CO 80132
Guccione, Bob *Publisher*
%Penthouse Magazine, 1965 Broadway, New York, NY 10023
Guenther, Johnny *Bowler*
%Professional Bowlers Assn, 1720 Merriman Rd, Akron, OH 44313
Guerard, Michel *Chef*
%William Morrow Co, 105 Madison Ave, New York, NY 10016
Guerin, Richie *Basketball Player*
%Bear Stearns Co, 55 Water St, New York, NY 10041
Guerrero, Pedro *Baseball Player*
535 S Plymouth Blvd, Los Angeles, CA 90020
Guerrero, Roberto *Auto Racing Driver*
%Championship Auto Racing Teams, 2655 Woodward Ave, Bloomfield Hills, MI 48013
Guerri, Sergio Cardinal *Religious Leader*
00120 Stato Citta del Vaticano, Rome, Italy
Guest, Douglas *Concert Organist*
Gables, Minchinhampton, Glos GL6 9JE, England
Guffey, J Roger *Financier*
%Kansas City Federal Reserve Bank, 925 Grand Ave, Kansas City, MO 64198
Guglielmi, Ralph *Football Player*
10812 Admiral Way, Potomac, MD 20854
Guidry, Ron *Baseball Player*
109 Conway, Lafayette, LA 70507
Guilbert, Ann *Actress*
550 Erskine Dr, Pacific Palisades, CA 90272
Guilford, Joy Paul *Psychologist*
PO Box 1288, Beverly Hills, CA 90213
Guillaume, Robert *Actor*
%Longridge Entertainment, PO Box 115, Studio City, CA 91614

Guillem, Sylvie *Ballerina*
%Paris Opera Ballet, Pl de l'Opera, 75009 Paris, France

Guillemin, Roger C L *Nobel Medicine Laureate*
%Salk Biological Studies Institute, PO Box 85800, San Diego, CA 92138

Guillerman, John *Movie Director*
309 S Rockingham Ave, Los Angeles, CA 90049

Guinan, Matthew *Labor Leader*
%Transportation Workers Union, 80 West End Ave, New York, NY 10023

Guindon, Richard G *Cartoonist (Guindon)*
321 W Lafayette Blvd, Detroit, MI 48231

Guinee, W Fenton, Jr *Businessman*
%Anderson Clayton & Co, 1100 Louisiana, #3800, Houston, TX 77002

Guinn, Donald E *Businessman*
%Pacific Telesis Grp, 140 New Montgomery St, San Francisco, CA 94105

Guinn, Kenny C *Financier*
%Nevada Savings & Loan Assn, 201 Las Vegas Blvd S, Las Vegas, NV 89125

Guinness, A F B *Businessman*
%Arthur Guinness & Sons, Park Royal Brewery, London NW10 7RR, England

Guinness, Alec *Actor*
Kettlebrook Meadows, Steep Marsh, Petersfield, Hants, England

Guisewite, Cathy *Cartoonist (Cathy)*
%Universal Press Syndicate, 4900 Main St, Kansas City, MO 64112

Gulager, Clu *Actor*
%J Michael Bloom Ltd, 9200 Sunset Blvd, #710, Los Angeles, CA 90069

Gulbinowicx, Henryk Roman *Religious Leader*
%Metropolita Wroclawski, Ul Katedraina 11, 50-328 Wroclaw, Poland

Gullett, Don *Baseball Player*
RR 2, Maloneton, KY 41158

Gullickson, Bill *Baseball Player*
300 Brentvale Ln, Brentwood, TN 37027

Gulliver, Harold *Editor*
%Atlanta Constitution, 72 Marieta St NW, Atlanta, GA 30302

Gumbel, Bryant *Broadcaster*
%NBC-TV, News Dept, 30 Rockefeller Plz, New York, NY 10020

Gumbel, Greg *Sportscaster*
%CBS-TV, Sports Dept, 51 W 52nd St, New York, NY 10019

Gumede, Josiah Z *President, Zimbabwe*
29 Barbour Fields, PO Mzilikazi, Bulawayo, Zimbabwe

Gunderson, Steve C *Representative, WI*
%House of Representatives, Washington, DC 20515

Gundling, Beulah *Synchronized Swimmer*
%Coral Ridge South, 3333 NE 34th St, #1517, Fort Lauderdale, FL 33308

Gunn, Moses *Actor*
395 Nut Plains Rd, Guilford, CT 06437

Gunn, Thom *Poet*
1216 Cole St, San Francisco, CA 94117

Gunness, Robert C *Businessman*
111 E Chestnut St, #41-H, Chicago, IL 60611

Gunsalus, Irwin C *Biochemist, Writer*
1709 Pleasant Cir, Urbana, IL 61801

Gur, Mordechai *Army General, Israel*
25 Mishmeret St, Ajeka, Tel-Aviv, Israel

Gura, Larry *Baseball Player*
PO Box 94, Litchfield Park, AZ 85350

Gurney, A R, Jr *Writer*
120 W 70th St, New York, NY 10023

Gurney, Edward J *Senator, FL*
617 N Interlachen Ave, Winter Park, FL 32789

Gushiken, Koji *Gymnast*
%Nippon Physical Education College, Tokyo, Japan

Gustafson, Tomas *Speed Skater*
%Olympic Committee, Idrottens Hus, 12387 Farsta, Sweden

Gustafsson, Bengt *Hockey Player*
%Washington Capitals, Capital Centre, 1 Truman Dr, Landover, MD 20785

Gustafsson, Sten *Businessman*
%Saab-Scania, S-581 88 Linkoping, Sweden

Guth, Alan H *Physicist*
%Massachusetts Institute of Technology, Physics Dept, Cambridge, MA 02139

Guth, Wilfried *Businessman*
%Daimler-Benz, Mercedesstrasse 136, 7000 Stuttgart 60, Germany

Guthardt, Helmut *Financier*
%Deutsche Genossenschaftsbank, 6000 Frankfurt am Main 1, Germany

Guthart, Leo A *Businessman*
%Pittway Corp, 333 Skokie Blvd, Northbrook, IL 60065

Guthman, Edwin O *Editor*
%Philadelphia Inquirer, 400 N Broad St, Philadelphia, PA 19101

Guthrie, Arlo *Singer*
The Farm, Washington, MA 01223

Guthrie, Randolph H *Businessman*
43 South Beach Lagoon Rd, Sea Pines Plantation, Hilton Head, SC 29928

Gutierrez, Gustavo *Theologian*
%Catholic University, Lima, Peru

Gutierrez, Horacio *Concert Pianist*
%Columbia Artists Mgmt Inc, 165 W 57th St, New York, NY 10019

Gutierrez, Sidney M *Astronaut*
%NASA, Johnson Space Ctr, Houston, TX 77058

Gutowsky, Herbert S *Physical Chemist*
%University of Illinois, Chemical Sciences School, Urbana, IL 61801

Guttenberg, Steve *Actor*
%William Morris Agency, 151 El Camino, Beverly Hills, CA 90212

Guttman, Zoltan (Lou) *Financier*
%New York Mercantile Exchange, 4 World Trade Ctr, New York, NY 10048

Guy, Jasmine *Actress*
%International Creative Mgmt, 8899 Beverly Blvd, Los Angeles, CA 90048

Guy, Ralph B, Jr *Judge*
%US Court of Appeals, PO Box 7910, Ann Arbor, MI 48107

Guy, William L *Governor, ND*
2920 Manitoba Ln, Bismarck, ND 58501

Guyon, John C *Educator*
%Southern Illinois University, President's Office, Carbondale, IL 62901

Guzzetti, Louis A, Jr *Businessman*
%United Brands Co, 1271 Ave of Americas, New York, NY 10020

Gwaltney, Eugene C *Businessman*
%Russell Corp, PO Box 272, Alexander City, AL 35010

Gwathmey, Charles *Architect*
1115 5th Ave, New York, NY 10028

Gwinn, Donald E *Businessman*
%Pacific Telesis Grp, 140 New Montgomery St, San Francisco, CA 94105

Gwinn, Mary Ann *Journalist*
%Seattle Times, Fairview Ave N & John St, Seattle, WA 98111

Gwinn, Robert P *Publisher*
%Encylopaedia Britannica, 310 S Michigan Ave, Chicago, IL 60604

Gwynn, Tony *Baseball Player*
3524 Delta, Long Beach, CA 90810

Gyarmati, Dezso *Water Polo Player, Coach*
Frankel Leo U 21/23, II-8, 1023 Budapest, Hungary

Gyenge Garay, Valerie *Swimmer*
5 Highland Ave, Toronto ON M4W 2A2, Canada

Gyll, Soren *Businessman*
%Stratsforetag Grp, Hamangatan 6, 103 97 Stockholm, Sweden

H

Haack, Robert W *Stock Exchange Executive, Businessman*
%Lockheed Aircraft Corp, 2555 Hollywood Way, Burbank, CA 91503

Haak, Harold H *Educator*
%California State University, President's Office, Fresno, CA 93740

Haas, Andrew T *Labor Leader*
%Auto Aero & Agricultural Union, 1300 Connecticut NW, Washington, DC 20036

Haas, Ernst *Photographer*
853 7th Ave, New York, NY 10019

Haas, James E *Businessman*
%National Intergroup Inc, 20 Stanwix St, Pittsburgh, PA 15222

Haas, Jay *Golfer*
%Professional Golf Assn, PO Box 109601, Palm Beach Gardens, FL 33410

Haas, Lukas *Actor*
%Harry Gold Assoc, 3500 W Olive Ave, #1400, Burbank, CA 91505

Haas, Paul R *Businessman*
%Corpus Christi Oil & Gas Co, PO Box 779, Corpus Christi, TX 78403

Haas, Peter E *Businessman*
%Levi Strauss Co, PO Box 7215, San Francisco, CA 94120

Haas, Robert D *Businessman*
%Levi Strauss Co, PO Box 7215, San Francisco, CA 94120

Haas, Walter A, Jr *Businessman*
%Levi Strauss Co, PO Box 7215, San Francisco, CA 94120

Haavelmo, Trygve *Nobel Economics Laureate*
%University of Oslo, Economics Dept, Oslo, Norway

Habash, George *Palestinian Nationalist Leader*
Palais Essaada La Marsa, Tunis, Tunisia

Habel, Karl *Medical Researcher*
%Reading Institute of Rehabilitation, Rt 1, Box 252, Reading, PA 19607

Haber, Bill *Entertainment Executive*
%Creative Artists Agency, 9830 Wilshire Blvd, Beverly Hills, CA 90212

Haber, Joyce *Columnist*
1005 N Rexford Dr, Beverly Hills, CA 90210

Haberberger, Art *Businessman*
%American Equipment Leasing, 1 American Pl, Baton Rouge, LA 70821

Haberler, Gottfried *Economist*
4108 48th St NW, Washington, DC 20016

Habib, Munir *Cosmonaut, Syria*
141 160 Svyosdny Gorodok, Moskovskoi Oblasti, Potchta Kosmonavtov, Russsia

Habib, Philip C *Diplomat*
1606 Courtland Rd, Belmont, CA 94002

Habig, Douglas A *Businessman*
%Kimball International, 1600 Royal St, Jasper, IN 47546

Habig, Thomas L *Businessman*
%Kimball International, 1600 Royal St, Japser, IN 47546

Habyarimana, Juvenal *President, Rwanda*
%President's Office, Kigali, Rwanda

Hack, Shelley *Model, Actress*
209 12th St, Santa Monica, CA 90402

Hackett, Buddy *Comedian*
800 N Whittier Dr, Beverly Hills, CA 90210

Hackett, Richard C *Mayor*
%Mayor's Office, 125 N Main St, Memphis, TN 38103

Hackford, Taylor *Movie Director*
2003 La Brea Terr, Los Angeles, CA 90046

Hackman, Gene *Actor*
%Creative Artists Agency, 9830 Wilshire Blvd, Beverly Hills, CA 90212

Hackney, F Sheldon *Educator*
%University of Pennsylvania, President's Office, Philadelphia, PA 19104

Haddix, Harvey *Baseball Player*
2105 Cheviot Hills Dr, Springfield, OH 45505

Haddon, Larry *Actor*
%Atkins Assoc, 303 S Crescent Heights Blvd, Los Angeles, CA 90048

Haden, Pat *Football Player, Sportscaster*
%Riodan & McKinzie, 300 S Grand Ave, Los Angeles, CA 90071

Hadley, Jerry *Opera Singer*
%Edward Lew, 204 W 10th St, New York, NY 10014

H

Haegg, Gunder *Track Athlete*
%Swedish Olympic Committee, Idrottens Hus, 12387 Farsta, Sweden
Haehl, John G, Jr *Businessman*
%Niagara Mohawk Power Corp, 300 Erie Blvd W, Syracuse, NY 13202
Haendel, Ida *Concert Violinist*
%Harold Holt Ltd, 31 Sinclair Rd, London W14 0N8, England
Haensel, Vladimir *Catalytic Chemist*
924 Oakwood Terr, Hinsdale, IL 60521
Haeusgen, Helmut *Financier*
%Dresdner Bank, Jurgen-Ponto-Platz 1, Frankfurt am Main 1, Germany
Haffner, Charles C, III *Businessman*
%R R Donnelley & Sons, 2223 Martin Luther King Dr, Chicago, IL 60616
Hafstein, Johann *Prime Minister, Iceland*
Sjalfstaedisflokkurinn, Laufasvegi 46, Reykjavik, Iceland
Hagan, Cliff *Basketball Player*
125 Chinoe Rd, Lexington, KY 40502
Hagan, Darian *Football Player*
%University of Colorado, Athletic Dept, Campus Box 357, Boulder, CO 80309
Hagan, Molly *Actress*
%Ellis Artists Agency, 119 N San Vicente Blvd, #202, Beverly Hills, CA 90211
Hagan, Ward S *Businessman*
%Warner-Lambert Co, 201 Tabor Rd, Morris Plains, NJ 07950
Hagar, Sammy *Singer*
%Steady State Inc, PO Box 687, Mill Valley, CA 94942
Hagegard, Hakan *Opera Singer*
Gunnarsbyn, 670 30 Edane, Sweden
Hagemeister, Charles C *Vietnam War Army Hero (CMH)*
811 N 16th Terrace Ct, Leavenworth, KS 66048
Hagen, Kevin *Actor*
%Alex Brewis Agency, 12429 Laurel Terrace Dr, Studio City, CA 91604
Hagen, Uta *Actress*
%Kroll, 390 West End Ave, New York, NY 10024
Hager, Robert *Commentator*
%NBC-TV, News Dept, 4001 Nebraska Ave NW, Washington, DC 20016
Hagerty, Julie *Actress*
%International Creative Mgmt, 40 W 57th St, New York, NY 10019
Haggard, Merle *Singer, Songwriter*
%HAG Inc, Box 536, Palo Cedro, CA 96073
Hagge, Marlene *Golfer*
%Ladies Professional Golf Assn, 2570 Volusia Ave, #B, Daytona Beach, FL 32114
Haggerty, Dan *Actor*
%Eileen Procter, 7060 Hollywood Blvd, #1201, Los Angeles, CA 90028
Haggerty, Tim *Cartoonist (Ground Zero)*
%United Feature Syndicate, 200 Park Ave, New York, NY 10166
Hagler, Marvin *Boxer*
%Marvelous Enterprises, 1360 Washington St, Hanover, MA 02339
Hagman, Larry *Actor*
23730 Malibu Colony Rd, Malibu, CA 90265
Hagstrom, W R *Financier*
%Sooner Federal Savings & Loan, 5100 E Skelly Dr, Tulsa, OK 74135
Hagura, Nobuya *Financier*
%Daialchi Kangyo Bank, 1-5 Uchisaiwaicho, Chiyodaku, Tokyo 100, Japan
Hahn, Carl H *Businessman*
%Volkswagenwerk AG, 3180 Wolfsburg 1, Germany
Hahn, Erwin L *Physicist*
69 Stevenson Ave, Berkeley, CA 94720
Hahn, K Robert *Businessman*
%Lear Siegler Inc, 2850 Ocean Park Blvd, Santa Monica, CA 90405
Hahn, T Marshall, Jr *Businessman*
%Georgia-Pacific Corp, 133 Peachtree St NE, Atlanta, GA 30303
Haid, Charles *Actor*
4376 Forman Ave, North Hollywood, CA 91602
Haig, Alexander M, Jr *Secretary, State; Army General*
%United Technologies Bldg, Hartford, CT 06101
Haignere, Jean-Pierre *Astronaut, France*
%Personnel Navigant, Bretigny Aerodrome, 91220 Bretigny Sur Orge, France

Hailey - Hall

Hailey, Arthur *Writer*
Lyford Cay, PO Box N-7776, Nassau, Bahamas

Hailsham of St Marylebone (Q M Hogg) *Government Official, England*
Corner House, Heathview Gdns, London SW15, England

Haim, Corey *Actor*
%Light Co, 901 Bringham Ave, Los Angeles, CA 90049

Haimovitz, Matt *Concert Cellist*
%International Creative Mgmt, 40 W 57th St, New York, NY 10019

Haines, Connie *Singer*
PO Box 1, Toluca Lake, CA 91602

Haines, George *Swimming Coach*
1218 Cordelia Ave, San Jose, CA 95129

Haines, Larry *Actor*
Hidden Meadow Rd, Weston, CT 06883

Hair, Jay *Environmentalist*
%National Wildlife Federation, 1412 16th St NW, Washington, DC 20036

Hairston, Carl *Football Player*
%Cleveland Browns, Cleveland Stadium, Cleveland, OH 44114

Hairston, Jester J *Composer*
5047 Valley Ridge Ave, Los Angeles, CA 90043

Haise, Fred W, Jr *Astronaut*
%Grumman Space Station, Program Support Div, PO Box 4650, Reston, VA 22090

Hajt, Bill *Hockey Player*
%Buffalo Sabres, Memorial Auditorium, Buffalo, NY 14202

Hakamada, Kunio *Businessman*
%Daido Steel Co, 11-18 Nishiki, Nakaku, Nagoya 460, Japan

Hakansson, Nils *Economist*
252 Clyde Dr, Walnut Creek, CA 94548

Hakashima, Tamotsu *Businessman*
%Nihon Cement Co, 1-6-1 Otemachi, Chiyodaku, Tokyo 100, Japan

Hakulinen, Veikko *Nordic Skier*
%General Delivery, Valkeakoski, Finland

Halaby, Najeeb E *Businessman*
239 Glenville Rd, Greenwich, CT 06830

Halas, John *Animator*
%Educational Film Center, 5-7 Kean St, London WC2B 4AT, England

Halberstam, David *Writer*
%Alfred A Knopf, 201 E 50th St, New York, NY 10022

Hale, Barbara *Actress*
22807 Lenora Dr, Woodland Hills, CA 91364

Hale, Clara McBride *Social Activist*
%Hale House, 154 W 122nd St, New York, NY 10027

Hale, David *Businessman*
%Hybritech Inc, 11095 Torneyana Rd, San Diego, CA 92121

Hale, Georgia *Actress*
74-A St John's Wood, High St, London NW8, England

Hale, James H *Publisher*
%Kansas City Star-Tribune, 1729 Grand Ave, Kansas City, MO 64108

Hale, John H *Businessman*
%Alcan Aluminum, 1 Pl Ville Marie, Montreal PQ H3C 3H2, Canada

Haley, Charles *Football Player*
%San Francisco 49ers, 4949 Centennial Blvd, Santa Clara, CA 95054

Haley, Jack, Jr *Movie Director, Producer*
1443 Devlin Dr, Los Angeles, CA 90069

Half, Robert *Businessman*
%Robert Half International, 522 5th Ave, New York, NY 10036

Halford, Rob *Singer (Judas Priest)*
%Judas Priest, Columbia Records, 1801 Century Park West, Los Angeles, CA 90067

Hall Adams, Evelyne *Track Athlete*
2000-69 N El Camino Real, Oceanside, CA 92054

Hall Greff, Kaye *Swimmer*
PO Box 538, Mukilteo, WA 98275

Hall, Arnold A *Businessman*
%Hawker Siddeley Grp, 18 St James's Sq, London SW1Y 4LJ, England

Hall, Arsenio *Entertainer*
%Paramount Pictures, 5555 Melrose Ave, Los Angeles, CA 90038

Hall, Charles *Inventor (Waterbed)*
%Basic Designs, 5815 Bennett Valley Rd, Santa Rosa, CA 95404
Hall, Conrad *Cinematographer*
%G G Gundry Agency, 3900 Cross Creek Rd, #6, Malibu, CA 90265
Hall, Cynthia Holcomb *Judge*
%US Court of Appeals, 125 S Grand, Pasadena, CA 91109
Hall, Daryl *Singer (Hall & Oates)*
%Champion Enterprises, 130 W 57th St, New York, NY 10019
Hall, David *Editor*
%Los Angeles Times, Times Mirror Sq, Los Angeles, CA 90053
Hall, Deidre *Actress*
%Agency for Performing Arts, 9000 Sunset Blvd, #1200, Los Angeles, CA 90069
Hall, Delores *Singer, Actress*
%Agency for Performing Arts, 888 7th Ave, New York, NY 10106
Hall, Donald *Writer*
Eagle Pond Farm, Danbury, NH 03230
Hall, Donald J *Businessman*
%Hallmark Cards, 2501 McGee Trafficway, Kansas City, MO 64141
Hall, Donald P *Navy Admiral*
%Navy Department, Pentagon, Washington, DC 20350
Hall, Doug *Cartoonist (Simple Beasts)*
%Tribune Media Services, 34 E Concord St, Orlando, FL 32801
Hall, Edward T *Antropologist, Writer*
2700 "Q" St NW, Washington, DC 20007
Hall, Edwin L *Educator*
%Hardin-Simmons University, President's Office, Abilene, TX 79698
Hall, Erv *Track Athlete*
%Citicorp Mortgage, 670 Mason Ridge Ctr Dr, St Louis, MO 63141
Hall, Floyd *Businessman*
%Grand Union Co, 100 Broadway, Elmwood Park, NJ 07407
Hall, Galen *Football Coach*
%University of Florida, Athletic Dept, Gainesville, FL 32611
Hall, Gary *Swimmer*
3123 E Vermont Ave, Phoenix, AZ 85016
Hall, Gary C *Test Pilot, Engineer*
PO Box 715, Rosamond, CA 93560
Hall, George E *Businessman*
%SCM Corp, 299 Park Ave, New York, NY 10171
Hall, Glenn *Hockey Player*
Stony Plain, Alberta, Canada
Hall, Gus *Political Party Official*
%Communist Party of America, 235 W 23rd St, 7th Floor, New York, NY 10011
Hall, Harold H *Businessman*
%Norfolk Southern Corp, 1 Commerce Pl, Norfolk, VA 23510
Hall, James E *Auto Race Car Builder, Driver*
Rt 7, Box 640, Midland, TX 79701
Hall, Jerry *Model*
81 Wimple St, London W1, England
Hall, Joe B *Basketball Coach*
%Central Bank & Trust Co, 300 W Vine St, Lexington, KY 40508
Hall, John G *Businessman*
200 Park Ave, New York, NY 10017
Hall, John R *Businessman*
%Ashland Oil Inc, Ashland Dr, Russell, NY 41169
Hall, Karen *Screenwriter*
%Broder, 9046 Sunset Blvd, Los Angeles, CA 90046
Hall, Kenneth K *Judge*
%US Court of Appeals, PO Box 75058, Charleston, WV 25375
Hall, Kevan *Fashion Designer*
%Kevan Hall Studio, 756 S Spring St, #11-E, Los Angeles, CA 90014
Hall, Lani *Singer*
31930 Pacific Coast Hwy, Malibu, CA 90265
Hall, Lars *Pentathlon Athlete*
%General Delivery, 18350 Taby, Stockholm, Sweden
Hall, Llody M, Jr *Religious Leader*
%Congregation Christian Churches National Assn, Box 1620, Oak Creek, MI 53154

Hall, Monty *Entertainer*
519 N Arden Dr, Beverly Hills, CA 90210

Hall, Parker *Football Player*
4712 Cole Rd, Memphis, TN 38117

Hall, Peter *Theater, Opera, Movie Director*
%Peter Hall Co, 18 Exeter St, London WC2E 7DU, England

Hall, Ralph M *Representative, TX*
%House of Representatives, Washington, DC 20515

Hall, Sam B, Jr *Representative, TX*
PO Box 1349, Marshall, TX 75670

Hall, Tom T *Singer*
PO Box 1246, Franklin, TN 37064

Hall, Tony P *Representative, OH*
%House of Representatives, Washington, DC 20515

Hall, William E *WW II Navy Hero (CMH)*
212 Kingsbury Dr, Muskogee, OK 74401

Hallahan, Charles *Actor*
%Triad Artists, 10100 Santa Monica Blvd, #1600, Los Angeles, CA 90067

Halle, Claus M *Businessman*
%Coca-Cola Co, 310 North Ave NW, Atlanta, GA 30313

Halligan, James E *Educator*
%New Mexico State University, President's Office, Las Cruces, NM 88003

Halligan, Thomas W *Businessman*
%Guy F Atkinson Co, 10 W Orange Ave, South San Francisco, CA 94080

Hallis, David M *Businessman*
%Maxicare Health Plans, 5525 W Slauson, Los Angeles, CA 90056

Hallstein, D Wayne *Businessman*
%Ingersoll-Rand Co, 200 Chestnut Ridge Rd, Woodcliff Lake, NJ 07675

Hallstrom, Lasse *Movie Director*
%Weintraub Entertainment, 11111 Santa Monica Blvd, 2001, Los Angeles, CA 90025

Halperin, Robert M *Businessman*
%Raychem Corp, 300 Constitution Dr, Menlo Park, CA 94025

Halprin, Lawrence *Landscape Architect, Planner*
1620 Montgomery St, San Francisco, CA 94111

Halsell, James D, Jr *Astronaut*
%NASA, Johnson Space Center, Houston, TX 77058

Halsey, Brenton S *Businessman*
%James River Corp of Virginia, Tredegar St, Richmond, VA 23217

Halstead, Lindsay *Businessman*
%Ford Brasil, Ave Dr Rudge Ramos 1501, 09 720 Rudge Ramos SP, Brazil

Halvorsen, Andrew C *Financier*
%Beneficial Corp, 1100 Carr Rd, Wilmington, DE 19899

Ham, Jack *Football Player*
409 Broad St, Sewickley, PA 15143

Ham, James M *Educator*
%University of Toronto, President's Office, Toronto ON M4W 2A4, Canada

Hamada, Hiroshi *Businessman*
%Ricoh Co, 1-5-5 Minami-Aoyama, Minatoku, Tokyo 107, Japan

Hamann, H J *Businessman*
%Schering, Mullerstrasse 170-178, 1000 Berlin 65, Germany

Hamari, Julia *Opera Singer*
%Metropolitan Opera Assn, Lincoln Ctr, New York, NY 10023

Hamblen, Lapsley W, Jr *Judge*
%US Tax Court, 400 2nd St NW, Washington, DC 20217

Hambrecht, William R *Businessman*
%Hambrecht & Quist Inc, 235 Montgomery St, San Francisco, CA 94104

Hambro, Leonid *Concert Pianist*
%California Institute of Arts, Music Dept, Valencia, CA 91355

Hameed, Abdul Majid *Financier*
%Rafidain Bank, New Banks St, Massarif, Baghdad, Iraq

Hamel, Veronica *Actress*
%Agency for Performing Arts, 9000 Sunset Blvd, #1200, Los Angeles, CA 90069

Hamerow, Theodore S *Educator*
%University of Wisconsin, German & European History Dept, Madison, WI 53706

Hamill, Dorothy *Figure Skater*
2331 Century Hill, Los Angeles, CA 90067

Hamill, Mark *Actor*
PO Box 55, Malibu, CA 90265

Hamill, Pete *Columnist*
%Esquire Magazine, 1790 Broadway, New York, NY 10019

Hamilton, Carrie *Actress*
2114 Ridgemont Dr, Los Angeles, CA 90046

Hamilton, Chico *Drummer*
%American Broadcasting Co, 1995 Broadway, New York, NY 10019

Hamilton, David *Photographer*
41 Blvd du Montparnasse, 75006 Paris, France

Hamilton, George *Actor*
4616 Willis Ave, #212, Sherman Oaks, CA 91403

Hamilton, Guy *Movie Director*
%London Management Ltd, 235-241 Regent St, London W1A 2JT, England

Hamilton, Lee H *Representative, IN*
%House of Representatives, Washington, DC 20515

Hamilton, Linda *Actress*
721 Via de la Paz, Pacific Palisades, CA 90272

Hamilton, R W *Businessman*
%Moore Corp, 1 First Canadian Pl, Toronto ON M5X 1G5, Canada

Hamilton, Robert A (Bones) *Football Player*
9255 Doheny Rd, Los Angeles, CA 90069

Hamilton, Scott *Figure Skater*
%International Management Grp, 1 Erieview Plz, Cleveland, OH 44114

Hamilton, Tom *Football Player*
7580 Caminito Avola, La Jolla, CA 92037

Hamilton, William *Cartoonist, Writer*
358 S Reeves Dr, Beverly Hills, CA 90212

Hamlin, Harry *Actor*
%Dolores Robinson Mgmt, 335 N Maple Dr, #250, Beverly Hills, CA 90210

Hamlisch, Marvin *Composer*
970 Park Ave, #501, New York, NY 10028

Hammack, Felix M *Businessman*
%Willamette Industries, 3800 First Interstate Tower, Portland, OR 97201

Hammer *Singer*
%Capitol Records, 1750 N Vine St, Los Angeles, CA 90028

Hammer, Frederick S *Financier*
%Meritor Financial Grp, 1212 Market St, Philadelphia, PA 19107

Hammer, Susan *Mayor*
%Mayor'Office, City Hall, 801 N 1st St, San Jose, CA 95110

Hammerschmidt, John P *Representative, AR*
PO Box 999, Harrison, AR 72601

Hammerstein, Mike *Football Player*
%Cincinnati Bengals, 200 Riverfront Stadium, Cincinnati, OH 45202

Hammett, Louis P *Chemist*
288 Medford Leas, Medford, NJ 08055

Hammond Innes, Ralph *Writer*
Ayres End, Kersey by Ipswich, Suffolk 1P7 6EB, England

Hammond, Caleb D *Publisher, Cartographer*
61 Woodland Rd, Maplewood, NJ 07040

Hammond, Caleb, III *Businessman*
%Hammond Inc, 515 Valley St, Maplewood, NJ 07040

Hammond, George S *Chemist*
43 Noe Ave, Madison, NJ 07940

Hammond, J T *Religious Leader*
%Pentecostal Free Will Baptist Church, Box 1568, Dunn, NC 28334

Hammond, Jay S *Governor, AK*
Lake Charles Lodge, Port Alsworth, AK 99652

Hammond, Joan *Opera Singer*
46 Lansell Rd, Toorak Vic 3142, Australia

Hammond, L Blaine, Jr *Astronaut*
%NASA, Johnson Space Ctr, Houston, TX 77058

Hammond, Robert D *Army General*
CG, USA Strategic Defense Command, PO Box 15280, Arlington, VA 22215

Hammond, Trevor A *Air Force General*
DCS/Logistics Command, Hq USAF, Washington, DC 20330

H

Hammons, Roger *Religious Leader*
%Primitive Advent Christian Church, 395 Frame Rd, Elkview, WV 25071

Hamnett, Katharine *Fashion Designer*
83 Shepperton Rd, London N1, England

Hampers, C L *Businessman*
%National Medical Care Inc, Hancock Tower, Boston, MA 02116

Hampshire, Susan *Actress*
Billing Rd, London SW1, England

Hampton, Colin C *Businessman*
%Union Mutual Life Insurance, 2211 Congress St, Portland, ME 04122

Hampton, Dan *Football Player*
%Chicago Bears, 250 N Washington, Lake Forest, IL 60045

Hampton, James *Actor*
%Artists Group, 1930 Century Park West, Los Angeles, CA 90067

Hampton, Lionel *Jazz Vibraharpist, Conductor*
20 W 64th St, #28-K, New York, NY 10023

Hampton, Philip M *Financier*
%Bankers Trust New York Corp, 16 Wall St, New York, NY 10005

Hampton, Ralph *Religious Leader*
%Free Will Baptists, PO Box 1088, Nashville, TN 37202

Han Suyin *Writer*
37 Montoie, Lausanne, Switzerland

Han, Maggie *Actress*
%J Michael Bloom Ltd, 9200 Sunset Blvd, #710, Los Angeles, CA 90069

Hanafusa, Hidesaburo *Microbiologist*
%Rockefeller University, 1230 York Ave, New York, NY 10021

Hanauer, Chip *Speed Boat Racer*
%Hanauer Enterprises, 2702 NE 88th St, Seattle, WA 98115

Hanburger, Chris *Football Player*
2540 Riva Rd, Annapolis, MD 21401

Hanbury-Tenison, Robin *Explorer*
%Maidenwell, Cardinham, Bodmin, Cornwall PL3O 4DW, England

Hancock, Herbie *Jazz Pianist, Composer*
1250 N Doheny Dr, Los Angeles, CA 90069

Hancock, John *Actor*
%Dave Schultz, 11846 Ventura Blvd, #100, Studio City, C A 91601

Hancock, Walker *Artist*
Lanesville, PO Box 133, Gloucester, MA 01930

Hand, Jon *Football Player*
%Indianapolis Colts, 7001 W 56th St, Indianapolis, IN 46254

Handelman, Rubin *Labor Leader*
%National Postal Supervisors Assn, 490 L'Enfant Plz SW, Washington, DC 20024

Handelsman, Walt *Editorial Cartoonist*
%New Orleans Times-Picayune, 3800 Howard Ave, New Orleans, LA 70140

Handleman, David *Businessman*
%Handleman Co, 500 Kirts Blvd, Troy, MI 48084

Handler, Mark S *Businessman*
%R H Macy Co, 151 W 34th St, New York, NY 10001

Handler, Ruth *Businesswoman*
%Nearly Me, 2245 Pontius Ave, Los Angeles, CA 90064

Handley, Ray *Football Coach*
%New York Giants, Giants Stadium, East Rutherford, NJ 07073

Handlin, Oscar *Historian, Educator*
18 Agassiz St, Cambridge, MA 02140

Hands, Bill *Baseball Player*
Willow Terr, Orient, NY 11957

Haney, Lee *Body Builder*
%Lee Haney Enterprises, PO Box 491269, Atlanta, GA 30349

Hanfmann, George M A *Archaeologist*
%Fogg Art Museum, Cambridge, MA 02138

Hanifan, Jim *Football Coach*
%Washington Redskins, PO Box 17247, Dulles Airport, Washington, DC 20041

Hanigan, John L *Businessman*
%Genesco Inc, Genesco Park, Nashville, TN 37202

Hanks, Sam *Auto Racing Driver*
17766 Tramonto Dr, Pacific Palisades, CA 90272

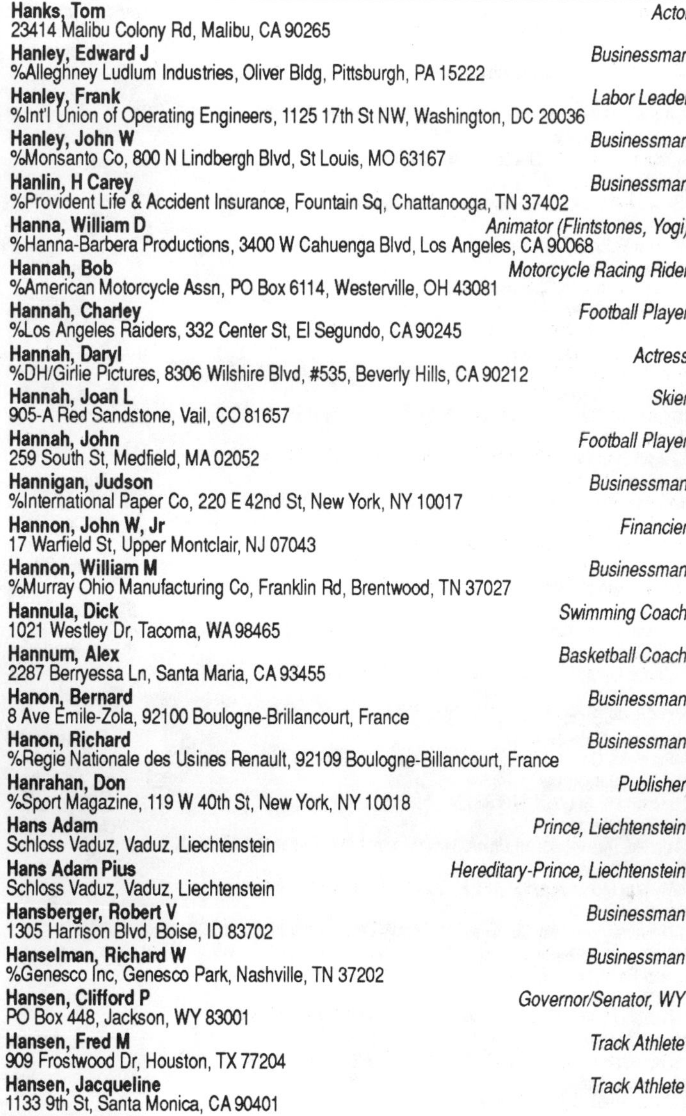

Hanks, Tom *Actor*
23414 Malibu Colony Rd, Malibu, CA 90265
Hanley, Edward J *Businessman*
%Alleghney Ludlum Industries, Oliver Bldg, Pittsburgh, PA 15222
Hanley, Frank *Labor Leader*
%Int'l Union of Operating Engineers, 1125 17th St NW, Washington, DC 20036
Hanley, John W *Businessman*
%Monsanto Co, 800 N Lindbergh Blvd, St Louis, MO 63167
Hanlin, H Carey *Businessman*
%Provident Life & Accident Insurance, Fountain Sq, Chattanooga, TN 37402
Hanna, William D *Animator (Flintstones, Yogi)*
%Hanna-Barbera Productions, 3400 W Cahuenga Blvd, Los Angeles, CA 90068
Hannah, Bob *Motorcycle Racing Rider*
%American Motorcycle Assn, PO Box 6114, Westerville, OH 43081
Hannah, Charley *Football Player*
%Los Angeles Raiders, 332 Center St, El Segundo, CA 90245
Hannah, Daryl *Actress*
%DH/Girlie Pictures, 8306 Wilshire Blvd, #535, Beverly Hills, CA 90212
Hannah, Joan L *Skier*
905-A Red Sandstone, Vail, CO 81657
Hannah, John *Football Player*
259 South St, Medfield, MA 02052
Hannigan, Judson *Businessman*
%International Paper Co, 220 E 42nd St, New York, NY 10017
Hannon, John W, Jr *Financier*
17 Warfield St, Upper Montclair, NJ 07043
Hannon, William M *Businessman*
%Murray Ohio Manufacturing Co, Franklin Rd, Brentwood, TN 37027
Hannula, Dick *Swimming Coach*
1021 Westley Dr, Tacoma, WA 98465
Hannum, Alex *Basketball Coach*
2287 Berryessa Ln, Santa Maria, CA 93455
Hanon, Bernard *Businessman*
8 Ave Emile-Zola, 92100 Boulogne-Brillancourt, France
Hanon, Richard *Businessman*
%Regie Nationale des Usines Renault, 92109 Boulogne-Billancourt, France
Hanrahan, Don *Publisher*
%Sport Magazine, 119 W 40th St, New York, NY 10018
Hans Adam *Prince, Liechtenstein*
Schloss Vaduz, Vaduz, Liechtenstein
Hans Adam Pius *Hereditary-Prince, Liechtenstein*
Schloss Vaduz, Vaduz, Liechtenstein
Hansberger, Robert V *Businessman*
1305 Harrison Blvd, Boise, ID 83702
Hanselman, Richard W *Businessman*
%Genesco Inc, Genesco Park, Nashville, TN 37202
Hansen, Clifford P *Governor/Senator, WY*
PO Box 448, Jackson, WY 83001
Hansen, Fred M *Track Athlete*
909 Frostwood Dr, Houston, TX 77204
Hansen, Jacqueline *Track Athlete*
1133 9th St, Santa Monica, CA 90401
Hansen, James V *Representative, UT*
%House of Representatives, Washington, DC 20515
Hansen, Kenneth N *Businessman*
%ServiceMaster Industries, 2300 Warrenville Rd, Downers Grove, IL 60515
Hansen, Patti *Model*
Redlands, W Wittering, Chichester, Sussex, England
Hansen, Peter *Actor*
%Atkins Assoc, 303 S Crescent Heights Blvd, Los Angeles, CA 90048
Hansen, Robert B *Businessman*
%Zenith Electronics Corp, 1000 Milwaukee Ave, Glenview, IL 60025
Hanson, Allen D *Businessman*
%Harvest States Cooperatives, 1667 Snelling Ave N, St Paul, MN 55164
Hanson, Duane *Sculptor*
6109 SW 55th Ct, Davie, FL 33314

Hanson, Howard *Composer, Conductor*
362 Oakdale Dr, Rochester, NY 14618

Hanson, James *Businessman*
%Hanson Trust, 180 Brompton Rd, London SW3 1HF, England

Hanson, Joseph J *Publisher*
%Hanson Publishing Grp, 6 River Bend, Stamford, CT 06907

Hanson, Robert A *Businessman*
%Deere & Co, John Deere Rd, Moline, IL 61265

Harada, Ernest *Actor*
13952 Moorpark St, #1, Sherman Oaks, CA 91423

Harald V *King, Norway*
%Royal Palace, Oslo, Norway

Harbaugh, Gregory J *Astronaut*
%NASA, Johnson Space Ctr, Houston, TX 77058

Harbaugh, Robert E *Neurosurgeon*
%Dartmouth-Hitchcock Medical Ctr, Hanover, NH 03756

Harbert, John Murdoch, III *Businessman*
%Harbart Corp, 1 Riverchase Pkwy S, Birmingham, AL 35244

Harbert, M R (Chick) *Golfer*
16 Caloosa Rd, Key Largo, FL 33037

Harbin, John Pickens *Businessman*
%Halliburton Co, 2600 Southland Ctr, Dallas, TX 75201

Harbison, Earle H, Jr *Businessman*
%Monsanto Co, 800 N Lindbergh Blvd, St Louis, MO 63167

Harbison, John H *Composer*
563 Franklin St, Cambridge, MA 02139

Hard, Darlene *Tennis Player*
22924 Erwin St, Woodland Hills, CA 91367

Hardaway, Tim *Basketball Player*
%Golden State Warriors, Oakland Colisem Arena, Oakland, CA 94621

Harder, Henry U *Businessman*
%Chubb Corp, 15 Mountain View Rd, Warren, NJ 07061

Harder, Mel *Baseball Player*
130 Center St, #6-A, Chardon, OH 44024

Hardesty, C Howard, Jr *Businessman*
%Purolator Courier Corp, 131 Morristown Rd, Basking Ridge, NJ 07920

Hardin, Clifford M *Secretary, Agriculture*
10 Roan Ln, St Louis, MO 63124

Hardin, Fred A *Labor Leader*
%United Transportation Union, 14600 Detroit Ave, Cleveland, OH 44107

Hardin, Melora *Actress*
%William Morris Agency, 151 El Camino, Beverly Hills, CA 90212

Hardin, Paul, III *Educator*
%University of North Carolina, President's Office, Chapel Hill, NC 27599

Harding of Petherton, John *Army Field Marshal*
Lower Farm, Nether Compton Near Sherborne, Dorset, England

Harding, John H *Businessman*
%National Life Insurance, National Life Dr, Montpelier, VT 05604

Hardt, Eloise *Actress*
%Dale Garrick Agency, 8831 Sunset Blvd, #402, Los Angeles, CA 90069

Hardwick, Billy *Bowler*
1576 S White Station, Memphis, TN 38117

Hardy, George *Labor Leader*
%Service Employees Union #399, 1247 W 7th St, Los Angeles, CA 90017

Hardy, Hugh *Architect*
%Hardy Holzman Pfeiffer, 902 Broadway, New York, NY 10010

Hardy, Norman E (Pete) *Businessman, Baseball Executive*
%John Labatt Ltd, 451 Ridout St N, London ON N6A 2PG, Canada

Hare, David *Playwright*
95 Linden Gdns, London WC2, England

Harewood, Dorian *Actor*
1203 Greenacre Ave, Los Angeles, CA 90046

Hargis, Billy James *Clergyman*
Rose of Sharon Farm, Neosho, MO 64850

Hargrove, Linda *Songwriter*
PO Box 120755, Nashville, TN 37212

Haring, Robert %Tulsa World, 315 S Boulder Ave, Tulsa, OK 74102	*Editor*	**H**
Harker, David 56 Lexington Ave, Buffalo, NY 14222	*Biophysicist*	
Harkin, Thomas R %US Senate, Washington, DC 20510	*Senator, IA*	
Harkins, Kenneth R %US Claims Court, 717 Madison Pl NW, Washington, DC 20005	*Judge*	
Harkness, Rebekah 4 E 75th St, New York, NY 10021	*Philanthropist, Ballet Director*	
Harlan, Neil E %McKesson Corp, 1 Post St, San Francisco, CA 94104	*Businessman*	
Harleston, Bernard W %City College of New York, President's Office, New York, NY 10031	*Educator*	
Harlin, Renny %Carolco Pictures, 8800 Sunset Blvd, Los Angeles, CA 90069	*Movie Director*	
Harlow, Harry F 672 Roller Coaster Rd, Tucson, AZ 85704	*Psychologist*	
Harmon, Mark %Wings Inc, 2236 Encinitas Blvd, #A, Encinitas, CA 92024	*Actor*	
Harmon, Merle 424 Lamar Blvd E, #210, Arlington, TX 76011	*Sportscaster*	
Harmon, Millard %General Delivery, Delmar, NY 12054	*Aviator*	
Harness, Edward G %Procter & Gamble Co, 301 E 6th St, Cincinnati, OH 45202	*Businessman*	
Harney, Paul 72 Club Valley Dr, East Falmouth, MA 02536	*Golfer*	
Harnick, Sheldon M %David J Cogan, 350 5th Ave, New York, NY 10001	*Lyricist*	
Harnoncourt, Nikolaus 38 Piaristangasse, 1080 Vienna, Austria	*Conductor*	
Harout, Magda %Erika Wain Agency, 1418 N Highland Ave, #102, Los Angeles, CA 90028	*Actress*	
Harper, Chandler %Bide-a-Wee Golf Club, PO Box 7398, Portsmouth, VA 23707	*Golfer*	
Harper, Charles M %ConAgra Inc, Congra Ctr, 1 Central Park Plz, Omaha, NE 68102	*Businessman*	
Harper, Craig %Chicago Bulls, 980 N Michigan Ave, Chicago, IL 60611	*Basketball Player*	
Harper, Derek %Dallas Mavericks, Reunion Arena, 777 Sports St, Dallas, TX 75207	*Basketball Player*	
Harper, Donald J %Insilco Corp, 1000 Research Pkwy, Meriden, CT 06450	*Businessman*	
Harper, Edwin L %Campbell Soup Co, Campbell Pl, Camden, NJ 08101	*Businessman*	
Harper, Heather 20 Milverton Rd, London NW6 7AS, England	*Opera Singer*	
Harper, Jessica %Century Artists, 9744 Wilshire Blvd, #308, Beverly Hills, CA 90212	*Actress*	
Harper, Paul 1107 5th Ave, New York, NY 10028	*Businessman*	
Harper, Ron %Los Angeles Clippers, Sports Arena, 3939 Figueroa St, Los Angeles, CA 90037	*Basketball Player*	
Harper, Tess 2271 Betty Ln, Beverly Hills, CA 90210	*Actress*	
Harper, Valerie 616 N Maple Dr, Beverly Hills, CA 90210	*Actress*	
Harrah, Toby 6120 Ten Mile Bridge Rd, Fort Worth, TX 76115	*Baseball Player*	
Harrar, J George 125 Puritan Dr, Scarsdale, NY 10583	*Nutritionist*	
Harrell, Henry H %Universal Leaf Tobacco Co, Hamilton & Broad, Richmond, VA 23230	*Businessman*	
Harrell, Lynn %Columbia Artists Mgmt Inc, 165 W 57th St, New York, NY 10019	*Concert Cellist*	**Haring – Harrell**

Harrelson – Harris

Harrelson, Ken *Baseball Player*
150 Crossways Park W, Woodbury, NY 11797

Harrelson, Woody *Actor*
%Creative Artists Agency, 9830 Wilshire Blvd, Beverly Hills, CA 90212

Harrick, Jim *Basketball Coach*
%University of California, Athletic Dept, Los Angeles, CA 90024

Harrigan, John F *Financier*
%Union Bank, 445 S Figueroa St, Los Angeles, CA 90071

Harrington, Donald J *Educator*
%St John's University, President's Office, Jamaica, NY 11439

Harrington, Fred H *Educator*
87 Oak Creek Trl, Madison, WI 53717

Harrington, Michael J *Representative, MA*
Bay View Ave, Beverly, MA 01915

Harrington, Pat *Actor*
2259 Linda Flora Dr, Los Angeles, CA 90024

Harris, Arthur T *Air Force Marshal*
Ferry House, Goring-on-Thames RG8 9DX, England

Harris, Barbara *Actress*
31 W 11th St, New York, NY 10010

Harris, Barbara C *Religious Leader*
%Episcopal Diocese of Massachusetts, 1 Joy St, Boston, MA 02108

Harris, Bernard A, Jr *Astronaut*
%NASA, Johnson Space Center, Houston, TX 77058

Harris, Bill *Movie Critic*
201 N Robertson Blvd, #A, Beverly Hills, CA 90211

Harris, Bill J *Businessman*
%Central & South West Corp, 2121 San Jacinto St, Dallas, TX 75266

Harris, Chauncy D *Geographer, Educator*
%University of Chicago, International Studies Ctr, Chicago, IL 60637

Harris, Claude *Representative, AL*
%House of Representatives, Washington, DC 20515

Harris, Cliff *Football Player*
%Penta Exploration Co, 6820 LBJ Fwy, #140, Dallas, TX 75240

Harris, D George *Businessman*
%SCM Corp, 299 Park Ave, New York, NY 10171

Harris, Danny *Track Athlete*
%Iowa State University, Athletic Dept, Ames, IA 50011

Harris, Del *Basketball Coach*
%Milwaukee Bucks, 901 N 4th St, Milwaukee, WI 53203

Harris, Ed *Actor*
%Creative Artists Agency, 9830 Wilshire Blvd, Beverly Hills, CA 90212

Harris, Elihu *Mayor*
%Mayor's Office, City Hall, 1 City Hall Plz, Oakland, CA 94612

Harris, Emmylou *Singer*
PO Box 1481, Murfreesboro, TN 37133

Harris, Franco *Football Player*
400 W North Ave, Old Allegheny, PA 15212

Harris, Irving B *Businessman*
%Pittway Corp, 333 Skokie Blvd, Northbrook, IL 60065

Harris, J Ira *Businessman*
%Salomon Brothers, 8700 Sears Tower, Chicago, IL 60606

Harris, John G *Financier*
%Crocker National Corp, 1 Montgomery St, San Francisco, CA 94104

Harris, Jonathan *Actor*
16830 Marmaduke Pl, Encino, CA 91316

Harris, Julie *Actress*
132 Barn Hill Rd, West Chatham, MA 02669

Harris, King W *Businessman*
%Pittway Corp, 333 Skokie Blvd, Northbrook, IL 60065

Harris, Lew *Editor*
%Los Angeles Magazine, 1888 Century Park East, Los Angeles, CA 90067

Harris, Louis *Public Opinion Analyst*
%Louis Harris Assoc, 630 5th Ave, New York, NY 10020

Harris, Mel *Actress*
%Gersh Agency, 232 N Canon Dr, Beverly Hills, CA 90210

Harris, Milton M *Businessman*
%Univar Corp, 1600 Norton Bldg, Seattle, WA 98104

Harris, Neil Patrick *Actor*
%Booh Schut Agency, 11350 Ventura Blvd, #206, Studio City, CA 91604

Harris, Neison *Businessman*
%Pittway Corp, 333 Skokie Blvd, Northbrook, IL 60065

Harris, Phil *Comedian*
49400 John F Kennedy Trl, Palm Desert, CA 92260

Harris, Richard *Actor*
502 Park Ave, New York, NY 10022

Harris, Richard H *Radio Executive*
%Westinghouse Broadcasting Co, 90 Park Ave, New York, NY 10016

Harris, Sidney *Cartoonist*
51 Maple Dr, Great Neck, NY 11021

Harris, Tim *Football Player*
%San Francisco 49ers, 4949 Centennial Blvd, Santa Clara, CA 95054

Harris, Virginia S *Religious Leader*
%Church of Christ Scientist, 175 Huntington Ave, Boston, MA 02115

Harrison Breetzke, Joan *Swimmer*
16 Clevedon Rd, East London 5201, South Africa

Harrison, Albertis S, Jr *Governor, VA; Judge*
Saddletree Farm, Box 108, Lawrenceville, VA 23868

Harrison, Ernest T *Businessman*
%Racal Electronics, Western Rd, Bracknell, Berks RB12 1RG, England

Harrison, George *Singer (Beatles)*
Fair Park Rd, Henley-On-Thames, England

Harrison, Jennilee *Actress*
%Twentieth Century Artists, 3800 Barham Blvd, Los Angeles, CA 90068

Harrison, Kathleen *Actress*
30 Cottenham Park Rd, London SW20 0SA, England

Harrison, Lester *Basketball Executive*
79 Nye Park, Rochester, NY 14621

Harrison, Mark *Editor*
%The Gazette, 250 St Antoine St W, Montreal PQ H2Y 3R7, Canada

Harrison, Noel *Actor*
5-11 Mortimer St, London W1, England

Harrison, Richard D *Businessman*
%Fleming Companies, 6301 Waterford Blvd, Oklahoma City, OK 73126

Harrison, William B *Financier*
%Chemical Banking Corp, 277 Park Ave, New York, NY 10172

Harrold, Kathryn *Actress*
%Gersh Agency, 232 N Canon Dr, Beverly Hills, CA 90210

Harry, Debbie *Singer*
%Overland, 1775 Broadway, #701, New York, NY 10019

Harryhausen, Ray *Movie Director*
2 Ilchester Pl, W Kensington, London W14, England

Harsch, Joseph C *Commentator*
275 Highland Dr, Jamestown, RI 02835

Harshfield, Edward G *Financier*
%Columbia Savings & Loan Assn, 8840 Wilshire Blvd, Beverly Hills, CA 90211

Harshman, Marv *Basketball Coach*
%Basketball Hall of Fame, PO Box 179, Springfield, MA 01101

Hart, Doris *Tennis Player*
600 Biltmore Way, #306, Coral Gables, FL 33134

Hart, Gary W *Senator, CO*
%Davis Graham Stubbs, 370 17th Ave E, Denver, CO 80203

Hart, H L A *Solicitor*
11 Manor Pl, Oxford, England

Hart, Jim *Football Player, Sports Administrator*
%Southern Illinois University, SIU Arena, Carbondale, IL 62901

Hart, John *Actor*
5650 Ranchito Ave, Van Nuys, CA 91401

Hart, John C *Businessman*
%Louisiana-Pacific Corp, 111 SW 5th Ave, Portland, OR 97204

Hart, John R *Commentator*
%International Creative Mgmt, 40 W 57th St, New York, NY 10019

Hart, Johnny (John L) *Cartoonist (BC, Wizard of Id)*
%Creators Syndicate, 5777 W Century Blvd, #700, Los Angeles, CA 90045

Hart, Leon *Football Player*
1155 Puritan St, Birmingham, MI 48009

Hart, Mary *Entertainer*
%William Morris Agency, 151 El Camino, Beverly Hills, CA 90212

Hart, Terry J *Astronaut*
%AT&T Bell Labs, Military & Space Applications, Whippany Rd, Whippany, NJ 07981

Hartack, Willie *Thoroughbred Racing Jockey*
%ABC-TV, Sports Dept, 1330 Ave of Americas, New York, NY 10019

Harte, Houston H *Publisher*
%Harte-Hanks Communications, 40 NE Loop 410, San Antonio, TX 78216

Harter, Carol C *Educator*
%State University of New York, President's Office, Potsdam, NY 13676

Hartford, Huntington *Financier, Art Patron*
600 3rd Ave, New York, NY 10016

Hartford, John *Singer, Songwriter*
PO Box 40989, Nashville, TN 37204

Harth, Sidney *Concert Violinist*
135 Westland Dr, Pittsburgh, PA 15217

Hartigan, Grace *Artist*
1701 1/2 Eastern Ave, Baltimore, MD 21231

Hartigan, James L *Businessman*
%Allegis Corp, 1200 Algonquin Rd, Elk Grove Township, IL 60007

Hartke, Vance *Senator, IN*
%Hartke & Hartke, 7637 Leesburg Pike, Falls Church, VA 22043

Hartley, Harry J *Educator*
%University of Connecticut, President's Office, Storrs, CT 06269

Hartley, John T *Businessman*
%Harris Corp, 1025 W NASA Blvd, Melbourne, FL 32919

Hartley, Mariette *Actress*
%Arlene Dayton Mgmt, 9744 Wilshire Blvd, #305, Beverly Hills, CA 90212

Hartling, Poul *Prime Minister, Denmark*
%Office for Refugees, Palais des Nations, 1211 Geneva 10, Switzerland

Hartman, Arthur A *Diplomat*
%State Department, 2201 "C" St NW, Washington, DC 20520

Hartman, Bill (William C, Jr) *Football Player*
%National Life of Vermont, 1160 S Milledge Ave, #220, Athens, GA 30605

Hartman, David *Actor, Commentator*
222 Cedar Ln, Teaneck, NJ 07666

Hartman, Lisa *Actress*
304 Broom Wy, Los Angeles, CA 90049

Hartmann, Alfred *Businessman*
%Roche Hoffmann-LA, Grenzacherstrasse 124, 4002 Basel, Switzerland

Hartmann, Erich *WW II Air Force Hero, Germany*
Vogelsangstrasse 1, 7031 Weil Im Schoenbuch, Germany

Hartmann, Frederick W *Editor*
%Florida Times-Union, 1 Riverside Ave, Jacksonville, FL 32202

Hartmann, Roy D *Financier*
%Security Pacific Corp, 333 S Hope St, Los Angeles, CA 90071

Hartsfield, Henry W *Astronaut*
%NASA, Johnson Space Ctr, Houston, TX 77058

Hartung, James *Gymnast*
3621 Portia, Lincoln, NE 68521

Hartwell of Peterborough Court, Baron *Publisher*
18 Cowley St, Westminister SW1, England

Hartwig, Cleo *Sculptor*
5 W 16th St, New York, NY 10011

Hartz, Jim *Commentator*
%Public Broadcasting System, News Dept, 475 L'Enfant Plz, Washington, DC 20024

Hartzog, George B, Jr *Government Official*
1643 Chain Bridge Rd, McLean, VA 22101

Harup, Karen *Swimmer*
Noerremarksvej 27, 2650 Hvidovre, Denmark

Harvey, Cynthia *Ballerina*
%Royal Ballet, Covent Gdn, Bow St, London W12E 7QA, England

Harvey, Doug *Baseball Umpire*
10231 Vera Cruz Ct, San Diego, CA 92124

Harvey, George B *Businessman*
%Pitney Bowes, Walter H Wheeler Jr Dr, Stamford, CT 06926

Harvey, James R *Businessman*
%Transamerica Corp, 600 Montgomery St, San Francisco, CA 94111

Harvey, Ken *Football Player*
%Phoenix Cardinals, PO Box 888, Phoenix, AZ 85001

Harvey, Paul *Commentator*
%Paulyanne, 1035 Park Ave, River Forest, IL 60305

Harvey, Raymond *Korean War Army Hero (CMH)*
8780 E McKellips Rd, #380, Scottsdale, AZ 85257

Harvey-Jones, John H *Businessman*
%Imperial Chemicals Industries, Millbank, London SW1P 3JF, England

Harvin, R A *Businessman*
%Church's Fried Chicken, 355 Spencer Ln, San Antonio, TX 78284

Harwell, Ernie *Sportscaster*
%CBS-TV, Sports Dept, 51 W 52nd St, New York, NY 10019

Hasegawa, Kenko *Businessman*
%Kawasaki Heavy Industries, 2-1-18 Nakamachidori, Chuoko, Kobe 650, Japan

Hasegawa, Masao *Businessman*
%Nippon Seiko, 2-3-2 Marunouchi, Chiyodaku, Tokyo 100, Japan

Hasehawa, Norishige *Businessman*
%Sumitomo Chemical Co, 15 Kitahama, Higashiku, Osaka, Japan

Haselton, William R *Businessman*
%Champion International Corp, 1 Champion Plz, Stamford, CT 06921

Hashida, Taizo *Financier*
%Fuji Bank Ltd, 1-5-5 Otemachi, Chiyodaku, Tokyo, Japan

Hashimoto, Namio *Businessman*
%Oki Electric Industry Co, 7-12 Toranomon, Minatoku, Tokyo 105, Japan

Haskell, Peter *Actor*
19924 Acre St, Northridge, CA 91324

Haskell, Robert N *Governor, ME*
645 Hammond St, Bangor, ME 04401

Haskins, Clem *Basketball Player, Coach*
%University of Minnesota, Athletic Dept, Minneapolis, MN 55455

Haskins, Sam *Photographer*
9-A Caloone Rd, London SW19 5HH, England

Haslam, Robert *Businessman*
%British Steel Corp, 9 Albert Embankment, London SE1 7SN, England

Hasler, Arthur D *Zoologist*
1233 Sweet Briar Rd, Madison, WI 53705

Hasluck, Paul M C *Government Official, Australia*
2 Adams Rd, Dalkeith WA 6009, Australia

Hassan Ibn Talal *Crown Prince, Jordan*
%Crown Prince's Office, Royal Palace, Amman, Jordan

Hassan II *King, Morocco*
Royal Palace, Rabat, Morocco

Hassanal Bolkiah Muizzaddin Waddaulah *Sultan, Brunei*
Royal Residence, Bandar Seri Begawan, Brunei

Hassel, Odd *Nobel Chemistry Laureate*
Holsteinveien 10, Oslo 8, Norway

Hasselhoff, David *Actor*
4310 Sutton Pl, Sherman Oaks, CA 91413

Hasselmo, Nils *Educator*
%University of Minnesota, President's Office, Minneapolis, MN 55455

Hassenfeld, Alan G *Businessman*
%Hasbro Inc, 1027 Newport Ave, Pawtucket, RI 02862

Hassett, Marilyn *Actress*
%Contemporary Artists, 132 Lasky Dr, #B, Beverly Hills, CA 90212

Hasso, Signe *Actress*
215 W 90th St, #7-F, New York, NY 10024

Hasson, Maurice *Concert Violinist*
18 W Heath Ct, North End Rd, London NW11, England

Hast, Adele *Editor*
%Marquis Who's Who, 200 E Ohio St, Chicago, IL 60611

H

Hastert, J Dennis *Representative, IL*
%House of Representatives, Washington, DC 20515

Hastings, A Baird *Chemist*
233 Prospect Ave, La Jolla, CA 92037

Hastings, Don *Actor*
%"As the World Turns" Show, CBS-TV, 51 W 52nd St, New York, NY 10019

Hatakeyama, Seiji *Businessman*
%EBARA Corp, 11-1 Hanedacho, Otaku, Tokyo 144, Japan

Hatch, H Clifford, Jr *Businessman*
%Hiram Walker Resources, 1 First Canadian Pl, Toronto M5X 1CS, Canada

Hatch, Harold A *Marine Corps General*
%Marine Corps Headquarters, Washington, DC 20380

Hatch, Henry J *Army General*
Chief, Corps of Engineers, 20 Massachusetts Ave NW, Washington, DC 20314

Hatch, Orrin G *Senator, UT*
2127 Galloping Way, Vienna, VA 22180

Hatch, Richard *Actor*
%Artists Group, 1930 Century Park West, #403, Los Angeles, CA 90067

Hatch, Robert W *Businesman*
%Interstate Bakeries Corp, 12 E Armout Blvd, Kansas City, MO 64111

Hatcher, Charles *Representative, GA*
%House of Representatives, Washington, DC 20515

Hatcher, Dale *Football Player*
%Los Angeles Rams, 2327 W Lincoln Ave, Anaheim, CA 92801

Hatcher, Jack *Businessman*
%H H Robertson Co, 2 Gateway Ctr, Pittsburgh, PA 15222

Hatcher, Kevin *Hockey Player*
%Washington Capitals, Capital Centre, 1 Truman Dr, Landover, MD 20785

Hatcher, Richard G *Mayor*
%Mayor's Office, City Hall, 401 Broadway, Gary, IN 46402

Hatcher, Teri *Actress*
PO Box 1101, Sunland, CA 91040

Hatcher, William C *Businessman*
%Genuine Parts Co, 2999 Circle 75 Pkwy, Atlanta, GA 30339

Hatchett, Joseph W *Judge*
%US Court of Appeals, 810 Lewis State Bank Bldg, Tallahassee, FL 32302

Hatfield, Bobby *Singer (Righteous Brothers)*
1824 Port Wheeler Dr, Newport Beach, CA 92660

Hatfield, Hud *Actor*
Ballinterry House, Rathcormac, Co Cork, Ireland

Hatfield, James E *Labor Leader*
%Glass Pottery & Plastics Union, 608 E Baltimore Pike, Media, PA 19063

Hatfield, Ken *Football Coach*
%Clemson University, Athletic Dept, Clemson, SC 29634

Hatfield, Mark O *Governor/Senator, OR*
%US Senate, Washington, DC 20510

Hatfield, Robert S *Businessman*
%Continental Grp, 633 3rd Ave, New York, NY 10017

Hathaway, Earl B *Businessman*
482 St Andrews Dr, Akron, OH 44307

Hathaway, Stanley K *Secretary, Interior; Governor, WY*
2424 Pioneer Ave, Cheyenne, WY 82001

Hathaway, William D *Senator, ME*
80 Orchard St, Auburn, ME 04210

Hatoyama, Iichiro *Government Official, Japan*
1-7-1 Otowa, Bunkyoku, Tokyo, Japan

Hatten, Tom *Actor*
%Agency for Performing Arts, 9000 Sunset Blvd, #1200, Los Angeles, CA 90069

Hattori, Kunio *Businessman*
%Bridgestone Tire Co, 1-10-1 Kyobashi, Chuoku, Tokyo 104, Japan

Hau Pei-Tsun *Prime Minister, Taiwan*
%Prime Minister's Office, Taipei, Taiwan

Hauck, Frederick H *Astronaut*
%Int'l Technical Underwriters (INTEC), 4800 Montgomery Ln, Bethesda, MD 20814

Hauer, Rutger *Actor*
%William Morris Agency, 151 El Camino, Beverly Hills, CA 90212

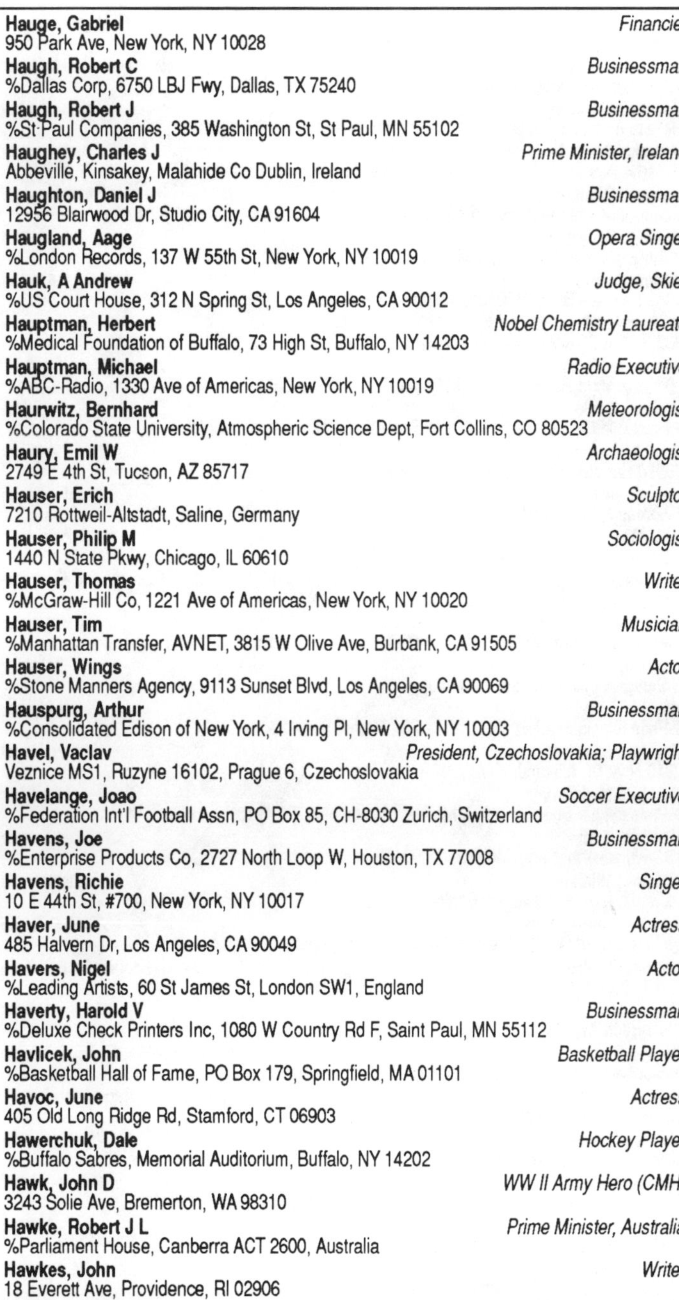

Hauge, Gabriel *Financier*
950 Park Ave, New York, NY 10028

Haugh, Robert C *Businessman*
%Dallas Corp, 6750 LBJ Fwy, Dallas, TX 75240

Haugh, Robert J *Businessman*
%St Paul Companies, 385 Washington St, St Paul, MN 55102

Haughey, Charles J *Prime Minister, Ireland*
Abbeville, Kinsakey, Malahide Co Dublin, Ireland

Haughton, Daniel J *Businessman*
12956 Blairwood Dr, Studio City, CA 91604

Haugland, Aage *Opera Singer*
%London Records, 137 W 55th St, New York, NY 10019

Hauk, A Andrew *Judge, Skier*
%US Court House, 312 N Spring St, Los Angeles, CA 90012

Hauptman, Herbert *Nobel Chemistry Laureate*
%Medical Foundation of Buffalo, 73 High St, Buffalo, NY 14203

Hauptman, Michael *Radio Executive*
%ABC-Radio, 1330 Ave of Americas, New York, NY 10019

Haurwitz, Bernhard *Meteorologist*
%Colorado State University, Atmospheric Science Dept, Fort Collins, CO 80523

Haury, Emil W *Archaeologist*
2749 E 4th St, Tucson, AZ 85717

Hauser, Erich *Sculptor*
7210 Rottweil-Altstadt, Saline, Germany

Hauser, Philip M *Sociologist*
1440 N State Pkwy, Chicago, IL 60610

Hauser, Thomas *Writer*
%McGraw-Hill Co, 1221 Ave of Americas, New York, NY 10020

Hauser, Tim *Musician*
%Manhattan Transfer, AVNET, 3815 W Olive Ave, Burbank, CA 91505

Hauser, Wings *Actor*
%Stone Manners Agency, 9113 Sunset Blvd, Los Angeles, CA 90069

Hauspurg, Arthur *Businessman*
%Consolidated Edison of New York, 4 Irving Pl, New York, NY 10003

Havel, Vaclav *President, Czechoslovakia; Playwright*
Veznice MS1, Ruzyne 16102, Prague 6, Czechoslovakia

Havelange, Joao *Soccer Executive*
%Federation Int'l Football Assn, PO Box 85, CH-8030 Zurich, Switzerland

Havens, Joe *Businessman*
%Enterprise Products Co, 2727 North Loop W, Houston, TX 77008

Havens, Richie *Singer*
10 E 44th St, #700, New York, NY 10017

Haver, June *Actress*
485 Halvern Dr, Los Angeles, CA 90049

Havers, Nigel *Actor*
%Leading Artists, 60 St James St, London SW1, England

Haverty, Harold V *Businessman*
%Deluxe Check Printers Inc, 1080 W Country Rd F, Saint Paul, MN 55112

Havlicek, John *Basketball Player*
%Basketball Hall of Fame, PO Box 179, Springfield, MA 01101

Havoc, June *Actress*
405 Old Long Ridge Rd, Stamford, CT 06903

Hawerchuk, Dale *Hockey Player*
%Buffalo Sabres, Memorial Auditorium, Buffalo, NY 14202

Hawk, John D *WW II Army Hero (CMH)*
3243 Solie Ave, Bremerton, WA 98310

Hawke, Robert J L *Prime Minister, Australia*
%Parliament House, Canberra ACT 2600, Australia

Hawkes, John *Writer*
18 Everett Ave, Providence, RI 02906

Hawking, Stephen W *Theoretical Physicist*
%University of Cambridge, Applied Math Dept, Cambridge CB3 9EW, England

Hawkins, Andy *Baseball Player*
PO Box 8812, Waco, TX 76714

Hawkins, Edwin *Vocal Group Leader*
1971 Hoover Ave, Oakland, CA 94602

H

Hawkins, Hersey %Philadelphia 76ers, PO Box 25040, Philadelphia, PA 19147	*Basketball Player*
Hawkins, Tommy %Los Angeles Dodgers, Dodger Stadium, Los Angeles, CA 90012	*Basketball Player, Sportscaster*
Hawkins, Whitley %Delta Air Lines, Hartsfield International Airport, Atlanta, GA 30320	*Businessman*
Hawley, Philip M %Carter Hawley Hale Stores, 444 S Flower St, Los Angeles, CA 90071	*Businessman*
Hawley, Richard E Commander, 5th Air Force, APO, AP 96328	*Air Force General*
Hawley, Steven A %Ames Research Center, Mail Stop 200-1A, Moffett Field, CA 94035	*Astronaut*
Hawn, Goldie 1849 Sawtelle Blvd, #500, Los Angeles, CA 90025	*Actress*
Haworth, Jill 300 E 51st St, New York, NY 10019	*Actress*
Haworth, Lionel 10 Hazelwood Rd, Sneryd Park, Bristol BS9 1PX, England	*Aeronautical Engineer*
Hawpe, David %Louisville Courier-Journal, 525 W Broadway, Louisville, KY 40202	*Editor*
Hay, Alexandria 20910 Bandera St, Woodland Hills, CA 91364	*Actress*
Hay, Jess T %Lomas & Nettleton Financial Corp, 2001 Bryan Tower, Dallas, TX 75201	*Financier*
Hay, Raymond A %LTV Corp, 2001 Ross Ave, Dallas, TX 75201	*Businessman*
Hayakawa, S I 225 Eldridge Ave, PO Box 100, Mill Valley, CA 94942	*Senator, CA; Educator*
Hayakawa, Saburo %Fujisawa Pharmaceutical Co, 4-3 Doshomachi, Hihasgiku, Osaka 541, Japan	*Businessman*
Haydee, Marcia %Stuttgart Ballet, Stuttgart, Germany	*Ballerina*
Hayden, Jim %Philadelphia Inquirer, 400 N Broad St, Philadelphia, PA 19101	*Publisher*
Hayden, Mike 3910 Rive Dr, Alexandria, VA 22309	*Governor, KS*
Hayden, Neil Steven %Philadelphia Bulletin, 30th & Market, Philadelphia, PA 19101	*Publisher*
Hayden, Tom 152 Wadsworth, Santa Monica, CA 90405	*Political Activist*
Hayden, William %Jaguar Motors, Coventry, England	*Businessman*
Haydon Jones, Ann 85 Westerfield Rd, Edgloaston, Birmingham 15, England	*Tennis Player*
Hayek, Friedrich A Von Urachstrasse 27, 7800 Freiburg im Breisgau, Germany	*Nobel Economics Laureate*
Hayes, Bill 4528 Beck Ave, North Hollywood, CA 91602	*Actor*
Hayes, Bob %Staubach Co, 6750 LBJ Fwy, #1100, Dallas, TX 75240	*Football Player, Track Athlete*
Hayes, Charles A %House of Representatives, Washington, DC 20515	*Representative, IL*
Hayes, Delbert J %Nike Inc, 3900 SW Murray Blvd, Beaverton, OR 97005	*Businessman*
Hayes, Denis %Cooley Godward Castro, Maritime Plz, 20th Fl, San Francisco, CA 94111	*Environmentalist*
Hayes, Helen 3003 Kalakaua Ave, #5-B, Honolulu 96815	*Actress*
Hayes, Isaac %Charter Mgmt, 9000 Sunset Blvd, #1112, Los Angeles, CA 90069	*Composer*
Hayes, James A (Jimmy) %House of Representatives, Washington, DC 20515	*Representative, LA*
Hayes, James B %Discover Magazine, Rockefeller Ctr, New York, NY 10020	*Publisher*
Hayes, John B %Coast Guard Headquarters, 2100 2nd St SW, Washington, DC 20593	*Coast Guard Admiral*

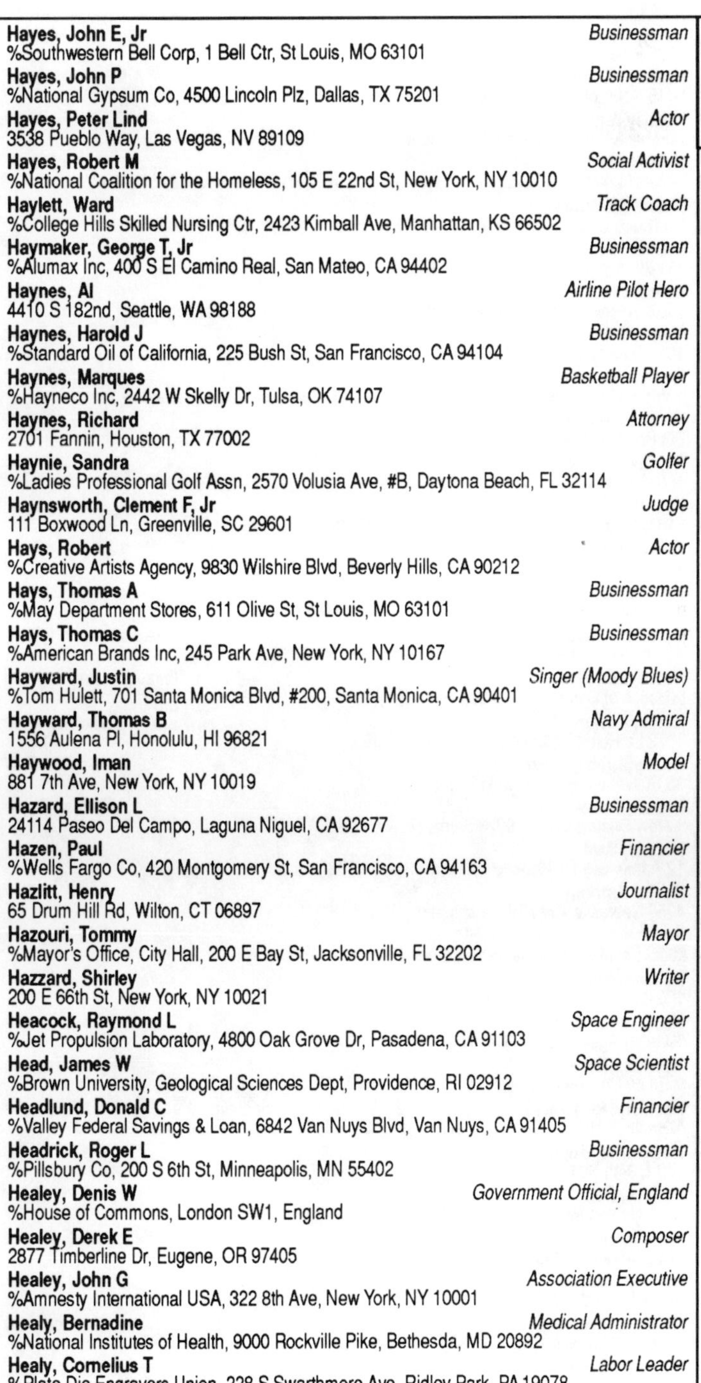

Hayes, John E, Jr — *Businessman*
%Southwestern Bell Corp, 1 Bell Ctr, St Louis, MO 63101

Hayes, John P — *Businessman*
%National Gypsum Co, 4500 Lincoln Plz, Dallas, TX 75201

Hayes, Peter Lind — *Actor*
3538 Pueblo Way, Las Vegas, NV 89109

Hayes, Robert M — *Social Activist*
%National Coalition for the Homeless, 105 E 22nd St, New York, NY 10010

Haylett, Ward — *Track Coach*
%College Hills Skilled Nursing Ctr, 2423 Kimball Ave, Manhattan, KS 66502

Haymaker, George T, Jr — *Businessman*
%Alumax Inc, 400 S El Camino Real, San Mateo, CA 94402

Haynes, Al — *Airline Pilot Hero*
4410 S 182nd, Seattle, WA 98188

Haynes, Harold J — *Businessman*
%Standard Oil of California, 225 Bush St, San Francisco, CA 94104

Haynes, Marques — *Basketball Player*
%Hayneco Inc, 2442 W Skelly Dr, Tulsa, OK 74107

Haynes, Richard — *Attorney*
2701 Fannin, Houston, TX 77002

Haynie, Sandra — *Golfer*
%Ladies Professional Golf Assn, 2570 Volusia Ave, #B, Daytona Beach, FL 32114

Haynsworth, Clement F, Jr — *Judge*
111 Boxwood Ln, Greenville, SC 29601

Hays, Robert — *Actor*
%Creative Artists Agency, 9830 Wilshire Blvd, Beverly Hills, CA 90212

Hays, Thomas A — *Businessman*
%May Department Stores, 611 Olive St, St Louis, MO 63101

Hays, Thomas C — *Businessman*
%American Brands Inc, 245 Park Ave, New York, NY 10167

Hayward, Justin — *Singer (Moody Blues)*
%Tom Hulett, 701 Santa Monica Blvd, #200, Santa Monica, CA 90401

Hayward, Thomas B — *Navy Admiral*
1556 Aulena Pl, Honolulu, HI 96821

Haywood, Iman — *Model*
881 7th Ave, New York, NY 10019

Hazard, Ellison L — *Businessman*
24114 Paseo Del Campo, Laguna Niguel, CA 92677

Hazen, Paul — *Financier*
%Wells Fargo Co, 420 Montgomery St, San Francisco, CA 94163

Hazlitt, Henry — *Journalist*
65 Drum Hill Rd, Wilton, CT 06897

Hazouri, Tommy — *Mayor*
%Mayor's Office, City Hall, 200 E Bay St, Jacksonville, FL 32202

Hazzard, Shirley — *Writer*
200 E 66th St, New York, NY 10021

Heacock, Raymond L — *Space Engineer*
%Jet Propulsion Laboratory, 4800 Oak Grove Dr, Pasadena, CA 91103

Head, James W — *Space Scientist*
%Brown University, Geological Sciences Dept, Providence, RI 02912

Headlund, Donald C — *Financier*
%Valley Federal Savings & Loan, 6842 Van Nuys Blvd, Van Nuys, CA 91405

Headrick, Roger L — *Businessman*
%Pillsbury Co, 200 S 6th St, Minneapolis, MN 55402

Healey, Denis W — *Government Official, England*
%House of Commons, London SW1, England

Healey, Derek E — *Composer*
2877 Timberline Dr, Eugene, OR 97405

Healey, John G — *Association Executive*
%Amnesty International USA, 322 8th Ave, New York, NY 10001

Healy, Bernadine — *Medical Administrator*
%National Institutes of Health, 9000 Rockville Pike, Bethesda, MD 20892

Healy, Cornelius T — *Labor Leader*
%Plate Die Engravers Union, 228 S Swarthmore Ave, Ridley Park, PA 19078

Healy, Jane — *Journalist*
%Orlando Sentinel, 633 N Orange Ave, Orlando, FL 32801

H

Healy, Mary *Actress*
3538 Pueblo Way, Las Vegas, NV 89109
Heaney, Gerald W *Judge*
%US Court of Appeals, Federal Bldg, Duluth, MN 55802
Heaney, Seamus *Writer*
%Faber & Faber, 3 Queen Sq, London WC1N 3RU, England
Heaps, Alvin E *Labor Leader*
%Retail Wholesale Department Store Union, 30 E 29th St, New York, NY 10016
Heard, Alexander *Educator*
2100 Golf Club Ln, Nashville, TN 37215
Heard, John *Actor*
853 7th Ave, #9-A, New York, NY 10019
Hearn, Chick *Sportscaster*
%Los Angeles Lakers, Great Western Forum, 3900 W Manchester, Inglewood, CA 90306
Hearn, Jim *Baseball Player*
1678 Beverly Wood Ct, Chamblee, GA 30341
Hearn, Thomas K, Jr *Educator*
%Wake Forest University, President's Office, Winston-Salem, NC 27109
Hearnes, Warren *Governor, MO*
PO Box 509, Charleston, MO 63834
Hearns, Thomas *Boxer*
19875 W 12 Mile Rd, Southfield, MI 48076
Hearst, George R, Jr *Publisher*
318 N Rockingham Ave, Los Angeles, CA 90049
Hearst, Randolph A *Publisher*
110 5th St, San Francisco, CA 94103
Hearst, William Randolph, Jr *Publisher*
%Hearst Corp, 959 8th Ave, New York, NY 10019
Hearth, Donald P *Aeronautical Engineer*
%Langley Research Ctr, NASA, Hampton, VA 23665
Heath, Edward *Prime Minister, England*
%House of Commons, London SW1, England
Heath, Howard D *Businessman*
1072 La Reina Dr, Lake San Marcos, CA 92069
Heath-Stubbs, John *Poet*
35 Sutherland Pl, London W2, England
Hebert, Bobby *Football Player*
%New Orleans Saints, 6928 Saints Dr, Metairie, LA 70003
Hebner, Paul C *Businessman*
12 Amber Sky Dr, Rancho Palos Verdes, CA 90274
Hecht, Anthony *Poet*
4256 Nebraska Ave NW, Washington, DC 20016
Hecht, Chic *Senator, NV; Ambassador*
%US Embassy, Mosmar Bldg, Queen St, Nassau, Bahamas
Heckart, Eileen *Actress*
135 Comstock Hill Rd, New Canaan, CT 06840
Heckerling, Amy *Movie Director*
%Gersh Agency, 232 N Canon Dr, Beverly Hills, CA 90210
Heckert, Richard E *Businessman*
%E I du Pont de Nemours Co, 1007 Market St, Wilmington, DE 19898
Heckler, Margaret M *Secretary, Health & Human Services*
%Health & Human Services Department, 200 Independence, Washington, DC 20201
Heckscher, August *Writer*
159 E 94th St, New York, NY 10028
Hedaya, Dan *Actor*
2101 N Beachwood Dr, Los Angeles, CA 90068
Hedberg, Hollis D *Petroleum Geologist*
118 Library Pl, Princeton, NJ 08540
Hedden, Alfred J *Financier*
%City Federal Savings & Loan, Rt 202-206, Bedminster, NJ 07921
Hedden, Russell A *Businessman*
%Cross & Trecker Corp, 505 N Woodward Ave, Bloomfield Hills, MI 48013
Hedison, David *Actor*
%Leading Artists, 445 N Bedford Dr, #PH, Beverly Hills, CA 90210
Hedren, Tippi *Actress*
6867 Soledad Canyon Rd, Acton, CA 93510

Hedrick, Jerry L %University of California, Biochemistry Dept, Davis, CA 95616	*Biochemist*
Heffernan, John 20 5th Ave, New York, NY 10011	*Actor*
Hefley, Joel %House of Representatives, Washington, DC 20515	*Representative, CO*
Heflin, Howell T 311 E 6th St, Tuscumbia, AL 35674	*Senator, AL*
Hefner, Christie %Playboy Enterprises, 680 N Lake Shore Dr, Chicago, IL 60611	*Publisher*
Hefner, Hugh M 10236 Charing Cross Rd, Los Angeles, CA 90024	*Publisher*
Hefner, W G (Bill) %House of Representatives, Washington, DC 20515	*Representative, NC*
Heft, Robert PO Box 131, Napoleon, OH 43545	*Flag Designer*
Hefti, Neal %Encino Music, 9454 Wilshire Blvd, #405, Beverly Hills, CA 90212	*Composer*
Heggtveit, Ann Hamilton %General Delivery, Grand Isle, VT 05458	*Skier*
Hegyes, Robert 12117 1/2 Hoffman St, Studio City, CA 91604	*Actor*
Heidel, Charles M %Detroit Edison Co, 2000 2nd Ave, Detroit, MI 48226	*Businessman*
Heidelberger, Charles 1495 Poppy Peak Dr, Pasadena, CA 91105	*Oncologist, Biochemist*
Heideloff, William R %Broadview Financial Corp, 6000 Rockside Woods Blvd, Cleveland, OH 44131	*Financier*
Heiden, Beth 3505 Blackhawk Dr, Madison, WI 53705	*Speed Skater*
Heiden, Eric 3505 Blackhawk Dr, Madison, WI 53705	*Speed Skater*
Heilbroner, Robert L 830 Park Ave, New York, NY 90210	*Economist*
Heilmeier, George H %Texas Instruments, 13500 North Central Expwy, Dallas, TX 75265	*Electronics Inventor*
Heimbinder, Isaac %US Home Corp, 1800 West Loop S, Houston, TX 77027	*Businessman*
Heimlich, Henry J %Xavier University, Clinical Sciences Dept, Cincinnati, OH 45207	*Physician*
Heineken, Alfred H %Heineken, 2-E Weteringplantsoen 21, 1017-ZD Amsterdam, Netherlands	*Businessman*
Heineman, Ben W %Northwest Industries, 6300 Sears Tower, Chicago, IL 60606	*Businessman*
Heinmann, John G %A G Paribus Becker Inc, 55 Water St, New York, NY 10041	*Financier*
Heinrich, Don PO Box 17704, Seattle, WA 98107	*Football Player*
Heinsohn, Tom 30 Indian Ridge Rd, Natick, MA 01760	*Basketball Player, Coach*
Heinze, Bernard T 101 Victoria Rd, Bellevue Hill, Sydney NSW, Australia	*Conductor*
Heiskell, Andrew 870 United Nations Plz, New York, NY 10017	*Publisher*
Hekman, Peter M, Jr Commander, Naval Sea Systems Command, Navy Department, Washington, DC 20362	*Navy Admiral*
Held, Al %Emmerich Gallery, 41 E 57th St, New York, NY 10022	*Artist*
Held, Franklin (Bud) 12474 Rock Crest Rd, Lakeside, CA 92040	*Track Athlete*
Heldman, Gladys 1002 Old Pecos Trl, Santa Fe, NM 87501	*Tennis Magazine Editor*
Helgenberger, Marg %STE Representation, 9301 Wilshire Blvd, #312, Beverly Hills, CA 90210	*Actress*
Heliker, John 865 West End Ave, #3-C, New York, NY 10025	*Artist*

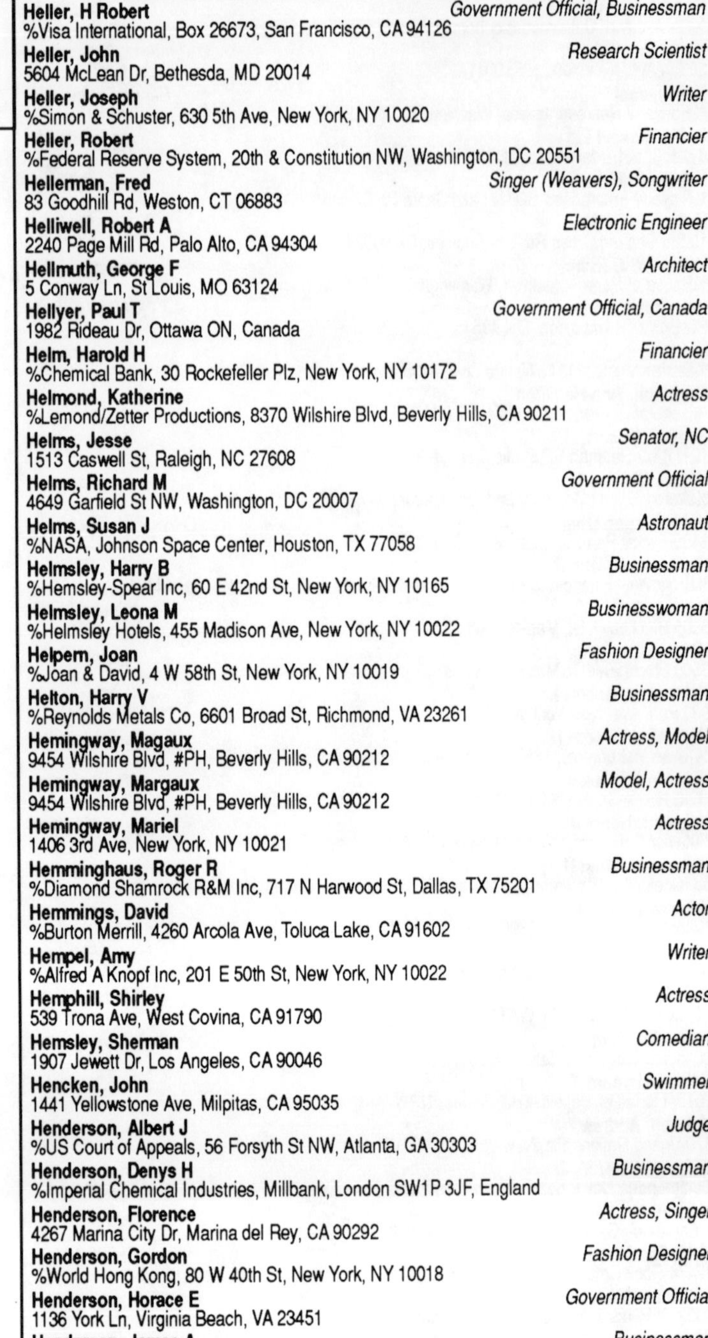

H

Heller – Henderson

Heller, H Robert *Government Official, Businessman*
%Visa International, Box 26673, San Francisco, CA 94126

Heller, John *Research Scientist*
5604 McLean Dr, Bethesda, MD 20014

Heller, Joseph *Writer*
%Simon & Schuster, 630 5th Ave, New York, NY 10020

Heller, Robert *Financier*
%Federal Reserve System, 20th & Constitution NW, Washington, DC 20551

Hellerman, Fred *Singer (Weavers), Songwriter*
83 Goodhill Rd, Weston, CT 06883

Helliwell, Robert A *Electronic Engineer*
2240 Page Mill Rd, Palo Alto, CA 94304

Hellmuth, George F *Architect*
5 Conway Ln, St Louis, MO 63124

Hellyer, Paul T *Government Official, Canada*
1982 Rideau Dr, Ottawa ON, Canada

Helm, Harold H *Financier*
%Chemical Bank, 30 Rockefeller Plz, New York, NY 10172

Helmond, Katherine *Actress*
%Lemond/Zetter Productions, 8370 Wilshire Blvd, Beverly Hills, CA 90211

Helms, Jesse *Senator, NC*
1513 Caswell St, Raleigh, NC 27608

Helms, Richard M *Government Official*
4649 Garfield St NW, Washington, DC 20007

Helms, Susan J *Astronaut*
%NASA, Johnson Space Center, Houston, TX 77058

Helmsley, Harry B *Businessman*
%Hemsley-Spear Inc, 60 E 42nd St, New York, NY 10165

Helmsley, Leona M *Businesswoman*
%Helmsley Hotels, 455 Madison Ave, New York, NY 10022

Helpern, Joan *Fashion Designer*
%Joan & David, 4 W 58th St, New York, NY 10019

Helton, Harry V *Businessman*
%Reynolds Metals Co, 6601 Broad St, Richmond, VA 23261

Hemingway, Magaux *Actress, Model*
9454 Wilshire Blvd, #PH, Beverly Hills, CA 90212

Hemingway, Margaux *Model, Actress*
9454 Wilshire Blvd, #PH, Beverly Hills, CA 90212

Hemingway, Mariel *Actress*
1406 3rd Ave, New York, NY 10021

Hemminghaus, Roger R *Businessman*
%Diamond Shamrock R&M Inc, 717 N Harwood St, Dallas, TX 75201

Hemmings, David *Actor*
%Burton Merrill, 4260 Arcola Ave, Toluca Lake, CA 91602

Hempel, Amy *Writer*
%Alfred A Knopf Inc, 201 E 50th St, New York, NY 10022

Hemphill, Shirley *Actress*
539 Trona Ave, West Covina, CA 91790

Hemsley, Sherman *Comedian*
1907 Jewett Dr, Los Angeles, CA 90046

Hencken, John *Swimmer*
1441 Yellowstone Ave, Milpitas, CA 95035

Henderson, Albert J *Judge*
%US Court of Appeals, 56 Forsyth St NW, Atlanta, GA 30303

Henderson, Denys H *Businessman*
%Imperial Chemical Industries, Millbank, London SW1P 3JF, England

Henderson, Florence *Actress, Singer*
4267 Marina City Dr, Marina del Rey, CA 90292

Henderson, Gordon *Fashion Designer*
%World Hong Kong, 80 W 40th St, New York, NY 10018

Henderson, Horace E *Government Official*
1136 York Ln, Virginia Beach, VA 23451

Henderson, James A *Businessman*
%Cummins Engine Co, PO Box 3005, Columbus, IN 47202

Henderson, Julia *International Official*
1735 Forest Rd, Venice, FL 33595

Henderson, Karen LeCraft *Judge*
%US Court of Appeals, 3rd & Constitution Ave NW, Washington, DC 20001

Henderson, Loy W *Diplomat*
2727 29th St NW, Washington, DC 20008

Henderson, Paul *Journalist*
%Seattle Times, Fairview & John, Seattle, WA 98111

Henderson, Rickey *Baseball Player*
10561 Englewood Dr, Oakland, CA 94621

Henderson, Skitch *Musician*
Hunt Hill Farm, 44 Upland Rd, RFD 3, New Milford, CT 06776

Henderson, T C *Businessman*
%Unocal Corp, 1201 W 5th St, Los Angeles, CA 90051

Hendrick, George *Baseball Player*
20893 Starshine Rd, Walnut, CA 91789

Hendricks, Barbara *Opera Singer*
%Opera & Concert, 19 Rue Vignon, 75008 Paris, France

Hendrix, Dennis R *Businessman*
%Halliburton Co, 2600 Southland Ctr, Dallas, TX 75201

Hendrix, James R *WW II Army Hero (CMH)*
PO Box 164, Davenport, FL 33837

Heng Samrin *President, Kampuchea*
%President's Office, Phnom-Penh, Kampuchea

Henize, Karl G *Astronaut*
%NASA/JSC, Code SN3, Johnson Space Ctr, Houston, TX 77058

Henkel, Konrad *Businessman*
%Degussa, Weissfrauenstrasse 9, 6000 Frankfurt 11, Germany

Henle, Gertrude *Virologist*
533 Ott Rd, Bala-Cynwyd, PA 19004

Henley, Beth *Playwright*
%William Morris Agency, 1350 Ave of Americas, New York, NY 10019

Henley, Don *Singer*
%Geffen Records, 9130 Sunset Blvd, Los Angeles, CA 90069

Henley, Edward T *Labor Leader*
%Hotel & Restaurant Employees Union, 1219 28th St NW, Washington, DC 20007

Henley, Henry H, Jr *Businessman*
%Cluett Peabody Co, 510 5th Ave, New York, NY 10036

Henley, J Smith *Judge*
%Federal Bldg, Harrison, AR 72601

Henley, William B *Educator*
Creston Circle Ranch, Paso Robles, CA 93446

Henne Hawkins, Jan *Swimmer*
1155 E Bishop Dr, Tempe, AZ 85282

Hennebach, Ralph L *Businessman*
%Asarco Inc, 180 Maiden Ln, New York, NY 10038

Henner, Marilu *Actress*
1440 Stone Canyon Rd, Los Angeles, CA 90077

Hennessey, Frank M *Businessman*
%Handleman Co, 500 Kirts Blvd, Troy, MI 48084

Hennessy, Edward L, Jr *Businessman*
%Allied-Signal Inc, PO Box 4000-R, Morristown, NJ 07960

Hennessy, John M *Financier*
%First Boston Corp, Park Ave Plz, New York, NY 10055

Henney, Edward N *Businessman*
%Safeway Stores, 4th & Jackson, Oakland, CA 94660

Hennig, Fred E *Businessman*
%Woolworth Corp, 233 Broadway, New York, NY 10279

Hennigan, Charlie *Football Player*
7800 Youree, #2700-G, Shreveport, LA 71105

Henning, Dan *Football Coach*
%Detroit Lions, Silverdome, 1200 Featherstone Rd, Pontiac, MI 48057

Henning, Doug *Illusionist*
6747 Odessa, #105, Van Nuys, CA 91406

Henning, John F, Jr *Publisher*
%Sunset Magazine, 80 Willow Rd, Menlo Park, CA 94025

Henning, Linda *Actress*
4250 Navajo St, North Hollywood, CA 91602

Henning – Herbig

Henning, Lorne — *Hockey Coach*
%Minnesota North Stars, 7901 Cedar Ave S, Bloomington, MN 55420

Henning-Walker, Anne — *Speed Skater*
2419 S Worchester Ct, #F, Aurora, CO 80014

Hennings, Chad — *Football Player*
%US Air Force Academy, Athletic Dept, Colorado Springs, CO 80840

Henreid, Paul — *Actor*
18068 Bluesail Dr, Pacific Palisades, CA 90272

Henrich, Tommy — *Baseball Player*
1347 Albino Trail, Dewey, AZ 86327

Henricks, Jon N — *Swimmer*
254 N Laurel Ave, Des Plaines, IL 60016

Henricks, Terrence T (Tom) — *Astronaut*
%NASA, Johnson Space Ctr, Houston, TX 77058

Henrik — *Prince, Denmark*
%Amalienborg Palace, Copenhagen, Denmark

Henriquez, Ron — *Television Host*
PO Box 38027, Los Angeles, CA 90038

Henry, Buck — *Actor*
760 N La Cienega Blvd, Los Angeles, CA 90069

Henry, David D — *Educator*
%University of Illinois, Education College, Urbana, IL 61801

Henry, Gloria — *Actress*
%Dade/Rosen/Schultz, 11846 Ventura Blvd, #100, Studio City, CA 91604

Henry, Paul B — *Representative, MI*
%House of Representatives, Washington, DC 20515

Henry, William H, Jr — *Publisher*
%Time-Life Books, Rockefeller Ctr, New York, NY 10020

Hensley, Kirby J — *Religious Leader*
%Universal Life Church, 601 3rd St, Modesto, CA 95351

Henson, Joe M — *Businessman*
%Prime Computer Inc, Prime Park, Natick, MA 01760

Henson, Lou — *Basketball Coach*
%University of Illinois, Athletic Dept, Assembly Hall, Champaign, IL 61820

Henson, Paul H — *Businessman*
%United Telecommunications, 2330 Johnson Dr, Westwood, KS 66205

Hentoff, Nat — *Jazz Critic*
25 5th Ave, New York, NY 10003

Henze, Hans Werner — *Composer, Conductor*
Via dei Laghi 18, Rome, Italy

Henze, Raymond F, III — *Businessman*
%Castle & Cooke Inc, 10900 Wilshire Blvd, Los Angeles, CA 90024

Hepburn, Audrey — *Actress*
Chalet Rice Bissenstrasse, Gstaad, Switzerland

Hepburn, Katherine — *Actress*
244 E 49th St, New York, NY 10017

Heppel, Leon A — *Biochemist*
%Cornell University, Biochemistry Dept, Ithaca, NY 14850

Heraeus, Jurgen — *Businessman*
%W C Heraeus, Heraeustr 12-14, 6450 Hannau 1, Germany

Herb, Raymond G — *Physicist*
RR 1, Box 223-A, Mazomanie, WI 53560

Herbert, Frank — *Writer*
%General Delivery, Port Townsend, WA 98368

Herbert, Gavin — *Businessman*
%Allergan Pharmaceuticals, 2525 Dupont Dr, Irvine, CA 92713

Herbert, Michael K — *Editor*
%Century Publishing Co, 1020 Church St, Evanston, IL 60201

Herbert, Ray — *Baseball Player*
32629 Five Mile Rd, Livonia, MI 48150

Herbert, Wally — *Explorer*
%Royal Geographical Society, London SW7, England

Herbig, George H — *Astronomer*
%University of Hawaii, Astronomy Inst, 2680 Woodlawn Dr, Honolulu, HI 96822

Herbig, Guenther — *Conductor*
%BBC Broadcasting House, Oxford Rd, Manchester M6O 1SJ, England

Herd, Richard *Actor*
%Harris & Goldberg Agency, 1999 Ave of Stars, #2850, Los Angeles, CA 90067
Herda, Frank A *Vietnam War Army Hero (CMH)*
PO Box 34239, Cleveland, OH 44134
Herger, Wally *Representative, CA*
%House of Representatives, Washington, DC 20515
Herlihy, James Leo *Writer*
%Jay Garon, 415 Central Park West, New York, NY 10025
Herman, Billy (William J) *Baseball Player*
%Suncrest Apartments #8, 3111 Garden E, #33, Palm Beach Gardens, FL 33410
Herman, Donald J *Businessman*
%NCR Corp, 1700 S Patterson Blvd, Dayton, OH 45479
Herman, George E *Commentator*
PO Box 88, Main St, Hancock, NH 03449
Herman, James R *Labor Leader*
%International Longshoremens Union, 1188 Franklin St, San Francisco, CA 94109
Herman, Pinky *Songwriter*
%Manor Music Co, 4705 NW 35th St, Lauderdale Lakes, FL 33319
Hermann, Allen *Physicist*
%University of Arkansas, Physics Dept, Fayetteville, AR 72701
Hermannsson, Steingrimur *Prime Minister, Iceland*
%Prime Minister's Office, Reykjavik, Iceland
Hermaszewski, Miroslaw *Cosmonaut, Poland*
Skrytka Pocztowa 17, 00 904 Warsaw 6, Poland
Hern, Dick *Thoroughbred Racing Trainer*
%West Ilsley Stables, West Ilsley, Newbury Berks RG16 0AE, England
Hernandez, Amalia *Dancer, Choreographer*
%Ballet Folklorico, Violeta 31 Esq Con Riva Palacio, Mexico DF, Mexico
Hernandez, Guillermo (Willie) *Baseball Player*
80 Espina Calle C, Box 125, Aguada, PR 00602
Hernandez, Keith *Baseball Player*
255 E 49th St, #28-D, New York, NY 10017
Hernandez, Rodolfo P *Korean War Army Hero (CMH)*
5328 Bluewater Pl, College Lakes, Fayetteville, NC 28311
Herr, Tommy *Baseball Player*
1077 Olde Forge Crossing, Lancaster, PA 17601
Herrera, Carolina *Fashion Designer*
%Carolina Herrera Ltd, 19 E 57th St, New York, NY 10022
Herrera, Silvestre S *WW II Army Hero (CMH)*
7222 W Windsor Blvd, Glendale, AZ 85303
Herrick, Kenneth G *Businessman*
%Tecumseh Products Co, 100 E Patterson, Tecumseh, MI 49286
Herrick, Todd W *Businessman*
%Tecumseh Products Co, 100 E Patterson, Tecumseh, MI 49286
Herring, Conyers *Physicist*
3945 Nelson Dr, Palo Alto, CA 94306
Herring, James P *Businessman*
247 River Dr, Tequesta, FL 33458
Herring, Leonard G *Businessman*
%Lowe's Companies, PO Box 1111, North Wilkesboro, NC 28656
Herring, Rufus G *WW II Navy Hero (CMH)*
PO Box 128, Roseboro, NC 28382
Herringer, Frank C *Businessman*
%Transamerica Corp, 600 Montgomery St, San Francisco, CA 94111
Herrington, John S *Secretary, Education; Businessman*
%Harcourt Brace Jovanovich Inc, 6277 Sea Harbor Dr, Orlando, FL 32821
Herriot, James *Writer*
Mire Beck, Thirlby, Thirsk, Yorkshire YO7 2DJ, England
Herrmann, Edward *Actor*
%William Morris Agency, 151 El Camino, Beverly Hills, CA 90212
Hersant, Robert J E *Publisher*
%Le Figaro, 12 Rue De Presbourg, 75116 Paris, France
Herschbach, Dudley R *Nobel Chemistry Laureate*
64 Linnaean St, Cambridge, MA 02138
Herschler, David *Artist*
PO Box 5859, Santa Barbara, CA 93108

H

Hersey, John *Writer*
719 Windsor Ln, Key West, FL 33040

Hersh, Seymour M *Writer*
1199 National Press Bldg, Washington, DC 20045

Hershberger, Gary *Actor*
%STE Representation, 9301 Wilshire Blvd, #312, Beverly Hills, CA 90210

Hershey, Alfred D *Nobel Medicine Laureate*
RD Box 1640, Moores Hill Rd, Syosset, NY 11791

Hershey, Barbara *Actress*
555 E Channel Rd, Santa Monica, CA 90406

Hershiser, Orel *Baseball Player*
1199 Madia St, Pasadena, CA 91103

Hertel, Dennis M *Representative, MI*
%House of Representatives, Washington, DC 20515

Hertz, C Hellmuth *Physicist*
%Lund Institute of Technology, Lund, Sweden

Hertz, Roy *Obstetrician*
Rt 3, Box 582, Hollywood, MD 20636

Hertzberg, Arthur *Religious Leader*
83 Glenwood Rd, Englewood, NJ 07631

Hertzberg, Daniel *Journalist*
%Wall Street Journal, 22 Cortlandt St, New York, NY 10038

Hertzberger, Herman *Architect*
Sarphatipark 132, 1073 EE Amsterdam, Netherlands

Hertzog, Merlin F *Businessman*
%Pennsylvania Power & Light Co, 2 N 9th St, Allentown, PA 18101

Hervey, Fred *Businessman*
%Circle K Corp, 7th St & McDowell, Phoenix, AZ 85006

Herz, Gunter *Businessman*
Reemtsma Cigarettenfabriken, Parkstr 51, 2000 Hamburg 52, Germany

Herzberg, Gerhard *Nobel Chemistry Laureate*
190 Lakewood Dr, Rockcliffe Park, Ottawa ON K1L 5B3, Canada

Herzog, Arthur, III *Writer*
PO Box 1012, Cooper Station, New York, NY 10003

Herzog, Chaim *President, Israel*
25 Ibn Gvirol St, Tel-Aviv, Israel

Herzog, George *Anthropologist*
%Holt Rinehart & Winston, 383 Madison Ave, New York, NY 10017

Herzog, Maurice *Mountaineer*
La Tournette, Chamoinix, Haute Savoie, France

Herzog, Werner *Movie Director*
%Werner Herzog Film Productions, Turkenstra 91, D-8000 Munich 40, Germany 90265

Herzog, Whitey (Dorrel N E) *Baseball Manager, Executive*
9426 Sappington Estates Dr, St Louis, MO 63127

Hesburgh, Theodore M *Educator*
%University of Notre Dame, President Emeritus' Office, Notre Dame IN 46556

Heseltine, Michael *Government Official, England*
Thenford House, Near Banbury, Oxon OX17 2BX, England

Hess, Erika *Skier*
Aeschi, 6388 Gratenort, Switzerland

Hess, Leon *Businessman*
%Amerada Hess Corp, 1185 Ave of Americas, New York, NY 10036

Hesselbach, Walter *Financier*
%Bank fur Gemeinwirtschaft AG, 6 Frankfurt am Main, Germany

Hesseltine, Michael *Government Official, England*
%House of Commons, London SW1A 0AA, England

Hesseman, Howard *Actor*
7146 La Pesa Dr, Los Angeles, CA 90068

Hessler, Curtis A *Businessman*
%Unisys Corp, 1 Burroughs Pl, Detroit, MI 48232

Hester, Jessie *Football Player*
%Los Angeles Raiders, 332 Center St, El Segundo, CA 90245

Hester, W E, Jr (Slew) *Tennis Player*
PO Box 1057, Jackson, MS 39205

Heston, Charlton *Actor*
2859 Coldwater Canyon, Beverly Hills, CA 90210

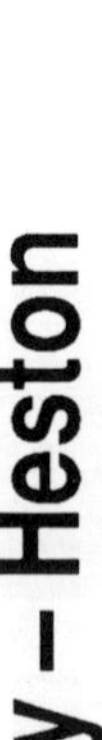

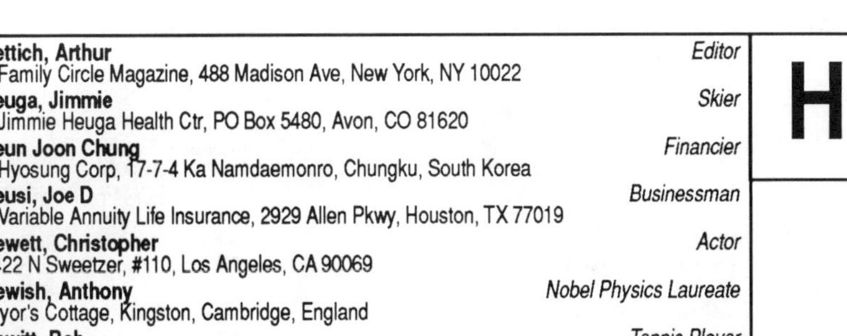

Hettich, Arthur *Editor*
%Family Circle Magazine, 488 Madison Ave, New York, NY 10022

Heuga, Jimmie *Skier*
%Jimmie Heuga Health Ctr, PO Box 5480, Avon, CO 81620

Heun Joon Chung *Financier*
%Hyosung Corp, 17-7-4 Ka Namdaemonro, Chungku, South Korea

Heusi, Joe D *Businessman*
%Variable Annuity Life Insurance, 2929 Allen Pkwy, Houston, TX 77019

Hewett, Christopher *Actor*
1422 N Sweetzer, #110, Los Angeles, CA 90069

Hewish, Anthony *Nobel Physics Laureate*
Pryor's Cottage, Kingston, Cambridge, England

Hewitt, Bob *Tennis Player*
%Pender Sports Corp, 29 Tower Rd, Newton, MA 02161

Hewitt, Don S *Television Producer*
%CBS-TV, News Dept, 524 W 57th St, New York, NY 10019

Hewitt, William A *Businessman*
3800 Blackhawk Rd, Rock Island, IL 61201

Hewlett, William R *Businessman*
%Hewlett-Packard Co, 3000 Hanover St, Palo Alto, CA 94304

Hextall, Ron *Hockey Player*
%Philadelphia Flyers, Spectrum, Pattison Pl, Philadelphia, PA 19148

Heyerdahl, Thor *Explorer, Anthropologist*
Colla Micheri, 7020 Laigueglia, Italy

Heyman, Richard *Geneticist (9-Cis Retinoic Acid Hormone)*
%Ligand Pharmaceuticals, 9393 Town Center Dr, #100, San Diego, CA 92121

Heyman, Samuel J *Businessman*
%GAF Corp, 1361 Alps Rd, Wayne, NJ 07470

Heywood, Anne *Actress*
9966 Liebe Dr, Beverly Hills, CA 90210

Hiatt, Andrew *Molecular Biologist*
%Scripps Clinic-Research Foundation, 10666 N Torrey Pines Rd, La Jolla, CA 92093

Hiatt, Arnold S *Businessman*
%Stride Rite Corp, 5 Cambridge Ctr, Cambridge, MA 02142

Hibbert, Donald R *Businessman*
%Kimberly-Clark Corp, PO Box 619100, Dallas, TX 75261

Hick, John H *Theologian*
%Claremont Graduate School, Religious Philosophy Dept, Claremont, CA 91711

Hickcox, Charlie *Swimmer*
1215 Northfield Rd, Colorado Springs, CO 80919

Hickel, Walter J *Secretary, Interior; Governor, AK*
935 W 5th, Anchorage, AK 99501

Hickerson, Gene *Football Player*
12700 Lake Ave, Lakewood, OH 44107

Hickey, Frank G *Businessman*
%General Instrument Co, 767 5th Ave, New York, NY 10153

Hickey, James Cardinal *Religious Leader*
%Archbishop's Residence, 1721 Rhode Island Ave NW, Washington, DC 20036

Hickey, Maurice *Publisher*
%Denver Post, 650 15th St, Denver, CO 80201

Hickey, Thomas J *Air Force General*
Deputy Chief of Staff/Personnel, Hq USAF, Washington, DC 20330

Hickman, Dwayne *Actor*
812 16th St, #1, Santa Monica, CA 90403

Hickman, Ed L *Financier*
%Guarantee Financial Corp, 1177 Fulton Mall, Fresno, CA 93721

Hickman, Fred *Sportscaster*
%Cable News Network, Sports Dept, 1 CNN Ctr, PO Box 105366, Atlanta, GA 0348

Hicks, Catherine *Actress*
%J Michael Bloom Ltd, 9200 Sunset Blvd, #710, Los Angeles, CA 90069

Hicks, Louise Day *Representative, MA; Mayor*
493 Broadway, South Boston, MA 02127

Hicks, Marshall M *Labor Leader*
%Utility Workers Union of America, 815 16th St NW, Washington, DC 20006

Hidalgo, John *Government Official*
%Mays Valentine Davenport Moore, 1899 "L" St NW, Washington, DC 20036

Hieb, Richard J *Astronaut*
%NASA, Johnson Space Ctr, Houston, TX 77058

Hiebert, Erwin Nick *Historian*
40 Payson Rd, Belmont, MA 02178

Hier, Marvin *Religious Leader, Social Activist*
%Simon Wiesenthal Holocaust Ctr, 9766 W Pico Blvd, Los Angeles, CA 90035

Hieronymus, Clara *Art & Drama Critic*
%The Tennessean, 1100 Broadway, Nashville, TN 37203

Higdon, Bruce *Cartoonist*
2631 Birdsong Ave, Murfreesboro, TN 37130

Higdon, Ernest D *Labor Leader*
%Coopers International Union, 400 Sherburn Ln, #207, Louisville, KY 40207

Higginbotham, A Leon, Jr *Judge*
%US Court of Appeals, US Courthouse, 601 Market St, Philadelphia, PA 19106

Higginbotham, Patrick E *Judge*
%US Court of Appeals, 1100 Commerce St, Dallas, TX 75242

Higgins, Alec W *Businessman*
Somersby, 12 Priestlands Park Rd, Sideup, Kent DA15 7HR, England

Higgins, Colin *Movie Director*
2844 Hutton Dr, Beverly Hills, CA 90210

Higgins, George V *Writer*
15 Brush Hill Ln, Milton, MA 02186

Higgins, Jack *Editorial Cartoonist*
%Chicago Sun-Times, 401 N Wabash Ave, Chicago, IL 60611

Higgins, Jack *Writer*
September Tide, Mont de la Roque, Jersey, Channel Islands, England

Higgins, Jay F *Financier*
%Salomon Bros, 1 New York Plz, New York, NY 10004

Higgins, Joel *Actor*
%Triad Artists, 10100 Santa Monica Blvd, #1600, Los Angeles, CA 90067

Higgins, John *Swimmer, Swimming Coach*
40 Williams Dr, Annapolis, MD 21401

Higgins, Ralph *Track Coach*
108 Spindrift PBC, Rancho Palos Verdes, CA 90274

Higginson, John *Pathologist*
9650 Rockville Pike, Bethesda, MD 20814

Higham, John *Historian*
309 Tuscany Rd, Baltimore, MD 21210

Highsmith, Patricia *Writer*
%Diogenes Verlag, Sprecherstrasse 8, Zurich 8032, Switzerland

Hightower, John B *Museum Director*
333 Central Park West, New York, NY 10025

Higuera, Teodoro *Baseball Player*
%Milwaukee Brewers, County Stadium, Milwaukee, WI 53214

Hijikata, Takeshi *Businessman*
%Sumitomo Chemical Co, 15 Kitahama, Higashiku, Osaka, Japan

Hijuelos, Oscar *Writer*
%Farrar Straus Girox, 19 Union Sq W, New York, NY 10003

Hilbe, Alfred J *Head of Government, Liechtenstein*
FL-9494 Schaan, Garsill 11, Liechtenstein

Hildegarde *Singer*
230 E 48th St, New York, NY 10017

Hilfiger, Tommy *Fashion Designer*
%Murjani International, 1411 Broadway, New York, NY 10018

Hilgard, Ernest R *Psychologist*
850 Webster, Palo Alto, CA 94301

Hilger, Wolfgang *Businessman*
%Hoechst AG, Postfach 800320, 6230 Frankfurt/Main 80, Germany

Hill of Luton, Baron *Government Official, Journalist*
5 Bamville Wood, East Common, Harpenden, Herts, England

Hill, Albert Alan *Government Official*
%Environmental Quality Council, 722 Jackson Pl NW, Washington, DC 20006

Hill, Anita *Educator*
%Oklahoma University, Law School, Norman, OK 73069

Hill, Arthur *Actor*
1515 Club View Dr, Los Angeles, CA 90024

Hill, Benny *Comedian*
2 Queens Gate, #7, London SW7, England

Hill, Dan *Football Player*
171 Montrose Dr, Dunbarton, Durham, NC 27707

Hill, Dave *Golfer*
%Professional Golfers Assn, PO Box 109601, Palm Beach Gardens, FL 33410

Hill, Draper *Editorial Cartoonist*
368 Washington Rd, Grosse Point, MI 48230

Hill, Drew *Football Player*
%Houston Oilers, 6910 Fannin St, Houston, TX 77030

Hill, Dusty *Musician (ZZ Top)*
PO Box 19744, Houston, TX 77024

Hill, Eddie *Drag Racing Driver*
2130 McGrath Ln, Wichita Falls, TX 76309

Hill, George Roy *Movie Director*
%Pan Arts Productions, 1325 Ave of Americas, New York, NY 10019

Hill, Harlon *Football Player*
Rt 2, Killen, AL 35645

Hill, James C *Judge*
%US Court of Appeals, 56 Forsyth St NW, Atlanta, GA 30303

Hill, Jim *Sportscaster*
%KABC-TV, Sports Dept, 4151 Prospect Ave, Los Angeles, CA 90027

Hill, John A *Businessman*
%Hospital Corp of Americas, 1 Park Plz, Nashville, TN 37202

Hill, John R, Jr *Businessman*
%Gifford-Hill Co, 300 E John W Carpenter Fwy, Irving, TX 75062

Hill, Margaret Hunt *Businesswoman*
%Hunt Resources Corp, 3600 First International Bldg, Dallas, TX 75270

Hill, Phil *Auto Racing Driver*
%Hill & Vaughan, 1607 Lincoln Blvd, Santa Monica, CA 90404

Hill, S Richardson *Educator*
%University of Alabama, President's Office, Birmingham, AL 35294

Hill, Terence *Actor*
PO Box 818, Stockbridge, MA 01262

Hill, Terrell L *Biophysicist, Chemist*
9626 Kensington Pkwy, Kensington, MD 20895

Hill, Virgil *Boxer*
%Top Rank Inc, 3900 Paradise Rd, #227, Las Vegas, NV 89109

Hill, Walter *Movie Director*
31368 Broad Beach Rd, Malibu, CA 90265

Hill-Norton, Baron *Navy Fleet Admiral*
King's Mill House, South Nutfield, Surrey, England

Hillaire, Marcel *Actor*
637 1/2 S Burnside Ave, Los Angeles, CA 90036

Hillary, Edmund *Mountaineer, Explorer*
278-A Remuera Rd, Auckland SE2, New Zealand

Hillas, Roger *Businessman*
Meritor Financial Grp, 1212 Market St, Philadelphia, PA 19107

Hille, Einar *Mathematician*
8862 La Jolla Scenic Dr N, La Jolla, CA 92037

Hilleman, Maurice R *Virologist*
%Merck Institute for Therapeutic Research, West Point, PA 19486

Hillenbrand, Daniel A *Businessman*
%Hillenbrand Industries, Highway 46, Batesville, IN 47006

Hillenbrand, Martin J *Diplomat*
%Atlantic Institute, 120 Rue de Longchamp, 75116 Paris, France

Hillenbrand, W August *Businessman*
%Hillenbrand Industries, Highway 46, Batesville, IN 47006

Hiller, Arthur *Movie Director*
1218 Benedict Canyon, Beverly Hills, CA 90210

Hiller, Wendy *Actress*
Spindles, Stratton Rd, Beaconsfield, Bucks, England

Hiller, William A *Businessman*
%Agway Inc, PO Box 4933, Syracuse, NY 13221

Hillerman, John *Actor*
%Metropolitan Talent Agency, 9320 Wilshire Blvd, #300, Beverly Hills, CA 90212

Hillerman, Tony *Writer*
2729 Texas NE, Albuquerque, NM 87110

Hillery, Patrick J *President, Ireland*
Aras An Uachtarain, Phoenix Park, Dublin 8, Ireland

Hillhouse, Gordon E *Businessman*
%Sun Co, 100 Matsonford Rd, Radnor, PA 19087

Hilliard, William A *Editor*
%Portland Oregonian, 1320 SW Broadway, Portland, OR 97201

Hillis, Danny *Computer Scientist*
%Thinking Machines Corp, 245 1st St, Cambridge, MA 02142

Hillman, Henry L *Businessman*
%Hillman Co, Grant Bldg, Pittsburgh, PA 15219

Hills, Carla A *Secretary, Housing & Urban Development*
3125 Chain Bridge Rd NW, Washington, DC 20016

Hills, Lee *Publisher, Editor*
%Knight-Ridder Newspapers, 1 Herald Plz, Miami, FL 33101

Hills, Roderick M *Government Official*
3125 Chain Bridge Rd NW, Washington, DC 20016

Hilmers, David C *Astronaut*
%NASA, Johnson Space Ctr, Houston, TX 77058

Hilmes, Jerome B *Army General*
Dir, Information Systems for Cmd, Control & Comm (C4), OSA, Washington, DC 20310

Hilsman, Roger *Diplomat*
Hamburg Cove, Lyme, CT 06371

Hilton, Barron *Businessman*
%Hilton Hotels Corp, 9336 Santa Monica Blvd, Beverly Hills, CA 90210

Himes, Chester *Writer*
%Rosalyn Targ, 250 W 57th St, New York, NY 10019

Himmelfarb, Gertrude *Historian*
%City University of New York, Graduate School, New York, NY 10036

Hinault, Bernard *Bicycle Racer*
%Le Poteries, Quessoy, 22120 Yffiniac, France

Hinds, Bruce J *Test Pilot*
2848 W Perfect Pl, Lancaster, CA 93534

Hinds, William E *Cartoonist (Tank McNamara)*
1301 Spring Oaks Cir, Houston, TX 77055

Hine, Maynard K *Dentist*
1121 W Michigan St, Indianapolis, IN 46202

Hines, Gerald D *Businessman*
%Gerald D Hines Interests, 2020 Post Oak Tower, Houston, TX 77055

Hines, Gregory *Dancer*
377 W 11th St, #PH, New York, NY 10014

Hines, Jerome *Opera Singer*
%Shaw Concerts, 1900 Broadway, New York, NY 10023

Hines, Patrick *Actor*
46 W 95th St, New York, NY 10025

Hingle, Pat *Actor*
41 Viola Rd, Suffern, NY 10901

Hingsen, Jurgen *Track Athlete*
4942 Sawyer Ave, Carpinteria, CA 93013

Hinkle, Carl *Football Player*
213 Cambridge Pl, Little Rock, AK 72212

Hinkle, Paul D (Tony) *Basketball Coach*
415 W 46th St, Indianapolis, IN 46208

Hino, Kazuyoshi *Fashion Designer*
%Hino & Malee Inc, 3701 N Ravenswood Ave, Chicago, IL 60613

Hinshaw, Horton C *Physician*
450 Sutter St, #1023, San Francisco, CA 94108

Hinson, Roy *Basketball Player*
%New Jersey Nets, Meadowlands Arena, East Rutherford, NJ 07073

Hinton of Bankside, Christopher *Government Official, England; Engineer*
Tiverton Lodge, Dulwich Common, London SG2 7EW, England

Hinton, Chris *Football Player*
%Atlanta Falcons, Suwanee Rd, Suwanee, GA 30174

Hinton, John D *WW II Army Hero (VC)*
30 Waitaki St, Bexley, Christchurch 7, New Zealand

Hinton, S(usan) E(loise) — *Writer*
%Delacorte Press, 1 Dag Hammarskjold Plz, New York, NY 10017

Hinton, Sam — *Singer, Songwriter*
9420 La Jolla Shores Dr, La Jolla, CA 92037

Hintz, Robert L — *Businessman*
%CSX Corp, 901 E Cary St, Richmond, VA 23219

Hiranandani, Hiro R — *Businessman*
%Pitney Bowes, Walter H Wheeler Jr Dr, Stamford, CT 06926

Hirano, Fubito — *Businessman*
%Nippondenso, 1-1 Showamachi, Kariya City 448, Japan

Hirata, Kusuo — *Businessman*
%Fuji Photo Film Co, 26-30 Nishiazabu, Minatoku, Tokyo 106, Japan

Hirata, Yutaka — *Businessman*
%Unitaka Ltd, 468 Kita-Kyutaromachi, Higashiku, Osaka 541, Japan

Hird, Thora — *Actress*
Old Loft, 21 Leinster Mews, Lancaster Gate, London W2, England

Hiro, Keitaro — *Businessman*
%Kubota Ltd, 2-47 Shikitsuhigashi, Naniwaku, Osaka 556, Japan

Hirsch, Elroy (Crazy Legs) — *Football Player*
50 Oak Creek Trl, Madison, WI 53717

Hirsch, Judd — *Actor*
%Bresler Kelly Kipperman, 15760 Ventura Blvd, #1730, Encino, CA 91436

Hirsch, Laurence E — *Businessman*
%Centex Corp, 4600 RepublicBank Tower, Dallas, TX 75201

Hirsch, Robert Paul — *Actor*
1 Pl du Palais Bourbon, 75017 Paris, France

Hirschfeld, Albert — *Cartoonist*
122 E 95th St, New York, NY 10028

Hirschfield, Alan J — *Movie Executive*
%Wertheim Schroder Co, 10900 Wilshire Blvd, Los Angeles, CA 90024

Hirt, Al — *Jazz Trumpeteer*
6135 Catalina St, New Orleans, LA 70124

Hisle, Larry — *Baseball Player*
%Ferguson, PO Box 84, Portsmouth, OH 45662

Hiss, Alger — *Attorney*
%Helen Buttenweiser, 575 Madison Ave, New York, NY 10022

Hitch, Charles J — *Educator*
1515 Oxford St, Berkeley, CA 94709

Hitchcock, Henry R — *Architectural Historian*
152 E 62nd St, New York, NY 10021

Hitchings, George H — *Nobel Medicine Laureate*
3030 Cornwallis Rd, Research Triangle, NC 27709

Hite, Shere — *Writer*
PO Box 5282, FDR Station, New York, NY 10022

Hittinger, William C — *Businessman*
%RCA Corp, 30 Rockefeller Plz, New York, NY 10020

Hix, Charles — *Fashion Expert, Writer*
%Simon & Schuster, 1230 Ave of Americas, New York, NY 10020

Hlass, I Jerry — *Aeronautical Engineer*
%National Space Technology Laboratories, NSTL Station, MS 39529

Hlinka, Nichol — *Ballerina*
%New York City Ballet, Lincoln Center Plz, New York, NY 10023

Hnizdovsky, Jacques — *Artist*
5270 Post Rd, Riverdale, NY 10471

Ho, Don — *Singer*
2005 Kalia Ave, Honolulu, HI 96815

Ho, Ya-Ming — *Biochemist*
%Massachusetts Institute of Technology, Biology Dept, Cambridge, MA 02139

Hoad, Lew — *Tennis Player*
Campo do Tenis, Apartado III, Fuengirola, Via Malaga, Spain

Hoag, David H — *Businessman*
%LTV Corp, 2001 Ross Ave, Dallas, TX 75201

Hoag, Peter C — *Test Pilot*
%AFFTC/SCV, Edwards Air Force Base, CA 93523

Hoage, Terry — *Football Player*
%Washington Redskins, Dulles Airport, Box 17247, Washington, DC 20041

Hoagland, Edward — *Writer*
Westbeth, 463 West St, New York, NY 10014

Hoagland, Jim — *Journalist*
%Washington Post, 1150 15th St NW, Washington, DC 20071

Hoagland, Mahlon B — *Biochemist*
Academy Rd, Thetford, VT 05074

Hoagland, Peter — *Representative, NE*
%House of Representatives, Washington, DC 20515

Hoaglin, Fred — *Football Player, Coach*
%New York Giants, Giants Stadium, East Rutherford, NJ 07073

Hoar, Joseph P — *Marine Corps General*
%Commander, US Central Command, MacDill AFB, FL 33608

Hoard, James L — *Chemist*
42 Cornell St, Ithaca, NY 14850

Hobart, Nick — *Cartoonist*
133 Indiana Ave, New Port Richey, FL 33552

Hobby, Oveta Culp — *Secretary, Health Education Welfare*
3050 Post Oak Blvd, #1330, Houston, TX 77056

Hoberman, Ben — *Radio Executive*
%ABC-Radio, 1330 Ave of Americas, New York, NY 10019

Hobson, David L — *Representative, OH*
%House of Representatives, Washington, DC 20515

Hoch, Orion L — *Businessman*
%Litton Industries, 360 N Crescent Dr, Beverly Hills, CA 90210

Hoch, Scott — *Golfer*
%Professional Golfers Assn, PO Box 109601, Palm Beach Gardens, FL 33410

Hochbrueckner, George J — *Representative, NY*
%House of Representatives, Washington, DC 20515

Hochhuth, Rolf — *Playwright*
CH-4125, Riehen, Schellenberg 117, Balse, Switzerland

Hockaday, Irvine O, Jr — *Businessman*
%Hallmark Cards Inc, 2501 McGee Trafficway, Kansas City, MO 64141

Hockney, David — *Artist*
2907 Montcalm Ave, Los Angeles, CA 90046

Hodge, Charlie — *Hockey Player*
%Winnipeg Jets, 15-1430 Maroons Rd, Winnipeg MA R3G 0L5, Canada

Hodges, Bill — *Basketball Coach*
%Georgia College, Athletic Dept, Milledgeville, GA 31061

Hodges, Carl N — *Environmental Scientist*
%University of Arizona, Environmental Research Laboratory, Tucson, AZ 85721

Hodges, Robert H, Jr — *Judge*
%US Claims Court, 717 Madison Pl NW, Washington, DC 20005

Hodgkin, Alan Lloyd — *Nobel Medicine Laureate*
Master's Lodge, Trinity College, Cambridge, England

Hodgson, James D — *Secretary, Labor*
10132 Hillgrove Dr, Beverly Hills, CA 90210

Hodgson, Maurice — *Businessman*
%Dunlop Holdings, Dunlop House, 25 Ryder St, London SW1Y 6PX, England

Hodsoll, Frank — *Government Official*
%National Endowment for Arts, 1100 Pennsylvania Ave NW, Washington, DC 20506

Hoefer, James B — *Publisher*
%Fortune Magazine, Rockefeller Ctr, New York, NY 10020

Hoeft, Billy — *Baseball Player*
36427 Sherwood, Livonia, MI 48154

Hoegh, Leo A — *Governor, IA*
2135 Glenhill Rd, Colorado Springs, CO 80906

Hoerni, Jean A — *Electronics Consultant*
East Fork Rd, Hailey, ID 87333

Hoeveler, William M — *Judge*
%US District Court, 301 N Miami Ave, Miami, FL 33128

Hoff, Lawrence C — *Businessman*
%Upjohn Co, 7000 Portage Rd, Kalamazoo, MI 49001

Hoff, Philip H — *Governor, VT*
%Hoff Wilson Powell Lang, 192 College St, Burlington, VT 05402

Hoff, Syd — *Writer, Cartoonist*
PO Box 2463, Miami Beach, FL 33140

H

Hoffman, Basil *Actor*
%Harry Gold Assoc, 3500 W Olive Ave, #1400, Burbank, CA 91505

Hoffman, Edwin K *Businessman*
%Woodward & Lothrop Inc, 11th & "F" NW, Washington, DC 20013

Hoffman, Gene D *Businessman*
2859 Gale Rd, Woodland, Wayzata, MN 55391

Hoffman, Grace *Opera Singer*
Bergstrasse 19, 7441 Neckartailfingen, Germany

Hoffman, Jeffrey A *Astronaut*
%NASA, Johnson Space Ctr, Houston, TX 77058

Hoffman, Leonard J *Religious Leader*
%Christian Reformed Church, 2850 Kalamazoo Ave SE, Grand Rapids, MI 49560

Hoffman, Michael L *Economist, Journalist*
RFD, Vineyard Haven, MA 02568

Hoffman, Robert B *Businessman*
%Staley Continental, 1701 Golf Rd, Rolling Meadows, IL 60008

Hoffman, Ted, Jr *Bowling Executive*
1568 Partarian Way, San Jose, CA 95129

Hoffmann, Frank (Nordy) *Football Player*
400 N Capitol St NW, #327, Washington, DC 20001

Hoffmann, Martin R *Government Official*
%Gardner Carton Douglas, 1875 "I" St NW, #1050, Washington, DC 20006

Hoffmann, Roald *Nobel Chemistry Laureate*
4 Sugarbush Ln, ithaca, NY 14850

Hoffs, Susanna *Singer*
%Columbia Records, Sony Music, 1801 Century Park West, Los Angeles, CA 90067

Hofman, Leonard J *Religious Leader*
%Christian Reformed Church, 2850 Kalamazoo Ave SE, Grand Rapids, MI 49560

Hofmann, Douglas *Artist*
8602 Saxon Cir, Baltimore, MD 21236

Hofmann, Isabella *Actress*
%Susan Smith Assoc, 121 N San Vicente Blvd, Beverly Hills, CA 90211

Hofmann, Peter *Opera Singer*
%Columbia Artists Mgmt Inc, 165 W 57th St, New York, NY 10019

Hofstad, Ralph *Businessman*
%Land O'Lakes Inc, 4001 Lexington Ave N, Arden Hills, MN 55112

Hogan, A Paul *Editor*
%Tampa Tribune, 202 S Parker St, Tampa, FL 33601

Hogan, Ben *Golfer*
2912 W Pafford St, Fort Worth, TX 76110

Hogan, Hulk *Wrestler*
10901 Winnetka Ave, Chatsworth, CA 91311

Hogan, Jack *Actor*
%Alex Brewis Agency, 12429 Laurel Terrace Dr, Studio City, CA 91604

Hogan, Paul *Actor*
1900 Ave of Stars, #2270, Los Angeles, CA 90067

Hogan, Robert *Actor*
%Borinstein-Oreck-Bogart, 8271 Melrose, #110, Los Angeles, CA 90046

Hogan, Ronald P *Businessman*
%Georgia-Pacific Corp, 133 Peachtree St NE, Atlanta, GA 30303

Hoge, James *Publisher*
%Daily News, 220 E 42nd St, New York, NY 10017

Hogg, Christopher A *Businessman*
%Courtaulds, 18 Hanover Sq, London W1A 2BB, England

Hoglund, Forrest E *Businessman*
%Enron Corp, 1400 Smith Enron Bldg, 3 Riverway, Houston, TX 77056

Hogwood, Christopher *Concert Harpsichordist, Conductor*
2 Claremont, Hills Rd, Cambridge, England

Hohenberg, John *Journalist, Educator*
3120 NW 51st Pl, Gainesville, FL 32601

Hohmann, John *Anthropologist*
%Louis Berger Assoc, 1110 E Missouri Ave, #200, Phoenix, AZ 85014

Hoiby, Lee *Composer, Concert Pianist*
Box 71, Rock Valley, Long Eddy, NY 12760

Holbrook, Anthony B *Businessman*
%Advanced Micro Devices Inc, 901 Thompson Pl, Sunnyvale, CA 94088

H

Holbrook, Bill *Cartoonist (On the Fastrack)*
1321 Weatherstone Way, Atlanta, GA 30324

Holbrook, Hal *Actor*
%William Morris Agency, 151 El Camino, Beverly Hills, CA 90212

Holchak, Vic *Actor*
%Raper Enterprises, 159 Shoshone, Flagstaff, AZ 86001

Holden, Edward *Businessman*
%AGRI Industries, PO Box 4887, Des Moines, IA 50306

Holden, Rebecca *Actress, Singer*
33 Music Square W, #104-B, Nashville, TN 37203

Holder, Geoffrey *Actor, Dancer*
%Donald Buchwald Assoc, 10 E 44th St, New York, NY 10017

Holder, Richard G *Businessman*
%Reynolds Metals Co, 6601 Broad Street Rd, Richmond, VA 23261

Holderman, James B *Educator*
%University of South Carolina, President's Office, Columbia, SC 29208

Holdorf, Willi *Track Athlete*
%Adidas KG, 8522 Herzogenaurach, Germany

Holdren, John P *Educator*
%University of California, Energy & Resources Dept, Berkeley, CA 94720

Holdsworth, Trevor *Businessman*
%Guest Keen Nettlefolds, 7 Cleveland Row, London SW1A 1DB, England

Holdt, Roy H *Businessman*
%White Consolidated Industries, 11770 Berea Rd, Cleveland, OH 44111

Holiday, Harry, Jr *Businessman*
%Armco Inc, 703 Curtis St, Middletown, OH 45043

Holl, Steven *Architect*
655 5th Ave, New York, NY 10009

Holland, David S *Businessman*
%Pennzoil Exploration & Production Co, Pennzoil Pl, Houston, TX 77252

Holland, John R *Religious Leader*
%Foursquare Gospel Int'l Church, 1100 Glendale Blvd, Los Angeles, CA 90026

Holland, Terry *Basketball Coach, Administrator*
%Davidson College, Athletic Dept, Davidson, NC 28036

Holland, Tom *Artist*
227 Tunnel Rd, Berkeley, CA 94705

Hollander, John *Poet*
Yale University, English Dept, New Haven, CT 06520

Hollander, Lorin *Concert Pianist*
210 W 101st St, #PH, New York, NY 10025

Hollein, Hans *Architect*
Eiskellerstrasse 1, 4000 Dusseldorf, Austria

Hollenbeck, Harold C *Representative, NJ; Judge*
%New Jersey Superior Court, Bergen County Justice Complex, Hackensack, NJ 07601

Hollerer, Walter F *Writer, Critic*
Heerstrasse 99, 1 Berlin 19, Germany

Holley, Cyrus H *Businessman*
%Engelhard Corp, Menlo Park, Edison, NJ 08818

Holley, Robert W *Nobel Medicine Laureate*
7381 Rue Michael, La Jolla, CA 92037

Holliday, Fred *Actor*
4610 Forman Ave, North Hollywood, CA 91602

Holliday, Jennifer *Singer, Actress*
%Raymond Katz Enterprises, 9255 Sunset Blvd, Los Angeles, CA 90069

Holliday, Polly *Singer, Actress*
%Lantz Office, 888 7th Ave, #2500, New York, NY 10106

Holliger, Heinz *Concert Oboist, Composer*
%Ingpen & Williams, 14 Kensington Ct, London W8, England

Holliman, Earl *Actor*
PO Box 1969, Studio City, CA 91604

Hollings, Ernest F *Senator, SC*
Boyce's Wharf, Charleston, SC 29401

Hollins, Lionel *Basketball Player*
%Houston Rockets, Summit, Greenway Plz, #10, Houston, TX 77046

Hollis, Peter *Businessman*
%Ames Department Stores, 2418 Main St, Rocky Hill, CT 06067

Holloway, Benjamin D *Financier*
%Donaldson Lufkin Jenrette, 140 Broadway, New York, NY 10005
Holloway, Clyde C *Representative, LA*
%House of Representatives, Washington, DC 20515
Holloway, James L, III *Navy Admiral*
1694 Epping Farms Ln, Annapolis, MD 21401
Holloway, Randy *Football Player*
%New England Patriots, Sullivan Stadium, Foxboro, MA 02035
Holloway, Sterling *Actor*
%Kingsley Colton Assoc, 16661 Ventura Blvd, #400, Encino, CA 91436
Holloway, William J, Jr *Judge*
%US Court of Appeals, PO Box 1767, Oklahoma City, OK 73101
Holm Whalen, Eleanor *Swimmer*
1800 NE 114th St, #1503, North Miami, FL 33161
Holm, Celeste *Actress*
88 Central Park West, New York, NY 10023
Holm, Gerald L *Financier*
%Beneficial Corp, 1100 Carr Rd, Wilmington, DE 19899
Holm, Hanya *Choreographer, Dancer*
%Selma Tamber, 45 W 54th St, New York, NY 10019
Holm, Ian *Actor*
%Julian Belfage Assoc, 60 St James St, London SW1, England
Holman, Marshall *Bowler*
%Professional Bowlers Assn, 1720 Merriman Rd, Akron, OH 44313
Holman, Nat *Basketball Player, Coach*
28 E 73rd St, New York, NY 10021
Holmes, E Paul *Navy Admiral*
4329 Alfriends Trl, Virginia Beach, VA 23455
Holmes, J Michael *Financier*
%NAFCO Financial Grp, 5801 Pelican Bay Blvd, Naples, FL 33940
Holmes, Jennifer *Actress*
5329 Sunnyslope Ave, Van Nuys, CA 91401
Holmes, Larry *Boxer*
%Holmes Enterprises, 43 Northampton St, Easton, PA 18042
Holmes, Ron *Football Player*
%Tampa Bay Buccaneers, 1 Buccaneer Pl, Tampa, FL 33607
Holmes, Thomas A *Businessman*
%Ingersoll-Rand Co, 200 Chestnut Ridge Rd, Woodcliff Lake, NJ 07675
Holmes, Tommy *Baseball Player*
1 Pine Dr, Woodbury, NY 11797
Holmgren, Mike *Football Coach*
%Green Bay Packers, 1265 Lombardi Ave, Green Bay, WI 54307
Holmgren, Paul *Hockey Player, Coach*
%Philadelphia Flyers, Pattison Pl, Philadelphia, PA 19148
Holmquest, Donald L *Astronaut*
%Wood Lucksinger Epstein, 1221 Lamar, #1400, Houston, TX 77010
Holmstrom, Carl *Skier*
1703 E 3rd St, #101, Duluth, MN 55812
Holovak, Mike *Football Player, Coach*
Links Rd, Gloucester, MA 01930
Holroyd, Michael *Writer*
%A P Watt Ltd, 20 John St, London WC1N 2DL, England
Holshouser, James E *Governor, NC*
PO Box 1227, Pinehurst, NC 28374
Holt, Glenn L *Labor Leader*
%Metal Workers Union, 5578 Montgomery Rd, Cincinnati, OH 45212
Holt, Leon C, Jr *Businessman*
%Air Products & Chemicals Inc, PO Box 538, Allentown, PA 18105
Holtermann, E Louis, Jr *Publisher*
%Glamour Magazine, 350 Madison Ave, New York, NY 10017
Holtfreter, Johannes F C *Zoologist*
29 Knolltop Dr, Rochester, NY 14610
Holton, A Linwood, Jr *Governor, VA*
6010 Claiborne Dr, McLean, VA 22101
Holton, Gerald *Physicist*
14 Trotting Horse Dr, Lexington, MA 02173

H

Holton – Hoover

Holton, Richard H *Educator*
87 Southampton Ave, Berkeley, CA 94707

Holton, Robert J *Labor Leader*
Plasters/Cement Masons International Assn, 1125 17th St NW, Washington, DC 20036

Holtz, Lou *Football Coach*
%University of Notre Dame, Athletic Dept, Notre Dame, IN 46556

Holtzman, Jerome *Sportswriter*
1225 Forest Ave, Evanston, IL 60202

Holtzman, Ken *Baseball Player*
933 Providence, Buffalo Grove, IL 60089

Holub, E J *Football Player*
%General Delivery, Copan, OK 74022

Holum, Dianne *Speed Skater*
280 Weldwood Dr, Elgin, IL 60120

Holyfield, Evander *Boxer*
%Shelly Finkel, 310 Madison Ave, #804, New York, NY 10017

Holyrod, Michael *Writer*
85 St Marks Rd, London W10 6JS, England

Holzer, Jenny *Artist*
245 Eldridge St, New York, NY 10022

Holzman, Malcolm *Architect*
%Hardy Holzman Pfeiffer, 902 Broadway, New York, NY 10010

Holzman, William (Red) *Basketball Coach*
%New York Knicks, Madison Square Gdn, 4 Pennsylvania Plz, New York, NY 10001

Home of Hirsel, Baron *Prime Minister, England*
Hirsel, Coldstream, Berwickshire, Scotland

Homeier, Skip *Actor*
261 S Robertson Blvd, Beverly Hills, CA 90211

Homfeld, Conrad *Equestrian Rider*
%Sandron, 11744 Marblestone Ct, West Palm Beach, FL 33414

Honderich, Beland H *Publisher*
%Toronto Star, 1 Yonge St, Toronto ON M5E 1E6, Canada

Honegger, Fritz *President, Switzerland*
Schloss-Strasse 29, 8803 Ruschlikon, Switzerland

Honeycutt, Rick *Baseball Player*
207 Forrest Rd, Fort Oglethorpe, GA 30742

Hong, James *Actor*
11684 Ventura Blvd, #948, Studio City, CA 91604

Honochick, Jim *Baseball Umpire*
10 S Ott St, Allentown, PA 18104

Hood, Edward E, Jr *Businessman*
%General Electric Co, 3135 Easton Turnpike, Fairfield, CT 06431

Hood, Kenneth *Religious Leader*
%799 Bloomfield Ave, Verona, NJ 07044

Hood, LeRoy *Biologist*
1453 E California Blvd, Pasadena, CA 91106

Hood, Robert *Editor*
%Boys Life Magazine, 1325 Walnut Hill Ln, Irving, TX 75062

Hood, Robin *Golfer*
%Ladies Professional Golf Assn, 2570 Volusia Ave, #B, Daytona Beach, FL 32114

Hooglandt, Jan D *Businessman*
Hoogovens Grp, 1970 CA Nijmegen, Netherlands

Hook, Harold S *Businessman*
%American General Corp, 2929 Allen Pkwy, Houston, TX 77019

Hooker, John Lee *Singer*
%Rosebud Agency, PO Box 210103, San Francisco, CA 94121

Hooks, Benjamin L *Civil Rights Leader*
%NAACP, 1790 Broadway, New York, NY 10019

Hookstratten, Edward G *Attorney*
9012 Beverly Blvd, Los Angeles, CA 90048

Hoopman, Harold D *Businessman*
%Marathon Oil Co, 539 S Main St, Findlay, OH 45840

Hooton, Burt *Baseball Player*
3619 Grandby Ct, San Antonio, TX 78217

Hoover, Charles M *Businessman*
%Roper Corp, 1905 W Court St, Kankakee, IL 60901

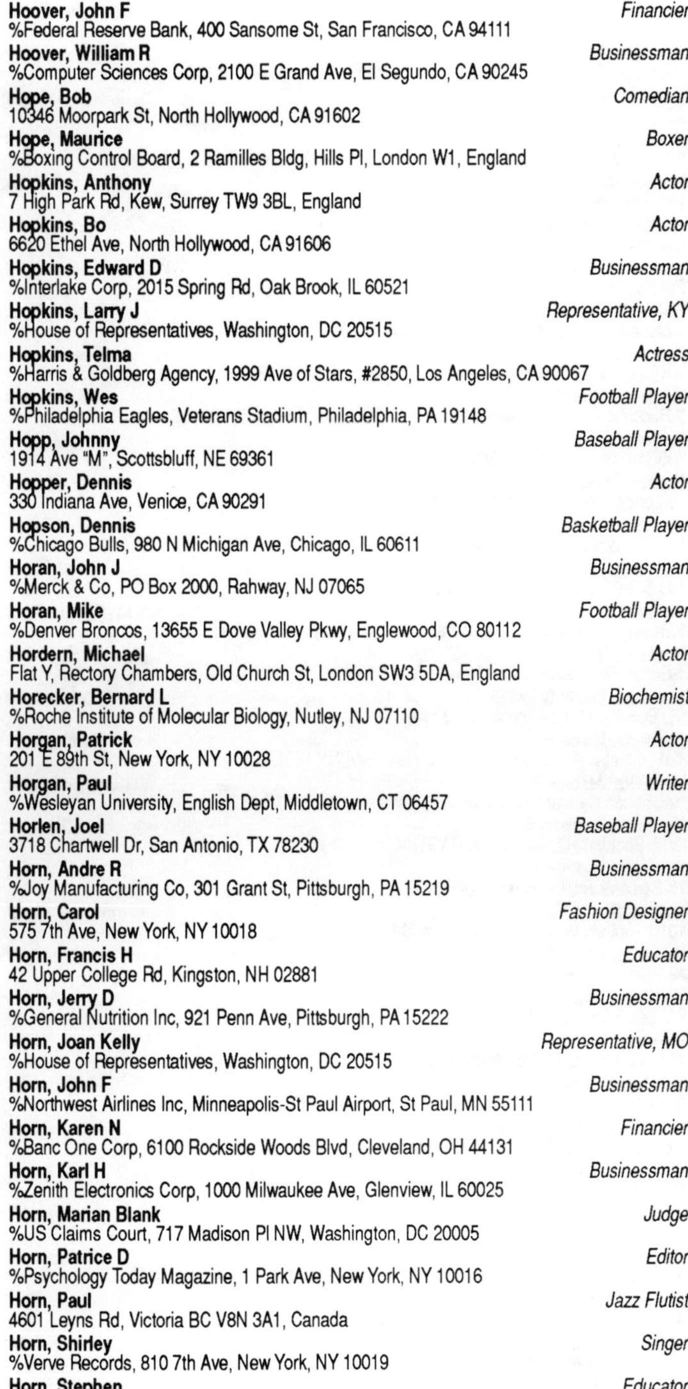

Hoover, John F *Financier*
%Federal Reserve Bank, 400 Sansome St, San Francisco, CA 94111

Hoover, William R *Businessman*
%Computer Sciences Corp, 2100 E Grand Ave, El Segundo, CA 90245

Hope, Bob *Comedian*
10346 Moorpark St, North Hollywood, CA 91602

Hope, Maurice *Boxer*
%Boxing Control Board, 2 Ramilles Bldg, Hills Pl, London W1, England

Hopkins, Anthony *Actor*
7 High Park Rd, Kew, Surrey TW9 3BL, England

Hopkins, Bo *Actor*
6620 Ethel Ave, North Hollywood, CA 91606

Hopkins, Edward D *Businessman*
%Interlake Corp, 2015 Spring Rd, Oak Brook, IL 60521

Hopkins, Larry J *Representative, KY*
%House of Representatives, Washington, DC 20515

Hopkins, Telma *Actress*
%Harris & Goldberg Agency, 1999 Ave of Stars, #2850, Los Angeles, CA 90067

Hopkins, Wes *Football Player*
%Philadelphia Eagles, Veterans Stadium, Philadelphia, PA 19148

Hopp, Johnny *Baseball Player*
1914 Ave "M", Scottsbluff, NE 69361

Hopper, Dennis *Actor*
330 Indiana Ave, Venice, CA 90291

Hopson, Dennis *Basketball Player*
%Chicago Bulls, 980 N Michigan Ave, Chicago, IL 60611

Horan, John J *Businessman*
%Merck & Co, PO Box 2000, Rahway, NJ 07065

Horan, Mike *Football Player*
%Denver Broncos, 13655 E Dove Valley Pkwy, Englewood, CO 80112

Hordern, Michael *Actor*
Flat Y, Rectory Chambers, Old Church St, London SW3 5DA, England

Horecker, Bernard L *Biochemist*
%Roche Institute of Molecular Biology, Nutley, NJ 07110

Horgan, Patrick *Actor*
201 E 89th St, New York, NY 10028

Horgan, Paul *Writer*
%Wesleyan University, English Dept, Middletown, CT 06457

Horlen, Joel *Baseball Player*
3718 Chartwell Dr, San Antonio, TX 78230

Horn, Andre R *Businessman*
%Joy Manufacturing Co, 301 Grant St, Pittsburgh, PA 15219

Horn, Carol *Fashion Designer*
575 7th Ave, New York, NY 10018

Horn, Francis H *Educator*
42 Upper College Rd, Kingston, NH 02881

Horn, Jerry D *Businessman*
%General Nutrition Inc, 921 Penn Ave, Pittsburgh, PA 15222

Horn, Joan Kelly *Representative, MO*
%House of Representatives, Washington, DC 20515

Horn, John F *Businessman*
%Northwest Airlines Inc, Minneapolis-St Paul Airport, St Paul, MN 55111

Horn, Karen N *Financier*
%Banc One Corp, 6100 Rockside Woods Blvd, Cleveland, OH 44131

Horn, Karl H *Businessman*
%Zenith Electronics Corp, 1000 Milwaukee Ave, Glenview, IL 60025

Horn, Marian Blank *Judge*
%US Claims Court, 717 Madison Pl NW, Washington, DC 20005

Horn, Patrice D *Editor*
%Psychology Today Magazine, 1 Park Ave, New York, NY 10016

Horn, Paul *Jazz Flutist*
4601 Leyns Rd, Victoria BC V8N 3A1, Canada

Horn, Shirley *Singer*
%Verve Records, 810 7th Ave, New York, NY 10019

Horn, Stephen *Educator*
%California State University, Political Science Dept, Long Beach, CA 90840

H

Hornacek – Horton

Hornacek, Jeff *Basketball Player*
%Phoenix Suns, 2910 N Central, Phoenix, AZ 85012

Hornaday, William *Religious Leader*
%Church of Religious Science, 3251 W 6th St, Los Angeles, CA 90020

Horne, Lena *Singer*
23 E 74th St, New York, NY 10021

Horne, Marilyn *Opera Singer*
%Columbia Artists Mgmt Inc, 165 W 57th St, New York, NY 10019

Horner, Bob *Baseball Player*
209 Steeplechase Dr, Irving, TX 75062

Horner, Charles A *Air Force General*
Commander, 9th Air Force, Shaw Air Force Base, SC 29152

Horner, Freeman V *WW II Army Hero (CMH)*
PO Box 6092, Columbus, GA 31907

Horner, Jack *Palentologist*
%Museum of the Rockies, Montana State University, Bozeman, MT 59717

Horner, Larry D *Businessman*
%KPMG Peat Marwick, 345 Park Ave, New York, NY 10022

Horner, Matina *Educator*
%Radcliffe College, President Emeritus' Office, Cambridge, MA 02138

Horner, Richard E *Businessman*
905 11th St NE, Waseca, MN 56093

Hornig, Donald F *Chemist*
16 Longfellow Park, Cambridge, MA 02138

Hornsby, Bruce *Singer*
%RCA Records, 6363 Sunset Blvd, #417, Los Angeles, CA 90028

Hornung, Paul *Football Player*
133 S 3rd St, Louisville, KY 40202

Horovitz, Adam *Singer (Beastie Boys)*
%Beastie Boys, Rush Productions, 1133 Broadway, New York, NY 10010

Horovitz, Israel *Playwright*
%Safier, 667 Madison Ave, New York, NY 10021

Horowitz, David C *Commentator*
PO Box 4524, Los Angeles, CA 90049

Horowitz, David H *Businessman*
%MTV Network, 75 Rockefeller Plz, New York, NY 10019

Horowitz, Jerome P *Medical Researcher*
%Michigan Cancer Foundation, 110 E Warren, Detroit, MI 48201

Horowitz, Norman H *Biologist*
2495 Brighton Rd, Pasadena, CA 91104

Horowitz, Paul *Physician*
15 Barberry Rd, Lexington, MA 02173

Horrell, Edwin (Babe) *Football Player*
10101 Angelo View Dr, Beverly Hills, CA 90210

Horsfall, James G *Plant Pathologist*
49 Woodstock Rd, Hamden, CT 06517

Horsford, Anna Maria *Actress*
PO Box 29765, Los Angeles, CA 90027

Horsley, Lee *Actor*
1941 Cummings Dr, Los Angeles, CA 90027

Horsley, Nicholas *Businessman*
%Northern Foods, St Stephen's Sq, Hull HU1 3XG, England

Horszowski, Mieczyslaw *Concert Pianist*
%Curtis Institute of Music, 1726 Locust St, Philadelphia, PA 19103

Horton, Frank E *Educator*
%University of Toledo, President's Office, Toledo, OH 43606

Horton, Frank J *Representative, NY*
2123 East Ave, Rochester, NY 14610

Horton, Jack K *Businessman*
%Southern California Edison Co, 2244 Walnut Grove Ave, Rosemead, CA 91770

Horton, Peter *Actor*
222 Adelaide Dr, Santa Monica, CA 90402

Horton, Robert *Actor*
5317 Andasol Ave, Encino, CA 91316

Horton, Willie *Baseball Player*
%Reid, 15124 Warwick, Detroit, MI 48233

Horvath, Les *Football Player*
2667 Bogue Dr, Glendale, CA 91208
Hosie, William C *Businessman*
%Sun-Diamond Growers, 1050 S Diamond St, Stockton, CA 95205
Hosking, Robert L *Radio Executive*
%CBS Radio, 51 W 52nd St, New York, NY 10019
Hoskins, Bob *Actor*
%Hope & Lyne, 5 Milner Pl, London N1, England
Hosmer, Bradley C *Air Force General*
%Superintendent's Office, USAF Air Force Academy, CO 80840
Hoss, Richard W *Businessman*
%Roadway Services Inc, 1077 Gorge Blvd, Akron, OH 44309
Hossein, Robert *Actor*
17 Rue de la Tremoille, 75008 Paris, France
Hostage, G Michael *Businessman*
%Howard Johnson Co, 220 Forbes Rd, Braintree, MA 02184
Hostetler, Robert D *Businessman*
%CTS Corp, 905 North West Blvd, Elkhart, IN 46514
Hotani, Hirokazu *Microbiotics Engineer*
%Teikyo University, Biosciences Dept, Toyosatodai, Utsunomiya 320, Japan
Hotchkiss, Rollin D *Bacterial Physiologist*
500 E 63rd St, New York, NY 10021
Hotson, Leslie *Educator*
White Hollow Rd, Northford, CT 06472
Hottel, Hoyt C *Chemical Engineer*
27 Cambridge St, Winchester, MA 01890
Hottelet, Richard C *Commentator*
%CBS-TV, News Dept, 530 W 57th St, New York, NY 10019
Hotter, Hans *Opera Singer*
%Bayerische Staatsoper, 8000 Munich, Germany
Hou, Ya-Ming *Biologist*
%Massachusetts Institute of Technology, Biology Dept, Cambridge, MA 02139
Houbregs, Bob *Basketball Player*
3403 207th Ave SE, Issaquah, WA 98027
Hough, Charlie *Baseball Player*
2266 Shade Tree Cir, Brea, CA 92621
Hough, Lawrence A *Businessman*
%Student Loan Marketing Assn, 1050 Thomas Jefferson St, Washington, DC 20007
Hough, Richard *Swimmer*
RR 2, Box 294, Concord, NH 03301
Houghton, Amory, Jr *Representative, NY*
%House of Representatives, Washington, DC 20515
Houghton, Anthony, Jr *Businessman*
%Corning Inc, Houghton Park, Corning, NY 14831
Houghton, James R *Businessman*
%Corning Inc, Houghton Park, Corning, NY 14831
Houghton, Katherine *Actress*
134 Steele Rd, West Hartford, CT 06119
Houk, Ralph *Baseball Manager*
3000 Plantation Rd, Winter Haven, FL 33884
Houle, Cyril O *Educator*
5510 Woodlawn Ave, Chicago, IL 60637
Hounsfield, Godfrey N *Nobel Medicine Laureate*
15 Crane Park Rd, Whitton, Twickenham, Middx, England
Houphouet-Boigny, Felix *President, Ivory Coast*
%President's Office, Abidjan, Ivory Coast
House, Karen E *Journalist*
%Wall Street Journal, 22 Cortlandt St, New York, NY 10007
Houseman, John J, Jr *Financier*
%Irving Bank Corp, 1 Wall St, New York, NY 10005
Houser, Allan *Artist*
1020 Camino Carlos Rey, Santa Fe, NM 87501
Houser, Clarence (Bud) *Track Athlete*
1220 S Lyon St, Santa Ana, CA 92705
Housley, Phil *Hockey Player*
%Buffalo Sabres, Memorial Auditorium, Buffalo, NY 14202

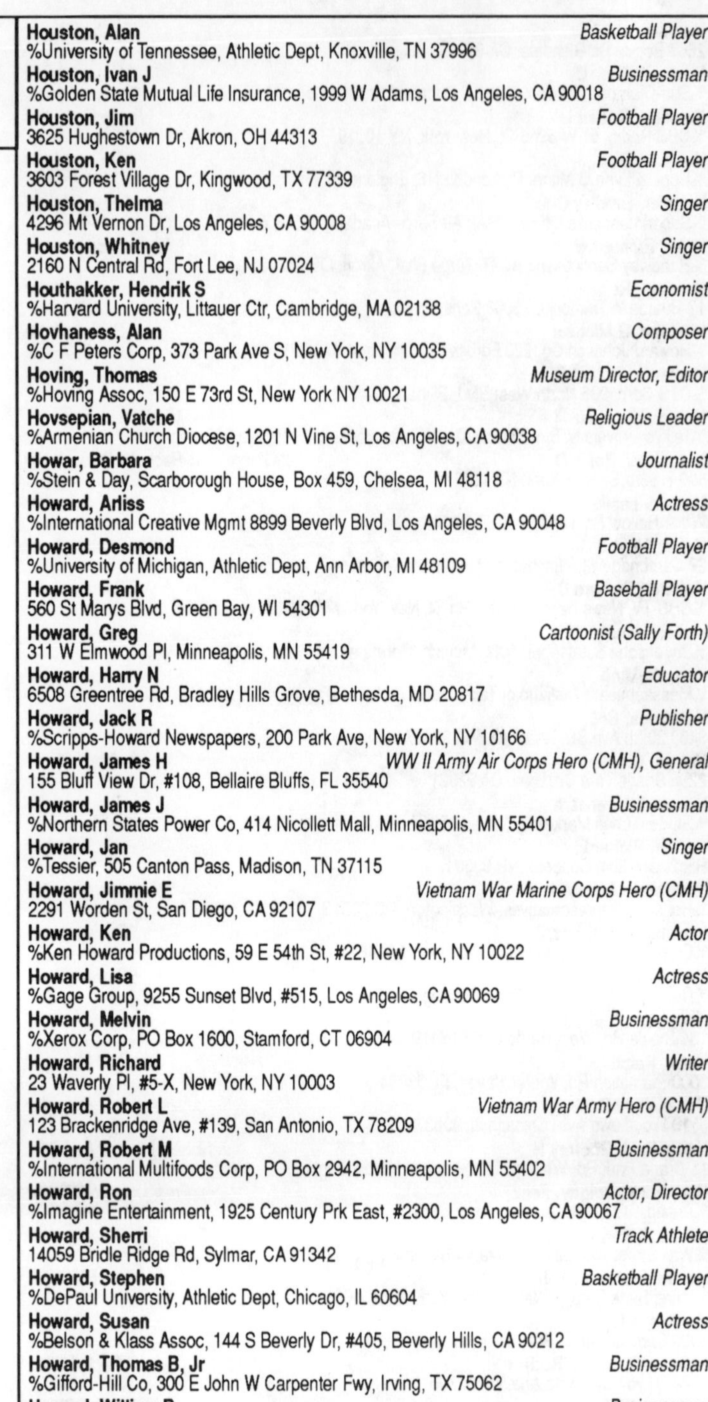

H

Houston - Howard

Houston, Alan *Basketball Player*
%University of Tennessee, Athletic Dept, Knoxville, TN 37996

Houston, Ivan J *Businessman*
%Golden State Mutual Life Insurance, 1999 W Adams, Los Angeles, CA 90018

Houston, Jim *Football Player*
3625 Hughestown Dr, Akron, OH 44313

Houston, Ken *Football Player*
3603 Forest Village Dr, Kingwood, TX 77339

Houston, Thelma *Singer*
4296 Mt Vernon Dr, Los Angeles, CA 90008

Houston, Whitney *Singer*
2160 N Central Rd, Fort Lee, NJ 07024

Houthakker, Hendrik S *Economist*
%Harvard University, Littauer Ctr, Cambridge, MA 02138

Hovhaness, Alan *Composer*
%C F Peters Corp, 373 Park Ave S, New York, NY 10035

Hoving, Thomas *Museum Director, Editor*
%Hoving Assoc, 150 E 73rd St, New York NY 10021

Hovsepian, Vatche *Religious Leader*
%Armenian Church Diocese, 1201 N Vine St, Los Angeles, CA 90038

Howar, Barbara *Journalist*
%Stein & Day, Scarborough House, Box 459, Chelsea, MI 48118

Howard, Arliss *Actress*
%International Creative Mgmt 8899 Beverly Blvd, Los Angeles, CA 90048

Howard, Desmond *Football Player*
%University of Michigan, Athletic Dept, Ann Arbor, MI 48109

Howard, Frank *Baseball Player*
560 St Marys Blvd, Green Bay, WI 54301

Howard, Greg *Cartoonist (Sally Forth)*
311 W Elmwood Pl, Minneapolis, MN 55419

Howard, Harry N *Educator*
6508 Greentree Rd, Bradley Hills Grove, Bethesda, MD 20817

Howard, Jack R *Publisher*
%Scripps-Howard Newspapers, 200 Park Ave, New York, NY 10166

Howard, James H *WW II Army Air Corps Hero (CMH), General*
155 Bluff View Dr, #108, Bellaire Bluffs, FL 35540

Howard, James J *Businessman*
%Northern States Power Co, 414 Nicollett Mall, Minneapolis, MN 55401

Howard, Jan *Singer*
%Tessier, 505 Canton Pass, Madison, TN 37115

Howard, Jimmie E *Vietnam War Marine Corps Hero (CMH)*
2291 Worden St, San Diego, CA 92107

Howard, Ken *Actor*
%Ken Howard Productions, 59 E 54th St, #22, New York, NY 10022

Howard, Lisa *Actress*
%Gage Group, 9255 Sunset Blvd, #515, Los Angeles, CA 90069

Howard, Melvin *Businessman*
%Xerox Corp, PO Box 1600, Stamford, CT 06904

Howard, Richard *Writer*
23 Waverly Pl, #5-X, New York, NY 10003

Howard, Robert L *Vietnam War Army Hero (CMH)*
123 Brackenridge Ave, #139, San Antonio, TX 78209

Howard, Robert M *Businessman*
%International Multifoods Corp, PO Box 2942, Minneapolis, MN 55402

Howard, Ron *Actor, Director*
%Imagine Entertainment, 1925 Century Prk East, #2300, Los Angeles, CA 90067

Howard, Sherri *Track Athlete*
14059 Bridle Ridge Rd, Sylmar, CA 91342

Howard, Stephen *Basketball Player*
%DePaul University, Athletic Dept, Chicago, IL 60604

Howard, Susan *Actress*
%Belson & Klass Assoc, 144 S Beverly Dr, #405, Beverly Hills, CA 90212

Howard, Thomas B, Jr *Businessman*
%Gifford-Hill Co, 300 E John W Carpenter Fwy, Irving, TX 75062

Howard, William R *Businessman*
%Piedmont Aviation, Smith Reynolds Airport, Winston-Salem, NC 27156

Howe, Art *Baseball Player, Manager*
711 Kahlddon Ct, Houston, TX 77079

Howe, Arthur *Journalist*
%Philadelphia Inquirer, 400 N Broad St, Philadelphia, PA 19101

Howe, G Woodson *Editor*
%Omaha World-Herald, World-Herald Sq, Omaha, NE 68102

Howe, Geoffrey *Government Official, England*
%Deputy Prime Minister's Office, House of Commons, London SW11, England

Howe, Gordie *Hockey Player*
32 Plank Ave, Glastonbury, CT 06033

Howe, Harold, II *Educator*
RD 2, Pawcatuck, CT 06379

Howe, Mark *Hockey Player*
%Philadelphia Flyers, Spectrum, Pattison Pl, Philadelphia, PA 19148

Howe, Oscar *Artist*
128 Walker St, Vermillion, SD 57069

Howe, Richard J *Businessman*
%Pennzoil Co, Pennzoil Pl, Houston, TX 77252

Howe, Stanley M *Businessman*
%HON Industries, 414 E 3rd St, Muscatine, IA 52761

Howe, Steve *Baseball Player*
318 W 6th St, Whitefish, MT 59937

Howe, Tina *Writer*
333 West End Ave, New York, NY 10023

Howe, Wesley J *Businessman*
%Becton Dickinson Co, Mack Centre Dr, Paramus, NJ 07652

Howell, C Thomas *Actor*
928 N LaJolla Ave, West Hollywood, CA 90046

Howell, Francis C *Anthropologist*
1994 San Antonio, Berkeley, CA 94707

Howell, Harry *Hockey Player*
Carslyle ON L0R 1H0, Canada

Howell, John O, Jr *Businessman*
4006 Brush Hill Rd, Nashville, TN 37216

Howell, W Nathaniel, III *Diplomat*
%Department of State, NEA/ARP Room 4224, Washington, DC 20520

Howell, William R *Businessman*
%J C Penney Co, 1301 Ave of Americas, New York, NY 10019

Howells, Anne *Opera Singer*
Milestone, Broom Close, Esher, Surrey, England

Howells, William W *Anthropologist*
General Delivery, Kittery Point, ME 03905

Howerd, Frankie *Actor*
306-16 Euston Rd, London NW13, England

Howland, Beth *Actress*
255 Amalfi Dr, Santa Monica, CA 90402

Howley, Chuck *Football Player*
%Howley Uniform Rental Inc, 5422 Redfield, Dallas, TX 75235

Hoyer, Steny H *Representative, MD*
%House of Representatives, Washington, DC 20515

Hoyle, Fred *Astronomer, Mathematician*
%Royal Society, 6 Carlton House Terr, London SW1Y 5AG, England

Hoyt, Charles O *Businessman*
%Carter-Wallace Inc, 767 5th Ave, New York, NY 10153

Hoyt, Henry H, Jr *Businessman*
%Carter-Wallace Inc, 767 5th Ave, New York, NY 10153

Hoyte, Hugh Desmond *President, Guyana*
%President's Office, Georgetown, Guyana

Hrabosky, Al *Baseball Player*
16216 Pepper View Ct, Chesterfield, MO 63017

Hrbek, Kent *Baseball Player*
9109 4th Ave S, Bloomington, MN 55420

Hruska, Roman L *Senator, NE*
2139 S 38th St, Omaha, NE 68105

Hu Qili *Government Official, China*
%Chinese Communist Party, Beijing, China

Huarte – Huggins

Huarte, John *Football Player*
%Arizona Tile Supply, 2002 W Southern Ave, Tempe, AZ 85282

Hubbard, Carroll, Jr *Representative, KY*
%House of Representatives, Washington, DC 20515

Hubbard, Phil *Basketball Player*
%Cleveland Cavaliers, 2923 Statesboro Rd, Richfield, OH 44286

Hubbard, William N, Jr *Businessman*
%Upjohn Co, 7000 Portgae Rd, Kalamazoo, MI 49001

Hubbell, Wilson (Bill) *Labor Leader*
%International Woodworkers of America, 25 Cornell, Gladstone, OR 97027

Hubel, David H *Nobel Medicine Laureate*
98 Collins Rd, Waban, MA 02168

Hubenthal, Karl *Editorial Cartoonist*
5536-A Via La Mesa, Laguna Hills, CA 92653

Huber, Ludwig *Financier*
%Bayerische Landesbank Girozentrale, 8000 Munich 2, Germany

Huber, Robert *Nobel Chemistry Laureate*
%Max Planck Biochemie Institut, 8033 Martinsried bei Munchen, Germany

Hubley, Faith *Animator*
%Hubley Studio, 355 E 50th St, New York, NY 10022

Hubley, John *Animator*
%Hubley Studio, 355 E 50th St, New York, NY 10022

Hubley, Season *Actress*
%Gersh Agency, 232 N Canon Dr, Beverly Hills, CA 90210

Huckaby, Thomas J *Representative, LA*
PO Box 544, Ringgold, LA 71068

Huddleston, David *Actor*
%Triad Artists Agency, 10100 Santa Monica Blvd, #1600, Los Angeles, CA 90067

Huddleston, Trevor *Religious Leader*
%Bishop's House, Phoenix, Mauritius

Huddleston, Walter D *Senator, KY*
Seminole Rd, Elizabethtown, KY 42701

Hudiburg, J J *Businessman*
%FPL Grp, 9250 W Flagler St, Miami, FL 33174

Hudner, Thomas J, Jr *Korean War Navy Hero (CMH)*
31 Allen Farm Ln, Concord, MA 01742

Hudson, Bannus B *Businessman*
%US Shoe Corp, 1 Eastwood Dr, Cincinnati, OH 45227

Hudson, Harold J, Jr *Businessman*
%General Re Corp, Financial Ctr, Stamford, CT 06904

Hudson, Hugh *Movie Director*
%Hudson Films Ltd, 11 Queen's Gate Pl Mews, London SW7 5BG, England

Hudson, James *Psychiatrist, Bulimia Researcher*
%Harvard Medical School, 25 Shattuck St, Boston, MA 02115

Hudson, Sally *Skier*
2922 Pasatiempo Pl, Sacramento, CA 95833

Huebner, Robert J *Medical Research Scientist*
12100 Whippoorwil Ln, Rockville, MD 20852

Huet, Phillippe *Businessman*
%Charbonnages de France, Bp 396 08, 73560 Paris Cedex, France

Huff, Paul B *Korean War Army Hero (CMH)*
580 Lafayette Rd, Clarkesville, TN 37042

Huff, Sam *Football Player*
824 Emerald Dr, Wellington, VA 22308

Huffington, Arianna *Writer*
%Morton L Janklow Assoc, 598 Madison Ave, New York, NY 10022

Hufstedler, Shirley *Secretary, Education*
%Hufstedler Miller Kaus Beardsley, 355 S Grand Ave, Los Angeles, CA 90071

Hug, Peter, Jr *Judge*
%US Court of Appeals, 50 W Liberty St, Reno, NV 89501

Hugel, Charles E *Businessman*
%Combustion Engineering Inc, 900 Long Ridge Rd, Stamford, CT 06902

Huggins, Charles B *Nobel Medicine Laureate*
5807 Dorchester Ave, Chicago, IL 60637

Huggins, Edwin V *Businessman*
22 Canterbury Ln, Summit, NJ 07901

Hugh-Kelly, Daniel — *Actor*
%Gersh Agency, 232 N Canon Dr, Beverly Hills, CA 90210

Hughes, Barnard — *Actor*
%J Michael Bloom Ltd, 9200 Sunset Blvd, #710, Los Angeles, CA 90069

Hughes, David A — *Businessman*
%Hughes Supply Inc, 521 W Central Blvd, Orlando, FL 32802

Hughes, Dick — *Baseball Player*
PO Box 598, Stephens, AR 71764

Hughes, Donald R — *Businessman*
%Burlington Industries, 3330 W Friendly Ave, Greensboro, NC 27410

Hughes, Finola — *Actress, Dancer*
%Gersh Agency, 232 N Canon Dr, Beverly Hills, CA 90210

Hughes, Harold E — *Governor, IA*
%Harold Hughes Ctrs, 600 E 14th St, Des Moines, IA 50316

Hughes, Harold E — *Senator, NJ*
%Democratic National Committee, 1625 Massachusetts NW, Washington, DC 20036

Hughes, Harry R — *Governor, MD*
9 Roland Mews, Baltimore, MD 21210

Hughes, John — *Movie Director, Screenwriter*
%Directors Guild, 7950 Sunset Blvd, Los Angeles, CA 90046

Hughes, Ken — *Movie Director*
950 N Kings Rd, #364, Los Angeles, CA 90067

Hughes, Mark — *Businessman*
%Herbalife, 9800 La Cienega, Inglewood, CA 90301

Hughes, Richard J — *Governor, NJ*
18 Morton Ct, Lawrenceville, NJ 08648

Hughes, Robert — *Art Critic*
%Time Magazine, Rockefeller Ctr, New York, NY 10020

Hughes, Ted — *Poet*
%Faber & Faber Ltd, 3 Queen Sq, London WC1N 3AN, England

Hughes, William J — *Representative, NJ*
1019 Wesley Rd, Ocean City, NJ 08226

Hughes-Fulford, Millie — *Astronaut*
%GE Government Services, 1050 Bay Area Blvd, Houston, TX 77058

Hughson, Cecil (Tex) — *Baseball Player*
135 W Sierra, San Marcos, TX 78666

Hugstedt, Petter — *Ski Jumper*
General Delivery, 3600 Kongsberg, Norway

Huizenga, Wayne — *Businessman*
%Blockbuster Entertainment Corp, 10460 Miller Rd, Dallas, TX 75238

Hulce, Tom — *Actor*
2305 Stanley Hills Dr, Los Angeles, CA 90046

Hull, Bobby (Robert M)) — *Hockey Player*
%Winnipeg Jets, 15-1430 Maroons Rd, Winnipeg MB R3G 0L5, Canada

Hull, Brett — *Hockey Player*
%St Louis Blues, 5700 Oakland Ave, St Louis, MO 63110

Hull, Kent — *Football Player*
%Buffalo Bills, 1 Bills Dr, Orchard Park, NY 14127

Hullar, Theodore L — *Educator*
%University of California, Chancellor's Office, Davis, CA 95616

Hulme, Denis — *Auto Racing Driver*
Cl 6, RDTE Puke, Bay of Plenny, New Zealand

Hulse, Frank W — *Businessman*
%Republic Airlines, 7500 Airline Dr, Minneapolis, MN 55450

Hulse, John E — *Businessman*
%Pacific Telesis Grp, 140 New Montgomery St, San Francisco, CA 94105

Humbard, Rex — *Evangelist*
2690 State Rd, Cuyahoga Falls, OH 44421

Humbert, John O — *Religious Leader*
%Christian Church Disciples of Christ, 222 S Downey, Indianapolis, IN 46206

Humble, Weldon — *Football Player*
12219 Broken Bough Dr, Houston, TX 77024

Hume, Basil Cardinal — *Religious Leader*
%Archbishop's House, Westminister, London SW1, England

Hume, Brit — *Commentator*
%ABC-TV, News Dept, 1717 De Sales St NW, Washington, DC 20036

Hume, Douglas *Actor*
%Abrams-Rubaloff & Lawrence, 8075 W 3rd St, #303, Los Angeles, CA 90048

Hume, Stephen *Editor*
%Edmonton Journal, 10006 101st St, Edmonton AB T5J 2S6, Canada

Humes, John P *Diplomat*
Forest Mill Rd, Mill Neck, NY 11765

Humke, Ramon L *Businessman*
%Indiana Bell Telephone Co, 240 N Meridian St, Indianapolis, IN 46204

Hummel, Arthur W, Jr *Diplomat*
4923 Essex Ave, Chevy Chase, MD 20815

Humperdinck, Englebert *Singer*
%International Creative Mgmt, 8899 Beverly Blvd, Los Angeles, CA 90048

Humphrey, Claude *Football Player*
%Atlanta Falcons, Suwanee Rd, Suwanee, GA 30174

Humphrey, Gordon J *Senator, NH*
%US Senate, Washington, DC 20510

Humphrey, Neil D *Educator*
%Youngstown State University, President's Office, Youngstown, OH 44555

Humphrey, Ralph *Artist*
%Bykert Gallery, 24 E 81st St, New York, NY 10028

Humphries, Jay *Basketball Player*
10644 N 11th St, Phoenix, AZ 85020

Hun Sen *Prime Minister, Cambodia*
%Prime Minister's Office, Supreme National Council, Phnom Penh, Cambodia

Hundertwasser, Friedensreich *Artist*
PO Box 45, 1013 Vienna, Austria

Hundley, (Hot) Rod *Basketball Player, Sportscaster*
%Utah Jazz, Salt Palace, 100 SW Temple, Salt Lake City, UT 84101

Hundley, Randy *Baseball Player*
122 E Forrest Ln, Palatine, IL 60067

Hunley, Leeann *Actress*
%Leading Artists, 445 N Bedford Dr, Beverly Hills, CA 90210

Hunnicutt, Gayle *Actress*
%Susan Smith Assoc, 121 N San Vicente Blvd, Beverly Hills, CA 90211

Hunstad, Robert E *Businessman*
%Minnesota Mutual Life Insurance, 400 N Robert St, St Paul, MN 55101

Hunsucker, Robert D *Businessman*
%Panhandle Eastern Corp, 3000 Bissonnet, Houston, TX 77005

Hunt of Llanfair Waterdine, Baron *Mountaineer*
Highway Cottage, Aston, Henley-on-Thames, England

Hunt, Bryan *Artist*
31 Great Jones St, New York, NY 10012

Hunt, Guy *Governor, AL*
%Governor's Office, State Capitol, 11 S Union St, Montgomery, AL 36130

Hunt, Helen *Actress*
%Creative Artists Agency, 9830 Wilshire Blvd, Beverly Hills, CA 90212

Hunt, James *Auto Racing Driver*
85 Lillie Rd, London SW6 1UD, England

Hunt, James B *Governor, NC*
3600 Glenwood Ave, Raleigh, NC 27609

Hunt, Joe H *Businessman*
%Southwestern Bell Corp, 1 Bell Ctr, St Louis, MO 63101

Hunt, John R *Religious Leader*
%Evangelical Covenant Church, 5101 N Francisco Ave, Chicago, IL 60625

Hunt, Lamar *Football Executive*
2800 Thanksgiving Tower, 1601 Elm, Dallas, TX 75021

Hunt, Linda *Actress*
%Triad Artists, 10100 Santa Monica Blvd, #1600, Los Angeles, CA 90067

Hunt, Marsha *Actress*
13131 Magnolia Blvd, Van Nuys, CA 91403

Hunt, Nelson Bunker *Businessman*
%Hunt Resources Corp, 3600 First International Bldg, Dallas, TX 75270

Hunt, Richard *Sculptor*
1017 W Lill Ave, Chicago, IL 60614

Hunt, Robert M *Publisher*
%New York Daily News, 220 E 42nd St, New York, NY 10017

Hunt, Ron *Baseball Player*
2806 Jackson Rd, Wentzville, MO 63385

Hunt, Ronald F *Businessman*
%Student Loan Marketing Assn, 1050 Thomas Jefferson St, Washington, DC 20007

Hunt, W Herbert *Businessman*
%Hunt Resources Corp, 3600 First International Bldg, Dallas, TX 75270

Hunter, Charles D *Businessman*
%Walgreen Co, 200 Wilmot Rd, Deerfield, IL 60015

Hunter, David W *Financier*
%Parker/Hunter Inc, 4000 US Steel Bldg, Pittsburgh, PA 15219

Hunter, Duncan L *Representative, CA*
%House of Representatives, Washington, DC 20515

Hunter, Evan (Ed McBain) *Writer*
%William Morris Agency, 1350 Ave of Americas, New York, NY 10019

Hunter, Holly *Actress*
%Paul Kohner Inc, 9169 Sunset Blvd, Los Angeles, CA 90069

Hunter, Ian *Singer*
%Associated Talent International, 888 7th Ave, New York, NY 10106

Hunter, James, 3rd *Judge*
%US Court of Appeals, 601 Market St, Philadelphia, PA 19106

Hunter, Jim *Skier*
%"Jungle" Jim Hunter Mgmt, 864 Woodpark Way SW, Calgary AB T2W 2V8, Canada

Hunter, Jim (Catfish) *Baseball Player*
RR1, Box 895, Hertford, NC 27944

Hunter, Kaki *Actress*
%Gersh Agency, 232 N Canon Dr, Beverly Hills, CA 90210

Hunter, Kim *Actress*
42 Commerce St, New York, NY 10014

Hunter, Rachel *Model*
%Ford Model Agency, 344 E 59th St, New York, NY 10022

Hunter, Rita *Opera Singer*
Cornways, 70 Embercourt Rd, Thams Ditton, Surrey KT7 0LW, England

Hunter, Ross *Movie Producer*
370 Trousdale Pl, Beverly Hills, CA 90210

Hunter, Tab *Actor*
PO Box 11167, Beverly Hills, CA 90213

Hunter-Gault, Charlayne *Commentator*
%McNeill/Lehrer News Hour, 256 W 58th St, New York, NY 10019

Hunthausen, Raymond G *Religious Leader*
%Catholic Archdiocese of Seattle, 910 Marion, Seattle, WA 98104

Huntington, Ellery C *Football Player*
219 Wolfe St, Alexandria, VA 22314

Huntley, Robert E R *Businessman*
%Best Products Co, Parham & Interstate 95, Richmond, VA 23227

Huntsman, Stanley H *Track Coach*
5532 Timbercrest Trl, Knoxville, TN 37919

Hunyadfi, Steven *Swimming Coach*
838 Ridgewood Dr, #12, Fort Wayne, IN 46805

Huo Yaobang *General Secretary, China*
%Communist Party Central Committee, Zhongguo Gongchan Dang, Bejing, China

Hupp, Robert P *Religious Leader, Social Worker*
%Father Flanagan's Boys Home, Boys Town, NE 68010

Huppert, Isabelle *Actress*
%Artmedia, 10 Ave George V, 75008 Paris, France

Hurd, Douglas *Government Official*
5 Mitford Cottages, Westwell, Burford, Oxon, England

Hurdey, Kelly *Hockey Player*
%New York Islanders, Nassau Coliseum, Uniondale, NY 11553

Hurley, Denis *Religious Leader*
%Archdiocese, Durban, South Africa

Hurley, Kevin *Businessman*
%Haagen-Dazs Inc, 1 Amboy Ave, Woodbridge, NJ 07075

Hurrell, George *Photographer*
6702 Saint Clair Ave, North Hollywood, CA 91606

Hurt, John *Actor*
23 Back Ln, London NW2, England

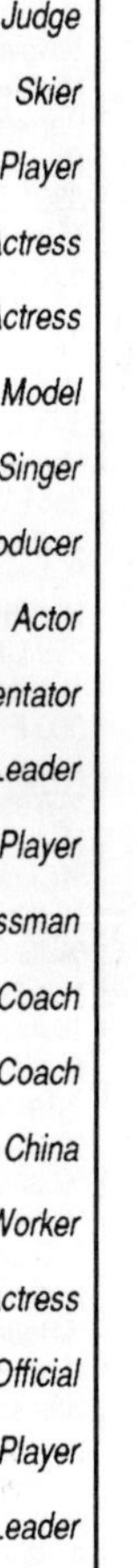

Hurt, Mary Beth *Actress*
1619 Broadway, #900, New York, NY 10019
Hurt, William *Actor*
%Triad Artists, 888 7th St, #1602, New York, NY 10019
Hurtt, Caleb B *Businessman*
%Martin Marietta Corp, 6801 Rockledge Dr, Bethesda, MD 20817
Hurwitz, Charles E *Financier*
%United Financial Grp, 10333 Harwin, Houston, TX 77036
Hurwitz, Jerard *Molecular Biologist*
%Einstein College of Medicine, Yeshiva University, Bronx, NY 10461
Husa, Karel *Composer, Conductor*
%Cornell University, Music Dept, Ithaca, NY 14853
Husen, Torsten *Educator*
%Institute for International Education, 10691 Stockholm, Sweden
Husky, Ferlin *Singer*
38 Music Square E, #116, Nashville, TN 37203
Hussein Ibn Talal *King, Jordan*
Royal Palace, Amman, Jordan
Hussein, Saddam *President, Iraq*
%Revolutionary Command Council, Baghdad, Iraq
Hussey, Olivia *Actress*
Barrett Benson McCartt Weston, 9320 Wilshire Blvd, #301, Beverly Hills, CA 90212
Hussey, Ruth *Actress*
3361 Don Pablo Dr, Carlsbad, CA 92008
Hutchcraft, A Stephens, Jr *Businessman*
%Kaiser Aluminum & Chemical Corp, 300 Lakeside Dr, Oakland, CA 94643
Hutcherson, Bobby *Jazz Vibraphonist*
2490 Channing Way, #406, Berkeley, CA 94704
Hutchins, Robert M *Educator*
%Public Affairs Press, 419 New Jersey Ave SE, Washington, DC 20003
Hutchins, Will *Actor*
3461 Waverly Dr, Los Angeles, CA 90027
Hutchinson, Barbara *Labor Leader*
%American Federation of Labor, 815 15th St NW, Washington, DC 20006
Hutchinson, G Evelyn *Zoologist*
269 Canner St, New Haven, CT 06511
Hutchinson, Josephine *Actress*
360 E 55th St, New York, NY 10022
Hutchinson, Pemberton *Businessman*
%Westmoreland Coal Co, 2500 Fidelity Bldg, Philadelphia, PA 19109
Hutchinson, Robert E *Businessman*
%Circle K Corp, 7th St & McDowell, Phoenix, AZ 85006
Hutchinson, William D *Judge*
%US Court of Appeals, Court House, 410 W Market St, Pottsville, PA 17901
Hutchison, Clyde A, Jr *Chemist*
%University of Chicago, Chemistry Dept, Chicago, IL 60637
Hutchison, William L *Businessman*
%Texas Oil & Gas Co, 2700 Fidelity Union Tower, Dallas, TX 75201
Huth, Edward J *Editor*
%Lancet, 4200 Pine St, Philadelphia, PA 19101
Hutson, Don *Football Player*
%Thunderbird Country Club, PO Box Y, Rancho Mirage, CA 92270
Hutto, Earl *Representative, FL*
%House of Representatives, Washington, DC 20515
Hutton, Betty *Actress*
Harrison Ave, Newport, RI 02840
Hutton, Edward L *Businessman*
%Chemed Corp, 1200 DuBois Tower, Cincinnati, OH 45202
Hutton, Lauren *Model, Actress*
54 Bond St, New York, NY 10012
Hutton, Leonard *Cricket Player*
Ebor House, 1 Coombe, Surrey KT2 7HW, England
Hutton, Ralph *Swimmer*
%Vancouver Police Department, 312 Main St, Vancouver BC, Canada
Hutton, Timothy *Actor*
PO Box 9078, Van Nuys, CA 91409

Huxley, Andrew F *Nobel Medicine Laureate*
Master's Lodge, Trinity College, Cambridge CB2 1TQ, England

Huxtable, Ada Louise *Architectural Critic*
969 Park Ave, New York, NY 10028

Huyck, Willard *Movie Director*
39 Oakmont Dr, Los Angeles, CA 90049

Hwang, David Henry *Playwright*
%International Production Assoc, 853 Broadway, #2120, New York, NY 10003

Hyams, Joe *Writer*
540 N Beverly Glen Blvd, Los Angeles, CA 90024

Hyatt, Chuck (Charles) *Basketball Player*
%Basketball Hall of Fame, PO Box 179, Springfield, MA 01101

Hyatt, Joel Z *Attorney, Businessman*
%Hyatt Legal Services, 4410 Main, Kansas City, MO 64111

Hybl, William J *Sports Official*
%US Olympic Committee, 1750 E Boulder St, Colorado Springs, CO 80909

Hyde, Henry J *Representative, IL*
50 E Oak St, Addison, IL 60101

Hyde, Lawrence H *Businessman*
%Harris Graphics Corp, 200 Seminole Ave, Melbourne, FL 32901

Hyer, Martha *Actress*
4100 W Alameda Ave, #204, Toluca Lake, CA 91503

Hylton, Thomas J *Journalist*
%Pottstown Mercury, Hanover & King Sts, Pottstown, PA 19464

Hyman, Dick *Jazz Pianist*
4146 Lankershim Blvd, #300, North Hollywood, CA 99162

Hyman, Earle *Actor*
%Manhattan Towers, 484 W 43rd St, #33-E, New York, NY 10036

Hyman, Phyllis *Singer*
%Zoo Entertainment, 6363 Sunset Blvd, Los Angeles, CA 90028

Hynde, Chrissie *Singer, Songwriter*
%Pretenders, Cheval Music Ltd, 73 Market St, Venice, CA 90292

Hyndman, Robert C *Businessman*
%Morton Thiokol Inc, 110 N Wacker Dr, Chicago, IL 60606

Hyser, Joyce *Actress*
%Chasin Agency, 190 N Canon Dr, #201, Beverly Hills, CA 90210

I

Iacobellis – Iliescu

Iacobellis, Sam F *Businessman, Aeronautical Engineer*
%Rockwell International Corp, 600 Grant St, Pittsburgh, PA 15219

Iacocca, Lee A *Businessman*
%Chrysler Corp, 12000 Chrysler Dr, Highland Park, MI 48203

Iafrate, Al *Hockey Player*
%Washington Capitals, Capital Ctr, Landover, MD 20785

Iakovos, Primate Archbishop *Religious Leader*
%Greek Orthodox Archdiocese, 8-10 E 79th St, New York, NY 10021

Ian, Janis *Singer*
611 Broadway, #822, New York, NY 10012

Iba, Hank (Henry P) *Basketball Coach*
Crestview Dr, Stillwater, OK 74074

Ibbetson, Arthur *Cinematographer*
%Tanglewood, Chalfont Ln, Chorlry Wood, Herts, England

Ibiam, Francis A *Religious Leader*
Ganymede, Unwana, PO Box 240, Afikpo, Imo State, Nigeria

Ibuka, Masaru *Inventor, Businessman*
%Sony Corp, 6-7-35 Kitashinagawa, Shinagawaku, Tokyo 141, Japan

Ibuka, Yaeko *Social Worker*
%Fukusei Byoin, Leprosarium, Mount Fuji, Japan

Icahn, Carl C *Businessman*
%Trans World Airlines, 605 3rd Ave, New York, NY 10158

Idle, Eric *Comedian (Monty Python)*
20 Fitzroy Sq, London W1P 6BB, England

Idol, Billy *Singer*
7267 Outpost Cove, Los Angeles, CA 90068

Iduarte Foucher, Andres *Writer*
Calle Edimburgo 3, Colonia del Valle, Mexico City 12 DF, Mexico

Iglesias, Enrique *Financier; Government Official, Uruguay*
%Inter-American Development Bank, 808 17th St NW, Washington, DC 20577

Ignatius IV of Antioch, Patriarch *Religious Leader*
%Antiochian Orthodox Church, Damascus, Syria

Ignatius, Paul R *Government Official*
3650 Fordham Rd, Washington, DC 20016

Ignatow, David *Poet*
PO Box 1458, East Hampton, NY 11937

Ihara, Michio *Sculptor*
63 Wood St, Concord, MA 01742

Ihnatowicz, Zbigniew *Architect*
Ul Mokotowska 31 m 15, 00-560 Warsaw, Poland

Iida, Yotaro *Businessman*
%Mitsubishi Heavy Industries, 2-5-1 Marunouchi, Chiyodaku, Tokyo, Japan

Ikard, Todd B *Financier*
%Society for Savings, 31 Pratt St, Hartford, CT 06103

Ike, Reverend *Evangelist*
910 Commonwealth Ave, Boston, MA 02215

Ikeda, Daisaku *Religious Leader*
%Soka Gakkai, 32 Shinanomachi, Shinjuku, Tokyo 160, Japan

Ikeda, Ichiro *Financier*
%Daiwa Bank, 2-21 Bingomachi, Higashiku, Osaka 541, Japan

Ikeda, Shunichiro *Businessman*
%Sanyo-Kokusaku Pulp Co, 1-4-5 Marunouchi, Chiyodaku, Tokyo, Japan

Ikenaga, Jiro *Businessman*
%Nichiro Gyogyo Kaisha Ltd, 12-1 Yurakucho, Chiyodaku, Tokyo 100, Japan

Ikle, Fred C *Social Scientist*
7010 Glenbrook Rd, Washington, DC 20014

Ikura, Kisaburo *Financier*
%Industrial Bank of Japan, 3-3 Marunouchi, Chiyodaku, Tokyo 100, Japan

Ilchman, Alice Stone *Educator*
%Sarah Lawrence College, President's Office, Bronxville, NY 10708

Iley, Barbara *Actress*
%STE Representation, 9301 Wilshire Blvd, #312, Beverly Hills, CA 90210

Ilg, Raymond P *Navy Admiral*
OPNAV FURASPERS, 4401 Ford Ave, Alexandria, VA 22302

Iliescu, Ion *President, Romania*
%President's Office, Bucharest, Romania

Ilitch, Mike *Hockey Executive*
%Detroit Red Wings, 600 Civic Center Dr, Detroit, MI 48226
Illich, Ivan *Educator, Writer, Theologian*
Apdo Postal 479, 62000 Cuernavaca, Mexico
Imai, Kenji *Architect*
4-12-28, Kitazawa, Setagayaku, Tokyo, Japan
Imbert, Bertrand S M *Explorer, Engineer*
50 Rue de Turenne, 75003 Paris, France
Imbrie, Andrew W *Composer*
2625 Rose St, Berkeley, CA 94708
Imhoff, Gary *Actor*
1430 N Martel Ave, #401, Los Angeles, CA 90046
Imshenetsky, Aleksandr A *Microbiologist*
%Russian Academy of Sciences, Profsoyuznaya Ul 7, Moscow, Russia
Inaba, Kosaku *Businessman*
%Ishikawajima-Harima Heavy Industries, 2-1 Ohtemachi, Tokyo 100, Japan
Inagawa, Tatsu *Businessman*
%Kanto Auto Works, Taura-Minatomachi, Yokosuka City 237, Japan
Inai, Yoshihiro *Businessman*
%Mitsubishi Metal Corp, 1-5-2 Otemachi, Chiyodaku, Tokyo 100, Japan
Inbal, Eliahu *Conductor*
Hessischer Rundfunk, Bertramstrasse 8, 6000 Frankfurt, Germany
Incaviglia, Pete *Baseball Player*
PO Box 526, Pebble Beach, CA 93953
Indiana, Robert *Artist*
Star of Hope, Vinalhaven, ME 04863
Iness, Sim *Track Athlete*
455 W Oak Ave, Porterville, CA 93257
Infill, O Urcille, Jr *Religious Leader*
%African Methodist Church, Box 19039, Germantown Station, Philadelphia, PA 19138
Ingalls, Daniel H H *Orientalist*
The Yard, Hot Springs, VA 24445
Ingalls, Joyce *Actress*
%Abrams-Rubaloff & Lawrence, 8075 W 3rd St, #303, Los Angeles, CA 90048
Ingels, Marty *Actor, Comedian*
%Ingels Inc, 8322 Beverly Blvd, Los Angeles, CA 90048
Ingersoll, Mary *Actress*
%Associated Talent International, 1320 Armacost Ave, Los Angeles, CA 90025
Ingersoll, Ralph, II *Publisher*
%Ingersoll Publications, PO Box 1869, Lakeville, CT 06039
Ingersoll, Robert S *Businessman*
1 First National Plz, Chicago, IL 60603
Inghram, Mark G *Physicist*
1534 E 59th St, Chicago, IL 60637
Ingle, Robert *Editor*
%San Jose Mercury News, 750 Ridder Park Dr, San Jose, CA 95190
Ingman, Einar H, Jr *Korean War Army Hero (CMH)*
W-4053 N Silver Lake Rd, Irma, WI 54442
Ingram, E Bronson *Businessman*
%Ingram Industries, 4304 Harding Rd, Nashville, TN 37205
Ingram, James *Singer*
867 Muirfield Rd, Los Angeles, CA 90005
Ingram, M Darrell *Businessman*
100 N Broadway, St Louis, MO 63102
Ingram, Vernon M *Biochemist*
%Massachusetts Institute of Technology, Biochemistry Dept, Cambridge, MA 02139
Ingrao, Pietro *Government Official, Italy*
%Centro Studie Inisiative per la Riforma, Via IV Novembre, Rome, Italy
Ingstad, Helge M *Explorer*
Vettalivei 24, 0389 Oslo 3, Norway
Inkeles, Alex *Sociologist*
1001 Hamilton Ave, Palo Alto, CA 94305
Inman, John *Actor*
%W&J Theatrical Ent, 51-A Oakwood Rd, London NW!! 6RJ, England
Innauer, Toni *Ski Jumper*
%Olympic Committee, Prinz-Eugen-Strasse 12, 1040 Vienna, Austria

I

Innaurato – Irwin

Innaurato, Albert *Playwright*
%William Morris Agency, 1350 Ave of Americas, New York, NY 10019

Innis, Roy E A *Civil Rights Activist*
%Congress of Racial Equality, 30 Cooper Sq, New York, NY 10003

Innocenti, Antonio Cardinal *Religious Leader*
Via Pancrazio Pfeiffer 10, 00193 Rome, Italy

Inoue, Shinya *Biologist, Photographer*
%Marine Biological Laboratory, 167 Water St, Woods Hole, MA 02543

Inoue, Yuichi *Artist*
Ohkamiyashiki, 2475-2 Kurami, Samakawamachi 253-01, Kozagun, Kam, Japan

Inouye, Daniel K *Senator, HI*
469 Edna Rd, Honolulu, HI 96814

Insko, Del *Harness Racing Driver*
Rt 1, Box 65, South Beloit, IL 61080

Insley, Will *Artist*
231 Bowery, New York, NY 10002

Insolia, Anthony *Editor*
%Newsday, 235 Pinelawn, Melville, NY 11747

Ioannisiani, Bagrat K *Astronomer*
%State Institute of Optics, St Petersburg, Russia

Iofan, Boris M *Architect*
%Russian Union of Architects, 3 Ul Shchuseva, Moscow, Russia

Ionesco, Eugene *Writer*
96 Blvd du Montparnasse, 75014 Paris, France

Ipcar, Dahlov *Illustrator, Artist*
Star Route 2, Bath, ME 04530

Ippolito, Angelo *Artist*
Friendsville Stage, Binghamton, NY 13903

Irani, Ray R *Businessman*
%Occidental Petroleum, 10889 Wilshire Blvd, Los Angeles, CA 90024

Iredale, Randle W *Architect*
1100 W 7th Ave, Vancouver BC V6H 1B4, Canada

Ireland, Andy *Representative, FL*
%House of Representatives, Washington, DC 20515

Ireland, John *Actor*
PO Box 5211, Santa Barbara, CA 93150

Ireland, Kathy *Model*
%Elite Model Mgmt, 111 E 22nd St, New York, NY 10010

Irobe, Yoshiaki *Financier*
%Kyowa Bank, 1-1-2 Otemachi, Chiyodaku, Tokyo 100, Japan

Irons, Jeremy *Actor*
%Hutton Mgmt, 200 Fulham Rd, London SW10 9PN, England

Irsay, Robert *Football Executive*
%Indianapolis Colts, 7001 W 56th St, Indianapolis, IN 46254

Irvan, Ernie *Auto Racing Driver*
80 Louve Ave, Conford, NC 28025

Irvin, John *Movie Director*
6 Lower Common S, London SW10, England

Irvin, Monte *Baseball Player*
11 Douglas Court S, Homosassa, FL 32646

Irvin, Tinsley H *Businessman*
%Alexander & Alexander Services, 1211 Ave of Americas, New York, NY 10036

Irving, Amy *Actress*
%Triad Artists, 10100 Santa Monica Blvd, #1600, Los Angeles, CA 90067

Irving, Herbert *Businessman*
%Sysco Corp, 1177 West Loop S, Houston, TX 77027

Irving, John W *Writer*
%Elsevier-Dutton Co, 2 Park Ave, New York, NY 10016

Irwin, Bill *Entertainer, Clown*
56 7th Ave, #4-E, New York, NY 10011

Irwin, Hale S *Golfer*
745 Old Frontenac Sq, #260, St Louis, MO 63131

Irwin, John C *Coast Guard Admiral*
%Vice Commandant's Office, US Coast Guard, Washington, DC 20593

Irwin, John Nichol, II *Government Official*
848 Weed St, New Canaan, CT 06840

Irwin, Malcolm R *Biologist*
4720 Regent St, Madison, WI 53705

Irwin, Robert W *Artist*
10966 Strathmore Dr, Los Angeles, CA 90024

Isaac, William M *Financier*
%Federal Deposit Insurance Corp, 550 17th St NW, Washington, DC 20429

Isaacs, Jeremy I *Opera Director*
%Royal Opera House, Covent Garden, Bow St, London WC2, England

Isaacs, John *Basketball Player*
1412 Crotona Ave, Bronx, NY 10456

Isaacs, Susan *Writer*
%Harper Collins Publishers, 10 E 53rd St, New York, NY 10022

Isaacson, Julius *Labor Leader*
%Novelty & Production Workers Union, 1815 Franklin Ave, Valley Stream, NY 11581

Isacksen, Peter *Actor*
%Stone Manners Agency, 9113 Sunset Blvd, Los Angeles, CA 90069

Isard, Walter *Regional Scientist*
3218 Garrett Rd, Drexel Hill, PA 19026

Isenburger, Eric *Artist*
140 E 56th St, New York, NY 10022

Ishaq Khan, Ghulam *President, Pakistan*
%President's Office, Islamabad, Pakistan

Isherwood, John S *Businessman*
%G Heileman Brewing Co, 100 Harborview Plz, La Crosse, WI 54601

Ishibashi, Kanichiro *Businessman*
%Bridgestone Tire Co, 1-10-1 Kyobashi, Chuoku, Tokyo 104, Japan

Ishida, Jim *Actor*
871 N Vail Ave, Montebello, CA 90640

Ishida, Taizo *Businessman*
%Toyota Motor Co, 1 Toyotacho, Toyotashi, Aichiken 471, Japan

Ishigami, Minoru *Businessman*
%Jujo Paper Co, 1-12-1 Yuraku, Chiyodaku, Tokyo 100, Japan

Ishiguro, Kazu *Writer*
%Faber & Faber, 3 Queens Sq, London WC1N 3AO, England

Ishihara, Takashi *Businessman*
%Nissan Motor Co, 6-17-1 Ginza, Chuoku, Tokyo 104, Japan

Ishizaka, Kimishige *Allergist*
%Good Samaritan Hospital, 5601 Loch Raven Blvd, Baltimore, MD 21239

Ishizaka, Teruko *Allergist*
%Good Samaritan Hospital, 5601 Loch Raven Blvd, Baltimore, MD 21239

Ismail, Ahmed Sultan *Mechanical Engineer*
43 Ahmed Abdel Aziz St, Dokki, Cairo, Egypt

Ismail, Raghib *Football Player*
%Toronto Argonauts, Exhibition Stadium, Toronto ON M6K 3C3, Canada

Ison, Chris *Journalist*
%Minneapolis-St Paul Star Tribune, 425 Portland Ave, Minneapolis, MN 55488

Isozaki, Arata *Architect*
16-12 Akasaka 9-chome, Minatoku, Tokyo 107, Japan

Issel, Dan *Basketball Player*
%Denver Nuggets, McNichols Arena, 1635 Clay St, Denver, CO 80204

Istomin, Eugene *Concert Pianist*
225 W 71st St, New York, NY 10023

Italiaander, Rolf *Writer, Explorer*
St Benedictstrasse 29, 2000 Hamburg 13, Germany

Itami, Juzo *Movie Director*
%Film Industry Federation, Sankei Bldg, 7-2-1 Otemachi, Tokyo 100, Japan

Ito, Kenichi *Businessman*
%Ito Ham Foods, 4-27 Takahatacho, Nishinomiya City 663, Japan

Ito, Masayoshi *Government Official, Japan*
%Liberal Democratic Part, Diet, Tokyo, Japan

Ito, Robert *Actor*
%Gray/Goodman Inc, 211 S Beverly Dr, #100, Beverly Hills, CA 90212

Ito, Shinsui *Artist*
Kita-Kamakura, Kanagawa Prefecture, Japan

Ito, Yoshikazu *Businessman*
%Toray Industries, 2-2 Nihonbashi-Muromachi, Chuoku, Tokyo 103, Japan

I

Itoh, Junji *Businessman*
%Kanebo Ltd, 1-2-2 Umeda, Kitaku, Osaka 530, Japan

Iue, Satoshi *Businessman*
%Sanyo Electric Co, 2-18 Keihan-Hondori, Moriguchi City 570, Japan

Ivan, Thomas N *Hockey Player*
557 N King Muir Rd, Lake Forest, IL 60045

Ivanchenkov, Alexander *Cosmonaut*
141 160 Svyosdny Gorodok, Moskovskoi Oblasti, Potchta Kosmonavtov, Russia

Iveagh, Earl of *Businessman*
%Arthur Guinness & Sons, Park Royal Brewery, London NW10 7RR, England

Iveroth, C Axel *Businessman*
Brantstigen 12, 16139 Bromma, Sweden

Iverson, F Kenneth *Businessman*
%Nucor Corp, 4425 Randolph Rd, Charlotte, NC 28211

Ives, Burl *Actor, Singer*
2804 Oakes Ave, Anacortes, WA 98221

Ives, J Atwood *Businessman*
%General Cinema Corp, 27 Boylston St, Chestnut Hill, MA 02176

Ivey, James B *Editorial Cartoonist*
561 Obispo Ave, Orlando, FL 32807

Ivey, Judith *Actress*
222 W 15th St, New York, NY 10011

Ivins, Marsha S *Astronaut*
%NASA, Johnson Space Ctr, Houston, TX 77058

Ivor, D M *Businessman*
%Imperial Oil, 111 St Clair Ave W, Toronto ON, Canada

Ivory, James *Movie Director*
%Merchant-Ivory Productions, 400 E 52nd St, New York, NY 10022

Iwago, Mitsuaki *Photographer*
%Chronicle Books, 1 Hallidie Plz, San Francisco, CA 94102

Iwamura, Eiro *Businessman*
%Kawasaki Steel Corp, 2-3 Uchisaiwaidio, Chiyodaku, Tokyo, Japan

Iwasawa, Masaji *Businessman*
%Mazda Motor Corp, 3-1 Fuchacho-Shinchi, Akigun, Hiroshima, Japan

Iwata, Kazuo *Businessman*
%Toshiba Corp, 72 Horikawacho, Sawwaiku, Kawasaki 210, Japan

J

Jabara, Paul *Songwriter, Singer*
%Warner Bros Records, 3300 Warner Blvd, Burbank, CA 91505

Jablonsky, Harvey (Jabo) *Football Player, Army General*
7400 Crestway, #1120, San Antonio, TX 78239

Jackee (Harry) *Actress*
%Metropolitan Talent Agency, 9320 Wilshire Blvd, #320, Beverly Hills, CA 90212

Jacklin, Tony *Golfer*
Chestnut Lea, St Marys, Jersey, Channel Islands

Jackson, Alan *Singer*
%Triad Artists, 10100 Santa Monica Blvd, #1600, Los Angeles, CA 90067

Jackson, Anne *Actress*
90 Riverside Dr, New York, NY 10024

Jackson, Arthur J *WW II Marine Corps Hero (CMH)*
PO Box 6402, Boise, ID 83707

Jackson, Bo *Football, Baseball Player*
%Chicago White Sox, 333 W 35th St, Chicago, IL 60616

Jackson, Danny *Baseball Player*
31 Newark, #C, Aurora, CO 80012

Jackson, Donald *Figure Skater*
504 Gordon Baker Rd, Willowdale ON M2H 3B4, Canada

Jackson, Frederick W, III *Publisher*
%Town & Country Magazine, 959 8th Ave, New York, NY 10019

Jackson, Glenda *Actress*
51 Harvey Rd, Blackheath, London SE3, England

Jackson, Harold *Football Player*
%New England Patriots, Sullivan Stadium, Foxboro, MA 02035

Jackson, Harry A *Artist*
Sage Creek, Cody, WY 82414

Jackson, Janet *Singer*
%Virgin Records, 30 W 21st St, New York, NY 10010

Jackson, Jesse *Civil Rights Activist*
400 "T" St NW, Washington, DC 20515

Jackson, Jim *Basketball Player*
%Ohio State University, Athletic Dept, Columbus, OH 43210

Jackson, Joe *Singer, Songwriter*
%Basement Music, Trinity House, 6 Pembridge Rd, London W11, England

Jackson, Joe M *Vietnam War Air Force Hero (CMH)*
25320 38th Ave S, Kent, WA 98032

Jackson, Kate *Actress*
%Triad Artists, 10100 Santa Monica Blvd, #1600, Los Angeles, CA 90067

Jackson, Keith *Sportscaster*
%ABC-TV, Sports Dept, 1330 Ave of Americas, New York, NY 10019

Jackson, Keith *Football Player*
%Philadelphia Eagles, Veterans Stadium, Philadelphia, PA 19148

Jackson, Larry R *Labor Leader*
%Graphic Communications Int'l Union, 1900 "L" St NW, Washington, DC 20036

Jackson, LaToya *Singer*
106 Central Park South, New York, NY 10019

Jackson, Mark *Basketball Player*
%New York Knicks, Madison Square Grdn, 4 Pennsylvania Plz, New York, NY 10001

Jackson, Mary *Actress*
%Writers & Artists Agency, 11726 San Vicente Blvd, #300, Los Angeles, CA 90049

Jackson, Michael *Commentator*
%KABC-Radio, News Dept, 3321 S LaCienega Blvd, Los Angeles, CA 90016

Jackson, Michael *Singer*
Sycamore Valley Ranch, Zacca Landeras, Santa Ynez, CA 93460

Jackson, Phil *Basketball Player, Coach*
%Chicago Bulls, 980 N Michigan Ave, Chicago, IL 60611

Jackson, R Graham *Architect*
7011 Southwest Pkwy, Houston, TX 77074

Jackson, Richard A *Religious Leader*
%North Phoenix Baptist Church, 5757 N Central Ave, Phoenix, AZ 85012

Jackson, Rickey *Football Player*
%New Orleans Saints, 6928 Saints Dr, Metairie, LA 70003

Jackson, Roy I *International Civil Servant*
%Food/Agriculture Organization, Via delle Terme di Caracalla, Rome, Italy

J

Jackson – Jacobson

Jackson, Sherry *Actress*
4933 Encino Ave, Encino, CA 91316

Jackson, Stoney *Actor*
%The Agency, 10351 Santa Monica Blvd, #211, Los Angeles, CA 90025

Jackson, Tom *Football Player*
%Denver Broncos, 13655 E Dove Valley Pkwy, Englewood, CO 80112

Jackson, Travis *Baseball Player*
101 S Olive St, Waldo, AR 71770

Jaco, Charles *News Correspondent*
%Cable News Network, 1 CNN Center, PO Box 105366, Atlanta, GA 30348

Jaco, Neal T *Army General*
Commanding General, 5th US Army, Fort Sam Houston, TX 78234

Jacob, Francois *Nobel Medicine Laureate*
%Institut Pasteur, 28 Rue du Dr Roux, 75015 Paris, France

Jacob, John E *Civil Rights Activist*
%National Urban League, 500 E 62nd St, New York, NY 10021

Jacob, Richard J *Businessman*
%Dayco Corp, 333 W 1st St, Dayton, OH 45402

Jacob, Stanley W *Surgeon (Co-Discoverer of DMSO)*
1055 SW Westwood Ct, Portland, OR 97201

Jacobi, Derek *Actor*
%International Creative Mgmt, 388/396 Oxford St, London W1N 9HE, England

Jacobi, Lou *Actor*
240 Central Park South, New York, NY 10019

Jacobs, Andrew, Jr *Representative, IN*
%House of Representatives, Washington, DC 20515

Jacobs, Bernard *Theater Producer*
%Shubert Organization, 225 W 44th St, New York, NY 10036

Jacobs, Harry A, Jr *Financier*
%Prudential-Bache Securities, 100 Gold St, New York, NY 10038

Jacobs, Helen Hull *Tennis Player*
26 Joanne Ln, Weston, CT 06883

Jacobs, Irwin L *Businessman*
%Minstar Inc, 1215 Marshall St NE, Minneapolis, MN 55413

Jacobs, Jack H *Vietnam War Army Hero (CMH)*
%AutoFinance Grp, 15301 Ventura Blvd, #230, Sherman Oaks, CA 91403

Jacobs, Jane *Writer*
%Random House, 201 E 50th St, New York, NY 10022

Jacobs, Jim *Playwright*
%International Creative Mgmt, 40 W 57th St, New York, NY 10019

Jacobs, Julien I *Judge*
%US Tax Court, 400 2nd St NW, Washington, DC 20217

Jacobs, Lawrence-Hilton *Actor*
2110 Mt Olympus Dr, Los Angeles, CA 90046

Jacobs, Marc *Fashion Designer*
%Perry Ellis Co, 575 7th Ave, New York, NY 10018

Jacobs, Norman J *Publisher*
%Century Publishing Co, 1020 Church St, Evanston, IL 60201

Jacobs, Robert *Pharmacologist*
%University of California, Pharmacology Dept, Santa Barbara, CA 93106

Jacobs, Robert A *Architect*
1065 Lexington Ave, New York, NY 10021

Jacobs, Walther J *Businessman*
%Jacobs Suchard, 107 Ave de Cour, 1007 Lausanne, Switzerland

Jacobsen, Peter *Golfer*
%Fred Meyer Challenge, 8700 SW Nimbus Ave, #B, Beaverton, OR 97005

Jacobsen, Steven C *Microbiotics Engineer*
%University of Utah, Center for Engineering Design, Salt Lake City, UT 84112

Jacobson, Allen F *Businessman*
%Minnesota Mining & Manufacturing Co, 3-M Ctr, St Paul, MN 55144

Jacobson, Herbert L *Diplomat, Journalist*
Apartado 160, Escazu, Costa Rica

Jacobson, John *Businessman*
%Idle Wild Foods, 256 Franklin St, Worcester, MA 01604

Jacobson, John, Jr *Businessman*
%Idle Wild Foods, 256 Franklin St, Worcester, MA 01604

Jacobson, Leon O *Medical Researcher*
5801 Dorchester Ave, Chicago, IL 60637

Jacobson, M Howard *Businessman*
%Idle Wild Foods, 256 Franklin St, Worcester, MA 01604

Jacobson, Nathan *Mathematician*
2 Prospect Ct, Hamden, CT 06514

Jacobson, Thurl *Petroleum Geologist*
358 Oxford Dr, Short Hills, NJ 07078

Jacoby, Joe *Football Player*
%Washington Redskins, Dulles Airport, Box 17247, Washington, DC 20041

Jacoby, Robert E, Jr *Businessman*
%Ted Bates Co, 1515 Broadway, New York, NY 10036

Jacoby, Scott *Actor*
%Harold Gold Assoc, 3500 W Olive Ave, #1400, Burbank, CA 91505

Jacot, Michele *Skier*
Residence du Brevent, 74 Chamonix, France

Jacquot, Pierre E *Army General, France*
15 Ave de Villars, 75007 Paris, France

Jadot, Jean L O *Religious Leader*
%Secretariat for Non-Christians, Vatican City, 00102 Rome, Italy

Jaeckel, Richard *Actor*
PO Box 1818, Santa Monica, CA 90406

Jaeger, Andrea *Tennis Player*
%Bardmoor Country Club, Largo, FL 33543

Jaffe, Arthur M *Mathematical Physicist*
27 Lancaster St, Cambridge, MA 02140

Jaffe, Leo *Movie Executive*
425 E 58th St, New York, NY 10022

Jaffe, Rona *Writer*
%Delacorte Press, 666 5th Ave, New York, NY 10103

Jaffe, Stanley *Entertainment Executive*
%Paramount Pictures, 5555 Melrose Ave, Los Angeles, CA 90038

Jaffe, Susan *Ballerina*
%American Ballet Theatre, 890 Broadway, New York, NY 10003

Jaffee, Richard *Businessman*
%Oil-Dri Corp of America, 520 N Michigan Ave, Chicago, IL 60611

Jagan, Cheddi *Premier, Guyana*
65 Pln Bel Air, ECD, Guyana

Jagger, Mick *Singer*
2 Munro Terr, London SW10, England

Jaglom, Henry *Movie Director*
8235 Monteel Rd, Los Angeles, CA 90069

Jaharis, Michael, Jr *Businessman*
%Key Pharmaceuticals, 50 NW 176th St, Miami, FL 33169

Jahn, Helmut *Architect*
224 S Michigan Ave, Chicago, IL 60604

Jahn, Sigmund *Cosmonaut, East Germany*
Postfach 66650, 1080 Berlin, Germany

Jaicks, Frederick G *Businessman*
%Inland Steel Co, 30 W Monroe St, Chicago, IL 60603

Jaidah, Ali Mohammed *Government Official, Qatar*
%Qatar Petroleum Corp, PO Box 3212, Doha, Qatar

Jakes, John *Writer*
PO Box 3248, Harbour Town Station, Hilton Head Island, SC 29928

Jaki, Stanley L *Physicist, Theologian*
%Seton Hall University, Physics Dept, South Orange, NJ 07079

Jakobovits, Immanuel *Religious Leader*
%Chief Rabbi's Residence, Adler House, Tavistock Sq, London WC1, England

Jakobson, Max *Journalist; Government Official, Finland*
Rahapajankatu 3B 17, 00160 Helsinki 16, Finland

Jalloud, Abdul Salam *Prime Minister, Libya*
General Secretariat of General People's Congress, Tripoli, Libya

Jamail, Joseph D, Jr *Attorney*
%Jamail & Kolius, 1 Allen Ctr, #3300, Houston, TX 77002

Jambor, Agi *Concert Pianist*
103 Pine Tree Rd, Radnor, PA 19087

J

James, Anthony *Actor*
%Alisha Tamburri, 10625 Magnolia Blvd, North Hollywood, CA 91601

James, Charmayne *Rodeo Rider*
%General Delivery, Clayton, NM 88415

James, Clifton *Actor*
95 Buttonwood Dr, Dix Hills, NY 11726

James, Craig *Football Player*
%New England Patriots, Sullivan Stadium, Foxboro, MA 02035

James, Craig *Representative, FL*
%House of Representatives, Washington, DC 20515

James, D Clayton *Historian*
1702 Linden Cir, Starkville, MS 39759

James, Dennis *Entertainer*
3581 Caribeth Dr, Encino, CA 91316

James, Don *Football Coach*
%University of Washington, Athletic Dept, Seattle, WA 98195

James, Etta *Singer*
PO Box 5025, Gardena, CA 90249

James, F L *Businessman*
%Winn-Dixie Stores, 5050 Edgewood Ct, Jacksonville, FL 32202

James, Forrest H (Fob), Jr *Governor, AL*
General Delivery, Magnolia Springs, AL 36555

James, Gene A *Businessman*
%Southern States Cooperative, 6606 W Broad St, Richmond, VA 23230

James, Harold L *Geologist*
%US Geological Survey, 1617 Washington St, Port Townsend, WA 98368

James, Howard P *Businessman*
%Sheraton Corp, 60 State St, Boston, MA 02109

James, John *Actor*
7310 Mulholland Dr, Los Angeles, CA 90046

James, John V *Businessman*
%Dresser Industries, 1505 Elm St, Dallas, TX 75221

James, Joseph W *Businessman*
%Household International, 2700 Sanders Rd, Prospect Heights, IL 60070

James, Larry *Track Athlete*
%Stockton State College, Athletic Dept, Pomona, NJ 08240

James, Lionel *Football Player*
%San Diego Chargers, 9449 Friars Rd, San Diego, CA 92108

James, P D *Writer*
%Faber & Faber Ltd, 3 Queen Sq, London WC1N 3AU, England

James, Rick *Singer*
8116 Mulholland Terr, Los Angeles, CA 90046

Jamieson, David A *WW II British Army Hero (VC)*
Drove House, Thornham, Hunstandton, Norfolk, England

Jamieson, John K *Businessman*
1100 Milam Bldg, #4601, Houston, TX 77002

Jamison, Judith *Dancer*
%Alvin Ailey American Dance Theater, 1515 Broadway, New York, NY 10036

Janecyk, Bob *Hockey Player*
%Los Angeles Kings, Great Western Forum, 3900 W Manchester, Inglewood, CA 90306

Janeway, Eliot *Economist*
15 E 80th St, New York, NY 10021

Janeway, Michael *Editor*
%Houghton Mifflin Co, 52 Vanderbilt Ave, New York, NY 10017

Janis, Conrad *Actor, Musician*
300 N Swall Dr, #251, Beverly Hills, CA 90211

Janis, Jay *Financier*
%Gibraltar Financial Corp, 9111 Wilshire Blvd, Beverly Hills, CA 90210

Janklow, Morton L *Literary Agent, Attorney*
%Morton L Janklow Assoc, 598 Madison Ave, New York, NY 10022

Jankowski, Gene F *Television Executive*
%CBS Broadcast Grp, 51 W 52nd St, New York, NY 10019

Janofsky, Leonard S *Law Enforcement Official*
661 Thayer Ave, Los Angeles, CA 90024

Janowicz, Vic *Football Player*
1966 Jervis Rd, Columbus, OH 43221

Janowitz, Gundula *Opera Singer*
Rehetobelstrasse 81, 9000 St Gallen, Switzerland

Janowitz, Tama *Writer*
92 Horatio St, #5-E, New York, NY 10014

Janowitz, Walter *Actor*
12325 Chandler Blvd, #211, North Hollywood, CA 91607

Jansen, Dan *Speedskater*
4428 S 85th St, Greenfield, WI 53228

Jansen, Larry *Baseball Player*
RR2, Box 413-A, Forest Grove, OR 97116

Janss, William C *Businessman*
%General Delivery, Sun Valley, ID 83353

January, Don *Golfer*
%Professional Golfers Assn, PO Box 109601, Palm Beach Gardens, FL 33410

January, Lois *Actress*
20938 De Mina St, Woodland Hills, CA 91364

Jany, Alex *Swimmer*
104 Blvd Livon, 13007 Marseille, France

Janzen, David H *Biologist*
%University of Pennsylvania, Biology Dept, Philadelphia, PA 19104

Janzen, Edmund *Religious Leader*
%General Conference of Mennonite Brethren, 8000 W 21st St, Wichita, KS 67212

Jaquish, John E *Air Force General*
Prin Dep Asst SecAF for Acquisition, Hq USAF, Washington, DC 20330

Jarman, Franklin M *Businessman*
%North American Financial Corp, 1 Commerce Pl, Nashville, TN 37239

Jarmen, Claude, Jr *Actor*
%Shakelee, 444 Market St, San Francisco, CA 94111

Jarratt, Alexander A *Businessman*
%Reed International, Reed House, 83 Piccadilly, London W1A 1EJ, England

Jarre, Maurice *Composer*
27011 Sea Vista Dr, Malibu, CA 90265

Jarrett, Keith *Jazz Pianist, Composer*
635 E 11th St, New York, NY 10009

Jarrett, Will *Editor*
%Dallas Times Herald, Herald Sq, Dallas, TX 75202

Jarriel, Tom *Commentator*
%ABC-TV, News Dept, 77 W 66th St, New York, NY 10023

Jarring, Gunnar *Government Official, Sweden*
Karlavaegen 85, 11459 Stockholm, Sweden

Jarrott, Charles *Movie Director*
%Thompson, High Park Rd, Kew, Richmond, Surrey, England

Jaruzelski, Wojciech *Chairman, Council of Polish Ministers*
%Zjiednoczona Partia Robotnicza, 6 Nowy Swiat, 00-497 Warsaw, Poland

Jarvi, Neeme *Conductor*
PO Box 305, Sea Bright, NJ 07760

Jarvie, Charles L *Businessman*
%Rapid-American Corp, 888 7th Ave, New York, NY 10106

Jarvis, Doug *Hockey Player*
%Hartford Whalers, 1 Civic Center Plz, Hartford, CT 06103

Jarvis, Graham *Actor*
15351 Via De Las Olas, #531, Pacific Palisades, CA 90272

Jason, Sybil *Actress*
PO Box 573, Los Angeles, CA 90078

Jastremski, Chet *Swimmer*
424 Meadowbrook, Bloomington, IN 47401

Jastrow, Robert *Physicist, Writer*
22 Riverside Dr, New York, NY 10023

Jastrow, Terry *Actor*
10510 Sandal Ln, Los Angeles, CA 90077

Jatoi, Ghulan Mustafa *Prime Minister, Pakistan*
%Parliament, Islamabad, Pakistan

Jatras, Stephen J *Businessman*
%Telex Corp, 6422 E 41st St, Tulsa, OK 74135

Javan, Ali *Physicist*
12 Hawthorne St, Cambridge, MA 02138

Javers, Ron *Editor*
%Philadelphia Magazine, 1500 Market St, Philadelphia, PA 19102

Javierre Ortas, Antonio Maria Cardinal *Religious Leader*
%Biblioteca Apostolica Vatican, Vatican City, Rome, Italy

Jawara, Dwarda K *President, Gambia*
%President's Office, State House, Banjul, Gambia

Jaworski, Leon *Attorney, Watergate Prosecutor*
%Travis & Walker, Bank of Southwest Bldg, Houston, TX 77002

Jaworski, Ron *Football Player*
%Kansas City Chiefs, 1 Arrowhead Dr, Kansas City, MO 64129

Jay, John *Ski Photographer*
PO Box 3131, Rancho Santa Fe, CA 92067

Jay, Peter *Government Official, England*
39 Castlebar Rd, London W5 2DJ, England

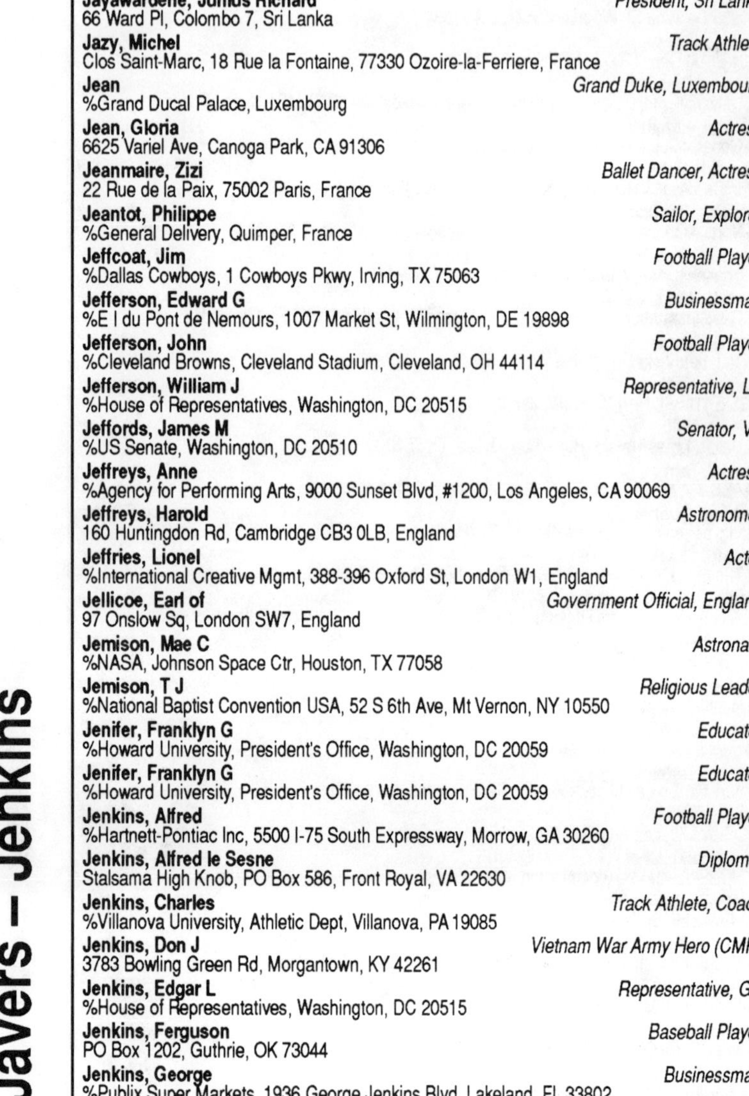

Jayawardene, Junius Richard *President, Sri Lanka*
66 Ward Pl, Colombo 7, Sri Lanka

Jazy, Michel *Track Athlete*
Clos Saint-Marc, 18 Rue la Fontaine, 77330 Ozoire-la-Ferriere, France

Jean *Grand Duke, Luxembourg*
%Grand Ducal Palace, Luxembourg

Jean, Gloria *Actress*
6625 Variel Ave, Canoga Park, CA 91306

Jeanmaire, Zizi *Ballet Dancer, Actress*
22 Rue de la Paix, 75002 Paris, France

Jeantot, Philippe *Sailor, Explorer*
%General Delivery, Quimper, France

Jeffcoat, Jim *Football Player*
%Dallas Cowboys, 1 Cowboys Pkwy, Irving, TX 75063

Jefferson, Edward G *Businessman*
%E I du Pont de Nemours, 1007 Market St, Wilmington, DE 19898

Jefferson, John *Football Player*
%Cleveland Browns, Cleveland Stadium, Cleveland, OH 44114

Jefferson, William J *Representative, LA*
%House of Representatives, Washington, DC 20515

Jeffords, James M *Senator, VT*
%US Senate, Washington, DC 20510

Jeffreys, Anne *Actress*
%Agency for Performing Arts, 9000 Sunset Blvd, #1200, Los Angeles, CA 90069

Jeffreys, Harold *Astronomer*
160 Huntingdon Rd, Cambridge CB3 0LB, England

Jeffries, Lionel *Actor*
%International Creative Mgmt, 388-396 Oxford St, London W1, England

Jellicoe, Earl of *Government Official, England*
97 Onslow Sq, London SW7, England

Jemison, Mae C *Astronaut*
%NASA, Johnson Space Ctr, Houston, TX 77058

Jemison, T J *Religious Leader*
%National Baptist Convention USA, 52 S 6th Ave, Mt Vernon, NY 10550

Jenifer, Franklyn G *Educator*
%Howard University, President's Office, Washington, DC 20059

Jenifer, Franklyn G *Educator*
%Howard University, President's Office, Washington, DC 20059

Jenkins, Alfred *Football Player*
%Hartnett-Pontiac Inc, 5500 I-75 South Expressway, Morrow, GA 30260

Jenkins, Alfred le Sesne *Diplomat*
Stalsama High Knob, PO Box 586, Front Royal, VA 22630

Jenkins, Charles *Track Athlete, Coach*
%Villanova University, Athletic Dept, Villanova, PA 19085

Jenkins, Don J *Vietnam War Army Hero (CMH)*
3783 Bowling Green Rd, Morgantown, KY 42261

Jenkins, Edgar L *Representative, GA*
%House of Representatives, Washington, DC 20515

Jenkins, Ferguson *Baseball Player*
PO Box 1202, Guthrie, OK 73044

Jenkins, George *Businessman*
%Publix Super Markets, 1936 George Jenkins Blvd, Lakeland, FL 33802

Jenkins, George *Stage Designer, Movie Art Director*
740 Kingman Ave, Santa Monica, CA 90402
Jenkins, Hayes Alan *Figure Skater*
809 Lafayette Dr, Akron, OH 44303
Jenkins, Jackie (Butch) *Actor*
G-5 Northwest Plaza, Box 72, Asheville, NC 28801
Jenkins, Loren *Journalist*
%Washington Post, 1150 15th St NW, Washington, DC 20071
Jenkins, Paul *Artist*
831 Broadway, New York, NY 10003
Jenkins, Roy *Government Official, England*
2 Kensington Park Gdns, London W11, England
Jenkins, William *Businessman*
%CalMat Co, 3200 San Fernando Rd, Los Angeles, CA 90065
Jenkins, William Maxwell *Financier*
PO Box 3586, Seattle, WA 98124
Jenks, Downing B *Businessman*
8 Greenbriar, St Louis, MO 63124
Jenner, Bruce *Track Athlete, Actor*
6342 Sycamore Meadows Dr, Malibu, CA 90265
Jennings, Elizabeth *Writer*
%David Higham Assoc, 5-8 Lower John St, London W1R 4HA, England
Jennings, Lynn *Track Athlete*
33 Spring St, Newmarket, NH 03857
Jennings, Peter *Commentator*
%ABC-TV, News Dept, 47 W 66th St, New York, NY 10023
Jennings, Waylon *Singer*
1114 17th St, #101, Nashville, TN 37212
Jenrette, Richard H *Businessman*
%Equitable Life Assurance Society, 787 7th Ave, New York, NY 10019
Jenrette, Rita *Actress, Model*
250 W 57th St, #2530, New York, NY 10107
Jens, Salome *Actress*
%Harris & Goldberg Agency, 1999 Ave of Stars, #2850, Los Angeles, CA 90067
Jens, Walter *Writer*
Sonnenstrasse 5, 74 Tubingen, Germany
Jensen, Arthur R *Educational Psychologist*
30 Canyon View Dr, Orinda, CA 94563
Jensen, Elwood V *Biochemist*
5650 Dorchester Ave, Chicago, IL 60637
Jensen, Harry A *Businessman*
%Armstrong World Industries, Box 3001, Lancaster, PA 17604
Jensen, James *Geologist*
%Brigham Young University, Geology Dept, Provo, UT 84602
Jensen, Karen *Actress*
4501 Vista del Monte, #8, Sherman Oaks, CA 91403
Jensen, Maren *Actress*
8033 Sunset, #1420, Los Angeles, CA 90046
Jensen, Robert P *Businessman*
%Tiger International, 1888 Century Park East, Los Angeles, CA 90067
Jepsen, Roger W *Senator, IA*
112 W Price St, Eldridge, IA 52748
Jerde, Jon *Architect*
%Jerde Grp, 363 5th Ave, Los Angeles, CA 90013
Jeremiah, David E *Navy Admiral*
%Joint Chiefs of Staff, Vice Chairman's Office, Pentagon, Washington, DC 20301
Jernberg, Sixten *Skier*
Fritidsby 780, 64 Lima, Sweden
Jerne, Niels *Nobel Medicine Laureate*
Chateau de Bellevue, Castillon-du-Gard, 30210 Gard, France
Jernigan, Tamara E *Astronaut*
%NASA, Johnson Space Ctr, Houston, TX 77058
Jerritts, Stephen G *Businessman*
%Storage Technology Corp, 2270 S 88th St, Louisville, CO 80028
Jethroe, Sam *Baseball Player*
340 E 14th St, Erie, PA 16503

J

Jewison – Johnsen

Jewison, Norman *Movie Director, Producer*
23752 Malibu Rd, Malibu, CA 90265

Jhabvala, Ruth Prawer *Writer*
%Harper & Row, 10 E 53rd St, New York, NY 10022

Jiang Zemin *Government Official, China*
%General Secretary's Office, Central Communist Party, Beijing, China

Jillian, Ann *Actress*
4241 Woodcliffe Rd, Sherman Oaks, CA 91403

Jillson, Joyce *Actress, Astrologist*
%Tribune Media Services, 64 E Concord St, Orlando, FL 32801

Jobert, Michel *Government Official, France*
21 Quai Alphonse-Le Gallo, 92100 Boulogne-Billancourt, France

Jobim, Antonio Carlos *Jazz Guitarist*
233 1/2 E 48th St, New York, NY 10017

Jobs, Steven P *Businessman*
%Next Inc, 3475 Deer Creek Rd, Palo Alto, CA 94304

Jockers, Harold W *Businessman*
%Mercantile Stores Co, 1100 N Market St, Wilmington, DE 19801

Joel, Billy *Singer*
%Maritime Music, 200 W 57th St, New York, NY 10019

Joel, Lucille A *Labor Leader*
%American Nurses Assn, 2420 Pershing Rd, Kansas City, MO 64108

Joffe, Roland *Movie Director*
%Lightmotive, 662 N Robertson Blvd, Los Angeles, CA 90069

Johann, Zita *Actress*
Sickletown Rd, West Nyack, NY 10994

Johannesson, Olafur *Prime Minister, Iceland*
%Althing, Reykjavik, Iceland

Johanos, Donald *Conductor*
%Honolulu Symphony Orchestra, 1000 Bishop St, Honolulu, HI 96813

Johanson, Donald C *Anthropologist*
%Institute of Human Origins, 2453 Ridge Rd, Berkeley, CA 94709

Johansson, Ingemar *Boxer*
Rakegaton 9, S-41320 Goteborg, Sweden

Johansson, Lennart V *Businessman*
%SKF (AB), Hornsgatan 1, 1415 50, Goteborg, Sweden

John Paul II, Pope *Religious Leader*
Palazzo Apostolico, Vatican City, Italy

John, Caspar *Fleet Admiral, England*
Trethewey, Mousehole, Penzance, Cornwall, England

John, David D *Museum Official, Explorer*
7 Cyncoed Ave, Cardiff CF2 6ST, Wales

John, Fritz *Mathematician*
%Courant Mathematical Sciences Institute, 251 Mercer St, New York, NY 10012

John, Tommy *Baseball Player*
32 Adams St, Cresskill, NY 07626

John-Roger (Hinkins) *Religious Leader*
%John Roger Foundation, 2101 Wilshire Blvd, Santa Monica, CA 90403

Johncock, Gordon *Auto Racing Driver*
2239 W Windrose Dr, Phoenix, AZ 85029

Johns, Charley E *Governor, FL*
%Community State Bank, 131 S Walnut St, Starke, FL 32091

Johns, Glynis *Actress*
11645 Gorham Ave, #309, Los Angeles, CA 90049

Johns, Jasper *Artist*
225 E Houston St, New York, NY 10002

Johns, John E *Educator*
%Furman University, President's Office, Greenville, SC 29613

Johns, Lori *Drag Racing Driver*
4418 Congressional, Corpus Christi, TX 78413

Johns, Mervyn *Actor*
%Richards, 42 Hazlebury Rd, London SW6, England

Johns, R Kenneth *Businessman*
%Sea-Land Corp, 10 Parsonage Rd, Edison, NJ 08837

Johnsen, Arve *Businessman*
%Stats Olijeselskap, Den Norske A/S, 4001 Stavanger, Norway

Johnson, Alex — *Baseball Player*
7650 Grand River, Detroit, MI 48206

Johnson, Arte — *Comedian*
2725 Bottlebrush Dr, Los Angeles, CA 90077

Johnson, Axel A — *Businessman*
Karlavagen 85, #300, S-114 59 Stockholm, Sweden

Johnson, Ben — *Track Athlete*
62 Blacktoft, Scarborough ON M1B 2H6, Canada

Johnson, Betsey — *Fashion Designer*
209 W 38th St, New York, NY 10018

Johnson, Beverly — *Model, Actress*
%Robert Kosden Agency, 7135 Hollywood Blvd, #PH 2, Los Angeles, CA 90046

Johnson, Bill — *Skier*
472-750 Richmond Rd, Susanville, CA 96130

Johnson, Billy — *Football Player*
%Washington Redskins, Dulles Airport, Box 17247, Washington, DC 20041

Johnson, Brad — *Model, Actor*
%International Creative Mgmt, 8899 Beverly Blvd, Los Angeles, CA 90048

Johnson, Brooks — *Track Coach*
%Stanford University, Athletic Dept, Stanford, CA 94305

Johnson, Butch — *Football Player*
%Denver Broncos, 13655 E Dove Valley Pkwy, Englewood, CO 80112

Johnson, Charles E, II — *Businessman*
%Sealed Power Corp, 100 Terrace Plz, Muskegon, MI 49443

Johnson, Clarence E — *Businessman*
%Borg-Warner Corp, 200 S Michigan Ave, Chicago, IL 60604

Johnson, Cletus — *Artist*
%Leo Castelli Gallery, 420 W Broadway, New York, NY 10012

Johnson, Darrell — *Baseball Manager*
3 Bussell Park, Ord, NE 68882

Johnson, Davey — *Baseball Manager*
4245 Bear Gulley Rd, Winter Park, FL 32789

Johnson, David G — *Economist*
5617 S Kenwood Ave, Chicago, IL 60637

Johnson, David W — *Businessman*
%Campbell Soup Co, Campbell Pl, Camden, NJ 08101

Johnson, Deane F — *Businessman*
%Time Warner Inc, 75 Rockefeller Plz, New York, NY 10019

Johnson, Dennis — *Basketball Player*
%Boston Celtics, 151 Merrimac St, Boston, MA 02114

Johnson, Deron — *Baseball Player*
13881 Poway Valley Rd, Poway, CA 92064

Johnson, Don J — *Bowler*
%Professional Bowlers Assn, 1720 Merriman Rd, Akron, OH 44313

Johnson, Donald E — *Businessman*
1500 Olde Hickory Ln, Coralville, IA 52241

Johnson, Donald M — *Businessman*
%Industrial Idemnity Co, 255 California St, San Francisco, CA 94111

Johnson, Earvin (Magic) — *Basketball Player*
%Los Angeles Lakers, Great Western Forum, 3900 W Manchester, Inglewood, CA 90306

Johnson, Eddie — *Basketball Player*
%Seattle SuperSonics, 190 Queen Ann Ave N, Seattle, WA 98109

Johnson, Edward C, III — *Financier*
%Fidelity Grp, 82 Devonshire St, Boston, MA 02109

Johnson, F Ross — *Businessman*
%RJR Nabisco Inc, 4385 Whitewater Creek Rd NW, Atlanta, GA 30327

Johnson, Frank M, Jr — *Judge*
%US Court of Appeals, PO Box 35, Montgomery, AL 36101

Johnson, G Griffith, Jr — *Government Official*
PO Box 804, Sherwood Forest, MD 21405

Johnson, G Thomas — *Businessman*
%Redman Homes Inc, 2550 Walnut Hill Ln, Dallas, TX 75229

Johnson, Georgann — *Actress*
%Gage Group, 9255 Sunset Blvd, #515, Los Angeles, CA 90069

Johnson, George E — *Businessman*
%Johnson Products Co, 8522 S Lafayette Ave, Chicago, IL 60620

Johnson, George W *Educator*
%George Mason University, President's Office, Fairfax, VA 22030

Johnson, Hansford T *Air Force General*
USCINTRANS, Scott Air Force Base, IL 62225

Johnson, Harold *Boxer*
139 W Tulpehocken St, #H-2, Philadelphia, PA 19144

Johnson, Haynes B *Journalist*
%Washington Post, 1150 15th St NW, Washington, DC 20071

Johnson, Hazel W *Army General*
%Army Nurse Corps, Army Department, Pentagon, Washington, DC 20310

Johnson, Henry A *Businessman*
%Spiegel Inc, 1515 W 22nd, Regency Towers, Oak Brook, IL 60521

Johnson, Howard *Baseball Player*
%New York Mets, Shea Stadium, Flushing, NY 11368

Johnson, Howard B *Businessman*
%Howard Johnson Co, 1 Howard Johnson Plz, Boston, MA 02125

Johnson, Howard Wesley *Educator*
100 Memorial Dr, Cambridge, MA 02142

Johnson, Hugh A *Financier*
%First Albany Corp, 41 State St, Albany, NY 12207

Johnson, J J *Jazz Trombonist, Composer*
4001 Murietta Ave, Sherman Oaks, CA 91423

Johnson, James H, Jr *Army General*
Commanding General, 1st US Army, Fort George G Meade, MD 20755

Johnson, James L *Businessman*
%GTE Corp, 1 Stamford Forum, Stamford, CT 06904

Johnson, Jannette *Skier*
PO Box 901, Sun Valley, ID 83353

Johnson, Jerome L *Navy Admiral*
Vice Chief of Naval Operations, Navy Department, Washington, DC 20350

Johnson, Jim *Football Player*
656 Amaranth Blvd, Mill Valley, CA 94941

Johnson, Jimmy *Football Coach*
%Dallas Cowboys, 1 Cowboys Pkwy, Irving, TX 75063

Johnson, John H *Publisher*
%Johnson Publishing Co, 820 S Michigan Ave, Chicago, IL 60605

Johnson, John Henry *Football Player*
%Pittsburgh Steelers, Three Rivers Stadium, Pittsburgh, PA 15212

Johnson, Johnnie (James E) *WW II Royal Air Force Hero, England*
Stables, Hargate Hall, Buxton, Derbyshire SK17 8TA, England

Johnson, Joseph B *Governor, VT*
1 Hillcrest Rd, Springfield, VT 05156

Johnson, Joseph H *Businessman*
%Associated Dry Goods Corp, 417 5th Ave, New York, NY 10016

Johnson, Keith *Labor Leader*
%Woodworkers of America Union, 1622 N Lombard St, Portland, OR 97217

Johnson, Kevin *Basketball Player*
%Phoenix Suns, 2910 N Central, Phoenix, AZ 85012

Johnson, Lady Bird *Wife of US President*
LBJ Ranch, Stonewall, TX 78671

Johnson, Lamont *Movie Director*
601 Paseo Miramar, Pacific Palisades, CA 90272

Johnson, Larry *Basketball Player*
%Charlotte Hornets, 2 First Union Center, #2600, Charlotte, NC 28282

Johnson, Laura *Actress*
%Gersh Agency, 232 N Canon Dr, Beverly Hills, CA 90210

Johnson, Leon W *WW II Air Force Hero (CMH), General*
1129 Litton Ln, McLean, VA 22101

Johnson, Lloyd P *Financier*
%Norwest Corp, 1200 Peavey Bldg, Minneapolis, MN 55479

Johnson, Lynn-Holly *Actress*
%Badgley Connor, 9229 Sunset Blvd, #607, Los Angeles, CA 90069

Johnson, Manuel H *Economist, Government Official*
%George Mason University, Global Market Studies Ctr, Fairfax, VA 22030

Johnson, Nancy L *Representative, CT*
%House of Representatives, Washington, DC 20515

Johnson, Nicholas *Attorney, Writer*
PO Box 1876, Iowa City, IA 52244

Johnson, Ora J *Religious Leader*
%General Assn of General Baptists, 100 Stinson Dr, Popular Bluff, MO 63901

Johnson, Oscar G *WW II Army Hero (CMH)*
1300 Michigan Ave, #19, Iron Mountain, MI 49801

Johnson, Pamela H (Lady Snow) *Writer*
85 Eaton Terr, London SW1, England

Johnson, Paul *Mayor*
%Mayor's Office, City Hall, 251 W Washington St, Phoenix, AZ 85003

Johnson, Pepper *Football Player*
%New York Giants, Giants Stadium, East Rutherford, NJ 07073

Johnson, Philip C *Architect*
375 Park Ave, New York, NY 10022

Johnson, R E *Labor Leader*
%Train Dispatchers Assn, 1401 S Harlem Ave, Berwyn, IL 60402

Johnson, R Scott *Architect*
%Johnson Fain Pereira, 6100 Wilshire Blvd, Los Angeles, CA 90048

Johnson, Rafer *Track Athlete*
%Special Olympics California, 501 Colorado Ave, #200, Santa Monica, CA 90401

Johnson, Ralph *Architect*
%Perkins & Will, 123 N Wacker Dr, Chicago, IL 60606

Johnson, Richard J V *Publisher*
%Houston Chronicle, 801 Texas Ave, Houston, TX 77002

Johnson, Rick *Motorcycle Racing Rider*
%American Honda Racing, 100 W Alondra Blvd, Gardena, CA 90247

Johnson, Robert *Businessman*
%Lederle Laboratories, Middletown Rd, Pearl River, NJ 10965

Johnson, Ron *Football Player*
126 Hillside Ave, Cresskill, NJ 07626

Johnson, Roy *Labor Leader*
%Roofers & Waterproofers Union, 1125 17th St NW, Washington, DC 20036

Johnson, S A *Businessman*
%Pentair Inc, 1700 W Highway 36, St Paul, MN 55113

Johnson, Samuel C *Businessman*
%S C Johnson & Son, 1525 Howe St, Racine, WI 53403

Johnson, Samuel D *Judge*
%US Court of Appeals, 999 Bank One Tower, 221 W 6th St, Austin, TX 78701

Johnson, Sonia *Women's, Religious Activist*
3318 2nd St S, Arlington, VA 22204

Johnson, Steve *Basketball Player*
%Seattle SuperSonics, 190 Queen Ann Ave N, Seattle, WA 98109

Johnson, Thomas S *Financier*
%Manufacturers Hanover Trust, 270 Park Ave, New York, NY 10017

Johnson, Tim *Representative, SD*
%House of Representatives, Washington, DC 20515

Johnson, Tish *Bowler*
%Ladies Professional Bowlers Assn, 7171 Cherryvale Blvd, Rockford, IL 61112

Johnson, Tom *Hockey Player*
%Boston Bruins, 150 Causeway St, Boston, MA 02114

Johnson, U Alexis *Diplomat*
%Department of State, 2201 "C" St NW, Washington, DC 20520

Johnson, Uwe *Writer*
%Suhrkamp Verlag, Postfach 4229, 6000 Frankfurt/Main, Germany

Johnson, Van *Actor*
%Studio Artists, 305 W 52nd St, New York, NY 10019

Johnson, Victor S *Businessman*
%Aladdin Industries, 703 Murfreesboro Rd, Nashville, TN 37210

Johnson, Virginia *Ballerina*
%Dance Theatre of Harlem, 466 W 152nd St, New York, NY 10031

Johnson, Virginia E *Sex Therapist*
4910 Forest Park Blvd, St Louis, MO 63108

Johnson, W Thomas, Jr *Television Executive*
%Cable News Network, 1 CNN Ctr, PO Box 105366, Atlanta, GA 30348

Johnson, Walter *Historian*
Bass Lake, Pentwater MI 49449

J

Johnson – Jones

Johnson, Warren C *Chemist*
946 Bellclair Rd SE, Grand Rapids, MI 49506

Johnson, William B *Businessman*
%IC Industries, 111 E Wacker Dr, Chicago, IL 60601

Johnson, William S *Chemist*
101 Meadowood Dr, Portola Valley, CA 94025

Johnston, Alastair *Sports Agent*
%International Mgmt Group, 1 Erieview Plz, Cleveland, OH 44114

Johnston, Allen H *Religious Leader*
%Bishop's House, 3 Wymer Terr, PO Box 21, Hamilton, New Zealand

Johnston, Cathy *Golfer*
%Ladies Professional Golf Assn, 2570 Volusia Ave, #B, Daytona Beach, FL 32114

Johnston, David L *Educator*
%McGill University, Chancellor's Office, Montreal PQ H3A 2T5, Canada

Johnston, David W, Jr *Businessman*
%Dan River Inc, 107 Frederick St, Greenville, SC 29606

Johnston, Don *Businessman*
%J Walter Thompson Co, 420 Lexington Ave, New York, NY 10017

Johnston, Douglas *Publisher*
%Vanity Fair Magazine, 350 Madison Ave, New York, NY 10017

Johnston, Gerald A *Businessman*
%McDonnell Douglas Corp, PO Box 516, St Louis, MO 63166

Johnston, Harold S *Chemist*
132 Highland Blvd, Berkeley, CA 94708

Johnston, J Bennett *Senator, LA*
%US Senate, Washington, DC 20510

Johnston, James W *Businessman*
%RJR Nabsico Inc, Reynolds Blvd, Winston-Salem, NC 27102

Johnston, John Dennis *Actor*
%LA Talent, 8335 Sunset Blvd, Los Angeles, CA 90069

Johnston, Lynn *Cartoonist (For Better or For Worse)*
%Universal Press Syndicate, 4900 Main St, Kansas City, MO 64112

Johnston, Mary *Astronaut*
%Marshall Space Flight Ctr, Mettallurgist Dept, Huntsville, AL 35812

Johnston, W Eugene *Representative, NC*
%Small Business Administration, 1441 "L" St NW, Washington, DC 20416

Johnstone, John W, Jr *Businessman*
%Olin Corp, 120 Long Ridge Rd, Stamford, CT 06904

Johore *Sultan, Malaysia*
Istana Bukit Serene, Johore Bahru, Johore, Malaysia

Joiner, Charlie *Football Player*
%San Diego Chargers, 9449 Friars Rd, San Diego, CA 92108

Jolly, Allison *Yachtswoman*
3440 Knoxville Ave, Long Beach, CA 90808

Jolly, E Grady *Judge*
%US Court of Appeals, Eastland Courthouse, 245 E Capitol St, Jackson, MS 39201

Jonckheer, Efrain *Prime Minister, Netherlands Antilles*
%Royal Netherlands Embassy, Calle 21, Avda 10, San Jose, Costa Rica

Jones, Alan *Auto Racing Driver*
%Williams Engineering, Station Rd Industrial Estate, Didcot, Oxon, England

Jones, Allan *Singer, Actor*
10 W 66th St, New York, NY 10023

Jones, Allen *Artist*
%Leslie Waddington Gallery, 1 Cork St, London W1, England

Jones, Arthur *Inventor (Nautilus Exercise Machine)*
%MedX, 1155 NE 77th St, Ocala, FL 32670

Jones, Benjamin F *Businessman*
%Monarch Capital Corp, 1 Financial Plz, Springfield, MA 01102

Jones, Bobby *Basketball Player*
5109 Panview Dr, Mathews, NC 28105

Jones, Brereton *Governor, KY*
%Governor's Office, State Capitol Bldg, #100, Frankfort, KY 40601

Jones, Charles W *Labor Leader*
%Brotherhood of Boilermakers, 8th & State, Kansas City, KS 66101

Jones, Charlie *Sportscaster*
NBC-TV, 30 Rockefeller Plz, New York, NY 10020

Jones, Chuck (Charles M) *Animator (Road Runner, Pepe le Pew)*
PO Box 2319, Costa Mesa, CA 92628

Jones, Courtney J L *Figure Skating Executive*
%National Skating Assn, 15-27 Gee St, London EC1V 3RE, England

Jones, Cranston E *Editor*
8 E 96th St, New York, NY 10028

Jones, Davey *Singer (The Monkees)*
21 Elms Rd, Fareham, Hampshire, England

Jones, David (Deacon) *Football Player*
%Calgary Stampeders, 1817 Crowchild Trl NW, Calgary AB T2M 4R6, Canada

Jones, David A *Businessman*
%Humana Inc, 500 W Main St, Louisville, KY 40201

Jones, Dean *Actor*
%Bresler Kelly Kipperman, 15760 Ventura Blvd, #1730, Encino, CA 91436

Jones, Dub *Football Player*
223 Glendale, Rusten, LA 71270

Jones, E Bradley *Businessman*
%LTV Steel Corp, PO Box 6778, Cleveland, OH 44101

Jones, E Fay *Architect*
1330 N Hillcrest St, Fayetteville, AR 72701

Jones, E Richard *Businessman*
%Safeway Stores, 4th & Jackson, Oakland, CA 94660

Jones, Earl *Track Athlete*
15114 Petroskey, Detroit, MI 48238

Jones, Ed *Representative, TN*
%General Delivery, Yorkville, TN 38389

Jones, Edith H *Judge*
%US Court of Appeals, 515 Rusk Ave, Houston, TX 77002

Jones, George *Singer*
38 Music Square E, #300, Nashville, TN 37203

Jones, Geraint I *Conductor*
Long House, Arkley Ln, Barnet Rd, Arkley, Herts, England

Jones, Gilbert E *Businessman*
%IBM World Trade Corp, 821 United Nations Plz, New York, NY 10017

Jones, Grace *Model, Actress*
PO Box 82, Great Neck, NY 11021

Jones, Grandpa *Comedian*
Box 853, Goodlettsville, TN 37072

Jones, Greg *Skier*
Box 500, Tahoe City, CA 95730

Jones, Gwyneth *Opera Singer*
PO Box 556, CH-8037 Zurich, Switzerland

Jones, Hayes *Track Athlete*
11799 Corbett, Detroit, MI 48213

Jones, Henry *Actor*
%Bauman Hiller Assoc, 5750 Wilshire Blvd, Los Angeles, CA 90036

Jones, Horace C *Businessman*
271 Westbay Point Moorings, 6200 Flotilla Dr, Holmes Beach, FL 33510

Jones, Jack *Singer*
%Senoj Productions, 9000 Sunset Blvd, #515, Los Angeles, CA 90069

Jones, Jack (James L) *Labor Leader*
74 Ruskin Park House, Champion Hill, London SE5, England

Jones, James Earl *Actor*
PO Box 55337, Sherman Oaks, CA 91413

Jones, James R *Representative, OK; Financier*
%American Stock Exchange, 86 Trinity Pl, New York, NY 10006

Jones, Janet *Actress*
14135 Beresford Dr, Beverly Hills, CA 90210

Jones, Jeffrey *Actor*
%J Michael Bloom Ltd, 9200 Sunset Blvd, #710, Los Angeles, CA 90069

Jones, John E *Businessman*
%CBI Industries, 800 Jorie Blvd, Oak Brook, IL 60521

Jones, John Paul *Sculptor*
22370 3rd Ave, South Laguna, CA 92677

Jones, Johnny (Lam) *Football Player*
%Dallas Cowboys, 1 Cowboy Pkwy, Irving, TX 75063

J

Jones – Jones

Jones, Joseph L — *Businessman*
%Armstrong World Industries, West Liberty St, Lancaster, PA 17604

Jones, L Q — *Actor*
%Charter Mgmt, 9000 Sunset Blvd, #1112, Los Angeles, CA 90069

Jones, Landon Y — *Editor*
%People Magazine, Rockefeller Ctr, New York, NY 10020

Jones, Lawrence M — *Businessman*
%Coleman Co, 250 N St Francis Ave, Wichita, KS 67202

Jones, LeRoi (Amiri Baraka) — *Poet*
%CAP, 502 High St, Newark, NJ 07102

Jones, Marcia Mae — *Actress*
4541 Hazeltine, #4, Sherman Oaks, CA 91423

Jones, Marvin — *Football Player*
%Florida State University, Athletic Dept, Tallahassee, FL 32306

Jones, Nathaniel R — *Judge*
%US Court of Appeals, US Courthouse Bldg, 5th & Walnut Sts, Cincinnati, OH 45202

Jones, Norman M — *Financier*
%Metropolitan Financial Corp, 215 N High St, Fargo, ND 58108

Jones, Parnelli — *Auto Racing Driver, Builder*
PO Box W, Torrance, CA 90507

Jones, Paul Tudor, II — *Financier*
%Tudor Investment Corp, 160 Broadway, New York, NY 10038

Jones, Quincy — *Composer*
1100 Bel Air Pl, Los Angeles, CA 90077

Jones, Randy — *Publisher*
%Esquire Magazine, 1790 Broadway, New York, NY 10019

Jones, Randy — *Baseball Player*
13379 Via Stephen, Poway, CA 92064

Jones, Reginald H — *Businessman*
%General Electric Co, Easton Turnpike, Fairfield, CT 06431

Jones, Reginald V — *Physicist*
8 Queen's Terr, Aberdeen AB1 1XL, Scotland

Jones, Richard M — *Businessman*
%Sears Roebuck Co, Sears Tower, Chicago, IL 60684

Jones, Rickie Lee — *Singer, Songwriter*
%Geffen Records, 9169 Sunset Blvd, Los Angeles, CA 90069

Jones, Robert T — *Aerospace Scientist*
25005 La Loma Dr, Los Altos, CA 94022

Jones, Robert Trent — *Golf Course Architect*
7 Church St, Montclair, NJ 07042

Jones, Rulon — *Football Player*
%Denver Broncos, 13655 E Dove Valley Pkwy, Englewood, CO 80112

Jones, Sam — *Basketball Player*
15417 Tierra Dr, Wheaton, MD 20906

Jones, Shirley — *Actress*
701 N Oakhurst Dr, Beverly Hills, CA 90210

Jones, Stan — *Football Player, Coach*
12-2 Clear Pond Dr, Walpole, MA 02081

Jones, Steve — *Golfer*
%Professional Golfers Assn, PO Box 109601, Palm Beach Gardens, FL 33410

Jones, Steven — *Physicist*
%Brigham Young University, Physics Dept, Provo, UT 84602

Jones, Thomas D — *Astronaut*
%NASA, Johnson Space Center, Houston, TX 77058

Jones, Thomas V — *Businessman*
%Northrop Corp, 1840 Century Park East, Los Angeles, CA 90067

Jones, Tom — *Singer*
363 Copa de Oro Rd, Los Angeles, CA 90024

Jones, Tommy Lee — *Actor*
PO Box 966, San Saba, TX 76877

Jones, Tristan — *Explorer, Writer*
246 W 10th St, #31-G, New York, NY 10014

Jones, Vernon T — *Businessman*
%Williams Companies, 1 Williams Ctr, Tulsa, OK 74172

Jones, Walter B — *Representative, NC*
May Blvd, Farmville, NC 27828

Jones, Warren L *Judge*
PO Box 60, Jacksonville, FL 32201

Jones, William (Dub) *Football Player*
326 Glendale, Ruston, LA 51277

Jones, William K *Marine Corps General*
1211 Huntly Pl, Alexandria, VA 22307

Jong, Erica *Writer*
%Harper Collins, 10 E 57th St, New York, NY 10022

Jong, Petrus J S de *Prime Minister, Netherlands*
%Christian Democratic Appel, The Hague, Netherlands

Jonsson, Emil *Prime Minister, Iceland*
Kirkjuvegur 7, Hafnarfjordur, Iceland

Jontz, James *Representative, IN*
%House of Representatives, Washington, DC 20515

Joo Hyong Kyong *Businessman*
%Samsung Co, 250 Ka Taepyungro, Chungku, Seoul, South Korea

Joon Silk Koh *Businessman*
%Pohang Iron & Steel, 5 Dongchondon, Pohang City, Kyungbok, South Korea

Jordan, Barbara *Representative, TX*
%University of Texas, LBJ Public Affairs School, Austin, TX 78713

Jordan, Charles M *Automobile Designer*
3955 Kirkland Ct, Bloomfield Hills, MI 48013

Jordan, Don D *Businessman*
%Houston Industries, 611 Walker Ave, Houston, TX 77002

Jordan, Frank *Mayor*
%Mayor's Office, City Hall, 400 Van Ness Ave, San Francisco, CA 94102

Jordan, Glenn *Movie Director*
9401 Wilshire Blvd, #700, Beverly Hills, CA 90212

Jordan, Hamilton *Government Official, Publisher*
%Whittle Books, 505 Market, Knoxville, TN 37902

Jordan, I King *Educator*
%Gallaudet University, President's Office, 800 Florida NW, Washington, DC 20002

Jordan, I King *Educator*
%Gallaudet University, President's Office, Washington, DC 20002

Jordan, Kathy *Tennis Player*
1604 Union St, San Francisco, CA 94213

Jordan, Lee Roy *Football Player*
%Redwood Lumber Co, 2425 Burbank St, Dallas, TX 75235

Jordan, Lloyd P *Football Coach*
21 Malvern Ave, #4, Richmond, VA 23221

Jordan, Michael *Basketball Player*
%Chicago Bulls, 980 N Michigan Ave, Chicago, IL 60611

Jordan, Michael H *Businessman*
%PepsiCo Inc, Anderson Hill Rd, Purchase, NY 10577

Jordan, Payton *Track Coach*
439 Knoll Dr, Los Altos, CA 94022

Jordan, Richard *Actor*
3704 Carbon Canyon, Malibu, CA 90265

Jordan, Steve *Football Player*
%Minnesota Vikings, 9520 Viking Dr, Eden Prairie, MN 55344

Jordan, Vernon E, Jr *Civil Rights Activist*
500 E 52nd St, New York, NY 10021

Jordan, William *Actor*
%Henderson/Hogan Agency, 247 S Beverly Dr, #102, Beverly Hills, CA 90210

Jorgensen, Anker *Prime Minister, Denmark*
Borgbjergvej 1, 2450 SV Copenhagen, Denmark

Jorgenson, Dale *Economist*
%Harvard University, Economics Dept, Cambridge, MA 02138

Joseph, Frederick H *Financier*
%Drexel Burnham Lambert Inc, 60 Broad St, New York, NY 10004

Joseph, Jackie *Comedienne*
111 N Valley St, Burbank, CA 91505

Joseph, Stephen *Physician*
%New York City Department of Health, 125 Worth St, New York, NY 10013

Josephine Charlotte *Princess, Belgium*
%Grand Ducal Palace, Luxembourg

J

Josephs, Wilfred *Composer*
6 Parsifal Rd, West Hampstead NW6, England

Josephson, Brian D *Nobel Physics Laureate*
Cavendish Laboratory, Madingley Rd, Cambridge CB3 0HE, England

Josephson, Erland *Actor*
%Royal Dramatic Theatre, Nybroplan, Box 5037, 102 41 Stockholm, Sweden

Josephson, Karen *Synchronized Swimmer*
1079 Mohr Ln, #E-19, Concord, CA 94518

Josephson, Sarah *Synchronized Swimmer*
1079 Mohr Ln, #E-19, Concord, CA 94518

Joulwan, George A *Army General*
CinC, US Southern Command, Quarry Heights, Panama, APO, AA 34003

Jourdan, Louis *Actor*
1139 Maybrook Dr, Beverly Hills, CA 90210

Jovan, Claude *Financier*
%Credit Commercial, 103 Ave des Champs-Elysees, 75008 Paris, France

Jovanovich, Peter *Publisher*
%Harcourt Brace Jovanovich Inc, 6277 Sea Harbor Dr, Orlando, FL 32821

Jovanovich, William I *Publisher*
%Harcourt Brace Jovanovich Inc, 6277 Sea Harbor Dr, Orlando, FL 32821

Joyce, Andrea *Sportscaster*
%CBS-TV, Sports Dept, 51 W 52nd St, New York, NY 10019

Joyce, Edward M *Television Executive*
%Columbia Broadcasting System, 51 W 52nd St, New York, NY 10019

Joyce, Elaine *Actress*
724 N Roxbury Dr, Beverly Hills, CA 90210

Joyce, Joan *Softball Player, Golfer*
22856 Marbella Cir, Boca Raton, FL 33433

Joyce, John T *Labor Leader*
%Bricklayers & Allied Craftsmen, 815 15th St NW, Washington, DC 20005

Joyner, Wally *Baseball Player*
2186 Tudor Castle Way, Decatur, GA 30035

Joyner-Kersee, Jackie *Track Athlete*
%World Class Mgmt, PO Box 21053, Long Beach, CA 90801

Jozwiak, Brian *Football Player*
%Kansas City Chiefs, 1 Arrowhead Dr, Kansas City, MO 64129

Juan Carlos I *King, Spain*
Palacio de la Zarzuela, Madrid, Spain

Juan, Count of Barcelona *Prince, Spain*
Giralda, Guisando 25, Puerta de Hierro, 28035 Madrid, Spain

Juantorena, Alberto *Track Athlete*
%National Institute for Sports, Sports City, Havana, Cuba

Jubany Arnau, Narciso Cardinal *Religious Leader*
%Arquebisbe de Barcelone, Bisbe Irurita 5, 08002 Barcelona, Spain

Juckes, Gordon W *Hockey Executive*
General Delivery, Zurich ON N0M 2T0, Canada

Judd, Donald C *Sculptor*
PO Box 218, Marfa, TX 79843

Judd, Howard L *Obstetrician*
%University of California, Health Sciences, Los Angeles, CA 90024

Judd, Naomi *Singer (The Judds)*
PO Box 17325, Nashville, TN 37217

Judd, Walter H *Representative, MN*
3083 Ordway St NW, Washington, DC 20008

Judd, Wynonna *Singer (The Judds)*
PO Box 17325, Nashville, TN 37217

Judelson, David N *Businessman*
%Gulf & Western Industries, 1 Gulf & Western Plz, New York, NY 10023

Judge, Thomas L *Governor, MT*
579 Diehl Dr, Helena, MT 59601

Jugnauth, Aneerood *Prime Minister, Mauritius*
%Government House, Port Louis, Mauritius

Juhl, Finn *Furniture Designer*
%Kratvaenget 15, 2920 Chartottenlund, Denmark

Julian, Alexander *Fashion Designer*
19 W 55th St, New York, NY 10019

Julian, Janet *Actress*
%Borinstein Oreck Bogart Agency, 8271 Melrose Ave, #110, Los Angeles, CA 90046

Juliana *Queen, Netherlands*
Palace of Soestdijk, Amsterdamsestraatweg 1, 3744 A A Baarn, Netherlands

Julien, Max *Actor*
5107 Coldwater Canyon Ave, Sherman Oaks, CA 90028

Jumblatt, Walid *Government Official, Lebanon*
%Druze Headquarters, Mokhtara, Lebanon

Jump, Gordon *Actor*
1631 Hillcrest Ave, Glendale, CA 91202

Juneau, Pierre *Commentator*
%Canadian Broadcast Co, 1500 Bronson Ave, Ottawa ON N1G 3J5, Canada

Jung, Richard *Neurologist*
Waldhofstrasse 42, D 78 Freiburg, Germany

Jungers, Francis *Businessman*
PO Box 3242, Sunriver, OR 97702

Junior, E J *Football Player*
%Miami Dolphins, Robbie Stadium, 2269 NW 199th St, Miami, FL 33056

Junkins, Jerry R *Businessman*
%Texas Instruments, 13500 N Central Expressway, Dallas, TX 75265

Juran, Joseph Moses *Engineer, Management Consultant*
%Juran Institute, 88 Danbury Rd, Wilton, CT 06897

Jurasik, Peter *Actor*
969 1/2 Manzanita St, Los Angeles, CA 90029

Juren, Dennis F *Businessman*
%Tesoro Petroleum Co, 8700 Tesoro Dr, San Antonio, TX 78286

Jurgensen, Sonny *Football Player*
%WDVM-TV, Sports Dept, 4001 Brandywine St NW, Washington, DC 20016

Juriga, Jim *Football Player*
%Denver Broncos, 13655 E Dove Valley Pkwy, Englewood, CO 80112

Jurinac, Sena *Opera Singer*
%State Opera House, Vienna 1, Austria

Just, Walter *Publisher*
%Milwaukee Journal, 333 W State St, Milwaukee, WI 53201

Just, Ward *Writer*
36 Ave Junot, Paris, France

Justice, Charlie (Choo Choo) *Football Player*
PO Box 819, Cherryville, NC 28021

Justice, Donald R *Poet, Educator*
1665 Ridge Rd, Iowa City, IA 52240

K

Kaat – Kamara-Taylor

Kaat, Jim *Baseball Player*
100 SE 5th Ave, #509, Boca Raton, FL 33432

Kabat, E A *Immunochemist*
730 Haven Ave, New York, NY 10032

Kael, Pauline *Writer*
%New Yorker Magazine, 20 W 43rd St, New York, NY 10036

Kaes, Herbert *Businessman*
%OMV, Otto Wagner-Platz 5, Vienna, Austria

Kagan, Jeremy Paul *Movie Director*
2024 N Curson Ave, Los Angeles, CA 90046

Kagoshima, Juzo *Dollmaker*
1-14 Toyotamakami, Nerimaku, Tokyo, Japan

Kahane, Jeffrey *Concert Pianist*
%IMG Artists, 22 E 71st St, New York, NY 10021

Kahn, Alfred E *Government Official*
RD 3, Trumansburg, NY 14886

Kahn, Jenette S *Publisher*
%DC Comics, 75 Rockefeller Plz, New York, NY 10019

Kahn, Madeline *Actress*
975 Park Ave, #9-A, New York, NY 10028

Kahn, Philippe *Businessman*
%Borland International, 4585 Scotts Valley Dr, Scotts Valley, CA 95066

Kain, Karin *Ballet Dancer*
%National Ballet of Canada, 157 E King St, Toronto ON M5C 1G9, Canada

Kairamo, Kari *Businessman*
%Nokia Grp, Mikonkatu 15 A, SF-00101 Helsinki 10, Finland

Kaiser, A Dale *Biochemist*
832 Santa Fe Ave, Stanford, CA 94305

Kaiser, Edgar F *Businessman*
%Kaiser Bldg, 300 Lakeside Dr, Oakland, CA 94643

Kaiser, Philip M *Diplomat*
%Department of State, 2201 "C" St NW, Washington, DC 20520

Kaiserman, William *Fashion Designer*
29 W 56th St, New York, NY 10019

Kaku, Ryuzaburo *Businessman*
%Canon Inc, 3-30-2 Shimomaruko, Otaku, Tokyo 146, Japan

Kalb, Marvin *Commentator*
%Harvard University, Barone Press Ctr, 79 J F Kennedy St, Cambridge, MA 02138

Kalber, Floyd *Commentator*
%NBC-TV, News Dept, 30 Rockefeller Plz, New York, NY 10020

Kalember, Patricia *Actress*
%Gersh Agency, 232 N Canon Dr, Beverly Hills, CA 90210

Kalikow, Peter *Publisher*
%H J Kalikow Co, 101 Park Ave, New York, NY 10178

Kalina, Mike *Chef*
%"Travelin' Gourmet" Show, PBS-TV, 1320 Braddock Pl, Alexandria, VA 22314

Kalina, Richard *Artist*
139 Bowery, New York, NY 10002

Kaline, Al *Baseball Player*
945 Timberlake Dr, Bloomfield Hills, MI 48013

Kalinowsky, Lothar B *Neuropsychiatrist*
155 E 76th St, New York, NY 10021

Kalish, Martin *Labor Leader*
%School Administrators Federation, 853 Broadway, New York, NY 10003

Kallai, Gyula *Prime Minister, Hungary*
Patriotic People's Front Council, Belgrad Rakpart 24, Budapest 5, Hungary

Kalleres, Michael P *Navy Admiral*
Commander, 2nd Fleet, FPO, AE 09501

Kallman, Donald H *Businessman*
%Manhattan Industries, 1155 Ave of Americas, New York, NY 10036

Kalmbach, Leland J *Businessman*
1295 State St, Springfield, MA 01101

Kamali, Norma *Fashion Designer*
11 W 56th St, New York, NY 10019

Kamara-Taylor, Christian A *Prime Minister, Sierra Leone*
%Vice President's Office, Freetown, Sierra Leone

Kamei, Masao *Businessman*
%Sumitomo Electric Industries, 5-15 Kitahama, Higashiku, Osaka 541, Japan

Kamen, Martin D *Chemist*
5768 Holly Oak Dr, Los Angeles, CA 90068

Kamm, Henry *Journalist*
%New York Times, 229 W 43rd St, New York, NY 10036

Kammhuber, Josef *Air Force General, West Germany*
Schwindstrasse 24, 8000 Munich 40, Germany

Kampelman, Max M *Government Official*
3154 Highland Pl NW, Washington, DC 20008

Kan, Yuet Wai *Geneticist*
%University of California, Genetics Dept, #U-426, San Francisco, CA 94143

Kanaly, Steve *Actor*
3611 Longridge Ave, Sherman Oaks, CA 91423

Kanamori, Masao *Businessman*
%Mitsubishi Heavy Industries, 2-5-1 Marunouchi, Chiyodaku, Tokyo, Japan

Kanao, Minoru *Businessman*
%Nippon Kokan, 1-1-2 Marunouchi, Chiyodaku, Tokyo 100, Japan

Kanazawa, Shuzo *Businessman*
%Mitsubishi Paper Co, 2-3-19 Kyobashi, Chuoku, Tokyo 104, Japan

Kandel, Eric R *Neurobiologist*
9 Sigma Pl, Riverdale, NY 10471

Kander, John *Composer*
%Dramatist Guild, 234 W 44th St, New York, NY 10036

Kane Elson, Marion *Synchronized Swimmer*
4669 Badger Rd, Santa Rosa, CA 95405

Kane, Art *Photographer*
%Art Center School of Design, Photography Dept, 1700 Lida, Pasadena, CA 91103

Kane, Bob *Cartoonist (Batman)*
8455 Fountain Ave, #725, Los Angeles, CA 90069

Kane, Carol *Actress*
2400 Broadway St, #100, Santa Monica, CA 90404

Kane, Charles J *Financier*
%Third National Corp, 201 4th Ave N, Nashville, TN 37201

Kane, Edward R *Businessman*
%E I du Pont de Nemours, 1007 Market St, Wilmington, DE 19898

Kane, James *Labor Leader*
%United Electrical Workers Union, 11 E 51st St, New York, NY 10022

Kane, Joseph Nathan *Historian*
%H W Wilson Co, 950 University Ave, Bronx, NY 10452

Kane, William J *Businessman*
%Great Atlantic & Pacific Tea Co, 420 Lexington Ave, New York, NY 10017

Kanew, Jeff *Movie Director*
%Gersh Agency, 232 N Canon Dr, Beverly Hills, CA 90210

Kangas, Edward A *Businessman*
%Deloitte & Touche Co, 1633 Broadway, New York, NY 10019

Kanin, Fay *Writer*
653 Ocean Front Walk, Santa Monica, CA 90402

Kanin, Garson *Writer*
200 W 57th St, #1203, New York, NY 10019

Kanjorski, Paul E *Representative, PA*
%House of Representatives, Washington, DC 20515

Kankaapaa, Matti *Businessman*
%Valmet Corp, Punanotkonkatu 2, PL 155, 00131 Helsinki 13, Finland

Kann Valar, Paula *Skier*
PO Box 906, Franconia, NH 03580

Kann, Peter R *Businessman, Publisher*
%Dow Jones Co, 200 Liberty St, New York, NY 10281

Kanne, Michael S *Judge*
%US Court of Appeals, PO Box 1340, Lafayette, IN 47902

Kannenberg, Bernd *Track Athlete*
Sportschule, Sonthofen/Allgau, Germany

Kanter, Hal *Movie, Television Writer, Producer*
15941 Woodvale Rd, Encino, CA 91316

Kantrowitz, Adrian *Heart Surgeon*
6767 W Outer Dr, Detroit, MI 48253

K

Kantrowitz, Arthur *Physicist*
24 Pinewood Village West, Lebanon, NH 03784

Kaplan, Gabe *Actor, Comedian*
9551 Hidden Valley Rd, Beverly Hills, CA 90210

Kaplan, Jeremiah *Publisher*
%Macmillan Inc, 866 3rd Ave, New York, NY 10022

Kaplan, Jonathan *Movie Director*
760 N LaCienega Blvd, Los Angeles, CA 90069

Kaplan, Justin *Writer*
PO Box 219, Truro, MA 02666

Kaplan, Marvin *Actor*
%Erika Wain Agency, 1418 N Highland Ave, #102, Los Angeles, CA 90028

Kaplan, Morton A *Educator*
5828 S University, Chicago, IL 60637

Kaplan, Nathan O *Biochemist*
8587 La Jolla Scenic Dr, La Jolla, CA 92037

Kaplan, Richard *Editor*
%US Magazine, 215 Lexington Ave, New York, NY 10016

Kaplansky, Irving *Mathematician*
5825 S Dorchester Ave, Chicago, IL 60637

Kaplow, Herbert E *Commentator*
211 Van Buren St, Falls Church, VA 22046

Kapnick, Harvey E, Jr *Financier*
100 Woodley Rd, Winnetka, IL 60093

Kapoor, Shashi *Actor*
%Film Valas, Juhu Beach, Bombay, India

Kapor, Mitchell *Computer Programer*
%ON Technology Inc, 1 Cambridge Ctr, Cambridge, MA 02142

Kapp, Joe *Football Player, Coach*
%British Columbia Lions, 765 Pacific Blvd, S Vancouver BC V6B 4Y9, Canada

Kappel, Frederick R *Businessman*
343 W Royal Flamingo Dr, Sarasota, FL 33577

Kaptur, Marcy *Representative, OH*
%House of Representatives, Washington, DC 20515

Karageorghis, Vassos *Archaeologist*
12 Kastoria St, Nicosia, Cyprus

Karan, Donna *Fashion Designer*
%Donna Karan Co, 550 7th Ave, New York, NY 10018

Karathanasis, Sotirios K *Medical Researcher*
%Harvard Medical School, 25 Shattuck St, Boston, MA 02115

Karatz, Bruce E *Businessman*
%Kaufman & Broad Inc, 11601 Wilshire Blvd, Los Angeles, CA 90025

Karch, George Frederick *Financier*
2720 Wicklow Rd, Shaker Heights, OH 44120

Karcher, Carl *Businessman*
%Carl Karcher Enterprises, 1200 N Harbor Blvd, Anaheim, CA 92801

Karelskaya, Rimma K *Ballerina*
%State Academic Bolshoi Theatre, 1 Ploshchad Sverdlova, Moscow, Russia

Karina, Anna *Actress*
12 Rue Saint Severin, 75005 Paris, France

Karkow, Richard E *Businessman*
%Minstar Inc, 1215 Marshall St NE, Minneapolis, MN 55413

Karl, George *Basketball Coach*
%Portland Trail Blazers, 700 Multnomah St, Portland, OR 97232

Karle, Jerome *Nobel Chemistry Laureate*
US Navy Structure of Matter Research Laboratory, Code 6030, Washington, DC 20375

Karlen, John *Actor*
PO Box 5617, Beverly Hills, CA 90210

Karlin, Samuel *Mathematician*
%Stanford University, Mathematics Dept, Stanford, CA 94305

Karling, John S *Mycologist*
1219 Tuckahoe Ln, West Lafayette, IN 47904

Karlson, Phil *Movie Director*
3094 Patricia Ave, Los Angeles, CA 90064

Karnes, William G *Businessman*
%Beatrice Foods Co, 2 N La Salle St, Chicago, IL 60602

Karnow, Stanley *Journalist*
10850 Springknoll Dr, Potomac, MD 20854

Karolyi, Bela *Gymnastics Coach*
%Karolyi's World Gym, 17203 Bamwood Dr, Houston, TX 77090

Karp, David *Writer*
1116 Corsica Dr, Pacific Palisades, CA 90272

Karpati, Gyorgy *Water Polo Player*
II Liva U 1, 1025 Budapest, Hungary

Karpatkin, Rhoda H *Publisher*
%Consumer Reports Magazine, 256 Washington St, Mount Vernon, NY 10553

Karplus, Martinmila *Chemist*
%Harvard University, Chemistry Dept, Cambridge, MA 02138

Karpov, Anatoly *Chess Player*
%Russian Chess Federation, Luzhnetskaya 8, Moscow 119270, Russia

Karppinen, Pentti *Rowing Athlete*
General Delivery, Turku, Finland

Karras, Alex *Football Player, Actor*
%William Morris Agency, 151 El Camino, Beverly Hills, CA 90212

Karrass, Chester L *Writer*
1633 Stanford St, Santa Monica, CA 90404

Karsh, Yousuf *Photographer*
%Chateau Laurier Hotel, #660, 1 Rideau St, Ottawa ON K1N 8S7, Canada

Kasaks, Sally Frame *Businesswoman*
%AnnTaylor Stores Corp, 3 E 57th, New York, NY 10022

Kasama, Yuichiro *Businessman*
%Mitsui Toatsu Chemicals, 205 Kasumigaseki, Chiyodaku, Tokyo, Japan

Kasatkina, Natalya *Ballerina, Choreographer*
St Karietny Riad, H 5/10, B 37, Moscow, Russia

Kasem, Casey *Entertainer*
%Westwood One, 9540 Washington Blvd, Culver City, CA 90232

Kasem, Jean *Actress*
%Commercials Unlimited, 7461 Beverly Blvd, #400, Los Angeles, CA 90036

Kasha, Al *Composer*
337 S El Camino Dr, Beverly Hills, CA 90212

Kashiwagi, Yusuke *Financier*
%Bank of Tokyo, 1-6-3 Nihombashi, Hongokucho, Chuoku, Tokyo 106, Japan

Kasich, John R *Representative, OH*
%House of Representatives, Washington, DC 20515

Kaske, Karlheinz *Businessman*
%Siemens AG, Wittelsbacherplatz 2, 8000 Munich, Germany

Kaslik, Vaclav *Composer, Conductor*
Skretova 10, Prague II, Czecholslovakia

Kasparov, Gary *Chess Player*
%Russian Chess Federation, Luzhnetskaya 8, Moscow 119270, Russia

Kasper, Steve *Hockey Player*
%Boston Bruins, 150 Causeway St, Boston, MA 02114

Kasrashvili, Makvala *Opera Singer*
%State Academy Bolshoi Theatre, 1 Ploschad Sverdlova, Moscow, Russia

Kassar, Mario *Movie Producer*
%Carolco Pictures, 8800 W Sunset Blvd, Los Angeles, CA 90069

Kassebaum, Nancy Landon *Senator, KS*
%US Senate, Washington, DC 20510

Kassirer, Jerome P *Physician, Editor*
%New England Journal of Medicine, 1440 Main St, Waltham, MA 02554

Kassorla, Irene *Psychologist*
PO Box 11001, Beverly Hills, CA 90213

Kassulke, Karl *Football Player*
%Bethel College, Athletic Dept, St Paul, MN 55112

Kasten, Robert W, Jr *Senator, WI*
%US Senate, Washington, DC 20510

Kastenmeier, Robert W *Representative, WI*
745 Pony Ln, Sun Prairie, WI 53590

Katayama, Nihachiro *Businessman*
%Mitsubishi Electric Corp, 2-2-3 Marunouchi, Chiyodaku, Tokyo 100, Japan

Katims, Milton *Conductor, Concert Violinist*
%University of Houston, Music School, Houston, TX 77004

Katin, Peter *Concert Pianist*
%Direction Arts, Box 7275, Station A, Toronto M5W 1X9, Canada
Katleman, Harris J *Entertainment Executive*
%Twentieth Century Fox Television, 10201 W Pico Blvd, Los Angeles, CA 90035
Kato, Benzabure *Businessman*
%Kyowa Hakko Kogyo Co, 1-6-1 Otemachi, Chiyodaku, Tokyo 100, Japan
Kato, Reiji *Businessman*
%Rengo Co, 4-18 Hirnomachi, Higashiku, Osaka 541, Japan
Kato, Ryuichi *Financier*
%Tokai Bank, 3-21-24 Nishiki, Nakaku, Nagoya, Japan
Katt, William *Actor*
PO Box 1980, Studio City, CA 91614
Katz, Abraham *Diplomat*
%Department of State, 2201 "C" St NW, Washington, DC 20520
Katz, Alex *Artist*
435 W Broadway, New York, NY 10012
Katz, Bernard *Nobel Medicine Laureate*
%University College, Biophysics Dept, Gower St, London WC1, England
Katz, Hilda *Artist*
915 West End Ave, #5-D, New York, NY 10025
Katz, Howard *Basketball Executive*
%Chicago Bulls, 333 N Michigan Ave, Chicago, IL 60601
Katz, Kurt *Businessman*
%Peabody International Corp, 4 Landmark Sq, Stamford, CT 06904
Katz, Lillian Hochberg *Businesswoman*
%Lillian Vernon Corp, 510 S Fulton Ave, Mount Vernon, NY 10550
Katz, Milton *Attorney, Educator*
6 Berkeley St, Cambridge, MA 02138
Katz, Omri *Actor*
%Eerie, Indiana Co, 4024 Radford Ave, Studio City, CA 91604
Katzenbach, Nicholas deB *Attorney General*
117 Library Pl, Princeton, NJ 08540
Katzenberg, Jeffrey *Entertainment Executive*
%Walt Disney Studios, 500 S Buena Vista Blvd, Burbank, CA 91521
Katzir, Ephraim *President, Israel*
%Weizmann Institute of Science, PO Box 26, Rehovot, Israel
Kauffman, Ewing *Baseball Executive*
%Kansas City Royals, PO Box 1969, Royals Stadium, Kansas City, MO 64141
Kauffman, John T *Businessman*
%Pennsylvania Power & Light Co, 2 N 9th St, Allentown, PA 18101
Kauffmann, Howard C *Businessman*
%Exxon Corp, 1251 Ave of Americas, New York, NY 10020
Kaufman, Henry *Financier*
%Phibro-Salomon Inc, 1221 Ave of Americas, New York, NY 10020
Kaufman, Philip *Movie Director*
%Creative Artists Agency, 9830 Wilshire Blvd, Beverly Hills, CA 90212
Kaufman, Stephen P *Businessman*
%Arrow Electronics Inc, 767 5th Ave, New York, NY 10153
Kaufman, Victor A *Entertainment Executive*
%Columbia Pictures Entertainment, 711 5th Ave, New York, NY 10022
Kaufmann, Bob *Basketball Player*
1677 Rivermist Dr, Lilburn, GA 30247
Kautner, Helmut *Movie Director*
18-C Konigsalle, Berlin 33, Germany
Kavanaugh, Ken *Football Player*
4907 Palm Aire Dr, Sarasota, FL 34243
Kawai, Ryoichi *Businessman*
%Komatsu Ltd, 2-3-6 Akasaka, Minatoku, Tokyo 107, Japan
Kawakami, Genichi *Businessman*
%Yamata Motor Co, 2500 Shingai, Iwata City 438, Japan
Kawakami, Tetsuro *Businessman*
%Sumitomo Electric Industries, 5-15 Kitahama, Higashiku, Osaka 541, Japan
Kawakatsu, Kenji *Financier*
%Sanwa Bank, 4-10 Fushimimachi, Higashiku, Osaka 541, Japan
Kawake, Jiro *Businessman*
%Oji Paper Co, 4-7-5 Ginza, Chuoku, Tokyo 104, Japan

K

Kawamoto, Nobuhiko *Businessman*
%Konishiroku Photo Industry, 1-26-2 Nishi, Shinjuku, Tokyo 160, Japan

Kawamura, Shigekuni *Businessman*
%Dainippon Ink & Chemicals, 3-7-20 Nihombashi, Chuoku, Tokyo 103, Japan

Kawamura, Yoshibumi *Businessman*
%Sankyo Co, 2-7-12 Ginza, Chuoku, Tokyo 104, Japan

Kawawa, Rashidi Mfaume *Prime Minister, Tanzania*
%Ministry of Defense, Dar es Salaam, Tanzania

Kay, Clarence *Football Player*
%Denver Broncos, 13655 E Dove Valley Pkwy, Englewood, CO 80112

Kay, Connie *Jazz Drummer (Modern Jazz Quartet)*
%Atlantic Records, 75 Rockefeller Plz, New York, NY 10019

Kay, Dianne *Actress*
%Harry Gold Assoc, 3500 W Olive Ave, #1440, Burbank, CA 91505

Kay, Hershy *Composer*
N George Hill Rd, Southbury, CT 06488

Kaye, Judy *Actress*
%William Morris Agency, 151 El Camino, Beverly Hills, CA 90212

Kaysen, Carl *Economist*
1 Hilliard Pl, Cambridge, MA 02138

Kayser, Elmer L *Historian*
2921 34th St NW, Washington, DC 20008

Kayser, Julius G *Businessman*
%S S Pierce Co, 74 Seneca St, Dundee, NY 14837

Kaysone Phomvihane *President, Laos*
%President's Office, Vientiane, Laos

Kazan, Elia *Movie Director*
174 E 95th St, New York, NY 10128

Kazan, Lainie *Singer*
9903 Santa Monica Blvd, #283, Beverly Hills, CA 90212

Kazin, Alfred *Writer*
%City University of New York, English Dept, 33 W 42nd St, New York, NY 10036

Kazmaier, Dick *Football Player*
676 Elm St, Concord, MA 01742

Keach, Stacy *Actor*
27425 Winding Way, Malibu, CA 90265

Kean, Jane *Actress*
4332 Ben Ave, Studio City, CA 91604

Kean, Michael *Actor*
%Triad Artists, 10100 Santa Monica Blvd, #1600, Los Angeles, CA 90067

Kean, Thomas H *Governor, NJ*
%Drew University, 36 Madison Ave, Madison, NJ 07940

Keanan, Staci *Actress*
%Michael Slessinger Assoc, 8730 Sunset Bld, #220, Los Angeles, CA 90069

Keane, Bil *Cartoonist (Family Circus)*
5815 E Joshua Tree Ln, Paradise Valley, AZ 85253

Keane, Diane *Actress*
23 Primrose Hill, Charleton Mackrell, Someton, Summerset, England

Keane, Glen *Animator (Little Mermaid)*
%Walt Disney Studios, 500 S Buena Vista St, Burbank, CA 91521

Keane, Kerrie *Actress*
%Century Artists, 9744 Wilshire Blvd, #308, Beverly Hills, CA 90212

Kear, David *Geologist*
14 Christiana Grover, Lower Hutt, Ohope, Wellington, New Zealand

Kearney, Richard D *Government Official*
167 Friar Tuck Hill, Sherwood Forest, MD 21405

Kearns, David T *Businessman*
%Xerox Corp, PO Box 1600, Stamford, CT 06904

Kearns, Henry *Financier*
1960 Vallejo St, San Francisco, CA 94123

Kearse, Amalya Lyle *Judge*
%US Court of Appeals, US Courthouse, Foley Sq, New York, NY 10007

Keating, Paul *Prime Minister, Australia*
%Prime Minister's Office, Parliament House, Canberra ACT 2600, Australia

Keating, Stephen F *Businessman*
688 Hillside Dr, Wayzata, MN 55391

K

Keaton, Diane *Actress*
%Arlyne Rothberg Inc, 145 Central Park West, New York, NY 10023

Keaton, Micheal *Actor*
821 Napoli, Pacific Palisades, CA 90272

Keck, Herman, Jr *Religious Leader*
%Calvary Grace Christian Church of Faith, US Box 4266, Norton AFB, CA 92409

Keck, Howard B *Philanthropist*
%Keck Foundation, 555 S Flower St, #3640, Los Angeles, CA 90071

Keck, William *Architect*
5551 University Ave, Chicago, IL 60637

Kedah *Sultan, Kedah*
Alor Setar, Kedah, Malaysia

Kedrova, Lila *Actress*
50 Forest Manor Rd, #3, Willowdale ON M2J 1M1, Canada

Keefe, Mike *Editorial Cartoonist*
%Denver Post, PO Box 1709, Denver, CO 80201

Keefer, Don *Actor*
4146 Allott Ave, Sherman Oaks, CA 91423

Keegan, John *Historian*
%Jonathan Cape Ltd, 32 Bedford Sq, London WC1B 3EL, England

Keehn, Grant *Financier*
8623 NE 10th St, Bellevue, MA 98004

Keehn, Silas *Financier*
%Federal Reserve Bank, 230 S LaSalle St, Chicago, IL 60690

Keeler, Ruby *Actress*
71029 Early Times Rd, Rancho Mirage, CA 92270

Keenan, John F *Judge*
%US District Court, Foley Sq, New York, NY 10007

Keenan, Joseph D *Labor Leader*
2727 29th St NW, Washington, DC 20008

Keenan, Mike *Hockey Coach*
%Chicago Black Hawks, 1800 W Madison Ave, Chicago, IL 60612

Keene, Christopher *Conductor*
650 West End Ave, New York, NY 10024

Keener, Jefferson W *Businessman*
265 Hampshire Rd, Akron, OH 44313

Keesee, Roger N *Businessman*
%Bally Manufacturing Corp, 8700 W Bryn Mawr Ave, Chicago, IL 60631

Keeshan, Bob *Actor (Captain Kangaroo)*
%Robert Keeshan Assoc, 40 W 57th St, 16th Fl, New York, NY 10019

Kehoe, Paul J *Businessman*
%Kellogg Co, 235 Porter St, Battle Creek, MI 49016

Kehoe, Rick *Hockey Player*
%Pittsburgh Penguins, Civic Arena, Pittsburgh, PA 15219

Keiffer, E Gene *Businessman*
%E-Systems Inc, 6250 LBJ Fwy, Dallas, TX 75266

Keightley, David N *Historian*
%University of California, History Dept, Berkeley, CA 94720

Keillor, Garrison *Writer, Broadcaster*
%American Humor Institute, 80 8th Ave, #1216, New York, NY 10011

Keiser, John H *Educator*
%Boise State University, President's Office, Boise, ID 83725

Keitel, Harvey *Actor*
PO Box 49, Palisades, NY 10964

Keith, Brian *Actor*
%Camden ITG, 822 S Robertson Blvd, #200, Los Angeles, CA 90035

Keith, Damon J *Judge*
%US Court of Appeals, US Courthouse, 231 W Lafayette Blvd, Detroit, MI 48226

Keith, David *Actor*
%Triad Artists, 10100 Santa Monica Blvd, #1600, Los Angeles, CA 90067

Keith, Garnett L, Jr *Businessman*
%Prudential Insurance, Prudential Plz, Newark, NJ 07101

Keith, Louis *Physician*
333 E Superior St, #476, Chicago, IL 60611

Keith, Penelope *Actress*
%London Mgmt, 235/241 Regent St, London W1A 2JT, England

K

Keith, R Drake *Businessman*
%Entergy Corp, 225 Baronne St, New Orleans, LA 70112
Keith, Robert *Financier*
%Northeast Savings, 147 Charter Oak Ave, Hartford, CT 06106
Keleti, Agnes *Gynmast*
%Wingate Institute for Physical Education & Sport, Matanya 42902, Israel
Kell, George *Baseball Player*
PO Box 158, Swifton, AR 72471
Kellaway, Roger *Composer*
%Pat Phillips Mgmt, 520 E 81st St, #PH-C, New York, NY 10028
Kelleher, Herbert D *Businessman*
%Southwest Airlines Co, Love Field, Dallas, TX 75235
Keller, Erhard *Speed Skater*
Sudl Munchneustrassw 6-A, 8022 Grunwald, Germany
Keller, George M *Businessman*
%Chevron Corp, 255 Bush St, San Francisco, CA 94104
Keller, Greta *Singer*
405 E 54th St, New York, NY 10022
Keller, Marthe *Actress*
%Lemonstrasse 9, 8 Munich 80, Germany
Keller, Mary Page *Actress*
%Triad Artists, 10100 Santa Monica Blvd, #1600, Los Angeles, CA 90067
Keller, Richard C *Financier*
%Marine Midland Banks Inc, 1 Marine Midland Ctr, Buffalo, NY 14240
Kellerman, Sally *Actress*
%Agency for Performing Arts, 9000 Sunset Blvd, #1200, Los Angeles, CA 90069
Kellermann, Susan *Actress*
%Judy Schoen Assoc, 606 N Larchmont Blvd, #309, Los Angeles, CA 90004
Kelley, Clarence M *Director, FBI*
Alameda Towers, 400 W 49th Terr, Kansas City, MO 64112
Kelley, DeForest *Actor*
15463 Greenleaf St, Sherman Oaks, CA 91403
Kelley, Edward *Government Official, Financier*
%Federal Reserve Board, 20th & Constitution NW, Washington, DC 20551
Kelley, Edward F *Physicist*
%National Standards & Technology Institute, Rt I-270, Gaithersburg, MD 20878
Kelley, Gaynor N *Businessman*
%Perkin-Elmer Corp, 761 Main Ave, Norwalk, CT 06859
Kelley, John A (Marathon) *Marathon Runner*
136 Cedar Hill Rd, East Dennis, MA 02641
Kelley, John J *Track Athlete*
415 Pequot Ave, Mystic, CT 06355
Kelley, Kitty *Writer*
%Bantam Books, 666 5th Ave, New York, NY 10103
Kelley, Larry *Football Player*
5917 Strickland Pl, Pensacola, FL 32506
Kelley, Steve *Editorial Cartoonist*
%San Diego Union, 350 Camino de la Reina, PO Box 191, San Diego, CA 92112
Kelley, Thomas G *Vietnam War Navy Hero (CMH)*
4411 Rena Rd, #4, Forestville, MD 20746
Kelley, Wendell J *Businessman*
%Illinois Power Co, 500 S 27th St, Decatur, IL 62525
Kellin, Mike *Actor*
23 Clinton Ave, Nyack, NY 10960
Kellner, Alex *Baseball Player*
3716 N Jackson Ave, Tucson, AZ 85719
Kelly, Donald P *Businessman*
%Beatrice Companies, 2 N LaSalle St, Chicago, IL 60602
Kelly, Eamon M *Educator*
%Tulane University, President's Office, New Orleans, LA 70118
Kelly, Ellsworth *Artist*
RD, PO Box 170-B, Chatham, NY 12037
Kelly, Gene *Actor, Dancer*
725 N Rodeo Dr, Beverly Hills, CA 90210
Kelly, Hugh J *Businessman*
%Ocean Drilling & Exploration Co, 1600 Canal St, New Orleans, LA 70161

K

Kelly – Kendall

Kelly, Jim *Football Player*
%Buffalo Bills, 1 Bills Dr, Orchard Park, NY 14127

Kelly, John *Labor Leader*
%Office/Professional Employees International, 265 W 14th St, New York, NY 10011

Kelly, Leroy *Football Player*
7210 Ardleigh St, #C-2, Philadelphia, PA 19119

Kelly, Patsy *Comedienne*
%Gloria Safier, 667 Madison Ave, New York, NY 10021

Kelly, Paula *Actress, Dancer*
%CNA Assoc, 1801 Ave of Stars, #1250, Los Angeles, CA 90067

Kelly, Petra *Government Official, West Germany*
Bundeshaus HT 718, 5300 Bonn, Germany

Kelly, Robert J *Navy Admiral*
Commander, US Pacific Fleet, Pearl Harbor, HI 96860

Kelly, Thomas L, Jr *Businessman*
%TIE/Communications Inc, 5 Research Dr, Shelton, CT 06484

Kelly, Thomas W *Army General*
%George Washington University, Engineering School, Washington, DC 20052

Kelly, Tom *Baseball Manager*
%Minnesota Twins, 501 Chicago Ave S, Minneapolis, MN 55415

Kelly, William M, Jr *Publisher*
%Money Magazine, Rockefeller Ctr, New York, NY 10020

Kelly, William R *Businessman*
%Kelly Services Inc, 999 W Big Beaver Rd, Troy, MI 48084

Kelsey, Frances O *Pharmacologist*
%Federal Drug Administration, 5600 Fishers Ln, Rockville, MD 20857

Kelsey, Linda *Actress*
%Harris & Goldberg Agency, 1999 Ave of Stars, #2850, Los Angeles, CA 90067

Kelso, Frank B, II *Navy Admiral*
Chief of Naval Operations, Navy Dept, Washington, DC 20350

Kemal, Yashal *Writer*
PK 14, Basinkoy, Istanbul, Turkey

Kemball-Cook, Denis B *Businessman*
58 Andrews Dr, Darien, CT 06820

Kemble, Edwin Crawford *Physicist*
8 Ash Street Pl, Cambridge, MA 02138

Kemeny, John G *Mathematician, Philosopher*
PO Box 195, Etna, NH 03750

Kemme, Thomas *Labor Leader*
%Stove Furnance & Appliance Union, 2929 S Jefferson Ave, St Louis, MO 63118

Kemp, Jack F *Secretary, Housing & Urban Development*
%Department of Housing & Urban Development, 451 7th St SW, Washington, DC 20410

Kemp, Jeremy *Actor*
%Leading Artists Ltd, 600 St James St, London SW1, England

Kemp, Steve *Baseball Player*
12979 Claymont Ct, San Diego, CA 92130

Kemper, James M, Jr *Financier*
%Commerce Bancshares Inc, 720 Main St, Kansas City, MO 64199

Kemper, James S, Jr *Businessman*
%Kemper Corp, Rt 22, Long Grove, IL 60049

Kemper, R Crosby, Jr *Financier*
%United Missouri Bancshares Inc, 10th & Grand, Kansas City, MO 64141

Kemper, Victor W *Cinematographer*
10313 W Pico Blvd, Los Angeles, CA 90064

Kempton, Murray *Journalist*
%Newsday, 235 Pinelawn Rd, Melville, NY 11747

Kendal, Felicity *Actress*
%Chatto & Linnit, Prince of Wales Theatre, Coventry St, London W1, England

Kendall, Bruce *Boardsailor*
6 Pedersen Pl, Bucklands Beach, Auckland, New Zealand

Kendall, Donald M *Businessman*
%PepsiCo Inc, Anderson Hill Rd, Purchase, NY 10577

Kendall, Felicity *Actress*
%Chatto & Linnit, Prince of Wales Theatre, London W1V 7FE, England

Kendall, Henry W *Nobel Physics Laureate*
%Massachusetts Institute of Technology, Physics Dept, Cambridge, MA 02139

Kendall, Tom *Auto Racing Driver*
708 Ivy St, Glendale, CA 91204

Kendall, William H *Businessman*
6602 Deep Creek Dr, Prospect, KY 40059

Kendler, Bob *Handball, Raquetball Player*
%US Handball Assn, 4101 Dempster St, Skokie, IL 60076

Kendrew, John C *Nobel Chemistry Laureate*
4 Church Ln, Linton, Cambridge CB1 6JX, England

Keneally, Thomas *Writer*
24 The Serpentine, Bilgola Beach NSW 2107, Australia

Keneflick, John C *Businessman*
%Union Pacific Railroad Co, 1416 Dodge St, Omaha, NE 68179

Kenn, Mike *Football Player*
%Atlanta Falcons, Suwanee Rd, Suwanee, GA 30174

Kenna, E Douglas *Businessman, Football Player*
%G L Ohrstrom & Co, 540 Madison Ave, New York, NY 10022

Kenna, Edward *WW II Australian Army Hero (VC)*
121 Coleraine Rd, Hamilton, Vic 3300, Australia

Kennan, Elizabeth Topham *Educator*
%Mount Holyoke College, Presidents' Office, South Hadley, MA 01075

Kennan, George F *Diplomat*
%Institute for Advanced Study, Princeton, NJ 08540

Kenneally, John P *WW II Irish Army Hero (VC)*
7 Station Ln, Lapworth, Warwks, England

Kennedy, Anthony M *Supreme Court Justice*
%US Supreme Court, 1 Ist St NE, Washington, DC 20543

Kennedy, Bernard J *Businessman*
%National Fuel Gas Co, 30 Rockefeller Plz, New York, NY 10112

Kennedy, Bruce R *Businessman*
%Alaska Air Grp, PO Box 68947, Seattle, WA 98168

Kennedy, Burt *Movie Director*
%Brigade Productions, 13138 Magnolia Blvd, Sherman Oaks, CA 91423

Kennedy, Cornelia G *Judge*
%US Court of Appeals, US Courthouse, 231 W Lafayette Blvd, Detroit, MI 48226

Kennedy, Cortez *Football Player*
%Seattle Seahawks, 11220 NE 53rd St, Kirkland, WA 98033

Kennedy, D James *Religious Leader*
%Coral Ridge Presbyterian Church, 5554 N Federal Hwy, Fort Lauderdale, FL 33308

Kennedy, David M *Secretary, Treasury*
33 Meadow View Dr, Northfield, IL 60093

Kennedy, Donald *Educator*
%Stanford University, President's Office, Stanford, CA 94305

Kennedy, Edward M (Ted) *Senator, MA*
636 Chain Bridge Rd, McLean, VA 22101

Kennedy, Eugene Patrick *Biological Chemist*
63 Buckminister Rd, Brookline, MA 02146

Kennedy, George *Actor*
1900 Ave of Stars, #2270, Los Angeles, CA 90067

Kennedy, George D *Businessman*
%International Minerals & Chemical Corp, 2315 Sanders, Northbrook, IL 60062

Kennedy, James Cox *Businessman*
%Cox Communications Inc, 1400 Lake Hearn Dr NE, Atlanta, GA 30319

Kennedy, Jayne *Actress*
944 17th St, #1, Santa Monica, CA 90403

Kennedy, Joey *Journalist*
%Birmingham News, PO Box 2553, Birmingham, AL 35202

Kennedy, John Milton *Actor*
7100 Balboa Blvd, #606, Van Nuys, CA 91406

Kennedy, John R, Jr *Businessman*
%Federal Paper Board Co, 75 Chestnut Ridge Rd, Montvale, NJ 07645

Kennedy, Joseph P, II *Representative, MA*
%House of Representatives, Washington, DC 20515

Kennedy, Kathleen *Movie Producer*
%Amblin Entertainment, 100 Universal City Plz, Universal City, CA 91608

Kennedy, Leon Isaac *Actor*
%Fred Amsel Assoc, 6310 San Vicente Blvd, #407, Los Angeles, CA 90048

K

Kennedy – Kerr

Kennedy, Mimi *Actress*
%Triad Artists, 10100 Santa Monica Blvd, #1600, Los Angeles, CA 90067

Kennedy, Nigel *Concert Violinist*
%Artists Mgmt, 9-A Penzance Pl, London W11 4PE, England

Kennedy, Robert D *Businessman*
%Union Carbide Corp, 39 Old Ridgbury Rd, Danbury, CT 06817

Kennedy, Ted *Hockey Player*
290 Russell Hill Rd, Toronto ON M4V 2T6, Canada

Kennedy, Terry *Baseball Player*
PO Box 220, Riderwood, MD 21139

Kennedy, Tom *Television Host*
%William Morris Agency, 151 El Camino, Beverly Hills, CA 90212

Kennedy, Vern *Baseball Player*
RR 1, Box 164, Mendon, MO 64660

Kennedy, William J, III *Businessman*
%North Carolina Mutual Life Insurance, Mutual Plz, Durham, NC 27701

Kennedy, X J *Writer*
4 Fern Way, Bedford, MA 01730

Kennelly, Barbara B *Representative, CT*
95 Scarborough St, Hartford, CT 06105

Kenny G *Saxophonist*
%Fritz/Turner Mgmt, 648 N Robertson Blvd, Los Angeles, CA 90048

Kenny, Douglas T *Educator*
%University of British Columbia, President's Office, Vancouver BC, Canada

Kenrich, John L *Businessman*
%Chemed Corp, 1200 DuBois Tower, Cincinnati, OH 45202

Kent, Allegra *Ballerina*
%New York City Ballet, Lincoln Ctr, New York, NY 10023

Kent, Arthur *Commentator*
%NBC-TV, News Dept, 30 Rockefeller Plz, New York, NY 10112

Kent, Geoffrey C *Businessman*
%Imperial Grp, 1 Grosvenor Pl, London SW1X 7HB, England

Kent, Jean *Actress*
%London Mgmt, 235-241 Regent St, London W1A 2JT, England

Kent, Julia *Ballerina*
%American Ballet Theatre, 890 Broadway, New York, NY 10003

Kent, Peter *Geologist*
43 Trinity Ct, Gray's Inn Rd, London WC1, England

Kentner, Louis P *Concert Pianist*
1 Mallord St, London SW3, England

Kenyon, Mel *Auto Racing Driver*
2645 S 25 West, Lebanon, IN 46052

Kenzo *Fashion Designer*
3 Pl des Victoires, 75001 Paris, France

Keogh, James *Government Official*
Byram Dr, Belle Haven, Greenwich, CT 06830

Keohane, Nannerl O *Educator*
%Wellesley College, President's Office, Wellesley, MA 02181

Keon, Dave *Hockey Player*
%Toronto Maple Leafs, 60 Carlton St, Toronto ON M5B 1L1, Canada

Keough, Donald R *Businessman*
%Coca-Cola Co, 310 North Ave NW, Atlanta, GA 30313

Kepes, Gyorgy *Artist*
90 Larchwood Dr, Cambridge, MA 02138

Kercheval, Ken *Actor*
570 N Rossmare Ave, Los Angeles, CA 90004

Kerkorian, Kirk *Businessman*
%MGM Inc, 10202 W Washington Blvd, Culver City, CA 90230

Kerley, James J *Businessman*
%Emerson Electric Co, 8000 W Florissant Ave, St Louis, MO 63136

Kern, Geof *Photographer*
1337 Crampton, Dallas, TX 75207

Kerns, David V, Jr *Microbiotics Engineer*
%Vanderbilt University, Electrical Engineering Dept, Nashville, TN 37235

Kerr, Clark *Educator*
8300 Buckingham Dr, El Cerrito, CA 94530

Kerr, Deborah *Actress*
Wyhergut, 7250 Klosters, Grisons, Switzerland
Kerr, Donald M, Jr *Physicist*
%EG&E Inc, 45 William St, Wellesley, MA 02181
Kerr, Graham *Food Expert, Writer*
%Simon & Schuster, 1230 Ave of Americas, New York, NY 10022
Kerr, James R *Businessman*
%Avco Corp, 1275 King St, Greenwich, CT 06830
Kerr, Jean *Writer*
1 Beach Ave, Larchmont, NY 10538
Kerr, John *Basketball Player*
%WMAQ-AM, Merchandise Mart, Chicago, IL 60654
Kerr, John G *Actor*
10203 Santa Monica Blvd, #400, Los Angeles, CA 90067
Kerr, Judy *Actress*
6827 Pacific View Dr, Los Angeles, CA 90068
Kerr, Pat *Fashion Designer*
%Pat Kerr Inc, 200 Wagner Pl, Memphis, TN 38103
Kerr, Tim *Hockey Player*
%Philadelphia Flyers, Spectrum, Pattison Pl, Philadelphia, PA 19148
Kerr, Walter F *Drama Critic*
1 Beach Ave, Larchmont, NY 10538
Kerrey, J Robert *Governor/Senator, NE; Vietnam Navy Hero*
%US Senate, Washington, DC 20010
Kerry, John F *Senator, MA*
%US Senate, Washington, DC 20510
Kersey, Jerome *Basketball Player*
%Portland Trail Blazers, 700 NE Multnomah St, Portland, OR 97232
Kershaw, Doug *Fiddler*
6537 Kessler Ave, Woodland Hills, CA 91364
Kershner, Irvin *Movie Director*
Box 232, Rt 7 N, Kent, CT 06757
Kerst, Donald W *Physicist*
425 Date Palm Rd, Vero Beach, FL 32963
Kerwin, Joseph P *Astronaut*
%Lockheed Houston Program, 1150 Gemini, Houston, TX 77058
Kerwin, Lance *Actor*
PO Box 237, Lake Elsinore, CA 92326
Kerwin, Larkin *Physicist*
%National Research Council, Ottawa ON K1A 0R6, Canada
Kesey, Ken *Writer*
Rt 8, Box 477, Pleasant Hill, OR 97401
Keshtmand, Sultan Ali *Prime Minister, Afghanistan*
%Prime Minister's Office, Revolutionary Council, Kabul, Afghanistan
Kessel, Dimitri *Photographer*
46 Ave Gabriel, 75008 Paris, France
Kessler, David A *Physician, Government Official*
%Food & Drug Administration, 5600 Fishers Ln, Rockville, MD 20857
Kest, Sol *Businessman*
%Goldrich & Kest Industries, 5150 Overland Ave, Culver City, CA 90230
Kesten, Hermann *Writer*
Im Tiefen Boden 25, 4059 Basel, Switzerland
Kestner, Boyd *Actor*
%Metropolitan Tallent Agency, 9320 Wilshire Blvd, #300, Beverly Hills, CA 90212
Ketcham, Hank *Cartoonist (Dennis the Menace)*
PO Box 800, Pebble Beach, CA 93953
Ketchum, Henry *Football Player*
801 McGilvra Blvd E, Seattle, WA 98112
Ketchum, Howard *Color Engineer*
3800 Washington Rd, West Palm Beach, FL 33405
Ketner, Ralph W *Businessman*
%Food Lion Inc, Harrison Rd, Salisbury, NC 28145
Kety, Seymour S *Physiologist, Psychobiologist*
%Mailman Research Ctr, McLean Hospital, Belmont, MA 02178
Keves, Gyorgy *Architect*
Vinceller U 26/C, 1113 Budapest, Hungary

K

Key – Kieschnick

Key, Ted — *Cartoonist (Hazel)*
1694 Glenhardie Rd, Wayne, PA 19087

Keyes, E L, Jr — *Businessman*
%Emerson Electric Co, 8000 W Florissant Ave, St Louis, MO 63136

Keyes, Evelyn — *Actress*
999 N Doheny Dr, #50, Los Angeles, CA 90069

Keyes, James H — *Businessman*
%Johnson Controls Inc, 5757 N Green Bay Ave, Milwaukee, WI 53201

Keyes, Leroy — *Football Player*
8527 Cratin Pl, Philadelphia, PA 19153

Keys, Donald — *Educator*
%Planetary Citizens, 777 United Nations Plz, New York, NY 10017

Keyser, F Ray, Jr — *Governor, VT*
29 S Main, Rutland, VT 05701

Keyworth, George A, III — *Government Official*
%Keyworth Meyer International, PO Box 25566, Washington, DC 20007

Khalifa, Sheikh Hamed bin Isa al- — *Crown Prince, Bahrain*
%Crown Prince's Office, Rifa's Palace, Manama, Bahrain

Khalifa, Sheikh Isa bin Sulman al- — *Emir, Bahrain*
%Rifa's Palace, Manama, Bahrain

Khalifa, Sheikh Khalifa bin Sulman al- — *Prime Minister, Bahrain*
%Prime Minister's Office, Manama, Bahrain

Khalil, Mustafa — *Prime Minister, Egypt*
%National Democratic Party, Cairo, Egypt

Khamenei, Hojatolislam Ali — *President, Iran*
%President's Office, Teheran, Iran

Khan, Chaka — *Singer*
%Steve Margo Mgmt, 4444 Via Marina, #818, Marina del Rey, CA 90292

Khatib, Ahmed al- — *President, Syria*
%Syrian Ba'ath Party, Damascus, Syria

Kheel, Theodore W — *Labor Mediator*
280 Park Ave, New York, NY 10017

Khokhlov, Boris I — *Ballet Dancer*
%State Academic Bolshoi Theatre, 1 Ploshchad Sverdlova, Moscow, Russia

Khoraiche, Antoine Pierre Cardinal — *Religious Leader*
Patriarcat Maronite, Bkerke, Lebanon

Khorana, Har Gobind — *Nobel Medicine Laureate*
%Massachusetts Institute of Technology, Biology Dept, Cambridge, MA 02139

Khrennikov, Tikhon N — *Composer*
%Composers Union, Ul Nezhdanovoi 8/10, Moscow, Russia

Khrunov, Yevgeny V — *Cosmonaut*
141 160 Svyosdny Gorodok, Moskovskoi Oblasti, Potchta Kosmonavtov, Russia

Kiam, Victor K, II — *Businessman*
119 Wire Mill Rd, Stamford, CT 06903

Kidd, Billy — *Skier*
PO Box 1178, Steamboat Springs, CO 80477

Kidd, Michael — *Choreographer*
%William Morris Agency, 1350 Ave of Americas, New York, NY 10019

Kidder Lee, Barbara — *Skier*
1308 W Highland, Phoenix, AZ 85013

Kidder, Margot — *Actress*
%Dolores Robinson Mgmt, 335 N Maple Dr, #250, Beverly Hills, CA 90210

Kidder, Tracy — *Writer*
%Houghton-Mifflin Co, 666 3rd Ave, New York, NY 10017

Kidman, Nicole — *Actress*
%Creative Artists Agency, 9830 Wilshire Blvd, Beverly Hills, CA 90212

Kiefer, Adolph — *Swimmer*
2040 Suffork Rd, Northfield, IL 60093

Kiefer, Anselm — *Artist*
%General Delivery, Hornbach/Odenwald, Germany

Kiel, Richard — *Actor*
500 Grand Ave, South Pasadena, CA 91030

Kielland, Kaspar K — *Businessman*
%Elkem, PO Box 5430, Maj Middelthunsgt 27, Oslo 3, Norway

Kieschnick, William F — *Businessman*
%Atlantic Richfield Co, 515 S Flower, Los Angeles, CA 90071

Kight Wingard, Lenore *Swimmer*
6281 Cary Ave, Cincinnati, OH 45224

Kihune, Robert K U *Navy Admiral*
Assistant CNO Surface Warfare, Navy Department, Washington, DC 20350

Kikutake, Kiyonori *Architect*
1-11-15 Otsuka, Bunkyoku, Tokyo, Japan

Kilbourne, Wendy *Actress*
9300 Wilshire Blvd, #410, Beverly Hills, CA 90212

Kilburn, Terry *Actor*
%Meadowbrook Theatre, Oakland University, Rochester, MI 48063

Kilby, Jack S *Inventor*
7723 Midbury St, Dallas, TX 75230

Kildee, Dale E *Representative, MI*
1434 Jane St, Flint, MI 48506

Kiley, Richard *Actor*
14323 Collins St, Van Nuys, CA 91401

Kilgore, Al *Cartoonist*
216-55 113th Dr, Queens Village, NY 11429

Kilkenny, John F *Judge*
%Pioneer Courthouse, 555 SW Yamhill St, Portland, OR 97204

Killanin, Baron *Olympics Official*
St Annins, Spiddal, County Galway, Ireland

Killebrew, Harmon *Baseball Player*
RR 2, Box 626, Ontario, OR 97914

Killen, Buddy *Businessman*
%Tree International, 8 Music Sq W, Nashville, TN 37203

Killy, Jean-Claude *Skier*
13 Chemin Bellefontaine, 1223 Cologny-GE, Switzerland

Kilmer, Val *Actor*
PO Box 362, Tesuque, NM 87574

Kilpatrick, James J *Columnist*
White Walnut Hill, Woodville, VA 22749

Kilpatrick, James L *Businessman*
%Ocean Drilling & Exploration Co, 1600 Canal St, New Orleans, LA 70161

Kilpatrick, Lincoln *Actor*
12834 McLennan Ave, Granada Hills, CA 91344

Kilpatrick, Robert D *Businessman*
Top O'World Farm, Litchfield, CT 06759

Kilroy, Frank *Football Coach*
%New England Patriots, Sullivan Stadium, Foxboro, MA 02035

Kilroy, Richard I *Labor Leader*
%Transportation Communications Int'l, 3 Research Pl, Rockville, MD 20850

Kilzer, Lou *Journalist*
%Minneapolis-St Paul Star-Tribune, 425 Portland Ave, Minneapolis, MN 55488

Kim Dae Jung *Political Leader, South Korea*
%Korean Human Rights Institute, PO Box 11618, Alexandria, VA 22312

Kim Il Sung *President, North Korea*
%President's Office, Pyongyang, North Korea

Kim Jong Pil *President, South Korea*
340-38, Sindang 4-Dongku, Seoul, South Korea

Kim Woo-Chong *Businessman*
%Daewoo Industrial Grp, 541-5 Ga Namdaemunro, Seoul, South Korea

Kim, Nelli *Gymnast*
%Russian Sports Council, Skaternyi per 4, Moscow, Russia

Kim, Stephan S Cardinal *Religious Leader*
Archbishop's House, 2-KA 1 Myong Dong, Chung-ku, Seoul 100, South Korea

Kimball, David T *Businessman*
%General Signal Corp, High Ridge Park, Stamford, CT 06904

Kimball, Dick *Diver, Diving Coach*
%University of Michigan, Athletic Dept, Ann Arbor, MI 48109

Kimball, Ward *Animator, Director*
8910 Ardendale Ave, San Gabriel, CA 91775

Kimberly, John R *Businessman*
Rt 1, Box 303, Queenstown, MD 21658

Kimble, Bo *Basketball Player*
%Los Angeles Clippers, Sports Arena, 3939 S Figueroa St, Los Angeles, CA 90037

K

Kimbrough, John *Football Player*
PO Box 535, Haskell, TX 79521

Kime, J William *Coast Guard Admiral*
Commandant, US Coast Guard, 2100 2nd St SW, Washington, DC 20593

Kimery, James L *Association Executive*
%Veterans of Foreign Wars, 405 W 34th St, Kansas City, MO 64111

Kimmel, George S *Businessman*
%Combustion Engineering, 900 Long Ridge Rd, Stamford, CT 06902

Kimura, Kazuo *Industrial Designer*
%Japan Design Foundation, 2-2 Cenba Chuo, Higashiku, Osaka 541, Japan

Kimura, Motoo *Geneticist, Biologist*
%Institute of Genetics, Yata 1, 111, Mishima, Shizuoka-ken 411, Japan

Kinard, Terry *Football Player*
%Houston Oilers, PO Box 1516, Houston, TX 77030

Kincaid, Aron *Actor*
%Coast to Coast Talent Grp, 12307-C Ventura Blvd, North Hollywood, CA 91601

Kind, Peter A *Army General*
Commanding General, US Army Information Systems Cmd, Fort Huachuca, AZ 85613

Kinder, Melvyn *Psychologist*
521 N LaCienega Blvd, #209, Los Angeles, CA 90048

Kindleberger, Charles P *Economist*
Bedford Rd, Lincoln, MA 01773

Kindred, David A *Sportswriter*
%Atlanta Constitution, 72 Marietta St, Atlanta, GA 30303

Kiner, Ralph *Baseball Player*
271 Silver Spur Trl, Palm Desert, CA 92260

King Hogue, Micki *Diver*
PO Box 918, Lexington, KY 40587

King, Don *Boxing Promoter*
%Don King Promotions, 1350 E Flamingo, Las Vegas, NV 89119

King, Albert *Basketball Player*
%San Antonio Spurs, 600 E Market St, San Antonio, TX 78292

King, B B *Singer, Guitarist*
PO Box 16707, Memphis, TN 38131

King, Bernard *Basketball Player*
%Washington Bullets, Capital Centre, 1 Truman Dr, Landover, MD 20785

King, Betsy *Golfer*
%General Delivery, Limekiln, PA 19535

King, Billie Jean *Tennis Player*
%Domino's Pizza Team Tennis, 101 W 79th St, New York, NY 10024

King, Bruce *Governor, NM*
PO Box 83, Stanley, NM 87056

King, Carole *Composer, Singer*
Robinson Bar Ranch, Stanley, ID 83278

King, Carolyn Dineen *Judge*
%US Court of Appeals, 515 Rusk Ave, Houston, TX 77002

King, Coretta *Civil Rights Leader*
234 Sunset Ave NW, Washington, DC 30314

King, Doyle D *Financier*
%United First Federal Savings & Loan, 1390 Main St, Sarasota, FL 33577

King, Edward J *Governor, MA*
%A J Lane Co, 1500 Worcester Rd, Framingham, MA 01701

King, Francis H *Writer*
19 Gordon Pl, London W8 4JE, England

King, Henry H *Businessman*
%Texas Eastern Corp, 1221 McKinney St, Houston, TX 77010

King, James A *Opera Singer*
%Denis Laggelier Artists, 40 Alexander St, Toronto ON M4Y 1B5, Canada

King, James B *Editor*
%Seattle Times, PO Box 70, Fairview & John, Seattle, WA 98111

King, John (Dusty) *Actor*
PO Box 487, Rancho Santa Fe, CA 92067

King, John Leonard *Businessman*
%Babcock International, St James's Sq, London SW17 4LA, England

King, John W *Governor, NH*
Kennedy Hill Rd, RD 1, Goffstown, NH 03045

King, Larry *Entertainer*
%"Larry King Live" Show, CNN, 111 Massachusetts Ave NW, Washington, DC 20001

King, Maxwell *Editor*
%Philadelphia Inquirer, 400 N Market St, Philadelphia, PA 19101

King, Morgana *Actress*
%Associated Talent Mgmt, 17226 Palisades Cir, Pacific Palisades, CA 90272

King, Pee Wee *Singer, Songwriter*
%Record Shop, Coleman Bldg, 240 W Jefferson St, Louisville, KY 40202

King, Perry *Actor*
%Creative Artists Agency, 9830 Wilshire Blvd, Beverly Hills, CA 90212

King, Phillip *Sculptor*
%Juda Rowan Gallery, 31-A Bruton Pl, Berkeley Sq, London W1X 7AB, England

King, Robert E *Businessman*
%Square D Co, 1415 S Roselle, Palatine, IL 60067

King, Stacey *Basketball Player*
%Chicago Bulls, 980 N Michigan Ave, Chicago, IL 60611

King, Stephen *Writer*
49 Florida Ave, Bangor, ME 04401

King, Thomas L *Businessman*
%Standex International Corp, 6 Manor Pkwy, Salem, NH 03079

King, Tony *Actor*
1333 N Sweetzer, #2-G, Los Angeles, CA 90046

King, William T *Businessman*
%Avondale Mills, Avondale Ave, Sylacauga, AL 35150

King, Woodie, Jr *Theater Producer*
417 Convent Ave, New York, NY 10031

King, Zalman *Movie Director*
%Triad Artists, 10100 Santa Monica Blvd, #1600, Los Angeles, CA 90067

Kingdom, Roger *Track Athlete*
146 S Fairmont St, #1, Pittsburgh, PA 15206

Kingman, Dong *Artist*
21 W 58th St, New York, NY 10019

Kings Norton (Harold R Cox) *Engineer, Scientist*
Westcote House, Chipping Campden, Glos, England

Kingsbury-Smith, Joseph *Journalist*
1701 Pennsylvania Ave NW, Washington, DC 20006

Kingsley, Alfred D *Businessman*
%ACF Industries, 3301 Rider Trl S, Earth City, MO 63045

Kingsley, Ben *Actor*
New Penworth House, Stratford Upon Avon, Warwickshire 0V3 7QX, England

Kingsley, Michael *Editor*
%New Republic Magazine, 1220 19th St NW, Washington, DC 20036

Kingsley, Sidney *Writer*
%Dramatist Guild, 234 W 44th St, New York, NY 10036

Kingston, Maxine Hong *Writer*
%John Schaffner Literary Agency, 264 5th Ave, New York, NY 10001

Kinison, Sam *Comedian*
%Starship Mgmt, 7365 Carnelian, #213, Rancho Cucamonga, CA 91730

Kinmont Boothe, Jill *Skier*
Rt 1, Box 11, 310 Sunland Dr, Bishop, CA 93514

Kinmont, Kathleen *Actress*
%Sutton Barth Vennari, 145 S Fairfax, Los Angeles, CA 90036

Kinnear, George E R, II *Navy Admiral*
%NATO Military Command, APO, New York, NY 09667

Kinnear, James W *Businessman*
%Texaco Inc, 2000 Westchester Ave, White Plains, NY 10650

Kinnear, Roy *Actor*
%Richard Stone Agency, 18-20 York Bldgs, Adelphi, London WC2N 6JY, England

Kinnell, Galway *Writer*
RFD, Sheffield, VT 05866

Kinney, E Robert *Businessman*
%General Mills Inc, PO Box 1113, Minneapolis, MN 55440

Kinnock, Neil *Government Official, England*
%House of Commons, London SW1, England

Kinnune, William P *Businessman*
%Willamette Industries, 3800 First Interstate Tower, Portland, OR 97201

K

Kinoshita – Kirkpatrick

Kinoshita, Keisuke *Movie Director*
1366 Tsujido, Fujisawa, Kanagawa Prefecture, Japan

Kinoshita, Shukuo *Businessman*
%Kyowa Hakko Kogyo Co, 1-6-1 Otemachi, Chiyodaku, Tokyo 100, Japan

Kinsella, John *Swimmer*
Canterberry Ct, Hinsdale, IL 60521

Kinsella, Thomas *Poet*
47 Percy Pl, Dublin 4, Ireland

Kinskey, Leonid *Actor*
11652 Huston St, North Hollywood, CA 90024

Kinski, Nastassja *Actress*
11 W 81st St, New York, NY 10024

Kinsley, Michael *Editor*
%New Republic Magazine, 1220 19th St NW, Washington, DC 20036

Kinsman, T Jim *Vietnam Army Hero (CMH)*
111 Howe Rd E, Winlock, WA 98596

Kintner, William R *Political Scientist*
%Foreign Policy Research Institute, 3508 Market St, Philadelphia, PA 19104

Kinugasa, Sachio *Baseball Player*
%Hiroshima Toyo Carp, 5-25 Moto-Machi, Nakaku, Hiroshima 730, Japan

Kiplinger, Austin *Publisher*
1729 "H" St NW, Washington, DC 20006

Kipnis, Igor *Concert Harpsichordist*
20 Drummer Ln, RFD 2, West Redding, CT 06896

Kipniss, Robert *Artist*
26 E 33rd St, New York, NY 10016

Kiraly, Karch *Volleyball Player, Coach*
%Pepperdine University, Athletic Dept, Malibu, CA 90265

Kirby, Bruce *Actor*
%Century Artists, 9744 Wilshire Blvd, #308, Beverly Hills, CA 90212

Kirby, Robert E *Businessman*
%Westinghouse Bldg, Gateway Ctr, Pittsburgh, PA 15222

Kirchner, Leon *Composer*
%Harvard University, Music Dept, Cambridge, MA 02138

Kirchschlager, Rudolf *President, Austria*
Hofburg, 1014 Vienna, Austria

Kirgo, George *Actor, Screenwriter*
178 N Carmelina Ave, Los Angeles, CA 90049

Kirk, Claude R, Jr *Governor, FL*
%Kirk Co, PO Box 668, Palm Beach, FL 33480

Kirk, Grayson *Educator*
28 Sunnybrook Rd, Bronxville, NY 10708

Kirk, Phyllis *Actress*
1225 Sunset Plaza Dr, #1, Los Angeles, CA 90069

Kirk, Robert L *Businessman*
%Allied-Signal Inc, PO Box 4000-R, Morristown, NJ 07960

Kirk, Russell A *Writer*
Piety Hill, Mecosta, MI 49332

Kirkland, Gelsey *Ballerina*
945 5th Ave, New York, NY 10021

Kirkland, Lane *Labor Leader*
%AFL-CIO, 815 16th St NW, Washington, DC 20006

Kirkland, Sally *Actress*
%Sally Kirkland Productions, 1930 Ocean Ave, #11, Santa Monica, CA 90405

Kirkley, Terry A *Businessman*
%Esso Eastern Inc, 2401 S Gessner, Houston, TX 77063

Kirkman, Rick *Cartoonist (Baby Blues)*
%Creators Syndicate, 5777 W Century Blvd, #700, Los Angeles, CA 90045

Kirkpatrick, Clayton *Editor*
156 Sunset Ave, Glen Ellyn, IL 60137

Kirkpatrick, Elwood *Businessman*
%Michigan Milk Producers Assn, PO Box 5087, Southfield, MI 48037

Kirkpatrick, Jeane *Ambassador, United Nations*
6812 Granby St, Bethesda, MD 20034

Kirkpatrick, Ralph *Concert Harpsichordist*
Old Quarry, Guilford, CT 06437

Kirkup, James *Writer*
BM-Box 2780, London WC1V 6XX, England
Kirpal, Prem Nath *Educator*
%UNESCO Executive Board, Pl de Fintenoy, 75700 Paris, France
Kirschner, Sidney *Businessman*
%National Service Industries, 1180 Peachtree St NE, Atlanta, GA 30309
Kirschstein, Ruth L *Physician*
%National Institutes of Health, 9000 Rockville Pike, Bethesda, MD 20205
Kirshbaum, Laurence *Publisher*
%Warner Books, 75 Rockefeller Plz, New York, NY 10019
Kirshner, Don *Concert Promoter*
8961 Sunset Blvd, #C, Los Angeles, CA 90069
Kirstein, Lincoln *Ballet Promoter*
%School of American Ballet, 144 W 66th St, New York, NY 10023
Kirsten, Dorothy *Opera Singer*
%Metropolitan Opera Assn, Lincoln Ctr, New York, NY 10023
Kirszenstein-Szewinska, Irena *Track Athlete*
Ul Bagno 5 m 80, 00-112 Warsaw, Poland
Kiser, Terry *Actor*
%Bauman Hiller Assoc, 5750 Wilshire Blvd, #512, Los Angeles, CA 90036
Kishimoto, Yasunobu *Businessman*
%Showa Denko, 1-13-9 Shiba Daimon, Minatoku, Tokyo, Japan
Kison, Bruce *Baseball Player*
1403 Riverside Cir, Bradenton, FL 33529
Kissick, John H *Financier*
%Drexel Burnham Lambert Inc, 131 S Rodeo Dr, Beverly Hills, CA 90212
Kissinger, Henry *Secretary, State; Nobel Peace Laureate*
River House, 435 E 52nd St, New York, NY 10022
Kissinger, Walter B *Businessman*
%Allen Grp, 534 Broad Hollow Rd, Melville, NY 11747
Kistler, William A, Jr *Businessman*
%Hughes Tool Co, 6500 Texas Commerce Tower, Houston, TX 77002
Kitaen, Tawny *Actress*
11075 Santa Monica Blvd, #150, Los Angeles, CA 90025
Kitaj, R B *Artist*
%Marlborough Fine Art Ltd, 6 Albemarle St, London W1, England
Kitajima, Yoshitoshi *Businessman*
%Dai Nippon Printing Co, 1-12 Ichigaya-Kagacho, Tokyo 162, Japan
Kitamura, Kusuo *Swimmer*
%Nippon Suiei Renmei, 25 Kannami, Shibuyaku, Tokyo, Japan
Kitaoka, Toru *Businessman*
%Nihon Cement Co, 1-6-1 Otemachi, Chiyodaku, Tokyo 100, Japan
Kitbunchu, M Michai Cardinal *Religious Leader*
Assumption Cathedral, 51 Oriental Ave, Bangkok 10500, Thailand
Kitchen, Lawrence O *Businessman*
%Lockheed Corp, 2555 N Hollywood Way, Burbank, CA 91520
Kite, Tom *Golfer*
%Pros Inc, PO Box 673, Richmond, VA 23206
Kittel, Charles *Physicist*
%University of California, Physics Dept, Berkeley, CA 94720
Kittinger, Joe *Parachutist, Balloonist*
300 N Main St, Las Vegas, NV 89101
Kittle, Ron *Baseball Player*
8080 E 109th, Crown Point, IN 46307
Kittrell, C M *Businessman*
%Phillips Petroleum Co, Phillips Bldg, Bartlesville, OK 74004
Kitzmiller, John W *Football Player*
403 Oak St, Dallas, OR 97338
Kivitt, Ted *Ballet Dancer*
%Milwaukee Ballet Co, PO Box 1225, Milwaukee, WI 53201
Kiyokawa Seiji, Masaji *Swimmer*
%Kanematsu-Gosho Ltd, CPO Box 141, Tokyo, Japan
Kizim, Leonid *Cosmonaut*
141 160 Svyosdny Gorodok, Moskovskoi Oblasti, Potchta Kosmonavtov, Russia
Kjorlien, Clarence J *Businessman*
%West Point-Pepperell Inc, 400 W 10th St, West Point, GA 31833

Klabunde - Klimuk

Klabunde, Charles S — *Artist*
68 W 3rd St, New York, NY 10012

Klammer, Franz — *Skier*
Mooswald 22, 9712 Frescch/Ktn, Austria

Klamon, Lawrence P — *Businessman*
%Fuqua Industries, 4900 Georgia-Pacific Ctr, Atlanta, GA 30303

Klatsky, Bruce J — *Businessman*
%Phillips-Van Heusen Corp, 1290 Ave of Americas, New York, NY 10104

Klatte, Gunther — *Businessman*
%Rheinische Braunkohlenwerke, Stuttgenweg 2, 5000 Koln 41, Germany

Klaus, Josef — *Chancellor, Austria*
Osterreichische Volkspartei, 1 Karntnerstrasse 51, Vienna, Austria

Klaw, Spencer — *Editor*
%Columbia Journalism Review Magazine, Columbia University, New York, NY 10027

Klebe, Giselher — *Composer*
Bruchstrasse 16, 4930 Detmold 1, Germany

Klecko, Joe — *Football Player*
%Indianapolis Colts, 7001 W 56th St, Indianapolis, IN 46254

Kleczka, Gerald D — *Representative, WI*
%House of Representatives, Washington, DC 20515

Kleene, Stephen Cole — *Mathematician*
%University of Wisconsin, Math Dept, Madison, WI 53706

Kleiman, Ansel — *Businessman*
%Telex Corp, 6422 E 41st St, Tulsa, OK 74135

Klein, Calvin — *Fashion Designer*
55 Central Park West, #19-F, New York, NY 10023

Klein, George — *Tumor Biologist*
Kottlavagen 10, 181 61 Lidingo, Sweden

Klein, Heinrich J — *Businessman*
%Carl-Zeiss-Stiftung, Postfach 1369, 7982 Oberkochen, Germany

Klein, Lawrence R — *Nobel Economics Laureate*
1317 Medford Rd, Wynnewood, PA 19096

Klein, Lester A — *Urologist*
%Scripps Clinic, Urology Dept, 10666 N Torrey Pines Rd, La Jolla, CA 92121

Klein, Robert — *Comedian*
10656 Lindamere Dr, Los Angeles, CA 90024

Klein, Robert J — *Businessman*
%Worthington Industries, 1205 Dearborn Dr, Columbus, OH 43085

Klein, Yves — *Artist*
%Marisa del Re Gallery, 41 E 57th St, New York, NY 10022

Kleindienst, Richard G — *Attorney General*
%Lesher Kimble & Rucker, 3773 E Broadway, Tucson, AZ 85716

Kleine, Joe — *Basketball Player*
%Boston Celtics, 151 Merrimac St, Boston, MA 02114

Kleinert, Harold E — *Microsurgeon*
250 E Liberty St, Louisville, KY 40202

Kleinrock, Leonard — *Computer Scientist*
%University of California, Computer Science Dept, Berkeley, CA 90024

Klemmer, John — *Saxophonist*
%Boardman, 10548 Clearwood Ct, Los Angeles, CA 90077

Klemperer, Werner — *Actor*
44 W 62nd St, 10th Fl, New York, NY 10023

Klemt, Becky — *Attorney*
%Pence & MacMillan, PO Box 1285, Laramie, WY 82070

Klensch, Else — *Fashion Commentator*
%Cable News Network, 1 CNN Center, PO Box 105366, Atlanta, GA 30348

Kleppe, Thomas S — *Secretary, Interior*
7100 Darby Rd, Bethesda, MD 20817

Kliesmet, Robert B — *Labor Leader*
%Union of Police Assns, 815 16th St NW, #307, Washington, DC 20006

Kliks, Rudolf R — *Architect*
%Russian Chamber of Commerce, Ul Kuibysheva 6, Moscow, Russia

Klimke, Reiner — *Equestrian Rider*
Krummestrrasse 3, 4400 Munster, Germany

Klimuk, Pyotr I — *Cosmonaut*
141 160 Svyosdny Gorodok, Moskovskoi Oblasti, Potchta Kosmonavtov, Russia

Kline, David I — *Businessman*
%Sunkist Growers Inc, 14130 Riverside Dr, Sherman Oaks, CA 91423
Kline, Kevin — *Actor*
%Creative Artists Agency, 9830 Wilshire Blvd, Beverly Hills, CA 90212
Klinger, Georgette — *Beauty Expert*
312 N Rodeo Dr, Beverly Hills, CA 90210
Klingler, Robert M — *Financier*
%Freedom Savings & Loan, 111 N Dale Mabry Hwy, Tampa, FL 33609
Klopman, William A — *Businessman*
%Burlington Industries, 3330 W Friendly Ave, Greensboro, NC 27410
Klos, Elmar — *Movie Director*
Strahovska 293, Hradcany, Prague 1, Czechoslovakia
Kloska, Ronald F — *Businessman*
%Skyline Corp, 2520 By-Pass Rd, Elkhart, IN 46515
Kloss, John — *Fashion Designer*
10 W 66th St, New York, NY 10023
Klotz, Irvin Myron — *Chemist, Biochemist*
2515 Pioneer Rd, Evanston, IL 60201
Klug, Aaron — *Nobel Physics Laureate*
%Medical Research Council Centre, Hills Rd, Cambridge CB2 2QH, England
Klug, Scott L — *Representative, WI*
%House of Representatives, Washington, DC 20515
Kluge, John W — *Businessman*
215 E 67th St, New York, NY 10021
Klugman, Jack — *Actor*
22548 W Pacific Coast Hwy, #110, Malibu, CA 90265
Klutznick, Philip M — *Secretary, Commerce*
875 N Michigan Ave, #4044, Chicago, IL 60611
Klyszewski, Waclaw — *Architect*
Ul Gornoslaska 16, m 15a, 00-432 Warsaw, Poland
Knape Lindberg, Ulrike — *Diver*
Drostvagen 7, 691 33 Karlskoga, Sweden
Knapp, Charles B — *Educator*
%University of Georgia, President's Office, Athens, GA 30602
Knapp, Cleon T — *Publisher*
6420 Wilshire Blvd, Los Angeles, CA 90036
Knapp, J Burke — *Financier*
4144 River St N, Arlington, VA 22207
Knapp, John W — *Educator, Army General*
%Virginia Military Institute, Superintendent's Office, Lexington, VA 24450
Knapp, Richard E — *Financier*
%Landmark Savings, 335 5th Ave, Pittsburgh, PA 15222
Knappenberger, Alton W — *WW II Army Hero (CMH)*
PO Box 364, Schwenksville, PA 19473
Knauer, Virginia M — *Consumer Advocate, Government Official*
%White House, 1600 Pennsylvania Ave NW, Washington, DC 20500
Knauss, Dalton L — *Businessman*
%Square D Co, 1415 S Roselle, Palatine, IL 60067
Knebel, Fletcher — *Writer*
208 Edgerstoune Rd, Princeton, NJ 08450
Knebel, John A — *Secretary, Agriculture*
1418 Laburnum St, McLean, VA 22101
Knepper, Bob — *Baseball Player*
2045 Oakhill Rd, Roseburg, OR 97470
Kness, Richard — *Opera Singer*
240 Central Park South, #3-N, New York, NY 10019
Knight Pulliam, Keshia — *Actress*
%Kaufman, 34-12 36th St, Astoria, NY 11106
Knight, Andrew — *Editor*
25 St James's St, London SW1, England
Knight, Bobby — *Basketball Coach*
%Indiana University, Athletic Dept, Bloomington, IN 47405
Knight, Charles F — *Businessman*
%Emerson Electric Co, 8000 W Florissant Ave, St Louis, MO 63136
Knight, Christopher — *Actor*
%Marshak-Wyckoff Assoc, 280 S Beverly Dr, #400, Beverly Hills, CA 90212

K

Knight – Knutson

Knight, Curt *Football Player*
5300 Holmes Run Pkwy, #301, Alexandria, VA 22304

Knight, Douglas M *Educator*
Rt 3, Box 539, Stockton, NJ 08559

Knight, Gladys *Singer*
9200 Sunset Blvd, #PH-15, Los Angeles, CA 90069

Knight, Philip H *Businessman*
%Nike Inc, 3900 SW Murray Blvd, Beaverton, OR 97005

Knight, Ray *Baseball Player*
2308 Tara Dr, Albany, GA 31707

Knight, Shirley *Actress*
4 Greenwood Ln, Westport, CT 06880

Knight, William J (Pete) *Test Pilot*
220 Eagle, Palmdale, CA 93551

Knipling, Edward F *Entomologist*
2623 Military Rd, Arlington, VA 22207

Knoell, William H *Businessman*
%Cyclops Corp, 650 Washington Rd, Pittsburgh, PA 15228

Knol, Monique *Cyclist*
Draarlier 6, 3766 Et Soest, Holland

Knoll, Jozseph *Pharmacologist (Deprenyl for Parkinsons)*
%Semmelweis Medical University, Pharmacology Dept, Budapest, Hungary

Knopoff, Leon *Geophysicist*
%University of California, Geophysics Institute, Los Angeles, CA 90024

Knotts, Don *Comedian*
%Artists Group, 1930 Century Park West, #403, Los Angeles, CA 90067

Knowles, John *Writer*
PO Box 939, Southampton, NY 11968

Knowles, Michael R *Medical Researcher (Cystic Fibrosis)*
%University of North Carolina, Medical School, Chapel Hill, NC 27599

Knowles, Patric *Actor*
6243 Randi Ave, Woodland Hills, CA 91367

Knowles, Warren P *Governor, WI*
3039 E Newport Ct, Milwaukee, WI 53211

Knowlton, R L *Businessman*
%Geo A Hormel Co, 501 16th Ave NE, Austin, MN 55912

Knowlton, Steve R *Skier*
%Palmer Yeager Assoc, 6600 E Hampden Ave, #210, Denver, CO 80224

Knox, Alexander *Actor*
%International Creative Mgmt, 388-396 Oxford St, London W1, England

Knox, Chuck *Football Coach*
%Los Angeles Rams, 2327 W Lincoln Ave, Anaheim, CA 92801

Knox, Elyse *Actress*
320 N Gunston Ave, Los Angeles, CA 90049

Knox, Northrup R *Financier*
%Marine Midland Banks Inc, 1 Marine Midland Ctr, Buffalo, NY 14240

Knox, Terence *Actor*
%International Creative Mgmt, 8899 Beverly Blvd, Los Angeles, CA 90048

Knox-Johnston, Robin *Sailor*
26 Sefton St, Putney, London SW15, England

Knudsen, Arthur G *Skier*
311 Blaine Ave, Racine, WI 53405

Knudsen, C C *Businessman*
%MacMillan Bloedel Ltd, 1075 W Georgia St, Vancouver BC V6E 3R9, Canada

Knudsen, Semon Emil *Businessman*
1700 N Woodward Ave, Bloomfield Hills, MI 48013

Knudson, Alfred G, Jr *Geneticist*
%Institute for Cancer Research, 7701 Burlhome Ave, Philadelphia, PA 19111

Knudson, Darrell G *Financier*
%First Bank System, 1200 First Bank Pl E, Minneapolis, MN 55402

Knudson, Gene D *Businessman*
%Willamette Industries, 3800 First Interstate Tower, Portland, OR 97201

Knudson, Thomas J *Journalist*
%Des Moines Register, Box 957, Des Moines, IA 50304

Knutson, Ronald *Religious Leader*
%Free Lutheran Congregations Assn, 402 W 11th St, Canton, SD 57013

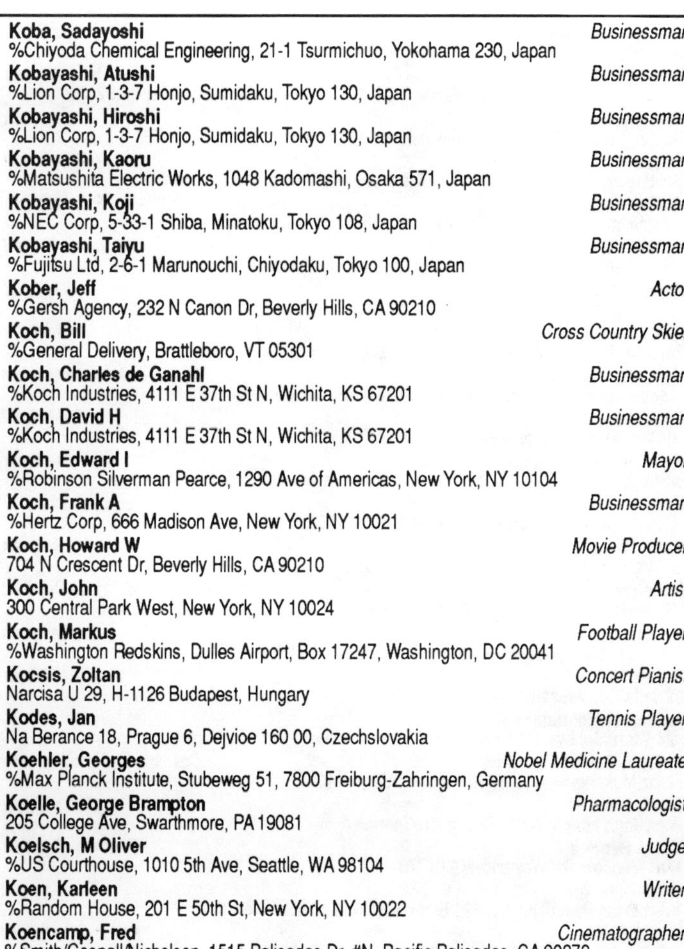

Koba, Sadayoshi *Businessman*
%Chiyoda Chemical Engineering, 21-1 Tsurmichuo, Yokohama 230, Japan

Kobayashi, Atushi *Businessman*
%Lion Corp, 1-3-7 Honjo, Sumidaku, Tokyo 130, Japan

Kobayashi, Hiroshi *Businessman*
%Lion Corp, 1-3-7 Honjo, Sumidaku, Tokyo 130, Japan

Kobayashi, Kaoru *Businessman*
%Matsushita Electric Works, 1048 Kadomashi, Osaka 571, Japan

Kobayashi, Koji *Businessman*
%NEC Corp, 5-33-1 Shiba, Minatoku, Tokyo 108, Japan

Kobayashi, Taiyu *Businessman*
%Fujitsu Ltd, 2-6-1 Marunouchi, Chiyodaku, Tokyo 100, Japan

Kober, Jeff *Actor*
%Gersh Agency, 232 N Canon Dr, Beverly Hills, CA 90210

Koch, Bill *Cross Country Skier*
%General Delivery, Brattleboro, VT 05301

Koch, Charles de Ganahl *Businessman*
%Koch Industries, 4111 E 37th St N, Wichita, KS 67201

Koch, David H *Businessman*
%Koch Industries, 4111 E 37th St N, Wichita, KS 67201

Koch, Edward I *Mayor*
%Robinson Silverman Pearce, 1290 Ave of Americas, New York, NY 10104

Koch, Frank A *Businessman*
%Hertz Corp, 666 Madison Ave, New York, NY 10021

Koch, Howard W *Movie Producer*
704 N Crescent Dr, Beverly Hills, CA 90210

Koch, John *Artist*
300 Central Park West, New York, NY 10024

Koch, Markus *Football Player*
%Washington Redskins, Dulles Airport, Box 17247, Washington, DC 20041

Kocsis, Zoltan *Concert Pianist*
Narcisa U 29, H-1126 Budapest, Hungary

Kodes, Jan *Tennis Player*
Na Berance 18, Prague 6, Dejvioe 160 00, Czechslovakia

Koehler, Georges *Nobel Medicine Laureate*
%Max Planck Institute, Stubeweg 51, 7800 Freiburg-Zahringen, Germany

Koelle, George Brampton *Pharmacologist*
205 College Ave, Swarthmore, PA 19081

Koelsch, M Oliver *Judge*
%US Courthouse, 1010 5th Ave, Seattle, WA 98104

Koen, Karleen *Writer*
%Random House, 201 E 50th St, New York, NY 10022

Koencamp, Fred *Cinematographer*
%Smith/Gosnell/Nicholson, 1515 Palisades Dr, #N, Pacific Palisades, CA 90272

Koenig, Allen E *Educator*
%Chapman College, President's Office, Orange, CA 92666

Koenig, Franz Cardinal *Religious Leader*
Erzbischofliches Sekretariat, Rotenturmstrasse 2, 1010 Vienna, Austria

Koenig, Mark *Baseball Player*
RR 3, Box 3654, Orland, CA 95963

Koenig, Walter *Actor*
PO Box 4395, North Hollywood, CA 91601

Koenigswald, G H Ralph von *Paleoanthropologist*
%Senckenberg Museum, Senckenberganlage 25, 6 Frankfurt/Maim, Germany

Kogovsek, Ray P *Representative, CO*
1627 Horseshoe Dr, Pueblo, CO 81001

Kohde-Kilsch, Claudia *Tennis Player*
Elsa-Brandstrom-Str 22, 6800 Saarbrucken 1, Germany

Kohl, Helmut *Chancellor, Germany*
Marbacherstrasse 11, 6700 Ludwigshafen/Rhein, Germany

Kohl, Herb *Senator, WI; Basketball Executive*
%US Senate, Washington, DC 20510

Kohlberg, Jerome *Financier*
%Kohlberg Kravis Roberts & Co, 9 W 57th St, New York, NY 10019

Kohlsaat, Peter *Cartoonist (Single Slices)*
%Los Angeles Times Syndicate, Times Mirror Sq, Los Angeles, CA 90053

K

Kohn - Koncak

Kohn, A Eugene *Architect*
%Kohn Pedersen Fox Assoc, 111 W 57th St, New York, NY 10019

Kohn, Edwin R, Jr *Navy Admiral*
Commander, Naval Air Force, Pacific Fleet, NAS North Island, San Diego, CA 92135

Kohner, Susan *Actress*
%John Weitz, 710 Park Ave, New York, NY 10021

Kohoutek, Lubos *Astronomer*
%Hamburg Observatory, Hamburg, Germany

Koike, Hisao *Businessman*
%Yamaha Motor Co, 2500 Shingai, Iwata City 438, Japan

Koivisto, Mauno H *President, Finland*
%President's Office, Presidential Palace, Helsinki, Finland

Kojac, George *Swimmer*
13015 Point Pleasant Dr, Fairfax, VA 22030

Kok Oudegeest, Mary *Swimmer*
Escuela Nacional de Natacion, Izarra, Alava, Spain

Kokonin, Vladimir *Opera, Ballet Administrator*
%State Academy Bolshoi Theatre, 1 Ploshchad Sverdlova, Moscow, Russia

Kolar, Jiri *Poet, Artist*
96 Blvd du Montparnasse, Paris, France

Kolb Thomas, Claudia *Swimmer*
%Stanford University, Athletic Dept, Stanford, CA 94305

Kolbe, Jim *Representative, AZ*
%House of Representatives, Washington, DC 20515

Kolff, Willem J *Surgeon*
2894 Crestview Dr, Salt Lake City, UT 84108

Kolingba, Andre *President, Central African Republic*
%President's Office, Bangui, Central African Republic

Koll, Donald M *Businessman*
%Koll Co, 4343 Von Karman Ave, Newport Beach, CA 92660

Kollek, Teddy *Mayor*
22 Jaffa Rd, Jerusalem, Israel

Kollias, Konstantinos V *Prime Minister, Greece*
124 Vassil Sophias St, Ampelokipi, Athens, Greece

Kollner, Oberst Eberhard *Cosmonaut, East Germany*
Franz-Mehring-Strasse, 8290 Kamenz, Germany

Kollo, Rene *Opera Singer*
Wilmelmstrasse 4, 8000 Munich 40, Germany

Kolm, Henry V *Electrical Engineer*
Weir Meadow Rd, Wayland, MA 01778

Kolpakova, Irina *Ballerina*
%American Ballet Theatre, 890 Broadway, New York, NY 10003

Kolsti, Paul *Editorial Cartoonist*
%Dallas News, Communications Center, Dallas, TX 75265

Kolter, Joe *Representative, PA*
%House of Representatives, Washington, DC 20515

Kolthoff, Izaak Maurits *Analytical Chemist*
%University of Minnesota, Chemistry School, Minneapolis, MN 55455

Kolvenbach, Peter-Hans *Religious Leader*
Borgo S Spirito 5, CP 6139, 00195 Rome, Italy

Komack, James *Telvision Producer, Director*
617 N Beverly Dr, Beverly Hills, CA 90210

Komar, Vitaly *Artist*
%Ronald Freeman Fine Arts, 31 Mercer St, New York, NY 10013

Komarkova, Vera *Mountaineer*
%University of Colorado, INSTAAR, Boulder, CO 80302

Komarov, Vladimir M *Cosmonaut*
141 160 Svyosdny Gorodok, Moskovskoi Oblasti, Potchta Kosmonavtov, Russia

Komatsu, Koh *Financier*
%Sumitomo Bank, 1-3-2 Marunouchi, Chiyodaku, Tokyo, Japan

Komatsubara, Shunichi *Businessman*
%Mitsui Mining Co, 1-1 Nihonbashi Muromachi, Chuoku, Tokyo 103, Japan

Komlos, Peter *Concert Violinist*
Torokvesz Ut 94, 1025 Budapest, Hungary

Koncak, Jon *Basketball Player*
%Atlanta Hawks, 100 Techwood Dr NW, Atlanta, GA 30303

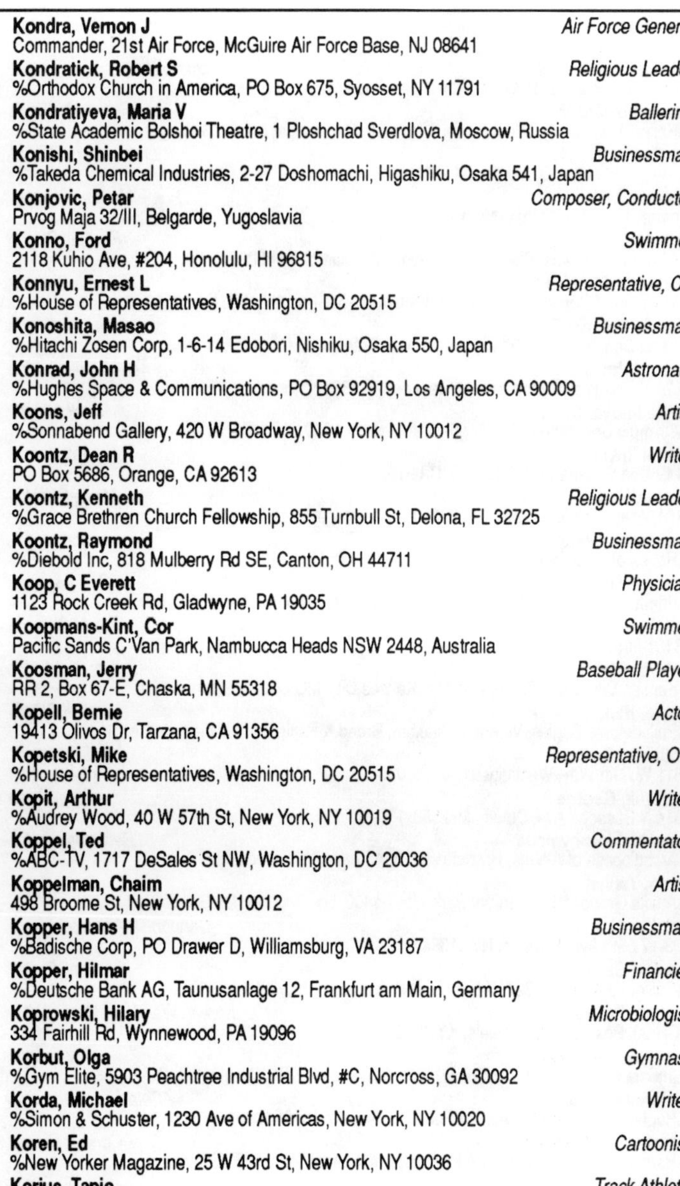

Kondra, Vernon J — *Air Force General*
Commander, 21st Air Force, McGuire Air Force Base, NJ 08641

Kondratick, Robert S — *Religious Leader*
%Orthodox Church in America, PO Box 675, Syosset, NY 11791

Kondratiyeva, Maria V — *Ballerina*
%State Academic Bolshoi Theatre, 1 Ploshchad Sverdlova, Moscow, Russia

Konishi, Shinbei — *Businessman*
%Takeda Chemical Industries, 2-27 Doshomachi, Higashiku, Osaka 541, Japan

Konjovic, Petar — *Composer, Conductor*
Prvog Maja 32/III, Belgarde, Yugoslavia

Konno, Ford — *Swimmer*
2118 Kuhio Ave, #204, Honolulu, HI 96815

Konnyu, Ernest L — *Representative, CA*
%House of Representatives, Washington, DC 20515

Konoshita, Masao — *Businessman*
%Hitachi Zosen Corp, 1-6-14 Edobori, Nishiku, Osaka 550, Japan

Konrad, John H — *Astronaut*
%Hughes Space & Communications, PO Box 92919, Los Angeles, CA 90009

Koons, Jeff — *Artist*
%Sonnabend Gallery, 420 W Broadway, New York, NY 10012

Koontz, Dean R — *Writer*
PO Box 5686, Orange, CA 92613

Koontz, Kenneth — *Religious Leader*
%Grace Brethren Church Fellowship, 855 Turnbull St, Delona, FL 32725

Koontz, Raymond — *Businessman*
%Diebold Inc, 818 Mulberry Rd SE, Canton, OH 44711

Koop, C Everett — *Physician*
1123 Rock Creek Rd, Gladwyne, PA 19035

Koopmans-Kint, Cor — *Swimmer*
Pacific Sands C'Van Park, Nambucca Heads NSW 2448, Australia

Koosman, Jerry — *Baseball Player*
RR 2, Box 67-E, Chaska, MN 55318

Kopell, Bernie — *Actor*
19413 Olivos Dr, Tarzana, CA 91356

Kopetski, Mike — *Representative, OR*
%House of Representatives, Washington, DC 20515

Kopit, Arthur — *Writer*
%Audrey Wood, 40 W 57th St, New York, NY 10019

Koppel, Ted — *Commentator*
%ABC-TV, 1717 DeSales St NW, Washington, DC 20036

Koppelman, Chaim — *Artist*
498 Broome St, New York, NY 10012

Kopper, Hans H — *Businessman*
%Badische Corp, PO Drawer D, Williamsburg, VA 23187

Kopper, Hilmar — *Financier*
%Deutsche Bank AG, Taunusanlage 12, Frankfurt am Main, Germany

Koprowski, Hilary — *Microbiologist*
334 Fairhill Rd, Wynnewood, PA 19096

Korbut, Olga — *Gymnast*
%Gym Elite, 5903 Peachtree Industrial Blvd, #C, Norcross, GA 30092

Korda, Michael — *Writer*
%Simon & Schuster, 1230 Ave of Americas, New York, NY 10020

Koren, Ed — *Cartoonist*
%New Yorker Magazine, 25 W 43rd St, New York, NY 10036

Korjus, Tapio — *Track Athlete*
%General Delivery, Lapua, Finland

Korman, Harvey — *Comedian*
1136 Stradella Rd, Los Angeles, CA 90024

Korman, Lewis J — *Entertainment Executive*
%Columbia Pictures Entertainment, 711 5th Ave, New York, NY 10022

Korn, Lester B — *Businessman*
%Korn/Ferry International, 1800 Ave of Stars, Los Angeles, CA 90067

Kornberg, Arthur — *Nobel Medicine Laureate*
365 Golden Oak Dr, Portola Valley, CA 94025

Korner, Jules J, III — *Judge*
%US Tax Court, 400 2nd St NW, Washington, DC 20217

K

Kornfield – Kove

Kornfield, Lewis F, Jr *Businessman*
%Tandy Corp, 1800 One Tandy Cir, Fort Worth, TX 76102

Koroma, Sorie Ibrahim *Prime Minister, Sierra Leone*
%First Vice President's Office, Tower Hill, Freetown, Sierra Leone

Korry, Edward M *Diplomat*
%Harvard University, International Affairs Ctr, Cambridge, MA 02138

Korth, Fred *Government Official*
El Retiro, PO Box 13, Ecleto, TX 78111

Korvald, Lars *Prime Minister, Norway*
Utsynet 18-A, 1500 Moss, Norway

Kosar, Bernie *Football Player*
%Cleveland Browns, Cleveland Stadium, Cleveland, OH 45202

Koshalek, Richard *Museum Director*
%Museum of Contemporary Art, 205 S Grand Ave, Los Angeles, CA 90012

Kosnik, Edward F *Businessman*
%Penn Central Corp, 500 W Putnam Ave, Greenwich, CT 06836

Koss, John C *Television Inventor*
4129 N Port Washington Ave, Milwaukee, WI 53212

Kostadinova, Stefka *Track Athlete*
%Olympic Committee, Rue Anghel Kantchev 4, 1000 Sofia, Bulgaria

Kostal, Irwin *Conductor*
3149 Don Susana Dr, Studio City, CA 91604

Koster, Henry *Movie Director*
3101 Village, #3, Camarillo, CA 93010

Kostmayer, Peter H *Representative, PA*
%House of Representatives, Washington, DC 20515

Kosuga, Usaji *Businessman*
%Prima Meat Packers Ltd, 2-5 Kasumigaseki, Chiyodaku, Tokyo 100, Japan

Kotcheff, Ted *Movie Director*
13451 Firth Dr, Beverly Hills, CA 90210

Koterba, Jeff *Sports Cartoonist*
%Kansas City Star, 1729 Grand Ave, Kansas City, MO 64108

Kotite, Rick *Football Coach*
%Philadelphia Eagles, Veterans Stadium, Broad & Pattison, Philadelphia, PA 19148

Kotlarek, Gene *Ski Jumper*
4611 W 89th Way, Westminster, CO 80030

Kotlarek, George *Skier*
1614 N Bassood Ave, Duluth, MN 55811

Kotsonis, Ieronymous *Religious Leader*
%Archdiocese of Athens, Hatzichristou 8, Athens 402, Greece 53212

Kotto, Yaphet *Actor*
%Artists Group, 1930 Century Park West, #403, Los Angeles, CA 90067

Kotzky, Alex S *Cartoonist (Apartment 3-G)*
203-17 56th Ave, Bayside, NY 11364

Koufax, Sandy *Baseball Player*
%California Angels, 2327 W Lincoln Ave, Anaheim, CA 92801

Kouma, Ernest R *Korean War Army Hero (CMH)*
HCR 60, Box 31-D, McDaniels, KY 40152

Kourpias, George J *Labor Leader*
%International Assn of Machinists, 1300 Connecticut NW, Washington, DC 20036

Koushouris, John L *Television Executive*
%Hughes Television Network, 4 Penn Plz, New York, NY 10001

Kovacevich, Stephen *Concert Pianist*
%Harrison Operations Ltd, 9-A Penzance Pl, London W11 4PE, England

Kovach, William *Editor*
%Nieman Fellows Program, Harvard University, Cambridge, MA 02138

Kovacic-Ciro, Zdravko *Water Polo Player*
JP Kamova 57, 51000 Rijeka, Yugoslavia

Kovacs, Denes *Concert Violinist*
Iranyi Utca 12, Budapest V, Hungary

Kovacs, Laszlo *Cinematographer*
%Nicholson/Landers, 13791 Riverside Dr, #314, Sherman Oaks, CA 91423

Kovalenak, Vladimir *Cosmonaut*
141 160 Svyosdny Gorodok, Moskovskoi Oblasti, Potchta Kosmonavtov, Russia

Kove, Martin *Actor*
2150 Sunset Crest Dr, Los Angeles, CA 90046

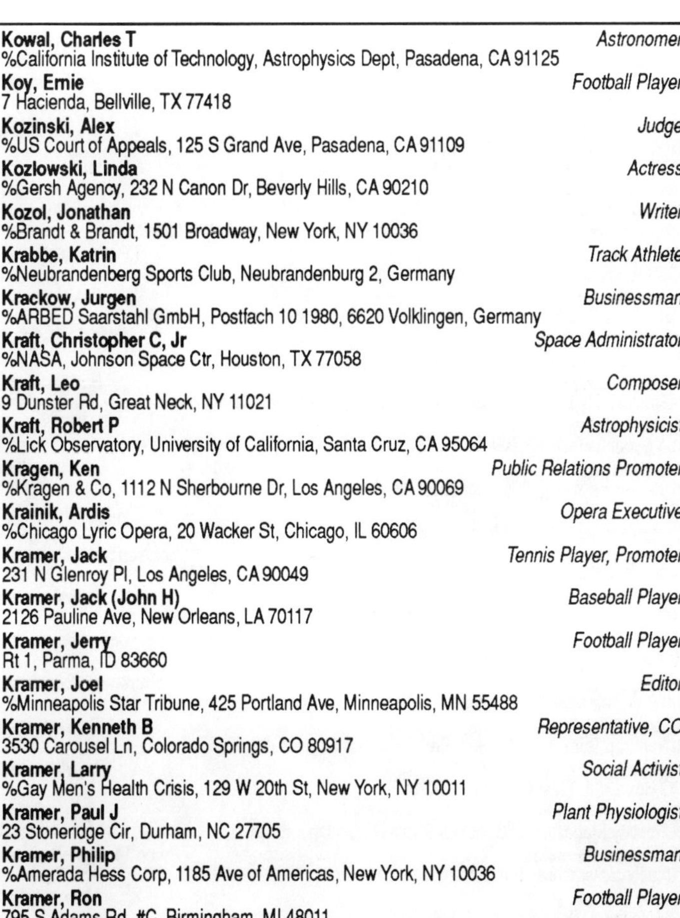

Kowal, Charles T *Astronomer*
%California Institute of Technology, Astrophysics Dept, Pasadena, CA 91125

Koy, Ernie *Football Player*
7 Hacienda, Bellville, TX 77418

Kozinski, Alex *Judge*
%US Court of Appeals, 125 S Grand Ave, Pasadena, CA 91109

Kozlowski, Linda *Actress*
%Gersh Agency, 232 N Canon Dr, Beverly Hills, CA 90210

Kozol, Jonathan *Writer*
%Brandt & Brandt, 1501 Broadway, New York, NY 10036

Krabbe, Katrin *Track Athlete*
%Neubrandenberg Sports Club, Neubrandenburg 2, Germany

Krackow, Jurgen *Businessman*
%ARBED Saarstahl GmbH, Postfach 10 1980, 6620 Volklingen, Germany

Kraft, Christopher C, Jr *Space Administrator*
%NASA, Johnson Space Ctr, Houston, TX 77058

Kraft, Leo *Composer*
9 Dunster Rd, Great Neck, NY 11021

Kraft, Robert P *Astrophysicist*
%Lick Observatory, University of California, Santa Cruz, CA 95064

Kragen, Ken *Public Relations Promoter*
%Kragen & Co, 1112 N Sherbourne Dr, Los Angeles, CA 90069

Krainik, Ardis *Opera Executive*
%Chicago Lyric Opera, 20 Wacker St, Chicago, IL 60606

Kramer, Jack *Tennis Player, Promoter*
231 N Glenroy Pl, Los Angeles, CA 90049

Kramer, Jack (John H) *Baseball Player*
2126 Pauline Ave, New Orleans, LA 70117

Kramer, Jerry *Football Player*
Rt 1, Parma, ID 83660

Kramer, Joel *Editor*
%Minneapolis Star Tribune, 425 Portland Ave, Minneapolis, MN 55488

Kramer, Kenneth B *Representative, CO*
3530 Carousel Ln, Colorado Springs, CO 80917

Kramer, Larry *Social Activist*
%Gay Men's Health Crisis, 129 W 20th St, New York, NY 10011

Kramer, Paul J *Plant Physiologist*
23 Stoneridge Cir, Durham, NC 27705

Kramer, Philip *Businessman*
%Amerada Hess Corp, 1185 Ave of Americas, New York, NY 10036

Kramer, Ron *Football Player*
795 S Adams Rd, #C, Birmingham, MI 48011

Kramer, Stepfanie *Actress*
%William Morris Agency, 151 El Camino, Beverly Hills, CA 90212

Kramer, Tommy *Football Player*
%Minnesota Vikings, 9520 Vikings Dr, Eden Prairie, MN 55344

Krasnow, Robert A *Businessman*
%Elektra/Asylum/Nonesuch Records, 962 N La Cienega Blvd, Los Angeles, CA 90069

Kratochilova, Jarmila *Track Athlete*
Golouv Jenikov, 582 82, Czechoslovakia

Krauch, Carl-Heinrich *Businessman*
%Chemische Werke Huels, PO Box 1320, 4370 Marl 1, Germany

Kraus, Alfredo *Opera Singer*
61 W 62nd St, #6-F, New York, NY 10023

Kraus, Otakar *Opera Singer*
223 Hamlet Gdns, London W6, England

Krause, Chester *Publisher*
Krause Publications, 700 E State St, Iola, WI 54990

Krause, Edward (Moose) *Basketball Player*
1519 Marigold Way, South Bend, IN 46617

Krause, Richard M *Immunologist*
%National Allergy Institute, 9000 Rockville Pike, Bethesda, MD 20205

Krauskopf, Konrad B *Geologist*
806 La Mesa Dr, Menlo Park, CA 94025

Krauthammer, Charles *Journalist*
%Washington Post Writers Grp, 1150 15th St NW, Washington, DC 20071

K

Kravchuk – Kristof

Kravchuk, Leonid M *President, Ukraine*
%President's Office, Kiev, Ukraine

Kravis, Henry *Financier*
%Kohlberg Kravis Roberts Co, 9 W 57th St, New York, NY 10019

Kravitch, Phyllis A *Judge*
%US Court of Appeals, PO Box 8085, Savannah, GA 31402

Krayer, Otto Hermann *Pharmacologist*
3940 E Timrod St, #202, Tucson, AZ 85711

Kreager, H Dewayne *Financier*
%Pacific First Federal Savings Bank, 11th & Pacific, Tacoma, WA 98401

Krebs, John H *Representative, CA*
1383 W Sample St, Fresno, CA 93711

Krebs, Robert D *Businessman*
%Santa Fe Southern Pacific Corp, 224 S Michigan Ave, Chicago, IL 60604

Krebs, Susan *Actress*
2709 1/2 Strongs Dr, Venice, CA 90291

Kreile, Reinhold *Businessman*
%Friedrich Flick Grp, Monchenwerther Str 15, Dusseldorf, Germany

Kreiner, Kathy *Skier*
194 Sydenham St, #2, Kingston ON K7K 3M2, Canada

Krementz, Jill *Photographer*
%Dial Books Young, 375 Hudson St, New York, NY 10014

Kremer, Gidon *Concert Violinist*
%International Creative Mgmt Artists, 40 W 57th St, New York, NY 10019

Krens, Thomas *Museum Administrator*
%Solomon Guggenheim Museum, 1071 5th Ave, New York, NY 10128

Krenz, Donald A *Businessman*
%Ogden Corp, 277 Park Ave, New York, NY 10172

Krenz, Jan *Composer, Conductor*
Al 1 Armii Wojska Polskiego 16/38, 00-582 Warsaw, Poland

Kreps, Juanita *Secretary, Commerce*
1407 W Pettigrew St, Durham, NC 27708

Kresa, Kent *Businessman*
%Northrop Corp, 1840 Century Park East, Los Angeles, CA 90067

Kreskin *Illusionist*
PO Box 1383, West Caldwell, NJ 07006

Kretchmer, Arthur *Editor*
%Playboy Magazine, 680 N Lake Shore Dr, Chicago, IL 60611

Kriangsak Chomanan *Prime Minister, Thailand*
%National Assembly, Bangkok, Thailand

Krick, Irving P *Meteorologist*
754 Vella Rd, Palm Springs, CA 92264

Krieg, Dave *Football Player*
%Seattle Seahawks, 11220 NE 53rd St, Kirkland, WA 98033

Kriemelman, Arthur *Radio Executive*
%Mutual Broadcasting System, 708 3rd Ave, New York, NY 10017

Krige, Alice *Actress*
%Creative Artists Agency, 9830 Wilshire Blvd, Beverly Hills, CA 90212

Krikalev, Sergei *Cosmonaut*
141 160 Svyosdny Gorodok, Moskovskoi Oblasti, Potchta Kosmonavtov, Russia

Krikorian, Robert V *Businessman*
%Rexnord, 350 Sunny Slope Rd, Brookfield, WI 53005

Krim, Arthur *Movie Executive*
%Orion Pictures, 711 5th Ave, New York, NY 10022

Krim, Mathilde *Philanthropist*
%American Foundation for AIDS Research, 1515 Broadway, New York, NY 10036

Krimsky, John, Jr *Sports Executive*
%US Olympic Committee, 1750 E Boulder St, Colorado Springs, CO 80909

Krinsky, P L *Admiral, Educator*
%US Merchant Marine Academy, Superintendent's Office, Kings Point, NY 11024

Kristiansen, Ingrid *Track Athlete*
%VG Sportsredaksjonen, Akersgaten 34, Sentrum 0107 Oslo 1, Norway

Kristiansen, Kjeld Kirk *Businessman*
%Interlego A/S, Billund, Denmark

Kristof, Kathy M *Columnist*
%Los Angeles Times, Times Mirror Sq, Los Angeles, CA 90053

Kristof, Nicholas D *Journalist*
%New York Times, 229 W 43rd St, New York, NY 10036

Kristofferson, Kris *Singer, Songwriter*
3179 Sumac Ridge, Malibu, CA 90265

Kristol, Irving *Educator*
%Public Interest Magazine, 10 E 53rd St, New York, NY 10022

Kroc, Joan B *Businesswoman*
%Joan B Kroc Foundation, 8989 Villa La Jolla Dr, La Jolla, CA 92038

Kroeger, Gary *Actor*
%Harris & Goldberg Agency, 1999 Ave of Stars, #2850, Los Angeles, CA 90067

Krofft, Marty *Puppeteer*
7710 Woodrow Wilson Dr, Los Angeles, CA 90046

Krofft, Sid *Puppeteer*
7710 Woodrow Wilson Dr, Los Angeles, CA 90046

Krogh, Harry M *Businessman*
%Interco Inc, 10 Broadway, St Louis, MO 63102

Krogman, Wilton *Physical Anthropologist*
1127 Spring Grove Ave, Lancaster, PA 17603

Krol, John Cardinal *Religious Leader*
%Philadelphia Archdiocese, 222 N 17th St, Philadelphia, PA 19103

Kroll, Fred J *Labor Leader*
%Railway Clerks Brotherhood, 3 Research Pl, Rockville, MD 20850

Kroll, Lucien *Architect*
Ave Louis Berlaimont 20, Boite 9, 1190 Brussels, Belgium

Krombholc, Jaroslav *Conductor*
%National Theatre, Anenskenan 2, Prague, Czechoslovakia

Kromm, Bob *Hockey Coach*
%Detroit Red Wings, 600 Civic Center Dr, Detroit, MI 48226

Kronberger, Petra *Skier*
Ellmautal 37, A-5452 Pfarrwerfen, Austria

Krone, Julie *Thoroughbred Racing Jockey*
%Monmouth Park Race Track, Oceanport Ave, Oceanport, NJ 07757

Kropfeld, Jim *Boat Racing Driver*
%Hydroplanes Inc, 3660 Hermes Dr, Cincinnati, OH 45247

Krotine, F Thomas *Businessman*
%Sherwin-Williams Co, 101 Prospect Ave NW, Cleveland, OH 44115

Kruegar, Charlie *Football Player*
44 Regency Dr, Clayton, CA 94517

Kruger, Hardy *Actor*
%Artists Agency, 10000 Santa Monica Blvd, #305, Los Angeles, CA 90067

Krugman, Saul *Physician*
300 E 33rd St, New York, NY 10016

Krugman, Wilton *Physical Anthropologist*
1127 Spring Grove Ave, Lancaster, PA 17603

Krumm, Daniel J *Businessman*
%Maytag Co, 403 W 4th St, Newton, IA 50208

Krumrie, Tim *Football Player*
%Cincinnati Bengals, 200 Riverfront Stadium, Cincinnati, OH 45202

Krupansky, Robert B *Judge*
%US Court of Appeals, US Courthouse, 201 Superior Ave NE, Cleveland, OH 44114

Kruschen, Jack *Actor*
%Lew Sherrell Agency, 1354 Los Robles, Palm Springs, CA 92262

Kruse, Earl J *Labor Leader*
%Roofers/Waterproofers/Allied Workers, 1125 17th St NW, Washington, DC 20036

Krzyzewski, Mike *Basketball Coach*
%Duke University, Cameron Indoor Stadium, Durham, NC 27706

Kubasov, Valery *Cosmonaut*
141 160 Svyosdny Gorodok, Moskovskoi Oblasti, Potchta Kosmonavtov, Russia

Kubbu, Sadoon *Financier*
%Rafidain Bank, New Banks St, PO Box 11360, Massarif, Baghdad, Iraq

Kubek, Tony *Baseball Player, Sportscaster*
N-8323 North Shore Rd, Menasha, WI 54952

Kubelik, Rafael *Conductor*
CH-6047 Kastaienbaum, Haus im Sand, Switzerland

Kubiak, Gary *Football Player, Coach*
%Texas A&M University, Athletic Dept, College Station, TX 77843

Kubota, Teruo *Financier*
%Hokuriko Bank, 1-2-26 Tsutsumicho-Dori, Toyama City 930, Japan

Kubota, Yoshifumi *Businessman*
%Daicel Chemical Industries, 8-1 Kasumigaseki, Chiyodaku, Tokyo 100, Japan

Kubrick, Stanley *Movie Director*
PO Box 123, Borehamwood, Herts, England

Kucharski, John M *Businessman*
%EG&G Inc, 45 William St, Wellesley, MA 02181

Kuchel, Thomas H *Senator, CA*
%Wyman Bautzer Rothman, 2049 Century Park East, Los Angeles, CA 90067

Kucinich, Dennis *Mayor*
12217 Milan, Cleveland, OH 44111

Kudlow, Lawrence A *Government Official*
%Office of Management & Budget, Executive Office Bldg, Washington, DC 20503

Kudrna, Julius *Canoeist*
Sekaninova 36, 120 00 Prague 2, Czechoslovakia

Kuehl, Hal C *Financier*
%First Wisconsin Corp, 777 E Wisconsin Ave, Milwaukee, WI 53201

Kuehler, Jack D *Businessman*
%International Business Machines Corp, Old Orchard Rd, Armonk, NY 10504

Kuehn, Ronald I, Jr *Businessman*
%Sonat Inc, First National-Southern Natural Bldg, Birmingham, AL 35203

Kuharic, Franjo Cardinal *Religious Leader*
%Archdiocese of Zagreb, 41101 Zagreb, Yugoslavia

Kuhn, Bowie *Baseball Executive*
%Kent Ridge Crawford, 225 Water St, Jacksonville, FL 32250

Kuhnen, Harald *Businessman*
%Thyssen, Kaiser-Wilhelm-Strasse 100, 4100 Duisburg 11, Germany

Kuhns, William G *Businessman*
%General Public Utilities Corp, 100 Interpace Pkwy, Parsippany, NJ 07054

Kulikov, Viktor G *Army Marshal, USSR*
%Ministry of Defense, 34 Naberezhnaya M Thoreza, Moscow, Russia

Kullberg, Duane E *Businessman*
%Arthur Andersen & Co, 1345 Ave of Americas, New York, NY 10105

Kullman, Charles *Opera Singer*
26 Chapman Ave, Madison, CT 06443

Kumagai, Yoshiro *Businessman*
%Sumitomo Metal Industries, 1-1-3 Otemachi, Chiyodaku, Tokyo 100, Japan

Kume, Tadashi *Businessman*
%Honda Motor Co, 27-8-6 Jingumae, Shibuyaku, Tokyo 150, Japan

Kume, Yutaka *Businessman*
%Nissan Motor Co Ltd, 6-17-1 Ginza, Chuoku, Tokyo 104, Japan

Kumin, Maxine *Writer*
Joppa Rd, Warner, NH 03278

Kummer, Glenn F *Businessman*
%Fleetwood Enterprises, 3125 Myers St, Riverside, CA 92523

Kundera, Milan *Writer*
%University of Rennes, 6 Ave Gaston Berger, 35043 Rennes, France

Kung, Hans *Theologian*
Waldhauserstr 23, 74 Tubingen, Germany

Kunin, Madeline M *Governor, VT*
%Governor's Office, State Capitol, Montpelier, VT 05602

Kunisch, Robert D *Businessman*
%PHH Grp, 11333 McCormick Rd, Hunt Valley, MD 21301

Kunitz, Stanley J *Writer*
37 W 12th St, New York, NY 10011

Kunkel, Louis *Pediatrician*
%Children's Hospital, 300 Longwood Ave, Boston, MA 02146

Kunkle, John F *Religious Leader*
%Evangelical Methodist Church, 3000 W Kellogg Dr, Wichita, KS 67213

Kunstler, William M *Attorney, Human Rights Activist*
%Center for Constitutional Rights, 666 Broadway, New York, NY 10012

Kunz, Erich *Opera Singer*
Grinzingerstrasse 35, 1190 Vienna, Austria

Kunz, Larry *Businessman*
%Payless Cashways Inc, 2301 Main, Kansas City, MO 64141

Kupchak, Mitch *Basketball Player*
1123 Manning Ave, Los Angeles, CA 90024

Kupcinet, Irv *Columnist*
5400 N St Louis Ave, Chicago, IL 60625

Kupfer, Carl *Ophthalmologist*
%National Eye Institute, 9000 Rockville Pike, Bethesda, MD 20205

Kupfer, Harry *Opera Director*
%Komische Oper, Chefregisseur, Berlin, Germany

Kupfer, Robert D *Businessman*
%Turner Corp, 633 3rd Ave, New York, NY 10017

Kuralt, Charles *Commentator*
%CBS-TV, News Dept, 524 W 57th St, New York, NY 10019

Kurland, Bob *Basketball Player*
1200 Brookside, Bartlesville, OK 34006

Kurokawa, Kisho *Architect*
Aoyama Bldg, 11th Floor, 1-2-3 Kita Aoyama, Minatoku, Tokyo, Japan

Kurosawa, Akira *Movie Director*
%Kurosawa Production, 3-2-1 Kirigaoka Midori-ku, Yokohama, Japan

Kurri, Jari *Hockey Player*
%Los Angeles Kings, Great Western Forum, 3900 W Manchester, Inglewood, CA 90306

Kurtz, Efrem *Conductor*
%19 Air St, Regent St, London W1R 6QL, England

Kurtz, Swoozie *Actress*
%William Morris Agency, 151 El Camino, Beverly Hills, CA 90212

Kurtzig, Sandra L *Businesswoman*
%ASK Computer Systems, 2440 W El Camino Real, Mountain View, CA 94040

Kurtzman, Harvey *Cartoonist (Little Annie Fanny)*
%Playboy Magazine, 919 N Michigan Ave, Chicago, IL 60611

Kurzweil, Raymond *Inventor*
%Kurzweil Applied Intelligence, 411 Waverly Oaks Rd, Waltham, MA 02154

Kusaba, Toshiro *Financier*
%Mitsui Bank, 1-1-2 Yuraku, Chiyodaku, Tokyo 100, Japan

Kusakabe, Etsuji *Businessman*
%Furukawa Electric Co, 6-1 Marunouchi, Chiyodaku, Tokyo 100, Japan

Kusch, Polykarp *Nobel Physics Laureate*
%University of Texas at Dallas, PO Box 688, Richardson, TX 75080

Kuschak, Metropolitan Andrei *Religious Leader*
%Ukranian Orthodox Church in America, 90-34 139th St, Jamaica, NY 11435

Kuter, Kay E *Actor*
5331 Denny Ave, North Hollywood, CA 91601

Kutner, Mal *Football Player*
3 River Hollow Ln, Houston, TX 77027

Kuttner, Stephan G *Historian*
771 Euclid Ave, Berkeley, CA 94708

Kutyna, Donald J *Air Force General*
Commander, AFSPACECOM, Peterson Air Force Base, CO 80914

Kuykendall, John W *Educator*
%Davidson College, President's Office, Davidson, NC 28036

Kuzyk, Mimi *Actress*
%J Michael Bloom Ltd, 9200 Sunset Blvd, #710, Los Angeles, CA 90069

Kwan, Nancy *Actress*
4154 Woodman Ave, Sherman Oaks, CA 91403

Kwestel, Sidney *Religious Leader*
%Union of Orthodox Jewish Congregations, 45 W 36th St, New York, NY 10018

Kwoh, Yik San *Electrical Engineer*
%Memorial Medical Center, PO Box 1428, Long Beach, CA 90801

Ky, Nguyen Cao *Prime Minister, South Vietnam*
15701 Sunburst Ln, Huntington Beach, CA 92647

Kylberg, Lars *Businessman*
%Saab-Scania, S-581 Linkoping, Sweden

Kyle, John *Representative, AZ*
%House of Representatives, Washington, DC 20515

Kylian, Jiri *Ballet Dancer*
%Netherlands Dance Theatre, Postbus 15697, 2501 Gravenhage, Netherlands

Kyprianou, Spyros *President, Cyprus*
Elia Papakyriakou 29, Acropolis, Nicosia, Cyprus

La Belle, Patti *Singer*
%Paz Inc, 526 S 3rd, Philadelphia, PA 19147

La Fosse, Robert *Choreographer*
%New York City Ballet, Lincoln Center Plz, New York, NY 10023

La Planche, Rosemary *Actress*
13914 Hartsook St, Sherman Oaks, CA 91423

La Rue, Lash *Actor*
PO Box 2484, Sanford, NC 27330

La Sala, James *Labor Leader*
%Amalgamated Transit Workers, 5025 Wisconsin Ave NW, Washington, DC 20016

Laage, Gerhart *Architect*
Jungfrauenthal 18, 2000 Hamburg 13, Germany

Labaff, Ernie *Labor Leader*
%Aluminum Brick Glass Workers Union, 3362 Hollenberg, Bridgeton, MO 63044

Labarre, Robert *Businessman*
%SAGEM, 6 Ave d'Iena, 75783 Paris Cedex 16, France

Labis, Attilo *Ballet Dancer, Choreographer*
36 Rue du Chemin-de-fer, 78380 Bougival, France

Labonte, Terry *Auto Racing Driver*
PO Box 4617, Archdale, NC 27263

Laborde, Alden J *Businessman*
%Ocean Drilling & Exploration Co, 1600 Canal St, New Orleans, LA 70161

Laborde, John P *Businessman*
%Tidewater Inc, 1440 Canal St, New Orleans, LA 70112

Labrecque, Thomas G *Financier*
%Chase Manhattan Corp, 1 Chase Manhattan Plz, New York, NY 10081

Labyorteaux, Matthew *Actor*
%David Shapira Assoc, 15301 Ventura Blvd, #345, Sherman Oaks, CA 91403

Labyorteaux, Patrick *Actor*
PO Box 1399, Burbank, CA 91507

Lacey, G F *Businessman*
%Simplicity Pattern Co, 200 Madison Ave, New York, NY 10016

Lach, Elmer J *Hockey Player*
4557 Rosedale Ave, Montreal PQ H4B 2H1, Canada

Lachey, Jim *Football Player*
%Washington Redskins, Dulles Airport, Box 17247, Washington, DC 20041

Lackey, Brad *Motorcycle Racing Rider*
%Badco, 35 Monument Plz, Pleasant Hill, CA 94523

Laclavere, Georges *Geophysicist*
53 Ave de Breteuil, 70075 Paris, France

Laco, Thomas *Businessman*
%Procter & Gamble Co, 1 Procter & Gamble Plz, Cincinnati, OH 45202

Lacombe, Henri *Oceanographer*
20 Bis Ave de Lattre de Tassigny, 92340 Bourg-La-Reine, France

Lacoste, Catherine *Golfer*
Calle B-6, #4, El Soto de la Moraleja Alcobendas, Madrid, Spain

Lacoste, Rene *Tennis Player*
1 Ave du Marechal Maunoury, 75016 Paris, France

Lacroix, Christian *Fashion Designer*
73 Rue du Faubourg St Honore, 75008, Paris, France

Ladd, Alan, Jr *Movie Producer*
706 N Elm Dr, Beverly Hills, CA 90210

Ladd, Cheryl *Actress*
9051 Oriole Way, Los Angeles, CA 90069

Ladd, Diane *Actress*
%Light Co, 901 Bringham Ave, Los Angeles, CA 90049

Ladd, Margaret *Actress*
444 21st St, Santa Monica, CA 90402

Laettner, Christian *Basketball Player*
%Duke University, Athletic Dept, Durham, NC 27706

LaFalce, John J *Representative, NY*
800 Starin Ave, Buffalo, NY 14223

Laffer, Arthur *Economist*
608 Silver Spur Rd, #229, Rolling Hills Estates, CA 90274

Lafleur, Guy *Hockey Player*
%New York Rangers, Madison Square Grdn, 4 Pennsylvania Plz, New York, NY 10001

Lafontaine, Oskar *Political Leader, West Germany*
Staatskanzle, Am Ludwigplatz 14, 6600 Saarbrucken, Germany

LaFontaine, Pat *Hockey Player*
%Buffalo Sabres, Memorial Auditorium, Buffalo, NY 14202

Lagerfeld, Karl *Fashion Designer*
202 Rue de Rivoli, 75000 Paris, France

Laghi, Pio Cardinal *Religious Leader*
%Congregation on Catholic Education, Vatican City, Rome, Italy

Lagomarsino, Robert J *Representative, CA*
%House of Representatives, Washington, DC 20515

Lahti, Christine *Actress*
%Creative Artists Agency, 9830 Wilshire Blvd, Beverly Hills, CA 90212

Lai, Francis *Composer*
%Editions 23, 15 Ave Hoche, 75008 Paris, France

Laidig, William R *Businessman*
%Great Northern Nekoosa Corp, 75 Prospect St, Stamford, CT 06904

Laimbeer, Bill *Basketball Player*
%Detroit Pistons, Palace, 1 Championship Dr, Auburn Hills, MI 48057

Laine, Cleo *Singer*
Old Rectory, Wavendon, Milton Keynes MK17 8LT, England

Laine, Frankie *Singer*
352 San Gorgonio St, San Diego, CA 92106

Laing, Hector *Businessman*
%United Biscuits Holdings, Isleworth, Middlesex TW7 5NN, England

Laingen, L Bruce *Diplomat*
%National War College, Washington, DC 20006

Laird, Melvin *Secretary, Defense*
Box 279, Marshfield, WI 54449

Laird, Melvin E *Secretary, Defense; Businessman*
%Communications Satellite Corp, 950 L'Enfant Plz SW, Washington, DC 20024

Laird, Peter *Cartoonist (Ninja Turtles)*
%Creators Syndicate, 5777 W Century Blvd, #700, Los Angeles, CA 90045

Laird, Ron *Track Athlete*
5525 Mansfield Ct, Colorado Springs, CO 80907

Laitman, Jeffrey *Anatomist*
%Mt Sinai Medical Center, Anatomy Dept, 1 Gustave Levy Pl, New York, NY 10029

Lake, Charles W, Jr *Businessman*
%R R Donnelley & Sons Co, 2223 Martin Luther King Dr, Chicago, IL 60616

Lake, Meno T *Businessman*
%Transamerica Occidental Insurance, Transamerica Ctr, Los Angeles, CA 90015

Lake, Thomas H *Businessman*
%Eli Lilly Co, Lilly Corporate Ctr, Indianapolis, IN 46285

Lakein, Alan *Time-Planning Advisor*
2918 Webster St, San Francisco, CA 94123

Laker, Freddie *Businessman*
%Cheapside House, 138 Cheapside, London EC2V 6BL, England

Laker, Jim *Cricketer*
Oak End, 9 Portinscale Rd, Putney, London SW15, England

Lakes, Gary *Opera Singer*
%Herbert Barrett Mgmt, 1776 Broadway, New York, NY 10019

LaLanne, Jack *Physical Fitness Expert*
PO Box 2, Los Angeles, CA 90078

Lalla Latifa *Royal Mother, Morocco*
%Royal Palace, Rabta, Morocco

Lalli, Frank *Editor*
%Money Magazine, Rockefeller Ctr, New York, NY 10020

LaMantia, Charles R *Businessman*
%Arthur D Little Inc, 25 Acorn Park, Cambridge, MA 02140

Lamarr, Hedy *Actress*
568 Orange Dr, #47, Altamonte Springs, FL 32701

Lamas, Lorenzo *Actor*
%David Shapira Assoc, 15301 Ventura Blvd, #345, Sherman Oaks, CA 91403

Lamb, Gil *Comedian*
6476 San Marcos Cir, Los Angeles, CA 90069

Lamb, Willis E, Jr *Nobel Physics Laureate*
%University of Arizona, Physics Dept, Tucson, AZ 85721

Lambro, Phillip *Composer, Musician*
%Trigram Music, 1888 Century Park East, Los Angeles, CA 90067
Lambsdorff, Otto *Government Official, West Germany*
Villemombler Strasse, 5300 Bonn, Germany
Lamm, Harvey H *Businessman*
%Subaru of America Inc, 7040 Central Hwy, Pennsauken, NJ 08109
Lamm, Norman *Educator*
101 Central Park West, New York, NY 10023
Lamm, Richard D *Governor, CO*
400 E 8th Ave, Denver, CO 80203
Lamonica, Roberta de *Artist*
Rua Anibal de Mendanca 180, AP 202, Rio de Janeiro ZC-37 RJ, Brazil
LaMothe, William E *Businessman*
%Kellogg Co, 235 Porter St, Battle Creek, MI 49016
LaMotta, Jake *Boxer*
400 E 57th St, New York, NY 10022
LaMotta, Vickie *Model*
520 East Ave, North Miami, FL 33162
Lamour, Dorothy *Actress*
5309 Goodland Ave, North Hollywood, CA 91607
Lamparski, Richard *Writer*
3289 Carse Dr, Los Angeles, CA 90068
Lampley, Jim *Sportscaster*
%KCBS-TV, Sports Dept, 6121 Sunset Blvd, Los Angeles, CA 90028
Lampton, Michael *Astronaut*
%Space Science Laboratory, University of California, Berkeley, CA 94720
Lancaster, Burt *Actor*
2220 Ave of Stars, #1805, Los Angeles, CA 90067
Lance, Bert *Government Official*
409 E Line St, PO Box 637, Calhoun, GA 30701
Lanchberg, John A *Conductor*
%Roger Stone Mgmt, W Grove, Hammers Ln, Mill Hill, London NW7 4DY, England
Landau, Irvin *Editor*
%Consumer Reports Magazine, 256 Washington St, Mount Vernon, NY 10553
Landau, Jacob *Artist*
2 Pine Dr, Roosevelt, NJ 08555
Landau, Martin *Actor*
241 Barlock Ave, Los Angeles, CA 90049
Landazuri Ricketts, Juan Cardinal *Religious Leader*
Arzobispado, Plazo de Armas, Apartado Postal 1512, Lima, Peru
Landeck, Armin *Artist*
RD 1, Litchfield, CT 06759
Lander, David L *Actor*
7009 Senalda Rd, Los Angeles, CA 90068
Landers, Ann (Eppie Lederer) *Columnist*
%Chicago Tribune, 435 N Michigan Ave, Chicago, IL 60611
Landers, Audrey *Actress, Singer*
%Queen Bee Productions, 3112 Nicada Dr, Bel Air, CA 90077
Landers, Judy *Actress*
9849 Denbight Dr, Beverly Hills, CA 90210
Landes, David S *Historian*
24 Highland St, Cambridge, MA 02138
Landeta, Sean *Football Player*
%New York Giants, Giants Stadium, East Rutherford, NJ 07073
Landini, Richard G *Educator*
%Indiana State University, President's Office, Terre Haute, IN 47809
Landrieu, Moon *Secretary, Housing & Urban Development*
4301 S Prieur St, New Orleans, LA 70125
Landry, Greg *Football Player, Coach*
%Chicago Bears, 250 N Washington Rd, Lake Forest, IL 60045
Landry, Tom *Football Executive*
PO Box 9108, Dallas, TX 75209
Landsbergis, Vytautas *President, Lithuania*
%Government Offices, Vilnius, Lithuania
Lane, Abbe *Singer*
444 N Faring Rd, Los Angeles, CA 90077

L

Lane, Bernard B *Businessman*
%Lane Co Inc, E Franklin Ave, Altavista, VA 24517

Lane, Burton *Songwriter*
146 Central Park West, New York, NY 10023

Lane, C B *Businessman*
%Campbell Tagget Inc, 6211 Lemmon Ave, Dallas, TX 75209

Lane, Charles *Actor*
321 Gretna Green Way, Los Angeles, CA 90049

Lane, Cristy *Singer*
1225 Apache Ln, Madison, TN 37115

Lane, Diane *Actress*
210 W 55th St, #1103, New York, NY 10019

Lane, Jeffrey B *Businessman*
%Smith Barney Harris Upham Co, 1350 Ave of Americas, New York, NY 10105

Lane, Kenneth Jay *Fashion Designer*
23 Park Ave, New York, NY 10016

Lane, Lawrence W, Jr *Publisher, Diplomat*
%Sunset Magazine, 80 Willow Rd, Menlo Park, CA 94025

Lane, Mark *Attorney, Political Activist*
1177 Central Ave, Memphis, TN 38104

Lane, Melvin B *Publisher*
%Sunset Magazine, 80 Willow Rd, Menlo Park, CA 94025

Lane, Mike *Editorial Cartoonist*
%Baltimore Evening Sun, 501 N Calvert St, Baltimore, MD 21278

Lane, Priscilla *Actress*
RR 1, North Shore Rd, Derry, NH 03038

Lane, Richard (Night Train) *Football Player*
10729 Santa Maria, #11, Detroit, MI 48221

Lane, Stephen L *Businessman*
%Emerson Radio Corp, 1 Emerson Ln, North Bergen, NJ 07047

Lane, William W *Businessman*
%Emerson Radio Corp, 1 Emerson Ln, North Bergen, NJ 07047

Laney, Al *Tennis Player*
241 Hungry Hollow Rd, Spring Valley, NY 10977

Laney, James T *Educator*
%Emory University, President's Office, Atlanta, GA 30322

Lang, Dale *Publisher*
%Lang Communications, 342 Madison Ave, 22nd Fl, New York, NY 10173

Lang, Eugene M *Businessman*
%REFAC Technology Development, 122 E 42nd St, New York, NY 10017

Lang, Jack *Government Official, France*
10 Rue Danton, 75006 Paris, France

Lang, Jack *Sportswriter*
%Baseball Writers' Assn, 36 Brookfield Rd, Fort Salonga, NY 11768

Lang, K D *Singer*
%Bumstead Productions, 1616 W 3rd Ave, Vancouver BC V6J 1K2, Canada

Lang, Otto *Skier*
%National Ski Hall of Fame, PO Box 191, Ishpeming, MI 49849

Lang, Pearl *Dancer, Choreographer*
382 Central Park West, New York, NY 10025

Langbo, Arnold G *Businessman*
%Kellogg Co, 235 Porter St, Battle Creek, MI 49016

Langdon, Harry *Photographer*
8826 Burton Way, Beverly Hills, CA 90211

Langdon, Jervis, Jr *Businessman*
Quarry Farm, Elmira, NY 14902

Langdon, Michael *Opera Singer*
34 Warnham Ct, Grand Ave, Hove, Sussex, England

Langdon, Sue Ann *Actress*
%Brewis Agency, 12429 Laurel Terrace Dr, Studio City, CA 91604

Lange, David *Prime Minister, New Zealand*
282 Massey Rd, Mangeren, Auckland, New Zealand

Lange, Hope *Actress*
320 Skyewiay, Los Angeles, CA 90049

Lange, Jessica *Actress*
%Creative Artists Agency, 9830 Wilshire Blvd, Beverly Hills, CA 90212

Lange, Ted *Actor*
19305 Redwing St, Tarzana, CA 91356

Langella, Frank *Actor*
%Harris & Goldberg Agency, 1999 Ave of Stars, #2850, Los Angeles, CA 90067

Langenberg, Frederick C *Businessman*
%Interlake Corp, 2015 Spring Rd, Oak Brook, IL 60521

Langer, Bernhard *Golfer*
1120 SW 21st Ln, Boca Raton, FL 33486

Langer, Jim *Football Player*
%Pro Football Hall of Fame, 2121 George Halas Dr NW, Canton, OH 44708

Langford, Frances *Singer*
PO Box 96, Jensen Beach, FL 33457

Langford, John *Aeronautical Engineer*
%Daedalus Project, Edwards Air Force Base, CA 93523

Langley, N L *Businessman*
%Pargas Inc, PO Box 67, Waldorf, MD 20601

Langley, Roger *Skier*
Broad St, Barre, MA 01005

Langlois, Lisa *Actress*
%Lantz Office, 888 7th Ave, #2500, New York, NY 10106

Langsam, Walter C *Educator*
%University of Cincinnati, President Emeritus' Office, Cincinnati, OH 45221

Langston, J William *Neurologist*
%Parkinson's Foundation, 2444 Moorpark Ave, San Jose, CA 95128

Langston, Mark *Baseball Player*
2935 Marietta Dr, Santa Clara, CA 95051

Langway, Rod *Hockey Player*
%Washington Capitals, Capital Ctr, 1 Truman Dr, Landover, MD 20785

Lanier, Hal *Baseball Manager*
11250 SW Rio Vista Dr, Dunellon, FL 32630

Lanier, J Hicks *Businessman*
%Oxford Industries, 222 Piedmont Ave NE, Atlanta, GA 30308

Lanier, Joseph L, Jr *Businessman*
%West Point-Pepperell Inc, 400 W 10th St, West Point, GA 31833

Lanier, Max *Baseball Player*
11250 SW Rio Vista Dr, Dunellon, FL 31630

Lanier, Sartain *Businessman*
%Oxford Industries, 222 Piedmont Ave NE, Atlanta, GA 30308

Lanier, William D *Mayor, Houston*
%Mayor's Office, City Hall, 900 Brazos St, Houston, TX 77002

Lanier, Willie E *Football Player*
2911 W Brigstock Rd, Midlothian, VA 23113

Lanigan, Robert J *Businessman*
%Owens-Illinois Inc, 1 SeaGate, Toledo, OH 43666

Lanin, Lester *Musician*
%Lester Lanin Orchestra, 157 W 57th St, New York, NY 10019

Lanker, Brian *Photographer*
1993 Kimberly Dr, Eugene, OR 97405

Lanni, J Terrance *Businessman*
%Caesars World Inc, 1801 Century Park East, Los Angeles, CA 90067

Lansbury, Angela *Actress*
635 N Bonhill Rd, Los Angeles, CA 90049

Lansdowne, J Fenwick *Artist*
941 Victoria Ave, Victoria BC V8S 4N6, Canada

Lansford, Carney *Baseball Player*
RR 1, Box 50, Baker, OR 97814

Lansing, Robert *Actor*
%Don Buchwald Assoc, 10 E 44th St, New York, NY 10017

Lansing, Sherry *Movie Producer*
1500 San Ysidro Dr, Beverly Hills, CA 90210

Lantos, Thomas P *Representative, CA*
%House of Representatives, Washington, DC 20515

Lantz, Walter *Animator (Woody Woodpecker)*
444 Lakeside Dr, #310, Burbank, CA 91505

Lanvin, Bernard *Fashion Designer*
22 Rue du Faubourg St Honore, 70008 Paris, France

Lanza, Frank C *Businessman*
%Loral Corp, 600 3rd Ave, New York, NY 10016
Lapensky, M Joseph *Businessman*
%Northwest Airlines, Minneapolis-St Paul Airport, St Paul, MN 55111
Laperriere, Jacques *Hockey Player*
%Montreal Canadiens, 2313 St Catherine St W, Montreal PQ H3H 1N2, Canada
Lapham, Lewis Abbot *Financier*
John St, Greenwich, CT 06830
Lapham, Lewis H *Editor*
%Harper's Magazine, 666 Broadway, New York, NY 10012
Lapides, Morton M *Businessman*
%Allegheny Beverage Corp, Allegheny Cir, Cheverly, MD 20781
Lapidus, Alan *Architect*
%Lapidus Assoc, 43 W 61st St, New York, NY 10023
Lapierre, Dominique *Writer, Historian*
%Simon & Schuster, 1230 Ave of Americas, New York, NY 10020
LaPorte, Danny *Motorcycle Racing Rider*
253 Via Buena Ventura, Redondo Beach, CA 90277
Laporte, William F *Businessman*
685 3rd Ave, New York, NY 10017
Laposata, Joseph S *General, Army*
Chief of Staff, Allied Forces Southern Europe, APO, AE 09620
Lapotaire, Jane *Actress*
92-C Oxford Gdns, London W10, England
Laragh, John H *Physician, Educator*
435 E 70th St, New York, NY 10021
Larch, John *Actor*
4506 Varna Ave, Sherman Oaks, CA 91423
Lardinois, P J *Financier*
%Rabobank Nederland, Catharijnesingel, 3503 SE Utrecht, Netherlands
Lardner, Ring, Jr *Writer*
55 Central Park West, New York, NY 10023
Largent, Steve *Football Player*
5941 E 88th, Tulsa, OK 74137
Larkin, Barry *Baseball Player*
6818 Elwynne Dr, Cincinnati, OH 45236
Larkin, Francis X *Businessman*
%Fieldcrest Mills, 326 E Stadium Dr, Eden, NC 27288
Larmer, Steve *Hockey Player*
%Chicago Black Hawks, 1800 W Madison St, Chicago, IL 60612
LaRocco, Larry *Representative, ID*
%House of Representatives, Washington, DC 20515
LaRocque, Gene R *Government Official, Navy Admiral*
3140 Davenport St NW, Washington, DC 20008
LaRouche, Lyndon *Political Activist*
%National Caucus of Labor Committees, Leesburg, VA 22075
Larrabee, Martin Glover *Biophysicist*
4227 Long Green Rd, Glen Arm, MD 21057
Larroquette, John *Actor*
PO Box 6303, Malibu, CA 90265
Larsen, Art *Tennis Player*
203 Lorraine Blvd, San Leandro, CA 94577
Larsen, Bruce *Editor*
%Vancouver Sun, 2250 Granville St, Vancouver BC V6H 3G2, Canada
Larsen, Don *Baseball Player*
17090 Copper Hill Dr, Morgan Hill, CA 95037
Larsen, Libby *Composer*
2205 Kenwood Pkwy, Minneapolis, MN 55405
Larsen, Paul E *Religious Leader*
%Evangelical Convenant Church, 5101 N Francisco Ave, Chicago, IL 60625
Larson, Charles R *Navy Admiral*
Commander, US Pacific Commander, Camp H M Smith, HI 96861
Larson, Eric *Publisher*
%TV Guide Magazine, Radnor, PA 19088
Larson, Gary *Cartoonist (Far Side)*
%Universal Press Syndicate, 4900 Main St, Kansas City, MO 64112

Larson, Glen *Television Producer, Singer*
351 Delfern Dr, Los Angeles, CA 90077

Larson, Jack *Actor*
449 Skyewiay Rd N, Los Angeles, CA 90049

Larson, Lance *Swimmer*
1872 N Tustin Ave, Orange, CA 92665

Larson, Nicolette *Singer, Songwriter*
%Craig Agency, 8485 Melrose Pl, #E, Los Angeles, CA 90069

Larson, Robert E *Financier*
%Bankers Life Co, 711 High St, Des Moines, IA 50307

Larsson, Gunnar *Swimmer*
Synalsvagen 9, 724 76 Vasteras, Sweden

LaRussa, Tony *Baseball Manager*
338 Golden Meadow Pl, Danville, CA 94526

Lary, Frank *Baseball Player*
RR 8, Box 142, Northport, AL 35476

Lary, Yale *Football Player*
%Mid-Cities National Bank, 500 Grapevine Hwy, Hurst, TX 76053

LaSalle, Denise *Singer*
%Rodgers Redding Assoc, PO Box 4603, Macon, GA 31208

Lasch, Christopher *Historian*
%University of Rochester, History Dept, Rochester, NY 14627

Lash, Bill *Skier*
PO Box 509, Sun Valley, ID 83353

Lash, Don *Track Athlete*
RR 4, Box 288-A, Rockville, IN 47872

Lashutka, Greg *Mayor*
%Mayor's Office, City Hall, 90 W Broad St, Columbus, OH 43215

Lasker, Mary *Civic Worker*
870 United Nations Plz, New York, NY 10017

Lasnick, Julius *Businessman*
%M Lowenstein Corp, 1430 Broadway, New York, NY 10018

Lasorda, Tom *Baseball Manager*
1473 W Maxzim Ave, Fullerton, CA 92633

Lassally, Walter *Cinematographer*
The Abbey, Eye, Suffolk, England

Lassaw, Ibram *Sculptor*
PO Box 487, East Hampton, NY 11937

Lassen, Clyde E *Vietnam War Navy Hero (CMH)*
6230 Dunfieth Pl, Pensacola, FL 32504

Lasser, Louise *Actress, Comedienne*
200 E 71st St, #20-C, New York, NY 10021

Lassila, Jaakko *Businessman*
%Rauma-Repola Oy, PL 203, Snellmaninkatu 13, 00170 Helsinki 17, Finland

Lassiter, Ronald C *Businessman*
%Zapata Corp, Zapata Tower, PO Box 4240, Houston, TX 77210

Lasswell, Fred *Cartoonist (Barney Google)*
1111 N Westshore Blvd, #604, Tampa, FL 33607

Laszlo, Andrew *Cinematographer*
%Smith/Gosnell/Nicholson, 15151 Palisades Dr, #N, Pacific Palisades, CA 90272

Lateef, Yusef *Jazz Saxophonist, Flutist*
527 Madison Ave, #1012, New York, NY 10022

Latham, Louise *Actress*
%Badgley Connor, 9229 Sunset Blvd, #607, Los Angeles, CA 90069

Lathiere, Bernard *Businessman*
%Airbus-Industrie, 5 Ave de Villiers, 75017 Paris, France

Lathon, Lamar *Football Player*
%Houston Oilers, PO Box 1516, Houston, TX 77030

Latimer, George *Mayor*
%Mayor's Office, City Hall, #347, St Paul, MN 55102

Latimer, Thomas P *Businessman*
%Chicago Pneumatic Tool Co, 6 E 44th St, New York, NY 10017

Latta, Delbert L *Representative, OH*
%House of Representatives, Washington, DC 20515

Lattimore, Richard *Writer*
123 Locust Grove Rd, Rosemont, PA 19010

Lattner, Johnny *Football Player*
933 Wenonah Ave S, Oak Park, IL 60304

Laub, Larry *Bowler*
%Professional Bowlers Assn, 1720 Merriman Rd, Akron, OH 44313

Laubach, Gerald D *Businessman*
%Pfizer Inc, 235 E 42nd St, New York, NY 10017

Lauda, Niki *Auto Racing Driver*
A-5322 Hof/Salzburg, Austria

Lauder, Estee *Businesswoman*
%Estee Lauder Inc, 767 5th Ave, New York, NY 10153

Lauder, Leonard *Businessman*
%Estee Lauder Inc, 767 5th Ave, New York, NY 10022

Lauer, John N *Businessman*
%B F Goodrich Co, 500 S Main St, Akron, OH 44318

Lauer, Martin *Track Athlete*
Hardstrasse 41, 8566 Lauf, Germany

Laughlin, Don *Businessman*
%Riverside Casino, Laughlin, NV 89046

Laughlin, James *Publisher*
Meadow House, Mountain Rd, Norfolk, CT 06058

Laughlin, Tom *Actor*
12953 Marlboro St, Los Angeles, CA 90049

Laughlin, W Price *Businessman*
%Saga Corp, 1 Saga Ln, Menlo Park, CA 94025

Lauper, Cyndi *Singer*
%Premier Talent, 3 E 54th St, New York, NY 10022

Laurance, Matthew *Actor*
%International Creative Mgmt, 8899 Beverly Blvd, Los Angeles, CA 90048

Laurel, Salvador H *Prime Minister, Philippines*
%Vice President's Office, Executive House, Manila, Philippines

Lauren, Ralph *Fashion Designer*
1107 5th Ave, New York, NY 10128

Laurens, Andre *Editor*
%Le Monde, 5 Rue des Italiens, 75009 Paris, France

Laurents, Arthur *Playwright*
Dune Rd, Quogue, NY 11959

Laurenzo, Vincent D *Businessman*
%Massey-Ferguson Ltd, 595 Bay St, Toronto ON M5G 2C3, Canada

Lauria, Dan *Actor*
%Twentieth Century Artists, 3800 Barham Blvd, Los Angeles, CA 90068

Lauricella, Francis (Hank) *Football Player*
%Lauricella Land Co, 900 Commerce Rd E, #100, Harahan, LA 70123

Laurie, Piper *Actress*
907 12th St, Santa Monica, CA 90403

Laurin, Michael *Businessman*
%Valley Federal Savings & Loan, 6842 Van Nuys Blvd, Van Nuys, CA 91405

Lautenberg, Frank R *Senator, NJ*
%US Senate, Washington, DC 20510

Lauter, Ed *Actor*
%Gersh Agency, 232 N Canon Dr, Beverly Hills, CA 90210

Lauterbach, Robert E *Businessman*
115 Forest Dr, Pittsburgh, PA 15238

Lauterbur, Paul C *Chemist*
%State University of New York, Chemistry Dept, Stony Brook, NY 11794

Laveikin, Alexander *Cosmonaut*
141 160 Svyosdny Gorodok, Moskovskoi Oblasti, Potchta Kosmonavtov, Russia

Lavelli, Dante *Football Player*
%Lavelli Furniture, 19680 Center Ridge Rd, Rocky River, OH 44116

Lavelli, Tony *Basketball Player*
37 Spring St, Somerville, MA 02143

Laventhol, David *Publisher*
%Los Angeles Times, Times Mirror Sq, Los Angeles, CA 90053

Laventhol, Hank *Artist*
RD 1, Box 44, Hanover St, Yorktown Heights, NY 10598

Lavery, Sean *Ballet Dancer*
%New York City Ballet, Lincoln Ctr, New York, NY 10023

L

Lavi, Daliah *Actress*
5900 SW 117th St, Miami, FL 33156

Lavin, Leonard H *Businessman*
%Alberto-Culver Co, 2525 Armitage Ave, Melrose Park, IL 60160

Lavin, Linda *Actress*
20781 Big Rock Rd, Malibu, CA 90265

Law, Bernard Cardinal *Religious Leader*
%Archdiocese of Boston, 2101 Commonwealth Ave, Brighton, MA 02135

Law, John Phillip *Actor*
1339 Miller Dr, Los Angeles, CA 90069

Law, Vernon *Baseball Player*
1748 N Cobblestone Dr, Provo, UT 84604

LaWare, John P *Government Official*
%Federal Reserve Board, 20th & Constitution Ave NW, Washington, DC 20551

Lawless, Robert W *Businessman*
%Southwest Airlines Co, Love Field, Dallas, TX 75235

Lawley, William R, Jr *WW II Army Air Corps Hero (CMH)*
3547 Dalraida Ct, Montgomery, AL 36109

Lawn, John *Law Enforcement Official*
%New York Yankees, Yankee Stadium, Bronx, NY 10451

Lawrence, Andrea Meade *Skier*
%Board of Supervisors, Mono County, Mammoth Lakes, CA 93546

Lawrence, Carol *Actress, Singer*
9033 Briarcrest Ln, Beverly Hills, CA 90210

Lawrence, David, Jr *Publisher*
%Miami Herald, 1 Herald Plz, Miami, FL 33101

Lawrence, Henry *Football Player*
%Los Angeles Raiders, 332 Center St, El Segundo, CA 90245

Lawrence, Henry S *Physician, Immunologist*
345 E 30th St, New York, NY 10016

Lawrence, Jacob *Artist*
4316 37th Ave NE, Seattle, WA 98105

Lawrence, Marc *Actor*
14016 Bora Bora Way, #19, Marina del Rey, CA 90292

Lawrence, Steve *Singer, Actor*
%Stage 2 Productions, PO Box 5140, Beverly Hills, CA 90210

Lawrence, Vicki *Actress, Singer*
%Lawrence/Schultz Inc, 132 S Rodeo Dr, Beverly Hills, CA 90212

Lawson, Eddie *Motorcycle Racing Rider*
%Gary Howard, International Racers, 1633 E 4th St, #132, Santa Ana, CA 92701

Lawson, Nigel *Government Official, England*
32 Sutherland Walk, London SE17, England

Lawson, Richard *Actor*
%Muchnick, 432 S Ogden Dr, Los Angeles, CA 90036

Lawton, Richard S *Financier*
%Perpetual American Bank, 2034 Eisenhower Ave, Alexandria, VA 22314

Lawwill, Theodore *Ophthalmologist*
1900 Drury Ln, Mission Hills, KS 66208

Laxalt, Paul *Governor/Senator, NV*
%Laxalt Washington, Willard, 1455 Pennsylvania NW, #975, Washington, DC 20004

Lay, Donald P *Judge*
%US Court of Appeals, PO Box 75908, St Paul, MN 55175

Lay, Herman Warden *Businessman*
4935 Radbrook Pl, Dallas, TX 75220

Lay, Kenneth L *Businessman*
%HNG/InterNorth Inc, 2223 Dodge St, Omaha, NE 68102

Layden, Frank *Basketball Coach, Executive*
%Utah Jazz, 5 Triad Ctr, Salt Lake City, UT 84180

Laye, Evelyn *Actress*
60 Dorset House, Gloucester Pl, London NW1, England

Layton, Joe *Dancer, Choreographer*
%Roy Gerber Assoc, 9200 Sunset Blvd, #620, Los Angeles, CA 90069

Lazar, Irving *Literary Agent*
1840 Carla Ridge, Beverly Hills, CA 90210

Lazar, Laurence *Religious Leader*
%Romanian Orthodox Episcopate, 2522 Grey Tower Rd, Jackson, MI 49201

Lazarev, Alexander %Christopher Tennant Artists, 11 Lawrence St, London SW3 5NB, England	*Conductor*
Lazarev, Vasily G 141 160 Svyosdny Gorodok, Moskovskoi Oblasti, Potchta Kosmonavtov, Russia	*Cosmonaut*
Lazarus, Charles %Toys "R" Us Inc, 395 W Passaic St, Rochelle Park, NJ 07662	*Businessman*
Lazarus, Mell %North America Syndicate, 1703 Kaiser Ave, Irvine, CA 92714	*Cartoonist (Miss Peach, Momma)*
Lazenby, George 1127 21st St, Santa Monica, CA 90403	*Actor*
Le Beauf, Sabrina %Henderson/Hogan Agency, 247 S Beverly Dr, #102, Beverly Hills, CA 90210	*Actress*
Le Bel, Robert 26 Rue St Pierre, Cite de Chambly PQ J3L 1L7, Canada	*Hockey Executive*
Le Carre, John Tregiffian, St Buryan, Penzance, Cornwall, England	*Writer*
Le Clerc, Jean %STE Representation, 9301 Wilshire Blvd, #312, Beverly Hills, CA 90210	*Actor*
Le Mat, Paul 1100 N Alta Loma Rd, Los Angeles, CA 90069	*Actor*
Le Mesurier, John 56 Barron's Keep, London W14, England	*Actor*
Le Pelley, Guernsey 841 Whitecap Cir, Venice, FL 33595	*Editorial Cartoonist*
Le Shana, David %Seattle Pacific University, President's Office, Seattle, WA 98119	*Educator*
Le Vier, Anthony W (Tony) %SAFE, 5108 Solliden Ln, La Canada, CA 91011	*Test Pilot*
Le Witt, Jan 10 Highfield Ave, Cambridge CB4 2AL, England	*Artist*
Le Witt, Sol %Susanna Singer, 308 E 79th St, New York, NY 10021	*Sculptor*
Lea, Charlie 4237 Fairmont Ave, Memphis, TN 38108	*Baseball Manager*
Leach, Henry Wonston Lodge, Wonston, Winchester, Hants SO21 3LS, England	*Fleet Admiral, England*
Leach, Howard H %Sybron Corp, Park 80 W, Plaza I, Saddle Brook, NJ 07662	*Businessman*
Leach, John A S 2625 Wood Ln, Davenport, IA 52803	*Representative, IA*
Leach, Robin %Leach Entertainment Features, 875 3rd Ave, #1800, New York, NY 10022	*Television Producer, Entertainer*
Leachman, Cloris 13127 Boca De Canon Ln, Los Angeles, CA 90049	*Actress*
Leader, George M %Country Meadows, 830 Cherry Dr, Hershey, PA 17033	*Governor, PA*
Leaf, Alexander 1 Curtis Cir, Winchester, MA 01890	*Physician*
Leahy, Pat %New York Jets, 598 Madison Ave, New York, NY 10022	*Football Player*
Leahy, Patrick J 31 Green Acres Dr, Burlington, VT 05402	*Senator, VT*
Leakey, Mary %National Museum, PO Box 30239, Nairobi, Kenya	*Geologist*
Leali, Richard L, Sr %Citizens Savings Financial Corp, 999 Brockell Ave, Miami, FL 33131	*Financier*
Lear, Evelyn %Columbia Artists Mgmt Inc, 165 W 57th St, New York, NY 10019	*Opera Singer*
Lear, Frances %Lear Publishing Co, 655 Madison Ave, New York, NY 10022	*Publisher*
Lear, Norman 255 Chadbourne Ave, Los Angeles, CA 90049	*Movie Producer, Director*
Learned, Michael %Henderson-Hogan Agency, 247 S Beverly Dr, #102, Beverly Hills, CA 90210	*Actress*
Learned, W Wayne %Sooner Federal Savings & Loan, 5100 E Skelly Dr, Tulsa, OK 74135	*Financier*

Learoyd, Roderick A B *WW II British Royal Air Force Hero (VC)*
12 Fittleworth Garden, Rustington, West Sussex BN16 3EW, England

Leary, Timothy *Psychologist*
10106 Sunbrook, Beverly Hills, CA 90210

Lease, Joseph A *Mayor*
%Mayor's Office, City Hall Building, #1109, Norfolk, VA 23501

Leather, Richard B *Businessman*
%Newmont Mining Corp, 200 Park Ave, New York, NY 10166

Leatherdale, Douglas W *Businessman*
%St Paul Companies, 385 Washington St, St Paul, MN 55102

Leavy, Edward *Judge*
%US Court of Appeals, 620 SW Main St, Portland, OR 97205

LeBaron, Eddie *Football Player*
6350 River Chase Cir, Atlanta, GA 30328

LeBeau, Dick *Football Player*
%Cincinnati Bengals, 200 Riverfront Stadium, Cincinnati, OH 45202

Lebed, Hartzel Z *Businessman*
%Cigna Corp, 1 Logan Sq, Philadelphia, PA 19103

Lebedev, Valentin *Cosmonaut*
141 160 Svyosdny Gorodok, Moskovskoi Oblasti, Potchta Kosmonavtov, Russia

LeBlanc, Sherri *Ballerina*
%New York City Ballet, Lincoln Ctr, New York, NY 10023

Lebowitz, Fran *Writer*
%Random House, 201 E 50th St, New York, NY 10022

Leboyer, Frederick *Physician*
%Georges Borchardt, 136 E 57th St, New York, NY 10022

LeBrock, Kelly *Actress*
PO Box 727, Los Olivos, CA 93441

Lecerf, Olivier *Businessman*
%Lafarge Copper, 28 Rue Emile Menier, 75116 Paris, France

LeClair, J M *Businessman*
%Grand Trunk Corp, 131 W Lafayette, Detroit, MI 48226

Leconte, Henri *Tennis Player*
58 Chemin Hauts-Crets, CH-1223 Cologny, Switzerland

Ledbetter, Donald N *Labor Leader*
%Postal Supervisors Assn, 490 L'Enfant Plz SW, Washington, DC 20005

Leder, Philip *Geneticist*
%Harvard University Medical School, 25 Shattuck St, Boston, MA 02115

Lederberg, Joshua *Nobel Medicine Laureate*
%Rockefeller University, President's Office, New York, NY 10021

Lederer, Francis *Actor*
23134 Sherman Way, Canoga Park, CA 91304

Lederman, Leon M *Nobel Physics Laureate*
%Fermi National Accelerator Laboratory, PO Box 500, Batavia, IL 60510

Ledford, Frank F, Jr *Army General*
%Surgeon General's Office, 5109 Leesburg Pike, Falls Church, VA 22041

Ledgerwood, Ian *Editor*
%Modern Maturity Magazine, 3200 E Carson St, Lakewood, CA 90712

Ledley, Robert S *Medical Researcher (CT Scanner)*
%Georgetown University, Medical Ctr, Washington, DC 20007

Lee Kuan Yew *Prime Minister, Singapore*
%Vice Prime Minister's Office, 8 Shenton Way, Singapore 0106, Singapore

Lee Teng-Hui *President, Taiwan*
%President's Office, Taipei 100, Taiwan

Lee Tsung-Dao *Nobel Physics Laureate*
25 Claremont Ave, New York, NY 10027

Lee, Anna *Actress*
%Andy Ronson, 868 W Knoll Dr, #A, Los Angeles, CA 90069

Lee, Bertram M *Basketball Executive*
%Denver Nuggets, 1635 Clay St, Denver, CO 80204

Lee, Bill (William F) *Baseball Player*
306 Pinetree Cir, Beaconsfield PQ H9W 5E1, Canada

Lee, Brenda *Singer*
2174 Carson St, PO Box 101188, Nashville, TN 37210

Lee, C Raymond *Financier*
%Fortune Financial Grp, 2120 US 19 S, Clearwater, FL 33546

L

Lee, Carl *Football Player*
%Minnesota Vikings, 9520 Viking Dr, Eden Prairie, MN 55344

Lee, Charles R *Businessman*
%GTE Corp, 1 Stamford Forum, Stamford, CT 06904

Lee, Chester M *Space Engineer*
%NASA, Code OT-6, 400 Maryland Ave SW, Washington, DC 20546

Lee, Dorothy *Actress*
434 Santa Dominga, Solana Beach, CA 92075

Lee, H Douglas *Educator*
%Stetson University, President's Office, Deland, FL 32720

Lee, H T *Businessman*
%Chinese Petroleum, 83 Chung Hwa Rd, Taipei, Taiwan

Lee, J Bracken *Governor, UT*
2031 Larid Dr, Salt Lake City, UT 84108

Lee, J Daniel, Jr *Businessman*
%TIAA-CREF, 730 3rd Ave, New York, NY 10017

Lee, James E *Businessman*
%Chevron Corp, 225 Bush St, San Francisco, CA 94104

Lee, Jared B *Cartoonist*
2942 Hamilton Rd, Lebanon, OH 45036

Lee, Johnny *Singer*
818 18th Ave S, Nashville, TN 37203

Lee, Jonna *Actress*
%Badgley Connor, 9229 Sunset Blvd, #607, Los Angeles, CA 90069

Lee, Keith *Basketball Player*
%Orlando Magic, Box 76, 1 Dupont Cir, Orlando, FL 32802

Lee, Lawrence H *Businessman*
%Delta Air Lines, 6060 Avion Dr, Los Angeles, CA 90045

Lee, Mark C *Astronaut*
%NASA, Johnson Space Ctr, Houston, TX 77058

Lee, Norman R *Businessman*
%Gulf States Utilities Co, 350 Pine St, Beaumont, TX 77701

Lee, Peggy *Singer*
7967 Mulholland Dr, Los Angeles, CA 90046

Lee, Pinky *Actor*
7110 Hwy 2, #22, Commerce City, CO 80022

Lee, Raphael C *Surgeon*
%Massassachusetts Institute Technology, Engineering Dept, Cambridge, MA 02139

Lee, Rex E *Government Official, Lawyer*
%Solicitor General's Office, Justice Department, Washington, DC 20530

Lee, Robert Edwin *Playwright*
15725 Royal Oak Rd, Encino, CA 91436

Lee, Ruta *Actress*
%Lew Sherrell Agency, 1354 Los Robles, Palm Springs, CA 92262

Lee, Sammy *Diver, Coach*
16537 Harbour Ln, Huntington Beach, CA 92649

Lee, Spike *Movie Director*
%Forty Acres & A Mule Filmworks, 124 DeKalb Ave, Brooklyn, NY 11217

Lee, Stan *Publisher, Cartoonist*
%Marvel Entertainment, 1440 S Sepulveda Blvd, #114, Los Angeles, CA 90025

Lee, Thornton *Baseball Player*
9054 Calle Norlo E, Tucson, AZ 85710

Lee, Tsung Dao *Nobel Physics Laureate*
%Columbia University, Physics Dept, New York, NY 10027

Lee, Vernon R *Religious Leader*
%Baptist Missionary Assn, PO Box 1203, Van, TX 75790

Lee, William S *Businessman*
%Duke Power Co, 422 S Church St, Charlotte, NC 28242

Lee, Yuan T *Nobel Chemistry Laureate*
%University of California, Chemistry Dept, Berkeley, CA 94720

Leeds, Laurence C, Jr *Businessman*
%Manhattan Industries, 1155 Ave of Americas, New York, NY 10036

Leeds, Phil *Actor*
%Sanders Agency, 8831 Sunset Blvd, #304, Los Angeles, CA 90069

Leek, Sybil *Self-Acclaimed Witch*
%Prentice-Hall Inc, Rt 9-W, Englewood Cliffs, NJ 07632

L

Leenhardt – Leighton

Leenhardt, Arnaud *Businessman*
%Vallourec, 7 Pl du Chancelier Adenauer, 75764 Paris Cedex 16, France

Leese, Howard *Guitarist (Heart)*
219 1st Ave N, #333, Seattle, WA 98109

Leestma, David C *Astronaut*
%NASA, Johnson Space Ctr, Houston, TX 77058

Leetch, Brian *Hockey Player*
%New York Rangers, Madison Square Grdn, 4 Pennsylvania Plz, New York, NY 10001

LeFebure, Estelle *Model*
%Elite Model Mgmt, 111 E 22nd St, New York, NY 10010

LeFrak, Samuel J *Businessman*
%LeFrak Organization, 97-77 Queens Blvd, Forest Hills, NY 11374

Leftwich, Samuel G *Businessman*
%K Mart Corp, 3100 W Big Beaver Rd, Troy, MI 48084

Lego, Paul E *Businessman*
%Westinghouse Electric Corp, Gateway Ctr, Pittsburgh, PA 15222

Legorreta Vilchis, Ricardo *Architect*
Palacio de Versalles 285, Codigo Postal 11020, Mexico City 10 DF, Mexico

Legrand, Michel *Composer*
Le Grand Moulin, 28 Rouves, France

LeGuin, Ursula K *Writer*
3321 NW Thurman St, Portland, OR 97210

Lehman, John F, Jr *Secretary, Navy; Businessman*
%PaineWebber Grp, 1285 Ave of Americas, New York, NY 10019

Lehman, Richard H *Representative, CA*
%House of Representatives, Washington, DC 20515

Lehman, William *Representative, FL*
%House of Representatives, Washington, DC 20515

Lehn, Jean-Marie P *Nobel Chemistry Laureate*
21 Rue d'Oslo, 67000 Strasbourg, France

Lehninger, Albert L *Biochemist*
15020 Tanyard Rd, Sparks, MD 21152

Lehr, Lewis W *Businessman*
%Minnesota Mining & Manufacturing Co, 3-M Ctr, St Paul, MN 55144

Lehrer, Jim *Commentator*
3356 Macomb, Washington, DC 20016

Lehrer, Peter M *Architect*
%Lehrer McGovern Bovis, 141 E 48th St, New York, NY 10017

Lehrer, Robert I *Molecular Biologist*
%UCLA Medical Ctr, Hematology & Oncology Div, Los Angeles, CA 90024

Lehrer, Tom *Entertainer*
%Cowell College, University of California, Santa Cruz, CA 95064

Lehrman, Lewis E *Businessman*
%Lehrman Institute, 641 Lexington Ave, New York, NY 10022

Lehtinen, Dexter *Attorney, Government Official*
%US Attorney's Office, Justice Dept, 155 S Miami Ave, Miami, FL 33130

Leiber, Hank *Baseball Player*
RR 2, Box 811, Tucson, AZ 85715

Leibler, Kenneth R *Financier*
%American Stock Exchange, 86 Trinity Pl, New York, NY 10006

Leibman, Morris I *Attorney*
1550 Lake Shore Dr, Chicago, IL 60603

Leibman, Ron *Actor*
10530 Strathmore Dr, Los Angeles, CA 90024

Leibman, Ron *Actor*
15535 Huston St, Encino, CA 91436

Leigh, Janet *Actress*
1625 Summitridge Dr, Beverly Hills, CA 90210

Leigh, Jennifer Jason *Actress*
%Edrick/Rich Mgmt, 2400 Whitman Pl, Los Angeles, CA 90068

Leigh, W Colston *Entertainment Executive*
26 Edgerstoune Rd, Princeton, NJ 08540

Leigh-Pemberton, Robert *Financier*
Torry Hill, Sittingbourne, Kent ME9 0SP, England

Leighton, Robert B *Physicist*
%California Institute of Technology, Physics Dept, Pasadena, CA 91125

Leimkuehler, Paul *Amputee Skier, Businessman*
351 Darbys Run, Bay Village, OH 44140

Lein, Don C *Businessman*
%Jostens Inc, 5501 Norman Center Dr, Minneapolis, MN 55437

Leisenring, E B, Jr *Businessman*
%Westmoreland Coal Co, 2500 Fidelity Bldg, Philadelphia, PA 19109

Leist, Neil Steven *Businessman*
%American Bakerless Co, 10 Riverside Plz, Chicago, IL 60606

Leisure, David *Actor*
%Cunningham-Escott-Dipene, 261 S Robertson Blvd, Beverly Hills, CA 90211

Leitz, George *Labor Leader*
%Transport Workers Union, 80 West End Ave, New York, NY 10023

Lejeune, Jerome *Geneticist*
31 Rue Galande, 75005 Paris, France

Lekang, Anton *Ski Jumper*
47 Pratt St, Winsted, CT 06098

Leland, Edwin S, Jr *Army General*
Director, Strategic Plans & Policy (J-5), Joint Staff, Washington, DC 20301

Lelouch, Claude *Movie Director*
15 Ave Hoche, 75008 Paris, France

Lem, Stanislaw *Writer*
%Franz Rottensteiner, Marchettigasse 9/17, 1060 Vienna, Austria

Lemaire, Jacques *Hockey Player*
%Montreal Canadiens, 2313 St Catherine St W, Montreal PQ H3H 1N2, Canada

Lemieux, Claude *Hockey Player*
%Montreal Canadiens, 2313 St Catherine St W, Montreal PQ H3H 1N2, Canada

Lemieux, Mario *Hockey Player*
%Pittsburgh Penguins, Civic Arena, 300 Auditorium Pl, Pittsburgh, PA 15219

Lemmon, Jack *Actor*
%Jalem Productions, 141 El Camino Dr, #201, Beverly Hills, CA 90212

Lemon, Bob *Baseball Player, Manager*
1141 Clairborne Dr, Long Beach, CA 90807

Lemon, Chet *Baseball Player*
4805 Highlands Place Dr, Lakeland, FL 33813

Lemon, Meadowlark *Basketball Player*
PO Box 398, Sierra Vista, AZ 85635

Lemon, Peter C *Vietnam War Army Hero (CMH)*
4820 Harvest Ct, Colorado Springs, CO 80917

LeMond, Greg *Cyclist*
%Greg LeMond Pro Centers, 235 Hillcrest Dr, Reno, NV 89509

Lemons, A E (Abe) *Basketball Coach*
%Oklahoma City University, Athletic Dept, Oklahoma City, OK 73106

Lemper, Ute *Singer*
%Marek Lieverberg, Hansaallee 19, 6000 Frankfurt/Main 1, Germany

Lenahan, Edward Patrick *Publisher*
%Fortune Magazine, Rockefeller Ctr, New York, NY 10020

Lendl, Ivan *Tennis Player*
%International Management Grp, 1 Erieview Plz, Cleveland, OH 44114

Lenfant, Claude J M *Physician*
%National Heart Institute, 9000 Rockville Pike, Bethesda, MD 20205

Lenhartz, Rudolf *Businessman*
%Saabergwerke, Trierer Str 1, 6600 Saarbrucken, Germany

Lenk, Maria *Swimmer*
Rua Cupertino Durao 16, Leblon, Rio de Janeiro 22441, Brazil

Lenk, Thomas *Sculptor*
7176 Tierberg, Gemeinde Braunsbach, Schloss Tierberg, Germany

Lennon, Max *Educator*
%Clemson University, President's Office, Clemson, SC 29634

Lennox, Annie *Singer (Eurythmics)*
%Mary Chambers, RCA Records, 6550 E 30th St, Indianapolis, IN 46219

Lennox, Donald D *Businessman*
%Schlegel Corp, 400 East Ave, Rochester, NY 14692

Leno, Jay *Comedian*
1151 Tower Dr, Beverly Hills, CA 90210

Lenoir, William B *Astronaut*
%Space Flight & Station Office, NASA Hdqs, Code M/S, Washington, DC 20546

L

Lenon – Lessing

Lenon, Richard A *Businessman*
%International Minerals & Chemical Corp, 2315 Sanders, Northbrook, IL 60062

Lenz, Kay *Actress*
%Gage Group, 9255 Sunset Blvd, #515, Los Angeles, CA 90069

Leonard, Bobby *Basketball Player, Coach*
%WTTV, 3490 Bluff Rd, Indianapolis, IN 46217

Leonard, Dennis *Baseball Player*
4102 Evergreen Ln, Blue Springs, MO 64015

Leonard, Elmore *Writer*
2192 Yarmouth Rd, Bloomfield Village, MI 48301

Leonard, George E *Financier*
%First Federal Savings & Loan, 3003 N Central Ave, Phoenix, AZ 85012

Leonard, Hugh *Playwright*
Theros, Coliemore Rd, Dalkey, County Dublin, Ireland

Leonard, Joseph B *Businessman*
%Eastern Air Lines, Miami International Airport, Miami, FL 33148

Leonard, Nelson Jordan *Chemist*
606 W Indiana Ave, Urbana, IL 61801

Leonard, Richard H *Editor*
%Milwaukee Journal, 333 W State St, Milwaukee, WI 53203

Leonard, Sheldon *Actor, Producer*
1141 Loma Vista, Beverly Hills, CA 90210

Leonard, Sugar Ray *Boxer*
1505 Brady Ct, Mitchellville, MD 20716

Leonard, Walter (Buck) *Baseball Player*
605 Atlantic Ave, Rocky Mount, NC 27801

Leone, Giovanni *Prime Minister, Italy*
%Senato, Piazzi Madama 1, 00186 Rome, Italy

Leonetti, Andrew F *Cinematographer*
%American Society of Cinematographers, 1782 N Orange, Los Angeles, CA 90028

Leonhard, William E *Businessman*
%Parsons Corp, 100 W Walnut St, Pasadena, CA 91124

Leonhart, William *Diplomat*
2618 30th St NW, Washington, DC 20008

Leonov, Aleksei A *Cosmonaut*
141 160 Svyosdny Gorodok, Moskovskoi Oblasti, Potchta Kosmonavtov, Russia

Leontief, Wassily *Nobel Economics Laureate*
%New York University, Economic Analysis Institute, New York, NY 10003

Leopold, Luna *Hydraulic Engineer*
400 Vermont Ave, Berkeley, CA 94707

Leppard, Raymond *Conductor*
1045 Park Ave, New York, NY 10028

Lerner, Max *Columnist*
25 East End Ave, New York, NY 10028

Lerner, Michael *Actor*
%Gersh Agency, 232 N Canon Dr, Beverly Hills, CA 90210

LeRoy, Gloria *Actress*
%Harry Gold Assoc, 3500 W Olive, #1400, Burbank, CA 91505

Lesch, George H *Businessman*
2817 Casey Key Rd, Nokomis, FL 33555

Lesch, James R *Businessman*
12210 Broken Bough, Houston, TX 77024

Leslie, Bethel *Actress*
%Burton Moss Agency, 113 N San Vicente Blvd, #202, Beverly Hills, CA 90211

Leslie, Donald S, Jr *Businessman*
%Hammermill Paper Co, PO Box 10050, Erie, PA 16533

Leslie, Joan *Actress*
2228 N Catalina St, Los Angeles, CA 90027

Leslie, Robert W *Businessman*
%Jostens Inc, 5501 Norman Center Dr, Minneapolis, MN 55437

Less, Anthony A *Navy Admiral*
Commander, Naval Air Force, US Atlantic Fleet, Norfolk, VA 23511

Lesser, Len *Actor*
934 N Evergreen St, Burbank, CA 91505

Lessing, Doris *Writer*
11 Kingscroft Rd, #3, London NW2 3QE, England

Lester, Ketty *Actress, Singer*
5931 Comey Ave, Los Angeles, CA 90034
Lester, Mark L *Movie Director*
17628 Camino Yatasto, Pacific Palisades, CA 90272
Lester, Richard *Movie Director*
River Ln, Petersham, Surrey, England
Letlow, W R (Russ) *Football Player*
1876 Thelma Dr, San Luis Obispo, CA 93401
Letsie David *Prince, Lesotho*
%Royal Palace, PO Box 524, Maseru, Lesotho
Letterman, David *Actor, Comedian*
30 Rockefeller Plz, #1410-W, New York, NY 10112
Leutze, James R *Educator*
%Hampden-Sydney College, President's Office, Hampden-Sydney, VA 23943
Levander, Harold *Governor, MN*
2323 Thompson Ave, South St Paul, MN 55175
Levchenko, Alexandr *Cosmonaut*
141 160 Svyosdny Gorodok, Moskovskoi Oblasti, Potchta Kosmonavtov, Russia
Levenson, Robert J *Businessman*
%Automatic Data Processing, 1 ADP Blvd, Roseland, NJ 07068
Leventhal, Kenneth *Businessman*
%Kenneth Leventhal Co, 2049 Century Park East, Los Angeles, CA 90067
Leventhol, Robert S *Businessman*
%Western Union Corp, 1 Lake St, Upper Saddle River, NJ 07458
Lever, Lafayette *Basketball Player*
%Dallas Mavericks, Reunion Arena, 777 Sports St, Dallas, TX 75207
Levergood, John H *Businessman*
%Scientific-Atlanta Inc, 1 Technology Pkwy, Atlanta, GA 30348
Levetown, Robert A *Businessman*
%Bell Atlantic Corp, 1600 Market St, Philadelphia, PA 19103
Levi, Edward H *Attorney General*
4950 Chicago Beach Dr, Chicago, IL 60615
Levi-Montalcini, Rita *Nobel Medicine Laureate*
%Instituto di Neurobiologia Cellulare, Via Marx 15, 00156 Rome, Italy
Levi-Strauss, Claude *Educator*
2 Rue Des Marronniers, 75016 Paris, France
Levin Cooper, Amy *Editor*
%Mademoiselle Magazine, 350 Madison Ave, New York, NY 10017
Levin, Carl *Senator, MI*
%US Senate, Washington, DC 20510
Levin, Gerald M *Publisher*
%Time Inc, Rockefeller Ctr, New York, NY 10020
Levin, Harry T *Educator, Writer*
14 Kirkland Pl, Cambridge, MA 02138
Levin, Ira *Writer*
%Harry Ober Agency, 40 E 49th St, New York, NY 10017
Levin, Jerry W *Businessman*
%Revlon Inc, 625 Madison Ave, New York, NY 10022
Levin, Robert J *Businessman*
%Stop & Shop Companies, PO Box 369, Boston, MA 02101
Levin, Sander M *Representative, MI*
%House of Representatives, Washington, DC 20515
Levine, David *Artist*
161 Henry St, Brooklyn, NY 11201
Levine, Ellen K *Editor*
%Redbook Magazine, 224 W 57th St, New York, NY 10019
Levine, Irving R *Commentator*
%NBC-TV, News Dept, 4001 Nebraska Ave NW, Washington, DC 20016
Levine, Jack *Artist*
68 Morton St, New York, NY 10014
Levine, James *Conductor*
%Metropolitan Opera Assn, Lincoln Ctr, New York, NY 10023
Levine, James *Conductor*
PO Box 698, Canal Street Station, New York, NY 10014
Levine, Mel *Representative, CA*
%House of Representatives, Washington, DC 20515

Levine, Robert N *Businessman*
%Laventhol & Horwath, 919 3rd Ave, New York, NY 10022

Levine, Ted *Actor*
%Harris & Goldberg Agency, 1999 Ave of Stars, #2850, Los Angeles, CA 90067

Levingston, Cliff *Basketball Player*
%Atlanta Hawks, 100 Techwood Dr NW, Atlanta, GA 30303

Levingstone, Ken *Government Official*
%House of Commons, London SW1A 0AA, England

Levinson, Barry *Movie Director*
%Creative Artists Agency, 9830 Wilshire Blvd, Beverly Hills, CA 90212

Levinson, Barry *Movie Director*
%Baltimore Pictures, 20th Century Fox, 10201 W Pico Blvd, Los Angeles, CA 90035

Levinson, Deirdre *Writer*
%Viking Press, 625 Madison Ave, New York, NY 10022

Levinthal, Cyrus *Biologist*
%Columbia University, Biological Sciences Dept, New York, NY 10027

Levitt, Richard S *Financier*
%Norwest Corp, 1200 Peavey Bldg, Minneapolis, MN 55479

Levy, Howard I *Businessman*
%Service Merchandise Co, 2968 Foster Creighton Dr, Nashville, TN 37204

Levy, Leon *Financier*
%Odyssey Partners, 437 Madison Ave, New York, NY 10022

Levy, Leonard *Historian*
820 N Cambridge Ave, Claremont, CA 91711

Levy, Lester A *Businessman*
%NCH Corp, 2727 Chemsearch Blvd, Irving, TX 75015

Levy, Marv *Football Coach*
%Buffalo Bills, 1 Bills Dr, Orchard Park, NY 14127

Levy, Michael R *Publisher*
%Texas Monthly Magazine, PO Box 1569, Austin, TX 78767

Levy, Paul *Editor*
%The Examiner, 5401 Broken Sound Blvd NW, Boca Raton, FL 33487

Levy, Raymond H *Businessman*
%Usninor, 4 Pl de la Pyramide, 92800 Puteaux, France

Levy, Stephen R *Businessman*
%Bolt Beranek Newman, 10 Moulton St, Cambridge, MA 02138

Levy, Walter J *Businessman*
300 Central Park West, New York, NY 10024

Lewin, Terence T *Navy Admiral*
%House of Lords, London SW1, England

Lewinsky, H C *Businessman*
%Mobil Oil, Steinstrasse 5, 2000 Hamburg 1, Germany

LeWinter, Nancy Nadler *Publisher*
%Esquire Magazine, 1790 Broadway, New York, NY 10019

Lewis, Al *Actor*
14755 Hartsook St, Van Nuys, CA 91403

Lewis, Albert *Football Player*
%Kansas City Chiefs, 1 Arrowhead Dr, Kansas City, MO 64129

Lewis, Allen *President, Saint Lucia*
Beaver Lodge, PO Box 1076, Castries, Saint Lucia

Lewis, Bill *Football Coach*
%Georgia Institute of Technology, Athletic Dept, Atlanta, GA 30332

Lewis, Carl *Track Athlete*
1801 Ocean Park Blvd, #112, Santa Monica, CA 90405

Lewis, David S *Businessman*
%General Dynamics Corp, Pierre Laclede Ctr, St Louis, MO 63105

Lewis, Drew *Secretary, Transportation*
%Union Pacific Corp, Martin Tower, 8th & Eaton Aves, Bethlehem, PA 18018

Lewis, Edward B *Geneticist*
%California Institute of Technology, Biology Dept, Pasadena, CA 91125

Lewis, Emmanuel *Actor*
518 N La Cienega Blvd, Los Angeles, CA 90048

Lewis, Flora *Journalist*
%New York Times, 229 W 43rd St, New York, NY 10036

Lewis, Frances A *Businesswoman*
%Best Products Co, Parham & Interstate 95, Richmond, VA 23227

Lewis, Geoffrey *Actor*
6120 Shirley Ave, Tarzana, CA 91356

Lewis, Henry *Conductor*
%Herbert H Breslin Inc, 119 W 57th St, New York, NY 10019

Lewis, Hobart *Editor*
%Reader's Digest, Pleasantville, NY 10570

Lewis, Huey *Singer*
%Hulex Corp, PO Box 819, Mill Valley, CA 94942

Lewis, Jerome A *Businessman*
%Petro-Lewis Corp, 717 17th St, Denver, CO 80201

Lewis, Jerry *Representative, CA*
%House of Representatives, Washington, DC 20515

Lewis, Jerry *Comedian*
%Muscular Dystrophy Assn, 810 7th Ave, New York, NY 10019

Lewis, Jerry Lee *Singer*
Lewis Farms, Nesbit, MS 38651

Lewis, John *Jazz Pianist, Composer*
%Atlantic Records, 9229 Sunset Blvd, Los Angeles, CA 90069

Lewis, John *Representative, GA*
%House of Representatives, Washington, DC 20515

Lewis, John C *Businessman*
%Amdahl Corp, 1250 E Arques Ave, Sunnyvale, CA 94088

Lewis, Juliette *Actress*
%William Morris Agency, 151 El Camino, Beverly Hills, CA 90212

Lewis, Monica *Singer*
%Lang, 606 Mountain Rd, Beverly Hills, CA 90210

Lewis, Ramsey *Jazz Pianist, Composer*
%Triad Artists, 10100 Santa Monica Blvd, #1600, Los Angeles, CA 90067

Lewis, Reggie *Basketball Player*
%Boston Celtics, 151 Merrimac St, Boston, MA 02114

Lewis, Reginald F *Businessman*
%TLC Group, 99 Wall St, New York, NY 10005

Lewis, Richard *Comedian*
9200 Sunset Blvd, #428, Los Angeles, CA 90069

Lewis, Robert *Writer*
%Stein & Day, 122 E 42nd St, New York, NY 10168

Lewis, Samuel W *Diplomat*
6232 Nelway Dr, McLean, VA 22101

Lewis, Shari *Ventriloquist*
603 N Alta Dr, Beverly Hills, CA 90210

Lewis, Sydney *Businessman*
%Best Products Co, Parham & Interstate 95, Richmond, VA 23227

Lewis, Tom *Representative, FL*
%House of Representatives, Washington, DC 20515

Lewit-Nirenberg, Julie *Publisher*
%Mademoiselle Magazine, 350 Madison Ave, New York, NY 10017

Lewitt, Sol *Artist*
%Susanna Singer, 50 Riverside Dr, New York, NY 10024

Lewitzky, Bella *Dancer, Choreographer*
849 S Broadway, #220, Los Angeles, CA 90014

Leyland, Jim *Baseball Manager*
30 Midway Rd, Pittsburgh, PA 15216

Leyton, John *Actor*
73 Grosvenor Sq, London W1A 4SA, England

Leyva, Nick *Baseball Manager*
%Philadelphia Phillies, PO Box 7575, Veterans Stadium, Philadelphia, PA 19101

Li Chonh-Ming *Educator*
81 Northampton Ave, Berkeley, CA 94707

Li Peng *Premier, China*
%Communist Central Committee, Beijing, China

Li Xiannian *President, China*
%Politburo, Chinese Communist Party, Beijing, China

Li, C H *Biochemist*
901 Arlington Ave, Berkeley, CA 94707

Liabo, Les C *Businessman*
%American Maize-Products Co, 41 Harbor Plaza Dr, Stamford, CT 06904

Liacouras, Peter J *Educator*
%Temple University, President's Office, Philadelphia, PA 19122

Liaklev, Reidar *Speed Skater*
General Delivery, 2770 Jaren, Norway

Liberman, Alexander *Editor*
%Conde Nast Publications, 350 Madison Ave, New York, NY 10017

Libertini, Richard *Actor*
%Writers & Artists Agency, 11726 San Vicente Blvd #300, Los Angeles, CA 90049

Lichfield, Patrick (Earl of) *Photographer*
Shugborough Hall, Stafford, England

Licht, Jeremy *Actor*
%Artists Agency, 10000 Santa Monica Blvd, #305, Los Angeles, CA 90067

Lichtenberg, Byron K *Astronaut*
%Payload Systems Inc, PO Box 38, Babson Park, Wellesley, MA 02157

Lichtenberg, Paul *Financier*
%Commerzbank, 32 Neue Mainzerstr, 6000 Frankfurt am Main, Germany

Lichtenberger, H William *Businessman*
%Union Carbide Corp, 39 Old Ridgbury Rd, Danbury, CT 06817

Lichtenfels, William C *Businessman*
%Emhart Corp, 426 Colt Hwy, Framington, CT 06032

Lichtenstein, Harvey *Musical Director*
%Brooklyn Academy of Music, 30 Lafayette Ave, Brooklyn, NY 11217

Lichtenstein, Roy *Artist*
PO Box 1369, Southampton, NY 11968

Lichti, Todd *Basketball Player*
%Denver Nuggets, 1635 Clay St, Denver, CO 80204

Lick, Dale W *Educator*
%University of Maine, President's Office, Orono, ME 04469

Liddy, G Gordon *Watergate Defendant*
9310 Ivanhoe Rd, Oxon Hill, MD 20010

Lidov, Arthur *Artist*
Pleasant Ridge Rd, Poughquag, NY 12570

Lieber, Larry *Cartoonist (Amazing Spider-Man)*
%Marvel Comics Grp, 387 Park Ave S, New York, NY 10016

Lieberman, Joseph I *Senator, CT*
%US Senate, Washington, DC 20510

Lieberman, Leonard *Businessman*
%Supermarkets General Corp, 301 Blair Rd, Woodbridge, NJ 07095

Lieberman, Myron *Educator*
%Ohio University, Education Dept, Athens, OH 45701

Lieberman, William S *Museum Curator*
%Metropolitan Museum of Art, 5th Ave & 82nd St, New York, NY 10028

Liebermann, Rolf *Opera Executive*
%Theatre National de l'Opera, Pl de l'Opera, 75009 Paris, France

Lieberson, Herbert *Businessman*
%National Small Business Assn, 1604 "K" St NW, Washington, DC 20006

Liebeskind, John *Brain Surgeon, Psychologist*
%University of California, Medical Ctr, Los Angeles, CA 90024

Lied, Finn *Businessman*
%Stats Olijeselskap, Den Norske A/S, 4001 Stavanger, Norway

Liedtke, J Hugh *Businessman*
%Pennzoil Co, Pennzoil Pl, Houston, TX 77252

Liepa, Adris *Ballet Dancer*
%Kirov Ballet Theatre, 1 Ploshchad Iskusstr, St Petersburg, Russia

Lieppe, Charles A *Businessman*
%West Point-Pepperell Inc, 400 W 10th St, West Point, GA 31833

Lietzke, Bruce *Golfer*
%Professional Golfers Assn, PO Box 109601, Palm Beach Gardens, FL 33410

Liffers, William A *Businessman*
%American Cyanamid Co, 1 Cyanamid Plz, Wayne, NJ 07470

Lifvendahl, Harold R *Publisher*
%Orlando Sentinel, 633 N Orange Ave, Orlando, FL 32801

Ligeti, Gyorgy *Composer*
Himmelhofgasse 34, 1130 Vienna, Austria

Light, Judith *Actress*
3410 Wrightview Dr, Studio City, CA 91604

Light, Murray *Editor*
%Buffalo News, 1 News Plaza, Buffalo, NY 14240

Lightfoot, Gordon *Singer*
1367 Yonge St, #207, Toronto ON M4T 2P7, Canada

Lightfoot, Jim R *Representative, IA*
%House of Representatives, Washington, DC 20515

Lightner, Candy *Social Activist*
22653 Pacific Coast Hwy, #I-289, Malibu, CA 90265

Likens, Gene E *Ecologist*
%Institute of Ecosystem Studies, New Botanical Gdns, Box AB, Millbrook, NY 12545

Likins, Peter W *Educator*
%Lehigh University, President's Office, Bethlehem, PA 18015

Lilienfeld, Abraham M *Epidemiologist*
3203 Old Post Dr, Pikesville, MD 21208

Lillee, Dennis K *Cricketer*
%WACA, WACA Ground, Nelson Crescent, East Perth 6000 WA, Australia

Lillehei, C Walton *Surgeon*
73 Otis Ln, St Paul, MN 55104

Lillie, John M *Businessman*
%Sequoia Assoc, 3000 Sand Hill Rd, #2-140, Menlo Park, CA 94025

Lilly, Bob *Football Player*
2250 Olender, Las Cruces, NM 80001

Lilly, Frank *Geneticist*
%Albert Einstein Medical College, Yeshiva University, Bronx, NY 10461

Lilly, John C *Dolphin Researcher*
%Human Dolphin Foundation, 33307 Decker School Rd, Malibu, CA 90265

Lilly, Sydney B *Businessman*
%Farm House Foods Corp, 111 E Wisconsin Ave, Milwaukee, WI 53202

Lima, Luis *Opera Singer*
%London Records, 137 W 55th St, New York, NY 10019

Liman, Arthur L *Attorney*
%Paul Weiss Rifkin Wharton Garrison, 345 Park Ave, New York, NY 10154

Limbaugh, Russ *Radio Entertainer*
%WABC-Radio, 2 Penn Plz, New York, NY 10121

Lin, Chia-Chiao *Applied Mathematician*
%Massachusetts Institute of Technology, Mathematics Dept, Cambridge, MA 02139

Lin, T Y *Civil Engineer*
8701 Don Carol Dr, El Cerrito, CA 94530

Lin, T-Y *Psychiatrist*
6287 MacDonald St, Vancouver BC V6N 1E7, Canada

Linander, Nils *Businessman*
%Saab-Scania, S-581 88 Linkoping, Sweden

Lind, Don L *Astronaut*
%Utah State University, Physics Dept, Logan, UT 84322

Lind, Joan *Rowing Athlete*
240 Euclid Ave, Long Beach, CA 90803

Lind, Marshall *Educator*
%University of Alaska, Chancellor's Office, Juneau, AK 99801

Lindars, Laurence E *Businessman*
%C R Bard Inc, 731 Central Ave, Murray Hill, NJ 07974

Lindbergh, Anne Morrow *Writer*
%Scott's Cove, Darien, CT 06820

Linden, Hal *Actor*
%Harold Cohen, 9200 Sunset Blvd, #808, Los Angeles, CA 90069

Lindfors, Viveca *Actress*
172 E 95th St, New York, NY 10028

Lindley, Audra *Actress*
%Harris & Goldberg Agency, 1999 Ave of Stars, #2850, Los Angeles, CA 90067

Lindner, Carl H *Financier*
%American Financial Corp, 1 E 4th St, Cincinnati, OH 45202

Lindner, Robert D *Financier*
%American Financial Corp, 1 E 4th St, Cincinnati, OH 45202

Lindner, William G *Labor Leader*
%Transport Workers Union, 80 West End Ave, New York, NY 10023

Lindsay, Jack *Writer*
56 Maids Causeway, Cambridge, England

L

Lindsay - Lipps

Lindsay, John V — *Mayor*
1 Rockefeller Plz, New York, NY 10020

Lindsay, Mark — *Singer, Songwriter*
%Carolyn Wood, PO Box 1442, Shelton, WA 98584

Lindsay, Robert — *Actor, Singer*
%Felix de Wolfe, 1 Robert St, London WC2N 6BH, England

Lindsay, Robert V — *Financier*
Box 296, Altamont Rd, Millbrook, NY 12545

Lindsay, Ted — *Hockey Player*
%Detroit Red Wings, 600 Civic Center Dr, Detroit, MI 48226

Lindsey, George — *Actor*
%Artists Agency, 10000 Santa Monica Blvd, #305, Los Angeles, CA 90067

Lindsey, Lawrence — *Government Official*
%Federal Reserve Board, 20th St & Constitution Ave NW, Washington, DC 20551

Lindsley, Donald B — *Psychologist, Physiologist*
471 23rd St, Santa Monica, CA 90402

Lindsley, Richard G — *Businessman*
%Farmers Grp, 4680 Wilshire Blvd, Los Angeles, CA 90010

Lindstrand, Per — *Balloonist*
%Thunder & Colt, Maesbury Rd, Oswestry, Shropshire SY10 8HA, England

Lindvall, Olle — *Neurologist*
%University of Lund, Medical Cell Research Dept, 233 62 Lund, Sweden

Lindwall, Raymond R — *Cricketer*
3 Wentworth Ct, Endeavour St, Mt Ommaney, Brisbane 4074 Old, Australia

Liney, John — *Cartoonist (Henry)*
%King Features Syndicate, 235 E 45th St, New York, NY 10017

Ling, James J — *Businessman*
14 Royal Way, Dallas, TX 75229

Ling, Maya Ying — *Sculptor*
%Yale University, Architecture School, New Haven, CT 06520

Lini, Walter — *Prime Minister, Vanuatu*
%Prime Minister's Office, PO Box 110, Port Vila, Vanuatu

Link, Arthur A — *Governor, ND*
2201 Grimsrud Dr, Bismarck, ND 58501

Linkert, Lo — *Cartoonist*
1333 Vivian Way, Port Coquitlam BC, Canada

Linkletter, Art — *Entertainer*
1100 Bel Air Rd, Los Angeles, CA 90024

Linkletter, John A — *Editor*
%Popular Mechanics Magazine, 224 W 57th St, New York, NY 10019

Linn-Baker, Mark — *Actor*
1033 Gayley Ave, #201, Los Angeles, CA 90024

Linowitz, Sol M — *Diplomat*
1 Farragut Sq S, Washington, DC 20006

Linson, Art — *Movie Director*
%William Morris Agency, 151 El Camino, Beverly Hills, CA 90212

Lint, Norman F, Jr — *Representative, NY*
48 Plymouth Rd, East Rockaway, NY 11518

Linton, Robert E — *Financier*
%Drexel Burnham Lambert Inc, 60 Broad St, New York, NY 10004

Linville, Joanne — *Actress*
3148 Fryman Rd, Studio City, CA 91604

Linville, Larry — *Actor*
%Gores/Fields Agency, 10100 Santa Monica Blvd, #700, Los Angeles, CA 90067

Lipinski, Ann Marie — *Journalist*
%Chicago Tribune, 435 N Michigan Ave, Chicago, IL 60611

Lipinski, William O — *Representative, IL*
%House of Representatives, Washington, DC 20515

Lipman, Allan M, Jr — *Businessman*
%Amalgamated Sugar Co, First Security Bank Bldg, Ogden, UT 84401

Lippincott, Philip E — *Businessman*
%Scott Paper Co, Scott Plz, Philadelphia, PA 19113

Lippold, Richard — *Artist*
PO Box 248, Locust Valley, NY 11560

Lipps, Louis — *Football Player*
%Pittsburgh Steelers, 300 Stadium Cir, Pittsburgh, PA 15212

Lipscomb, William Nunn *Chemist*
44 Langdon St, Cambridge, MA 02138

Lipset, Seymour M *Educator*
%Stanford University, Herbert Hoover Memorial Bldg, Stanford, CA 94305

Lipsett, Mortimer B *Physician*
%National Institutes of Health, 9000 Rockville Pike, Bethesda, MD 20205

Lipsey, Stanford *Publisher*
%Buffalo News, 1 News Plaza, Buffalo, NY 14240

Lipshutz, Bruce H *Organic Chemist*
%University of California, Chemistry Dept, Santa Barbara, CA 93106

Lipsig, Harry H *Attorney*
%Harry H Lipsig & Partners, 225 Broadway, #715, New York, NY 10007

Lipson, D Herbert *Publisher*
%Philadelphia Magazine, 1500 Walnut St, Philadelphia, PA 19102

Lipson, David E *Businessman*
%Beatrice Companies, 2 N LaSalle St, Chicago, IL 60602

Lipton, Martin *Attorney*
%Wachtell Lipton Rosen Katz, 299 Park Ave, New York, NY 10171

Lipton, Peggy *Actress*
%Triad Artists, 10100 Santa Monica Blvd, #1600, Los Angeles, CA 90067

Liquori, Marty *Track Athlete, Sportscaster*
2915 NW 58th Blvd, Gainesville, FL 32606

Lisa (Velez) *Singer (Lisa Lisa & Cult Jam)*
%Steve Salem Co, Full Force Productions, 450 6th Ave, #4-E, New York, NY 10018

Lisi, Virna *Actress*
Via di Filomarino 4, Rome, Italy

List, Robert *Governor, NV*
50 W Liberty, #210, Reno, NV 89501

Lister, Alton *Basketball Player*
%Golden State Warriors, Oakland Coliseum, Oakland, CA 94621

Lithgow, John *Actor*
%Creative Artists Agency, 9830 Wilshire Blvd, Beverly Hills, CA 90212

Little Anthony (Gordine) *Singer*
%Twan Productions, PO Box 3032, Palos Verdes Peninsula, CA 90274

Little Steven *Singer*
%Dusty, PO Box 1379, Radio City Station, New York, NY 10019

Little, Bernie *Boat Racing Driver, Owner*
%Hydroplanes Inc, 9117 Zoellner Dr, Cincinnati, OH 45251

Little, Cleavon *Actor*
%Susan Smith Assoc, 121 N San Vicente Blvd, Beverly Hills, CA 90211

Little, David *Football Player*
%Pittsburgh Steelers, Three Rivers Stadium, Pittsburg, PA 15212

Little, Floyd *Football Player*
2539 E Garvey, West Covina, CA 91791

Little, James D *Businessman*
%Columbia Gas System, 20 Montchanin Rd, Wilmington, DE 19807

Little, Rich *Comedian*
%Rich Little Enterprises, 21550 Oxnard St, #630, Woodland Hills, CA 91367

Little, Sally *Golfer*
%Ladies Professional Golf Assn, 2570 Volusia Ave, #B, Daytona Beach, FL 32114

Little, Tawny *Commentator*
%KABC-TV, 4151 Prospect Ave, Los Angeles, CA 90027

Littlefield, Clyde *Track Coach*
3702 Edgemont Dr, Austin, TX 78731

Littler, Gene *Golfer*
PO Box 1919, Rancho Santa Fe, CA 92067

Littleton, Harvey *Glass Sculptor*
Rt 1, Box 843, Spruce Pine, NC 28777

Litwack, Harry *Basketball Coach*
1818 Oakwynne Rd, Huntingdon Valley, PA 19006

Liut, Mike *Hockey Player*
%Washington Capitals, Capital Centre, Landover, MD 20785

Liuzzi, Robert C *Businessman*
%CF Industries, Salem Lake Dr, Long Grove, IL 60047

Lively, Pierce *Judge*
%US Court of Appeals, PO Box 1226, Louisville, KY 40422

Livingston, Barry *Actor*
11310 Blix St, North Hollywood, CA 91602

Livingston, James E *Vietnam Marine Corps Hero (CMH), General*
%Joint Staff, Pentagon, Room 2B906, Washington, DC 20318

Livingston, Robert L, Jr *Representative, LA*
701 Patterson St, New Orleans, LA 70114

Livingston, Stanley *Actor*
PO Box 1782, Studio City, CA 91604

LL Cool J *Singer*
%Def Jam/Columbia Records, 1801 Century Park West, Los Angeles, CA 90067

Llewellyn, John A *Astronaut*
%University of South Florida, Engineering Computing Dept, Tampa, FL 33620

Lloyd Weber, Andrew *Composer*
%Really Useful Group PLC, 20 Greek St, London W1V 5LF, England

Lloyd, Christopher *Actor*
%Managemint, PO Box 491246, Los Angeles, CA 90049

Lloyd, Emily *Actress*
%Triad Artists, 10100 Santa Monica Blvd, #1600, Los Angeles, CA 90067

Lloyd, Kathleen *Actress*
%Gores/Fields Agency, 10100 Santa Monica Blvd, #700, Los Angeles, CA 90067

Lloyd, Marilyn *Representative, TN*
%House of Representatives, Washington, DC 20515

Lloyd, Norman *Actor*
1813 Old Ranch Rd, Los Angeles, CA 90049

Lo Bianco, Tony *Actor*
1245 74th St, Brooklyn, NY 11228

Loach, Kenneth *Movie Director*
%Judy Daish Assoc, 83 Eastbourne Mews, London W2 6LQ, England

Lobkowicz, Nicholas *Philosopher*
Westpreussenstrasse 7, 8000 Munich 81, Germany

Locatelli, Paul L *Educator*
%Santa Clara University, President's Office, Santa Clara, CA 95053

Locher, Dick *Editorial Cartoonist*
%Chicago Tribune, 435 N Michigan Ave, Chicago, IL 60611

Lochner, Philip R, Jr *Government Official*
%Securities & Exchange Commission, 450 5th St NW, Washington, DC 20549

Locke, Charles S *Businessman*
%Morton International, 110 N Wacker Dr, Chicago, IL 60606

Locke, Sondra *Actress*
PO Box 69865, Los Angeles, CA 90069

Lockhart, Anne *Actress*
8577 Wonderland Ave, Los Angeles, CA 90046

Lockhart, Eugene *Football Player*
%Dallas Cowboys, 1 Cowboys Pkwy, Irving, TX 75063

Lockhart, June *Actress*
404 San Vicente Blvd, #208, Santa Monica, CA 90402

Locklear, Heather *Actress*
3208 W Cahuenga Blvd, PO Box 124, Los Angeles, CA 90068

Lockwood, Gary *Actor*
3083 1/2 Rambla Pacifica, Malibu, CA 90265

Lockwood, Julia *Actress*
112 Castlenan, London SW13, England

Loe, Harald A *Dentist*
%National Dental Research Institute, 9000 Rockville Pike, Bethesda, MD 20205

Loeb, Marshall *Editor*
%Money Magazine, Rockefeller Ctr, New York, NY 10020

Loeb, William *Editor*
%Nevada Star Ranch, 6995 Franktown Rd, Carson City, NV 89701

Loewhagen, Birger *Businessman*
%Sandvik AB Grp, Hamngatan 6, 103 97, Stockholm, Sweden

Lofgren, Nils *Singer*
1801 Century Park East, #1132, Los Angeles, CA 90067

Lofton, Fred C *Religious Leader*
%Progressive National Baptist Convention, 601 50th St NE, Washington, DC 20019

Lofton, James *Football Player*
%Buffalo Bills, 1 Bills Dr, Orchard Park, NY 14127

Loftus, Stephen F *Navy Admiral*
Deputy CNO, Logistics, Navy Department, Washington, DC 20350

Logan, David *Football Player*
%Tampa Bay Buccaneers, 1 Buccaneer Pl, Tampa, FL 33607

Logan, James K *Judge*
%US Court of Appeals, PO Box 790, 1 Patrons Plz, Olathe, KS 66061

Logan, James M *WW II Army Hero (CMH)*
801 Emmons, Kilgore, TX 75662

Logan, Johnny *Baseball Player*
6115 W Cleveland Ave, Milwaukee, WI 53219

Logan, Rayford W *Historian*
3001 Veazey Terr NW, Washington, DC 20008

Logan, Robert *Actor*
%BDP Assoc, 10637 Burbank Blvd, North Hollywood, CA 91601

Loggia, Robert *Actor*
10101 Angelo Cir, Beverly Hills, CA 90210

Loh, John M *Air Force General*
Commander, Tactical Air Command, Langley Air Force Base, VA 23665

Lolich, Mickey *Baseball Player*
6252 Robinhill, Washington, MI 48094

Lollobrigida, Gina *Actress*
Via Appino Antica 223, 00178 Rome, Italy

Lom, Herbert *Actor*
%William Morris Agency, 147-149 Wardour St, London W1V 37B, England

Lomax, Alan *Folk Song Collector, Producer*
%Cantometrics, 215 W 98th St, #12-E, New York, NY 10025

Lomax, Neil *Football Player*
%Phoenix Cardinals, PO Box 888, Phoenix, AZ 85001

Lombardi, John V *Educator*
%University of Florida, President's Office, Gainesville, FL 32611

Lombreglio, Ralph *Writer*
%Doubleday Press, 666 5th Ave, New York, NY 10103

Lonborg, Jim *Baseball Player*
498 First Parish Rd, Scituate, MA 02066

London, Irving Myer *Physician*
%Harvard-MIT Health Sciences, 77 Massachusetts Ave, Cambridge, MA 02139

London, Julie *Actress, Singer*
16075 Royal Oaks Rd, Encino, CA 91316

Long, Augustus C *Businessman*
Green Plains, North, VA 23128

Long, Chuck *Football Player*
%Detroit Lions, Silverdome, 1200 Featherstone Rd, Pontiac, MI 48057

Long, Dale W *Publisher*
%Working Woman Magazine, 342 Madison Ave, New York, NY 10173

Long, Franklin A *Chemist*
429 Warren Rd, Ithaca, NY 14850

Long, Howie *Football Player*
%Los Angeles Raiders, 332 Center St, El Segundo, CA 90245

Long, Jill *Representative, IN*
%House of Representatives, Washington, DC 20515

Long, Richard *Artist*
The Old School, Lower Failand, Bristol BS8 3SL, England

Long, Robert *Paleontologist*
%University of California, Paleontology Museum, Berkeley, CA 94720

Long, Robert L J *Navy Admiral*
%Camp H M Smith, HI 96861

Long, Russell B *Senator, LA*
%Finley Kumble Wagner, 1120 Connecticut Ave NW, Washington, DC 20036

Long, Sharon R *Molecular Geneticist*
%Stanford University, Biological Sciences Dept, Stanford, CA 94305

Long, Shelley *Actress*
905 Napoli Way, Pacific Palisades, CA 90272

Longbine, Robert F *Businessman*
%Champion International Corp, 1 Champion Plz, Stamford, CT 06921

Longden, Johnny *Thoroughbred Racing Jockey, Trainer*
Nar JL Ranch, 247 W Lemon Ave, Arcadia, CA 91006

L

Longhurst – Lorenzoni

Longhurst, Peter *Astronaut, England*
%Defense Ministry, 98 High Holburn, London WC1V 6LL, England

Longo, Robert *Artist*
%Editions Schellmann, 50 Greene St, New York, NY 10013

Longstreet, Stephen *Writer*
1133 Miradero Rd, Beverly Hills, CA 90210

Longuet-Higgins, Christopher *Chemist*
%Experimental Psych Lab, Sussex Univ, Falmer, Brighton BN1 9Q4, England

Lonning, Joseph E *Businessman*
%Kellogg Co, 235 Porter St, Battle Creek, MI 49016

Lonsbrough Porter, Anita *Swimmer*
6 Rivendell Gdns, Tettendall, Wolverhampton WV6 8SY, England

Loob, Hakan *Hockey Player*
%Calgary Flames, PO Box 1540, Station M, Calgary AB T2P 3B9, Canada

Loomis, Worth *Businessman*
%Dexter Corp, 1 Elm St, Windsor Locks, CT 06906

Looney, Donald L *Football Player*
1447 Wakefield, Houston, TX 77018

Looney, M O *Educator*
%University of Alaska, President's Office, Anchorage, AK 99508

Looney, Ralph *Editor*
%Rocky Mountain News, 400 W Colfax Ave, Denver, CO 80204

Looney, Wilton *Businessman*
%Genuine Parts Co, 2999 Circle 75 Pkwy, Atlanta, GA 30339

Lopat, Eddie *Baseball Player*
99 Oak Trail Rd, Hillsdale, NJ 07205

Lopes, Davey *Baseball Player*
16984 Ave de Santa Ynez, Pacific Palisades, CA 90272

Lopez, Al *Baseball Player*
3601 Beach Dr, Tampa, FL 33609

Lopez, Danny (Little Red) *Boxer*
1141 El Molino, Alhambra, CA 91801

Lopez, George *Comedian*
%Harvey Elkin Mgmt, 6515 Sunset Blvd, #305, Los Angeles, CA 90028

Lopez, Jose M *WW II Army Hero (CMH)*
3223 Hatton Dr, San Antonio, TX 78237

Lopez, Nancy *Golfer*
RR 2, Box 380-C, Albany, GA 31707

Lopez, Priscilla *Actress*
%Don Buchwald Assoc, 10 E 44th St, New York, NY 10017

Lopez, Robert Sabatino *Historian*
41 Richmond Ave, New Haven, CT 06515

Lopez-Cobos, Jesus *Conductor*
%Terry Harrison Artists, 9-A Penzance Pl, London W11 4PE, England

Lorant, Stefan *Writer*
PO Box 803, Lenox, MA 01240

Lord, Jack *Actor*
4999 Kahala Ave, Honolulu, HI 96816

Lord, M G *Editorial Cartoonist*
%Newsday, 235 Pinelawn, Melville, NY 11747

Lord, Marjorie *Actress*
1110 Maytor Pl, Beverly Hills, CA 90210

Lord, Michael *Artist*
14227 71st Ave, Surrey BC V3W 2K9, Canada

Lord, Walter *Writer*
116 E 68th St, New York, NY 10021

Loren, Sophia *Actress*
La Concordia Ranch, 1151 Hidden Valley Rd, Thousand Oaks, CA 91360

Lorengar, Pilar *Opera Singer*
19 Franken Allee 12, Berlin, Germany

Lorenz, Lee *Cartoonist*
%New Yorker Magazine, 25 W 43rd St, New York, NY 10036

Lorenzo, Francisco A *Businessman*
%Texas Air Corp, 333 Clay St, Houston, TX 77002

Lorenzoni, Andrea *Astronaut, Italy*
Via B Vergine del Carmelo 168, 00144 Rome, Italy

Loring, Gloria *Actress*
14746 Valley Vista Blvd, Sherman Oaks, CA 91423

Loring, Lynn *Actress*
506 N Camden Dr, Beverly Hills, CA 90210

Lorini, John C *Businessman*
%Shaklee Corp, 444 Market St, San Francisco, CA 94111

Lorring, Joan *Actress*
345 E 68th St, New York, NY 10021

Lorscheider, Aloisio Cardinal *Religious Leader*
%Arquidiocese de Fortaleza, CP D-6, 60.000 Fortaleza, Ceara, Brazil

Lortel, Lucille *Theater Producer*
%White Barn Theatre Foundation, Westport, CT 06880

Lortie, Louis *Concert Pianist*
%G Guibord, 4666 De Bullion, Montreal PQ H2T 1Y6, Canada

Loton, Brian Thorley *Businessman*
%Broken Hill Proprietary Co, 140 William St, Melbourne, Vic, Australia

Lott, Ronnie *Football Player*
%Los Angeles Raiders, 332 Center St, El Segundo, CA 90245

Lott, Trent *Senator, MS*
%US Senate, Washington, DC 20510

Loucks, Vernon R, Jr *Businessman*
%Baxter Travenol Laboratories, 1 Baxter Pkwy, Deerfield, IL 60015

Loudon, Aarnout A *Businessman*
%Akzo Group, Velperweg 76, 6800 LS Arnhem, Netherlands

Louganis, Greg *Diver*
PO Box 4068, Malibu, CA 90265

Loughery, Kevin *Basketball Player, Coach*
%Miami Heat, Miami Arena, Miami, FL 33136

Loughhead, Robert L *Businessman*
%Weirton Steel Corp, 400 Three Springs Dr, Weirton, WV 26062

Loughran, James N *Educator*
%Loyola Marymount University, Chancellor's Office, Los Angeles, CA 90045

Louis, John J, Jr *Diplomat, Publisher*
%Combined Communications Corp, 1 Northfield Plz, #510, Northfield, IL 60093

Louis-Dreyfus, Robert *Businessman*
%Saatchi & Saatchi Co, 80 Charlotte St, London W1, England

Louisa, Maria *Model*
%Next Model Mgmt, 115 E 57th St, #1540, New York, NY 10027

Louise, Tina *Actress*
9565 Lime Orchard Rd, Beverly Hills, CA 90210

Lounge, John M *Astronaut*
%NASA, Johnson Space Ctr, Houston, TX 77058

Lourdusamy, D Simon Cardinal *Religious Leader*
34 Via della Conciliazione, 00193 Rome, Italy

Lourie, Alan D *Judge*
%US Court of Appeals, 717 Madison Pl NW, Washington, DC 20439

Lousma, Jack *Astronaut*
PO Box 8689, Ann Arbor, MI 48107

Love, Ben F *Financier*
%Texas Commerce Bancshares Inc, 600 Travis St, Houston, TX 77002

Love, Gael *Editor*
%Connoisseur Magazine, 1790 Broadway, New York, NY 10019

Love, Howard M *Businessman*
%National Intergroup Inc, 20 Stanwix St, Pittsburgh, PA 15222

Love, John A *Governor, CO; Businessman*
%Ideal Basic Industries, 950 17th St, Denver, CO 80201

Love, Mike *Singer (Beach Boys)*
101 Mesa Ln, Santa Barbara, CA 93109

Love, Nancy *Editor*
%Mademoiselle Magazine, 350 Madison Ave, New York, NY 10017

Lovelace, Jon B, Jr *Financier*
%Capital Research Co, 333 S Hope St, Los Angeles, CA 90071

Loveless, Patty *Singer*
PO Box 24475, Nashville, TN 37202

Lovell, Bernard *Astronomer*
Quinta, Swettenham nr Congleton, Cheshire, England

Lovell, James A, Jr *Astronaut*
%Centel Business Systems, O'Hare Plz, 8725 Higgins Rd, Chicago, IL 60631

Lovell, James C *Businessman*
%Mercantile Stores Co, 1100 N Market St, Wilmington, DE 19801

Lovellette, Clyde *Basketball Player*
%Basketball Hall of Fame, PO Box 179, Springfield, MA 01101

Lovering, Thomas S *Geologist, Geochemist*
2663 Tallant Rd, Santa Barbara, CA 93105

Lovett, Lyle *Singer*
%MCA Records, 445 Park Ave, New York, NY 10022

Low, G David *Astronaut*
%NASA, Johnson Space Ctr, Houston, TX 77058

Low, George M *Space Scientist, Educator*
2005 Tibbits Ave, Troy, NY 12180

Low, Robert K *Businessman*
%Savin Corp, Columbus Ave, Valhalla, NY 10595

Low, Stephen *Diplomat*
1400 Key Blvd, #1200, Arlington, VA 22209

Lowe, Kevin *Hockey Player*
%Edmonton Oilers, Northlands Coliseum, Edmonton AL T5B 4M9, Canada

Lowe, Rob *Actor*
2817 Nichols Canyon Pl, Los Angeles, CA 90046

Lowe, Woodrow *Football Player*
%San Diego Chargers, 9449 Friars Rd, San Diego, CA 92108

Lowein, J C *Businessman*
%Mobil Oil Company Ltd, 54-60 Victoria St, London SW1E 6QB, England

Lowell, Carey *Actress*
%International Creative Mgmt, 8899 Beverly Blvd, Los Angeles, CA 90048

Lowenstein, Louis *Attorney, Educator*
1 Fountain Sq, Larchmont, NY 10538

Lowery, Joseph E *Civil Rights Activist*
%Southern Christian Leadership, 334 Auburn Ave NE, Atlanta, GA 30303

Lowery, Nick *Football Player*
%Kansas City Chiefs, 1 Arrowhead Dr, Kansas City, MO 64129

Lowery, William D *Representative, CA*
%House of Representatives, Washington, DC 20515

Lown, Bernard *Cardiologist*
%Harvard University Medical School, 25 Shattuck St, Boston, MA 02115

Lowry, Bates *Art Historian*
Lake Shore Rd, Essex, NY 12936

Lowry, Mike *Senator, WA*
%US Senate, Washington, DC 20510

Lowry, Oliver H *Pharmacologist*
%Washington University, Medical School, St Louis, MO 63110

Loy, Myrna *Actress*
425 E 63rd St, New York, NY 10021

Lozano, Silvia *Choreographer*
%Ballet Folklorico, 31 Esq Con Riva Palacio, Mexico City DF, Mexico

Lubachivsky, Myroslav Cardinal *Religious Leader*
%Vatican City, Rome, Italy

Lubbers, Ruud *Prime Minister*
%Prime Minister's Office, The Hague, Netherlands

Lubensky, Lloyd C *Businessman*
%Wheeling-Pittsburgh Steel Corp, 4 Gateway Ctr, Pittsburgh, PA 15230

Lubin, Arthur *Movie Director*
2881 Seattle Dr, Los Angeles, CA 90046

Lubovitch, Lar *Dancer, Choreographer*
17 W 18th, New York, NY 10011

Lubs, Herbert A *Medical Researcher (X Syndrome Gene)*
%University of Miami Med School, Pediatrics Dept, Box 016950, Miami, FL 33101

Lucas, George *Movie Director*
%LucasFilm Ltd, PO Box 2009, San Rafael, CA 94912

Lucas, Jack H *WW II Marine Corps Hero (CMH)*
PO Box 825, Bowie, MD 20715

Lucas, Jerry *Basketball Player*
340 Sunfish St, Foster City, CA 94404

Lucas, John *Basketball Player*
%Treatment/Recovery, Spring Branch Med Ctr, 8850 Long Point, Houston, TX 77055

Lucas, Maurice *Basketball Player, Coach*
%Portland Trail Blazers, 700 NE Multnomah St, Portland, OR 97232

Lucas, Richard J *Football Player*
%Pennsylvania State University, Athletic Dept, University Park, PA 16802

Lucas, Robert E, Jr *Economist*
5441 S Hyde Park Blvd, Chicago, IL 60615

Lucas, William *Government Official*
%Department of Justice, Constitution & 10th NW, Washington, DC 20530

Lucassen, Sigurd *Labor Leader*
%Brotherhood of Carpenters/Joiners, 101 Constitution NW, Washington, DC 20001

Lucchesini, Andrea *Concert Pianist*
%Columbia Artists Mgmt Inc, 165 W 57th St, New York, NY 10019

Lucci, Susan *Actress*
16 Carteret Pl, Garden City, NY 11530

Luce, Charles F *Businessman*
%Consolidated Edison Co, 4 Irving Pl, New York, NY 10003

Luce, Gordon C *Financier*
%Great American First Savings Bank, 600 "B" St, San Diego, CA 92183

Luce, Henry, III *Journalist*
4 Sutton Pl, New York, NY 10022

Lucey, Patrick J *Governor, WI*
6200 Hwy 57, Rt 3, Sturgeon Bay, WI 54235

Luciano, Robert P *Businessman*
%Schering-Plough Corp, 1 Giralda Farms, Madison, NJ 07940

Lucid, Shannon W *Astronaut*
%NASA, Johnson Space Ctr, Houston, TX 77058

Lucier, Francis P *Businessman*
%Black & Decker Manufacturing Co, 701 E Joppa Rd, Towson, MD 21204

Luck, Gary E *Army General*
Commanding General, XVIII Airborne Corps, Fort Bragg, NC 28307

Luckinbill, Lawrence *Actor*
470 Main St, #K, Ridgefield, CT 06877

Luckman, Charles *Architect*
%Luckman Management Co, 9220 Sunset Blvd, Los Angeles, CA 90069

Luckman, Sid *Football Player*
5303 St Charles Rd, Bellwood, IL 60104

Luckovich, Mike *Editorial Cartoonist*
%Atlanta Constitution, 72 Marietta St, Atlanta, GA 30303

Lucky, Robert *Research Scientist*
%AT&T Bell Laboratories, 295 N Maple Ave, Basking Ridge, NJ 07920

Ludington, John S *Businessman*
%Dow Corning Corp, 2200 W Salzburg Rd, Auburn, MI 48611

Ludlum, Robert *Writer*
%Dell Publishing, 1 Dag Hammarskjold Plz, New York, NY 10017

Ludwig, Christa *Opera Singer*
Rigistrasse 14, 6045 Meggen, Switzerland

Ludwig, Ken *Playwright*
%Steptoe & Johnson, 1330 Connecticut Ave NW, Washington, DC 20036

Ludwig, Robert H *Air Force General*
DCS/Comd, Cntrl, Comm & Comp, Hq USAF, Washington, DC 20330

Luecke, Joseph E *Businessman*
%Kemper Corp, Rt 22, Long Grove, IL 60049

Luening, Otto *Composer*
460 Riverside Dr, New York, NY 10027

Luerssen, Frank W *Businessman*
%Inland Steel Co, 30 W Monroe St, Chicago, IL 60603

Luft, Lorna *Actress*
%Lemond/Zetter Inc, 8370 Wilshire Blvd, #310, Beverly Hills, CA 90211

Lugar, Richard G *Senator, IN*
%US Senate, Washington, DC 20510

Lugbill, Jon *Kayak Athlete*
%American Canoe Assn, PO Box II90, Newington, VA 22122

Luigs, C Russell *Businessman*
%Global Marine Inc, 777 Eldridge Rd, Houston, TX 77079

L

Luisetti, Hank *Basketball Player*
%E F MacDonald Travel Co, 215 Market St, San Francisco, CA 94105

Luisi, James *Actor*
4319 Irvine Ave, Studio City, CA 91604

Luiso, Anthony *Businessman*
%Beatrice Companies, 2 N LaSalle St, Chicago, IL 60602

Lujack, Johnny *Football Player*
3700 Harrison St, Davenport, LA 52806

Lujan, Manuel, Jr *Secretary, Interior*
%Department of Interior, "C" & 18th Sts NW, Washington, DC 20240

Lukas, D Wayne *Thoroughbred Racing Trainer*
%Santa Anita Race Track, Barn 66, 285 W Huntington Dr, Arcadia, CA 91006

Lukas, J Anthony *Journalist, Writer*
890 West End Ave, #10-B, New York, NY 10025

Luke, David L, III *Businessman*
%Westvaco Corp, 299 Park Ave, New York, NY 10171

Luke, John A *Businessman*
%Westvaco Corp, 299 Park Ave, New York, NY 10171

Luken, Charles J *Representative, OH*
%House of Representatives, Washington, DC 20515

Lumbard, Edward *Judge*
%US Courthouse, Foley Sq, New York, NY 10007

Lumet, Sidney *Movie Director*
1380 Lexington Ave, New York, NY 10028

Lumley, Harry *Hockey Player*
680 4th Ave E, Owen Sound ON N4K 2N4, Canada

Luna, Barbara *Actress*
%Yvette Bikoff Agency, 8721 Santa Monica Blvd, #21, West Hollywood, CA 90067

Lund, Francis (Pug) *Football Player*
5229 Hollywood Rd, Edina, MN 55436

Lund, John *Actor*
2777 Coldwater Canyon, Beverly Hills, CA 90210

Lund, Olof *Businessman*
%Swedyards, Kyrogatan 35, 401 26 Goteborg, Sweden

Lund, Victor L *Businessman*
%American Stores Co, 709 E South Temple, Salt Lake City, UT 84102

Lundberg, George D *Editor, Physician*
%JAMA Magazine, 535 N Dearborn St, Chicago, IL 60610

Lundberg, Henry *Businessman*
%Sventskt Stal, PO Box 16344, 10326 Stockholm, Sweden

Lunden, Joan *Commentator*
%"Good Morning America" Show, ABC-TV, 77 W 66th St, New York, NY 10023

Lundgren, Dolph *Actor*
2079 Mount Olympus Dr, Los Angeles, CA 90046

Lundquist, Verne *Sportscaster*
%CBS-TV, Sports Dept, 51 W 52nd St, New York, NY 10019

Lundsgaard, Dennis *Businessman*
%Agri Industries, PO Box 4887, Des Moines, IA 50306

Lungren, Daniel E *Representative, CA*
5514 Britton Dr, Long Beach, CA 90815

Luns, Joseph M A H *Government Official, Holland*
%Secretary General of NATO, Blvd Leopold III, Brussels, Belgium

Lupberger, Edwin A *Businessman*
%Entergy Corp, 225 Baronne St, New Orleans, LA 70112

Lupino, Ida *Actress*
%Mary Ann Anderson, 13451 Erwin St, Van Nuys, CA 91401

Lupino, Ida *Actress*
23388 Mulholland Rd, Woodland Hills, CA 91364

LuPone, Patti *Singer, Actress*
%International Creative Mgmt, 8899 Beverly Blvd, Los Angeles, CA 90038

Lupton, John *Actor*
2528 Tilden Ave, Los Angeles, CA 90064

Lupu, Radu *Concert Pianist*
%Terry Harrison Artists, 9-A Penzance Pl, London W11 4PE, England

Lupus, Peter *Actor*
11375 Dona Lisa Dr, Studio City, CA 91604

Lurie, Alison *Writer*
%Cornell University, English Dept, Ithaca, NY 14850

Lurie, Ron *Mayor*
%Mayor's Office, City Hall, 400 Stewart St, Las Vegas, NV 89101

Lurton, H William *Businessman*
%Jostens Inc, 5501 Norman Center Dr, Minneapolis, MN 55437

Lussi, Gustave F *Figure Skating Coach*
%Swiss Meadows, Averyville Rd, Lake Placid, NY 12946

Lustiger, Jean-Marie Cardinal *Religious Leader*
Archeveche de Paris, 32 Rue Barbet de Jouy, 75007 Paris, France

Lutali, A P *Governor, AS*
%Governor's Office, Government Offices, Pago Pago, Tutuila, AS 90799

Luter, Joseph W, III *Businessman*
%Smithfield Foods, 1777 N Kent St, Arlington, VA 22209

Lutoslawski, Witold *Composer, Conductor*
Ul Smiala 39, 01-523 Warsaw, Poland

Lutz, Bob *Tennis Player*
%US Tennis Assn, 1212 Ave of Americas, New York, NY 10036

Lux, John H *Businessman*
%Ametek Inc, 410 Park Ave, New York, NY 10022

Lux, Philip G *Businessman*
%Coachmen Industries, 601 E Beardsley Ave, Elkhart, IN 46515

Luyten, Willem Jacob *Astronomer*
%University of Minnesota, Space Science Ctr, Minneapolis, MN 55455

Luyties, Ricci *Volleyball Player*
%USA Volleyball Team, National Team Ctr, PO Box 24219, San Diego, CA 92124

Luzinski, Greg *Baseball Player*
320 Jackson Rd, Medford, NJ 08055

Lwoff, Andre *Nobel Medicine Laureate*
69 Ave de Suffren, 75007 Paris, France

Lyakhov, Vladimir *Cosmonaut*
141 160 Svyosdny Gorodok, Moskovskoi Oblasti, Potchta Kosmonavtov, Russia

Lydon, Jimmy *Actor*
2746 Belden Dr, Los Angeles, CA 90068

Lydon, Thomas J *Judge*
%US Claims Court, 717 Madison Pl NW, Washington, DC 20005

Lyet, J Paul *Businessman*
%Sperry Corp, 1290 Ave of Americas, New York, NY 10104

Lyght, Todd *Football Player*
%Los Angeles Rams, 2327 W Lincoln Ave, Anaheim, CA 92801

Lyke, James P *Religious Leader*
%Archbishop of Atlanta, 680 W Peachtree St NW, Atlanta, GA 30308

Lyle, Sandy *Golfer*
%Professional Golfers Assn, PO Box 109601, Palm Beach Gardens, FL 33410

Lyle, Sparky *Baseball Player*
17 Signal Hill Dr, Voorhees, NJ 08043

Lyman, Richard W *Foundation Executive, Educator*
%Stanford University, International Studies Institute, Stanford, CA 94305

Lympany, Moura *Concert Pianist*
%Jacques Leiser Mgmt, Dorchester Towers, 155 W 68th St, New York, NY 10023

Lynagh, James T *Businessman*
%Multimedia Inc, 305 S Main St, Greenville, SC 29601

Lynam, Jim *Basketball Coach*
%Philadelphia 76ers, PO Box 25040, Veterans Stadium, Philadelphia, PA 19147

Lynch, Allen J *Vietnam War Army Hero (CMH)*
438 Belle Plaine Ave, Gurnee, IL 60031

Lynch, Charles A *Businessman*
%Saga Corp, 1 Saga Ln, San Francisco, CA 94025

Lynch, David K *Movie Director*
PO Box 93624, Los Angeles, CA 90093

Lynch, Dick *Football Player*
203 Manor Rd, Douglaston, NY 11363

Lynch, Frank W *Businessman*
%Northrop Corp, 1840 Century Park East, Los Angeles, CA 90067

Lynch, Jim *Football Player*
1009 W 67th St, Kansas City, MO 64113

Lynch, John *Prime Minister, Ireland*
21 Garville Ave, Rathgar, Dublin 6, Ireland

Lynch, Kelly *Actress, Model*
%Creative Artists Agency, 9830 Wilshire Blvd, Beverly Hills, CA 90212

Lynch, Peter *Financier*
%Fidelity Magellan Fund, 82 Devonshire St, Boston, MA 02109

Lynde, Phil *Rodeo Rider*
%General Delivery, George West, TX 78022

Lynden-Bell, Donald *Astronomer*
Institute of Astronomy, Madingley Rd, Cambridge CB3 0HA, England

Lynds, Roger *Astronomer*
%Kitt Peak National Observatory, Tucson, AZ 85726

Lyne, Adrian *Movie Director*
2825 Seattle Dr, Los Angeles, CA 90046

Lyngstad, Anni-Frida *Singer (ABBA)*
%ABBA, PO Box 26072, 100 41 Stockholm, Sweden

Lynley, Carol *Actress*
PO Box 2190, Malibu, CA 90265

Lynn Salomon, Janet *Figure Skater*
4215 Marsh Ave, Rockford, IL 61111

Lynn, Fred *Baseball Player*
801 Iverness Dr, Rancho Mirage, CA 92270

Lynn, John W *Businessman*
%Woolworth Corp, 233 Broadway, New York, NY 10279

Lynn, Loretta *Singer*
PO Box 120369, Nashville, TN 37212

Lynn, Vera *Actress, Singer*
4 Sandhurst Ave, Bispham, Blackpool, Lancs FY2 9AV, England

Lynne, Gillian *Dance Director, Choreographer*
%Lean2 Productions, 18 Rutland St, Knightsbridge, London SW7 1EF, England

Lynne, Jeff *Singer*
2621 Deep Canyon Dr, Beverly Hills, CA 90210

Lyon, Lisa *Body Builder*
%Jungle Gym, PO Box 585, Santa Monica, CA 90406

Lyon, Sue *Actress*
%Charter Mgmt, 9000 Sunset Blvd, #1112, Los Angeles, CA 90069

Lyon, Wayne B *Businessman*
%Masco Corp, 21001 Van Born Rd, Taylor, MI 48180

Lyon, William *Businessman*
%AirCal Inc, 3636 Birch St, Newport Beach, CA 92668

Lyons, Daniel J *Businessman*
%Guardian Life Insurance, 201 Park Ave, New York, NY 10003

Lyons, J Chisholm *Businessman*
%Allen Grp, 534 Broad Hollow Rd, Melville, NY 11747

Lyons, James F *Businessman*
%American Medical International, 414 N Camden Dr, Beverly Hills, CA 90210

Lyons, Robert F *Actor*
%LaRocca Entertainment, 3800 Barham Blvd, Los Angeles, CA 90068

Lyons, William P *Businessman*
%Ashton-Tate Corp, 20101 Hamilton Ave, Torrance, CA 90502

Lyst, John H *Editor*
%Indianapolis Star, 307 N Pennsylvania St, Indianapolis, IN 46204

Lyubimov, Yuri *Theater Director*
%Royal Opera, Covent Garden, Bow St, London WC2, England

M'Bow, Amadou-Mahtar *Government Official, Senegal*
BP 5276, Dakar-Fann, Senegal

Ma, Yo-Yo *Concert Cellist*
%International Creative Mgmt, 40 W 57th St, New York, NY 10019

Maag, Peter *Conductor*
%Dina Thoma-Tennenbaum, 23 Jennershausweg, 3098 Koniz-Bern, Switzerland

Maas, Bill *Football Player*
%Kansas City Chiefs, 1 Arrowhead Dr, Kansas City, MO 64129

Maas, Peter *Writer*
%Sterling Lord Agency, 660 Madison Ave, New York, NY 10021

Maazel, Lorin *Conductor, Concert Violinist*
%Pittsburgh Symphony, 600 Penn Ave, Pittsburgh, PA 15222

Mabbs, Edward C *Businessman*
%L B Foster Co, 415 Holiday Dr, Pittsburgh, PA 15220

Mabee, John *Thoroughbred Racing Executive*
4346 54th St, San Diego, CA 92115

Mabuchi, Tatsuo *Businessman*
%Mitsubishi Oil Co, 1-2-4 Toranomon, Minatoku, Tokyo 150, Japan

MacAfee, Ken *Football Player*
26 W Elm Terr, Brockton, MA 02401

MacAlister, Sue E *Financier*
%Nafco Financial Grp, 5801 Pelican Bay Blvd, Naples, FL 33940

MacAllister, Jack A *Businessman*
%US West Inc, 7800 E Orchard Rd, Englewood, CO 80111

MacArthur, Douglas, II *Diplomat*
2101 Connecticut Ave NW, Washington, DC 20008

MacArthur, James *Actor*
3003 Kalakaua, #5-B, Honolulu, HI 96815

MacArthur, John B *Publisher*
%Harper's Magazine, 2 Park Ave, New York, NY 10016

Macauley, Ed *Basketball Player*
1455 Reauville Dr, St Louis, MO 63122

MacBain, Gavin K *Businessman*
345 Park Ave, New York, NY 10022

Macchio, Ralph *Actor*
451 Deerpark Ave, Dix Hills, NY 17746

MacCorkindale, Simon *Actor*
%Agency for Performing Arts, 9000 Sunset Blvd, #1200, Los Angeles, CA 90069

MacCready, Paul B *Aeronautical Engineer*
%AeroVironment Inc, 222 E Huntington Dr, Monrovia, CA 91016

MacDermot, Galt *Composer*
%MacDermot Assoc, 12 Silver Lake Rd, Staten Island, NY 10301

Macdonald, Donald A *Businessman*
%Dow Jones Co, 200 Liberty St, New York, NY 10281

MacDonald, Gordon J F *Geophysicist*
%Mitre Corp, 1820 Dolly Madison Blvd, McLean, VA 22102

MacDonald, James G *Businessman*
%TIAA-CREF, 730 3rd Ave, New York, NY 10017

MacDonald, Ray W *Businessman*
%Burroughs Corp, World Bldgs, Detroit, MI 48232

MacEachen, Allan J *Government Official, Canada*
RR 1, Whycocomagh, NS, Canada

MacGraw, Ali *Actress*
27040 Malibu Cove Colony Dr, Malibu, CA 90265

MacGregor, George L *Businessman*
6322 Westchester Dr, Dallas, TX 75205

MacGregor, Ian K *Government Official, England*
%National Coal Board, Hobart House, Grosvenor Pl, London W1, England

Macharski, Franciszak Cardinal *Religious Leader*
%Metropolita Krakowski, Ul Franciszkanska 3, 31-004 Krakow, Poland

Machiz, Leon *Businessman*
%Avnet Inc, 767 5th Ave, New York, NY 10153

Machover, Tod *Composer*
%Massachusetts Institute of Technology, Media Laboratory, Cambridge, MA 02139

MacInnis, Al *Hockey Player*
%Calgary Flames, PO Box 1540, Station M, Calgary AB T2P 3B9, Canada

MacIntock, Craig *Cartoonist (Professor Doodle's)*
%Tribune Media Services, 34 E Concord St, Orlando, FL 32801

MacIntyre, Malcolm A *Businessman*
60 Mamaroneck Rd, Scarsdale, NY 10583

MacIver, Loren *Artist*
61 Perry St, New York, NY 10014

Mack, Connie, III *Senator, FL*
1342 Colonial Blvd, #27, Fort Myers, FL 33907

Mack, John E *Psychiatrist*
%Harvard University School of Medicine, 25 Shattuck St, Boston, MA 02115

Mack, Kevin *Football Player*
%Cleveland Browns, Cleveland Stadium, Cleveland, OH 44114

MacKay, Buddy *Representative, FL*
%House of Representatives, Washington, DC 20515

Mackay, Harvey *Writer*
%Mackay Envelope Corp, 2100 Elm St SE, Minneapolis, MN 55414

Macke, Richard C *Navy Admiral*
Director, Command/Control/Communications, Joint Staff, Washington, DC 20318

MacKenzie, Giselle *Singer*
13726 Magnolia Blvd, Sherman Oaks, CA 91423

MacKenzie, Kelvin *Editor*
%The Sun, PO Box 481, Virginia St, London EC1 9BD, England

MacKenzie, Patch *Actress*
%Harry Gold Assoc, 3500 W Olive Ave, #1400, Burbank, CA 91505

Mackerras, Charles *Conductor*
10 Hamilton Terr, London NW8 9UG, England

Mackey, George W *Mathematician*
25 Coolidge Hill Rd, Cambridge, MA 02138

Mackie, Bob *Fashion Designer*
550 7th Ave, New York, NY 10018

Mackin, B John *Businessman*
%Zapata Corp, Zapata Tower, PO Box 4240, Houston, TX 77210

MacKinnon, George E *Judge*
%US Courthouse, 3rd & Constitution Ave NW, Washington, DC 20001

Macklin, David *Actor*
%Dale Garrick Agency, 8831 Sunset Blvd, #402, Los Angeles, CA 90069

Macklin, Gordon S *Financier*
%Hambrecht & Quist Grp, 235 Montgomery St, San Francisco, CA 94104

Mackovic, John *Football Coach*
%University of Texas, Athletic Dept, Austin, TX 78712

MacLachlan, Janet *Actress*
1919 N Taft Ave, Los Angeles, CA 90068

MacLachlan, Kyle *AActor*
828 Venezia, Venice, CA 90291

MacLaine, Shirley *Actress*
25200 Old Malibu Rd, Malibu, CA 90265

MacLane, Saunders *Mathematician*
5712 S Dorchester Ave, Chicago, IL 60637

MacLaury, Bruce K *Educator*
%Brookings Institute, 1775 Massachusetts Ave NW, Washington, DC 20036

MacLean, Steve *Astronaut, Canada*
%National Research Council, Montreal Rd, Ottawa ON K1A 0R6, Canada

MacLeod, Gavin *Actor*
%David Shapira Assoc, 15301 Ventura Blvd, #345, Sherman Oaks, CA 91403

MacLeod, John *Basketball Coach*
%University of Notre Dame, Athletic Dept, Notre Dame, IN 46556

MacLeod, Robert *Football Player*
110 Malibu Colony Dr, Malibu, CA 90265

MacMahon, Brian *Physician*
89 Warren St, Needham, MA 02192

MacMillan, Kenneth *Choreographer*
%Royal Ballet, Convent Gdn, Bow St, London WL2E 7QA, England

MacNabb, B Gordon *Missile Engineer*
PO Box 312, West Yellowstone, MT 59758

MacNaughton, Angus A *Businessman*
%Genstar Corp, 1177 W Hastings St, Vancouver BC, Canada

MacNaughton, Donald S *Businessman*
109 Lynwood Terr, Nashville, TN 37203

Macnee, Patrick *Actor*
%Michael Ladkin, 11 Garrick St, London WC2, England

MacNeil, Cornell *Opera Singer*
%Columbia Artists Mgmt, 165 W 57th St, New York, NY 10019

MacNeil, Robert *Commentator*
%WNET-13, 356 W 58th St, New York, NY 10019

MacNelly, Jeff *Editorial Cartoonist*
333 E Grace St, Richmond, VA 23219

Macomber, George B H *Skier*
Russia Wharf, 530 Atlantic Ave, Boston, MA 02210

Macomber, John D *Businessman, Financier*
%Export-Import Bank, 811 Vermont Ave NW, Washington, DC 20571

Macomber, William B, Jr *Diplomat, Museum Official*
993 5th Ave, New York, NY 10028

MacPhail, Leland S, Jr *Baseball Executive*
%American League, 350 Park Ave, New York, NY 10022

MacPhee, Donald A *Educator*
%State University of New York, President's Office, Fredonia, NY 14063

MacPherson, Dick *Football Coach*
%New England Patriots, Sullivan Stadium, Foxboro, MA 02035

MacPherson, Duncan I *Editorial Cartoonist*
%Toronto Daily Star, 1 Yonge St, Toronto ON M5E 1E6, Canada

Macpherson, Elle *Model*
%Ford Model Agency, 344 E 59th St, New York, NY 10022

MacRae, Meredith *Actress*
13659 Victory Blvd, #588, Van Nuys, CA 91401

MacRae, Sheila *Actress, Singer*
%Talent Mgmt International, 9110 Sunset Blvd, Los Angeles, CA 90069

MacTaggart, Barry *Businessman*
%Pfizer Inc, 235 E 42nd St, New York, NY 10017

MacWilliams, John J *Businessman*
%Colonial Penn Grp, 5 Penn Center Plz, Philadelphia, PA 19181

Macy, Bill *Actor*
10130 Angelo Cir, Beverly Hills, CA 90210

Macy, Kyle *Basketball Player*
%Chicago Bulls, 333 N Michigan Ave, Chicago, IL 60601

Madden, D S *Religious Leader*
%American Baptist Assn, 4605 N State Line, Texarkana, TX 75503

Madden, John *Football Coach, Sportscaster*
%CBS-TV, Sports Dept, 201 E 50th St, New York, NY 10022

Madden, Kevin *Publisher*
%Self Magazine, 350 Madison Ave, New York, NY 10017

Madden, Richard B *Businessman*
%Potlatch Corp, 1 Maritime Plz, San Francisco, CA 94111

Maddox, David M *Army General*
Commanding General, V Corps, US Army Europe & 7th Army, APO, AE 09079

Maddox, Lester *Governor, GA*
3155 Johnson Ferry Rd NE, Marietta, GA 30062

Maddox, Rose *Singer*
749 E Nevada St, Ashland, OR 97520

Maddux, Greg *Baseball Player*
%Chicago Cubs, Wrigley Field, Chicago, IL 60613

Madigan, Amy *Actress*
%Triad Artists, 10100 Santa Monica Blvd, #1600, Los Angeles, CA 90067

Madigan, Edward R *Secretary, Agriculture*
%Department of Agriculture, 14th & Independence Ave SW, Washington, DC 20250

Madigan, John W *Publisher*
%Tribune Co, 435 N Michigan Ave, Chicago, IL 60611

Madison, Guy *Actor*
35022 1/2 Ave "H", Yucaipa, CA 92399

Madlock, Bill *Baseball Player*
453 E Decatur St, Decatur, IL 62521

Madonna *Singer*
930 Stradella Rd, Los Angeles, CA 90077

Madonna, Jon C *Businessman*
%KPMG Peat Marwick, 345 Park Ave, New York, NY 10022

Madrazo, Ignacio N *Medical Researcher*
%Specialities Hospital, La Raza Medical Ctr, Mexico City, Mexico

Madsen, Loren *Sculptor*
428 Broome St, New York, NY 10013

Madsen, Virginia *Actress*
%Rodkin Pett Co, 8730 Santa Monica Blvd, #1, Los Angeles, CA 90069

Maeda, Kazuo *Businessman*
%Mitsui Engineering & Shipbuilding, 5-6-4 Tsukiji, Tokyo 104, Japan

Maegle, Richard *Football Player*
%Tides II Motor Inn, 6700 S Main, Houston, TX 77005

Maehata Hyodo, Hideko *Swimmer*
1294 Nagamorikuramae, Gifu City, Japan

Maekawa, Kunio *Architect*
8 Honshiocho, Shinjukuku, Tokyo, Japan

Maggio, Kirk *Football Player*
%Green Bay Packers, 1265 Lombardi Ave, Green Bay, WI 54303

Magill, Frank J *Judge*
%US Court of Appeals, Federal Bldg, 657 2nd Ave N, Fargo, ND 58102

Magilton, Gerald E *Astronaut*
%RCA Astro-Electronics, PO Box 800, Princeton, NJ 08540

Maglie, Sal *Baseball Player*
77 Morningside Dr, Grand Island, NY 14072

Magnan, Larry B *Businessman*
%Westin Hotels Co, Westin Building, 2001 6th Ave, Seattle, WA 98121

Magnus, Edie *Commentator*
%ABC-TV, News Dept, 1717 De Sales St NW, Washington, DC 20036

Magoon, Bob *Powerboat Racing Driver*
1688 Meridian Ave, Miami Beach, FL 33139

Magruder, Jeb S *Government Official, Religious Leader*
%First Presbyterian Church, 171 Market, Lexington, KY 40503

Maguire, Bassett *Botanist*
%New York Botanical Garden, Botanical Sq, Bronx, NY 10458

Maguire, Deirdre *Model*
%Elite Model Mgmt, 111 E 22nd St, New York, NY 10010

Maguire, John D *Educator*
%Claremont Colleges, President's Office, Claremont, CA 91711

Maguire, Michael *Actor*
%Agency for Performing Arts, 9000 Sunset Blvd, #1200, Los Angeles, CA 90069

Magyar, Gabriel *Concert Cellist*
708 Dover Pl, Champaign, IL 61820

Mahaffey, John *Golfer*
3100 Richmond Ave, #500, Houston, TX 77098

Mahal, Taj *Musician, Composer*
%Folklore Productions, 1671 Appian Way, Santa Monica, CA 90401

Mahan, Larry *Rodeo Rider*
PO Box 41, Camp Verde, TX 78010

Mahanes, Walter J *Businessman*
%Minstar Inc, 1215 Marshall St NE, Minneapolis, MN 55413

Maharis, George *Actor*
13150 Mulholland Dr, Beverly Hills, CA 90210

Maharishi Mahesh Yogi *Religious Leader*
%Institute of World Leadership, Maharishi University, Fairfield, IA 52556

Mahathir Bin Mohamed *Prime Minister, Malaysia*
%Prime Minister's Office, Kuala Lumpur, Malaysia

Mahdi Mohamed, Ali *President, Somali*
%President's Office, Magadishu, Somalia

Maher, Bill *Comedian*
%Brillstein Co, 9200 Sunset Blvd, #428, Los Angeles, CA 90069

Maher, John F *Financier*
%Great Western Financial Corp, 8484 Wilshire Blvd, Beverly Hills, CA 90211

Mahfouz, Naguib *Nobel Literature Laureate*
%Cinema Organization, TV Building, Mapsero St, Cairo, Egypt

Mahfouz, Sheikh Salem Ahmed Bin *Financier*
%National Commercial Bank, PO Box 3555, Jedda 21481, Saudi Arabia

Mahoney, David J *Businessman*
277 Park Ave, New York, NY 10017

Mahoney, Edward P *Financier*
%American Savings & Loan Assn of Florida, 17801 NW 2nd Ave, Miami, FL 33169

Mahoney, J Daniel *Judge*
%US Court of Appeals, PO Box 3620, Milford, CT 06460

Mahoney, Richard J *Businessman*
%Monsanto Co, 800 N Lindbergh Blvd, St Louis, MO 63167

Mahoney, Robert W *Businessman*
%Diebold Inc, 818 Mulberry Rd SE, Canton, OH 44711

Mahony, Roger M Cardinal *Religious Leader*
%Archdiocese of Los Angeles, 1531 W 9th St, Los Angeles, CA 90015

Mahorn, Rick *Basketball Player*
%Philadelphia 76ers, Veterans Stadium, PO Box 25040, Philadelphia, PA 19147

Mahovlich, Frank *Hockey Player*
%Mahovlich Travel, 2066 Avenue Rd, Toronto ON M5M 4A6, Canada

Mahre, Phil *Skier*
Rt 9, Box 715-M, Yakima, WA 98901

Mahre, Steve *Skier*
%US Ski Assn, PO Box 100, Park City, UT 84060

Maier, Henry W *Mayor*
1324 W Birch St, Milwaukee, WI 53209

Maier, Sepp *Soccer Player*
Parkstrasse 62, 8011 Anzing, Germany

Mailer, Norman *Writer*
142 Columbia Heights, Brooklyn, NY 11201

Maines, Bruce *Businessman*
%Safeco Corp, Safeco Plz, Seattle, WA 98185

Maisel, Jay *Photographer*
190 The Bowery, New York, NY 10012

Maisel, Sherman J *Economist*
2164 Hyde St, San Francisco, CA 94109

Maisonrouge, Jacques G *Businessman*
%Liquid Air Corp, 1 Embarcadero Ctr, San Francisco, CA 94111

Majdarzavyn Ganzorig *Cosmonaut, Mongolia*
Lyotchik Kosmonaut MNR, Ulan Bator, Mongolia

Majerle, Dan *Basketball Player*
%Phoenix Suns, 2910 N Central, Phoenix, AZ 85012

Majerus, Rick *Basketball Coach*
%University of Utah, Athletic Dept, Salt Lake City, UT 84112

Majkowski, Don *Football Player*
%Green Bay Packers, 1265 Lombardi Ave, Green Bay, WI 54303

Majoni, Mario *Water Polo Player*
Via C N Rosselli 15, 16145 Genoa, Italy

Major, John *Prime Minister, England*
%Prime Minister's Office, 10 Downing St, London SW1A 2AA, England

Majors, Johnny *Football Player, Coach*
Beechwood Rd, Rt 23, Knoxville, TN 37920

Majors, Lee *Actor*
23826 Malibu Rd, Malibu, CA 90265

Makarov, Oleg G *Cosmonaut*
141 160 Svyosdny Gorodok, Moskovskoi Oblasti, Potchta Kosmonavtov, Russia

Makarova, Natalia *Ballerina*
%Herbert Breslin Inc, 119 W 57th St, New York, NY 10019

Maki, Fumihiko *Architect*
5-16-22 Higashi-Gotanda, Shinagawaku, Tokyo, Japan

Makino, Koji *Financier*
%Sumitomo Trust & Banking Ltd, 5-15 Kitahama, Osaka 540, Japan

Makita, Hisao *Businessman*
%Nippon Kokan, 1-1-2 Marunouchi, Chiyodaku, Tokyo 100, Japan

Mako *Actor*
%Fred Amsel Assoc, 6310 San Vicente Blvd, #407, Los Angeles, CA 90048

Mako, C Gene *Tennis Player*
430 S Burnside Ave, #M-C, Los Angeles, CA 90036

Maksymiuk, Jerzy *Conductor*
%BBC Scottish Symphony, Queen Margaret Dr, Glasgow G12 8BC, Scotland

M

Maktum, Sheikh Rashid bin Said al- *Prime Minister, United Arab Emirates*
%Royal Palace, Dubai, United Arab Emirates

Malandro, Kristina *Actress*
10647 Wilkins Ave, #307, Los Angeles, CA 90024

Malara, Anthony C *Television Executive*
%CBS-TV Network, 51 W 52nd St, New York, NY 10019

Malarchuk, Clint *Hockey Player*
%Quebec Nordiques, 2205 Ave du Colisee, Charlesbourg PQ G1L 4W7, Canada

Malden, Karl *Actor*
1845 Mandeville Canyon, Los Angeles, CA 90049

Malee, Chompoo *Fashion Designer*
%Hino & Malee Inc, 3701 N Ravenswood Ave, Chicago, IL 60613

Maleeva, Katerina *Tennis Player*
Mladostrasse I, #45, NH 14, Sofia 1174, Bulgaria

Maleeva, Manuela *Tennis Player*
%Women's Tennis Assn, 133 1st St NE, St Petersburg, FL 33701

Malek, Frederic V *Businessman*
%Northwest Airlines Inc, Minneapolis-St Paul Airport, St Paul, MN 55111

Malenick, Donal H *Businessman*
%Worthington Industries, 1205 Dearborn Dr, Columbus, OH 43085

Maletz, Herbert N *Judge*
101 W Lombard St, Baltimore, MD 21201

Malfitano, Catherine *Opera Singer*
%Metropolitan Opera Assn, Lincoln Ctr, New York, NY 10023

Malick, Wendy *Actress*
%Flick East-West Talents, 1608 N La Palmas, Los Angeles, CA 90068

Malicky, Neal *Educator*
%Baldwin-Wallace College, President's Office, Berea, OH 44017

Malietoa Tanumafili II *King, Western Samoa*
%Government House, Vailima, Apia, Western Samoa

Malinsky, Aaron *Businessman*
%Waldbaum Inc, Hemlock & Boulevard, Central Islip, NY 11722

Maliponte, Adrianna *Opera Singer*
%Gorlinsky Promotions, 35 Darer, London W1, England

Maljers, Floris *Businessman*
%Unilever PLC, PO Box 68, Unilever House, London EC4P 4BQ, England

Malkan, Matthew A *Astronomer*
%Steward Observatory, University of Arizona, Tucson, AZ 85721

Malkin, John *Businessman*
%JMB Realty Corp, 875 N Michigan Ave, Chicago, IL 60611

Malkovich, John *Actor*
346 S Lucerne Blvd, Los Angeles, CA 90020

Mallary, Robert *Sculptor*
PO Box 97, Conway, MA 01341

Malle, Louis *Movie Director*
Le Couel, 46260 Limogne en Quercy, France

Mallea, Eduardo *Writer*
Posadas 1120, Buenos Aires, Argentina

Mallender, William H *Businessman*
%Talley Industries, 2702 N 44th St, Phoenix, AZ 85008

Malley, Kevin J *Businessman*
%Desert Inn Hotel & Casino, 3145 Las Vegas Blvd S, Las Vegas, NV 89109

Mallory, Glynn C *Army General*
Commanding General, 6th US Army, Presidio of San Francisco, CA 94129

Mallory, Wilhelm A *Businessman*
%Wickes Companies, 3340 Ocean Park Blvd, Santa Monica, CA 90405

Malloy, Edward A *Educator*
%University of Notre Dame, President's Office, Notre Dame, IN 46556

Malloy, James B *Businessman*
%Jefferson Smurfit Corp, 401 Alton St, Alton, IL 62002

Maloff, Sam *Furniture Designer*
PO Box 51, Alta Loma, CA 91701

Malone, James W *Religious Leader*
%National Catholic Bishops Conference, 1312 Massachusetts, Washington, DC 20005

Malone, Jeff *Basketball Player*
%Utah Jazz, 5 Triad Ctr, Salt Lake City, UT 84180

Malone, John C *Television Executive*
%Tele-Communications, PO Box 22595, Wellshire Station, Denver, CO 80222

Malone, Karl *Basketball Player*
%Utah Jazz, 5 Triad Ctr, Salt Lake City, UT 84180

Malone, Moses *Basketball Player*
%Milwaukee Bucks, Bradley Center, 1001 N 4th St, Milwaukee, WI 53203

Malone, Nancy *Actress*
%Lilac Productions, 4507 Auckland Ave, North Hollywood, CA 91602

Malone, Thomas F *Geophysicist*
6421 Sunset Ln, Indianapolis, IN 46208

Maloney, Dan *Hockey Coach*
%Winnipeg Jets, 15-1430 Maroons Rd, Winnipeg MB R3G 0L5, Canada

Maloney, Don *Hockey Player*
%New York Rangers, Madison Square Grdn, 4 Pennsylvania Plz, New York, NY 10004

Maloney, George T *Businessman*
%C R Bard Inc, 731 Central Ave, Murray Hill, NJ 07974

Maloney, Jim *Baseball Player*
2217 W Keats, Fresno, CA 93705

Maloney, William R *Marine Corps General*
%Navy Mutual Aid Assn, Board of Directors, Arlington Annex, Washington, DC 20370

Malott, Adele *Editor*
%Friendly Exchange Magazine, 1999 Shepard Rd, St Paul, MN 55116

Malott, Deane W *Educator*
322 Wait Ave, Ithaca, NY 14853

Malott, Robert H *Businessman*
%FMC Corp, 200 E Randolph Dr, Chicago, IL 60601

Maloy, Robert *Librarian*
%Smithsonian Institution Libraries, Washington, DC 20560

Malozemoff, Plato *Businessman*
%Newmont Mining Corp, 200 Park Ave, New York, NY 10166

Maltby, Richard E, Jr *Lyricist*
83 Perry St, #2, New York, NY 10014

Malyshev, Yuri *Cosmonaut*
141 160 Svyosdny Gorodok, Moskvoskoi Oblasti, Potchta Kosmonavtov, Russia

Malzacher, H M *Businessman*
%Steyr-Daimler-Puch, Kartnerring 7, 1010 Vienna, Austria

Mamet, David A *Writer*
%General Delivery, Cabot, VT 05647

Mammel, R N *Businessman*
%Nash Finch Co, 3381 Gorham Ave, St Louis Park, MN 55426

Mamo, Anthony J *President, Malta*
49 Stella Maris St, Sliema, Malta

Manakov, Gennady *Cosmonaut*
141 160 Svyosdny Gorodok, Moskovskoi Oblasti, Potchta Kosmonavtov, Russia

Manarov, Musa *Cosmonaut*
141 160 Svyosdny Gorodok, Moskovskoi Oblasti, Potchta Kosmonavtov, Russia

Manatt, Charles T *Political Leader*
%Democratic National Committee, 1625 Massachusetts Ave, Washington, DC 20036

Mancha, Vaughn *Football Player*
1308 High Rd, Tallahassee, FL 32304

Mancham, James R M *President, Seychelles*
%Lloyd's Bank, 81 Edgware Rd, London W2 2HY, England

Mancheski, Frederick J *Businessman*
%Echlin Inc, 100 Double Beach Rd, Branford, CT 06405

Manchester, Melissa *Singer*
15822 High Knoll Rd, Encino, CA 91436

Manchester, William *Writer*
PO Box 329, Wesleyan Station, Middletown, CT 06457

Mancini, Henry *Composer, Conductor*
261 Baroda Dr, Los Angeles, CA 90077

Mancini, Ray (Boom Boom) *Boxer*
750 Bundy Dr, #108, Los Angeles, CA 90049

Mancuso, Nick *Actor*
%International Creative Mgmt, 8899 Beverly Blvd, Los Angeles, CA 90048

Mandan, Robert *Actor*
%The Agency, 10351 Santa Monica Blvd, #211, Los Angeles, CA 90025

M

Mandarich, Tony *Football Player*
%Green Bay Packers, 1265 Lombardi Ave, Green Bay, WI 54303

Mandel, Howie *Actor*
24710 Robert Guy Rd, Hidden Hills, CA 91302

Mandel, Marvin *Governor, MD*
%Frank A Defilippo, Cross Keys Rd, Baltimore, MD 21210

Mandel, Morton L *Businessman*
%Premier Industrial Corp, 4500 Euclid Ave, Cleveland, OH 44103

Mandela, Nelson *Social Activist*
Orlando West, Soweto, Johannesburg, South Africa

Mandela, Winnie *Social Activist*
Orlando West, Soweto, Johannesburg, South Africa

Mandelbrot, Benoit B *Mathematician*
21 Overhill Rd, Scarsdale, NY 10583

Mandlikova, Hanna *Tennis Player*
Vymolova 8, Prague 5 150 00, Czechslovakia

Mandrell, Barbara *Singer*
PO Box 100, Whites Creek, TN 37189

Mandrell, Louise *Singer*
%Mandrell Mgmt, 128 River Rd, Hendersonville, TN 37075

Maneatis, George A *Businessman*
%Pacific Gas & Electric Co, 77 Beale St, San Francisco, CA 94106

Manekshaw, Sam H F J *Army Field Marshal, India*
%Army Headquarters, DHQ PQ New Delhi 110011, India

Manella, Daniel J *Businessman*
%Rapid-American Corp, 888 7th Ave, New York, NY 10106

Manescu, Manea *Prime Minister, Romania*
%Consiliul de Ministri, Bucharest, Romania

Manetti, Larry *Actor*
4615 Winnetka Ave, Woodland Hills, CA 91364

Mangelsdorf, David *Geneticist (9-Cis Retinoic Acid Hormone)*
%Salk Institute, Gene Expression Laboratory, PO Box 85800, San Diego, CA 92138

Mangelsdorf, Paul C *Geneticist*
510 Caswell Rd, Chapel Hill, NC 27514

Mangione, Chuck *Jazz Trumpter, Composer*
%Gates Music, 476 Hampton Blvd, Rochester, NY 14612

Mangold, Sylvia *Artist*
1 Bull Rd, Washingtonville, NY 10992

Maniatis, Tom *Genetic Engineer*
%Harvard University, Engineering Dept, Cambridge, MA 02138

Manilow, Barry *Singer*
PO Box 69180, Los Angeles, CA 90069

Manion, Daniel A *Judge*
US Court of Appeals, 204 S Main St, South Bend, IN 46601

Manion, Jerry R *Businessman*
%Aztar Corp, 3838 E Van Buren St, Phoenix, AZ 85008

Mankiewicz, Frank F *Broadcast Executive*
%Hill & Knowlton, 1201 Pennsylvania Ave NW, Washington, DC 20004

Mankiewicz, Joseph L *Movie Director, Producer*
RFD 2, Box 82, Bedford, NY 10506

Mankiller, Wilma P *Social Activist*
%Cherokee Nation, PO Box 948, Tahlequah, OK 74465

Mankowitz, Wolf *Writer*
Bridge House, Ahakista, County Cork, Ireland

Manley, Elizabeth *Figure Skater*
%M A Rosenberg, Marco Entertainment, 2331 Century Hill, Los Angeles, CA 90067

Manley, Michael N *Prime Minister, Jamaica*
%Prime Minister's Office, Kingston, Jamaica

Mann, Abby *Writer*
1240 La Collina Rd, Beverly Hills, CA 90210

Mann, Carol *Golfer*
6 Cape Chestnut, The Woodlands, TX 77381

Mann, Charles *Football Player*
%Washington Redskins, Dulles Airport, Box 17247, Washington, DC 20041

Mann, David W *Religious Leader*
%Mennonite Church, 421 S 2nd St, Elkhart, IN 46516

Mann, Delbert *Movie Director, Producer*
%Caroline Productions, 401 S Burnside Ave, #11-D, Los Angeles, CA 90036

Mann, Gerald C *Football Player*
3631 Northwest Pkwy, Dallas, TX 75225

Mann, Herbie *Jazz Flutist*
119 W 57th St, #818, New York, NY 10019

Mann, Johnny *Composer, Conductor*
19764 Corbin Dr, Chatsworth, CA 91311

Mann, Larry D *Actor*
%Allen Goldstein Assoc, 5015 Lemona Ave, Sherman Oaks, CA 91423

Mann, Lowell K *Businessman*
5503 Currituck Pl, Greensboro, NC 27407

Mann, Maurice *Financier*
%Pacific Stock Exchange, 301 Pine St, San Francisco, CA 94104

Mann, Michael *Television Producer, Director*
13746 Sunset Blvd, Pacific Palisades, CA 90272

Mann, Robert *Football Player*
3500 David Stott Bldg, Detroit, MI 48226

Mann, Shelley *Swimmer*
315 S Ivy St, Arlington, VA 22204

Mann, Thomas C *Government Official*
8105 Middle Ct, Austin, TX 78759

Mann, Thompson *Swimmer*
6 Berkshire, Richmond, VA 23221

Manning Mims, Madeline *Track Athlete*
2506 51st St, Tulsa, OK 74105

Manning, Archie *Football Player*
%New Orleans Saints, 6928 Saints Dr, Metairie, LA 70003

Manning, Burton J *Businessman*
%Jordan Case Taylor McGrath, 445 Park Ave, New York, NY 10022

Manning, Danny *Basketball Player*
%Los Angeles Clippers, Sports Arena, 3939 S Figueroa St, Los Angeles, CA 90039

Manning, Rick *Baseball Player*
150 Miles Rd, Chagrin Falls, OH 44022

Manning, Robert J *Editor*
%Boston Publishing Co, 355 Commonwealth Ave, Boston, MA 02115

Manning, William S *Businessman*
%Bibb Co, 237 Coliseum Dr, Macon, GA 31208

Mannino, Franco *Conductor*
%Studio Mannino, Via Citta di Castello 14, 00191 Rome, Italy

Manoff, Dinah *Actress*
913 Amoroso Pl, Venice, CA 90291

Manoliu, Lia *Track Athlete*
%Olympic Committee, Strada Vasile Conta 16, Bucharest, Romania

Manoogian, Alex *Businessman*
%Masco Corp, 21001 Van Born Rd, Taylor, MI 48180

Manoogian, Richard A *Businessman*
%Masco Corp, 21001 Van Born Rd, Taylor, MI 48180

Manorov, Musa *Cosmonaut*
141 160 Svyosdny Gorodok, Moskovskoi Oblasti, Potchta Kosmonavtov, Russia

Mansager, Felix N *Businessman*
3421 Lindel Ct NW, Canton, OH 44718

Mansell, Nigel *Auto Racing Driver*
PO Box 1, Portland House, Station Rd, Ballasalla, Isle of Man

Mansholt, Sicco L *Government Official, Netherlands*
Oosteinde 18, 8351 HB Wapserveen, Netherlands

Manske, Edgar *Football Player*
1031 Lanza Ct, San Marcos, CA 92069

Mansmann, Carol L *Judge*
%US Court of Appeals, US Courthouse, 7th & Grants Sts, Pittsburgh, PA 15219

Mansouri, Lotfi *Opera Director*
%San Francisco War Memorial Opera House, 301 Van Ness, San Francisco, CA 94102

Mantee, Paul *Actor*
%ASH Mgmt, 7250 Beverly Blvd, #102, Los Angeles, CA 90036

Mantegna, Joe *Actor*
%Strain Assoc, 1500 Broadway, #2001, New York, NY 10036

M

Mantle, Mickey *Baseball Player*
42 Central Park South, New York, NY 10019

Manton, Edwin A G *Businessman*
%American International Grp, 70 Pine St, New York, NY 10270

Manton, Thomas J *Representative, NY*
%House of Representatives, Washington, DC 20515

Mantooth, Randolph *Actor*
%Bauman Hiller Assoc, 5750 Wilshire Blvd, #512, Los Angeles, CA 90036

Manzi, Jim P *Businessman*
%Lotus Development Corp, 55 Wheeler Ct, Cambridge, MA 02172

Mapelli, Roland L *Businessman*
%Monfort of Colorado Inc, PO Box G, Greeley, CO 80602

Mara, Kamisese K T *Prime Minister, Fiji*
11 Battery Rd, Suva, Fiji

Mara, Wellington *Football Executive*
%New York Giants, Giants Stadium, East Rutherford, NJ 07073

Marafino, Vincent N *Businessman*
%Lockheed Corp, 2555 N Hollywood Way, Burbank, CA 91520

Marai, Sandor *Writer*
100 Park Terr W, New York, NY 10034

Marburger, John H, III *Educator*
%State University of New York, President's Office, Stony Brook, NY 11794

Marbut, Robert G *Publisher*
%Harte-Hanks Communications, 40 NE Loop 410, San Antonio, TX 78216

Marca-Relli, Conrad *Artist*
7337 Point of Rocks Rd, Sarasota, FL 33581

Marceau, Marcel *Mime*
%School of Mime, 17 Rue Rene Boulander, 75010 Paris, France

Marchais, Georges *Government Official, France*
%Parti Communiste Francais, 2 Pl du Colonel Fabien, 75019 Paris, France

Marchand, Nancy *Actress*
205 W 89th St, New York, NY 10024

Marchese, Donald V *Businessman*
%McCulloch Corp, 5400 Alla Rd, Los Angeles, CA 90066

Marcheski, Frederick J *Businessman*
%Echlin Inc, 100 Double Beach Rd, Branford, CT 06405

Marchetti, Gino *Football Player*
%General Delivery, Cape May, NJ 08204

Marchetti, Leo V *Labor Leader*
%Fraternal Order of Police, 5613 Belair Rd, Baltimore, MD 21206

Marchibroda, Ted *Football Player, Coach*
%Indianapolis Colts, 7001 W. 56th St, Indianapolis, IN 46253

Marchuk, Guri I *Applied Mathematician*
%USSR Academy of Sciences, Leninsky Prosp 14, Moscow, Russia

Marcinkus, Paul C *Religious Leader*
%Institute for Religious Work, Vatican City, Rome, Italy

Marciulionis, Sarunas *Basketball Player*
%Golden State Warriors, Oakland Coliseum, Oakland, CA 94621

Marcovicci, Andrea *Actress*
%Artists Agency, 10000 Santa Monica Blvd, #305, Los Angeles, CA 90067

Marcum, Joseph L *Businessman*
%Ohio Casualty Corp, 136 N 3rd St, Hamilton, OH 45025

Marcus, Ken *Photographer*
6916 Melrose Ave, Los Angeles, CA 90036

Marcus, Robert *Businessman*
%Alumax Inc, 400 S El Camino Real, San Mateo, CA 94402

Marcus, Rudolph A *Theoretical Chemist*
331 S Hill Ave, Pasadena, CA 91106

Marcus, Stanley *Businessman*
1 Nonesuch Rd, Dallas, TX 75214

Marden, Brice *Artist*
54 Bond St, New York, NY 10012

Maree, Sidney *Track Athlete*
2 Braxton Rd, Rosemont, PA 19010

Margal, Albert M *Prime Minister, Sierra Leone*
8 Hornsey Rise Gdns, London N19, England

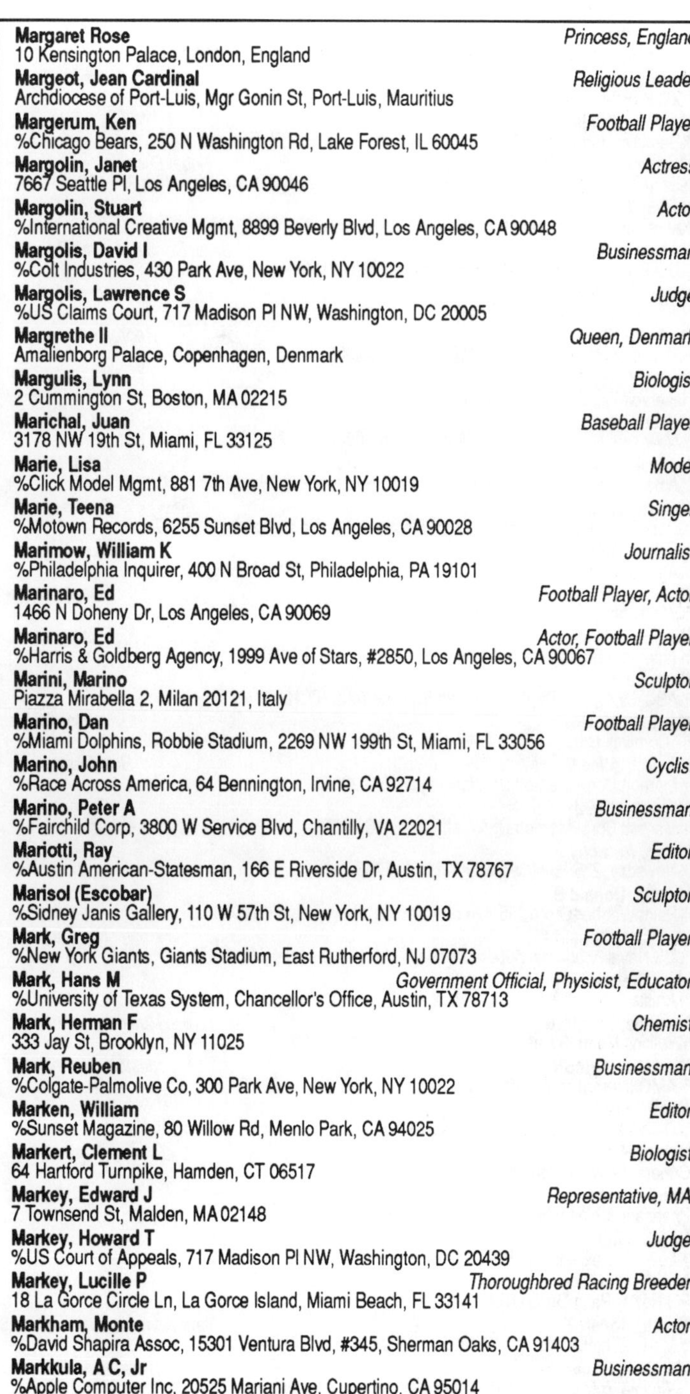

Margaret Rose — *Princess, England*
10 Kensington Palace, London, England

Margeot, Jean Cardinal — *Religious Leader*
Archdiocese of Port-Luis, Mgr Gonin St, Port-Luis, Mauritius

Margerum, Ken — *Football Player*
%Chicago Bears, 250 N Washington Rd, Lake Forest, IL 60045

Margolin, Janet — *Actress*
7667 Seattle Pl, Los Angeles, CA 90046

Margolin, Stuart — *Actor*
%International Creative Mgmt, 8899 Beverly Blvd, Los Angeles, CA 90048

Margolis, David I — *Businessman*
%Colt Industries, 430 Park Ave, New York, NY 10022

Margolis, Lawrence S — *Judge*
%US Claims Court, 717 Madison Pl NW, Washington, DC 20005

Margrethe II — *Queen, Denmark*
Amalienborg Palace, Copenhagen, Denmark

Margulis, Lynn — *Biologist*
2 Cummington St, Boston, MA 02215

Marichal, Juan — *Baseball Player*
3178 NW 19th St, Miami, FL 33125

Marie, Lisa — *Model*
%Click Model Mgmt, 881 7th Ave, New York, NY 10019

Marie, Teena — *Singer*
%Motown Records, 6255 Sunset Blvd, Los Angeles, CA 90028

Marimow, William K — *Journalist*
%Philadelphia Inquirer, 400 N Broad St, Philadelphia, PA 19101

Marinaro, Ed — *Football Player, Actor*
1466 N Doheny Dr, Los Angeles, CA 90069

Marinaro, Ed — *Actor, Football Player*
%Harris & Goldberg Agency, 1999 Ave of Stars, #2850, Los Angeles, CA 90067

Marini, Marino — *Sculptor*
Piazza Mirabella 2, Milan 20121, Italy

Marino, Dan — *Football Player*
%Miami Dolphins, Robbie Stadium, 2269 NW 199th St, Miami, FL 33056

Marino, John — *Cyclist*
%Race Across America, 64 Bennington, Irvine, CA 92714

Marino, Peter A — *Businessman*
%Fairchild Corp, 3800 W Service Blvd, Chantilly, VA 22021

Mariotti, Ray — *Editor*
%Austin American-Statesman, 166 E Riverside Dr, Austin, TX 78767

Marisol (Escobar) — *Sculptor*
%Sidney Janis Gallery, 110 W 57th St, New York, NY 10019

Mark, Greg — *Football Player*
%New York Giants, Giants Stadium, East Rutherford, NJ 07073

Mark, Hans M — *Government Official, Physicist, Educator*
%University of Texas System, Chancellor's Office, Austin, TX 78713

Mark, Herman F — *Chemist*
333 Jay St, Brooklyn, NY 11025

Mark, Reuben — *Businessman*
%Colgate-Palmolive Co, 300 Park Ave, New York, NY 10022

Marken, William — *Editor*
%Sunset Magazine, 80 Willow Rd, Menlo Park, CA 94025

Markert, Clement L — *Biologist*
64 Hartford Turnpike, Hamden, CT 06517

Markey, Edward J — *Representative, MA*
7 Townsend St, Malden, MA 02148

Markey, Howard T — *Judge*
%US Court of Appeals, 717 Madison Pl NW, Washington, DC 20439

Markey, Lucille P — *Thoroughbred Racing Breeder*
18 La Gorce Circle Ln, La Gorce Island, Miami Beach, FL 33141

Markham, Monte — *Actor*
%David Shapira Assoc, 15301 Ventura Blvd, #345, Sherman Oaks, CA 91403

Markkula, A C, Jr — *Businessman*
%Apple Computer Inc, 20525 Mariani Ave, Cupertino, CA 95014

Markle, C Wilson — *Film Engineer*
%Colorization Inc, 26 Soho St, Toronto ON M5T 1Z7, Canada

M

Markle – Marshall

Markle, Peter *Movie Director*
%Creative Artists Agency, 9830 Wilshire Blvd, Beverly Hills, CA 90212

Markov, Victor *Football Player*
1500 Westlake Ave N, Seattle, WA 98109

Markova, Alicia *Ballerina*
%Barclays Bank Ltd, 1-3 Brompton Rd, London SW3 1EB, England

Markowitz, Harry M *Nobel Economics Laureate*
%Baruch College, Economics & Finance Dept, 17 Lexington Ave, New York, NY 10010

Marks, Albert J *Pageant Director*
%Miss American Pageant, 1325 Broadway, Atlantic City, NJ 08401

Marks, Bruce *Ballet Dancer, Artistic Director*
%Boston Ballet Co, 42 Vernon St, Newton, MA 02158

Marland, Sidney P *Government Official*
N Bigelow Rd, Hampton, CT 06247

Marlenee, Ron *Representative, MT*
%House of Representatives, Washington, DC 20515

Marler, Peter R *Biologist*
Reservoir Rd, Staatsburg, NY 12580

Marlette, Doug *Editorial Cartoonist*
%New York Newsday, 780 3rd Ave, New York, NY 10017

Maroney, Daniel V, Jr *Labor Leader*
%Amalgamated Transit Union, 5025 Wisconsin Ave NW, Washington, DC 20016

Marotta, Nicholas G *Businessman*
%National Starch & Chemical Corp, Finderne Ave, Bridgewater, NJ 08807

Marotte, Gilles *Hockey Player*
%Agence Prestige, 4777 Blvd Bourque, Rock Forest PQ J1N 1A6, Canada

Marous, John C, Jr *Businessman*
%Westinghouse Electric Corp, Gateway Ctr, Pittsburgh, PA 15222

Marquard, William A *Businessman*
%American Standard Inc, 40 W 40th St, New York, NY 10018

Marr, Dave *Golfer*
%ABC-TV, Sports Dept, 77 W 66th St, New York, NY 10023

Marriner, Neville *Conductor*
67 Cornwell Gdns, London SW7 4BA, England

Marriott, Alice S *Businesswoman*
%Marriott Corp, Marriott Dr, Washington, DC 20058

Marriott, J W, Jr *Businessman*
%Marriott Corp, Marriott Dr, Washington, DC 20058

Marro, Anthony J *Editor*
%Newsday, 235 Pinelawn, Melville, NY 11747

Marron, Donald B *Businessman*
%PaineWebber Grp, 1285 Ave of Americas, New York, NY 10019

Marryout, Ronald F *Navy Admiral*
%US Naval Academy, Superintendent's Office, Annapolis, MD 21402

Mars, Kenneth *Actor*
%Artists Group, 1930 Century Park West, #403, Los Angeles, CA 90067

Marsalis, Branford *Musician, Composer*
%Wilkins Mgmt, 3 Hastings Sq, Cambridge, MA 02139

Marsalis, Wynton *Musician, Composer*
%AMG International, 4200 Argyle Terr NW, Washington, DC 20011

Marsh, Brad *Hockey Player*
%Detroit Red Wings, Louis Sports Arena, 600 Civic Center Dr, Detroit, MI 48226

Marsh, Henry *Track Athlete*
General Delivery, Bountiful, UT 84010

Marsh, Jean *Actress*
Pheasant, Chinnor Hill, Oxon OX9 4BN, England

Marsh, Linda *Actress*
%Lew Sherrell Agency, 1354 Los Robles, Palm Springs, CA 92262

Marsh, Marian *Actress*
PO Box 1, Palm Desert, CA 92260

Marsh, Robert T *Navy Admiral, Businessman*
%Morton Thiokel Inc, 110 W Wacker Dr, Chicago, IL 60606

Marshak, Robert E *Theoretical Physicist*
%Virginia Polytechnic Institute, Physics Dept, Blacksburg, VA 24061

Marshall, Burke *Attorney*
Castle Meadow Rd, Newton, CT 06470

Marshall, Carolyn M *Religious Leader*
%United Methodist Church, 204 N Newlin St, Veedersburg, IN 47987
Marshall, Catherine *Writer*
3003 Fernwood Dr, Boynton Beach, FL 33435
Marshall, Charles *Businessman*
%American Telephone & Telegraph Co, 550 Madison Ave, New York, NY 10022
Marshall, David L *Businessman*
%Pittston Co, 1 Pickwick Plz, Greenwich, CT 06830
Marshall, E G *Actor*
Bryam Lake Rd, RFD 2, Mt Kisco, NY 10549
Marshall, Esme *Model*
%Fame Models Ltd, 133 E 58th St, New York, NY 10022
Marshall, F Ray *Secretary, Labor*
%University of Texas, LBJ School of Public Affairs, Austin, TX 78712
Marshall, Frank *Movie Producer*
%Amblin Entertainment, 100 Universal City Plz, #477, Universal City, CA 91608
Marshall, Garry *Movie Director*
10067 Riverside Dr, Toluca Lake, CA 91602
Marshall, James *Actor*
%Harris & Goldbrg Agency, 1999 Ave of Stars, #2850, Los Angeles, CA 90067
Marshall, John *Prime Minister, New Zealand*
%Buddle Findlay Barristers, PO Box 2694, Wellington, New Zealand
Marshall, Leonard *Football Player*
%New York Giants, Giants Stadium, East Rutherford, NJ 07073
Marshall, Mike (Michael A) *Baseball Player*
13063 Ventura Blvd, Studio City, CA 91604
Marshall, Mike (Michael G) *Baseball Player*
%Henderson State College, Athletic Dept, Arkadelphia, AR 71923
Marshall, Penny *Actress, Director*
1849 Sawtelle Blvd, #500, Los Angeles, CA 90025
Marshall, Peter *Television Host*
16714 Oak View Dr, Encino, CA 91436
Marshall, Robert C *Businessman*
%Tandem Computers Inc, 19333 Vallco Pkwy, Cupertino, CA 95014
Marshall, Thurgood *Supreme Court Justice*
%US Supreme Court, 1 1st St NE, Washington, DC 20543
Marshall, Wilber *Football Player*
%Washington Redskins, Dulles Airport, Box 17247, Washington, DC 20041
Marshall, Willard *Baseball Player*
1090 Arcadian Wy, Fort Lee, NJ 07024
Marshall, William *Actor*
11351 Dronfield Ave, Pacoima, CA 91331
Martens, Wilfried *Prime Minister, Belgium*
%Prime Minister's Office, Wetstraat 16, 1000 Brussels, Belgium
Martin, Agnes *Artist*
%Pace Gallery, 32 E 57th St, New York, NY 10022
Martin, Alastair B *Tennis Contributor*
%Bessemer Trust Co, 630 5th Ave, New York, NY 10111
Martin, Albert C, Jr *Architect*
%Albert C Martin Assoc, 811 W 7th St, #800, Los Angeles, CA 90017
Martin, Andrea *Actress*
%International Creative Mgmt, 40 W 57th St, New York, NY 10019
Martin, Anne-Marie *Actress*
%Belson & Klass Assoc, 144 S Beverly Dr, #405, Beverly Hills, CA 90212
Martin, Archer John Porter *Nobel Chemistry Laureate*
47 Roseford Rd, Cambridge CB4 2HA, England
Martin, Boyce F, Jr *Judge*
%US Court of Appeals, US Courthouse, 601 W Broadway, Louisville, KY 40202
Martin, David *Commentator*
%CBS-News, 2020 "M" St NW, Washington, DC 20036
Martin, David O'B *Representative, NY*
41 Judson St, Canton, NY 13617
Martin, Dean *Singer, Actor*
613 N Linden Dr, Beverly Hills, CA 90210
Martin, Dewey *Actor*
1430 Stonewood Ct, San Pedro, CA 90732

M

Martin, Dick *Comedian*
11030 Chalon Rd, Los Angeles, CA 90077

Martin, Edmund F *Businessman*
437 Main St, #310, Bethlehem, PA 18018

Martin, Ernest H *Theater, Movie Producer*
505 Park Ave, New York, NY 10022

Martin, George C *Businessman*
Greenwillow, Box 282, Anchorage, KY 40223

Martin, Harry F *Financier*
%Northeast Savings, 147 Charter Oak Ave, Hartford, CT 06106

Martin, Harvey *Football Player*
%Dallas Cowboys, 1 Cowboys Pkwy, Irving, TX 75063

Martin, Helen *Actress*
%Irv Schechter Co, 9300 Wilshire Blvd, #410, Beverly Hills, CA 90212

Martin, Henry R *Cartoonist (Good News Bad News)*
17 Charlton St, Princeton, NJ 08540

Martin, J Landis *Businessman*
%NL Industries, 1230 Ave of Americas, New York, NY 10020

Martin, Jacques Cardinal *Religious Leader*
Casa Pontificia, Vatican City, Rome, Italy

Martin, James E *Businessman*
%Illinois Central Gulf Railroad, 233 N Michigan Ave, Chicago, IL 60601

Martin, James G *Governor, NC*
%Governor's Office, State Capitol, Raleigh, NC 27611

Martin, James S *Businessman*
%TIAA-CREF, 730 3rd Ave, New York, NY 10017

Martin, Jared *Actor*
%Paul Kohner Inc, 9169 Sunset Blvd, Los Angeles, CA 90069

Martin, Joe *Cartoonist (Mister Boffo)*
%Tribune Media Services, 34 E Concord St, Orlando, FL 32801

Martin, John E *Businessman*
%Dana Corp, 4500 Dorr St, Toledo, OH 43615

Martin, John H *Educator*
%JHM Corp, 3930 RCA Blvd, #3240, Palm Beach Gardens, FL 33410

Martin, Judith (Miss Manners) *Journalist*
1651 Harvard St NW, Washington, DC 20009

Martin, Kellie *Actress*
%Savage Agency, 6212 Banner Ave, Los Angeles, CA 90038

Martin, Lynn M *Secretary, Labor*
%Department of Labor, 200 Constitution Ave NW, Washington, DC 20210

Martin, Marilyn *Singer*
%Atlantic Records, 9229 Sunset Blvd, #710, Los Angeles, CA 90069

Martin, Millicent *Actress*
%Fred Amsel Assoc, 6310 San Vicente Blvd, #407, Los Angeles, CA 90048

Martin, Pamela Sue *Actress*
PO Box 1684, Studio City, CA 91604

Martin, Paul *Government Official, Canada*
2021 Ontario Ave, Windsor ON, Canada

Martin, Preston *Government Official, Financier*
1130 N Lake Shore Dr, #4-E, Chicago, IL 60611

Martin, Ray *Billiards Player*
11-05 Cadmus Pl, Fairlawn, NJ 07410

Martin, Ray *Financier*
%Coast Federal Savings, 855 S Hill St, Los Angeles, CA 90014

Martin, Rod *Football Player*
%Los Angeles Raiders, 332 Center St, El Segundo, CA 90245

Martin, Ronald D *Editor*
%Atlanta Journal-Constitution, 72 Marietta St, Atlanta, GA 30303

Martin, Slater *Basketball Player*
2615 Ella Blvd, Houston, TX 77008

Martin, Steve *Comedian*
PO Box 929, Beverly Hills, CA 90213

Martin, Tony *Singer*
10390 Wilshire Blvd, #1507, Los Angeles, CA 90024

Martin, William F *Businessman*
615 E 16th Pl, Bartlesville, OK 74003

Martin, William McChesney, Jr *Government Official, Tennis Contributor*
2861 Woodland Dr NW, Washington, DC 20008
Martinelli, Alfred W *Businessman*
%Penn Central Corp, 500 W Putnam Ave, Greenwich, CT 06836
Martinez, A *Actor*
%Dolores Robinson Mgmt, 335 N Maple Dr, #250, Beverly Hills, CA 90210
Martinez, Bob *Governor, FL*
%Office of National Drug Control Policy, Executive Office, Washington, DC 20500
Martinez, Matthew G *Representative, CA*
%House of Representatives, Washington, DC 20515
Martinez, Ramon *Baseball Player*
Bo San Miguel #9, Managuayaba, Santo Domingo, Dominican Republic
Martini, Carlo Maria Cardinal *Religious Leader*
Palazzo Arcivescovile, Piazza Fontana 2, 20122 Milan, Italy
Martini, Emil P, Jr *Businessman*
%Bergen Brunswig Corp, 1900 Ave of Stars, Los Angeles, CA 90067
Martini, Robert E *Businessman*
%Bergen Brunswig Corp, 1900 Ave of Stars, Los Angeles, CA 90067
Martino, Al *Musician*
927 N Rexford Dr, Beverly Hills, CA 90210
Martino, Frank D *Labor Leader*
%Chemical Workers Union, 1655 W Market St, Akron, OH 43313
Martins, Peter *Ballet Dancer, Artistic Director*
%New York City Ballet, Lincoln Ctr, New York, NY 10023
Marton, Eva *Opera Singer*
%Metropolitan Opera Assn, Lincoln Ctr, New York, NY 10023
Martre, Henri *Businessman*
%Aerospatiale, 37 Rue Blvd de Montmorency, 75781 Paris Cedex 16, France
Marty, Francois Cardinal *Religious Leader*
32 Rue Barbet de Jouy, 75007 Paris, France
Marty, Martin E *Theologian*
239 Scottswood Rd, Riverside, IL 60546
Martzke, Rudy *Sportswriter*
%USA Today, PO Box 500, Washington, DC 20044
Marusi, Augustine R *Businessman*
%Borden Inc, 277 Park Ave, New York, NY 10017
Maruta, Yoshio *Businessman*
%Kao Corp, 14-10 Nihonbashi Kayabacho, Chuoku, Tokyo 103, Japan
Marx, Gilda *Fashion Designer*
%Gilda Marx Industries, 11755 Exposition Blvd, Los Angeles, CA 90064
Marx, Jeffrey A *Journalist*
%Lexington Herald-Leader, Main & Midland, Lexington, KY 40507
Maryland, Russell *Football Player*
%Dallas Cowboys, 1 Cowboys Pkwy, Irving, TX 75063
Marzio, Peter *Museum Director*
%Houston Museum of Fine Arts, 1001 Bissonnet, PO Box 6826, Houston, TX 77265
Masak, Ron *Actor*
%Agency for Performing Arts, 9000 Sunset Blvd, #1200, Los Angeles, CA 90069
Masamune, Isao *Financier*
%Industrial Bank of Japan, 3-3 Marunouchi, Chiyodaku, Tokyo 100, Japan
Masco, Judit *Model*
%Ford Model Agency, 344 E 59th St, New York, NY 10022
Mascotte, John P *Businessman*
%Continental Corp, 180 Maiden Ln, New York, NY 10038
Mase, Seisuke *Financier*
%Hokuriko Bank, 1-2-26 Tsutumichodori, Toyama City 930, Japan
Mashat, Mohammed *Diplomat, Iraq*
%Embassy of Iraq, 1801 "P" St NW, Washington, DC 20036
Masina, Giulietta *Actress*
Via Margutta 110, 00187 Rome, Italy
Masire, Quett K J *President, Botswana*
%State House, Private Bag 001, Gaborone, Botswana
Maske, John T *Businessman*
%Prime Computer Inc, Prime Park, Natick, MA 01760
Maslansky, Paul *Movie Producer*
%Paul Maslansky Productions, 1041 Formosa Ave, Los Angeles, CA 90046

M

Masloff, Sophie %Mayor's Office, City Hall, 510 City-County Bldg, Pittsburgh, PA 15219	*Mayor, Pittsburgh*
Mason, Birny, Jr 6 Island Dr, Rye, NY 10580	*Chemical Engineer*
Mason, Bobbie Ann Box 340-C, RD 1, Mertztown, PA 19539	*Writer*
Mason, Jackie %William Morris Agency, 151 El Camino, Beverly Hills, CA 90212	*Comedian*
Mason, Marlyn %Diamond Artists, 9200 Sunset Blvd, #909, Los Angeles, CA 90069	*Actress*
Mason, Marsha %Collett & Levy, 10100 Santa Monica Blvd, #400, Los Angeles, CA 90067	*Actress*
Mason, Monica %Royal Opera House, Convent Gdn, Bow St, London WC2, England	*Ballerina*
Mason, Pamela 1013 Pamela Dr, Beverly Hills, CA 90210	*Actress*
Mason, R Steven %Pope & Talbot Inc, 1500 SW 1st Ave, Portland, OR 97201	*Businessman*
Mason, Rausey W %Fortune Financial Grp, 2120 US 19 S, Clearwater, FL 33546	*Financier*
Mason, Raymond K %Charter Co, 1 Charter Plz, Jacksonville, FL 32202	*Businessman*
Mason, Steven C %Mead Corp, Courthouse Plz NE, Dayton, OH 45463	*Businessman*
Mason, Tom %Gersh Agency, 232 N Canon Dr, Beverly Hills, CA 90210	*Actor*
Masotta, Robert E %Standex International, 6 Manor Pkwy, Salem, NH 03079	*Businessman*
Massagli, Mark Tully %American Federation of Musicians, 1501 Broadway, #600, New York, NY 10036	*Labor Leader*
Massengale, Martin A %University of Nebraska, President's Office, Lincoln, NE 68566	*Educator*
Masserman, Jules H 8 S Michigan Ave, Chicago, IL 60603	*Psychoanalyst*
Massevitch, Alla G %Astronomical Council, 48 Pjatnitskaja St, Moscow, Russia	*Astronomer*
Massey, Daniel 35 Tynehan Rd, London SW11, England	*Actor*
Massey, Marilyn Chapin %Pitzer College, President's Office, Claremont, CA 91711	*Educator*
Massie, Edward L %Commerce Clearing House, 4025 W Peterson Ave, Chicago, IL 60646	*Businessman*
Massimino, Rollie %Villanova University, Athletic Dept, Villanova, PA 19085	*Basketball Coach*
Masterhoff, Joe 2 Horatio St, New York, NY 10014	*Playwright*
Masters, John %McGraw-Hill, 1221 Ave of Americas, New York, NY 10020	*Writer*
Masters, William H 4529 Pershing Pl, St Louis, MO 63108	*Sex Therapist*
Masterson, Peter %Writer's Guild, 55 W 57th St, New York, NY 10019	*Writer, Director, Producer*
Masterson, Valerie %A M Halliday, 71 Holland Park, Flat 5-A, London W11 3SL, England	*Opera Singer*
Mastroianni, Marcello Via Maria Adelaide 8, Rome, Italy	*Actor*
Masur, Kurt %New York Philharmonic, Avery Fisher Hall, Lincoln Ctr, New York, NY 10023	*Conductor*
Masur, Richard 2847 Mandeville Canyon Rd, Los Angeles, CA 90049	*Actor*
Mata'aho %Royal Palace, Nuku'alofa, Tonga	*Queen, Tonga*
Mata, Eduardo %Dallas Symphony Orchestra, PO Box 26207, Dallas, TX 75226	*Conductor*
Matalon, David %Tri-Star Pictures, 711 5th Ave, New York, NY 10022	*Entertainment Executive*

Mathers, Jerry *Actor*
23965 Via Aranda, Valencia, CA 91355

Matheson, Scott M *Governor, UT*
2253 Hubbard Ave, Salt Lake City, UT 84108

Mathews, David *Secretary, Health Education Welfare*
%Charles F Kettering Foundation, 5335 Far Hills Ave, Dayton, OH 45429

Mathews, Eddie *Baseball Player*
13744 Recuerdo Dr, Del Mar, CA 92014

Mathias, Bob *Track Athlete; Representative, CA*
24011 Goldeneye Dr, Laguna Niguel, CA 92677

Mathias, Charles M, Jr *Senator, MD*
3808 Leland St, Chevy Chase, MD 20815

Mathiesen, Charles *Speed Skater*
Hans Lambachsv 8, 3000 Drammen, Norway

Mathis, Johnny *Singer*
PO Box 69278, Los Angeles, CA 90069

Mathis, Terance *Football Player*
%New York Jets, 598 Madison Ave, New York, NY 10022

Matlin, Marlee *Actress*
%International Creative Mgmt, 8899 Beverly Blvd, Los Angeles, CA 90048

Matlock, Jack F, Jr *Diplomat*
%American Embassy, 19-23 Ul Chaikovskogo, Moscow, Russia

Matson, Ollie *Football Player*
1319 S Hudson Ave, Los Angeles, CA 90019

Matson, Randy *Track Athlete*
%Assn of Former Students, Texas A&M University, College Station, TX 77840

Matsui, Robert T *Representative, CA*
%House of Representatives, Washington, DC 20515

Matsumoto, Shigeharu *Writer, Association Executive*
%International House of Japan, 11-16 Roppongi, Minatuku, Tokyo, Japan

Matsushita, Hiroshi *Financier*
%Toyo Trust & Banking Co, 4-3 Marunouchi, Chiyodaku, Tokyo 100, Japan

Matsushita, Masaharu *Businessman*
%Matsushita Electrical Industrial, 1006 Kadoma City, Osaka 571, Japan

Matsuyama, Tkashige *Businessman*
%Nissan Diesel Motor Co, 1-1 Ageo City 362, Japan

Matsuzawa, Takuji *Financier*
%Fuji Bank, 1-5-5 Otemachi, Chiyodaku, Tokyo 100, Japan

Matta del Meskin *Religious Leader*
Deir el Makarios Monastery, Cairo, Egypt

Matta, Roberto *Artist*
Boissy Sans Avoir, Seine-et-Oise, France

Mattea, Kathy *Singer*
PO Box 158482, Nashville, TN 37215

Mattesich, Rudi *Skier*
%General Delivery, Troy, VT 05868

Matteson, Thomas *Coast Guard Admiral*
%US Coast Guard Academy, Superintendent's Office, New London, CT 06320

Matthau, Walter *Actor*
278 Toyopa, Pacific Palisades, CA 90272

Matthes, Roland *Swimmer*
Storkower Strasse 118, 1055 Berlin, Germany

Matthews, Bruce *Football Player*
%Houston Oilers, 6910 Fannin St, Houston, TX 77030

Matthews, Clay *Football Player*
%Cleveland Browns, Cleveland Stadium, Cleveland, OH 44114

Matthews, Leonard *Association Executive*
%American Assn of Advertising Agencies, 666 3rd Ave, New York, NY 10017

Matthews, Norman S *Businessman*
%Federated Department Stores, 7 W 7th St, Cincinnati, OH 45202

Matthews, Raymond (Rags) *Football Player*
2700 Simondale Dr, Fort Worth, TX 76109

Matthews, Victor C *Businessman*
%Trafalgar House Ltd, 1 Berkeley St, London W1X 6NN, England

Matthiessen, Peter *Writer*
Bridge Ln, Sagaponack, NY 11962

M

Mattingly – Maxwell

Mattingly, Don *Baseball Player*
RR 5, Box 74, Evansville, IN 47711

Mattingly, Thomas K, II *Astronaut, Navy Admiral*
%Grumman Corp, 1760 Business Center, #60, Reston, VA 22090

Mattis, Louis P *Businessman*
%Sterling Drug Inc, 90 Park Ave, New York, NY 10016

Mattscheck, Fred J *Businessman*
%Harsco Corp, PO Box 8888, Camp Hill, PA 17011

Mattson, Robin *Actress*
917 Manning Ave, Los Angeles, CA 90024

Mattson, Walter E *Publisher*
%New York Times Co, 229 W 43rd St, New York, NY 10036

Mattus, Reuben *Businessman*
%Haagen-Dazs, 1 Amboy Ave, Woodbridge, NJ 07075

Mature, Victor *Actor*
PO Box 706, Rancho Santa Fe, CA 92067

Matz, Merton J *Financier*
%Atlantic Financial Federal, 50 Monument Rd, Bala Cynwyd, PA 19004

Mauch, Bill *Actor*
23427 Canzonet St, Woodland Hills, CA 91364

Mauch, Gene *Baseball Manager*
46 La Ronda Dr, Rancho Mirage, CA 92270

Maucher, Helmut *Businessman*
%Nestle SA, Ave Nestle, 1800 Vevey, Switzerland

Maugham, R H *Religious Leader*
%Christian & Missionary Alliance, PO Box 35000, Colorado Springs, CO 80935

Mauldin, Bill *Editorial Cartoonist*
%Chicago Sun-Times, 401 N Wabash Ave, Chicago, IL 60611

Maulnier, Thierry *Writer*
3 Rue Yves-Carriou, 92430 Marnes-la-Coquette, France

Maumenee, Alfred Edward *Ophthalmologist*
1700 Hillside Rd, Stevenson, MD 21153

Maura, Carmen *Actress*
%Official Body of Spanish Cinema, San Mateo 4, Madrid 28004, Spain

Maurer, Gilbert C *Publisher*
%Hearst Corp, 959 8th Ave, New York, NY 10019

Maurer, Ion Gheorghe *Premier, Romania*
Bul Aviatorilor 104, Bucharest, Romania

Maurin, Laurence *Skier, Conservationist*
6874 Schmidt Rd, West Bend, WI 53095

Mauroy, Pierre *Premier, France*
38 Ave Charles-Saint-Venant, 59000 Lille, France

Mauz, Henry H, Jr *Navy Admiral*
Deputy CNO, Navy Program Planning, Navy Department, Washington, DC 20350

Mavroules, Nicholas *Representative, MA*
%House of Representatives, Washington, DC 20515

Max, Peter *Artist*
118 Riverside Dr, New York, NY 10024

Maxim, Joey *Boxer*
2491 Natalie Ave, Las Vegas, NV 89121

Maxson, Robert *Educator*
%University of Nevada, President's Office, Las Vegas, NV 89154

Maxwell Reid, Daphne *Actress*
16540 Adlon Rd, Encino, CA 91436

Maxwell, Arthur E *Oceanographer*
%University of Texas, Oceanography Dept, Austin, TX 78712

Maxwell, Charlie *Baseball Player*
730 Mapleview Ave, Paw Paw, MI 49079

Maxwell, David O *Businessman*
%Federal National Mortgage Assn, 1133 15th St NW, Washington, DC 20005

Maxwell, Frank *Labor Leader*
%Federation of TV-Radio Artists, 260 Madison Ave, New York, NY 10016

Maxwell, Hamish *Businessman*
%Philip Morris Companies, 120 Park Ave, New York, NY 10017

Maxwell, Robert D *WW II Army Hero (CMH)*
3097 Stapp Dr, Eugene, OR 97401

Maxwell, Vera H *Fashion Designer*
530 7th Ave, New York, NY 10018

May, Alfred T *Financier*
%Home Federal Bank of Florida, 1901 Central Ave, St Petersburg, FL 33713

May, Arthur *Architect*
%Kohn Pedersen Fox Assoc, 111 W 57th St, New York, NY 10019

May, Charles A, Jr *Air Force General*
Asst Vice Chief of Staff, Hq USAF, Washington, DC 20330

May, Daniel F *Businessman*
%Republic Airlines, 7500 Airline Dr, Minneapolis, MN 55450

May, Don *Basketball Player*
108 Beverly Pl, Dayton, OH 45419

May, Elaine *Movie Director, Comedienne*
146 Central Park West, #4-E, New York, NY 10023

May, John L *Religious Leader*
%Archdiocese of St Louis, 4445 Lindell Blvd, St Louis, MO 63108

May, Lee *Baseball Player*
RR 1, Box 318, Bridgewater, VA 22812

May, Mark *Football Player*
%San Diego Chargers, 9449 Friars Rd, San Diego, CA 92120

May, Rollo *Psychiatrist*
%William Alanson White Institute, 20 W 74th St, New York, NY 10023

May, William F *Educator*
%New York University, Business Administration School, New York, NY 10003

Mayall, John *Musician, Composer*
%Artists/Heller Agency, 6430 Sunset Blvd, Los Angeles, CA 90028

Mayberry, John *Baseball Player*
11115 W 121st Terr, Overland Park, KS 66213

Mayehoff, Eddie *Actor*
369 Paseo de Playa, #411, Ventura, CA 93001

Mayer, Francois *Financier*
%L F Rothschild Unterberg Towbin, 55 Water St, New York, NY 10041

Mayer, H Robert *Judge*
%US Court of Appeals, 717 Madison Pl NW, Washington, DC 20439

Mayer, Jean *Nutrition Scientist, Educator*
%Tufts University, President's Office, Medford, MA 02155

Mayer, Joseph E *Chemical Physicist*
2345 Via Siena, La Jolla, CA 92037

Mayer, Milhaly *Water Poloist*
Bimbo Ut 103, 1022 Budapest II, Hungary

Mayer, Paul Augustin Cardinal *Religious Leader*
Ecclesia Dei, Vatican City, Rome, Italy

Mayer, Selma *Medical Missionary*
%Shaare Zedak Hospital, Jerusalem, Israel

Mayes, Rueben *Football Player*
%New Orleans Saints, 6928 Saints Dr, Metairie, LA 70003

Mayfield, Curtis *Jazz Musician, Composer, Singer*
5915 Lincoln Ave, Chicago, IL 60669

Maynard, Andrew *Boxer*
%Mike Trainer, 3922 Fairmont Ave, Bethesda, MD 20814

Maynard, Don *Football Player*
6545 Butterfield Dr, El Paso, TX 79932

Maynard, Mimi *Actress*
%Badgley Connor, 9229 Sunset Blvd, #607, Los Angeles, CA 90069

Maynard, Robert C *Editor, Publisher*
%Oakland Tribune, 409 13th St, Oakland, CA 94612

Mayne, Charles W *Editor*
%Foreign Policy Magazine, 11 Dupont Cir, Washington, DC 20036

Mayne, Ferdinand *Actor*
%Nat Stoller Accountancy, 315 S Beverly Dr, Beverly Hills, CA 90210

Mayne, William *Writer*
%Harold Ober Assoc, 40 E 49th St, New York, NY 10017

Mayo, Virginia *Actress*
109 E Ave de las Aboles, Thousand Oaks, CA 91360

Mayo, Whitman *Actor*
3210 W 80th St, Inglewood, CA 90305

Mayor Zaragoza, Federico *Government Official, Spain*
%UNESCO, Pl de Fonteroy, 75700 Paris, France

Mayoux, Jacques *Financier*
%Societe Generale, 29 Blvd Haussmann, 75009 Paris, France

Mayr, Ernst *Biologist*
11 Chauncy St, Cambridge, MA 02138

Mayron, Melanie *Actress*
%Triad Artists, 10100 Santa Monica Blvd, #1600, Los Angeles, CA 90067

Mays, Willie *Baseball Player*
51 Mt Vernon Ln, Atherton, CA 94025

Mayyers, George H *Businessman*
%US Home Corp, 1800 West Loop S, Houston, TX 77027

Mazaika, Robert J *Businessman*
%Uniroyal Inc, World Headquarters, Middlebury, CT 06749

Mazarin, Sanford S *Businessman*
%Whitehall Laboratories, 685 3rd Ave, New York, NY 10017

Mazeroski, Bill *Baseball Player*
RR 6, Box 130, Greensburg, PA 15601

Mazia, Daniel *Biologist*
%Hopkins Marine Station, Pacific Grove, CA 93950

Mazur, Jay *Labor Leader*
%International Ladies Garment Workers Union, 265 W 14th St, New York, NY 10019

Mazursky, Paul *Movie Director*
16 E 11th St, #3-A, New York, NY 10003

Mazzo, Kay *Ballerina*
%Sharon Wagner Artists, 150 West End Ave, New York, NY 10023

Mazzoli, Romano L *Representative, KY*
%House of Representatives, Washington, DC 20515

Mbasogo, Teodoro Obiang Nguema *President, Equatorial Guinea*
%President's Office, Malabo, Equatorial Guinea

McAfee, George *Football Player*
4011 Bristol Rd, Durham, NC 27707

McAlister, Maurice L *Financier*
%Downey Savings & Loan, 3200 Bristol St, Costa Mesa, CA 92626

McArdle, Andrea *Actress, Singer*
%Ambrosio/Mortimer Assoc, 301 N Canon Dr, #305, Beverly Hills, CA 90210

McArthur, John *Educator*
140 Old Connecticut Path, Wayland, MA 01778

McArthur, William S, Jr *Astronaut*
%NASA, Johnson Space Center, Houston, TX 77058

McArtor, T Allan *Government Official*
%Federal Aviation Administration, 800 Independence SW, Washington, DC 20591

McBain, Diane *Actress*
%Allen Goldstein Assoc, 5015 Lemona Ave, Sherman Oaks, CA 91423

McBee, Frank W, Jr *Businessman*
%Tracor Inc, 6500 Tracor Ln, Austin, TX 78725

McBride, Jon A *Astronaut*
PO Box 1050, Lewisburg, WV 24901

McBride, Patricia *Ballerina*
%Sharon Wagner Artists, 150 West End Ave, New York, NY 10023

McBride, Robert D *Businessman*
181 Ridge Rd, Grosse Point Farms, MI 48236

McBride, William James *Rugby Player*
Roebuck House, Clonskea, Dublin 14, Ireland

McBroom, Amanda *Singer, Songwriter*
22903 Mariano St, Woodland Hills, CA 91367

McCabe, Charles *Columnist*
%San Francisco Chronicle, 901 Mission St, San Francisco, CA 94119

McCabe, Thomas B *Businessman*
607 N Chester Rd, Swarthmore, PA 19081

McCaffrey, Barry R *Army General*
ADC, 24th Mechanized Infantry Division, Fort Stewart, GA 31314

McCaffrey, John F *Businessman*
%Frank B Hall Co, 549 Pleasantville Rd, Briarcliff Manor, NY 10510

McCaffrey, Robert H *Businessman*
%C R Bard Inc, 731 Central Ave, Murray Hill, NJ 07974

McCain, James A *Educator*
1711 Sunny Slope Ln, Manhattan, KS 66502

McCain, John S *Senator, AZ*
921 E Lamplighter Ln, Tempe, AZ 85283

McCain, Warren E *Businessman*
%Albertson's Inc, 250 Parkcenter Blvd, Boise, ID 83726

McCall, David *Businessman*
%McCaffney & McCall Inc, 575 Madison Ave, New York, NY 10022

McCall, Howard W, Jr *Financier*
68 Dorchester Rd, Darien, CT 06820

McCall, Robert T *Artist*
4816 Moonlight Way, Paradise Valley, AZ 85253

McCalla, Irish *Actress*
920 Oak Terr, Prescott, AZ 86301

McCallister, Lon *Actor*
PO Box 396, Little River, CA 95456

McCallum, David *Actor*
%The Agency, 10351 Santa Monica Blvd, #211, Los Angeles, CA 90025

McCallum, Napoleon *Football Player*
%Los Angeles Raiders, 332 Center St, El Segundo, CA 90245

McCambridge, Mercedes *Actress*
%Michael Hartig Agency, 114 E 28th St, New York, NY 10016

McCammon, Bob *Hockey Coach*
%Vancouver Canucks, 100 N Renfrew St, Vancouver BC V5K 3N7, Canada

McCampbell, David *WW II Navy Hero (CMH)*
725 Wright Dr, Lake Worth, FL 33461

McCandless, Alfred A *Representative, CA*
%House of Representatives, Washington, DC 20515

McCandless, Bruce, II *Astronaut*
%Martin Marietta Astronautics Grp, PO Box 179, Denver, CO 80201

McCann, Chuck *Comedian*
%Dade/Rosen/Schultz Agency, 11846 Ventura Blvd, #100, Studio City, CA 91403

McCann, David A *Publisher*
%Connosseur Magazine, 224 W 57th St, New York, NY 10019

McCann, Les *Jazz Pianist, Composer*
6248 Scenic Dr, Los Angeles, CA 90068

McCann, Owen Cardinal *Religious Leader*
%Archdicesan Chancery, 12 Bouquet St, Capetown, South Africa

McCants, Keith *Football Player*
%Tampa Bay Buccaneers, 1 Buccaneer Pl, Tampa, FL 33607

McCardell, Archie *Businessman*
%International Harvester Co, 401 N Michigan Ave, Chicago, IL 60611

McCarter, John W, Jr *Businessman*
450 Somonauk, Sycamore, IL 60178

McCarthy, Denis M *Businessman*
%Emery Air Freight Corp, Old Danbury Rd, Wilton, CT 06897

McCarthy, Donald W *Astronomer*
%University of Arizona, Steward Observatory, Tucson, AZ 85721

McCarthy, Donald W *Businessman*
%Northern States Power Co, 414 Nicollet Mall, Minneapolis, MN 55401

McCarthy, Eugene J *Senator, MN*
%EPM Publishing, 1003 Turkey Run Rd, McLean, VA 22101

McCarthy, Fred *Cartoonist (Brother Juniper)*
%Field Newspaper Syndicate, 1703 Kaiser Ave, Irvine, CA 92714

McCarthy, James P *Air Force General*
Deputy, USCINCEurope, Hq USEUCOM, APO, AE 09128

McCarthy, John *Computer Scientist*
%Stanford University, Computer Science Dept, Bldg 460, Stanford, CA 94305

McCarthy, Joseph J *WW II Marine Corps Hero (CMH); General*
2305 Lowson Rd, #D, Delray Beach, FL 33445

McCarthy, Kevin *Actor*
1032 6th St, #3, Santa Monica, CA 90403

McCarthy, Mary Frances *Writer, Educator*
%Trinity College, English Dept, Washington, DC 20017

McCarthy, Michael W *Businessman*
%Merrill Lynch Inc, 1 Liberty Plz, 165 Broadway, New York, NY 10006

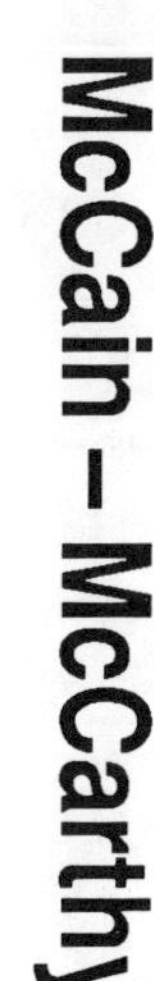

M

McCarthy, Walter J, Jr *Businessman*
%Detroit Edison Co, 2000 2nd Ave, Detroit, MI 48226

McCarthy, William J *Businessman*
%Montgomery Ward Co, 535 W Chicago Ave, Chicago, IL 60607

McCarthy, William J (Billy) *Labor Leader*
%International Teamsters Brotherhood, 25 Louisiana Ave NW, Washington, DC 20001

McCartney, Bill *Football Coach*
%University of Colorado, Athletic Dept, Boulder, CO 80309

McCartney, Linda *Singer, Photographer*
Waterfall Estate, Pearmarsh, St Leonard-on-Sea, Sussex, England

McCartney, Paul *Singer (Beatles)*
Waterfall Estate, Pearmarsh, St Leonard-on-Sea, Sussex, England

McCarver, Tim *Baseball Player, Sportscaster*
1518 Youngford Rd, Gladwynne, PA 19035

McCaskey, Mike *Football Executive*
%Chicago Bears, 250 N Washington, Lake Forest, IL 60045

McCaskill, Kirk *Baseball Player*
25 Mirador St, Irvine, CA 92715

McCaughan, John F *Businessman*
%Betz Laboratories, 4636 Somerton Rd, Trevose, PA 19047

McCauley, Barry *Opera Singer*
8 Pershing St, Emerson, NJ 07630

McCausland, Charles *Air Force General*
Director, Defense Logistics Agency, Cameron Station, VA 22304

McCay, Peggy *Actress*
%Agency for Performing Arts, 9000 Sunset Blvd, #1200, Los Angeles, CA 90069

McClanahan, Rue *Actress*
10894 Willow Crest Pl, Studio City, CA 91604

McCleery, Finnis D *Vietnam War Army Hero (CMH)*
826 Veck, #F, San Angelo, TX 76901

McClelland, David C *Psychologist*
81 Washington Ave, Cambridge, MA 02140

McClelland, W Craig *Businessman*
%Hammermill Paper Co, PO Box 10050, Erie, PA 16533

McClements, Robert, Jr *Businessman*
%Sun Co, 100 Matsonford Rd, Radnor, PA 19087

McClendon, Charles *Football Coach*
%American Football Coaches Assn, 7758 Wallace Rd, #10, Orlando, FL 32819

McClendon, Sarah *Writer, Journalist*
2933 28th St NW, Washington, DC 20008

McClintock, Barbara *Nobel Medicine Laureate*
%Carnegie Institute of Washington, Cold Spring Harbor, NY 11724

McCloskey, Frank *Representative, IN*
%House of Representatives, Washington, DC 20515

McCloskey, J Michael *Environmentalist*
%Sierra Club, 730 Polk St, San Francisco, CA 94109

McCloskey, Paul N, Jr *Representative, CA*
305 Grant Ave, Palo Alto, CA 94305

McCloskey, Robert J *Diplomat*
%Washington Post, 1150 15th St NW, Washington, DC 20071

McClure, Doug *Actor*
%William Morris Agency, 151 El Camino, Beverly Hills, CA 90212

McClure, James A *Senator, ID*
3467 N Venice St, Arlington, VA 22207

McClurg, Edie *Actress*
3306 Wonderview Plz, Los Angeles, CA 90068

McColl, Bill *Football Player*
2877 Monte Verde Dr, Covina, CA 91722

McColl, Hugh L, Jr *Financier*
%NCNB Corp, 1 NCNB Plz, Charlotte, NC 28255

McCollum, Bill *Representative, FL*
1801 Lee Rd, #301, Winter Park, FL 32789

McColough, C Peter *Businessman*
%Xerox Corp, PO Box 1600, Stamford, CT 06904

McComas, James D *Educator*
%Virginia Polutechnic Institute, President's Office, Blacksburg, VA 23284

McConnaughy, John E, Jr *Businessman*
%Peabody International Corp, 4 Landmark Sq, Stamford, CT 06904
McConnell, Harden M *Chemist*
%Stanford University, Chemistry Dept, Stanford, CA 94305
McConnell, John H *Businessman*
%Worthington Industries, 1205 Dearborn Dr, Columbus, OH 43085
McConnell, Mitch *Senator, KY*
%US Senate, Washington, DC 20510
McConnell, Robert *Publisher*
%The Gazette, 250 St Antoine St W, Montreal PQ H2Y 3R7, Canada
McConnell, Thomas R *Educator*
Grand Lake Gdns, 401 Santa Cruz Ave, #214, Oakland, CA 94610
McConnor, William S *Businessman*
%Unocal Corp, 1201 W 5th St, Los Angeles, CA 90051
McConville, Frank *Labor Leader*
%Union of Plant Guard Workers of America, 25510 Kelly Rd Roseville, MI 48066
McCoo, Marilyn *Singer*
%Davis, 9911 Mark Pl, Beverly Hills, CA 90210
McCool, Richard M *WW II Navy Hero (CMH)*
PO Box 11347, Bainbridge Island, WA 98110
McCord, Catherine *Model*
%Elite Model Mgmt, 111 E 22nd St, New York, NY 10010
McCord, Darris *Football Player*
%Photo Reproduction Services, 3144 Martin Rd, Walled Lake, MI 48390
McCord, Kent *Actor*
%David Shapira Assoc, 15301 Ventura Blvd, #345, Sherman Oaks, CA 91403
McCord, William C *Businessman*
%Enserch Corp, 300 S St Paul, Dallas, TX 75201
McCorkindale, Douglas H *Businessman*
%Gannett Co, 1100 Wilson Blvd, Arlington, VA 22209
McCorkindale, Simon *Actor*
1221 N Kings Rd, #104, Los Angeles, CA 90069
McCormack, John P *Businessman*
%Adam Opel, Bahnhofsplatz 1, 6090 Russelsheim, Germany
McCormack, Mark H *Attorney*
%Mark McCormack Enterprises, 1 Erieview Plz, #1300, Cleveland, OH 44114
McCormack, Mike *Football Coach, Executive*
%Seattle Seahawks 11220 NE 53rd St, Kirkland, WA 98033
McCormack, Patricia *Actress*
%Gores/Fields Agency, 10100 Santa Monica Blvd, #700, Los Angeles, CA 90067
McCormack, Patty *Actress*
3870 Avenida del Sol, Studio City, CA 91604
McCormick, Brooks *Businessman*
%International Harvester Co, 410 N Michigan Ave, #560, Chicago, IL 60611
McCormick, Donald F *Financier*
%Howard Savings Bank, 768 Broad St, Newark, NJ 07101
McCormick, Kevin *Cartoonist (Arnold)*
%News America Syndicate, 1703 Kaiser Ave, Irvine, CA 92714
McCormick, Mike *Baseball Player*
22330 Homestead Rd, #305, Cupertino, CA 95014
McCormick, Pat *Diver*
PO Box 250, Seal Beach, CA 90740
McCormick, Tim *Basketball Player*
%New York Knicks, Madison Square Gdn, 4 Pennsylvania Plz, New York, NY 10001
McCormick, William E *Publisher*
%Pittsburgh Post-Gazette & Press, 34 Blvd of Allies, Pittsburgh, PA 15230
McCormick, William T, Jr *Businessman*
%Consumers Power Co, 212 W Michigan Ave, Jackson, MI 49201
McCosky, Barney *Baseball Player*
66 Woodland Dr, #102, Vero Beach, FL 32962
McCovey, Willie *Baseball Player*
PO Box 620342, Woodside, CA 94062
McCowan, Robert T *Businessman*
%Ashland Oil Inc, Ashland Dr, Russell, KY 41169
McCowen, Alec *Actor*
%Conway, Eagle House, 109 Jermyn St, London SW1, England

McCoy, Charles B *Businessman*
%E I DuPont de Nemours, DuPont Bldg, Wilmington, DE 19801

McCoy, Dave *Ski Resort Builder*
%Mammoth Mountain Chairlifts, PO Box 24, Mammoth Lakes, CA 92014

McCoy, John B *Financier*
%Bank One Corp, 100 E Broad St, Columbus, OH 43215

McCoy, William O *Businessman*
%BellSouth Corp, 675 W Peachtree St NE, Atlanta, GA 30375

McCracken, G Herbert *Football Coach*
6830 N Ocean Blvd, Maisonette South 9, Ocean Ridge, FL 33435

McCracken, Paul W *Economist, Government Official*
2564 Hawthorne Rd, Ann Arbor, MI 48104

McCraig, Joseph J *Businessman*
%Grand Union Co, 100 Broadway, Elmwood Park, NJ 07407

McCrary, Douglas L *Businessman*
%Gulf Power Co, 75 N Pace Blvd, Pensacola, FL 32505

McCraw, Leslie G *Businessman*
%Fluor Corp, 3333 Michelson Dr, Irvine, CA 92730

McCray, Curtis L *Educator*
%California State University, President's Office, Long Beach, CA 90840

McCray, Rodney *Basketball Player*
%Dallas Mavericks, Reunion Arena, 777 Sports St, Dallas, TX 75207

McCrillis, John W *Skiing Executive, Writer*
%McCrillis & Eldredge Insurance, 17 Depot St, Newport, NH 03773

McCrimmon, Brad *Hockey Player*
%Calgary Flames, PO Box 1540, Station M, Calgary AB T2P 3B9, Canada

McCrory, Milt *Boxer*
%Escot Boxing Enterprises, 19600 W McNichols, Detroit, MI 48219

McCuaig, Donald D *Businessman*
%Gulf Resources & Chemical Corp, 1100 Milam Bldg, Houston, TX 77002

McCulley, Michael J *Astronaut*
%Lockheed Space Operations Co, LSO-383, 1100 Lockheed Way, Titusville, FL 32780

McCulloch, Frank W *Attorney, Educator, Arbitrator*
104 Falcon Dr, Charlottesville, VA 22901

McCulloch, Frank W *Editor*
%San Francisco Examiner, 110 5th St, San Francisco, CA 94103

McCullough, Colleen *Writer*
%Harper & Row, 10 E 53rd St, New York, NY 10022

McCumber, Mark *Golfer*
%Professional Golfers Assn, PO Box 109601, Palm Beach Gardens, FL 33410

McCune, Frank K *Businessman*
1564 Danny Dr, Sarasota, FL 33580

McCune, William J, Jr *Businessman*
%Polaroid Corp, 549 Technology Sq, Cambridge, MA 02139

McCurdy, Dave K *Representative, OK*
%House of Representatives, Washington, DC 20515

McCurdy, Richard C *Businessman*
Contentment Island, Darien, CT 06820

McCutchan, Arad *Basketball Coach*
Pine Dr, Santa Claus, IN 47579

McDade, Joseph M *Representative, PA*
%House of Representatives, Washington, DC 20515

McDaniel Singleton, Mildred *Track Athlete*
211 W Poppy Field Dr, Altadena, CA 91001

McDaniel, Boyce D *Physicist*
26 Woodcrest Ave, Ithaca, NY 14850

McDaniel, Lindy *Baseball Player*
PO Box 342, Las Vegas, NV 87701

McDaniel, Mel *Singer*
106 Cranwell Dr, Hendersonville, TN 37075

McDaniel, Randall *Football Player*
%Minnesota Vikings, 9520 Viking Dr, Eden Prairie, MN 55344

McDaniel, Xavier *Basketball Player*
%New York Knicks, Madison Square Gdn, 4 Pennsylvania Plz, New York, NY 10001

McDaniels, Darryl *Singer (Run-DMC)*
%Rush Productions, 1133 Broadway, New York, NY 10010

McDermott, Edward A *Government Official*
5400 Albemarle St NW, Washington, DC 20016

McDermott, Robert F *Businessman*
%United Services Automobile Assn, USAA Bldg, San Antonio, TX 78284

McDermott, Thomas C *Businessman*
%Bausch & Lomb Inc, 1 Lincoln First Sq, Rochester, NY 14601

McDivitt, James A *Astronaut, Air Force General*
%Rockwell International, 1745 Jefferson Davis Hwy, #1200, Arlington, VA 22202

McDonald, Alonzo L *Businessman*
255 Guilford Rd, Bloomfield Hills, MI 48013

McDonald, Charles C *Air Force General*
Commader, AF Logistics Command, Wright-Patterson Air Force Base, OH 45433

McDonald, Country Joe *Singer*
PO Box 7054, Berkeley, CA 94707

McDonald, David J *Businessman*
%Curtice-Burns Inc, 1 Lincoln First Sq, Rochester, NY 14603

McDonald, Duncan *Businessman*
19 North Park Terr, Edinburgh EH4 1DP, Scotland

Mcdonald, Gregory *Writer*
PO Box 193, Lincoln, MA 01773

McDonald, James F *Businessman*
%Gould Inc, 10 Gould Ctr, Rolling Meadows, IL 60008

McDonald, Lanny *Hockey Player*
%Calgary Flames, PO Box 1540, Station M, Calgary AB T2P 3B9, Canada

McDonald, Marshall *Businessman*
%FPL Grp, 9250 W Flagler St, Miami, FL 33174

McDonald, Randal *Businessman*
%Pennzoil Co, Pennzoil Pl, Houston, TX 77252

McDonald, Robert E *Businessman*
1125 Robin Rd, Gladwyne, PA 19035

McDonald, Tim *Football Player*
%Phoenix Cardinals, PO Box 888, Phoenix, AZ 85001

McDonald, Tommy *Football Player*
%Tommy McDonald Enterprises, PO Box 184, King of Prussia, PA 19406

McDonell, Horace G *Businessman*
%Perkin-Elmer Corp, 761 Main Ave, Norwalk, CT 06859

McDonell, Terry *Editor*
%Esquire Magazine, 1790 Broadway, New York, NY 10019

McDonnell, John F *Businessman*
%McDonnell Douglas Corp, PO Box 516, St Louis, MO 63166

McDonnell, Mary *Actress*
%Bresler Kelly Kipperman Assoc, 15760 Ventura Blvd, #1730, Encino. CA 91436

McDonnell, Sanford N *Businessman*
%McDonnell Douglas Corp, PO Box 516, St Louis, MO 63166

McDonough, Gerald C *Businessman*
%Leaseway Transportation Corp, 3700 Park East Dr, Beachwood, OH 44122

McDonough, Sean *Sportscaster*
%CBS-TV, Sports Dept, 51 W 52nd St, New York, NY 10019

McDonough, Will *Sportscaster*
4 Malcolm St, Hingham, MA 02043

McDonough, William *Architect*
%William McDonough Architects, 116 E 27th St, New York, NY 10016

McDormand, Frances *Actress*
%International Creative Mgmt, 8899 Beverly Blvd, Los Angeles, CA 90048

McDougald, Gil *Baseball Player*
10 Warren Ave, Spring Lake, NJ 07762

McDougall, Walter *Historian*
%University of California, History Dept, Berkeley, CA 94720

McDowall, Roddy *Actor*
%Badgley Connor, 9229 Sunset Blvd, #607, Los Angeles, CA 90069

McDowell, Frank *Plastic Surgeon*
100-F N Kalaheo, Kailua, HI 96734

McDowell, Malcolm *Actor*
%Camden ITG, 822 S Robertson Blvd, #200, Los Angeles, CA 90035

McDowell, Sam *Baseball Player*
7727 St Lawrence Ave, Pittsburgh, PA 15218

McDuffie, Robert *Concert Violinist*
111 E 85th St, New York, NY 10028

McEachran, Angus *Editor*
%Pittsburgh Press, 34 Blvd of Allies, Pittsburgh, PA 15230

McElhenny, Hugh *Football Player*
4023 171st Ave SE, Bellevue, WA 98008

McElroy, Joseph P *Writer*
%Georges Borchandt, 136 E 57th St, New York, NY 10022

McElroy, William David *Biochemist*
%University of California, Biology Dept, La Jolla, CA 92067

McElwaine, Guy *Businessman*
%Columbia Pictures Industries, 711 5th Ave, New York, NY 10022

McElwee, John G *Businessman*
%John Hancock Mutual Life Insurance, 200 Clarendon St, Boston, MA 02117

McEneaney, James F *Businessman*
%Ryland Homes, 10221 Wincopin Cir, Columbia, MD 21044

McEnery, Tom *Mayor*
%Mayor's Office, City Hall, 801 N 1st St, San Jose, CA 95110

McEnroe, John *Tennis Player*
23712 Malibu Colony Rd, Malibu, CA 90265

McEntee, Gerald W *Labor Leader*
%State County Municipal Employees Union, 1625 "L" St, Washington, DC 20036

McEntire, Reba *Singer*
PO Box 121966, Nashville, TN 37212

McEvoy, Nan Tucker *Businesswoman*
%San Francisco Chronicle Publishing Co, 901 Mission St, San Francisco, CA 94103

McEwen, Mike *Hockey Player*
%Hartford Whalers, 1 Civic Center Plz, Hartford, CT 06103

McEwen, Robert C *Representative, NY*
Rt 2, Ogdensburg, NY 13669

McEwen, Tom *Drag Racing Driver*
17368 Buttonwood, Fountain Valley, CA 92708

McFadden, James (Banks) *Football Player*
253 Riggs Dr, Clemson, SC 29631

McFadden, Mary *Fashion Designer*
264 W 35th St, New York, NY 10001

McFadin, Lewis (Bud) *Football Player*
%General Delivery, Victoria, TX 77902

McFarland, James P *Businessman*
%General Mills Inc, PO Box 1113, Minneapolis, MN 55440

McFarland, Spanky *Actor*
PO Box 80202, Fort Worth, TX 76180

McFarther, Larry *Labor Leader*
%Brotherhood of Locomotive Engineers, Standard Bldg, Cleveland, OH 44113

McFeeley, William S *Historian*
23 Ashfield Ln, South Hadley, MA 01075

McFerrin, Bobby *Singer*
%Linda Goldstein Original Artists, 129 W 69th St, New York, NY 10023

McGahey, James C *Labor Leader*
%Plant Guard Workers Union, 25510 Kelly Rd, Roseville, MI 48066

McGarity, Vernon *WW II Army Hero (CMH)*
4522 Quince Ave, Memphis, TN 38117

McGaugh, James L *Psychobiologist*
2327 Aralia St, Newport Beach, CA 92660

McGavin, Darren *Actor*
470 Park Ave, New York, NY 10022

McGaw, Foster G *Businessman*
%American Hospital Supply Corp, 1 American Plz, Evanston, IL 60201

McGee, Dean A *Businessman*
%Kerr-McGee Corp, Kerr-McGee Ctr, Oklahoma City, OK 73125

McGee, Gale W *Senator, WY; Diplomat*
1201 Pennsylvania Ave NW, #700, Washington, DC 20004

McGee, Mike *Basketball Player*
%New Jersey Nets, Meadowlands Arena, East Rutherford, NJ 07073

McGee, Mike *Football Player, Administrator*
%University of Southern California, Heritage Hall, Los Angeles, CA 90089

McGee, Tim *Football Player*
%Cincinnati Bengals, 200 Riverfront Stadium, Cincinnati, OH 45202
McGee, Vonetta *Singer*
%Writers & Artists, 11726 San Vicente Blvd, #300, Los Angeles, CA 90049
McGee, William G *Businessman*
%Piedmont Aviation, Smith Reynolds Airport, Winston-Salem, NC 27156
McGhee, Brownie *Singer*
688 43rd St, Oakland, CA 94609
McGill, Archie *Financier*
%Rothschild Inc, 1 Rockefeller Plz, New York, NY 10020
McGill, Everett *Actor*
%Triad Artists, 10100 Santa Monica Blvd, #1600, Los Angeles, CA 90067
McGill, William J *Educator*
2624 Costebelle Dr, La Jolla, CA 92037
McGillicuddy, John F *Financier*
%Manufacturers Hanover Trust, 270 Park Ave, New York, NY 10017
McGillis, Kelly *Actress*
9595 Wilshire Blvd, #505, Beverly Hills, CA 90212
McGinniss, Joe *Writer*
%Sterling Lord, 660 Madison Ave, New York, NY 10021
McGirt, James (Buddy) *Boxer*
%B Goodman, Madison Square Grdn Boxing, 4 Pennsylvania Plz, New York, NY 10001
McGlockin, Jon *Basketball Player*
%Bando-McGlocklin Investment Co, 13555 Bishops Ct, #205, Brookfield, WI 53005
McGlothlin, Ray, Jr *Businessman*
%E-Z Serve Inc, 901 S 1st St, Abilene, TX 79604
McGonagle, William L *Mediterrean Action Navy Hero (CMH)*
500 E Amado Rd, #612, Palm Springs, CA 92262
McGoohan, Patrick *Actor*
%The Agency, 10351 Santa Monica Blvd, #211, Los Angeles, CA 90025
McGoon, Dwight C *Surgeon*
%Mayo Clinic, 200 1st St SW, Rochester, MN 55901
McGovern, Elizabeth *Actress*
9161 Hazen Dr, Beverly Hills, CA 90210
McGovern, George S *Senator, SD*
1825 Connecticut Ave NW, #213, Washington, DC 20009
McGovern, Maureen *Singer*
%Barron Mgmt, 529 W 42nd St, #7-F, New York, NY 10036
McGovern, Patrick *Publisher*
%International Data Group, 60 Austin St, Framingham, MA 02160
McGowan, George V *Businessman*
%Baltimore Gas & Electric Co, Gas & Electric Bldg, Baltimore, MD 21203
McGowan, William G *Businessman*
%MCI Communications, 1133 19th St NW, Washington, DC 20036
McGranahan, Donald V *Social Scientist*
47 Chemin Moise Duboule, 1209 Geneva, Switzerland
McGrath, Raymond J *Representative, NY*
%House of Representatives, Washington, DC 20515
McGraw, Harold W, III *Publisher*
%Aviation Week Magazine, 1221 Ave of Americas, New York, NY 10020
McGraw, Harold W, Jr *Publisher*
%McGraw-Hill Inc, 1221 Ave of Americas, New York, NY 10020
McGraw, Tug (Frank E) *Baseball Player*
1 Dale Ln, Wallingford, PA 19086
McGregor, Maurice *Cardiologist*
%Royal Victoria Hospital, 687 Pine Ave W, Montreal PQ H3A 1A1, Canada
McGregor, Scott *Baseball Player*
Star Rt 1, Box 2800-1300, Tehachapi, CA 93561
McGriff, Hershel *Auto Racing Driver*
%General Delivery, Green Valley, AZ 85622
McGrory, Mary *Columnist*
%Universal Press Syndicate, 4400 Fairway Dr, Fairway, KS 66205
McGuff, Joe *Sportswriter*
%Kansas City Star, 1729 Grand Ave, Kansas City, MO 64108
McGuire, Al *Basketball Coach, Sportscaster*
%NBC-TV, Sports Dept, 30 Rockefeller Plz, New York, NY 10020

M

McGuire – McKeel

McGuire, Biff — *Actor*
1650 Broadway, #406, New York, NY 10019

McGuire, Dorothy — *Actress*
121 Copley Pl, Beverly Hills, CA 90210

McGuire, Frank J — *Basketball Coach*
268 Sandhurst Rd, Columbia, SC 29210

McGuire, Patricia A — *Educator*
%Trinity College, President's Office, Washington, DC 20017

McGuire, Willard H — *Labor Leader*
%National Education Assn, 1201 16th St NW, Washington, DC 20036

McGuirk, Terry — *Television Executive*
%Turner Broadcasting Systems, 1 CNN Ctr, #1300, Atlanta, GA 30303

McGwire, Mark — *Baseball Player*
%Oakland A's, Oakland-Alameda County Coliseum, PO Box 2220, Oakland, CA 94621

McHale, Kevin — *Basketball Player*
41 Stonybrook, Weston, MA 02193

McHenry, Donald F — *Diplomat*
%Georgetown University, Foreign Service School, Washington, DC 20057

McHugh, Matthew F — *Representative, NY*
1003 Triphammer Rd, Ithaca, NY 14850

McHugh, Peter T — *Businessman*
%Pan American Corp, 200 Park Ave, New York, NY 10166

McInally, Pat — *Football Player*
PO Box 17791, Fort Mitchell, KY 41017

McInerney, Thomas G — *Air Force General*
Commander, AAC & Alaskan NORAD Region, Elmendorf Air Force Base, AK 99506

McInnes, Harold A — *Businessman*
%AMP Inc, 470 Friendship Rd, Harrisburg, PA 17109

McIntosh, Thomas S — *Businessman*
%Zapata Corp, Zapata Tower, PO Box 4240, Houston, TX 77210

McIntyre, James A — *Businessman*
%Fremont General Corp, 525 S Virgil Ave, Los Angeles, CA 90020

McIntyre, James C — *Businessman*
%General American Life Insurance, PO Box 396, St Louis, MO 63166

McIntyre, James T, Jr — *Government Official*
%Hansell Post Brandon Dorsey, 1747 Pennsylvania Ave, Washington, DC 20006

McIntyre, Lee E — *Businessman*
%Fremont General Corp, 525 S Virgil Ave, Los Angeles, CA 90025

McIntyre, Richard — *Representative, IN*
%House of Representatives, Washington, DC 20515

McIntyre, Robert M — *Businessman*
%Pacific Lighting Corp, 810 S Flower St, Los Angeles, CA 90060

McIntyre, Thomas J — *Senator, NH*
2923 Garfield St NW, Washington, DC 20008

McKay, Gardner — *Actor*
9301 Cherokee Ln, Beverly Hills, CA 90210

McKay, Heather — *Squash, Raquetball Player*
48 Nesbitt Dr, Toronto ON M4W 2G3, Canada

McKay, Janet — *Educator*
%Mills College, President's Office, Oakland, CA 94613

McKay, Jim — *Sportscaster*
%ABC-TV, Sports Dept, 1330 Ave of Americas, New York, NY 10019

McKay, Monroe G — *Judge*
%US Court of Appeals, Federal Bldg, 125 S State St, Salt Lake City, UT 84138

McKechnie, Donna — *Dancer, Actress*
710 Park Ave, #7-B, New York, NY 10021

McKee, Frank S — *Labor Leader*
%United Steelworkers Union, 5 Gateway Ctr, Pittsburgh, PA 15222

McKee, James W, Jr — *Businessman*
%CPC International, International Plz, Englewood Cliffs, NJ 07632

McKee, Lewis K — *Businessman*
%Federal Co, PO Box 17236, Memphis, TN 38187

McKee, Maria — *Singer*
%Geffen Records, 9126 Sunset Blvd, Los Angeles, CA 90069

McKeel, Sam S — *Publisher*
%Philadelphia Inquirer, 400 N Broad St, Philadelphia, PA 19101

McKeever, Marlin *Football Player*
%Andreini & Co, 770 The City Dr, #1300, Orange, CA 92613

McKeithen, John J *Governor, LA*
%McKeithen Wear Ryland Woodard, 221 Wall St, Columbia, LA 71418

McKellar, Danica *Actress*
%Savage Agency, 6212 Banner Ave, Los Angeles, CA 90038

McKellen, Ian *Actor*
25 Earls Terr, London W8, England

McKenna, Alex G *Businessman*
%Kennametal Inc, Rt 981 & Westmoreland County Airport, Latrobe, PA 15650

McKenna, Quentin C *Businessman*
%Kennametal Inc, Rt 981 & Westmoreland County Airport, Latrobe, PA 15650

McKenna, Virginia *Actress*
Cherry Tree Cottage, Cold Harbour, Dorking, Surrey RH5 6HA, England

McKenna, William J *Businessman*
%Kellwood Co, 600 Kellwood Pkwy, St Louis, MO 63017

McKenny, Jere W *Businessman*
%Kerr-McGee Corp, Kerr-McGee Ctr, Oklahoma City, OK 73125

McKenzie, Kevin *Ballet Dancer*
%American Ballet Theatre, 890 Broadway, New York, NY 10003

McKenzie, Reggie *Football Player*
%Seattle Seahawks, 11220 NE 53rd St, Kirkland, WA 98033

McKeon, Nancy *Actress*
PO Box 6778, Burbank, CA 90510

McKeown, Bob *Commentator*
CBS-TV, News Dept, 524 W 57th St, New York, NY 10019

McKern, Leo *Actor*
International Creative Mgmt, 388-39696 Oxford St, London W1 9HE, England

McKernan, John R, Jr *Governor, ME*
%Governor's Office, Blaine House, Augusta, ME 04333

McKernan, Leo J *Businessman*
%Clark Equipment Co, 100 N Michigan St, South Bend, IN 46634

McKey, Derrick *Basketball Player*
%Seattle SuperSonics, 190 Queen Ann Ave N, Seattle, WA 98109

McKieman, John S *Governor, RI*
95 Hilltop Dr, East Greenwich, RI 02818

McKinney, Frank M, Jr *Swimmer*
%American Fletcher National Bank, 101 Monument Cir, Indianapolis, IN 46277

McKinney, John A *Businessman*
%Manville Corp, Ken-Caryl Ranch, Denver, CO 80217

McKinney, John R *WW II Army Hero (CMH)*
101 Shell Ln, Sylvania, GA 30467

McKinney, Joseph F *Businessman*
%Tyler Corp, 3200 San Jacinto Tower, Dallas, TX 75201

McKinney, Mark *Actor*
%Harry Gold Assoc, 3500 W Olive Ave, #1400, Burbank, CA 91505

McKinney, Rick *Archer*
%Hoyt/Easton USA, 549 E Silver Creek, Gilbert, AZ 85234

McKinney, Robert M *Publisher, Diplomat*
Rt 1, Box 64, Middleburg, VA 22117

McKinney, Tamara *Skier*
%Jimmy Heuga Health Ctr, PO Box 5480, Avon, CO 81620

McKinnon, Alan L *Financier*
%Bank of Boston Corp, 100 Federal St, Boston, MA 02110

McKinnon, Arnold B *Businessman*
%Norfolk Southern Corp, 1 Commerce Pl, Norfolk, VA 23510

McKinnon, John B *Businessman*
%Sara Lee Corp, 3 First National Plz, Chicago, IL 60602

McKone, Don T *Businessman*
%Libbey-Owens-Ford Co, 811 Madison Ave, Toledo, OH 43695

McKuen, Rod *Poet, Singer*
1155 Angelo Dr, Beverly Hills, CA 90210

McKusick, Victor A *Clinical Geneticist*
%Johns Hopkins Hospital, Genetics Dept, 600 N Wolfe St, Baltimore, MD 21205

McLaglen, Andrew V *Movie Director*
%Stanmore Productions, PO Box 1056, Friday Harbor, WA 98250

McLain, Denny *Baseball Player*
4933 Coventry Pkwy, Fort Wayne, IN 46804

McLane, Jimmy *Swimmer*
2-C Brockett Pl, Marblehead, MA 01945

McLaughlin, Ann Dore *Secretary, Labor*
%Urban Institute of Washington, 2100 "M" St NW, Washington, DC 20037

McLaughlin, Audrey *Government Official, Canada*
%New Democratic Party, House of Commons, Ottawa ON K1A 0A6, Canada

McLaughlin, Donald Hamilton *Businessman*
1450 Hawthorne Terr, Berkeley, CA 94708

McLaughlin, Edward F *Radio Executive*
%ABC Radio Network, 1330 Ave of Americas, New York, NY 10019

McLaughlin, John *Singer, Songwriter*
%Ted Kurland Assoc, 173 Brighton Ave, Boston, MA 02134

McLaughlin, Peter J *Businessman*
%Union Camp Corp, 1600 Valley Rd, Wayne, NJ 07470

McLean, Barney *Skier*
3355 Nelson St, Wheatridge, CO 80033

McLean, Don *Singer*
Old Manitou Rd, Garrison, NY 10524

McLean, Don *Basketball Player*
%University of California, Athletic Dept, Los Angeles, CA 90024

McLean, Malcom P *Businessman*
%McLean Industries, 660 Madison Ave, New York, NY 10021

McLean, Malcom P, Jr *Businessman*
%McLean Industries, 660 Madison Ave, New York, NY 10021

McLean, Vincent R *Businessman*
%Unisys Corp, 1290 Ave of Americas, New York, NY 10104

McLendon, John A *Businessman*
%Insilco Corp, 1000 Research Pkwy, Meriden, CT 06450

McLendon, John B, Jr *Basketball Coach*
6021 Clyde Dr, Downers Grove, IL 60515

McLeod, Catherine *Actress*
4146 Allott Ave, Van Nuys, CA 91423

McLeod, George J *Businessman*
%Noble Affiliates Inc, 330 Neustadt Plz, Ardmore, OK 73401

McLerie, Allyn Ann *Actress*
4234 Babcock Ave, Studio City, CA 91604

McLucas, John L *Businessman, Government Official*
6519 Dearborn Dr, Falls Churhc, VA 22044

McLure, Charles E, Jr *Government Official*
250 Yerba Santa Ana, Los Altos, CA 94022

McMackin, John J *Businessman*
%Brockway Inc, McCullough Ave, Brockway, PA 15824

McMahon, Donald A *Businessman*
%Royal Crown Companies, 41 Perimeter Ctr NE, Atlanta, GA 30346

McMahon, Ed *Entertainer*
12000 Crest Ct, Beverly Hills, CA 90210

McMahon, Jim *Football Player*
%Philadelphia Eagles, Veterans Stadium, Philadelphia, PA 19148

McMahon, Vince *Wrestling Promoter*
%World Wrestling Federation, Madison Square Gdn, New York, NY 10001

McManus, Jason *Editor*
%Time Warner Inc, Rockefeller Ctr, New York, NY 10020

McMath, Sid *Governor, AR*
711 W 3rd St, Little Rock, AR 72201

McMichael, Steve *Football Player*
%Chicago Bears, 250 N Washington Rd, Lake Forest, IL 60045

McMichen, Robert S *Labor Leader*
%International Typographical Union, PO Box 157, Colorado Springs, CO 80901

McMillan, Roy *Baseball Player*
1200 E 9th St, Bonham, TX 75418

McMillen, Dale W, Jr *Financier*
3415 S Washington Rd, Fort Wayne, IN 46804

McMillen, Tom *Basketball Player; Representative, MD*
#2 Village Green, Crofton, MD 21114

McMillian, J Alex *Representative, NC*
%House of Representatives, Washington, DC 20515

McMillian, Theodore *Judge*
%US Court of Appeals, US Courthouse, 1114 Market St, St Louis, MO 63101

McMonagle, Donald R *Astronaut*
%NASA, Johnson Space Ctr, Houston, TX 77058

McMorris, Donald L *Businessman*
%Yellow Freight System of Delaware, 10990 Roe Ave, Overland Park, KS 66207

McMullian, Amos R *Businessman*
%Flowers Industries, PO Box 1338, Thomasville, GA 31799

McMurray, W Grant *Religious Leader*
%Reorganized Church of Latter Day Saints, PO Box 1059, Independence, MO 64051

McMurren, W H *Businessman*
%Morrison-Knudsen Co, 1 Morrison-Knudsen Plz, Boise, ID 83707

McMurtry, Larry *Writer*
PO Box 552, Archer City, TX 76351

McNair, Barbara *Singer*
%Lew Sherrell Agency, 1353 Los Robles, Palm Springs, CA 92262

McNair, Robert E *Governor, SC*
Rt 2, Box 310, Columbia, SC 29210

McNall, Bruce *Hockey Executive*
%Los Angeles Kings, Great Western Forum, 3900 W Manchester, Inglewood, CA 90306

McNally, Andrew, III *Publisher*
%Rand McNally & Co, PO Box 7600, Chicago, IL 60680

McNally, Andrew, IV *Publisher*
%Rand McNally & Co, PO Box 7600, Chicago, IL 60680

McNally, Dave *Baseball Player*
3305 Ramada Dr, Billings, MT 59102

McNally, Stephen *Actor*
624 N Hillcrest Rd, Beverly Hills, CA 90210

McNally, Terrence *Playwright*
218 W 10th St, New York, NY 10014

McNamara, Brian *Actor*
%Gersh Agency, 232 N Canon Dr, Beverly Hills, CA 90210

McNamara, John *Baseball Manager*
158 Still Meadow Dr, Cincinnati, OH 45245

McNamara, Julianne *Gymnast*
%Barry Axelrod, 2236 Encinitas Blvd, #A, Encinitas, CA 90204

McNamara, Robert S *Secretary, Defense*
2412 Tracy Pl, Washington, DC 20008

McNamara, William *Actor*
%William Morris Agency, 151 El Camino, Beverly Hills, CA 90212

McNary, Gene *Government Official*
%US Immigration & Naturalization Service, 425 "I" St NW, Washington, DC 20536

McNaughton, Robert F, Jr *Computer Scientist*
2511 15th St, Troy, NY 12180

McNeer, Charles S *Businessman*
%Wisconsin Electric Power Co, 231 W Michigan St, Milwaukee, WI 53201

McNeil, Freeman *Football Player*
%New York Jets, 598 Madison Ave, New York, NY 10022

McNeil, Gerald *Football Player*
%Cleveland Browns, Cleveland Stadium, Cleveland, OH 44114

McNeil, Lori *Tennis Player*
%International Management Grp, 1 Erieview Plz, Cleveland, OH 44114

McNeill, James *Businessman*
%Broken Hill Proprietary Co, 140 William St, Melbourne, Australia

McNeill, W Donald *Tennis Player*
670 Eugenia Rd, Vero Beach, FL 32960

McNerney, David H *Vietnam War Army Hero (CMH)*
20322 New Moon Trl, Crosby, TX 77532

McNichols, Stephen L R *Governor, CO*
3404 S Race St, Englewood, CO 80110

McNichols, William H, Jr *Mayor*
754 Krameria St, Denver, CO 80220

McNulty, James F, Jr *Representative, AZ*
1605 N Wilmot Rd, #108, Tucson, AZ 85712

McNutt, Jack W *Businessman*
%Murphy Oil Corp, 200 Peach St, El Dorado, AK 71730

McPeak, Merrill A *Air Force General*
%Chief of Staff, US Air Force, Hq USAF, Washington, DC 20330

McPhee, John A *Writer*
475 Drake's Corner Rd, Princeton, NJ 08540

McPherson, Frank A *Businessman*
%Kerr-McGee Corp, Kerr-McGee Ctr, Oklahoma City, OK 73125

McPherson, Mary Patterson *Educator*
%Bryn Mawr College, President's Office, Bryn Mawr, PA 19010

McPherson, Rene C *Businessman*
%Dana Corp, 4500 Dorr St, Toledo, OH 43615

McPherson, Rolf K *Religious Leader*
%Church of Foursquare Gospel, 1100 Glendale Blvd, Los Angeles, CA 90026

McQuarrie, Gerald H *Financier*
%Downey Savings & Loan, 3200 Bristol St, Costa Mesa, CA 92626

McQueen, Butterfly *Actress*
31 Hamilton Terr, #3, New York, NY 10031

McRae, Carmen *Singer*
2200 Summit Ridge, Beverly Hills, CA 90201

McRae, Hal *Baseball Player*
2531 Landing Cir, Bradenton, FL 33529

McRaney, Gerald *Actor*
329 N Wetherly Dr, #101, Beverly Hills, CA 90211

McReynolds, Kevin *Baseball Player*
Camp Robinson, North Little Rock, AR 72118

McShane, Edward James *Mathematician*
209 Maury Ave, Charlottesville, VA 22903

McShane, Ian *Actor*
%Gersh Agency, 232 N Canon Dr, Beverly Hills, CA 90210

McSwiney, James Wilmer *Businessman*
%Mead Corp, Courthouse Plz NE, Dayton, OH 45463

McVie, Christine *Singer (Fleetwood Mac)*
9477 Lloydcrest Dr, Beverly Hills, CA 90210

McVie, Tom *Hockey Coach*
%New Jersey Devils, Meadowlands Arena, East Rutherford, NJ 07023

McWethy, John *Commentator*
%ABC-TV, News Dept, 1717 De Sales St NW, Washington, DC 20036

McWherter, Ned *Governor, TN*
%Governor's Office, State Capitol Bldg, Nashville, TN 37219

McWhirter, Norris *Publisher*
2 Cecil Ct, London Rd, Enfield EN2 6DJ, England

McWhorter, R Clayton *Businessman*
%Hospital Corp of America, 1 Park Plz, Nashville, TN 37203

McWilliams, Caroline *Actress*
%International Creative Mgmt, 8899 Beverly Blvd, Los Angeles, CA 90048

McWilliams, David *Football Coach, Administrator*
%University of Texas, Athletic Dept, Austin, TX 78712

McWilliams, Robert H *Judge*
US Courthouse, 1929 Stout St, Denver, CO 80294

Mead, George W *Businessman*
%Consolidated Papers Inc, 231 1st Ave N, Wisconsin Rapids, WI 54494

Mead, Shepherd *Writer*
3 W Eaton Pl, #B, London SW1X 8LU, England

Meade, Carl J *Astronaut*
%NASA, Johnson Space Ctr, Houston, TX 77058

Meade, James E *Nobel Economics Laureate*
40 High St, Little Shelford, Cambridge CB2 5ES, England

Meadlock, James W *Businessman*
%Intergraph Corp, 1 Madison Industrial Park, Huntsville, AL 35807

Meadow, David L *Religious Leader*
%Churches of God General Conference, 7176 Glenmeadow Dr, Frederick, MD 21701

Meadows, Audrey *Actress*
350 Trousdale Pl, Beverly Hills, CA 90210

Meadows, Earl *Track Athlete*
1220 W Fogg Ave, Fort Worth, TX 76110

Meadows, Jayne — *Actress*
16185 Woodvale Ave, Encino, CA 91316

Meagher, John W — *WW II Army Hero (CMH)*
38 Hyannis St, Toms River, NJ 08757

Meagher, Mary T — *Swimmer*
4100 Ormond Dr, Louisville, KY 40207

Means, Russell — *Indian Activist*
444 Crazy Horse Dr, Porcupine, SD 57772

Meara, Anne — *Comedienne*
118 Riverside Dr, #5-A, New York, NY 10024

Mears, Gary H — *Air Force General*
Director, Logistics, J-4, Joint Staff, Washington, DC 20318

Mears, Rick — *Auto Racing Driver*
%Championship Auto Racing Teams, 2655 Woodward Ave, Bloomfield Hills, MI 48013

Mears, Walter R — *Journalist*
%Associated Press, 2021 "K" St NW, Washington, DC 20006

Meatloaf (Marvin Lee Aday) — *Singer*
PO Box 68, Stockport, Cheshire SK30 JY, England

Mebiame, Leon — *Prime Minister, Gabon*
%Prime Minister's Office, BP 546, Libreville, Gabon

Mecham, Evan — *Governor, AZ*
%Mecham Pontiac-AMC-Renault, 4510 W Glendale Ave, Glendale, AZ 85301

Mechem, Charles S, Jr — *Sports Executive*
%Ladies Professional Golf Assn, 2570 Volusia Ave, #B, Daytona Beach, FL 32114

Mecklenburg, Karl — *Football Player*
%Denver Broncos, 13655 E Dove Valley Pkwy, Englewood, CO 80112

Mecom, John W, Jr — *Football Executive*
%New Orleans Saints, 6928 Saints Dr, Metairie, LA 70003

Mecum, Dudley C — *Businessman*
%Combustion Engineering Inc, 900 Long Ridge Rd, Stamford, CT 06902

Medaris, John Bruce — *Clergyman, Army General*
1050 Cottontail Ln, Maitland, FL 32751

Medavoy, Mike — *Entertainment Executive*
%Tri-Star Pictures, 1875 Century Park East, Los Angeles, CA 90067

Medberry, Chauncey J, III — *Financier*
%Bank of America, 555 S Flower St, Los Angeles, CA 90071

Medina, Patricia — *Actress*
1993 Mesa Dr, Palm Springs, CA 92264

Medley, Bill — *Singer (Righteous Brothers)*
%Rillera, 9841 Hot Springs Dr, Huntington Beach, CA 92646

Medoff, Mark — *Playwright*
%New Mexico State University, Theater Dept, Las Cruces, NM 88003

Medved, Aleksandr — *Wrestler*
%Central Soviet Sports Federation, Skatertny p 4, Moscow, Russia

Medvedev, Zhores A — *Geneticist*
%Institute for Medical Research, Ridgeway, London NW7 1AA, England

Meehan, Thomas E — *Writer*
Brook House, Obtuse Rd, Newtown, CT 88003

Meek, Paul D — *Businessman*
%American Petrofina Inc, Fina Plz, Dallas, TX 75206

Meek, Phillip J — *Publisher*
%Capital Cities/ABC Publishing Division, 7 E 12th St, New York, NY 10003

Meggett, David — *Football Player*
%New York Giants, Giants Stadium, East Rutherford, NJ 07073

Mehl, Lance — *Football Player*
%New York Jets, 598 Madison Ave, New York, NY 10022

Mehrabian, Robert — *Educator*
%Cranegie Mellon University, President's Office, Pittsburgh, PA 15213

Mehregany, Mehran — *Microbiotics Engineer*
%Case Western Reserve University, Electrical Engineer Dept, Cleveland, OH 44106

Mehta, Ved — *Writer*
%W W Norton Co, 500 5th Ave, New York, NY 10110

Mehta, Zubin — *Conductor*
%New York Philharmonic, Avery Fisher Hall, Lincoln Ctr, New York, NY 10023

Meier, Richard — *Architect*
%Richard Meier Partners, 457 10th Ave, New York, NY 10016

Meier, Vernon H *Labor Leader*
%National Rural Letter Carriers Assn, 1630 Duke St, 4th Fl, Alexandria, VA 22314

Meigher, S Christopher, III *Publisher*
%People Magazine, Rockefeller Ctr, New York, NY 10020

Meinert, John R *Businessman*
%Hartmarx Corp, 101 N Wacker Dr, Chicago, IL 60606

Meinwald, Jerrold *Chemist*
%Cornell University, Chemistry Dept, Ithaca, NY 14853

Meisner, Sanford *Actor, Director*
%Neighborhood Playhouse School of Theatre, 340 E 54th St, New York, NY 10022

Meister, Alton *Biochemist*
%Cornell University Medical College, 1300 York Ave, New York, NY 10021

Mejia, Paul *Choreographer*
%Chicago City Ballet, 76 W 69th St, New York, NY 10023

Mekka, Eddie *Actor*
%Coast-to-Coast Group, 4942 Vineland Ave, #200, North Hollywood, CA 91601

Melamid, Aleksandr *Artist*
%Ronald Freeman Fine Arts, 31 Mercer St, New York, NY 10013

Melcher, John *Senator, MT*
%General Delivery, Forsyth, MT 59327

Melchior, Ib *Writer*
8228 Marymount Ln, Los Angeles, CA 90069

Melendez, Bill *Animator*
438 N Larchmont Blvd, Los Angeles, CA 90004

Melinda (Saxe) *Illusionist*
%Sands Hotel Casino, 3355 Las Vegas Blvd S, Las Vegas, NV 89109

Mellanby, Kenneth *Entomologist, Ecologist*
38 Warkworth St, Cambridge CB1 1ER, England

Mellencamp, John *Singer*
Rt 1, Box 361, Nashville, IN 47448

Melles, Carl *Conductor*
Grunbergstrasse 4, 1130 Vienna, Austria

Mellinkoff, Sherman *Physician, Educator*
%University of California, Medical Ctr, Los Angeles, CA 90024

Mellon, Paul *Foundation Executive*
1729 "H" St NW, Washington, DC 20006

Mellor, James R *Businessman*
%General Dynamics Corp, Pierre Laclede Ctr, St Louis, MO 63105

Melnick, Bruce E *Astronaut*
%NASA, Johnson Space Ctr, Houston, TX 77058

Melnick, Daniel *Movie, Television Producer*
1123 Sunset Hills Dr, Los Angeles, CA 90067

Melone, Joseph J *Businessman*
%Equitable Life Assurance Society, 787 7th Ave, New York, NY 10019

Melrose, Kendrick B *Businessman*
%Toro Co, 8009 34th Ave S, Minneapolis, MN 55420

Melton, Sid *Actor*
5347 Cedros Ave, Van Nuys, CA 91410

Melville, Donald R *Businessman*
%Norton Co, 120 Front St, Worcester, MA 01608

Melvin, Allan *Actor*
%Gene Yusem Assoc, 9000 Sunset Blvd, #502, Los Angeles, CA 90069

Melzer, Thomas *Financier*
%Federal Reserve Bank of St Louis, PO Box 442, St Louis, MO 63166

Menard, Henry W *Geologist*
%Scripps Institute of Oceanography, La Jolla, CA 92093

Mendes, Sergio *Musician*
4849 Encino Ave, Encino, CA 91316

Menem, Carlos Saul *President, Argentina*
%President's Office, Casa Rosada, Buenos Aires, Argentina

Meneses, Antonio *Concert Cellist*
%International Creative Mgmt, 40 W 57th St, New York, NY 10019

Menge, Walter O *Businessman*
200 Beach Rd, Tequesta, FL 33458

Menges, Chris *Cinematographer*
%Harmony Pictures, 2921 W Alameda Ave, Burbank, CA 91505

Menk, Louis W *Businessman*
%International Harvester Co, 401 N Michigan Ave, Chicago, IL 60611

Mennea, Pietro *Track Athlete*
Via Cassia 1041, 00189 Rome, Italy

Mennin, Peter *Composer*
%Julliard School, Lincoln Ctr, New York, NY 10023

Meno, Chorepiscopus John *Religious Leader*
%Syrian Orthodox Church of Antioch, 45 Fairmount Ave, Hackensack, NJ 07601

Menotti, Gian-Carlo *Composer*
27 E 62nd St, New York, NY 10021

Menscer, Darrell V *Businessman*
%Public Service Co of Indiana, 1000 E Main St, Plainfield, IN 46168

Menuhin, Yehudi *Concert Violinist*
Chalet Chankly Bore, Buhlstrasse, CH-3780 Gstaad-Neuret, Switzerland

Menzies, Heather *Actress*
15930 Woodvale Rd, Encino, CA 91436

Meola, Eric *Photographer*
535 Greenwich St, New York, NY 10013

Merbold, Ulf *Astronaut, Germany*
%DFVLR, Linder Hohe, 5 Koln 90, Germany

Mercer, Marian *Actress, Singer*
25901 Piuma Rd, Calabasas, CA 91302

Mercer, Robert E *Businessman*
%Goodyear Tire & Rubber Co, 1144 E Market St, Akron, OH 44316

Mercouri, Melina *Actress; Government Official, Greece*
Anagnostropulon 25, Athens, Greece

Mercure, Alex P *Government Official*
%Department of Agriculture, 14th & Independence SW, Washington, DC 20250

Meredith, Burgess *Actor*
25 Malibu Colony Rd, Malibu, CA 90265

Meredith, Don *Football Player, Sportscaster*
PO Box 597, Santa Fe, NM 87504

Meredith, E T, III *Publisher*
%Meredith Corp, 1716 Locust St, Des Moines, IA 50336

Meredith, James H *Civil Rights Activist*
%Office of Sen Jesse Helms, US Senate, Washington, DC 20510

Meredith, Thomas C *Educator*
%Western Kentucky University, President's Office, Bowling Green, KY 42101

Meredith, William *Poet*
6300 Bradley Blvd, Bethesda, MD 20817

Merigan, Thomas C, Jr *Medical Researcher*
148 Goya Rd, Portola Valley, CA 94025

Meritt, Benjamin D *Philogist*
712 W 16th St, Austin, TX 78701

Meriwether, Lee *Actress*
1341 Ocean Ave, #261, Santa Monica, CA 90401

Merk, L W *Businessman*
%International Harvester Co, 401 N Michigan Ave, Chicago, IL 60611

Merkle, Hans L *Financier*
%Deutsche Bank, Taunusanlage 12, 6000 Frankfurt-am-Main, Germany

Merli, Gino J *WW II Army Hero (CMH)*
605 Gino Merli Dr, Peckville, PA 18452

Merlin, Jan *Actor*
9016 Wonderland Ave, Los Angeles, CA 90046

Merlo, Ellen *Businesswoman*
%Philip Morris, Marketing Services, 120 Park Ave, New York, NY 10017

Merlo, Harry A *Businessman*
%Louisiana-Pacific Corp, 111 SW 5th Ave, Portland, OR 97204

Merow, James F *Judge*
%US Claims Court, 717 Madison Pl NW, Washington, DC 20005

Merrick, David *Theater Producer*
246 W 44th St, New York, NY 10036

Merrifield, R Bruce *Nobel Medicine Laureate*
43 Mezzine Dr, Cresskill, NJ 07626

Merrill, Charles M *Judge*
PO Box 547, San Francisco, CA 94101

Merrill, Dina *Actress*
325 Dunemere Dr, La Jolla, CA 92037

Merrill, James *Writer*
107 Water St, Stonington, CT 06378

Merrill, John O *Architect*
101 Gardner Pl, Colorado Springs, CO 80906

Merrill, Maurice H *Attorney, Educator*
800 Elm Ave, Norman, OK 73069

Merrill, Richard G *Businessman*
%Prudential Insurance, Prudential Plz, Newark, NJ 07101

Merrill, Richard T *Businessman*
%Commerce Clearing House, 4025 W Peterson Ave, Chicago, IL 60646

Merrill, Robert *Opera Singer*
79 Oxford Dr, New Rochelle, NY 10801

Merriman, Brian *Businessman*
%Savin Corp, Columbus Ave, Valhalla, NY 10595

Merritt, C C I *WW II Canadian Army Hero (VC)*
1255 58th Ave W, Vancouver BC V6P 1V9, Canada

Merritt, Gilbert S *Judge*
%US Court of Appeals, US Courthouse, 701 Broadway, Nashville, TN 37203

Merritt, Jim *Baseball Player*
5924 Thelma Ave, LaPalma, CA 90623

Merritt, William A, Jr *Businessman*
%TIE/Communications Inc, 5 Research Dr, Shelton, CT 06484

Merrow, Susan *Association Executive*
%Sierra Club, 730 Polk St, San Francisco, CA 94109

Merry, Eugene W *Businessman*
%Mine Safety Appliances Co, 600 Penn Center Blvd, Pittsburgh, PA 15235

Merseth, Alf *Religious Leader*
%Evangelical Lutheran Synod, 106 13th St S, Northwood, IA 50459

Merton, Robert K *Sociologist*
%Columbia University, Fayerweather Hall, New York, NY 10027

Mertz, Francis J *Educator*
%Farleigh Dickinson University, President's Office, Rutherford, NJ 07070

Merwin, William Stanley *Poet*
%Atheneum Publishers, 122 E 42nd St, New York, NY 10017

Mese, John *Actor*
%Century Artists, 9744 Wilshsire Blvd, #308, Beverly Hills, CA 90212

Meselson, Matthew S *Biochemist*
%Harvard University, Fairchild Biochemistry Laboratories, Cambridge, MA 02138

Meskill, Thomas J *Governor, CT; Judge*
%US Court of Appeals, Old Post Office Plz, 114 W Main St, New Britain, CT 06051

Messer, Thomas A *Museum Director*
%Guggenheim Museum, 1071 5th Ave, New York, NY 10028

Messerschmid, Ernst *Astronaut, Germany*
%DFVLR, Linder Hohe, 5 Kohn 90, Germany

Messerschmidt, Andy *Baseball Player*
200 Lagunita Dr, Soquel, CA 95073

Messervy, Godfrey *Businessman*
%Lucas Industries, Great King St, Birmingham BI9 2XF, England

Messiaen, Olivier *Composer*
230 Rue Marcadet, 75018 Paris, France

Messier, Mark *Hockey Player*
%New York Rangers, Madison Square Gdn, 4 Pennsylvania Plz, New York, NY 10001

Messner, Reinhold *Explorer, Mountaineer*
Juval-Sudtirol, 39020 Stabel BZ, Italy

Messner, Zbigniew *Premier, Poland*
%Central Committee, Ul Nowy Swiat 6, 00-497 Warsaw, Poland

Metcalf, Gordon M *Businessman*
%Savings & Profit Fund of Sears Employees, Sears Tower, Chicago, IL 60684

Metcalf, Keyes D *Librarian*
68 Fairmont St, Belmont, MA 02178

Metcalf, Robert L *Entomologist*
1902 Golfview Dr, Urbana, IL 61801

Metcalf, Shelby *Basketball Coach*
%Texas A&M University, Athletic Dept, College Station, TX 77843

Metheny, Pat *Musician*
%Ted Kurland Assoc, 173 Brighton Ave, Boston, MA 02134

Metrano, Art *Actor*
%Harry Gold Assoc, 3500 W Olive Ave, #1400, Burbank, CA 91505

Metter, Bertrand M *Businessman*
%J Walter Thompson Co, 420 Lexington Ave, New York, NY 10017

Mettey, Lynette *Actress*
942 N Martel Ave, Los Angeles, CA 90046

Mettler, Ruben F *Businessman*
%TRW Inc, 1900 Richmond Rd, Cleveland, OH 44124

Metzenbaum, Howard M *Senator, OH*
18500 N Park Blvd, Shaker Heights, OH 44118

Meyer Reyes, Debbie *Swimmer*
1700 McClaren Dr, Carmichael, CA 95608

Meyer, Armin H *Diplomat*
4610 Reno Rd NW, Washington, DC 20008

Meyer, C E, Jr *Businessman*
%Hilton International, 301 Park Ave, New York, NY 10022

Meyer, Charles A *Businessman*
1320 N Sheridan Rd, Lake Forest, IL 60045

Meyer, Clifford R *Businessman*
%Cincinnati Milacron Inc, 4701 Marburg Ave, Cincinnati, OH 45209

Meyer, Edward H *Businessman*
%Grey Advertising, 777 3rd St, New York, NY 10017

Meyer, Emmanuel R *Businessman*
%Alusuisse, Feldeggstrasse 4, 8034 Zurich 8, Switzerland

Meyer, Frederick R *Businessman*
%Tyler Corp, 3200 San Jacinto Tower, Dallas, TX 75201

Meyer, Joey *Basketball Coach*
%DePaul University, Athletic Dept, Chicago, IL 60614

Meyer, John M, Jr *Financier*
%Morgan Guaranty Trust, 23 Wall St, New York, NY 10015

Meyer, Karl H *Biochemist*
642 Wyndham Rd, Teaneck, NJ 07666

Meyer, Larry *Writer, Educator*
19811 Bushard St, Huntington Beach, CA 92646

Meyer, Louis *Auto Racing Driver*
Box 922, Searchlight, NV 89046

Meyer, Randall *Businessman*
407 Shadywood, Houston, TX 77057

Meyer, Ray *Basketball Coach*
2518 Cedar Glen Dr, Arlington Heights, IL 60005

Meyer, Ron *Entertainment Executive*
%Creative Artists Agency, 9830 Wilshire Blvd, Beverly Hills, CA 90212

Meyer, Russ *Movie Producer, Photographer*
%RM Films International, PO Box 3748, Los Angeles, CA 90078

Meyer, Russell W, Jr *Businessman*
%Cessna Aircraft Co, 5800 E Pawnee Rd, Wichita, KS 67201

Meyers Drysdale, Ann *Basketball Player, Sportscaster*
1488 Rutherford Dr, Pasadena, CA 91103

Meyers, Ari *Actress*
%Dove Audio, 301 N Canon Dr, #203, Beverly Hills, CA 90210

Meyers, Gerald Carl *Businessman*
%Ford Motor Co, 27777 Franklin Rd, Southfield, MI 48034

Meyers, Jan *Representative, KS*
%House of Representatives, Washington, DC 20515

Meyers, John A *Publisher*
%Time Magazine, Rockefeller Ctr, New York, NY 10020

Meyerson, Martin *Educator*
%University of Pennsylvania, Von Pelt Library, Philadelphia, PA 19104

Meyerson, Morton H *Businessman*
%Electronic Data Systems Corp, 7171 Forest Ln, Dallas, TX 75230

Meyfarth, Ulrike *Track Athlete*
Friedensweg 59, 5047 Wesseling, Germany

Mezentseva, Galina *Ballerina*
%Kirov Ballet Theatre, 1 Ploshchad Iskusstr, St Petersburg, Russia

M

Mfume – Midler

Mfume, Kweisi *Representative, MD*
%House of Representatives, Washington, DC 20515

Mica, Daniel A *Representative, FL*
%House of Representatives, Washington, DC 20515

Michael *King, Romania*
Versoix, Lake Geneva, Switzerland

Michael (Shaheen), Archbishop *Religious Leader*
%Antiochian Orthodox Christian Archdiocese, 358 Mountain Rd, Englewood, NJ 07631

Michael, Gary G *Businessman*
%Albertson's Inc, 250 Parkcenter Blvd, Boise, ID 83726

Michael, Gene *Baseball Manager*
147 Grove St, Bergenfield, NJ 07621

Michael, George *Singer*
2 Eden Pl, London W8, England

Michaels, Al *Sportscaster*
%ABC-TV, Sports Dept, 77 W 66th St, New York, NY 10023

Michaels, Corinne *Actress*
%Allen Goldstein Assoc, 5015 Lemona Ave, Sherman Oaks, CA 91423

Michaels, James W *Editor*
%Forbes Magazine, 60 5th Ave, New York, NY 10011

Michaels, Leonard *Writer*
438 Beloit Ave, Kensington, CA 94708

Michaels, Lisa *Actress*
4942 Vineland Ave, #8, North Hollywood, CA 91601

Michaels, Walter *Football Player, Coach*
65 Park, Bayshore, NY 11706

Michals, Duane *Photographer*
109 E 19th St, New York, NY 10003

Michel, F Curtis *Astronaut*
%Rice University, Space Physics & Astronomy Dept, Houston, TX 77001

Michel, George J, Jr *Businessman*
%Stanadyne Inc, 100 Deerfield Rd, Windsor, CT 06095

Michel, Hartmut *Nobel Chemistry Laureate*
%Max Planck Biophysik Institut, 6000 Frankfurt/Main 71, Germany

Michel, Jean-Louis *Underwater Scientist*
%IFREMER, Ctr de Toulon, 83500 La Seyne dur Mer, Toulon, France

Michel, Paul R *Judge*
%US Court of Appeals, 717 Madison Pl NW, Washington, DC 20439

Michel, Robert H *Representative, IL*
1029 N Glenwood St, Peoria, IL 61606

Michelangeli, Arturo Benedetti *Concert Pianist*
%Columbia Artists Mgmt Inc, 165 W 57th St, New York, NY 10019

Michelin, Francois *Businessman*
%Michelin & Cie, 4 Rue du Terrail, 6300 Clermont Ferrand, France

Michener, Charles Duncan *Entomologist*
1706 W 2nd St, Lawrence, KS 66044

Michie, Donald *Computer Scientist*
10 Bellevue Cres, Edinburgh, Scotland

Michiko *Empress, Japan*
Imperial Palace, Tokyo, Japan

Michnik, Adam *Political Activist*
%Sejm, Parliament, Warsaw, Poland

Mickal, Abe *Football Player, Physician*
20 Wren St, New Orleans, LA 70124

Mickel, Buck *Businessman*
%Fluor Corp, 3333 Michelson Dr, Irvine, CA 92730

Mickelson, George *Governor, SD*
%Governor's Office, State Capitol, 500 E Capitol Ave, Pierre, SD 57501

Middendorf, J William, II *Secretary, Navy*
1453 Kirby Rd, McLean, VA 22101

Middlecoff, Cary *Golfer*
%Professional Golf Assn, PO Box 109601, Palm Beach Gardens, FL 33410

Middleton, Rick *Hockey Player*
%Boston Bruins, 150 Causeway St, Boston, MA 02114

Midler, Bette *Singer, Actress*
9481 Readcrest Dr, Beverly Hills, CA 90210

Midori %International Creative Mgmt, 40 W 57th St, New York, NY 10019	*Concert Violinist*
Miechur, Thomas F %Cement & Allied Workers Union, 2500 Brickdale, Elk Grove Village, IL 60007	*Labor Leader*
Mielke, Frederick W, Jr %Pacific Gas & Electric Co, 77 Beale St, San Francisco, CA 94106	*Businessman*
Mieto, Juha %General Delivery, Mieto, Finland	*Cross Country Skier*
Mieuli, Franklin %Golden State Warriors, Oakland Coliseum Arena, Oakland, CA 94621	*Basketball Executive*
Mifune, Toshiro %Mifune Productions, 9-30-7 Siejyo, Setagayaku, Tokyo, Japan	*Actor*
Migenes, Julia %Metropolitan Opera Assn, Lincoln Ctr, New York, NY 10023	*Opera Singer*
Mihalik, Zigmund (Red) 307 O'Connor St, Ford City, PA 16226	*Basketball Referee*
Mihalowski, John 10825 110th Ave N, Largo, FL 34648	*Navy Underwater Diving Hero (CMH)*
Mikami, Shinzo %Sanyo Manufacturing Corp, 3333 Sanyo Rd, Forrest City, AK 72335	*Businessman*
Mikan, George 7096 Cahill Rd, Minneapolis, MN 55435	*Basketball Player*
Mikhailov, A A %Pulkovo Observatory, 196140 St Petersburg, USSR	*Astronomer*
Mikita, Stan %Kemper Lake Golf Course, Pro Shop, Long Grove, IL 60047	*Hockey Player*
Mikulic, Branko %Federal Executive Council, Bul Lenjina 2, 11070 Novi Belgrad, Yugoslavia	*Prime Minister, Yugoslavia*
Mikulski, Barbara A %US Senate, Washington, DC 20510	*Senator, MD*
Mikva, Abner J %US Court of Appeals, 3rd & Constitution NW, Washington, DC 20001	*Judge*
Milano, Alyssa %Mel Pogue Enterprises, 3365 Cahuenga, Los Angeles, CA 90068	*Actress*
Milbank, Samuel R 1 E 75th St, New York, NY 10021	*Financier*
Milburn, H Ted %US Court of Appeals, PO Box 750, Chattanooga, TN 37401	*Judge*
Milch, David %Writers Guild, 55 W 57th St, New York, NY 10019	*Screenwriter*
Miles, Joanna %Bauman Hiller Assoc, 5750 Wilshire Blvd, #512, Los Angeles, CA 90036	*Actress*
Miles, Josephine 2275 Virginia St, Berkeley, CA 94709	*Poet*
Miles, Mark %Assn of Tennis Pros, 200 Tournament Players Rd, Ponte Vedra Beach, FL 32082	*Tennis Executive*
Miles, Michael A %Philip Morris Companies, 120 Park Ave, New York, NY 10017	*Businessman*
Miles, Sarah 7 Windmill St, London W1, England	*Actress*
Miles, Sylvia 240 Central Park South, New York, NY 10019	*Actress*
Miles, Vera PO Box 1704, Big Bear Lake, CA 92315	*Actress*
Milford, Penelope 219 Market St, Venice, CA 90291	*Actress*
Milgram, Stanley %City University of New York, Graduate Ctr, New York, NY 10036	*Social Psychologist*
Milius, John 888 Linda Flora, Los Angeles, CA 90027	*Movie Director*
Milken, Michael R %International Capital Access Grp, 450 N Roxbury Dr, Beverly Hills, CA 90210	*Financier*
Millar, Jeff %Universal Press Syndicate, 1301 Spring Oaks Cir, Houston, TX 77055	*Cartoonist (Tank McNamara)*
Millar, Margaret 4420 Via Esperanza, Santa Barbara, CA 93110	*Writer*

M

Millard – Miller

Millard, Keith — *Football Player*
%Minnesota Vikings, 9520 Viking Dr, Eden Prairie, MN 55344

Millen, Matt — *Football Player*
%Washington Redskins, Dulles Airport, Box 17247, Washington, DC 20041

Miller, Alice — *Golfer*
%Ladies Professional Golf Assn, 2570 Volusia Ave, #B, Daytona Beach, FL 32114

Miller, Ann — *Actress, Dancer*
151 Ainslie St, Brooklyn, NY 11211

Miller, Arjay — *Businessman*
225 Mountain Home Rd, Woodside, CA 94062

Miller, Arthur — *Writer*
RR 1, Box 320, Tophet Rd, Roxbury, CT 06783

Miller, Barry — *Actor*
%Gersh Agency, 232 N Canon Dr, Beverly Hills, CA 90212

Miller, C Ray — *Religious Leader*
%United Brethren in Christ, 302 Lake St, Huntington, IN 46750

Miller, Charles D — *Businessman*
%Avery International Corp, 150 N Orange Grove Blvd, Pasadena, CA 91103

Miller, Cheryl — *Basketball Player, Sportscaster*
%ABC-TV, Sports Dept, 1330 Ave of Americas, New York, NY 10019

Miller, Clarence E — *Representative, OH*
%House of Representatives, Washington, DC 20515

Miller, Creighton — *Football Player*
1610 Euclid Ave, Cleveland, OH 44115

Miller, David F — *Businessman*
%J C Penney Co, 1301 Ave of Americas, New York, NY 10019

Miller, Delvin — *Harness Racer*
PO Box 356, Meadow Lands, PA 15347

Miller, Denny — *Actor*
323 E Matilija St, #112, Ojai, CA 93023

Miller, Donald C — *Financier*
%Continental Illinois Corp, 231 S La Salle St, Chicago, IL 60693

Miller, Edward D — *Financier*
%Manufactuers Hanover Trust, 270 Park Ave, New York, NY 10017

Miller, Elizabeth C — *Medical Educator*
5517 Hammersely Rd, Madison, WI 53711

Miller, Elliott C — *Financier*
%Society for Savings, 31 Pratt St, Hartford, CT 06103

Miller, Frank — *Radio Executive*
%CBS Radio Network, 51 W 52nd St, New York, NY 10019

Miller, Franklin D — *Vietnam War Army Hero (CMH)*
3562 Alohea Ave, Honolulu, HI 96816

Miller, G William — *Secretary, Treasury; Businessman*
%G William Miller Co, 1215 19th St NW, Washington, DC 20036

Miller, Geoff — *Publisher*
%Los Angeles Magazine, 1888 Century Park East, Los Angeles, CA 90067

Miller, George — *Representative, CA*
%House of Representatives, Washington, DC 20515

Miller, George — *Movie Director*
30 Orwell St, King's Cross, Sydney 2011, Australia

Miller, George A — *Psychologist*
478 Lake Dr, Princeton, NJ 08540

Miller, Irwin — *Businessman*
%Stride Rite Corp, 5 Cambridge Ctr, Cambridge, MA 02142

Miller, J Irwin — *Businessman*
301 Washington St, Columbus, IN 47201

Miller, Jack R — *Senator, IA; Judge*
6710 Maybole Pl, Temple Terrace, FL 33617

Miller, James A — *Oncologist*
5517 Hammersely Rd, Madison, WI 53711

Miller, James C, III — *Government Official*
%Office of Management & Budget, Executive Office Bldg, Washington, DC 20503

Miller, Jason — *Playwright, Actor*
%Artists Agency, 10000 Santa Monica Blvd, #305, Los Angeles, CA 90067

Miller, Jeremy — *Actor*
%Harry Gold Assoc, 3500 W Olive Ave, #1400, Burbank, CA 91505

Miller, John *Representative, WA*
%House of Representatives, Washington, DC 20515

Miller, John A *Businessman*
%Provident Mutual Life Insurance Co, 1600 Market St, Philadelphia, PA 19103

Miller, Jon H *Businessman*
%Boise Cascade Corp, 1 Jefferson Sq, Boise, ID 83728

Miller, Jonathan *Stage, Opera Director*
63 Gloucester Cres, London NW1, England

Miller, Joyce D *Labor Leader*
%Amalgamated Clothing & Textile Workers, 15 Union Sq, New York, NY 10003

Miller, Keith H *Governor, AK*
3605 Arctic Blvd, #1001, Anchorage, AK 99503

Miller, Lennox *Track Athlete*
1213 N Lake Ave, Pasadena, CA 91104

Miller, Lenore *Labor Leader*
%Retail/Wholesale/Department Store Union, 30 E 29th St, New York, NY 10016

Miller, Linda *Ballerina*
890 Broadway, New York, NY 10003

Miller, Marvin J *Labor Leader*
%Baseball Players Assn, 1370 Ave of Americas, New York, NY 10019

Miller, Merton H *Nobel Economics Laureate*
%University of Chicago, Graduate Business School, 1101 E 58th, Chicago, IL 60637

Miller, Mildred *Opera Singer*
718 Devonshire St, Pittsburgh, PA 15213

Miller, Mitch *Musician*
345 W 58th St, New York, NY 10019

Miller, Neal E *Psychologist*
%Rockefeller University, Psychology Dept, New York, NY 10021

Miller, Paul A *Businessman*
%Pacific Lighting Corp, 810 S Flower St, Los Angeles, CA 90017

Miller, Paul D *Navy Admiral*
Commander, US Atlantic Fleet, Norfolk, VA 23511

Miller, Paul Lukens *Financier*
%First Boston Corp, Park Avenue Plz, New York, NY 10055

Miller, Peter North *Businessman*
%Lloyd's of London, Lime St, London EC3M 7HL, England

Miller, Reggie *Basketball Player*
%Indianapolis Pacers, 30 E Market St, Indianapolis, IN 46204

Miller, Richard A *Businessman*
%Cleveland Electric Illuminating Co, Illuminating Bldg, Cleveland, OH 44101

Miller, Richard B *Attorney*
%Miller Keeton, 909 Fannin, Houston, TX 77010

Miller, Robert *Governor, NV*
%Governor's Office, State Capitol, Carson City, NV 89710

Miller, Robert (Red) *Football Coach*
%Dean Witter Reynolds, 4582 S Ulster Pkwy, #300, Denver, CO 80237

Miller, Robert L *Publisher*
%Times Warner, Rockefeller Ctr, New York, NY 10020

Miller, Robert S, Jr *Businessman*
%Chrysler Corp, 12000 Chrysler Dr, Highland Park, MI 48203

Miller, Roger *Singer, Songwriter*
PO Box 2689, Danbury, CT 06813

Miller, Sherman *Financier*
%Nevada Savings & Loan Assn, 201 Las Vegas Blvd S, Las Vegas, NV 89125

Miller, Sidney *Actor*
%Tisherman Agency, 6767 Forest Lawn Dr, #115, Los Angeles, CA 90068

Miller, Stanley L *Chemist*
%University of California, Chemistry Dept, La Jolla, CA 92093

Miller, Steve *Musician*
PO Box 4127, Bellevue, WA 98040

Miller, Stu *Baseball Player*
3701 Ocaso Ct, Cameron Park, CA 95682

Miller, W Millard *Businessman*
%Southern States Cooperative, 6606 W Broad St, Richmond, VA 23230

Miller, Warren *Ski Photographer*
505 Pier Ave, Hermosa Beach, CA 90254

M

Miller, William *Financier*
165 Blackstone Blvd, Providence, RI 02906

Miller, William R *Businessman*
%Bristol-Myers Squibb Co, 345 Park Ave, New York, NY 10154

Miller, Zell *Governor, GA*
%Governor's Office, State Capitol Bldg, #203, Atlanta, GA 30334

Millett, Kate *Feminist Leader, Writer*
%Simon & Schuster, 1230 Ave of Americas, New York, NY 10020

Millett, Lewis L *Korean War Army Hero (CMH)*
%Korean War Memorial, Patriotic Hall, #700, 1816 Figueroa, Los Angeles, CA 90015

Milley, Norman G *Businessman*
%K Mart Corp, 3100 W Big Beaver Rd, Troy, MI 48084

Millhiser, Ross R *Businessman*
%Philip Morris Inc, 100 Park Ave, New York, NY 10017

Milligan, Spike *Actor, Director*
9 Orme Ct, London W2, England

Milliken, Gerrish H *Businessman*
%Milliken & Co, 1045 Ave of Americas, New York, NY 10018

Milliken, Minot K *Businessman*
%Milliken & Co, 1045 Ave of Americas, New York, NY 10018

Milliken, Roger *Businessman*
%Milliken & Co, PO Box 3167, Spartanburg, SC 29304

Milliken, William G *Governor, MI*
300 Grandview Pkwy, Traverse City, MI 49684

Millo, Aprile *Opera Singer*
%Columbia Artists Mgmt Inc, 165 W 57th St, New York, NY 10019

Milloro, Frank P *Religious Leader*
%American Carpatho, 312 Garfield St, Johnstown, PA 15906

Mills, Alley *Actress*
%Artists Group, 1930 Century Park West, #403, Los Angeles, CA 90067

Mills, Curtis *Track Athlete*
328 Lake St, Lufkin, TX 75901

Mills, Donna *Actress*
%Lorimar Telepictures, 3970 Overland Dr, Culver City, CA 90230

Mills, Hayley *Actress*
81 High St, Hampton, Middlesex, England

Mills, John *Actor*
Hill House, Denham Village, Buckinghamshire, England

Mills, Juliet *Actress*
%Craig Agency, 8485 Melrose Pl, #E, Los Angeles, CA 90069

Mills, Lorna H *Financier*
%Great American First Savings Bank, 600 "B" St, San Diego, CA 92183

Mills, Neil M *Businessman*
%Dower House, Upton Grey Near Basingstoke, Hants, England

Mills, Phoebe *Gymnast*
7 Country Ln, Northfield, IL 60093

Mills, Sam *Football Player*
%New Orleans Saints, 6928 Saints Dr, Metairie, LA 70003

Mills, Stephanie *Singer*
PO Box K-350, Tarzana, CA 91356

Mills, Terry *Basketball Player*
%New Jersey Nets, Meadowlands Arena, East Rutherford, NJ 07073

Mills, Wilbur *Representative, AR*
%Shea & Gould, 1775 Pennsylvania Ave NW, Washington, DC 20006

Millsaps, Knox *Aerospace Engineer*
PO Box 13857, Gainesville, FL 32604

Milne, J D *Businessman*
%Blue Circle Industries, Portland House, London SW1E 5BJ, England

Milner, G W *Businessman*
%Lanier Business Products, 1700 Chantilly Dr, Atlanta, GA 30324

Milner, Martin *Actor*
%Agency for Performing Arts, 9000 Sunset Blvd, #1200, Los Angeles, CA 90069

Milnes, Sherrill *Opera Singer*
%Herbert Barrett Mgmt, 1776 Broadway, #1800 New York, NY 10019

Milosz, Czeslaw *Nobel Literature Laureate*
%University of California, Slavic Languages Dept, Berkeley, CA 94720

Milsap, Ronnie *Singer*
%Dick Blake International, 12 Music Cir S, Nashville, TN 37202

Milstein, Cesar *Nobel Medicine Laureate*
%Medical Research Council Ctr, Hills Rd, Cambridge, England

Milstein, Nathan *Concert Violinist*
%Shaw Concerts, 1900 Broadway, New York, NY 10023

Mimieux, Yvette *Actress*
9626 Oak Pass Rd, Beverly Hills, CA 90210

Mimoun, Alain *Marathon Runner*
27 Ave Edouard-Jenner, 94500 Champigny-sur-Marne, France

Min, Gao *Diver*
%Olympic Committee, 9 Tiyuguan Rd, Beijing, Republic of China

Miner, Harold *Basketball Player*
%University of Southern Calaifornia, Heritage Hall, Los Angeles, CA 90089

Miner, Jan *Actress*
300 E 46th St, #9-J, New York, NY 10017

Miner, Roger J *Judge*
%US Court of Appeals, PO Box 858, Albany, NY 12201

Mineta, Norman Y *Representative, CA*
%House of Representatives, Washington, DC 20515

Minisi, Skip (Anthony S) *Football Player*
300 Continental Ln, Paoli, PA 19301

Mink, Patsy Takemoto *Representative, HI*
%House of Representatives, Washington, DC 20515

Minnelli, Liza *Actress, Singer*
150 E 69th St, #21-G, New York, NY 10021

Minnesota Fats (R W Wanderone Jr) *Billiards Player*
%Hermitage Park Suite Hotel, 231 6th Ave N, Nashville, TN 37219

Minnifield, Frank *Football Player*
%Cleveland Browns, Cleveland Stadium, Cleveland, OH 44114

Mino, Shigekazo *Businessman*
%Kubota Ltd, 2-47 Shikitsuhigashi, Naniwaku, Osaka 556, Japan

Minogue, Kylie *Singer*
PO Box 292, Watford, Hertsfordshire WD2 4ND, England

Minor, Ronald R *Religious Leader*
%Pentecostal Church of God, 4901 Pennsylvania, Joplin, MO 64802

Minoso, Minnie *Baseball Player*
4250 Marin Dr, Chicago, IL 60613

Minow, Newton N *Government Official*
375 Palos Rd, Glencoe, IL 60022

Minsky, Marvin L *Computer Scientist*
545 Main St, Cambridge, MA 02139

Minter, Alan *Boxer*
%Minter's Restaurant, 49 High St, Crawley, Sussex, England

Minter, Kelly *Actress*
%Marshak-Wyckoff Assoc, 280 S Beverly Dr, #400, Beverly Hills, CA 90212

Mintoff, Dominic *Prime Minister, Malta*
The Olives, Xintill St, Tarxien, Malta

Minton, John D *Businessman*
%Mutual of Omaha Life Insurance, Mutual of Omaha Plz, Omaha, NE 68175

Mintz, Shlomo *Concert Violinist*
%Internationaol Creative Mgmt, 40 W 57th St, New York, NY 10019

Minz, Alexander *Ballet Dancer*
2020 Broadway, New York, NY 10023

Mir, Isabelle *Skier*
65170 Saint-Lary, France

Mirabella, Grace *Editor*
%Mirabella Magazine, 200 Madison Ave, New York, NY 10016

Mirisch, Walter *Movie Producer*
647 Warner Ave, Los Angeles, CA 90024

Miro, Joan *Artist*
%Galerie Maeght, 13 Rue de Teheran, 75008 Paris, France

Mirren, Helen *Actress*
%Lantz Office, 888 7th Ave, #2500, New York, NY 10106

Mirvish, Edwin *Comedian, Theater Producer*
581 Bloor St W, Toronto ON M6G 1K3, Canada

M

Mischke – Mitsuda

Mischke, Rev Carl H *Religious Leader*
%Wisconsin Evangelical Lutheran Synod, 1270 N Dobson, Chandler, AZ 85224

Missar, Richard R *Businessman*
%DeSoto Inc, 1700 S Mount Prospect Rd, Des Plaines, IL 60017

Mita, Katsushige *Businessman*
%Hitachi Ltd, 1-5-1 Marunouchi, Chiyodaku, Tokyo 100, Japan

Mitarai, Takeshi *Businessman*
%Canon Inc, 3-30-2 Shimomaruko, Otaku, Tokyo 146, Japan

Mitchell, Andrea *Commentator*
%NBC-TV, News Dept, 4001 Nebraska Ave NW, Washington, DC 20016

Mitchell, Arthur *Dance Director*
%Dance Theatre of Harlem, 468 W 152nd St, New York, NY 10031

Mitchell, Bobby *Football Player, Executive*
%Washington Redskins, Dulles Airport, Box 17247, Washington, DC 20041

Mitchell, Brian *Actor*
%Agency for Performing Arts, 9000 Sunset Blvd, #1200, Los Angeles, CA 90069

Mitchell, Broadus *Economist*
49 Barrow St, New York, NY 10014

Mitchell, Cameron *Actor*
%Century Artists, 9744 Wilshire Blvd, #308, Beverly Hills, CA 90212

Mitchell, David W *Businessman*
%Avon Products, 9 W 57th St, New York, NY 10019

Mitchell, Don G *Businessman*
%Marriott Corp, Marriott Dr, Washington, DC 20058

Mitchell, Edgar D *Astronaut*
%Institute of Noetic Science, PO Box 909, Sausalito, CA 94966

Mitchell, George J *Senator, ME*
%US Senate, Washington, DC 20510

Mitchell, George P *Businessman*
%Mitchell Energy & Development Corp, 2001 Timberlach Pl, Woodlands, TX 77380

Mitchell, Gerald B *Businessman*
%Dana Corp, 4500 Dorr St, Toledo, OH 43615

Mitchell, Hamilton B *Financier*
%Dun & Bradstreet Inc, 99 Church St, New York, NY 10007

Mitchell, James *Prime Minister, St Vincent & Grenadines*
%Prime Minister's Office, Kingstown, St Vincent & Grenadines

Mitchell, Joan *Artist*
"La Tour", Rue Claude Monet, 95510 Vetheuil, France

Mitchell, John F *Businessman*
%Motorola Inc, 1303 E Algonquin Rd, Schaumberg, IL 60196

Mitchell, Joni *Singer, Songwriter*
644 N Doheny Dr, Los Angeles, CA 90069

Mitchell, Kevin *Baseball Player*
4372 "Z" St, San Diego, CA 92123

Mitchell, Leona *Opera Singer*
%Columbia Artists Mgmt Inc, 165 W 57th St, New York, NY 10019

Mitchell, Michele *Diver*
10664 San Bernadino Way, Boca Raton, FL 33428

Mitchell, Peter D *Nobel Chemistry Laureate*
Glynn House, Bodmin, Cornwall PL30 4AU, England

Mitchell, Sasha *Actor*
%Flick East-West Talents, 1608 Las Palmas Ave, Los Angeles, CA 90028

Mitchell, Warren I *Businessman*
%Southern California Gas Co, 810 S Flower St, Los Angeles, CA 90017

Mitchell, William S *Businessman*
%Safeway Stores, PO Box 660, Oakland, CA 94604

Mitchelson, Marvin *Attorney*
1801 Century Park East, #1900, Los Angeles, CA 90067

Mitchum, Robert *Actor*
860 San Ysidro Rd, Santa Barbara, CA 93108

Mitford, Jessica *Writer*
6411 Regent St, Oakland, CA 94618

Mitsotakis, Constantine *Prime Minister, Greece*
%Prime Minister's Office, Maximos Building, Athens, Greece

Mitsuda, Hirotaka *Businessman*
%Daikyo Oil Co, 2-4-1 Yaesu, Chuoku, Tokyo 100, Japan

Mittermaier, Rosi *Skier*
Munchnerstrasse 42, 8100 Garmisch-Partenkirchen, Germany

Mitterrand, Francois *President, France*
%Palais de L'Elysee, 55-57 Rue De Faubourg, 75008 Paris, France

Mitzel, Donald H *Financier*
%First Federal of Michigan, 1001 Woodward Ave, Detroit, MI 48226

Mix, Ron *Football Player*
1059 10th Ave, San Diego, CA 92101

Mixon, Wayne *Governor, FL*
2219 Demeron, Tallahassee, FL 32312

Miyake, Shigemitsu *Financier*
%Tokai Bank, 3-21-24 Nishiki, Nakaku, Nagoya, Japan

Miyamura, Hiroshi *Korean War Army Hero (CMH)*
1905 Mossman, Gallup, NM 87301

Miyazaki, Kagayaki *Businessman*
%Asahi Chemical Industry Grp, 1-1-2 Yurakucho, Tokyo 100, Japan

Miyazaki, Yasuji *Swimmer*
2-5-35 Izumicho, Hamamatsu, Postal #430, Shizuka Ken, Japan

Miyazawa, Kiichi *Prime Minister, Japan*
6-34-1 Jingu-mae, Shibuya-ku, Tokyo 150, Japan

Miyori, Kim *Actress*
%Susan Smith Assoc, 121 N San Vicente Blvd, Beverly Hills, CA 90211

Mize, Johnny *Baseball Player*
PO Box 112, Demorest, GA 30535

Mizell, Jason *Singer (Run-DMC)*
%Rush Productions, 1133 Broadway, New York, NY 10010

Mizell, Wilmer D *Representative, NC; Baseball Player*
RR 5, Box 333, Winston-Salem, NC 27107

Mizerak, Steve *Billiards Player*
140 Alfred St, Edison, NJ 08817

Mizrahi, Issac *Fashion Designer*
104 Wooster St, New York, NY 10012

Mizuno, Kazuo *Businessman*
%Ube Industries, 1-12-32 Nishi-Honmachi, Uve City 755, Japan

Moakley, John J *Representative, MA*
%House of Representatives, Washington, DC 20515

Mobley, Mary Ann *Actress*
2751 Hutton Dr, Beverly Hills, CA 90210

Mobley, William H *Educator*
%Texas A&M University, President's Office, College Station, TX 77843

Mobutu Sese Seko *President, Zaire*
%President's Office, Kinshasa, Zaire

Moch, Jules *Government Official, France*
La Griviere, Cabris, 06530 Peymeinade, France

Mockler, Robert H *Businessman*
%Gillette Co, Prudential Tower Bldg, Boston, MA 02199

Moctezuma, Edwardo Matos *Archeologist*
%Great Temple Museum, Mexico City, Mexico

Modell, Arthur B *Football Executive*
%Cleveland Browns, Cleveland Stadium, Cleveland, OH 44114

Modell, Frank *Cartoonist*
%New Yorker Magazine, 25 W 43rd St, New York, NY 10036

Modigliani, Franco *Nobel Economics Laureate*
25 Clark St, Belmont, MA 02178

Modine, Matthew *Actor*
9696 Culver Blvd, #203, Culver City, CA 90232

Modl, Martha *Opera Singer*
Perlacherstrasse 19, 8022 Munchen-Grunwald, Germany

Modrzejewski, Robert J *Vietnam War Marine Corps Hero (CMH)*
4725 Oporto Ct, San Diego, CA 92124

Modzelewski, Ernest F *Financier*
%First Federal Savings & Loan, 3003 N Central Ave, Phoenix, AZ 85012

Moe, Doug *Basketball Player, Coach*
%Denver Nuggets, McNichols Arena, 1635 Clay St, Denver, CO 80204

Moffat, Donald *Actor*
%Triad Artists, 10100 Santa Monica Blvd, #1600, Los Angeles, CA 90067

M

Moffet, John *Swimmer*
%US Olympic Training Camp, 1750 E Boulder St, Colorado Springs, CO 80909

Moffett, James R *Businessman*
%Freeport-McMoran Inc, 1615 Poydras St, New Orleans, LA 70161

Moffett, William A *Museum Official*
%Huntington Library, 1151 Oxford Rd S, San Marino, CA 91108

Moffo, Anna *Opera Singer*
%Carl Byoir Assoc, 380 Madison Ave, New York, NY 10022

Mogenburg, Dietmar *Track Athlete*
Pregelstrasse 16, 5090 Leverkuser, Germany

Mohmand, Abdul Ahad *Cosmonaut, Afghanistan*
141 160 Svyosdny Gorodok, Moskovskoi Oblasti, Potchta Kosmonavtov, Russia

Mohn, Reinhard *Publisher*
%Bertelsmann, Carl-Bertelsmann-Strasse 270, 4830 Guetersloh, Germany

Mohri, Mamoru *Astronaut, Japan*
NASDA, 2-4-1 Hamamatsucho, Minatoku, Tokyo 105, Japan

Moi, Daniel Arap *President, Kenya*
%President's Office, PO Box 30510, Nairobi, Kenya

Moir, G Russell *Businessman*
%Transway International Corp, 81 Main St, White Plains, NY 10601

Moiseyev, Igor *Dance Director; Choreographer*
%State Folk Dance Co, 20 Ploshchad Mayakivskogo, Moscow, Russia

Mokae, Zakes *Actor*
PO Box 5617, Beverly Hills, CA 90210

Moldofsky, Philip J *Cancer Researcher*
%Fox Chase Cancer Ctr, 7701 Burholme Ave, Philadelphia, PA 19111

Molina, Mario J *Physical Chemist*
11 Star Thistle, Irvine, CA 92714

Molinari, Guy V *Representative, NY*
21 Merrick Ave, Staten Island, NY 10301

Molitor, Paul *Baseball Player*
10239 N Waterleaf Dr, Mequon, WI 53092

Moll, Kurt *Opera Singer*
Billwerder Billdeich, 2050 Hamburg 80, Germany

Moll, Richard *Actor*
4139 Via Marina, #900, Marina del Rey, CA 90292

Moller, Hans *Artist*
2207 Allen St, Allentown, PA 18104

Mollohan, Alan B *Representative, WV*
%House of Representatives, Washington, DC 20515

Molson, Hartland *Hockey Executive*
21 Rosemount, Westmount PQ, Canada

Momaday, Scott *Writer*
%Stanford University, English Dept, Stanford, CA 94305

Momper, Walter *Mayor, Berlin*
%Fichtestrasse 15, 1000 Berlin 61, Germany

Monacelli, Amleto *Bowler*
%Professional Bowlers Assn, 1720 Merriman Rd, Akron, OH 44313

Monagham, Bernard A *Businessman*
%Vulcan Materials Co, 1 Metroplex Dr, Birmingham AL 35209

Monaghan, Tom *Businessman, Baseball Executive*
%Domino's Pizza, PO Box 997, Ann Arbor, MI 48106

Monan, J Donald *Educator*
%Boston College, President's Office, Chestnut Hill, MA 02167

Monbouquette, Bill *Baseball Player*
271 Clark Hill Rd, New Boston, NH 03070

Moncrief, Sidney *Basketball Player*
%Milwaukee Bucks, 1001 N 4th St, Milwaukee, WI 53203

Mondale, Walter F *Vice President*
%Dorsey & Whitney, 2300 First National Bank Bldg, Minneapolis, MN 55402

Mondavi, Robert *Businessman*
%Robert Mondavi Winery, 7801 St Helena Hwy, Oakville, CA 94562

Money, Eddie *Singer*
%Bill Graham Mgmt, PO Box 1994, San Francisco, CA 94101

Money, John W *Psychiatrist*
2104 E Madison St, Baltimore, MD 21205

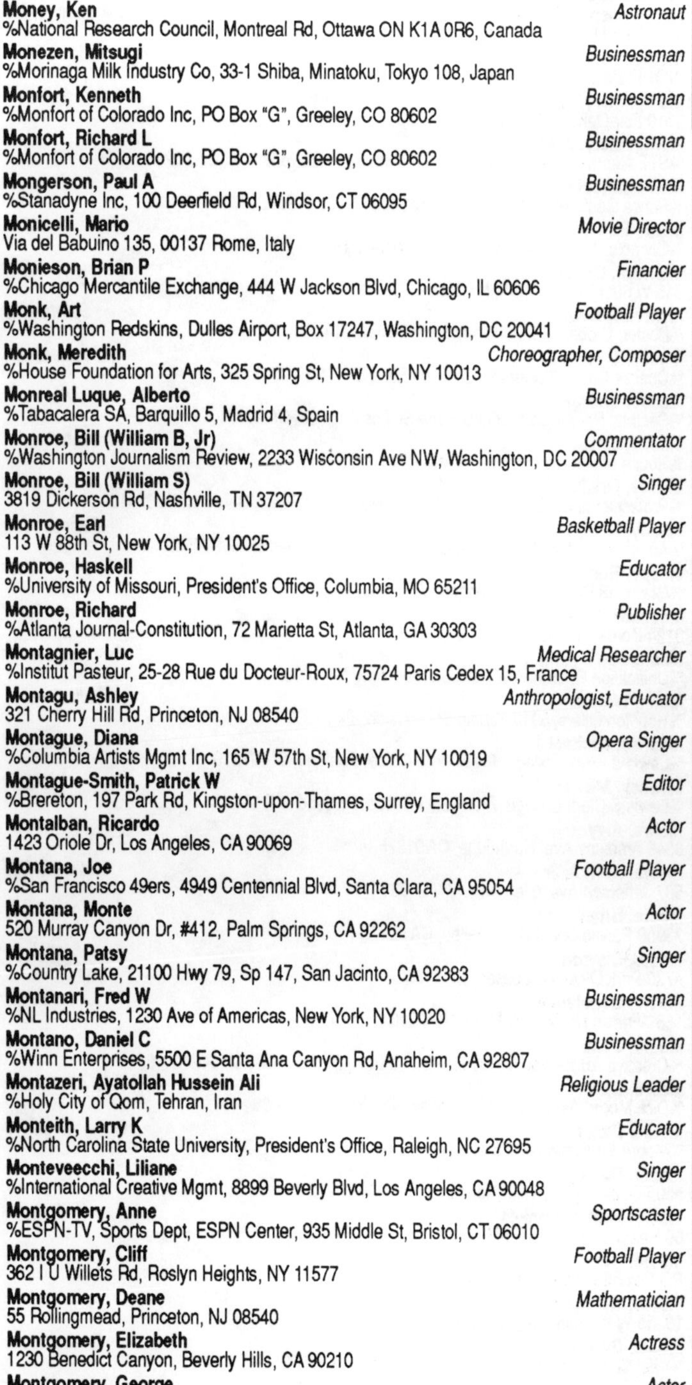

Money, Ken — *Astronaut*
%National Research Council, Montreal Rd, Ottawa ON K1A 0R6, Canada

Monezen, Mitsugi — *Businessman*
%Morinaga Milk Industry Co, 33-1 Shiba, Minatoku, Tokyo 108, Japan

Monfort, Kenneth — *Businessman*
%Monfort of Colorado Inc, PO Box "G", Greeley, CO 80602

Monfort, Richard L — *Businessman*
%Monfort of Colorado Inc, PO Box "G", Greeley, CO 80602

Mongerson, Paul A — *Businessman*
%Stanadyne Inc, 100 Deerfield Rd, Windsor, CT 06095

Monicelli, Mario — *Movie Director*
Via del Babuino 135, 00137 Rome, Italy

Monieson, Brian P — *Financier*
%Chicago Mercantile Exchange, 444 W Jackson Blvd, Chicago, IL 60606

Monk, Art — *Football Player*
%Washington Redskins, Dulles Airport, Box 17247, Washington, DC 20041

Monk, Meredith — *Choreographer, Composer*
%House Foundation for Arts, 325 Spring St, New York, NY 10013

Monreal Luque, Alberto — *Businessman*
%Tabacalera SA, Barquillo 5, Madrid 4, Spain

Monroe, Bill (William B, Jr) — *Commentator*
%Washington Journalism Review, 2233 Wisconsin Ave NW, Washington, DC 20007

Monroe, Bill (William S) — *Singer*
3819 Dickerson Rd, Nashville, TN 37207

Monroe, Earl — *Basketball Player*
113 W 88th St, New York, NY 10025

Monroe, Haskell — *Educator*
%University of Missouri, President's Office, Columbia, MO 65211

Monroe, Richard — *Publisher*
%Atlanta Journal-Constitution, 72 Marietta St, Atlanta, GA 30303

Montagnier, Luc — *Medical Researcher*
%Institut Pasteur, 25-28 Rue du Docteur-Roux, 75724 Paris Cedex 15, France

Montagu, Ashley — *Anthropologist, Educator*
321 Cherry Hill Rd, Princeton, NJ 08540

Montague, Diana — *Opera Singer*
%Columbia Artists Mgmt Inc, 165 W 57th St, New York, NY 10019

Montague-Smith, Patrick W — *Editor*
%Brereton, 197 Park Rd, Kingston-upon-Thames, Surrey, England

Montalban, Ricardo — *Actor*
1423 Oriole Dr, Los Angeles, CA 90069

Montana, Joe — *Football Player*
%San Francisco 49ers, 4949 Centennial Blvd, Santa Clara, CA 95054

Montana, Monte — *Actor*
520 Murray Canyon Dr, #412, Palm Springs, CA 92262

Montana, Patsy — *Singer*
%Country Lake, 21100 Hwy 79, Sp 147, San Jacinto, CA 92383

Montanari, Fred W — *Businessman*
%NL Industries, 1230 Ave of Americas, New York, NY 10020

Montano, Daniel C — *Businessman*
%Winn Enterprises, 5500 E Santa Ana Canyon Rd, Anaheim, CA 92807

Montazeri, Ayatollah Hussein Ali — *Religious Leader*
%Holy City of Qom, Tehran, Iran

Monteith, Larry K — *Educator*
%North Carolina State University, President's Office, Raleigh, NC 27695

Monteveecchi, Liliane — *Singer*
%International Creative Mgmt, 8899 Beverly Blvd, Los Angeles, CA 90048

Montgomery, Anne — *Sportscaster*
%ESPN-TV, Sports Dept, ESPN Center, 935 Middle St, Bristol, CT 06010

Montgomery, Cliff — *Football Player*
362 I U Willets Rd, Roslyn Heights, NY 11577

Montgomery, Deane — *Mathematician*
55 Rollingmead, Princeton, NJ 08540

Montgomery, Elizabeth — *Actress*
1230 Benedict Canyon, Beverly Hills, CA 90210

Montgomery, George — *Actor*
16351 Saticoy St, Van Nuys, CA 91406

Montgomery, Gillespie V (Sonny) *Representative, MS*
%House of Representatives, Washington, DC 20515

Montgomery, Jack C *WW II Army Hero (CMH)*
2701 Ft Davis Dr, Muskogee, OK 74403

Montgomery, Jim *Swimmer*
9510 Fair Oaks, #807, Dallas, TX 75231

Montgomery, Julia *Actress*
%STE Representation, 9301 Wilshire Blvd, #312, Beverly Hills, CA 90210

Monti, Antonio *Financier*
%Banca Commerciale Italiana, Plazza della Scala 6, 20121 Milan, Italy

Monti, Eugenio *Bobsled Athlete*
%Olympic Committee, Forco Italico, Rome, Italy

Montoya, Carlos *Concert Guitarist*
345 W 58th St, New York, NY 10019

Montville, Leigh *Sportswriter*
%Boston Globe, 135 Morrissey Blvd, Boston, MA 02107

Moody, D Thomas *Businessman*
%Charter Co, 1 Charter Plz, Jacksonville, FL 32202

Moody, George F *Financier*
%Security Pacific Corp, 333 S Hope St, Los Angeles, CA 90071

Moody, Jim *Representative, WI*
%House of Representatives, Washington, DC 20515

Moody, Orville *Golfer*
%Professional Golfers Assn, PO Box 109601, Palm Beach Gardens, FL 33410

Moody, Robert L *Businessman*
%American National Insurance Co, 1 Moody Plz, Galveston, TX 77550

Moody, Ron *Actor*
%Glass, 28 Berkeley Sq, London W1X 6HD, England

Moomaw, Donn *Football Player*
3124 Corda Dr, Los Angeles, CA 90049

Moon, Sun Myung *Religious Leader*
%Unification Church, 4 W 43rd St, New York, NY 10036

Moon, Warren *Football Player*
%Houston Oilers, 6910 Fannin St, Houston, TX 77030

Mooney, Michael J *Educator*
%Lewis & Clark College, President's Office, Portland, OR 97219

Mooney, Michael J *Educator*
%Lewis & Clark College, President's Office, Portland, OR 97219

Moore, Alvy *Actor*
8546 Amestoy Ave, Northridge, CA 91325

Moore, Arch A, Jr *Governor, WV*
507 Jefferson Ave, Glen Dale, WV 26038

Moore, Brian *Writer*
33958 Pacific Coast Hwy, Malibu, CA 90265

Moore, Clayton *Actor*
4720 Park Olivo, Calabasas, CA 91302

Moore, Constance *Actress*
1661 Ferrari Dr, Beverly Hills, CA 90210

Moore, Demi *Actress*
%Creative Artists Agency, 9830 Wilshire Blvd, Beverly Hills, CA 90212

Moore, Dick *Cartoonist (Our Gang)*
%Dick Moore Assoc, 1560 Broadway, New York, NY 10036

Moore, Dickie *Hockey Executive*
%Moore Equipments, 675 Montee de Liesse, St Laurent PQ H4T 1P5, Canada

Moore, Dudley *Comedian*
5505 Ocean Front Walk, Marina del Rey, CA 90292

Moore, Francis Daniels *Surgeon*
66 Heath St, Brookline, MA 02146

Moore, Gary *Actor*
PO Box 583, Northeast Harbor, ME 04662

Moore, George E *Surgeon*
13755 W Kentucky Dr, Lakewood, CO 80228

Moore, Gordon E *Businessman*
%Intel Corp, 3065 Bowers Ave, Santa Clara, CA 95052

Moore, Herman *Football Player*
%Detroit Lions, Silverdome, 1200 Featherstone Rd, Pontiac, MI 48057

Moore, Howard W *Businessman*
%Toys "R" Us Inc, 395 W Passiac St, Rochelle Park, NJ 07662

Moore, Jeremy *General, England*
%Lloyds Bank, Cox's & King's Branch, 6 Pall Mall, London SW1, England

Moore, Jesse W *Space Engineer*
%Ball Aerospace Corp, Boulder Industrial Park, Boulder, CO 80306

Moore, Joe *Baseball Player*
PO Box 65, Gause, TX 77857

Moore, John *Baseball Player*
4-A Swan Lake Village, Bradenton, FL 33507

Moore, John A *Biologist*
11522 Tulane Ave, Riverside, CA 92507

Moore, John P *Judge*
%US Court of Appeals, US Courthouse, 1929 Stout St, Denver, CO 80294

Moore, John W *Educator*
%California State University, President's Office, Turlock, CA 95380

Moore, Johnny *Basketball Player*
%New Jersey Nets, Meadowlands Arena, East Rutherford, NJ 07073

Moore, Lenny *Football Player*
8815 Stonehaven Rd, Randallstown, MD 21133

Moore, M Thomas *Businessman*
%Cleveland-Cliffs Co, Huntington Bldg, Cleveland, OH 44115

Moore, Malcolm *Medical Researcher*
%Memorial Sloan-Kettering Cancer Ctr, 1275 York Ave, New York, NY 10021

Moore, Mary Tyler *Actress*
PO Box 49032, Los Angeles, CA 90049

Moore, Melba *Singer*
%Hush Inc, 231 W 58th St, New York, NY 10019

Moore, Mike *Prime Minister, New Zealand*
%Labor Party, House of Representatives, Wellington, New Zealand

Moore, Patrick *Broadcaster, Writer*
Farthings, 39 West St, Selsey, Sussex, England

Moore, Paul, Jr *Religious Leader*
%Protestant Episcopal Church, 1047 Amsterdam Ave, New York, NY 10025

Moore, R Stuart *Businessman*
%Lane Co Inc, E Franklin Ave, Altavista, VA 24517

Moore, Roger *Actor*
Chalet Le Fenil, CH-3783 Grund Bei Staad, Switzerland

Moore, Steve *Cartoonist (In the Bleachers)*
%Tribune Media Syndicate, 64 E Concord St, Orlando, FL 32801

Moore, Terry *Actress*
833 Ocean Ave, #104, Santa Monica, CA 90403

Moore, Terry B *Baseball Player*
501 Ridgemont Dr, Collinsville, IL 62234

Moore, William Harreld *Businessman*
%Penn Central Transportation Co, 1846 Six Penn Ctr, Philadelphia, PA 19104

Moorer, Thomas H *Navy Admiral, Businessman*
6901 Lupine Ln, McLean, VA 22101

Moorhead, Carlos J *Representative, CA*
%House of Representatives, Washington, DC 20515

Moorman, Thomas S, Jr *Air Force General*
Commander, AFSPACECOM, Peterson Air Force Base, CO 80914

Mora, Jim *Football Coach*
%New Orleans Saints, 6928 Saints Dr, Metairie, LA 70003

Moran, Erin *Actress*
%Patrick McMinn Mgmt, 8721 Sunset Blvd, #104, Los Angeles, CA 90069

Moran, John *Religious Leader*
%Missionary Church, 3901 S Wayne Ave, Ft Wayne, IN 46516

Moran, Julie *Sportscaster*
%ABC-TV, Sports Dept, 77 W 66th St, New York, NY 10023

Moran, Lois *Actress*
PO Box 1088, Sedona, AZ 86336

Morast, Daniel J *Association Executive*
%International Wildlife Coalition, 634 N Falmouth Hwy, North Falmouth, MA 02556

Morath, Max *Singer*
529 W 42nd St, #3-B, New York, NY 10036

M

Moreau – Moriarty

Moreau, Jeanne *Actress*
193 Rue de l'Universite, 75007 Paris, France

Morella, Constance A *Representative, MD*
%House of Representatives, Washington, DC 20515

Moreno, Rita *Actress*
1620 Amalfi Dr, Pacific Palisades, CA 90272

Moret, Roger *Baseball Player*
RR 1, Box 6742, Guayama, PR 00654

Morgan, Barbara *Astronaut*
%Oklahoma State University, Teacher in Space Program, Stillwater, OK 74078

Morgan, Ben F, Jr *Businessman*
%Dairymen Inc, 10140 Linn Station Rd, Louisville, KY 40223

Morgan, Debbi *Actress*
%Artists Agency, 10000 Santa Monica Blvd, #305, Los Angeles, CA 90067

Morgan, Dennis *Actor*
PO Box 3036, Ahwahnee, CA 93601

Morgan, Frank J *Businessman*
%Quaker Oats Co, Merchandise Mart Plz, Chicago, IL 60654

Morgan, Graham J *Businessman*
%USG Corp, 101 S Wacker Dr, Chicago, IL 60606

Morgan, Harry *Actor*
13172 Boca de Canon Ln, Los Angeles, CA 90049

Morgan, Hugh J, Jr *Businessman*
%Sonat Inc, First National-Southern Natural Bldg, Birmingham, AL 35203

Morgan, Jane *Singer*
%Management Three, 4570 Encino Ave, Encino, CA 91316

Morgan, Jaye P *Singer, Actress*
30130 Cuthbert, Malibu, CA 90265

Morgan, Joe (Joseph L) *Baseball Player*
5588 Fernhoff Rd, Oakland, CA 94619

Morgan, Joe (Joseph M) *Baseball Manager*
15 Oak Hill Dr, Walpole, MA 02081

Morgan, Lee L *Businessman*
%Caterpillar Tractor Co, 100 NE Adams St, Peoria, IL 61629

Morgan, Lewis R *Judge*
PO Box 759, Newman, GA 30264

Morgan, Marabel *Writer*
%Total Woman Inc, 1300 NW 167th St, Miami, FL 33169

Morgan, Michele *Actress*
5 Rue Jacques Dulud, 92200 Neuilly-sur-Seine, France

Morgan, Nancy *Actress*
%Bauman Hiller Assoc, 9220 Sunset Blvd, #512, Los Angeles, CA 90069

Morgan, P J *Mayor*
%Mayor's Office, 1819 Farnam, #300, Omaha, NE 68183

Morgan, Robert *Businessman*
%Aamco Transmissions, 408 E 4th St, Bridgeport, PA 19405

Morgan, Robert B *Senator, NC*
PO Box 377, Lillington, NC 27546

Morgan, Roger L *Financier*
%First Columbia Financial Corp, 5850 S Ulster Cir, Irvine, CO 80217

Morgan, Stanley *Football Player*
%New England Patriots, Sullivan Stadium, Rt 1, Foxboro, MA 02035

Morgan, Walter T J *Biochemist*
57 Woodbury Dr, Sutton, Surrey, England

Morgan, William W *Astronomer*
%Yerkes Observatory, Williams Bay, WI 53191

Morgens, Howard *Businessman*
PO Box 222255, Carmel, CA 93922

Morgenthau, Robert M *District Attorney*
1085 Park Ave, New York, NY 10028

Mori, Hanae *Fashion Designer*
17 Ave Montaigne, 75008 Paris, France

Mori, Mamoru *Astronaut, Japan*
%NASDA, 2-4-1 Hamamatshucho, Minatoku, Tokyo 105, Japan

Moriarty, Cathy *Actress*
3601 Vista Pacifica, #12, Malibu, CA 90265

Moriarty, Michael *Actor*
200 W 58th St, #3-B, New York, NY 10019
Moriarty, Phil *Swimming Coach*
%Harbour Village, #20-E, Branford, CT 06045
Morin, Jim *Editorial Cartoonist*
%Miami Herald, Herald Plz, Miami, FL 33101
Morini, Erica *Concert Violinist*
1200 5th Ave, New York, NY 10029
Morinigo, Higinio *President, Paraguay*
Calle General Urguiza 625-Acassuso, Buenos Aires, Argentina
Morishima, Tozo *Businessman*
%Toyo Soda Manufacturing Co, 7-7 Akasaka, Minatoku, Tokyo 107, Japan
Morison, Patricia *Actress*
400 S Hauser Blvd, #9-L, Los Angeles, CA 90036
Morita, Akio *Businessman*
%Sony Corp, 6-7-35 Kitashinagawa, Shinagawaku, Tokyo 141, Japan
Morita, Chigazo *Financier*
%Toyo Trust & Banking Co, 4-3 Marunouchi, Chiyodaku, Tokyo 100, Japan
Morita, Noriyuki (Pat) *Actor*
PO Box 491278, Los Angeles, CA 90049
Moritz, Charles F *Editor*
%Current Biography, H W Wilson Co, 950 University Ave, Bronx, NY 10452
Moritz, Charles W *Businessman*
%Dun & Bradstreet Corp, 299 Park Ave, New York, NY 10171
Moritz, Louisa *Actress*
2354 Jupiter Dr, Los Angeles, CA 90046
Moriya, Gakuji *Businessman*
%Mitsubishu Heavy Industries, 2-5-1 Marunouchi, Chiyodaku, Tokyo, Japan
Morley, H Barclay *Businessman*
%Stauffer Chemical Co, Nyala Farm Rd, Westport, CT 06881
Morley, Robert *Actor*
Fairmans, Wargrave, Berks, England
Moro, Saburo *Businessman*
%Toyo Tire & Rubber Co, 17-18 Edobori, Nishiku, Osaka 550, Japan
Moroder, Giorgio *Composer*
4162 Lankershim Blvd, Universal City, CA 91602
Morosky, Robert H *Businessman*
%Allied Stores Corp, 1114 Ave of Americas, New York, NY 10036
Morrall, Earl *Football Player*
%Arrowhead Country Club, 8201 SW 24th St, Fort Lauderdale, FL 33324
Morrey, Charles B, Jr *Mathematician*
210 Yale Ave, Berkeley, CA 94708
Morrice, Norman *Ballet Choreographer*
%Royal Ballet, Convent Gdn, Bow St, London WC2E 7QA, England
Morrill, James L *Educator*
1752 Ardleigh Rd, Columbus, OH 43221
Morrill, Priscilla *Actress*
%Bauman Hiller Strain, 9220 Sunset Blvd, Los Angeles, CA 90069
Morris Wingerter, Pam *Synchronized Swimmer*
403 Boros Rd, New Bern, NC 28560
Morris, Betty *Bowler*
%Women's International Bowling Congress, 5301 S 76th St, Greendale, WI 53129
Morris, Charles B *Vietnam War Army Hero (CMH)*
1103 Riverside Cir, Spring Lake, NC 28390
Morris, Desmond *Writer, Zoologist*
%Jonathan Cape, 32 Bedford Sq, London WC1, England
Morris, Everett L *Businessman*
%Public Service Enterprise Grp, 80 Park Plz, Newark, NJ 07101
Morris, Garrett *Actor*
%Judy Schoen Assoc, 606 N Larchmont Blvd, #309, Los Angeles, CA 90004
Morris, George *Football Player*
6695 Peachtree Industrial Blvd, #108, Atlanta, GA 30360
Morris, Greg *Actor*
%Artists Group, 1930 Century Park West, #403, Los Angeles, CA 90067
Morris, Howard *Comedian*
%Fred Amsel Assoc, 6310 San Vicente Blvd, #407, Los Angeles, CA 90048

M

Morris – Mortimer Barrett

Morris, Jack *Baseball Player*
4705 Old Orchard Trl, Orchard Lake, MI 48033

Morris, James *Opera Singer*
%Colbert Artists Mgmt, 111 W 57th St, New York, NY 10019

Morris, Jan *Writer*
Trefan Morys, Chanystamdwy, Gwymedd, Cymru, Wales

Morris, Joe *Football Player*
%Cleveland Browns, Cleveland Stadium, Cleveland, OH 44114

Morris, John M *Editorial Cartoonist*
%Associated Press, 50 Rockefeller Plz, New York, NY 10020

Morris, Johnny *Football Player*
%WBBM-TV, 620 N McClurg Ct, Chicago, IL 60611

Morris, Joseph J *Businessman*
%Champion Home Builders Co, 5573 E North St, Dryden, MI 48428

Morris, Mark *Choreographer*
%Mark Morris Dance Group, 104 Franklin St, New York, NY 10013

Morris, Richard S *Businessman*
%El Paso Natural Gas, 1 Paul Kayser Ctr, El Paso, TX 79978

Morris, Robert *Sculptor*
%Hunter College, Art Dept, New York, NY 10021

Morris, Seth Irvin *Architect*
%Morris/Aubry Architects, 3465 W Alabama St, Houston, TX 77027

Morris, William S, III *Publisher*
%Florida Times-Union, 1 Riverside Ave, Jacksonville, FL 32202

Morris, Willie *Editor*
PO Box 702, Bridgehampton, NY 11932

Morris, Wright *Writer*
341 Laurel Way, Mill Valley, CA 94941

Morrison, James S *Businessman*
%Atlantic Richfield Co, 515 S Flower St, Los Angeles, CA 90071

Morrison, John W *Financier*
%Norwest Corp, 1200 Peavey Bldg, Minneapolis, MN 55479

Morrison, Philip *Astronomer*
%Massachusetts Institute of Technology, Astronomy Dept, Cambridge, MA 02139

Morrison, Sid *Representative, WA*
%House of Representatives, Washington, DC 20515

Morrison, Toni *Writer*
%Princeton University, Dickinson Hall, Princeton, NJ 08544

Morrison, Van *Singer*
12304 Santa Monica Blvd, #300, Los Angeles, CA 90025

Morrow, Bobby *Track Athlete*
1620 Sam Houston, Harlingen, TX 78550

Morrow, Bruce (Cousin Brucie) *Radio Entertainer*
%CBS Radio Network, 51 W 52nd St, New York, NY 10019

Morrow, Byron *Actor*
%Barr Agency, 8350 Santa Monica Blvd, #206-A, Los Angeles, CA 90069

Morrow, Rob *Actor*
%William Morris Agency, 151 El Camino, Beverly Hills, CA 90212

Morse, David *Actor*
%Yvette Bikoff Agency, 8721 Santa Monica Blvd, #21, West Hollywood, CA 90067

Morse, David E *Publisher*
%Christian Science Monitor, 1 Norway St, Boston, MA 02115

Morse, Ella Mae *Singer*
3232 W 152nd Pl, Gardena, CA 90249

Morse, F Bradford *Representative, MA*
%UN Development Program, 1 UN Plz, New York, NY 10017

Morse, Jeremy *Financier*
%Lloyds Bank, 71 Lombard St, London EC3P 3BS, England

Morse, Joseph *Financier*
%Morse Investments, Franklin Hill Rd, Lyme, NH 03768

Morse, Philip M *Physicist*
126 Wildwood St, Winchester, MA 01890

Morse, Robert *Actor*
13554 Valley Vista Blvd, Sherman Oaks, CA 91423

Mortimer Barrett, Angela *Tennis Player*
The Oaks, Coombe Hill Gl, Beverly Ln, Kingston-on-Thames, Surrey, England

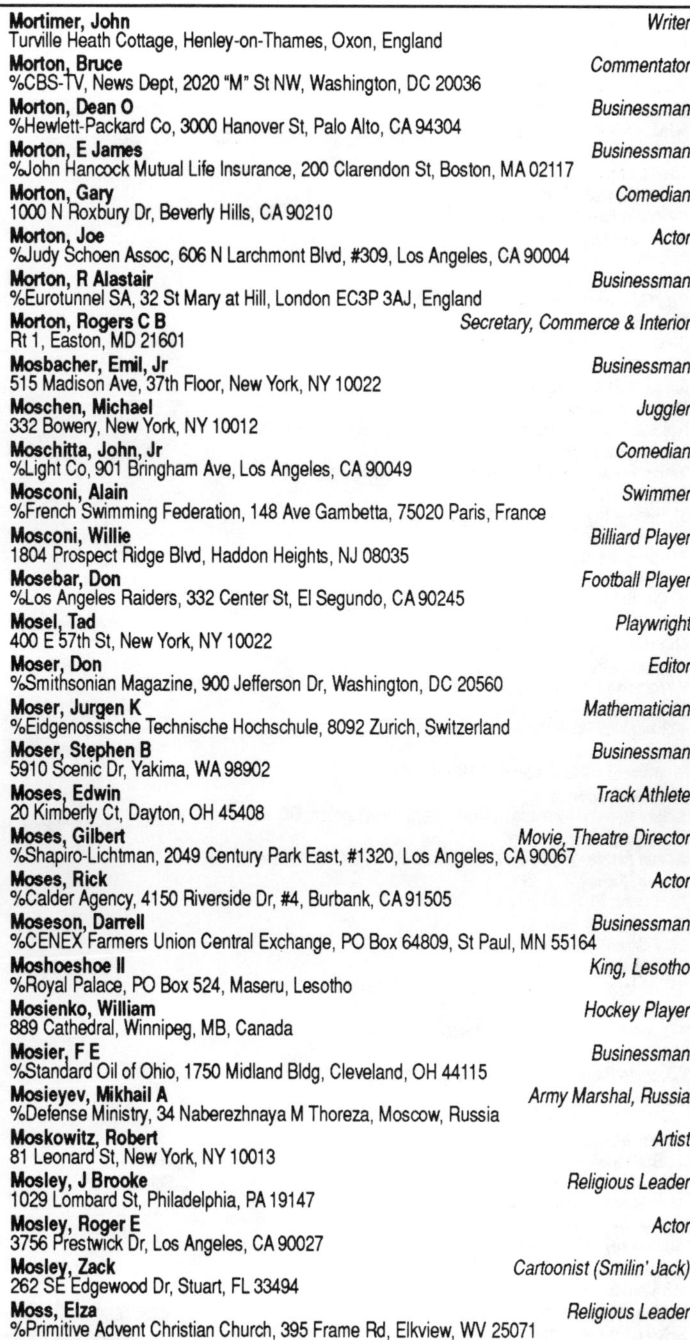

Mortimer, John *Writer*
Turville Heath Cottage, Henley-on-Thames, Oxon, England

Morton, Bruce *Commentator*
%CBS-TV, News Dept, 2020 "M" St NW, Washington, DC 20036

Morton, Dean O *Businessman*
%Hewlett-Packard Co, 3000 Hanover St, Palo Alto, CA 94304

Morton, E James *Businessman*
%John Hancock Mutual Life Insurance, 200 Clarendon St, Boston, MA 02117

Morton, Gary *Comedian*
1000 N Roxbury Dr, Beverly Hills, CA 90210

Morton, Joe *Actor*
%Judy Schoen Assoc, 606 N Larchmont Blvd, #309, Los Angeles, CA 90004

Morton, R Alastair *Businessman*
%Eurotunnel SA, 32 St Mary at Hill, London EC3P 3AJ, England

Morton, Rogers C B *Secretary, Commerce & Interior*
Rt 1, Easton, MD 21601

Mosbacher, Emil, Jr *Businessman*
515 Madison Ave, 37th Floor, New York, NY 10022

Moschen, Michael *Juggler*
332 Bowery, New York, NY 10012

Moschitta, John, Jr *Comedian*
%Light Co, 901 Bringham Ave, Los Angeles, CA 90049

Mosconi, Alain *Swimmer*
%French Swimming Federation, 148 Ave Gambetta, 75020 Paris, France

Mosconi, Willie *Billiard Player*
1804 Prospect Ridge Blvd, Haddon Heights, NJ 08035

Mosebar, Don *Football Player*
%Los Angeles Raiders, 332 Center St, El Segundo, CA 90245

Mosel, Tad *Playwright*
400 E 57th St, New York, NY 10022

Moser, Don *Editor*
%Smithsonian Magazine, 900 Jefferson Dr, Washington, DC 20560

Moser, Jurgen K *Mathematician*
%Eidgenossische Technische Hochschule, 8092 Zurich, Switzerland

Moser, Stephen B *Businessman*
5910 Scenic Dr, Yakima, WA 98902

Moses, Edwin *Track Athlete*
20 Kimberly Ct, Dayton, OH 45408

Moses, Gilbert *Movie, Theatre Director*
%Shapiro-Lichtman, 2049 Century Park East, #1320, Los Angeles, CA 90067

Moses, Rick *Actor*
%Calder Agency, 4150 Riverside Dr, #4, Burbank, CA 91505

Moseson, Darrell *Businessman*
%CENEX Farmers Union Central Exchange, PO Box 64809, St Paul, MN 55164

Moshoeshoe II *King, Lesotho*
%Royal Palace, PO Box 524, Maseru, Lesotho

Mosienko, William *Hockey Player*
889 Cathedral, Winnipeg, MB, Canada

Mosier, F E *Businessman*
%Standard Oil of Ohio, 1750 Midland Bldg, Cleveland, OH 44115

Mosieyev, Mikhail A *Army Marshal, Russia*
%Defense Ministry, 34 Naberezhnaya M Thoreza, Moscow, Russia

Moskowitz, Robert *Artist*
81 Leonard St, New York, NY 10013

Mosley, J Brooke *Religious Leader*
1029 Lombard St, Philadelphia, PA 19147

Mosley, Roger E *Actor*
3756 Prestwick Dr, Los Angeles, CA 90027

Mosley, Zack *Cartoonist (Smilin' Jack)*
262 SE Edgewood Dr, Stuart, FL 33494

Moss, Elza *Religious Leader*
%Primitive Advent Christian Church, 395 Frame Rd, Elkview, WV 25071

Moss, Frank E *Senator, UT*
1848 S Wasatch Dr, Salt Lake City, UT 84108

Moss, Geoffrey *Cartoonist, Illustrator*
%Washington Post Writers Grp, 1150 15th St NW, Washington, DC 20071

M

Moss – Muckler

Moss, Jerry *Record Company Executive*
%A & M Records, 1416 N La Brea Ave, Los Angeles, CA 90028

Moss, Ronn *Actor*
%Yvette Bikoff Agency, 8721 Santa Monica Blvd, #21, West Hollywood, CA 90067

Mossbauer, Rudolf *Nobel Physics Laureate*
%Institut Max von Laue, POB 156, 38042 Grenoble-Cedex, France

Mossi, Don *Baseball Player*
1340 Sanford Ranch Rd, Ukiah, CA 95482

Most, Donald *Actor*
%Chasin Agency, 190 N Canon Dr, #201, Beverly Hills, CA 90210

Most, Johnny *Sportscaster*
%Boston Celtics, 151 Merrimac St, Boston, MA 02114

Mota Pinto, Carlos *Prime Minister, Portugal*
Rua Gil Vicente 83, 3000 Coimbra, Portugal

Mota, Manny *Baseball Player*
3926 Los Olivos Ln, La Crescenta, CA 91214

Mota, Rosa *Marathon Athlete*
R Teatro 194 4 Esq, 4100 Porto, Portugal

Motelson, Benjamin *Nobel Physics Laureate*
Nordita, Blegdamsvej 17, DK-2100 Copenhagen 0, Denmark

Motoyama, Hideyo *Businessman*
%Kirin Brewery, 6-26-1 Jingumae, Shibuyaku, Tokyo 150, Japan

Mott, Nevill F *Nobel Physics Laureate*
31 Sedley Taylor Rd, Cambridge, England

Mott, Stewart *Political Activist*
515 Madison Ave, New York, NY 10022

Mott, William Penn *Government Official*
%National Park Service, Department of Interior, Washington, DC 20240

Moulton, Alexander E *Bicycle Engineer*
The Hall, Bradford-on-Avon, Wilts, England

Mounsey, Yvonne *Ballerina*
%Westside School of Ballet, 1711 Stewart St, Santa Monica, CA 90404

Mount, Rick *Basketball Player*
803 Hopkins Rd, Lebanon, IN 46052

Mountcastle, Vernon B, Jr *Neurophysiologist*
31 Warrenton Rd, Baltimore, MD 21210

Mourning, Alonzo *Basketball Player*
%Georgetown University, Athletic Dept, Washington, DC 20057

Mouskouri, Nana *Singer*
%Triad Artists, 10100 Santa Monica Blvd, #1600, Los Angeles, CA 90067

Mowat, Farley *Writer, Naturalist*
25 St John St, Port Hope ON, Canada

Mowerson, Robert *Swimmer*
3417 Downers Dr, Minneapolis, MN 55418

Mowry, William S, Jr *Businessman*
%Beatrice Companies, 2 N LaSalle St, Chicago, IL 60602

Moxley, David *Businessman*
%Deloitte Touche Co, 1633 Broadway, New York, NY 10019

Moyer, Alan *Editor*
%Arizona Republic, PO Box 1950, Phoenix, AZ 85001

Moyers, Bill D *Commentator*
524 W 57th St, New York, NY 10019

Moyet, Allison *Singer*
%CBS Records, Sony Music, 1801 Century Park West, Los Angeles, CA 90067

Moynihan, Daniel Patrick *Senator, NY; Educator*
%US Senate, Washington, DC 20510

Mphahlele, Ezekiel *Writer*
%University of Witwatersrand, Jan Smuts Ave, Johannesburg, South Africa

Mrazek, Robert J *Representative, NY*
143 Main St, Huntington, NY 11743

Mu'alla, Sheikh Rashid bin Ahmed al- *Ruler, Umm al Quwain*
%Royal Palace, Umm al Quwain, United Arab Emirates

Mubarak, Muhammad Hosni *President, Egypt*
%Presidential Palace, Abdeen, Cairo, Egypt

Muckler, John *Hockey Coach*
%Edmonton Oilers, Northlands Coliseum, Edmonton AL T5B 4M9, Canada

Mudd, Dennis I *Businessman*
%Allied Van Lines, 2120 S 25th St, Broadview, IL 60153

Mudd, Roger *Commentator*
7167 Old Dominion Dr, McLean, VA 22101

Mueller, George E *Electrical Engineer, Missile Scientist*
PO Box 3356, Santa Monica, CA 90403

Mueller, Robert J *Financier*
%Carteret Savings & Loan, 200 South St, Morristown, NJ 07960

Muench, David *Photographer*
PO Box 30500, Santa Barbara, CA 93105

Muench, John *Artist*
Flying Pt, Freeport, ME 04032

Muetterties, Earl Leonard *Chemist*
%University of California, Chemistry Dept, Berkeley, CA 94720

Muetzelfeldt, Bruno *Religious Leader*
%Lutheran World Federation, 150 Rt de Ferney, 1211 Geneva 20, Switzerland

Mugabe, Robert G *President, Zimbabwe*
%President's Office, Harare, Zimbabwe

Muhammad, Wallace D *Religious Leader*
%Elijah Muhammad Masjid, 7351 S Stony Island Blvd, Chicago, IL 60649

Muir DeGraad, Karen *Swimmer*
%Applebosch State Hospital, Ozwatini, Natal, South Africa

Muir, Jean *Fashion Designer*
59/61 Farringdon Rd, London EC1M 3HD, England

Mukai, Chiaki *Astronaut, Japan*
%NASDA, 2-4-1 Hamamatsucho, Minatoku, Tokyo 105, Japan

Mukhamedov, Irek *Ballet Dancer*
%Royal Ballet, Convent Grdn, Bow St, London WL2E 7QA, England

Muldaur, Diana *Actress*
259 Quadro Vecchio Dr, Pacific Palisades, CA 90272

Muldaur, Maria *Singer*
PO Box 5535, Mill Valley, CA 94942

Muldoon, Robert D *Prime Minister, New Zealand*
Vogel House, 75 Woburn Rd, Lower Hutt, New Zealand

Muldowney, Shirley *Drag Racing Driver*
%Roven Productions, PO Box 5192, Beverly Hills, CA 90210

Mulgrew, Kate *Actress*
%STE Representation, 9301 Wilshire Blvd, #312, Beverly Hills, CA 90210

Mulhare, Edward *Actor*
%First Artists Agency, 10000 Riverside Dr, #6, Toluca Lake, CA 91602

Mull, Martin *Actor*
338 Chapbourne Ave, Los Angeles, CA 90049

Mullane, Denis F *Businessman*
%Connecticut Mutual Life Insurance, 140 Garden St, Hartford, CT 06154

Mullane, Richard M (Mike) *Astronaut*
1301 Las Lomas Rd NE, Albuquerque, NM 87106

Mullane, Robert E *Businessman*
%Bally Manufacturing Corp, 8700 W Bryn Mawr Ave, Chicago, IL 60631

Mullavey, Greg *Actor*
4430 Hayvenhurst Ave, Encino, CA 91436

Mullen, Joe *Hockey Player*
%Pittsburgh Penguins, Civic Arena, Pittsburgh, PA 15219

Muller, Egon *Motorcyle Racer*
Dorfstrasse 9, 2307 Rodenbeck, Germany

Muller, Henry *Editor*
%Time Magazine, Rockefeller Ctr, New York, NY 10020

Muller, K Alex *Nobel Physics Laureate*
%IBM Research Laboratory, Saumerstrasse 4, CH-8803 Ruschlikon, Switzerland

Muller, Kirk *Hockey Player*
%New Jersey Devils, Meadowlands Arena, East Rutherford, NJ 07073

Muller, Peter *Skier*
Haldenstrasse 18, CH-8134 Adliswil, Switzerland

Muller, Richard S *Microbiotics Engineer*
%University of California, Sensor/Acutator Center, Berkeley, CA 94720

Muller, Robby *Cinematographer*
%Smith/Gosnell/Nicholson, 1515 Palisades Dr, #N, Pacific Palisades, CA 90272

Muller, Steven *Educator*
%Johns Hopkins University, President's Office, Baltimore, MD 21218

Mulligan, Gerry *Jazz Saxophonist*
%Willard Alexander Inc, 660 Madison Ave, New York, NY 10021

Mulligan, Richard *Actor*
%International Creative Mgmt, 8899 Beverly Blvd, Los Angeles, CA 90048

Mulligan, Richard C *Research Scientist*
11 Sumner Rd, Cambridge, MA 02138

Mulligan, Robert *Movie Director*
%United Talent Agency, 9560 Wilshire Blvd, #500, Beverly Hills, CA 90212

Mulliken, Bill *Swimmer*
7050 W 71st St, Chicago, IL 60638

Mullikin, Harry *Businessman*
%Westin Hotels Co, Westin Bldg, 2001 6th Ave, Seattle, WA 98121

Mullin, Chris *Basketball Player*
%Golden State Warriors, Oakland Coliseum Arena, Oakland, CA 94621

Mullin, J Stanley *Skier*
%Sheppard Mullin Richter Hampton, 333 S Hope St, Los Angeles, CA 90071

Mullins, David *Government Official*
%Federal Reserve Board, 20th St & Constitution Ave NW, Washington, DC 20551

Mullins, Jeff *Basketball Player, Coach*
%University of North Carolina Charlotte, Athletic Dept, Charlotte, NC 28223

Mullova, Viktoria *Concert Violinist*
%Columbia Artists Mgmt Inc, 165 W 57th St, New York, NY 10019

Mulloy, Gardner *Tennis Player*
%Fisher Island, 1 Fisher Island Dr, Fisher Island, FL 33109

Mulroney, Brian *Prime Minister, Canada*
Langevin Block, Parliamentary Bldgs, Ottawa ON K1A 0A2, Canada

Mulvoy, Mark *Editor, Publisher*
%Sports Illustrated Magazine, Rockefeller Ctr, New York, NY 10020

Mumford, Milton C *Businessman*
390 Park Ave, New York, NY 10022

Mumy, Billy *Actor*
2419 Laurel Pass Ave, Los Angeles, CA 90046

Munch, Guido *Astronomer*
%Max Planck Institute, 6900 Heidelberg-Konigstuhl, Germany

Munchak, Mike *Football Player*
%Houston Oilers, PO Box 1516, Houston, TX 77251

Munchinger, Karl *Conductor*
Haus am Rebenhang, 7000 Stuttgart-Rotenberg, Germany

Mundt, Donald K *Businessman*
%Northwestern Mutual Life Insurance, 720 E Wisconsin, Milwaukee, WI 53202

Mundt, Ray B *Businessman*
%Alco Standard Corp, PO Box 834, Valley Forge, PA 19482

Mundy, Carl E, Jr *Marine Corps General*
Commandant's Office, Hdq, US Marine Corps, Washington, DC 20380

Munger, Charles T *Businessman*
%Berkshire Hathaway Inc, 1440 Kiewit Plz, Omaha, NE 68131

Munger, George (Red) *Football Coach*
Matlack Ln & Newton Rd, Villanova, PA 19085

Munitz, Barry A *Educator*
%California State University System, 400 Golden Shore, Long Beach, CA 90802

Munk, Frank *Political Scientist*
3808 SW Mt Adams Dr, Portland, OR 97201

Munk, Walter H *Geophysicist*
9530 La Jolla Shores Dr, La Jolla, CA 92037

Munn, Stephen P *Businessman*
%Carlisle Corp, 1600 Columbia Plz, Cincinnati, OH 45202

Munoz Vega, Paolo Cardinal *Religious Leader*
%Palacio Arzobispal, Apartado 106, Quito, Ecuador

Munoz, Anthony *Football Player*
%Cincinnati Bengals, 200 Riverfront Stadium, Cincinnati, OH 45202

Munro, Dana G *Diplomat*
345 Harrison St, Princeton, NJ 08540

Munro, Ian *Editor*
%Annals of Internal Medicine, 34 Beacon St, Boston, MA 02106

M

Munro, J Richard *Publisher*
%Time Warner Inc, Rockefeller Ctr, New York, NY 10020
Munroe, George B *Businessman*
%Phelps Dodge Corp, 300 Park Ave, New York, NY 10022
Munsel, Patrice *Opera Singer*
337 Lattingtown, Locust Valley, NY 11560
Munson, Frank W *Businessman*
%General Re Corp, Financial Ctr, Stamford, CT 06904
Munzer, Rudolph J *Businessman*
%Petrolane Inc, 1600 E Hill St, Long Beach, CA 90806
Murakowski, Frank H *Senator, AK*
3 Mile Chena Pump Rd, Fairbanks, AK 99701
Murayama, Makio *Biochemist*
5010 Benton Ave, Bethesda, MD 20014
Murdoch, Bob *Hockey Coach*
%Winnipeg Jets, 15-1430 Maroons Rd, Winnipeg MB R3G 0L5, Canada
Murdoch, Iris *Writer*
Cedar Lodge, Steeple Aston, Oxon, England
Murdoch, Rupert *Publisher*
%News America Publishing Inc, 210 South St, New York, NY 10002
Murdock, David H *Businessman*
%Pacific Holding Corp, 10900 Wilshire Blvd, #1600, Los Angeles, CA 90024
Murdock, George *Actor*
%Barry Freed Co, 9255 Sunset Blvd, #603, Los Angeles, CA 90069
Murdock, George Peter *Anthropologist*
Wynnewood Plz, #107, Wynnewood, PA 19096
Murnaghan, Francis D, Jr *Judge*
%US Court of Appeals, 101 W Lombard St, Baltimore, MD 21201
Murphey, Michael Martin *Singer*
%Jim Halsey Assoc, 3225 S Norwood, Tulsa, OK 74135
Murphy, Austin J *Representative, PA*
%House of Representatives, Washington, DC 20515
Murphy, Ben *Actor*
3601 Vista Pacifica, #17, Malibu, CA 90265
Murphy, Caryle *Journalist*
Washington Post, 1150 15th St NW, Washington, DC 20071
Murphy, Charles (Stretch) *Basketball Player*
4002 Barcelona, Tampa, FL 33609
Murphy, Charles E, Jr *Businessman*
%Resorts International Inc, 915 NE 125th St, North Miami, FL 33161
Murphy, Charles H, Jr *Businessman*
%Murphy Oil Corp, 200 Peach St, El Dorado, AK 71730
Murphy, Charles S *Government Official*
100 Bluff View Dr, #503-C, Belleair Bluffs, FL 33540
Murphy, Daniel J *Navy Admiral*
%Gray & Co, 3020 "K" St NW, Washington, DC 20007
Murphy, Dwayne *Baseball Player*
1132 "W" St, #H-6, Lancaster, CA 93534
Murphy, Eddie *Comedian, Actor*
2727 Benedict Canyon Dr, Beverly Hills, CA 90210
Murphy, Franklin D *Educator, Publisher*
419 Robert Ln, Beverly Hills, CA 90210
Murphy, George A *Financier*
%Irving Trust Co, 1 Wall St, New York, NY 10005
Murphy, George L *Senator, CA*
100 Worth Ave, #419, Palm Beach, FL 33480
Murphy, Gerald D *Businessman*
%Early California Industries, 10960 Wilshire Blvd, Los Angeles, CA 90024
Murphy, Henry B *Businessman*
%Resorts International Inc, 915 NE 125th St, North Miami, FL 33161
Murphy, John A *Businessman*
%Philip Morris Companies, 120 Park Ave, New York, NY 10017
Murphy, John Cullen *Cartoonist (Prince Valiant)*
%King Features Syndicate, 235 E 45th St, New York, NY 10017
Murphy, John J *Businessman*
%Dresser Industries, 1505 Elm St, Dallas, TX 75221

M

Murphy, Mark — *Football Player*
%Colgate University, Athletic Dept, Hamilton, NY 13346

Murphy, Michael — *Actor*
%International Creative Mgmt, 8899 Beverly Blvd, Los Angeles, CA 90048

Murphy, Michael E — *Businessman*
%Sara Lee Corp, 3 First National Plz, Chicago, IL 60602

Murphy, Raymond G — *Korean War Marine Corps Hero (CMH)*
4677 Sutton NW, Albuquerque, NM 87114

Murphy, Reg — *Editor, Publisher*
%Baltimore Sun, 501 N Calvert St, Baltimore, MD 21278

Murphy, Rosemary — *Actress*
220 E 73rd St, New York, NY 10021

Murphy, Thomas A — *Businessman*
%General Motors Corp, 3044 W Grand Blvd, Detroit, MI 48202

Murphy, Thomas S — *Businessman*
%Capital Cities Communications, 24 E 51st St, New York, NY 10022

Murphy, William B — *Businessman*
110 Maplehill Rd, Gladwyne, PA 19035

Murray, Allen E — *Businessman*
%Mobil Corp, 150 E 42nd St, New York, NY 10017

Murray, Anne — *Singer*
%Balmur Ltd, 4881 Yonge St, Toronto ON M2N 5X3, Canada

Murray, Bill — *Comedian*
RFD 1, Box 250-A, Washington Springs Rd, Palisades, NY 10964

Murray, Bruce C — *Planetary Scientist*
%Jet Propulsion Laboratory, 4800 Oak Grove Dr, Pasadena, CA 91109

Murray, Bryan — *Hockey Coach*
%Philadelphia Flyers, Spectrum, Pattison Pl, Philadelphia, PA 19148

Murray, Charles A — *Social Scientist*
%Manhattan Policy Research Institute, 131 Spring St, New York, NY 10012

Murray, Charles P, Jr — *WW II Army Hero (CMH)*
5906 Northridge Rd, Columbia, SC 29206

Murray, Doug — *Cartoonist (The 'Nam)*
%Marvel Comic Grp, 387 Park Ave S, New York, NY 10016

Murray, Eddie — *Baseball Player*
13401 Blythenia Rd, Phoenix, MD 21131

Murray, Iain — *Yachtsman*
%International Management Group, 1 Eireview Plz, Cleveland, OH 44114

Murray, J Terrence — *Financier*
%Fleet Financial Group, 50 Kennedy Plz, Providence, RI 02903

Murray, Jan — *Comedian*
1157 Calle Vista Dr, Beverly Hills, CA 90210

Murray, Jim — *Sportswriter*
430 Bellagio Terr, Los Angeles, CA 90049

Murray, John E — *Educator*
%Duquesne University, President's Office, Pittsburgh, PA 15282

Murray, John L — *Businessman*
%Universal Foods Corp, 433 E Michigan St, Milwaukee, WI 53202

Murray, Joseph E — *Nobel Medicine Laureate*
108 Abbott Rd, Wellesley Hills, MA 02181

Murray, Kathryn — *Dancer*
2877 Kalakaua Ave, Honolulu, HI 96815

Murray, Michael — *Concert Organist*
1876-B Northwest Blvd, Columbus, OH 43212

Murray, Peg — *Actress*
41 Greenwich Ave, New York, NY 10014

Murray, R William — *Businessman*
%Philip Morris Companies, 120 Park Ave, New York, NY 10017

Murray, Robert E — *Businessman*
%North American Coal Corp, 12800 Shaker Blvd, Cleveland, OH 44120

Murray, Terry — *Hockey Coach*
%Washington Capitals, Capital Ctr, 1 Truman Dr, Landover, MD 20785

Murray, Troy — *Hockey Player*
%Chicago Black Hawks, 1800 W Madison Ave, Chicago, IL 60612

Murray, Ty — *Rodeo Rider*
Rt 6, Box 320, Stephenville, TX 76401

Murray, William *Businessman*
%Philip Morris Companies, 120 Park Ave, New York, NY 10017

Murrill, Paul W *Businessman*
%Gulf States Utilities Co, 350 Pine St, Beaumont, TX 77701

Murtagh, Kate *Actress*
15146 Moorpark St, Sherman Oaks, CA 91403

Murtha, John P *Representative, PA*
%House of Representatives, Washington, DC 20515

Musante, Tony *Actor*
%Artists Agency, 10000 Santa Monica Blvd, #305, Los Angeles, CA 90067

Musburger, Brent *Sportscaster*
%ABC-TV, Sports Dept, 1330 Ave of Americas, New York, NY 10019

Muse, William V *Educator*
%Auburn University, President's Office, Auburn, AL 36849

Museveni, Yoweri K *President, Uganda*
%President's Office, Kampala, Uganda

Musgrave, F Story *Astronaut*
%NASA, Johnson Space Ctr, Houston, TX 77058

Musgrave, R Kenton *Judge*
%US Court of International Trade, New York, NY 10007

Musgrave, Thea *Composer, Conductor*
%Theodore Presser Co, Presser Pl, Bryn Mawr, PA 19010

Musial, Stan *Baseball Player*
%St Louis Cardinals, 250 Stadium Plz, St Louis, MO 63102

Muskie, Edmund S *Secretary, State; Governor, ME*
%Chadborne Parke Whiteside Wolff, 1101 Vermont Ave NW, Washington, DC 20005

Musolino, Joseph R *Financier*
%RepublicBank Corp, 1800 RepublicBank Bldg, Dallas, TX 75201

Musso, George *Football Player*
604 W High St, Edwardsville, IL 62025

Mustard, Vernon *Labor Leader*
%United Textile Workers, 2 Echelon Plaza, Laurel Rd, Voorhees, NJ 08043

Muster, Brad *Football Player*
%Chicago Bears, 250 N Washington Rd, Lake Forest, IL 60045

Muth, Rene *Basketball Coach*
%Pennsylvania State University, Athletic Dept, University Park, PA 16802

Muti, Ornella *Actress*
376 Dalehurst Ave, Los Angeles, CA 90024

Muti, Riccardo *Conductor*
%Philadelphia Symphony, 1420 Locust St, Philadelphia, PA 19102

Mutoh, Hiroshi *Businessman*
%Showa Sangyo Co, 2-1 Uchi Kanda, Chiyodaku, Tokyo 101, Japan

Mutombo, Dikembe *Basketball Player*
%Denver Nuggets, McNichols Arena, 1635 Clay St, Denver, CO 80204

Mutter, Anne-Sophie *Concert Violinist*
%Columbia Artists Mgmt Inc, 165 W 57th St, New York, NY 10019

Muzzy, Richard W *Businessman*
%Owens-Corning Fiberglas Corp, Fiberglas Tower, Toledo, OH 43659

Mwinyi, Ali Hassam *President, Tanzania*
%State House, Dar-es-Salaam, Tanzania

Myers Tikalsky, Linda *Skier*
1500 N Cattle Dr, Dillon, MT 59725

Myers, Anne *Religious Leader*
%Church of the Brethren, 1451 Dundee Ave, Elgin, IL 60120

Myers, Barton *Architect*
%Barton Myers Assoc, 6834 Hollywood Blvd, Los Angeles, CA 90028

Myers, Dale D *Space Engineer*
%Dale Myers Assoc, Box 2455, Leucadia, CA 92024

Myers, Frederick M *Businessman*
%Lukens Inc, 50 S 1st Ave, Coatsville, PA 19320

Myers, Harry *Publisher*
%Scientific American Magazine, 415 Madison Ave, New York, NY 10017

Myers, Jack D *Physician*
%University of Pittsburgh, Scaife Hall, #1291, Pittsburgh, PA 15261

Myers, John T *Representative, IN*
%House of Representatives, Washington, DC 20515

M

Myers, John T *Army General*
Deputy Director General,, NATO Cmd/Info Systems Agency, APO, New York, NY 09667

Myers, Lisa *Commentator*
%NBC-TV, News Dept, 4001 Nebraska Ave NW, Washington, DC 20016

Myers, Malcolm C *Businessman*
%Carlisle Corp, 1600 Columbia Plz, Cincinnati, OH 45202

Myers, Minor, Jr *Educator*
%Illinois Wesleyan University, President's Office, Bloomington, IL 61702

Myers, Norman A *Businessman*
%Browning-Ferris Industries, 14701 St Mary's, Houston, TX 77079

Myers, Rochelle *Writer*
3827 California, San Francisco, CA 94118

Myers, Russell *Cartoonist (Broom Hilda)*
%Tribune Media Services, 64 E Concord St, Orlando, FL 32801

Myerson, Bernard *Businessman*
%Loews Corp, 666 5th Ave, New York, NY 10103

Myerson, Bess *Consumer Advocate*
6 E 43rd St, New York, NY 10017

Myerson, Harvey *Attorney*
%Finley Kumble Wagner Assoc, 425 Park Ave, New York, NY 10022

Myerson, Jacob M *Economist, Diplomat*
%OECD, 2 Rue Andre-Pascal, 75775 Paris Cedex 16, France

Myles, Alannah *Singer*
%Atlantic Records, 9229 Sunset Blvd, Los Angeles, CA 90069

Myrick, Sue *Mayor*
%Mayor's Office, City Hall, 600 E Trade St, Charlotte, NC 28202

Mzali, Mohamed *Prime Minister, Tunisia*
%Destourian Socialist Party, Blvd 9 April 1938, Tunis, Tunisia

N

Naber, John *Swimmer*
PO Box 50107, Pasadena, CA 91105
Nabors, Jim *Actor, Singer*
%William Morris Agency, 151 El Camino, Beverly Hills, CA 90212
Nabrit, Samuel M *Foundation Executive*
686 Beckwith St SW, Atlanta, GA 30314
Nachman, Jerry *Editor*
%New York Post, 210 South St, New York, NY 10002
Nachmansohn, David *Biochemist*
560 Riverside Dr, New York, NY 10027
Nader, George *Actor*
52 S Iwa Pl, La Haina, HI 96761
Nader, Michael *Actor*
%Gores/Fields Agency, 10100 Santa Monica Blvd, #700, Los Angeles, CA 90067
Nader, Ralph *Consumer Activist*
%Center for Study of Responsive Law, PO Box 19367, Washington, DC 20036
Nagako Kuni *Empress Mother, Japan*
%Imperial Palace, Tokyo, Japan
Nagamo, Takeshi *Businessman*
%Mitsubishi Metal Corp, 1-5-2 Otemachi, Chiyodaku, Tokyo 100, Japan
Nagamo, Wakichi *Businessman*
%Mitsubishi Gas & Chemical, 2-5-2 Marunouchi, Chiyodaku, Tokyo 100, Japan
Nagata, Takao *Businessman*
%Hitachi Zosen Corp, 1-6-14 Edobori, Nishiku, Osaka 550, Japan
Nagayama, Tokio *Businessman*
%Showa Oil Co, 2-7-3 Marunouchi, Chiyodaku, Tokyo 100, Japan
Nagel, Steven R *Astronaut*
%NASA, Johnson Space Ctr, Houston, TX 77058
Nageotte, Frank L *Businessman*
%Greyhound Corp, Greyhound Tower, Phoenix, AZ 85077
Nagle, David R *Representative, IA*
%House of Representatives, Washington, DC 20515
Nagler, Fred *Artist*
5742 Berkshire Ln, Dallas, TX 75209
Nahan, Stu *Sportscaster*
11274 Canton Dr, Studio City, CA 91604
Nahayan, Sheikh Zayed bin Sultan al- *President, United Arab Emirates*
%Amiri Palace, Abu Dhabi, Arabian Gulf
Naimi, Ali I *Businessman*
%Arabian American Oil Co, Box 4000, Daharan, Saudi Arabia
Naipaul, V S *Writer*
%Andre Deutsch Ltd, 105 Great Russell St, London WC1B 3LJ, England
Naisbitt, John *Writer*
%American Media Inc, 1454 30th St, West Des Moines, IA 50265
Naito, Chiaki *Astronaut, Japan*
NASDA, 2-4-1 Hamamatsucho, Minatoku, Tokyo 105, Japan
Najarian, John S *Surgeon*
%University of Minnesota, Health Science Ctr, Minneapolis, MN 55455
Najibullah, Muhammad *President, Afghanistan*
%Revolutionary Council, Da Khalkoo Koor, Kabul, Afghanistan
Nakabe, Tojiro *Businessman*
%Taiyo Fishery Co, 1-1-2 Otemachi, Chiyodaku, Tokyo 100, Japan
Nakagawa, Takeshi *Businessman*
%Meiji Seika Kaisha Ltd, 4-16 Kyobashi, Chuoku, Tokyo 104, Japan
Nakai, Norio *Businessman*
%Aisin Seiki Co, 2-1 Asahimachi, Kariya 448, Japan
Nakama, Keo *Swimmer*
1788 Laukahi St, Honolulu, HI 96821
Nakamura, Toshio *Financier*
%Mitsubishi Bank, 2-7-1 Marunochi, Chiyodaku, Tokyo 100, Japan
Nakamura, Utaemon *Kabuki Actor*
2551 Jikecho, Suzuka City, Japan
Nakano, Kiyonori *Businessman*
%Mitsui Petrochemical Industries, 2-5 Kasumigaseki, Tokyo 100, Japan
Nakasone, Yasuhiro *Prime Minister, Japan*
%Liberal-Democratic Party, Diet, Tokyo, Japan

N

Nakayama – Natori

Nakayama, Yoshiro *Businessman*
%Daikyo Oil Co, 2-4-1 Yaesu, Chuoku, Tokyo 100, Japan

Nakayasu, Kanichi *Businessman*
%Ube Industries, 1-12-32 Nishi-Honmachi, Ube City 755, Japan

Nalder, Eric *Journalist*
%Seattle Times, Fairview Ave N & John St, Seattle, WA 98111

Namaliu, Rabbie *Prime Minister, Papua New Guinea*
%Prime Minister's Office, Port Moresby, Papua New Guinea 40536

Namath, Joe *Football Player*
%Namanco Productions, 300 E 51st St, New York, NY 10022

Nambu, Masaji *Businessman*
%Toa Nenryo Kogyo, 1-1-1 Hitotsubashi, Chiyodaku, Tokyo 100, Japan

Namias, Jerome *Meteorologist*
%Scripps Institute of Oceanography, Sverdrup Hall, La Jolla, CA 92093

Nance, Jack *Actor*
%BDP Assoc, 10637 Burbank Blvd, North Hollywood, CA 91601

Nanne, Lou *Hockey Executive*
%Minnesota North Stars, Met Center, 7901 Cedar Ave S, Minneapolis, MN 55420

Nannen, Henri *Editor*
%Gruner und Jahr 2, Postfach 302040, 2 Hamburg 36, Germany

Nantz, Jim *Sportscaster*
%CBS-TV, Sports Dept, 51 W 52nd St, New York, NY 10019

Napier, Charles *Actor*
%Light Co, 901 Bringham Ave, Los Angeles, CA 90049

Napier, John *Stage Designer*
%MLR, 200 Fulham Rd, London SW10, England

Napier, John L *Judge*
%US Claims Court, 717 Madison Pl NW, Washington, DC 20005

Napier, W F Cardinal *Religious Leader*
%Archdiocese, 97 St John's St, PO Box 65, 4700 Kokstad, South Africa

Narayan, R K *Writer*
15 Vivekananda Rd, Yadavagir, Mysore 2, India

Narizzano, Silvio *Movie Director*
%Al Parker, 55 Park Ln, London, England

Narleski, Ray *Baseball Player*
1183 Chews Landing Rd, Laurel Springs, NJ 08021

Narz, Jack *Television Host*
1905 Beverly Pl, Beverly Hills, CA 90210

Nash, Graham *Singer, Songwriter*
%Siddons Assoc, 1588 Crossroads of World, Los Angeles, CA 90028

Nash, Jack *Financier*
%Odyssey Partners, 437 Madison Ave, New York, NY 10022

Nash, Johnny *Singer, Songwriter*
%CBS Records, 51 W 52nd St, New York, NY 10019

Nason, John W *Educator*
Rocky Pt, Keene, NY 12942

Nassau, Robert H *Businessman*
3 Evergreen Ct, St Paul, MN 55127

Nastase, Ilie *Tennis Player*
%Mitch Oprea, 107 W 75th St, #2-A, New York, NY 10023

Nasu, Tadami *Businessman*
%Sanyo-Kokusake Pulp Co, 1-4-5 Marunouchi, Chiyodaku, Tokyo, Japan

Nasution, Abdul Haris *Army General, Indonesia*
Jl Teuku Umar 40, Jakarta Pusat, Indonesia

Natalicio, Diana *Educator*
%University of Texas at El Paso, President's Office, El Paso, TX 79968

Natcher, William H *Representative, KY*
638 E Main St, Bowling Green, KY 42101

Nathaniel (Popp), Bishop *Religious Leader*
%Romanian Orthodox Episcopate, 2522 Grey Tower Rd, Jackson, MI 49201

Nathans, Daniel *Nobel Medicine Laureate*
%Johns Hopkins School of Medicine, Microbiology Dept, Baltimore, MD 21205

Natkin, Robert *Artist*
24 Mark Twain Ln, West Redding, CT 06896

Natori, Josie *Fashion Designer*
%Natori Co, 40 E 34th St, New York, NY 10016

Natt, Calvin *Basketball Player*
%Denver Nuggets, McNichols Arena, 1265 Clay St, Denver, CO 80204
Natus, Dietrich *Businessman*
%Metallgesellschaft, Reuterweg 14, Frankfurt am Main, Germany
Natwick, Mildred *Actress*
1001 Park Ave, New York, NY 10028
Naude, C F Beyers *Religious Leader*
%Council of Churches, 42 de Villiers St, Johannesburg, South Africa
Naughton, David *Actor*
2750 N Beachwood Dr, Los Angeles, CA 90068
Naughton, James *Actor*
%International Creative Mgmt, 8899 Beverly Blvd, Los Angeles, CA 90048
Naughton, Paul F *Businessman*
%Primark Corp, 8251 Greensboro Dr, McLean, VA 22102
Naulls, Willie *Basketball Player*
%Chuck & Willie's Auto Agency, 13900 Hawthorne Blvd, Hawthorne, CA 90250
Nauman, Bruce *Artist*
%Leo Castelli Gallery, 420 W Broadway, New York, NY 10012
Naumann, William L *Businessman*
3619 Scandia Dr, Peoria, IL 61604
Nauta, Walle J H *Anatomist*
%Massachusetts Institute of Technology, Psychology Dept, Cambridge, MA 02139
Navasky, Victor *Editor*
%Nation Magazine, 72 5th Ave, New York, NY 10011
Navratilova, Martina *Tennis Player*
%Women's Tennis Assn, 133 1st St NE, St Petersburg, FL 33701
Nazam, Hisham *Govenment Official, Saudi Arabia*
%Ministry of Petroleum & Mineral Resources, Riyadh, Saudi Arabia
Nazer, Hisham *Businessman*
%Arabian American Oil Co, Box 5000, Daharan, Saudi Arabia
Neal, James F *Attorney*
%Neal & Harwell, Third National Bank Bldg, #800, Nashville, TN 37219
Neal, Patricia *Actress*
PO Box 1043, Edgartown, MA 02539
Neal, Stephen L *Representative, NC*
1001 Wellington Rd, Winston-Salem, NC 27106
Neame, Ronald *Movie Director*
%Kimridge Corp, 2317 Kimridge Ave, Beverly Hills, CA 90210
Near, Holly *Singer*
%Redwood Records, 6400 Hollis St, #8, Emeryville, CA 94608
Near, James W *Businessman*
%Wendy's International, 4288 W Dublin Granville Rd, Dublin, OH 43017
Nebel, Dorothy Hoyt *Skier*
PO Box 69, Denville, NJ 07834
Neblett, Carol *Opera Singer*
%Philip Akre, 1117 10th St, Coronado, CA 92118
Nedderman, Wendell H *Educator*
%University of Texas at Arlington, President's Office, Arlington, TX 76019
Nederlander, James M *Theater Executive*
1564 Broadway, New York, NY 10036
Needham, Connie *Actress*
%Twentieth Century Artists, 3800 Barham Blvd, Los Angeles, CA 90068
Needham, Hal *Movie Director*
%Bandit Productions, 3518 Cahuenga Blvd W, #110, Los Angeles, CA 90068
Needham, James J *Exchange Executive*
665 5th Ave, #201, New York, NY 10022
Needham, Joseph *Biochemist*
%Needham Research Institute, 8 Sylvester Rd, Cambridge CB3 9AF, England
Needham, Tracey *Actress*
%Cunningham-Escott-Dipene Assoc, 261 S Robertson Blvd, Beverly Hills, CA 90211
Neel, James V G *Geneticist*
2235 Belmont Rd, Ann Arbor, MI 48104
Neel, Louis Boyd *Conductor*
%York Club, 135 St George St, Toronto ON M5B 2L8, Canada
Neel, Louis E F *Nobel Physics Laureate*
15 Rue Marcel Allegot, 92190 Meudon, France

Neely, Cam *Hockey Player*
%Boston Bruins, 150 Causeway St, Boston, MA 02114

Neeson, Liam *Actor*
%Harris & Goldberg Agency, 1999 Ave of Stars, #2850, Los Angeles, CA 90067

Nef, John U *Historian*
2726 "N" St NW, Washington, DC 20007

Neff, Francine *Government Official*
1509 Sagebrush Trl SE, Albuquerque, NM 87123

Neff, William D *Psychologist*
3505 Bradley St, Bloomington, IN 47401

Negulesco, Jean *Movie Director*
%Santa Margarita Marbella-Club, Marbella, Malaga, Costa-del-Sol, Spain

Neher, Erwin *Nobel Medicine Laureate*
%Max Planck Biophysical Chemistry Institute, D-3400 Gottingen, Germany

Nehlen, Don *Football Coach*
%West Virginia University, Athletic Dept, Morgantown, WV 26506

Neidlinger, Gustav *Opera Singer*
Wurtembergische Staatsoper, 5427 Lahnstrasse 57, 7000 Stuttgart, Germany

Neikirk, Joseph R *Businessman*
%Norfolk Southern Corp, 1 Commerce Pl, Norfolk, VA 23510

Neilan, Edwin P *Financier*
62 Town House Ln, Corpus Christi, TX 78412

Neill, Noel *Actress*
331 Sage Ln, Santa Monica, CA 90402

Neill, Rolfe *Publisher*
%Charlotte News-Observer, 600 S Tryon St, Charlotte, NC 28202

Neill, Sam *Actor*
%Lantz Office, 888 7th Ave, #2500, New York, NY 10106

Neilson, Roger *Hockey Coach*
1796 Westover Point Rd, RR 3, Lakefield ON K0L 2H0, Canada

Neilson-Bell, Sandra *Swimmer*
1598 Winford Ave, Ventura, CA 93004

Neiman, LeRoy *Artist*
1 W 67th St, New York, NY 10023

Nelissen, Roelof J *Financier*
%Amsterdam-Rotterdam Bank, Herengracht 595, 1017 CE Amsterdam, Netherlands

Nelligan, Kate *Actress*
%Larry Dalzell Assoc, 3 Goodwin's Ct, London WC2, England

Nelligan, Michael T *Businessman*
%Ideal Basic Industries, 950 17th St, Denver, CO 80201

Nelms, Mike *Football Player*
%Washington Redskins, Box 17247, Dulles Airport, Washington, DC 20041

Nelson, Barry *Actor*
134 W 58th St, New York, NY 10019

Nelson, Bill *Representative, FL; Astronaut*
780 S Apollo Dr, #12, Melbourne, FL 32901

Nelson, Byron *Golfer*
Fairway Ranch, Litsey Rd, Box 5, Roanoke, TX 76262

Nelson, Cindy *Skier*
%US Ski Assn, PO Box 100, Park City, UT 84060

Nelson, Craig T *Actor*
28872 Boniface Dr, Malibu, CA 90265

Nelson, Darrin *Football Player*
%San Diego Chargers, 9449 Friars Rd, San Diego, CA 92120

Nelson, David *Actor, Television Director*
%Western International Media, 8732 Sunset Blvd, Los Angeles, CA 90038

Nelson, David B *Judge*
%US Court of Appeals, US Courthouse Bldg, 5th & Walnut Sts, Cincinnati, OH 45202

Nelson, Don *Basketball Player, Coach*
%Golden State Warriors, Oakland Coliseum Arena, Oakland, CA 94621

Nelson, Dorothy W *Judge*
%US Court of Appeals, 125 S Grand Ave, Pasadena, CA 91109

Nelson, E Benjamin *Governor, NE*
%Governor's Office, State Capitol Bldg, Lincoln, NE 68509

Nelson, Gaylord *Governor/Senator, WI; Environmentalist*
%Wilderness Society, 1400 "I" St NW, Washington, DC 20005

Nelson, Gene — *Actor, Dancer*
2 Stern Ln, Atherton, CA 94025

Nelson, George D — *Astronaut*
%University of Washington, Astronomy Dept, Seattle, WA 98195

Nelson, James E — *Religious Leader*
%Baha'i Faith, 536 Sheridan Rd, Wilmette, IL 60091

Nelson, John W — *Conductor*
%Indianapolis Symphony, 4600 Sunset Ave, Indianapolis, IN 46208

Nelson, Judd — *Actor*
%William Morris Agency, 151 El Camino, Beverly Hills, CA 90212

Nelson, Kent C — *Businessman*
%United Parcel Service, Greenwich Park 5, Greenwich, CT 06830

Nelson, Larry — *Golfer*
%Professional Golfers Assn, PO Box 109601, Palm Beach Gardens, FL 33410

Nelson, Lindsey — *Sportscaster*
1431 Cherokee Trl, Cherokee Bluff, #82, Knoxville, TN 37920

Nelson, Michael A — *Air Force General*
Deputy Chief of Staff/Plans & Operations, Hq USAF, Washington, DC 20330

Nelson, Steve — *Football Player*
%New England Patriots, Sullivan Stadium, Foxboro, MA 02035

Nelson, Ted — *Computer Inventor (Xanadu)*
%Autodesk Inc, 2320 Marinship Way, Sausalito, CA 94965

Nelson, Tracy — *Actress*
%STE Representation, 9301 Wilshire Blvd, #312, Beverly Hills, CA 90210

Nelson, Willie — *Singer, Songwriter*
%Pedernails Studio, Rt 1, Briarcliff 2, Spicewood, TX 78669

Nemecek, Bohumil — *Boxer*
V Zahradkach 30, 400 00 Usti nad Labem, Czechoslovakia

Nemeth, Karoly — *Government Official, Hungary*
%Hungarian Socialist Party, Szechenyi Rakpart 19, Budapest, Hungary

Nemeth, Miklos — *Premier, Hungary*
%Premier's Office, Budapest, Hungary

Nenneman, Richard A — *Editor*
%Christian Science Monitor, 1 Norway St, Boston, MA 02115

Nepote, Jean — *Law Enforcement Official*
26 Rue Armengaud, 92210 Saint-Cloud, Hauts-de-Seine, France

Nerette, Joseph — *President, Haiti*
%Supreme Court, Chief Justice's Office, Port-au-Prince, Haiti

Neri Vela, Rudolfo — *Astronaut, Mexico*
Playa Copacabana 131, Col Marte, Mexico City DF 08830, Mexico

Nero, Peter — *Pianist, Conductor*
%Kolmer, 1776 Broadway, New York, NY 10019

Nerud, John — *Thoroughbred Racing Executive*
%Tartan Farms, 6775 SW 43rd Ave, Ocala, FL 32671

Nesbitt, Lowell — *Artist*
69 Wooster, New York, NY 10012

Nesi, Nerio — *Financier*
%Banco Nazionale dei Lavoro, Via Vittorio Veneto 19, 00187 Rome, Italy

Ness, Norman F — *Space Scientist*
%University of Delaware, Interplanetary Physics Dept, Newark, DE 19716

Nesterenko, Yevgeny — *Opera Singer*
%State Academy Bolshoi Theatre, 1 Ploshchad Sverdlova, Moscow, Russia

Nesty, Anthony — *Swimmer*
%University of Florida, Athletic Dept, Gainesville, FL 32611

Netsch, Walter A, Jr — *Architect*
30 Monroe St, Chicago, IL 60603

Nett, Robert B — *WW II Army Hero (CMH)*
5417 Kessington Dr, Columbus, GA 31907

Nettelsheim, Christine Cook — *Judge*
%US Claims Court, 717 Madison Pl NW, Washington, DC 20005

Nettles, Graig — *Baseball Player*
13 North Ln, Del Mar, CA 92014

Nettleton, Lois — *Actress*
1263 N Flores Ave, Los Angeles, CA 90069

Neuharth, Allen H — *Publisher*
%Gannett Co, 1100 Wilson Blvd, Arlington, VA 22209

Neuhaus, Max *Artist, Composer*
210 5th Ave, New York, NY 10010
Neuhaus, Richard J *Religious Leader*
%Center on Religion & Society, 152 Madison Ave, New Yirk, NY 10016
Neumann, Gerhard *Aeronautical Engineer*
%General Electric Co, 1000 Western Ave, West Lynn, MA 01910
Neumann, Jonathan *Journalist*
1325 18th St NW, #706, Washington, DC 20071
Neumann, Robert G *Diplomat, Educator*
4986 Sentinel Dr, #301, Bethesda, MD 20816
Neumann, Vaclav *Conductor*
Siroka 10, Prague 1-Stare Mesto, Czechoslovakia
Neumann, Wolfgang *Opera Singer*
%Metropolitan Opera Assn, Lincoln Center Plz, New York, NY 10023
Neurath, Hans *Biochemist*
5752 60th NE, Seattle, WA 98105
Neustadt, Richard E *Political Scientist, Educator*
985 Memorial Dr, Cambridge, MA 02138
Neuwirth, Bebe *Actress*
%Gage Group, 9255 Sunset Blvd, #515, Los Angeles, CA 90069
Neves, Lucas Moreira Cardinal *Religious Leader*
Palacio de Se, Praca da Se 1, 40-000 Salvador, BA, Brazil
Neville, Aaron *Singer*
%A&M Records, 1416 N La Brea Ave, Los Angeles, CA 90028
Nevin, John J *Businessman*
%Firestone Tire & Rubber Co, 1200 Firestone Pkwy, Akron, OH 44317
Nevins, Claudette *Actress*
%Gage Group, 9255 Sunset Blvd, #515, Los Angeles, CA 90069
Newberry, Tom *Football Player*
%Los Angeles Rams, 2327 W Lincoln Ave, Anaheim, CA 92801
Newbigging, William *Publisher*
%Edmonton Journal, 10006 101st St, Edmonton AB T5J 2S6, Canada
Newbury, Mickey *Songwriter, Singer*
2510 Franklin Rd, Nashville, TN 37204
Newcombe, Don *Baseball Player*
22507 Peale Dr, Woodland Hills, CA 91364
Newcombe, John *Tennis Player*
%John Newcombe's Tennis Ranch, PO Box 469, New Braunfels, TX 78130
Newcombe, John *Tennis Player*
25-B Orinocco, Pymble, Sydney NSW 2073, Australia
Newell, Allen *Computer Scientist*
%Carnegie-Mellon University, Schenley Park, Pittsburgh, PA 15213
Newell, Homer Edward *Physicist*
2567 Nicky Ln, Alexandria, VA 22311
Newell, Pete *Basketball Coach*
%Basketball Hall of Fame, PO Box 179, Springfield, MA 01101
Newgard, Christopher *Biochemist (Insulin-Making Cells)*
%University of Texas Southwestern Med Ctr, Biochemistry Dept, Dallas, TX
Newhart, Bob *Comedian, Actor*
215 Strada Corta Rd, Los Angeles, CA 90077
Newhouse, Donald E *Publisher*
%Advance Publications, 950 Fingerboard Rd, Staten Island, NY 10305
Newhouse, Samuel I, Jr *Publisher*
%Advance Publications, 950 Fingerboard Rd, Staten Island, NY 10305
Newhouser, Hal *Baseball Player*
2584 Marcy, Bloomfield Hills, MI 48013
Newley, Anthony *Actor, Singer*
3249 Hutton Dr, Beverly Hills, CA 90210
Newman, Arnold *Photographer*
33 W 67th St, New York, NY 10023
Newman, Barry *Actor*
425 N Oakhurst Dr, Beverly Hills, CA 90210
Newman, Bernard *Judge*
%US Court of International Trade, 1 Federal Plz, New York, NY 10007
Newman, Beryl R *WW II Army Hero (CMH)*
%General Delivery, Remlick, VA 23175

Newman, Harry *Football Player*
3145 Palm Aire Dr N, #102, Pompano Beach, FL 33069

Newman, James H *Astronaut*
%NASA, Johnson Space Center, Houston, TX 77058

Newman, John V *Businessman*
%Sunkist Growers, 14130 Riverside Dr, Sherman Oaks, CA 91423

Newman, Jon O *Judge*
%US Court of Appeals, 450 Main St, Hartford, CT 06103

Newman, Laraine *Comedienne*
10480 Ashton Ave, Los Angeles, CA 90024

Newman, Lionel *Composer*
PO Box 900, Beverly Hills, CA 90213

Newman, Paul *Actor*
%Deloitte & Touche, 2029 Century Park East, #300, Los Angeles, CA 90067

Newman, Pauline *Judge*
%US Court of Appeals, 717 Madison Pl NW, Washington, DC 20439

Newman, Phyllis *Singer, Actress*
529 W 42nd St, #7-F, New York, NY 10036

Newman, Randy *Singer, Songwriter*
601 Hightree Rd, Santa Monica, CA 90402

Newmar, Julie *Actress*
%Ruth Webb Enterprises, 7500 Devista Dr, Los Angeles, CA 90046

Newsom, David D *Diplomat*
3308 Woodley Rd NW, Washington, DC 20008

Newsome, Ozzie *Football Player*
%Cleveland Browns, Cleveland Stadium, Cleveland, OH 44144

Newton, C M *Basketball Coach, Administrator*
%University of Kentucky, Athletic Dept, Lexington, KY 40536

Newton, Juice *Singer*
%R Landis, 6856 Los Altos Pl, Los Angeles, CA 90068

Newton, Wayne *Singer*
6629 S Pecos, Las Vegas, NV 89120

Newton-John, Olivia *Singer*
PO Box 2710, Malibu, CA 90265

Ney, Edward N *Businessman, Diplomat*
%US Embassy, 100 Wellington St, Ottawa ON, Canada

Ney, Edward P *Physicist*
1925 Penn Ave S, Minneapolis, MN 55405

Ney, Richard *Actor*
PO Box 90215, Pasadena, CA 91109

Nezhat, Camran *Endocrinologist*
%Fertility/Endocrinology Ctr, 5555 Peachtree Dunwoody Rd NE, Atlanta, GA 30342

Ngor, Haing S *Actor*
%Marion Rosenberg, 8428 Melrose Pl, #C, Los Angeles, CA 90069

Nguyen Van Linh *Chairman, Vietnam*
%Communist Party, Ho Chi Minh City, Vietnam

Nguyen Van Thieu *President, South Vietnam*
White House, Coombe Park, Kingston-upon-Thames, Surrey, England

Niarchos, Stavros S *Businessman*
%Niarchos Ltd, 41-43 Park St, London W1, England

Nicandros, Constantine S *Businessman*
%Conoco Inc, 1007 Market St, Wilmington, DE 19801

Nicholas (Smisko), Bishop *Religious Leader*
%American Carpatho, 312 Garfield St, Johnstown, PA 15906

Nicholas, Denise *Actress*
%Hall Conner Agency, 9169 Sunset Blvd, Los Angeles, CA 90069

Nicholas, Henry *Labor Leader*
%Hospital & Health Care Union, 330 W 42nd St, #1905, New York, NY 10036

Nicholas, Nicholas J, Jr *Publisher*
%Time Warner Inc, Rockefeller Ctr, New York, NY 10020

Nicholls, Bernie *Hockey Player*
%New York Rangers, Madison Square Grdn, 4 Pennsylvania Plz, New York, NY 10001

Nichols, Bobby *Golfer*
8681 Glenlyon Ct, Fort Myers, FL 33912

Nichols, Carl W *Businessman*
%Cunningham & Walsh Inc, 260 Madison Ave, New York, NY 10016

N

Nichols, Dick *Representative, KS*
%House of Representatives, Washington, DC 20515

Nichols, John D *Businessman*
%Illinois Tool Works, 8501 W Higgins Rd, Chicago, IL 60631

Nichols, Kenneth C *Businessman*
%Home Life Insurance, 253 Broadway, New York, NY 10007

Nichols, Kyra *Ballerina*
%New York City Ballet, Lincoln Center Plz, New York, NY 10023

Nichols, Larry *Rubik Cube Designer*
%Moleculon Research Corp, 139 Main, Cambridge, MA 02142

Nichols, Mike *Movie Director, Comedian*
211 Central Park West, New York, NY 10024

Nichols, Nichelle *Actress*
%Artists Group, 1930 Century Park West, #403, Los Angeles, CA 90067

Nichols, Peter *Writer*
20 Piazza Della Toretta, Rome, Italy

Nichols, Robert L *Businessman*
%Kellogg Co, 235 Porter St, Battle Creek, MI 49016

Nichols, Stephen *Actor*
%David Shapira Assoc, 15301 Ventura Blvd, #345, Sherman Oaks, CA 91403

Nicholson, Bill *Baseball Player*
RR 3, Chestertown, MD 21620

Nicholson, Jack *Actor*
12850 Mulholland Dr, Beverly Hills, CA 90210

Nickelson, Donald E *Businessman*
%PaineWebber Grp, 1285 Ave of Americas, New York, NY 10019

Nickerson, Albert L *Businessman*
3 Lexington Rd, Lincoln, MA 01773

Nickerson, Donald A, Jr *Religious Leader*
%Episcopal Church, 815 2nd Ave, New York, NY 10017

Nicklaus, Jack *Golfer*
11397 Old Harbour Rd, North Palm Beach, FL 33048

Nickles, Donald L *Senator, OK*
1412 Meadowbrook, Ponca City, OK 74601

Nicks, Stevie *Singer*
PO Box 6907, Alhambra, CA 91802

Nickson, David W *Businessman*
%Scottish & Newcastle Breweries, Holrood Rd, Edinburgh EH8 8YS, Scotland

Nicol, Alex *Actor*
10601 Ohio Ave, Los Angeles, CA 90024

Nicol, Donald *Publisher*
%Winnipeg Free Press, 300 Carlton St, Winnipeg MB R3C 3A7, Canada

Nicolin, Curt *Businessman*
%ASEA AB, Box 7373, 103 91 Stockholm, Sweden

Nicollier, Claude *Astronaut, Switzerland*
%DFVLR, Linder Hohe, D-5000 Kohn 90, Germany

Nicolson, David *Businessman*
10 Fordie House, Sloane St, London SW1, England

Nicolson, Nigel *Writer*
Sissinghurst Castle, Kent, England

Nidetch, Jean *Businesswoman*
%Weight Watchers International, 3860 Crenshaw Blvd, Los Angeles, CA 90008

Nieder, Bill *Track Athlete*
%General Delivery, Mountain Ranch, CA 95246

Niederhoffer, Victor *Squash Player*
%Niederhoffer Cross Zeckhauser, 757 3rd Ave, New York, NY 10017

Niederland, William G *Psychiatrist*
108 Glenwood Rd, Englewood, NJ 07631

Niekro, Phil *Baseball Player*
6382 Nichols Rd, Flowery Branch, GA 30542

Nielsen, Arthur C, Jr *Businessman*
%A C Nielsen Co, Nielsen Plz, Northbrook, IL 60082

Nielsen, Brigitte *Actress, Model*
%William Morris Agency, 151 El Camino, Beverly Hills, CA 90212

Nielsen, Kenneth A *Businessman*
%Farmland Industries, 3315 N Oak Trafficway, Kansas City, MO 64116

Nielsen, Leslie *Actor*
1622 Viewmont Dr, Los Angeles, CA 90069
Nielson, Howard C *Representative, UT*
580 Sagewood Ave, Provo, UT 84601
Niemeyer, Gerhart *Political Scientist*
806 E Angela Blvd, South Bend, IN 46617
Niemeyer, Paul V *Judge*
%US Court of Appeals, 101 W Lombard St, Baltimore, MD 21201
Nier, Alfred O C *Physicist*
2001 Aldine St, St Paul, MN 55113
Nierenberg, William A *Physicist*
9581 La Jolla Farms Rd, La Jolla, CA 92037
Nierman, Leonardo *Artist*
Amsterdam 43 PH, Mexico City 11 DF, Mexico
Nies, Helen W *Judge*
%US Court of Appeals, 717 Madison Pl NW, Washington, DC 20439
Nieuwendyk, Joe *Hockey Player*
%Calgary Flames, PO Box 1540, Station M, Calgary AB T2P 3B9, Canada
Nigh, George P *Governor, OK*
8321 Pine Ln, Oklahoma City, OK 73127
Nigrelli, Ross F *Pathologist*
29 Barracuda Rd, East Quogue, NY 11942
Nikolais, Alwin *Choreographer*
%Nikolais Dance Theatre, 33 E 18th St, New York, NY 10003
Nikolayev, Andrian G *Cosmonaut*
141 160 Svyosdny Gorodok, Moskovskoi Oblasti, Potchta Kosmonavtov, Russia
Niles, Nicholas *Publisher*
%Changing Times Magazine, 220 E 42nd St, New York, NY 10017
Niles, Wendell *Entertainer*
%Wendell Niles Productions, 4555 Ledge Ave, North Hollywood, CA 91602
Nilles, William O *Financier*
%Metropolitan Financial Corp, 215 N 5th St, Fargo, ND 58108
Nilsson, Birgit *Opera Singer*
PO Box 527, Stockholm C, Sweden
Nilsson, Harry *Singer, Songwriter*
5460 Round Meadow Rd, Hidden Hills, CA 91302
Nilsson, Lennart *Photographer*
%Pantheon Books, 201 E 50th St, New York, NY 10022
Nimoy, Leonard *Actor*
%Gersh Agency, 232 N Canon Dr, Beverly Hills, CA 90210
Nims, Arthur L, III *Judge*
%US Tax Court, 400 2nd St NW, Washington, DC 20217
Nininger, Harvey H *Meteoriticist*
PO Box 420, Sedona, AZ 86336
Nirenberg, Louis *Mathematician*
221 W 82nd St, New York, NY 10024
Nirenberg, Marshall W *Nobel Medicine Laureate*
%National Heart Institute, Biochemical Genetics Lab, Bethesda, MD 20014
Nisbet, Robert A *Historian, Sociologist*
2828 Wisconsin Ave NW, Washington, DC 20007
Nishio, Suehiro *Government Official, Japan*
1 Shiba Sakuragawacho, Minatoku, Tokyo, Japan
Nishizawa, Junichi *Electronics Inventor*
%Semiconductor Research Institute, Sendai, Japan
Nishkian, Byron *Skier*
150 4th St, #PH, San Francisco, CA 94103
Niska, Maralin *Opera Singer*
%Tony Hartmann Assoc, 250 W 57th St, New York, NY 10019
Niskanen, William A *Government Official, Economist*
%Council of Economic Advisers, Executive Office Bldg, Washington, DC 20500
Nitschke, Ray *Football Player*
410 Peppermint Ct, RR 1, Oneida, WI 54155
Nitze, Paul H *Secretary, Navy; Diplomat*
3120 Woodley Rd NW, Washington, DC 20008
Nitzschke, Dale F *Educator*
%University of New Hampshire, President's Office, Durham, NH 03824

Niven, Kip *Actor*
20781 Big Rock Dr, Malibu, CA 90265

Niwa, Masaharu *Businessman*
%Matsushita Electric Works, 1048 Kadomashi, Osaka 571, Japan

Niwano, Shonosuke *Businessman*
%Nippon Mining Co, 2-10-1 Toranomon, Minatoku, Tokyo 105, Japan

Nixon, Edwin *Businessman*
%IBM United Kingdom Holdings, Portsmouth, Hants PO6 3AU, England

Nixon, Marni *Singer*
%Maxim Gershunoff Attractions, 502 Park Ave, New York, NY 10022

Nixon, Patricia *Wife of US President*
574 Chestnut Ridge Rd, Woodcliff Lake, NJ 07675

Nixon, Richard M *President, United States*
577 Chestnut Ridge Rd, Woodcliff Lake, NJ 07675

Nizer, Louis *Attorney, Writer*
Phillips Nizer Benjamin Krim Ballon, 40 W 57th St, New York, NY 10019

Nkomo, Joshua *Political Leader, Zimbabwe*
%House of Assembly, Salisbury, Zimbabwe

Noah, Yannick *Tennis Player, Coach*
%ProServe Europe, 20 Rue Billancourt, 92100 Boulogne, France

Nobis, Tommy *Football Player, Executive*
%Atlanta Falcons, Suwanee Rd, Suwanee, GA 30174

Noble, Chelsea *Actress*
%Michael Seleffinger, 8730 Sunset Blvd, #200, Los Angeles, CA 90069

Noble, Edward E *Businessman*
%US Synthetic Fuels Corp, 2121 "K" St NW, Washington, DC 20586

Noble, James *Actor*
%STE Representation, 9301 Wilshire Blvd, #312, Beverly Hills, CA 90210

Noble, Sam *Businessman*
%Noble Affiliates, 330 Neustadt Plz, Ardmore, OK 73401

Noe, Vergilius Cardinal *Religious Leader*
St Peter's Basilica, Vatican City, Rome, Italy

Noel, Philip W *Governor, RI*
21 Kirby Ave, Warwick, RI 02889

Nogales, Luis G *Businessman*
%United Press International, 800 Broadway, Cincinnati, OH 45202

Nogawa, Shoji *Businessman*
%Komatsu Ltd, 2-3-6 Akasaka, Minatoku, Tokyo 107, Japan

Noguchi, Teruo *Businessman*
%Koa Oil Co, 2-6-2 Otemachi, Chiyodaku, Tokyo 100, Japan

Noguchi, Thomas T *Coroner, Physician*
%Medical Examiner's Office, 1104 N Mission Rd, Los Angeles, CA 90033

Noiret, Philippe *Actor*
104 Rue des Sablons, 78750 Mareil-Marly, France

Nojima, Minoru *Concert Pianist*
%Hillyer Kazuko International, 250 W 57th St, New York, NY 10107

Nokes, Matt *Baseball Player*
13011 Avenida La Valencia, Poway, CA 92064

Nolan, Barry *Entertainer*
%"Hard Copy" Show, ABC-TV, 77 W 66th St, New York, NY 10023

Nolan, Christopher *Writer*
158 Vernon Ave, Clontanf, Dublin 3, Ireland

Nolan, Jeanette *Actress*
1417 Samona Way, Laguna Beach, CA 92651

Nolan, Kenny *Singer*
%Bennett, 211 S Beverly Dr, Beverly Hills, CA 90212

Nolan, Martin F *Editor*
%Boston Globe, 135 Morrissey Blvd, Boston, MA 02125

Nolan, Sidney *Artist*
%Bank of New South Wales, 9 Sackville St, London W1, England

Nolan, Thomas B *Geologist*
2219 California St NW, Washington, DC 20019

Nolan, William F *Writer*
22720 Cavalier St, Woodland Hills, CA 91364

Noland, Kenneth *Artist*
PO Box 125, South Salem, NY 10590

Noland, Robert L *Businessman*
%Ametek Inc, 410 Park Ave, New York, NY 10022
Nolte, Nick *Actor*
29555 Rainsford Pl, Malibu, CA 90265
Nolting, Paul F *Religious Leader*
%Church of Lutheran Confession, 620 E 50th St, Loveland, CO 80537
Nomellini, Leo *Football Player*
520 St Claire Dr, Palo Alto, CA 94306
Noonan, John T, Jr *Judge*
%US Court of Appeals, Court Bldg, San Francisco, CA 94101
Noonan, Peggy *Writer*
%Random House, 201 E 58th St, New York, NY 10022
Noone, Peter *Singer, Actor*
%J Michael Bloom Ltd, 9200 Sunset Blvd, #710, Los Angeles, CA 90069
Noor Al-Hussein *Queen, Jordan*
%Royal Palace, Amman, Jordan
Nordenstrom, Bjorn *Cancer Radiologist*
%Karolinska Institute, Radiology Dept, Stockholm, Sweden
Nordlund, Donald E *Businessman*
%Staley Continental Inc, 1701 Golf Rd, Rolling Meadows, IL 60008
Nordsieck, Kenneth H *Astronaut*
%University of Wisconsin, Space Astronomy Lab, Madison, WI 53706
Nordskog, Bob *Boat Racing Driver*
%Nordskog Industries, 16000 Strathern St, Van Nuys, CA 91406
Nordstrom, Bruce A *Businessman*
%Nordstrom Inc, 1501 5th Ave, Seattle, WA 98101
Nordstrom, James F *Businessman*
%Nordstrom Inc, 1501 5th Ave, Seattle, WA 98101
Nordstrom, John N *Businessman*
%Nordstrom Inc, 1501 5th Ave, Seattle, WA 98101
Noren, Irv *Baseball Player*
3215 Valley Glen Rd, Oceanside, CA 92056
Norian, Roger W *Businessman*
%Kerr Glass Maufacturing Corp, 501 S Shatto Pl, Los Angeles, CA 90020
Norick, Ronald J *Mayor*
%Mayor's Office, City Hall, 200 N Walker, #302, Oklahoma City, OK 73102
Norman, Greg *Golfer*
%International Mangement Group, 1 Erieview Plz, Cleveland, OH 44114
Norman, Jack, Sr *Attorney*
3723 West End Ave, Nashville, TN 37205
Norman, Jessye *Concert Singer*
%Harry Beall Mgmt, 119 W 57th St, New York, NY 10019
Norman, Ken *Basketball Player*
%Los Angeles Clippers, Sports Arena, 3939 S Figueroa St, Los Angeles, CA 90037
Norodom Sihanouk, Prince Samdech Preah *King, Cambodia*
%President's Office, Supreme National Council, Phnom Penh, Cambodia
Norquist, John *Mayor*
%Mayor's Office, City Hall, 200 E Wells St, Milwaukee, WI 53202
Norrington, Roger *Conductor*
%Byers Schwalbe Assoc, 1 5th Ave, New York, NY 10003
Norris, Alan E *Judge*
%US Court of Appeals, US Courthouse, 85 Marconi Blvd, Columbus, OH 43215
Norris, Christopher *Actress*
%Commerical's Unlimited, 7461 Beverly Blvd, #400, Los Angeles, CA 90036
Norris, Chuck *Actor*
18800 Wells Dr, Tarzana, CA 91356
Norris, Mike *Baseball Player*
1003 Imperial Dr, Hayward, CA 94541
Norris, William A *Judge*
%US Court of Appeals, 312 N Spring St, Los Angeles, CA 90012
Norris, William C *Businessman*
%Control Data Corp, 8100 34th Ave S, Minneapolis, MN 55440
Norsworthy, Lamar *Businessman*
%Holly Corp, 2600 Diamond Shamrock Tower, Dallas, TX 75201
North, Andy *Golfer*
%Professional Golfers Assn, PO Box 109601, Palm Beach Gardens, FL 33410

N

North – Noyd

North, Jay *Actor*
11532 Chiquita St, North Hollywood, CA 91604

North, Oliver *Government Official*
%North Defense Trust, PO Box 96577, Washington, DC 20090

North, Phil R *Businessman*
%Tandy Corp, 1 Tandy Ctr, #1800, Fort Worth, TX 76102

North, Sheree *Actress*
%Gage Group, 9255 Sunset Blvd, #515, Los Angeles, CA 90069

Northrip, Richard A *Labor Leader*
%Cement & Allied Workers Union, 2500 Brickdale, Elk Grove Village, IL 60007

Northrop, John H *Nobel Chemistry Laureate*
PO Box 1387, Wickenburg, AZ 85358

Northrop, Stuart J *Businessman*
%Huffy Corp, 7701 Byers Rd, Miamisburg, OH 45342

Northrup, Jim *Baseball Player*
1326 Otter Dr, Pontiac, MI 48054

Norton, Gerard Ross (Toys) *WW II Rhodesian Army Hero (VC)*
Box II2, PO Banket, Zimbabwe

Norton, James J *Labor Leader*
%Graphic Communications International, 1900 "L" St NW, Washington, DC 20036

Norton, Ken *Boxer*
16 S Peck Dr, Laguna Niguel, CA 92677

Norton, Peter *Computer Programmer*
225 Arizona Ave, 2nd Fl W, Santa Monica, CA 90401

Norton-Taylor, Judy *Actress*
10965 Fruitland Dr, #314, Studio City, CA 91604

Norville, Deborah *Commentator*
%NBC-TV, News Dept, 30 Rockefeller Plz, New York, NY 10020

Norvo, Kenneth N (Red) *Jazz Vibraphonist*
420 Alta Ave, Santa Monica, CA 90402

Norwood, Scott *Football Player*
%Buffalo Bills, 1 Bills Dr, Orchard Park, NY 14127

Nosseck, Noel *Movie Director*
20406 Seaboard Rd, Malibu, CA 90265

Notkins, Abner L *Virologist*
%National Institute of Dental Research, 9000 Rockville Pike, Bethesda, MD 20205

Noto, Lore *Theater Producer, Actor*
%Sullivan Street Playhouse, 181 Sullivan St, New York, NY 10012

Nott, John W *Government Official, England*
%House of Commons, Westminster, London SW1, England

Nottelmann, O Robert *Businessman*
%Inland Steel Co, 30 W Monroe St, Chicago, IL 60603

Nouira, Hedi *Prime Minister, Tunisia*
%Parti Socialiste Destourien, Blvd 9 April 1938, Tunis, Tunisia

Nouri, Michael *Actor*
%William Morris Agency, 1350 Ave of Americas, New York, NY 10019

Novak Popper, Ilona *Swimmer*
II-Orso-U 23, Budapest, Hungary

Novak, Kim *Actress*
24700 Outlook Dr, Carmel, CA 93923

Novak, Michael *Social Critic, Philosopher*
%North Agency, 660 Madison Ave, New York, NY 10021

Novak, Robert D S *Columnist*
%Field Newspaper Syndicate, 1703 Kaiser Ave, Irvine, CA 92714

Novella, Antonia *Medical Administrator*
%Surgeon General's Office, 200 Independence Ave SW, Washington, DC 20201

Novosel, Michael J *Vietnam War Army Hero (CMH)*
202 Oakwood Dr, Enterprise, AL 36330

Novotna, Jana *Tennis Player*
%Women's Tennis Assn, 133 1st St NE, St Petersbyrg, FL 33701

Novotna, Jarmila *Opera Singer*
162 E 80 St, New York, NY 10021

Nowak, Henry J *Representative, NY*
508 Linden Ave, Buffalo, NY 14216

Noyd, R Allen *Religious Leader*
%General Council, Christian Church, Box 141-A, RD 1, Transfer, PA 16154

Noyes, Albert, Jr *Chemist*
5102 Fairview Dr, Austin, TX 78731
Nozick, Robert *Philosopher*
%Harvard University, Emerson Hall, Cambridge, MA 02138
Ntombi *Queen, Swaziland*
%Royal Residence, Mbabane, Swaziland
Nuami, Sheikh Humaidbin Rashid al- *Ruler, Ajman*
%Royal Palace, Ajman, United Arab Emirates
Nucatola, John P *Basketball Referee*
61-47 210th St, Bayside, NY 11364
Nugent, Nelle *Theater Producer*
1501 Broadway, New York, NY 10036
Nugteren, Arie *Businessman*
%Kay Corp, 320 King St, Alexandria, VA 22314
Nujoma, Sam *President, Namibia*
%President's Office, Windhoek, Namibia
Numeiri, Jaafar Mohammed al- *President, Sudan*
%Tahera Palace, Cairo, Egypt
Nunley, Frank *Football Player*
12360 Hilltop Dr, Los Altos Hills, CA 94022
Nunn, Louie B *Governor, KY*
RR 3, Park, KY 42749
Nunn, Sam *Senator, GA*
%US Senate, Washington, DC 20510
Nunn, Trevor *Theater Director*
%Royal Shakespeare Theater, Stratford-upon-Avon, Warwickshire, England
Nureyev, Rudolf *Ballet Dancer*
1 W 72nd St, New York, NY 10023
Nussbaum, Karen *Labor Activist*
%9 to 5 National Assn of Working Women, 614 Superior Ave, Cleveland, OH 44113
Nussbaum, Luther J *Businessman*
%Evernet Systems, 5777 W Century Blvd, #1680, Los Angeles, CA 90045
Nusser, Edward *Financier*
%Mercury Savings & Loan, 7812 Edinger Ave, Huntington Beach, CA 92647
Nussle, Jim *Representative, IA*
%House of Representatives, Washington, DC 20515
Nutting, Anthony *Government Official, England*
1 Disbrowe Rd, London W6, England
Nutzle, Futzie (Bruce John Kleinsmith) *Artist, Cartoonist*
PO Box 325, Aromas, CA 95004
Nuwer, Hank *Writer, Journalist*
PO Box 776, Fogelsville, PA 18051
Nuxhall, Joe *Baseball Player*
5705 Lindenwood Ln, Fairfield, OH 45014
Nuyen, France *Actress*
1800 Franklin Canyon, Beverly Hills, CA 90210
Nyad, Diana *Swimmer, Sportscaster*
%Uptown Racquet Club, 151 E 86th St, New York, NY 10022
Nye, Carrie *Actress*
109 E 79th St, New York, NY 10019
Nye, Louis *Actor*
1241 Corsica Dr, Pacific Palisades, CA 90272
Nyerere, Julius K *President, Tanzania*
%State House, Dar-es-Salaam, Tanzania
Nygaard, Richard L *Judge*
%US Court of Appeals, First National Bank Bldg, 7171 State St, Erie, PA 16501
Nygren, Carrie *Model*
%Elite Model Mgmt, 111 E 22nd St, 2nd Floor, New York, NY 10010
Nykaenen, Matti *Ski Jumper*
%General Delivery, Jyvaseskylae, Finland
Nykvist, Sven *Cinematographer*
%Dove Films, 3518 Cahuenga Blvd, #216, Los Angeles, CA 90068
Nyro, Laura *Singer, Songwriter*
PO Box 186, Shoreham, NY 11786
Nyrop, Donald W *Businessman*
%Northwest Airlines, Minneapolis-St Paul Airport, St Paul, MN 55111

O'Boyle, Maureen *Entertainer*
%"A Current Affair" Show, Fox Broadcasting, PO Box 900, Beverly Hills, CA 90213

O'Brasky, David *Publisher*
%Vanity Fair Magazine, 350 Madison Ave, New York, NY 10017

O'Brian, Hugh *Actor*
3195 Benedict Canyon, Beverly Hills, CA 90210

O'Brien, Albert J *Businessman*
5 Doubletree Ln, St Louis, MO 63131

O'Brien, Brian *Physicist*
PO Box 166, North Hollywood, CT 06281

O'Brien, Conor Cruise *Writer; Diplomat, Ireland*
Whitewater, The Summit, Howth, Dublin, Ireland

O'Brien, G Dennis *Educator*
%University of Rochester, President's Office, Rochester, NY 14627

O'Brien, George H, Jr *Korean War Marine Corps Hero (CMH)*
2001 Douglas, Midland, TX 79701

O'Brien, Ian *Swimmer*
PO Box 36, Forestville NSW 2087, Australia

O'Brien, John F *Businessman*
%State Mutual Life Assurance, 440 Lincoln St, Worcester, MA 01605

O'Brien, Ken *Football Player*
%New York Jets, 598 Madison Ave, New York, NY 10022

O'Brien, Margaret *Actress*
1250 La Peresa Dr, Thousand Oaks, CA 91362

O'Brien, Parry *Track Athlete*
851 Euclid, Santa Monica, CA 90403

O'Brien, Pat *Sportscaster*
%NBC-TV, Sports Dept, 30 Rockefeller Plz, New York, NY 10020

O'Brien, Raymond F *Businessman*
%Consolidated Freightways, 3240 Hillview Ave, Palo Alto, CA 94303

O'Brien, Robert B, Jr *Financier*
%Carteret Savings & Loan, 200 South St, Morristown, NJ 07960

O'Brien, Thomas H *Financier*
%Pittsburgh National Bancorp, 5th & Wood, Pittsburgh, PA 15222

O'Brien, Tim *Writer*
17 Partride Ln, Boxford, MA 01921

O'Brien, Vincent *Thoroughbred Racing Trainer*
Ballydoyle House, Cashel, County Tipperary, Ireland

O'Brien, Virginia *Actress*
%Ruth Webb, 7500 Devista Dr, Los Angeles, CA 90046

O'Byrne, Bryan *Actor*
%Sue Goldin Agency, 5455 Wilshire Blvd, #1406, Los Angeles, CA 90036

O'Callaghan, Mike *Governor, NV*
%Las Vegas Sun, 121 S Martin Luther King Blvd, Las Vegas, NV 89106

O'Connell, Helen *Singer*
1260 S Beverly Glen Blvd, #108, Los Angeles, CA 90024

O'Connell, Neil *Educator*
%St Bonaventure University, President's Office, St Bonaventure, NY 14778

O'Connor, Bryan D *Astronaut*
%NASA, Johnson Space Ctr, Houston, TX 77058

O'Connor, Carroll *Actor*
30826 Broad Beach Rd, Malibu, CA 90265

O'Connor, Donald *Actor, Dancer*
3715 Alomar Dr, Sherman Oaks, CA 91423

O'Connor, Francis J *Financier*
%Orbanco Financial Services Corp, 1001 SW 5th Ave, Portland, OR 97204

O'Connor, Glynnis *Actress*
%Bauman Hiller Assoc, 5750 Wilshire Blvd, #512, Los Angeles, CA 90036

O'Connor, James J *Businessman*
%Commonwealth Edison Co, 1 First National Plz, Chicago, IL 60690

O'Connor, John J Cardinal *Religious Leader*
%Archdiocese of New York, 452 Madison Ave, New York, NY 10022

O'Connor, Martin J *Religious Leader*
Palazzo San Carlo, 00120 Vatican City, Rome, Italy

O'Connor, Maureen F *Mayor*
%Mayor's Office, City Hall, 202 "C" St, San Diego, CA 92101

O'Connor, Sandra Day *Supreme Court Justice*
%US Supreme Court, 1 1st St NE, Washington, DC 20543
O'Connor, Sinead *Singer*
%Chrysalis Records, 645 Madison Ave, New York, NY 10022
O'Connor, Thom *Artist*
Moss Rd, Voorheesville, NY 12186
O'Connor, Timothy J *Actor*
%Artists Agency, 10000 Santa Monica Blvd, #305, Los Angeles, CA 90067
O'Day, Anita *Singer*
%Emily Productions, 5010 Indian River Dr, #355, Las Vegas, NV 89103
O'Donnell, John J *Labor Leader*
%Air Line Pilots Assn, 1625 Massachusetts Ave NW, Washington, DC 20036
O'Donnell, William *Harness Racing Driver*
%O'Donnell Stable, 823 Chippewa Trl, Franklin Lakes, NJ 07417
O'Donnell, William T *Labor Leader*
%United Garment Workers, 4207 Lebanon Rd, Hermitage, TN 37076
O'Donovan, Leo J *Educator*
%Georgetown University, President's Office, Washington, DC 20057
O'Driscoll Appleton, Martha *Actress*
22 Indian Creek Island, Miami Beach, FL 33154
O'Grady, Lani *Actress*
%First Artists, 10000 Riverside Dr, #6, Toluca Lake, CA 91602
O'Grady, Mac *Golfer*
%Professional Golfers Assn, PO Box 109601, Palm Beach Gardens, FL 33410
O'Green, Fred W *Businessman*
%Litton Industries, 360 N Crescent Dr, Beverly Hills, CA 90210
O'Hair, Madalyn Murray *Social Activist*
2210 Hancock Dr, Austin, TX 78701
O'Hara, Jenny *Actress*
%Century Artists, 9744 Wilshire Blvd, #308, Beverly Hills, CA 90212
O'Hara, John A *Publisher*
%Reader's Digest Assn, Pleasantville, NY 10570
O'Hara, Maureen *Actress*
PO Box 1400, Christeansted, St Croix, VI 00820
O'Hare, Dean R *Businessman*
%Chubb Corp, 15 Mountain View Rd, Warren, NJ 07061
O'Hare, Don R *Businessman*
%Sundstrand Corp, 4751 Harrison Ave, Rockford, IL 61125
O'Hare, Joseph A *Educator*
%Fordham University, President's Office, Bronx, NY 10458
O'Herlihy, Daniel *Actor*
%Artists Group, 1930 Century Park West, #403, Los Angeles, CA 90067
O'Horgan, Tom *Composer, Director*
%William Morris Agency, 1350 Ave of Americas, New York, NY 10019
O'Kane, Richard H *WW II Navy Hero (CMH), Admiral*
6150 Guerneville Rd, Sebastopol, CA 95472
O'Keefe, Frank R, Jr *Businessman*
%Armstrong Rubber Co, 500 Sargent Dr, New Haven, CT 06536
O'Keefe, Miles *Actor*
PO Box 69365, Los Angeles, CA 90069
O'Konski, A E *Representative, WI*
361 Beloit Ave, Winter Park, FL 32789
O'Koren, Mike *Basketball Player*
%Washington Bullets, Capital Centre, 1 Harry Truman Dr, Landover, MD 20785
O'Leary, Thomas H *Businessman*
%Burlington Northern Inc, 999 3rd Ave, Seattle, WA 98104
O'Loughlin, Gerald S *Actor*
13907 Rayen St, Arleta, CA 91331
O'Malley, Peter *Baseball Executive*
%Los Angeles Dodgers, 1000 Elysian Park Ave, Los Angeles, CA 90012
O'Malley, Robert E *Vietnam War Marine Corps Hero (CMH)*
PO Box 775, Goldthwaite, TX 76844
O'Malley, Susan *Basketball Executive*
%Washington Bullets, Capital Centre, 1 Harry Truman Dr, Landover, MD 20785
O'Malley, Thomas D *Businessman*
%Phibro-Salomon Inc, 1221 Ave of Americas, New York, NY 10020

O

O'Malley – O'Scannlain

O'Malley, Thomas P — *Educator*
%Loyola Marymount University, President's Office, Los Angeles, CA 90045

O'Mara, Mark — *Harness Racing*
20083 Back Nine Dr, Boca Raton, FL 33498

O'Meara, Mark — *Golfer*
PO Box 3277, Escondido, CA 92025

O'Neal, A Daniel, Jr — *Government Official*
1613 Forest Ln, McLean, VA 22101

O'Neal, Edward A, Jr — *Financier*
%Chemical Banking Corp, 277 Park Ave, New York, NY 10172

O'Neal, Frederick — *Labor Leader*
%Associated Actors & Artists, 165 W 46th St, New York, NY 10036

O'Neal, Leslie — *Football Player*
%San Diego Chargers, 9449 Friars Rd, San Diego, CA 92108

O'Neal, Patrick — *Actor*
%Marian Rosenberg Office, 8428 Melrose Pl, #C, Los Angeles, CA 90069

O'Neal, Ryan — *Actor*
21368 Pacific Coast Hwy, Malibu, CA 90265

O'Neal, Shaquille — *Basketball Player*
%Louisiana State University, Athletic Dept, Baton Rouge, LA 70803

O'Neal, Tatum — *Actress*
23712 Malibu Colony Rd, Malibu, CA 90265

O'Neil, F J — *Actor*
12228 Cantura St, Studio City, CA 91604

O'Neil, M Gerald — *Businessman*
%GenCorp Inc, 175 Ghent Rd, Akron, OH 44313

O'Neil, Thomas F — *Businessman*
%General Tire & Rubber Co, 1 General St, Akron, OH 44329

O'Neil, Tricia — *Actress*
%David Shapira Assoc, 15301 Ventura Blvd, #345, Sherman Oaks, CA 91403

O'Neill, Dick — *Actor*
%International Creative Mgmt, 8899 Beverly Blvd, Los Angeles, CA 90048

O'Neill, Ed — *Actor*
%International Creative Mgmt, 8899 Beverly Blvd, Los Angeles, CA 90048

O'Neill, Eugene F — *Communications Engineer*
17 Dellwood Ct, Middletown, NJ 07748

O'Neill, Gerard K — *Physicist*
%Princeton University, Physics Dept, Princeton, NJ 08540

O'Neill, Jennifer — *Actress, Model*
32356 Mulholland Hwy, Malibu, CA 90265

O'Neill, Michael J — *Editor*
%New York Daily News, 220 E 42nd St, New York, NY 10017

O'Neill, Paul H — *Businessman*
%Aluminum Co of America, 1501 Alcoa Bldg, Pittsburgh, PA 15219

O'Neill, Shane — *Television Executive*
%RKO General Inc, 1440 Broadway, New York, NY 10018

O'Neill, Thomas P (Tip) — *Representative, MA; Speaker*
%O'Neill Federal Office Bldg, 10 Causeway St, #1008, Boston, MA 02222

O'Neill, William A — *Governor, CT*
Meeks Pt, East Hampton, CT 06424

O'Reilly, Anthony J F — *Businessman*
%H J Heinz Co, 600 Grant St, Pittsburgh, PA 15219

O'Rourke Keiski, Heidi — *Synchronized Swimmer*
400 NE 13th Ave, Gainesville, FL 32601

O'Rourke, Charles — *Football Player*
220 Bedford St, Bridgewater, MA 02324

O'Rourke, Dennis — *Businessman*
8 Heather Dr, Colorado Springs, CO 80906

O'Rourke, J Tracy — *Businessman*
%Varian Assoc, 611 Hansen Way, Palo Alto, CA 94303

O'Rourke, Patrick J — *Educator*
%University of Alaska, President's Office, Fairbanks, AK 99701

O'Rourke, Tracy — *Businessman*
%Allen-Bradley Co, 1201 S 2nd St, Milwaukee, WI 53204

O'Scannlain, Diarmuid F — *Judge*
%US Court of Appeals, Pioneer Courthouse, 555 SW Yamhill St, Portland, OR 97204

O'Shea, Kevin *Basketball Player*
%Marovich & O'Shea, 215 Leidesdorff, San Francisco, CA 94111
O'Shea, Milo *Actor*
%Bancroft Hotel, 40 W 72nd St, New York, NY 10023
O'Shields, Richard L *Businessman*
%Panhandle Eastern Corp, 3000 Bissonnet, Houston, TX 77005
O'Sullivan, Maureen *Actress*
1839 Union St, Schenectady, NY 12309
O'Sullivan, Peter *Editor*
%Houston Post, 4747 Southwest Fwy, Houston, TX 77001
O'Toole, Annette *Actress*
%William Morris Agency, 151 El Camino, Beverly Hills, CA 90212
O'Toole, John E *Businessman*
%Foote Cone & Belding Advertising, 200 Park Ave, New York, NY 10166
O'Toole, Peter *Actor*
98 Heath St, London NW3, England
O'Toole, Robert *Businessman*
%A O Smith Corp, 11270 W Park Pl, Milwaukee, WI 53224
Oakar, Mary Rose *Representative, OH*
%House of Representatives, Washington, DC 20515
Oakes, Gordon N, Jr *Businessman*
%Monarch Capital Corp, 1 Financial Plz, Springfield, MA 01102
Oakes, James L *Judge*
%US Court of Appeals, PO Box 696, Brattleboro, VT 05301
Oakes, John B *Editor*
1120 5th Ave, New York, NY 10036
Oakley, Charles *Basketball Player*
%New York Knicks, Madison Square Grdn, 4 Pennsylvania Plz, New York, NY 10001
Oaks, Robert C *Air Force General*
COMAIRCENT & CINCUSAFE, APO, AE 09094
Oates, John *Singer (Hall & Oates)*
%Champion Entertainment, 130 W 57th St, #2-A, New York, NY 10019
Oates, Joyce Carol *Writer*
%Princeton University, Creative Writing Program, Princeton, NJ 08540
Obando Bravo, Miguel Cardinal *Religious Leader*
Arzobispado, Apartado 3050, Managua, Nicaragua
Obata, Kenzo *Businessman*
%Sekisui Chemical Co, 2-4-4 Nishitenma, Kitaku, Osaka 530, Japan
Obato, Gyo *Architect*
100 N Broadway, St Louis, MO 63102
Ober, Eric *Television Executive*
%CBS-TV, News Dept, 51 W 52nd St, New York, NY 10019
Oberding, Mark *Basketball Player*
%Sacramento Kings, 1515 Sports Dr, Sacramento, CA 95834
Oberg, Margo *Surfer*
RR1, Box 73, Koloa, Kaui HI 96756
Obermeyer, Klaus F *Fashion Designer*
%Sport Obermeyer, 115 Atlantic Ave, Aspen, CO 81611
Oberstar, James L *Representative, MN*
317 NW 9th St, Chisholm, MN 55719
Obey, David R *Representative, WI*
%House of Representatives, Washington, DC 20515
Obraztsov, Sergei V *Puppeteer*
%Central Puppet Theatre, Sadovo Samotechnaya St 3, Moscow, Russia
Obraztsova, Elena *Opera Singer*
Bolshaya Doroga, Milovskaya 21, Moscow, Russia
Obregon, Alejandro *Artist*
Apartado Aereo 37, Barranquilla, Colombia
Ocean, Billy *Singer*
%Zomba Entertainment, Arista Records, 6 W 57th St, New York, NY 10019
Ochiltree, Ned A, Jr *Businessman*
%Ceco Industries, 1400 Kensington Rd, Oak Brook, IL 60521
Ochoa, Severo *Nobel Medicine Laureate*
%Roche Institute of Molecular Biology, Nutley, NJ 07110
Ockels, Wubbo *Astronaut, Netherlands*
%ESTEC, Postbus 299, 2200 AG Noordwijk, Netherlands

Oddi, Silvio Cardinal *Religious Leader*
Via Pompeo Magno 21, 00192 Rome, Italy

Odegaard, Charles E *Educator*
%University of Washington, Education College, Seattle, WA 98195

Odell, Bob *Football Player, Coach*
%Williams College, Athletic Dept, Williamstown, PA 02167

Odell, Noel E *Geological Researcher, Mountaineer*
5 Dean Ct, Cambridge, England

Odetta *Singer*
%Vanguard Records, 71 W 23rd St, New York, NY 10010

Odinga, A Oginga *Government Official, Kenya*
%KANU, PO Box 12394, Nairobi, Kenya

Odom, G R *Businessman*
%US Home Corp, 1177 West Loop S, Houston, TX 77001

Oelman, Robert S *Businessman*
2846 Upper Bellbrook Rd, Bellbrook, OH 45305

Oerter, Al *Track Athlete*
135 W Islip Rd, West Islip, NY 11797

Offerdahl, John *Football Player*
%Miami Dolphins, Robbie Stadium, 2269 NW 199th St, Miami, FL 33056

Office, G S, Jr *Businessman*
%Ponderosa Systems, PO Box 578, Dayton, OH 45401

Ogarkov, Nikolay V *Army Marshal, Russia*
%Ministry of Defense, 34 Naberezhnaya M Thoreza, Moscow, Russia

Ogata, Taro *Financier*
%Chiba Bank, 1-2 Chiba-Minato, Chiba City 260, Japan

Ogden, Carlos C *WW II Army Hero (CMH)*
6013 Calle de Felice, San Jose, CA 95124

Ogilvy, David M *Businessman*
Chateau de Touffou, 86300 Bonnes, France

Oglivie, Ben *Baseball Player*
917 Bodark Ln, Austin, TX 78745

Ogrodnick, John *Hockey Player*
%New York Rangers, Madison Square Grdn, 4 Pennsylvania Plz, New York, NY 10001

Oh, Sadaharu *Baseball Player*
%Yomiuri Giants, 1-7-1 Otemachi, Chiyodaku, Tokyo 100, Japan

Ohara, Elichi *Businessman*
%Fuji Heavy Industries, 1-7-2 Nishi-Shinjuku, Shinjukuku, Tokyo 160, Japan

Ohara, Sakae *Businessman*
%Daihatsu Motor Co, 1-1 Daihatsucho, Ikeda City 563, Japan

Ohga, Norio *Businessman*
%Sony Corp, 6-7-35 Kitashinagawa, Shingawaku, Tokyo 141, Japan

Ohira, Masayoshi *Prime Minister, Japan*
105 Komagome Hayashicho, Bunkyoku, Tokyo, Japan

Ohki, Shigetaki *Financier*
%Saitama Bank, 7-4-1 Tokiwa, Urawa City 336, Japan

Ohki, Tsuneshiro *Financier*
%Saitama Bank, 7-4-1 Tokiwa, Urawa City 336, Japan

Ohkuchi, Shunichi *Businessman*
%Nippon Suisan Kaisha Ltd, 2-6-2 Otemachi, Chiyodaku, Tokyo 100, Japan

Ohlmeyer, Don *Television Executive*
%Ohlmeyer Communications, 9 W 57th St, New York, NY 10019

Ohlsson, Carl-Olof *Businessman*
%SwedYards, Kyrogatan 35, 401 26 Goteborg, Sweden

Ohlsson, Garrick *Concert Pianist*
%Shaw Concerts, 1900 Broadway, New York, NY 10023

Ohman, Jack *Editorial Cartoonist*
%Portland Oregonian, 1320 SW Broadway, Portland, OR 97201

Ohnishi, Minoru *Businessman*
%Fuji Photo Film Co, 26-30 Nishiazabu, Minatoku, Tokyo 160, Japan

Ohta, Michio *Financier*
%Mitsui Trust & Banking Ltd, 2-1-1 Nihonbashi, Muromachi, Tokyo 103, Japan

Ohtani, Ichiji *Businessman*
%Toyobo Co, 2-2-8 Dojimahama, Kitaku, Osaka 530, Japan

Oimeon, Casper *Skier*
540 S Mountain Ave, Ashland, OR 97520

Ojukwu, Chukwuemeka Odumegwu *Head of State, Biafra*
%National Party of Nigeria, Lagos, Nigeria

Okamoto, Ayako *Golfer*
%Ladies Professional Golf Assn, 2570 Volusia Ave, #B, Daytona Beach, FL 32114

Okamoto, Sashiro *Businessman*
%Teijin Ltd, 11 Minamihonmachi, Higashiku, Osaka 541, Japan

Okamoto, Toshiro *Businessman*
%Isuzu Motors Ltd, 6-22-10 Minamioi, Shinagawaku, Tokyo 140, Japan

Okamura, Arthur *Artist*
155 Horseshoe Hill Rd, Bolinas, CA 94924

Okazaki, Masaharu *Businessman*
%Toyo Tire & Rubber Co, 17-18 Edobori, Nishiku, Osaka 550, Japan

Okello, Basilio Olara *Army General, Uganda*
%General Staff Headquarters, Kampala, Uganda

Okoso, Yoshinori *Businessman*
%Nippon Meat Packers, 4-47 Minamihonmachi, Higashiku, Osaka 541, Japan

Okoye, Christian *Football Player*
%Kansas City Chiefs, 1 Arrowhead Dr, Kansas City, MO 64129

Okubo, Susumu *Physicist*
1209 East Ave, Rochester, NY 14607

Okumura, Teruyuki *Financier*
%Taiyo Kobe Bank, 56 Naniwa, Chuoku, Kobe 650, Japan

Olajuwon, Hakeem *Basketball Player*
%Houston Rockets, Summit, Greenway Plaza, #10, Houston, TX 77046

Olberman, Keith *Sportscaster*
%ESPN, Sports Dept, ESPN Plaza, 935 Middle St, Bristol, CT 06010

Olczyk, Ed *Hockey Player*
%Winnipeg Jets, 15-1430 Maroons Rd, Winnipeg MB R3G 0L5, Canada

Old, Jonathan W, Jr *Businessman*
%GrandMet USA Inc, 100 Paragon Dr, Montvale, NJ 07645

Old, Lloyd J *Cancer Biologist*
%Sloan-Kettering Institute, 410 E 68th St, New York, NY 10021

Oldenburg, Claes *Sculptor*
556 Broome St, New York, NY 10013

Oldenburg, Richard E *Museum Director*
%Museum of Modern Art, 11 W 53rd St, New York, NY 10019

Olds, Robin *WW II Air Force Hero, Football Player*
PO Box 1478, Steamboat Springs, CO 80477

Olevsky, Julian *Concert Violinist*
68 Blue Hills Rd, Amherst, MA 01002

Oliansky, Joel *Movie Director*
%Triad Artists, 10100 Santa Monica Blvd, #1600, Los Angeles, CA 90067

Olin, James R *Representative, VA*
%House of Representatives, Washington, DC 20515

Olin, John Merrill *Businessman*
%Olin Corp, 7701 Forsyth Blvd, St Louis, MO 63105

Olin, Ken *Actor*
%Gersh Agency, 232 N Canon Dr, Beverly Hills, CA 90210

Olin, Lena *Actress*
%International Creative Mgmt, 8899 Beverly Blvd, Los Angeles, CA 90048

Oliphant, Patrick *Editorial Cartoonist*
%Universal Press Syndicate, 4900 Main St, Kansas City, MO 62114

Olitski, Jules *Artist*
RFD 1, Bear Island, Lovejoy Sands Rd, Meredith, NH 03253

Oliva, L Jay *Educator*
%New York University, President's Office, New York, NY 10012

Oliva, Tony *Baseball Player*
212 Spring Valley Dr, Bloomington, MN 55420

Olivares, Ruben *Boxer*
%Geno Productions, PO Box 113, Montebello, CA 90640

Oliveira, Elmar *Concert Violinist*
%Robert N Levin, 250 W 57th St, #1332, New York, NY 10019

Oliveira, Nathan *Artist*
785 Santa Maria Ave, Stanford, CA 94305

Oliver, Al *Baseball Player*
1598 Cleveland, Columbus, OH 43211

O

Oliver – Ono

Oliver, Covey T — *Attorney, Educator*
Ingleton-on-Miles, RFD 1, Box 194, Easton, MD 21601

Oliver, Daniel — *Government Official*
%Federal Trade Commission, Pennsylvania & 6th NW, Washington, DC 20580

Oliver, Edith — *Theater Critic*
%New Yorker Magazine, 25 W 43rd St, New York, NY 10036

Oliver, Mary — *Poet*
%Molly Malone Cook Agency, PO Box 338, Provincetown, MA 02657

Olivero, Magda — *Opera Singer*
%Matthews/Napal Ltd, 270 West End Ave, New York, NY 10023

Olmedo, Alex — *Tennis Player*
5067 Woodley Ave, Encino, CA 91436

Olmos, Edward James — *Actor*
%Artists Agency, 10000 Santa Monica BLvd, #305, Los Angeles, CA 90067

Olmsted, Mildred S — *Social Worker*
Rose Valley, Box 157, Moylan, PA 19065

Olney, Claude W — *Educator*
%Olney 'A' Seminars, PO Box 686, Scottsdale, AZ 85252

Olscamp, Paul J — *Educator*
%Bowling Green State University, President's Office, Bowling Green, OH 43403

Olsen, Jack — *Writer*
7954 NE Baker Hill Rd, Bainbridge Island, WA 98110

Olsen, Kenneth H — *Businessman*
%Digital Equipment Corp, 146 Main St, Maynard, MA 01754

Olsen, Kenneth O — *Businessman*
%Von's Grocery Co, PO Box 3338, Terminal Annex, Los Angeles, CA 90051

Olsen, Leif H — *Financier*
409 Carter St, New Canaan, CT 06840

Olsen, Merlin — *Football Player, Sportscaster*
%CBS-TV, Sports Dept, 51 W 52nd St, New York, NY 10020

Olsen, Paul E — *Geologist*
%Columbia University, Lamont-Doherty Geological Laboratory, New York, NY 10027

Olseth, D R — *Businessman*
%Metronic Inc, 3055 Hwy 8, Minneapolis, MN 55440

Olson, Allen I — *Governor, ND*
6951 Raven Ct, Eden Prairie, MN 55344

Olson, Eugene R — *Businessman*
%Deluxe Check Printers Inc, 1080 W County Rd F, St Paul, MN 55112

Olson, Frank A — *Businessman*
%Allegis Corp, 1200 Algonquin Rd, Elk Grove Township, IL 60666

Olson, H Everett — *Businessman*
%Carnation Co, 5045 Wilshire Blvd, Los Angeles, CA 90036

Olson, Harry F — *Physicist*
%RCA Laboratories, Princeton, NJ 08540

Olson, James — *Actor*
%Bauman Hiller Assoc, 5750 Wilshire Blvd, #512, Los Angeles, CA 90036

Olson, Lisa — *Sportswriter*
%Boston Herald, 300 Harrison Ave, Boston, MA 02106

Olson, Lute — *Basketball Coach*
%University of Arizona, Athletic Dept, Tucson, AZ 85721

Olson, Nancy — *Actress*
945 N Alpine Dr, Beverly Hills, CA 90210

Olsson, Curt G — *Financier*
%Esselte AB, Box 1371, 171 27 Stockholm-Solna, Sweden

Omar Ali Saifuddin Sa'adul — *Sultan, Brunei*
Istana Darul Hana, Brunei

Onanian, Edward — *Religious Leader*
%Diocese of Armenian Church, 630 2nd Ave, New York, NY 10016

Onassis, Jacqueline Bouvier Kennedy — *Wife of US President*
%Doubleday Co, 245 Park Ave, New York, NY 10167

Ong, John D — *Businessman*
%B F Goodrich Co, 500 S Main St, Akron, OH 44318

Ongais, Danny — *Auto Racing Driver*
3031 S Orange, Santa Ana, CA 92707

Ono, Yoko — *Filmmaker, Artist*
%Dakota Hotel, 1 W 72nd St, New York, NY 10023

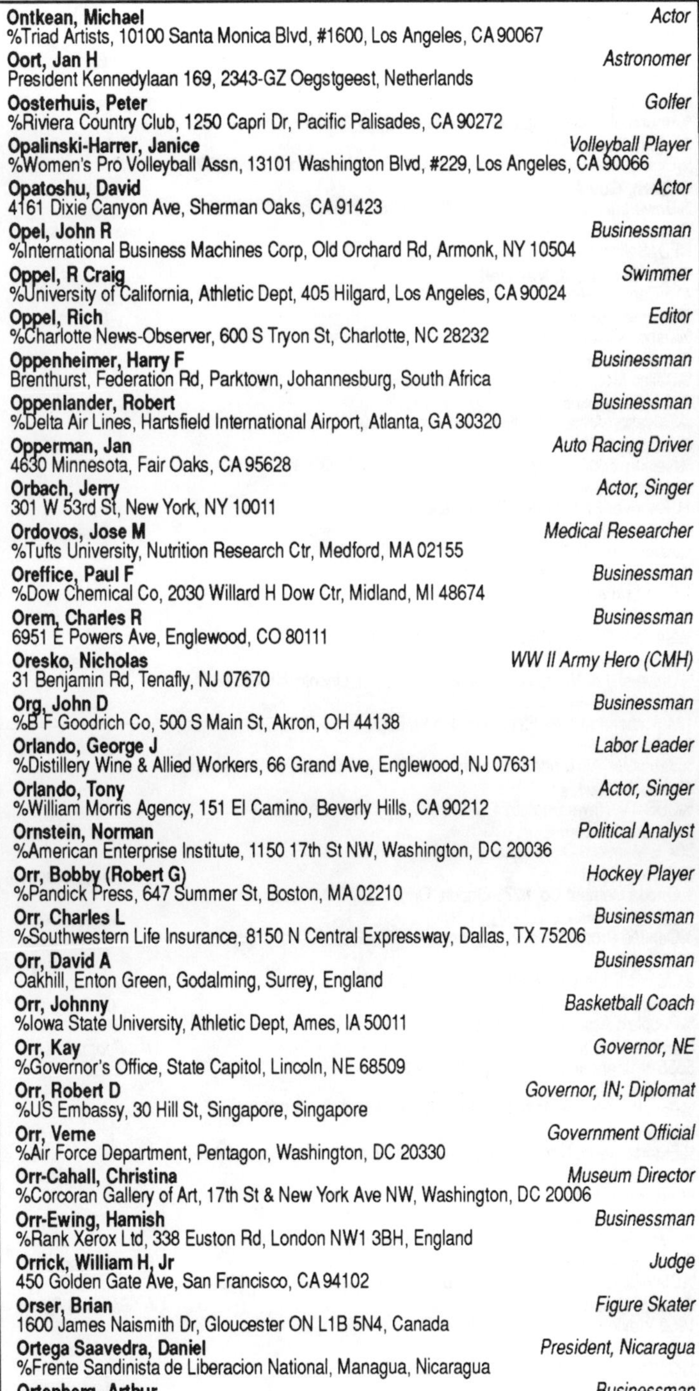

Ontkean, Michael *Actor*
%Triad Artists, 10100 Santa Monica Blvd, #1600, Los Angeles, CA 90067

Oort, Jan H *Astronomer*
President Kennedylaan 169, 2343-GZ Oegstgeest, Netherlands

Oosterhuis, Peter *Golfer*
%Riviera Country Club, 1250 Capri Dr, Pacific Palisades, CA 90272

Opalinski-Harrer, Janice *Volleyball Player*
%Women's Pro Volleyball Assn, 13101 Washington Blvd, #229, Los Angeles, CA 90066

Opatoshu, David *Actor*
4161 Dixie Canyon Ave, Sherman Oaks, CA 91423

Opel, John R *Businessman*
%International Business Machines Corp, Old Orchard Rd, Armonk, NY 10504

Oppel, R Craig *Swimmer*
%University of California, Athletic Dept, 405 Hilgard, Los Angeles, CA 90024

Oppel, Rich *Editor*
%Charlotte News-Observer, 600 S Tryon St, Charlotte, NC 28232

Oppenheimer, Harry F *Businessman*
Brenthurst, Federation Rd, Parktown, Johannesburg, South Africa

Oppenlander, Robert *Businessman*
%Delta Air Lines, Hartsfield International Airport, Atlanta, GA 30320

Opperman, Jan *Auto Racing Driver*
4630 Minnesota, Fair Oaks, CA 95628

Orbach, Jerry *Actor, Singer*
301 W 53rd St, New York, NY 10011

Ordovos, Jose M *Medical Researcher*
%Tufts University, Nutrition Research Ctr, Medford, MA 02155

Oreffice, Paul F *Businessman*
%Dow Chemical Co, 2030 Willard H Dow Ctr, Midland, MI 48674

Orem, Charles R *Businessman*
6951 E Powers Ave, Englewood, CO 80111

Oresko, Nicholas *WW II Army Hero (CMH)*
31 Benjamin Rd, Tenafly, NJ 07670

Org, John D *Businessman*
%B F Goodrich Co, 500 S Main St, Akron, OH 44138

Orlando, George J *Labor Leader*
%Distillery Wine & Allied Workers, 66 Grand Ave, Englewood, NJ 07631

Orlando, Tony *Actor, Singer*
%William Morris Agency, 151 El Camino, Beverly Hills, CA 90212

Ornstein, Norman *Political Analyst*
%American Enterprise Institute, 1150 17th St NW, Washington, DC 20036

Orr, Bobby (Robert G) *Hockey Player*
%Pandick Press, 647 Summer St, Boston, MA 02210

Orr, Charles L *Businessman*
%Southwestern Life Insurance, 8150 N Central Expressway, Dallas, TX 75206

Orr, David A *Businessman*
Oakhill, Enton Green, Godalming, Surrey, England

Orr, Johnny *Basketball Coach*
%Iowa State University, Athletic Dept, Ames, IA 50011

Orr, Kay *Governor, NE*
%Governor's Office, State Capitol, Lincoln, NE 68509

Orr, Robert D *Governor, IN; Diplomat*
%US Embassy, 30 Hill St, Singapore, Singapore

Orr, Verne *Government Official*
%Air Force Department, Pentagon, Washington, DC 20330

Orr-Cahall, Christina *Museum Director*
%Corcoran Gallery of Art, 17th St & New York Ave NW, Washington, DC 20006

Orr-Ewing, Hamish *Businessman*
%Rank Xerox Ltd, 338 Euston Rd, London NW1 3BH, England

Orrick, William H, Jr *Judge*
450 Golden Gate Ave, San Francisco, CA 94102

Orser, Brian *Figure Skater*
1600 James Naismith Dr, Gloucester ON L1B 5N4, Canada

Ortega Saavedra, Daniel *President, Nicaragua*
%Frente Sandinista de Liberacion National, Managua, Nicaragua

Ortenberg, Arthur *Businessman*
%Liz Claiborne Inc, 1441 Broadway, New York, NY 10018

Ortiz, Solomon P *Representative, TX*
%House of Representatives, Washington, DC 20515
Ortoli, Francois-Xavier *Businessman*
%Total Cie Francaise des Petroles, 5 Rue Michel-Ange, 75781 Paris, France
Orton, Bill *Representative, UT*
%House of Representatives, Washington, DC 20515
Orvick, George *Religious Leader*
%Evangelical Lutheran Synod, 106 13th St S, Northwood, IA 50459
Osborn, Guy A *Businessman*
%Universal Foods Corp, 443 E Michigan St, Milwaukee, WI 53202
Osborn, Robert *Cartoonist*
RFD, Salisbury, CT 06068
Osborne DuPont, Margaret *Tennis Player*
415 Camino Real, El Paso, TX 79922
Osborne, Adam *Businessman*
%Osborne Computer Corp, 26538 Danti Ct, Hayward, CA 94545
Osborne, Burl *Editor, Publisher*
%Dallas Morning News, Communications Ctr, Dallas, TX 75265
Osborne, James *Religious Leader*
%Salvation Army, 799 Bloomfield Ave, Verona, NJ 07044
Osborne, Jeffrey *Singer*
%Nelson, 5800 Valley Oak Dr, Los Angeles, CA 90068
Osborne, John *Playwright*
11 Hanover St, London W1, England
Osborne, Richard de J *Businessman*
%Asarco Inc, 180 Maiden Ln, New York, NY 10038
Osborne, Stanley de J *Businessman*
1 East End Ave, New York, NY 10021
Osborne, Stellanova *Writer*
%General Delivery, Sault Sainte Marie, MI 49783
Osborne, Tom *Football Coach*
%University of Nebraska, Athletic Department, Lincoln, NE 68588
Osbourne, Ozzy *Singer*
184 Sutherland Ave, Flat 2, London W, England
Oschmann, Fritz *Businessman*
%Veba Oel, Alexander-von-Humboldt-Str, 4650 Gelsenkirchen, Germany
Osgood, Charles *News Commentator*
%CBS-TV, News Dept, 524 W 57th St, New York, NY 10019
Osgood, Charles E *Psychologist, Educator*
304 E Mumford Dr, Urbana, IL 61801
Oshima, Kenji *Businessman*
%Onoda Cement Co, 6276 Onoda, Onoda City 756, Japan
Oshima, Nagisa *Movie Director*
%Oshima Productions, 2-15-7 Arasaka, Minatoku, Tokyo, Japan
Oslin, K T *Singer*
21 Music Square E, #180, Nashville, TN 37203
Osman, Osman Ahmed *Civil Engineer*
%People's Assembly, Cairo, Egypt
Osmanski, Bill *Football Player*
5555 N Sheridan Rd, Chicago, IL 60640
Osmond, Cliff *Actor*
%Paul Kohner Inc, 9169 Sunset Blvd, Los Angeles, CA 90069
Osmond, Donny *Singer*
%Entertainment Corp, 1570 Brookhollow Dr, #116, Santa Ana, CA 92705
Osmond, Marie *Singer*
PO Box 6000, Provo, UT 84603
Osnes, Larry G *Educator*
%Hamline University, President's Office, St Paul, MN 55104
Osrin, Raymond *Editorial Cartoonist*
%Cleveland Plain Dealer, 1801 Superior Ave, Cleveland, OH 44114
Osteen, Claude *Baseball Player*
1959 Wexford Rd, Palmyra, PA 17078
Osterbrock, Donald E *Astronomer*
120 Woodside Ave, Santa Cruz, CA 95060
Osterhoff, James M *Businessman*
%Digital Equipment Corp, 146 Main St, Maynard, MA 01754

Ostern, W C *Businessman*
%Mobay Chemical Corp, Mobay Rd, Pittsburgh, PA 15205
Osterwald, Bibi *Actress*
4219 Warner Blvd, Burbank, CA 91505
Ostin, Mo *Businessman*
%Warner Bros Records, 3300 Warner Blvd, Burbank, CA 91505
Ostos, Javier *Swimmer*
%FINA, Isabel La Catolica 13, Desp 401-2, Mexico City 1 DF, Mexico
Ostriker, Jeremiah P *Astrophysicist*
33 Philip Dr, Princeton, NJ 08540
Ostrom, John H *Vertebrate Paleontologist*
198 Towpath Ln, Cheshire, CT 06410
Oswald, Stephen S *Astronaut*
%NASA, Johnson Space Ctr, Houston, TX 77058
Othmer, Donald F *Chemical Engineer*
140 Columbia Heights, Brooklyn, NY 11201
Otis, Amos *Baseball Player*
13558 Freeport Rd, San Diego, CA 92129
Otis, Johnny *Singer*
7105 Baker Ln, Sebastopol, CA 95472
Otsott, Charles P *Army General*
Deputy Chairman, NATO Military Committee, APO, AE 09724
Ottenbrite, Anne *Swimmer*
%Olympic Assn, Olympic House, Cite du Harve, Montreal PQ H3C 3R4, Canada
Ottey, Merlene *Track Athlete*
%Jamaican Olympic Committee, PO Box 544, Kingston 10, Jamaica
Ottinger, Richard L *Representative, NY*
554 Alda Rd, Mamaroneck, NY 10543
Otto, A T, Jr *Labor Leader*
%Railroad Yardmasters Union, 1411 Peterson Ave, #201, Park Ridge, IL 60068
Otto, Frei *Architect*
Berghalde 19, 7250 Leonberg, 7 Warmbroun, Germany
Otto, Jim *Football Player*
00 Estates Dr, Auburn, CA 95603
Otumfuo Nana Opoku Ware II *Ruler, Ghana*
%Asantehene's Palace, Manhyia, Kumasi, Ashanti, Ghana
Otunga, Maurice Cardinal *Religious Leader*
%Cardinal's Residence, PO Box 14231, Nairobi, Kenya
Otwell, Ralph M *Editor*
%Chicago Sun-Times, 401 N Wabash Ave, Chicago, IL 60611
Ouchi, William G *Educator*
%University of California, Management School, Los Angeles, CA 90024
Oueddei, Goukouni *President, Chad*
%Conseil Supreme de la Revolutions, Badai, Chad
Ouedraogo, Gerard Kango *Prime Minister, Burkina Faso*
%Union Democratique Voltaique, Ouagadougou, Burkina Faso
Ovchinnikov, Yuri A *Biochemist*
%Academy of Sciences, Lenisky Prospeckt 14, Moscow, Russia
Overall, Park *Actress*
%Witt/Thomas/Harris Productions, 846 N Cahuenga Blvd, #A, Los Angeles, CA 90038
Overby, Andrew N *Financier*
20 Exchange Pl, New York, NY 10005
Overcash, Reece A, Jr *Businessman*
%Paramount Communications, 1 Paramount Communications Plz, New York, NY 10023
Overgard, Robert M, Sr *Religious Leader*
%Church of Lutheran Brethren, 707 Crestview Dr W, Union, IA 52175
Overgard, William *Cartoonist (Rudy)*
%United Feature Syndicate, 200 Park Ave, New York, NY 10166
Overholser, Geneva *Editor*
%Des Moines Register, Box 957, Des Moines, IA 50304
Overlock, Willard J, Jr *Financier*
%Goldman Sachs Co, 85 Broad St, New York, NY 10004
Overmyer, Robert F *Astronaut*
%McDonnell Douglas Space Station Div, 16055 Space Center Blvd, Houston, TX 77062
Overton, William W *Financier*
4830 Cedar Springs, Dallas, TX 75219

O

Ovitz, Michael S *Entertainment Executive*
%Creative Artists Agency, 9830 Wilshire Blvd, Beverly Hills, CA 90212

Ovshinsky, Stanford R *Ovionics Engineer*
%Ovitron Corp, 1675 W Maple Rd, Troy, MI 48084

Owen, David A L *Government Official, England*
%House of Commons, Westminster, London SW1, England

Owen, Gordon *Businessman*
%Cable & Wireless PLC, Mercury House, Theobald's Rd, London WC1, England

Owen, Henry *Diplomat*
%Brookings Institute, 1775 Massachusetts Ave NW, Washington, DC 20036

Owen, Mickey *Baseball Player*
2731 E Lombard, Springfield, MO 65802

Owen, Randy *Singer (Alabama)*
%Dale Morris Assoc, 818 19th Ave S, Nashville, TN 37203

Owen, Ray D *Biologist*
1583 Rose Villa St, Pasadena, CA 91106

Owen, Thomas J *Financer*
%Perpetual American Bank, 2034 Eisenhower Ave, Alexandria, VA 22314

Owens, Billy *Basketball Player*
%Golden State Warriors, Oakland Coliseum, Oakland, CA 94621

Owens, Buck *Singer*
%Buck Owens Production Co, 3223 Sillect Ave, Bakersfield, CA 93308

Owens, Donna *Mayor*
%Mayor's Office, 1 Government Ctr, Toledo, OH 43604

Owens, Gary *Entertainer*
PO Box 76860, Los Angeles, CA 90076

Owens, Ira C *Army General*
Deputy Chief of Staff for Intelligence, ODCSINT, US Army, Washington, DC 20310

Owens, Jim *Football Player, Coach*
%Rowan Companies, 2470 First City Tower, 1001 Fannin, Houston, TX 77002

Owens, Major R *Representative, NY*
335 Wyona St, Brooklyn, NY 11207

Owens, Wayne *Representative, UT*
%House of Representatives, Washington, DC 20515

Owens, William A *Navy Admiral*
Commander, 6th Fleet, Unit 50148, FPO, AE 09501

Oxenberg, Catherine *Actress*
PO Box 25909, Los Angeles, CA 90025

Oxenhorn, Harvey *Writer*
%Harvard University, School of Government, Cambridge, MA 02138

Oxley, Michael G *Representative, OH*
1995 Old Mill Rd, Findlay, OH 45849

Oyakawa, Yoshi *Swimmer*
4171 Hutchinson Rd, Cincinnati, OH 45248

Oz, Amos *Writer*
Kibbutz Hulda, Doar Na Nachal, Ayalon, Israel

Oz, Frank *Puppeteer*
%Henson Assoc, 117 E 69th St, New York, NY 10021

Ozal, Turgut *Prime Minister, Turkey*
Halaskargazi Cad 336/1 D 6 Sisli, Istanbul, Turkey

Ozark, Danny *Baseball Executive*
PO Box 6666, Vero Beach, FL 32960

Ozawa, Seiji *Conductor*
%Boston Symphony, 301 Massachusetts Ave, Boston, MA 02115

Ozbun, David *Educator*
%North Dakota State University, President's Office, Fargo, ND 58105

Ozick, Cynthia *Writer*
%Alfred A Knopf, 201 E 50th St, New York, NY 10022

Paar, Jack *Entertainer*
115 Pequot Ln, New Canaan, CT 06848

Pace, Darrell O *Archery Athlete*
%Diane Gerdau, 7417 Michael Rd, Middletown, OH 45042

Pace, Judy *Actress*
4139 Cloverdale, Los Angeles, CA 90008

Pacheco, Ferdie *Sportscaster*
%NBC-TV, Sports Dept, 30 Rockefeller Plz, New York, NY 10020

Pacheco, Manuel T *Educator*
%University of Arizona, President's Office, Tucson, AZ 85721

Pacino, Al *Actor*
%Creative Artists Agency, 9830 Wilshire Blvd, Beverly Hills, CA 90212

Pacino, Al *Actor*
301 W 57th St, #16-C, New York, NY 10017

Packard, David *Businessman*
%Hewlett-Packard Co, 3000 Hanover St, Palo Alto, CA 94304

Packard, Ron *Representative, CA*
%House of Representatives, Washington, DC 20515

Packard, Vance *Writer*
87 Mill Rd, New Canaan, CT 06840

Packer, Billy (A William) *Sportscaster*
105 Tescue Dr, Advance, NC 27001

Packwood, Robert W *Senator, OR*
%US Senate, Washington, DC 20510

Pacquer, Michel *Businessman*
%Elf-Aquitaine Societe Nationale, 75739 Paris Cedex 15, France

Pacula, Joanna *Actress*
%Gersh Agency, 232 N Canon Dr, Beverly Hills, CA 90210

Paddock, John *Hockey Coach*
%Winnipeg Jets, 15-1430 Maroons Rd, Winnipeg MA R3G 0L5, Canada

Padilla, Doug *Track Athlete*
%General Delivery, Orem, UT 84057

Padiyara, Anthony Cardinal *Religious Leader*
Archdiocese Curia, Post Bag 2580, Ernakulam, Cochin-68201, Kerela, India

Paez, Jorge (Maromero) *Boxer*
%Decor Depot, 677 Anita St, #D, Chula Vista, CA 92011

Pafko, Andy *Baseball Player*
1420 Blackhawk Dr, Mount Prospect, IL 60056

Paganelli, Robert P *Diplomat*
331 S Main St, Albion, NY 14411

Page, Alan *Football Player*
%Attorney General's Office, 444 Lafayette Rd, #200, St Paul, MN 55101

Page, Anita *Actress*
717 "A" St, Coronado, CA 92118

Page, David C *Geneticist*
%Whitehead Institute, 9 Cambridge Center, Cambridge, MA 02142

Page, Genevieve *Actress*
52 Rue de Vaugirard, 75006 Paris, France

Page, George K *Financier*
%United First Federal Savings & Loan, 1390 Main St, Sarasota, FL 33577

Page, Greg *Boxer*
%Don King Promotions, 32 E 69th St, New York, NY 10021

Page, La Wanda *Actress*
1607 N El Centro Ave, Los Angeles, CA 90028

Page, Oscar *Educator*
%Austin Peay State University, President's Office, Clarksville, TN 37044

Page, Patti *Singer, Actress*
1412 San Lucas Ct, Solana Beach, CA 92075

Page, Walter H *Financier*
%Morgan Guaranty Trust, 23 Wall St, New York, NY 10015

Pagels, Elaine H *Educator*
%Barnard College, Religion Dept, New York, NY 10027

Pagett, Nicola *Actress*
22 Victoria Rd, London SW14, England

Pagliarulo, Mike *Baseball Player*
164 W Wyoming St, Melrose, MA 02176

Pagniez, Regis *Publisher*
%Elle Magazine, 551 5th Ave, New York, NY 10176

Pagonis, William G *Army General*
Commanding General, 22nd TAACOM, US CENTCOM (Saudi Arabia), APO, AE 09808

Pahang, Sultan of *Ruler, Malaysia*
Pekan Lama, Kuantan, Pahang, Malaysia

Paige, Elaine *Singer*
%International Business Ctr, 90 Regent St, London W1R 5PA, England

Paige, Janis *Actress*
1700 Rising Glen Rd, Los Angeles, CA 90069

Paige, Mitchell *WW II Marine Corps Hero (CMH)*
PO Box 2358, Palm Desert, CA 92261

Paik, Nam June *Video Artist*
%Galerie Bonino, 48 Great Jones St, New York, NY 10012

Pailes, Bill *Astronaut*
%HQ Space Division, PO Box 92960, Worldway Postal Ctr, Los Angeles, CA 90009

Paine, Thomas O *Space Administrator, Businessman*
765 Bonhill Rd, Los Angeles, CA 90049

Painter, John W *Businessman*
%Eagle-Picher Industries, 580 Walnut St, Cincinnati, OH 45202

Pais, Abraham *Physicist*
450 E 63rd St, New York, NY 10021

Paisley, Ian *Political Leader, Northern Ireland*
%Parsonage, 17 Cyprus Ave, Belfast BZ5 5NT, Northern Ireland

Pak, Charles *Medical Researcher*
%University of Texas, Health Sciences Ctr, Dallas, TX 75235

Pakula, Alan *Movie Director*
%Pakula Co, 330 W 58th St, #5-H, New York, NY 10019

Palade, George E *Nobel Medicine Laureate*
%Yale University, Cell Biology Section, New Haven, CT 06510

Palance, Jack *Actor*
Cielo Ranch, Star Rt 1, Box 805, Tehachapi, CA 93561

Palau, Luis *Evangelist*
1100 NW Murray Rd, Portland, OR 97229

Palay, Gilbert *Businessman*
%Parker Pen Co, 1 Parker Pl, Janesville, WI 53545

Palazzini, Pietro Cardinal *Religious Leader*
Via Proba Petronia 83, Rome, Italy

Palevsky, Max *Businessman*
924 Westwood Blvd, #700, Los Angeles, CA 90024

Paley, Albert R *Sculptor*
Paley Studios, 25 N Washington St, Rochester, NY 14614

Paley, Grace *Writer*
%Sarah Lawrence College, Literature Dept, Bronxville, NY 10708

Palfrey Danzig, Sarah *Tennis Player*
993 Park Ave, New York, NY 10028

Palillo, Ron *Actor*
%Bauman Hiller Assoc, 5750 Wilshire Blvd, #512, Los Angeles, CA 90036

Palin, Michael *Actor, Writer (Monty Python)*
%Gumby Corporation Ltd, 68-A Delancey St, London NW1 7RY, England

Palmar, Derek *Businessman*
%Bass Ltd, 30 Portland Pl, London W1N 3DF, England

Palmer, Arnold *Golfer*
PO Box 52, Youngstown, PA 15696

Palmer, Betsy *Actress*
%Harry Gold Assoc, 3500 W Olive Ave, #1400, Burbank, CA 91505

Palmer, H Bruce *Businessman*
Rt 2, Ridge Rd, Hunting Country, Tryon, NC 28782

Palmer, Jim *Baseball Player, Sportscaster*
PO Box 145, Brooklandville, MD 21022

Palmer, Paul *Football Player*
%Cincinnati Bengals, 200 Riverfront Stadium, Cincinnati, OH 45202

Palmer, Robert *Singer*
%Triad Artists, 10100 Santa Monica Blvd, #1600, Los Angeles, CA 90067

Palmer, Russell E *Educator*
%University of Pennsylvania, Business School, Philadelphia, PA 19104

Palmer, Sandra *Golfer*
PO Box 986, La Quinta, CA 92253

Palmer, William R *Publisher*
%Detroit News, 615 Lafayette Blvd, Detroit, MI 48231

Palmieri, Paul *Religious Leader*
%Church of Jesus Christ, 6th & Lincoln Sts, Monongahela, PA 15063

Palmieri, Peter C *Financier*
%Irving Bank Corp, 1 Wall St, New York, NY 10005

Palms, John M *Educator*
%University of South Carolina, President's Office, Columbia, SC 29208

Paltrow, Bruce *Television Producer*
304 21st St, Santa Monica, CA 90402

Paluzzi, Luciana *Actress*
200 Old Palisade Rd, Ft Lee, NJ 07024

Pamplin, R B *Businessman*
%Riegel Textile Corp, 25 Woods Lake Rd, Greenville, SC 29607

Pandit, Korla *Organist*
PO Box 11614, Santa Rosa, CA 95406

Panetta, Leon E *Representative, CA*
%House of Representatives, Washington, DC 20515

Pankey, Irv *Football Player*
%Indianapolis Colts, 7001 W 56th St, Indianapolis, IN 46254

Panoff, Robert *Nuclear Engineer*
1140 Connecticut Ave NW, Washington, DC 20036

Panofsky, Wolfgang K H *Physicist, Educator*
25671 Chapin Rd, Los Altos, CA 94022

Panov, Valery *Ballet Dancer*
%Carson Office, 119 W 57th St, #903, New York, NY 10019

Panova, Galina *Ballerina*
%Carson Office, 119 W 57th St, #903, New York, NY 10019

Paolozzi, Eduardo *Sculptor*
Landemere, Thorpe-le-Soken, England

Papadopoulos, Georgios *President, Greece*
Kordallous Prison, Piraeus, Greece

Papandreou, Andreas *Prime Minister, Greece*
Papaia Anaktora, Athens, Greece

Papart, Max *Artist*
10 Rue Pernety, 75014 Paris, France

Papas, Irene *Actress*
Xenokratous 39, Atens-Kolonaki, Greece

Papert, Seymour *Mathematician*
%Massachusetts Institute of Technology, 20 Ames St, Cambridge, MA 02139

Papp, Lazlo *Boxer*
Ora-Utca 6, 1125 Budapest, Hungary

Pappalardo, Salvatore Cardinal *Religious Leader*
Via Matteo Bonello 2, Palermo, Italy

Pappas, George *Bowler*
%George Pappas's Park Lanes, 1700 Montford Dr, Charlotte, NC 28209

Pappas, Ike *Commentator, Television Producer*
%Pappas Network Productions, 2030 "M" St NW, #6N8, Washington, DC 20036

Pappas, Jimmy *Navy Admiral*
Director for Logistics, Joint Chiefs of Staff, Washington, DC 20318

Pappas, Milt *Baseball Player*
RR 1, Box 154, Ashland Ave, Beecher, IL 60401

Pappenheimer, John Richard *Physiologist, Educator*
15 Fayerweather St, Cambridge, MA 02138

Pappito, Ralph R *Businessman*
%Nortek Inc, 50 Kennedy Plz, Providence, RI 02903

Paquet, Jean Guy *Educator*
%Laval University, Rector's Office, Quebec PQ G1K 7P4, Canada

Paquette, Joseph F, Jr *Businessman*
%Philadelphia Electric Co, 2301 Market St, Philadelphia, PA 19101

Parayre, Jean-Paul *Businessman*
26 Rue Saint-James, 92200 Neuilly-sur-Seine, France

Parcells, Bill *Football Coach, Sportscaster*
%NBC-TV, Sports Dept, 30 Rockefeller Ctr, New York, NY 10020

P

Pardee – Parker

Pardee, Arthur B — *Biochemist, Educator*
30 Codman Rd, Brookline, MA 02146

Pardee, Jack — *Football Player, Coach*
%Houston Oilers, 6910 Fannin St, Houston, TX 77030

Pare, Michael — *Actor*
2804 Pacific Ave, Venice, CA 90291

Parent, Bernie — *Hockey Player*
%Philadelphia Flyers, Spectrum, Pattison Pl, Philadelphia, PA 19148

Parfet, Ray T, Jr — *Businessman*
%Upjohn Co, 7000 Portage Rd, Kalamazoo, MI 49001

Parfet, William U — *Businessman*
%Upjohn Co, 7000 Portage Rd, Kalamazoo, MI 49001

Parilli, Vito (Babe) — *Football Player*
545 Downing St, Denver, CO 80218

Paris, Mica — *Singer*
%Island Records, 6525 Sunset Blvd, Los Angeles, CA 90028

Parise, Ronald A — *Astronaut*
%Computer Science Corp, 8728 Colesville Rd, Silver Spring, MD 20910

Parish, Preston S — *Businessman*
%Upjohn Co, 7000 Portage Rd, Kalamazoo, MI 49001

Parish, Robert — *Basketball Player*
%Boston Celtics, 151 Merrimac St, Boston, MA 02114

Park Yung-Wok — *Businessman*
%Hyundai Corp, 140-2 Kyedong, Chongroku, Seoul, South Korea

Park, Brad — *Hockey Player, Coach*
%Bradan Corp, 22-B Cranes Ct, Woburn, MA 01801

Park, Merle — *Ballerina*
21 Millers Ct, Chiswick Mall, London W4 2PF, England

Park, W B — *Cartoonist (Off the Leash)*
%United Feature Syndicate, 200 Park Ave, New York, NY 10166

Parkening, Christopher — *Concert Guitarist*
%Columbia Artists Mgmt Inc, 165 W 57th St, New York, NY 10019

Parker, Alan — *Movie Director*
%Parker Film Co, Pinewood Studios, Iver Heath, Bucks, England

Parker, Bob — *Skier*
408 Camino Don Miguel, Santa Fe, NM 87501

Parker, Brant J — *Cartoonist (Wizard of Id)*
5668 Thorndyke Ct, Centreville, VA 22020

Parker, Bruce C — *Botanist*
841 Hutcheson Dr, Blacksburg, VA 24060

Parker, Charles O — *Businessman*
%Pacific Lighting Corp, 810 S Flower St, Los Angeles, CA 90060

Parker, Clarence (Ace) — *Football Player*
210 Snead Fairway, Portsmouth, VA 23701

Parker, Corey — *Actor*
%Gersh Agency, 232 N Canon Dr, Beverly Hills, CA 90210

Parker, Dave — *Baseball Player*
7864 Ridge Rd, Cincinnati, OH 45237

Parker, Edna G — *Judge*
%US Tax Court, 400 2nd St NW, Washington, DC 20217

Parker, Eleanor — *Actress*
2195 La Paz Way, Palm Springs, CA 92262

Parker, Ellis D — *Army General*
Director of Army Staff, Hq USA, Washington, DC 20310

Parker, Eugene N — *Physicist*
1323 Evergreen Rd, Homewood, IL 60430

Parker, Fess — *Actor*
%Parker's Red Lion Resort Hotel, 633 E Cabrillo Blvd, Santa Barbara, CA 93103

Parker, Frank A — *Tennis Player*
1625 Ridge Ave, Evanston, IL 60201

Parker, George — *Businessman*
%Parker Pen Co, 1 Parker Pl, Janesville, WI 53545

Parker, George M — *Labor Leader*
%Glass Workers Union, 1440 S Byrne Rd, Toledo, OH 43614

Parker, George R — *Businessman*
%Newmont Mining Corp, 200 Park Ave, New York, NY 10166

Parker, Graham *Singer*
%RCA Records, 6363 Sunset Blvd, #417, Los Angeles, CA 90028

Parker, Jackie *Football Player*
%Edmonton Eskimo, 90211 111th Ave, Edmonton AB T5B 0C3, Canada

Parker, Jameson *Actor*
%David Shapira Assoc, 15301 Ventura Blvd, #345, Sherman Oaks, CA 91403

Parker, Jim *Football Player*
5448 Wingborne Ct, Columbia, MD 21045

Parker, Lara *Actress*
%Twentieth Century Artists, 3800 Barham Blvd, Los Angeles, CA 90068

Parker, Mary-Louise *Actress*
%Triad Artists, 10100 Santa Monica Blvd, #1600, Los Angeles, CA 90067

Parker, Patrick S *Businessman*
%Parker Hannifin Corp, 17325 Euclid Ave, Cleveland, OH 44112

Parker, Robert A *Astronaut*
NASA Headquarters, Policy & Plans Div, Washington, DC 20546

Parker, Robert B *Writer*
555 W 57th St, #1230, New York, NY 10019

Parker, Robert L *Businessman*
%Parker Drilling Co, 8 E 3rd St, Tulsa, OK 74103

Parker, Robert L, Jr *Businessman*
%Parker Drilling Co, 8 E 3rd St, Tulsa, OK 74103

Parker, Sarah Jessica *Actress*
%Creative Artists Agency, 9830 Wilshire Blvd, Beverly Hills, CA 90212

Parker, Scott *Motorcyle Racing Rider*
6080 Grand Blanc Rd, Swartz Creek, MI 48473

Parker, Suzy *Model, Actress*
770 Hot Springs Rd, Santa Barbara, CA 93103

Parker, Wes *Baseball Player*
PO Box 550, Santa Monica, CA 90406

Parker, Willard *Actor*
74580 Fairway Dr, Indian Wells, CA 92260

Parkins, Barbara *Actress*
%Artists Group, 1930 Century Park West, #403, Los Angeles, CA 90067

Parkinson, C Northcote *Writer, Historian*
Anneville Manor, Anneville Rd, Vale Guernsey, Channel Islands, England

Parkinson, Charles J *Businessman*
2162 Arbor Ln, PO Box 17556, Salt Lake City, UT 84117

Parkinson, J David *Businessman*
%Thomas & Betts Corp, 920 Rt 202, Raritan, NJ 08869

Parkinson, Roger *Publisher*
%Minneapolis Star Tribune, 425 Portland Ave, Minneapolis, MN 55488

Parkos, Gregory T *Businessman*
%Whittaker Corp, 10880 Wilshire Blvd, Los Angeles, CA 90024

Parks, Gordon *Movie Director, Photographer*
860 United Nations Plz, New York, NY 10017

Parks, Hildy *Actress*
225 W 44th St, New York, NY 10036

Parks, Michael *Actor*
%Agency for Performing Arts, 9000 Sunset Blvd, #1200, Los Angeles, CA 90069

Parks, Rosa L *Civil Rights Activist*
%Rep John Conyers, Federal Bldg, 231 W Lafayette St, Dearborn, MI 48226

Parks, Van Dyke *Composer*
PO Box 1207, Studio City, CA 91604

Parnell, Mel *Baseball Player*
700 Turquoise St, New Orleans, LA 70124

Parr, Carolyn Miller *Judge*
%US Tax Court, 400 2nd St NW, Washington, DC 20217

Parravicini, Giannino *Financier*
%Banco di Sicilia, 1 Via Generale Magliocco, 90141 Palermo, Italy

Parretti, Giancarlo *Movie Producer*
%Pathe Communications, 640 S San Vicente Blvd, Los Angeles, CA 90048

Parris, Stanford E *Representative, VA*
903 Bay Cir, Woodbridge, VA 22191

Parrish, Lance *Baseball Player*
22370 Starwood Dr, Yorba Linda, CA 92686

P

Parry – Patrick

Parry, Charles W *Businessman*
%Aluminum Co of America, 1501 Alcoa Bldg, Pittsburgh, PA 15219

Parseghian, Ara *Football Coach, Sportscaster*
%St Joseph Bank Bldg, #1212, South Bend, IN 46601

Parsons, Alan *Singer*
%Arista Records, 6 W 57th St, New York, NY 10019

Parsons, Benny *Auto Racing Driver*
PO Box 540, 112 S Main St, Ellerbe, NC 28338

Parsons, E I *Businessman*
%Holly Corp, 2600 Diamond Shamrock Tower, Dallas, TX 75201

Parsons, Estelle *Actress*
505 West End Ave, New York, NY 10024

Parsons, James B *Judge*
%US District Court, US Courthouse, 219 S Dearborn Ave, Chicago, IL 60604

Partee, J Charles *Financier*
%Federal Reserve, 20th & Constitution NW, Washington, DC 20551

Parton, Dolly *Singer*
700 Dollywood Ln, Pigeon Forge, TN 37863

Pasarell, Charles *Tennis Player*
%Sportsworld, 8245 Ronson Rd, San Diego, CA 92111

Pasatieri, Thomas *Composer*
500 West End Ave, New York, NY 10024

Pascal, Donald D *Businessman*
%National Starch & Chemical Corp, Finderne Ave, Bridgewater, NJ 08807

Pascual, Camilo *Baseball Player*
7741 SW 32nd St, Miami, FL 33155

Paskai, Laszlo Cardinal *Religious Leader*
Berenyi Utca 2, Levelcim, 2501 Esztergom, Hungary

Pasman, James S *Businessman*
%Kaiser Aluminum & Chemical Corp, 300 Lakeside Dr, Oakland, CA 94643

Pasmore, Victor *Artist*
Dar Gamri, Gudja, Malta

Pass, Joe *Jazz Guitarist*
%Saue, 451 N Canon Dr, Beverly Hills, CA 90210

Passarelli, Pasquale *Greco-Roman Wrestler*
Ander Froschlache 23, 4400 Munster, Germany

Passeau, Claude *Baseball Player*
113 London St, Lucedale, MS 39452

Pastor, Ed *Representative, AZ*
%House of Representatives, Washington, DC 20515

Pastore, John O *Governor/Senator, RI*
81 Mountain Laurel Dr, Cranston, RI 02920

Pastorelli, Robert *Actor*
%Gage Group, 9255 Sunset Blvd, #515, Los Angeles, CA 90069

Pastrana Borrero, Misael *President, Colombia*
Calle 36, #16-56, Bogota DE, Colombia

Pastrano, Willie *Boxer*
4020 Rye St, #3, Metairie, LA 70002

Patat, Frederic *Spatinaut, France*
%Faculte de Medecine, 2 Bis Blvd Tonnelle, 37032 Tours Cedex, France

Pate, Jerry *Golfer*
1255 Country Club Rd, Gulf Breeze, FL 32561

Pate, Michael *Actor*
21 Bundarra Rd, Bellvue Hill NSW 2023, Australia

Paterno, Joe *Football Coach*
%Pennsylvania State University, Athletic Dept, University Park, PA 16802

Patinkin, Mandy *Actor*
200 W 90th St, New York, NY 10024

Patkin, Max *Baseball Clown*
2000 Valley Forge Cir, #837, King of Prussia, PA 19406

Paton, Angus *Civil Engineer*
Earley House, London Rd, Reading, Berks, England

Patric, Jason *Actor*
%Dolores Robinson Mgmt, 335 N Maple Dr, #250, Beverly Hills, CA 90210

Patrick, Dennis *Movie Director, Actor*
%Bauman Hiller Assoc, 5750 Wilshire Blvd, #512, Los Angeles, CA 90036

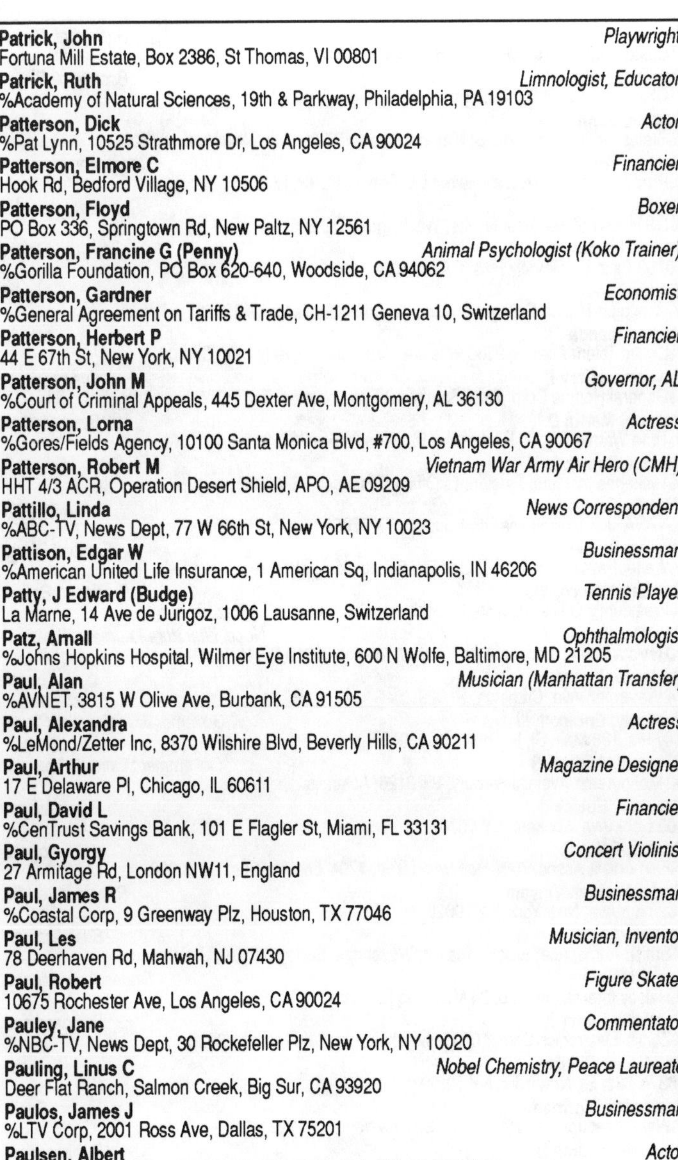

Patrick, John *Playwright*
Fortuna Mill Estate, Box 2386, St Thomas, VI 00801

Patrick, Ruth *Limnologist, Educator*
%Academy of Natural Sciences, 19th & Parkway, Philadelphia, PA 19103

Patterson, Dick *Actor*
%Pat Lynn, 10525 Strathmore Dr, Los Angeles, CA 90024

Patterson, Elmore C *Financier*
Hook Rd, Bedford Village, NY 10506

Patterson, Floyd *Boxer*
PO Box 336, Springtown Rd, New Paltz, NY 12561

Patterson, Francine G (Penny) *Animal Psychologist (Koko Trainer)*
%Gorilla Foundation, PO Box 620-640, Woodside, CA 94062

Patterson, Gardner *Economist*
%General Agreement on Tariffs & Trade, CH-1211 Geneva 10, Switzerland

Patterson, Herbert P *Financier*
44 E 67th St, New York, NY 10021

Patterson, John M *Governor, AL*
%Court of Criminal Appeals, 445 Dexter Ave, Montgomery, AL 36130

Patterson, Lorna *Actress*
%Gores/Fields Agency, 10100 Santa Monica Blvd, #700, Los Angeles, CA 90067

Patterson, Robert M *Vietnam War Army Air Hero (CMH)*
HHT 4/3 ACR, Operation Desert Shield, APO, AE 09209

Pattillo, Linda *News Correspondent*
%ABC-TV, News Dept, 77 W 66th St, New York, NY 10023

Pattison, Edgar W *Businessman*
%American United Life Insurance, 1 American Sq, Indianapolis, IN 46206

Patty, J Edward (Budge) *Tennis Player*
La Marne, 14 Ave de Jurigoz, 1006 Lausanne, Switzerland

Patz, Arnall *Ophthalmologist*
%Johns Hopkins Hospital, Wilmer Eye Institute, 600 N Wolfe, Baltimore, MD 21205

Paul, Alan *Musician (Manhattan Transfer)*
%AVNET, 3815 W Olive Ave, Burbank, CA 91505

Paul, Alexandra *Actress*
%LeMond/Zetter Inc, 8370 Wilshire Blvd, Beverly Hills, CA 90211

Paul, Arthur *Magazine Designer*
17 E Delaware Pl, Chicago, IL 60611

Paul, David L *Financier*
%CenTrust Savings Bank, 101 E Flagler St, Miami, FL 33131

Paul, Gyorgy *Concert Violinist*
27 Armitage Rd, London NW11, England

Paul, James R *Businessman*
%Coastal Corp, 9 Greenway Plz, Houston, TX 77046

Paul, Les *Musician, Inventor*
78 Deerhaven Rd, Mahwah, NJ 07430

Paul, Robert *Figure Skater*
10675 Rochester Ave, Los Angeles, CA 90024

Pauley, Jane *Commentator*
%NBC-TV, News Dept, 30 Rockefeller Plz, New York, NY 10020

Pauling, Linus C *Nobel Chemistry, Peace Laureate*
Deer Flat Ranch, Salmon Creek, Big Sur, CA 93920

Paulos, James J *Businessman*
%LTV Corp, 2001 Ross Ave, Dallas, TX 75201

Paulsen, Albert *Actor*
%Contemporary Artists, 132 Lasky Dr, #B, Beverly Hills, CA 90212

Paulsen, Pat *Comedian*
%Sutton Barth Vennari, 143 S Fairfax Ave, #310, Los Angeles, CA 90046

Paulson, Allen E *Businessman*
%Gulf Stream Aerospace, 5000 Rockwell, Bethany, OK 73008

Paupini, Giuseppe Cardinal *Religious Leader*
Via Rusticucci 13, 00193 Rome, Italy

Pavan, Pietro Cardinal *Religious Leader*
Via Sella Magliana 1240, Ponte Galeria, 00050 Rome, Italy

Pavarotti, Luciano *Opera Singer*
Via Giardini 941, 41040 Saliceta San Giuliano/Modena, Italy

Pavin, Corey *Golfer*
%International Management Group, 1 Erieview Plz, Cleveland, OH 44114

P

Paxson, Jim *Basketball Player*
%Boston Celtics, 151 Merrimac St, Boston, MA 02114

Paxson, John *Basketball Player*
%Chicago Bulls, 980 N Michigan Ave, Chicago, IL 60611

Paxton, John *Editor*
%Statesman's Year-Book, St Martin's Press, 175 5th Ave, New York, NY 10010

Paxton, Tom *Composer, Musician*
%Producers Inc, 5109 Oak Haven Ln, Tampa, FL 33617

Payne, Donald *Representative, NJ*
%US House of Representatives, Washington, DC 20515

Payne, Freda *Singer*
10160 Cielo Dr, Beverly Hills, CA 90210

Payne, Ladell *Educator*
%Randolph-Macon College, President's Office, Ashland, VA 23005

Pays, Amanda *Actress*
%United Talent Agency, 9560 Wilshire Blvd, #501, Beverly Hills, CA 90212

Payson, Jeffrey P *Businessman*
%General Homes Corp, 7322 Southwest Fwy, Houston, TX 77074

Payson, Martin D *Businessman*
%Time Warner Inc, 75 Rockefeller Plz, New York, NY 10019

Payton, Benjamin F *Educator*
%Tuskegee Institute, President's Office, Tuskegee, AL 36088

Payton, Gary *Astronaut*
%NASA, Johnson Space Ctr, Houston, TX 77058

Payton, Walter *Football Player*
%Walter Payton Inc, 1251 E Golf Rd, Schaumburg, IL 60195

Paz Estenssoro, Victor *President, Bolivia*
%President's Office, Palacio de Gobierno, Plaza Murillo, La Paz, Bolivia

Paz, Octavio *Nobel Literature Laureate, Diplomat*
%Revista Vuelta, Leonardo da Vinci 17, Mexico 03910 DF, Mexico

Pazienza, Vinny *Boxer*
64 Waterman Ave, Cranston, RI 02910

Peabody, Endicott, III *Governor, MA; Football Player*
City Plz, 188 Main St, Nashua, NH 03060

Peacock, Andrew S *Government Official, Australia*
30 Monomeath Ave, Canterbury, Vic 3126, Australia

Peacock, Eulace *Track Athlete*
100 Cook Ave, Yonkers, NY 10701

Peaker, E J *Actress*
%Film Artists Assoc, 7080 Hollywood Blvd, #704, Los Angeles, CA 90028

Peale, Norman Vincent *Religious Leader*
1025 5th Ave, New York, NY 10028

Pearce, Austin *Businessman*
%British Aerospace, Brooklands Rd, Weybridge, Surrey KT13 0SJ, England

Pearl, Minnie *Singer, Comedienne*
%Halsey International Co, 24 Music Sq E, Nashville, TN 37203

Pearlman, Jerry K *Businessman*
%Zenith Electronics Corp, 1000 Milwaukee Ave, Glenview, IL 60025

Pearlstein, Philip *Artist*
163 W 88th St, New York, NY 10024

Pearlstine, Norman *Editor*
%Wall Street Journal, 200 Liberty St, New York, NY 10281

Pearson, Andrall E *Businessman*
%Pepisco Inc, Anderson Hill Rd, Purchase, NY 10577

Pearson, David *Auto Racing Driver*
%NASCAR, 1801 Speedway Blvd, Daytona Beach, FL 32015

Pearson, James B *Senator, KS*
%Stroock Stroock & Lavan, 1150 17th St NW, Washington, DC 20036

Pearson, John E *Businessman*
%Northwestern National Life Insurance, 20 Washington S, Minneapolis, MN 55440

Pearson, Louis *Sculptor*
224 12th St, San Francisco, CA 94103

Pearson, Paul G *Educator*
%Miami University, President's Office, Oxford, OH 45056

Pearson, Richard D *Businessman*
%Trans World Airlines, 605 3rd Ave, New York, NY 10158

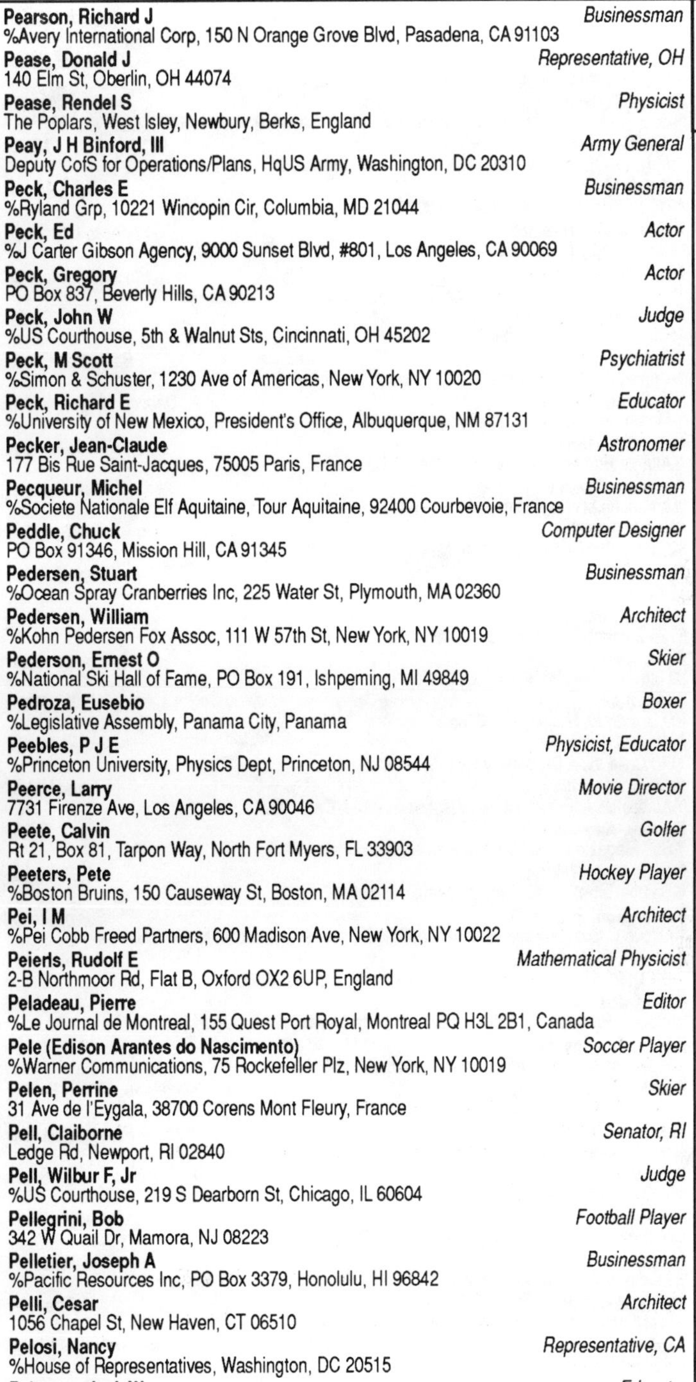

Pearson, Richard J *Businessman*
%Avery International Corp, 150 N Orange Grove Blvd, Pasadena, CA 91103

Pease, Donald J *Representative, OH*
140 Elm St, Oberlin, OH 44074

Pease, Rendel S *Physicist*
The Poplars, West Isley, Newbury, Berks, England

Peay, J H Binford, III *Army General*
Deputy CofS for Operations/Plans, HqUS Army, Washington, DC 20310

Peck, Charles E *Businessman*
%Ryland Grp, 10221 Wincopin Cir, Columbia, MD 21044

Peck, Ed *Actor*
%J Carter Gibson Agency, 9000 Sunset Blvd, #801, Los Angeles, CA 90069

Peck, Gregory *Actor*
PO Box 837, Beverly Hills, CA 90213

Peck, John W *Judge*
%US Courthouse, 5th & Walnut Sts, Cincinnati, OH 45202

Peck, M Scott *Psychiatrist*
%Simon & Schuster, 1230 Ave of Americas, New York, NY 10020

Peck, Richard E *Educator*
%University of New Mexico, President's Office, Albuquerque, NM 87131

Pecker, Jean-Claude *Astronomer*
177 Bis Rue Saint-Jacques, 75005 Paris, France

Pecqueur, Michel *Businessman*
%Societe Nationale Elf Aquitaine, Tour Aquitaine, 92400 Courbevoie, France

Peddle, Chuck *Computer Designer*
PO Box 91346, Mission Hill, CA 91345

Pedersen, Stuart *Businessman*
%Ocean Spray Cranberries Inc, 225 Water St, Plymouth, MA 02360

Pedersen, William *Architect*
%Kohn Pedersen Fox Assoc, 111 W 57th St, New York, NY 10019

Pederson, Ernest O *Skier*
%National Ski Hall of Fame, PO Box 191, Ishpeming, MI 49849

Pedroza, Eusebio *Boxer*
%Legislative Assembly, Panama City, Panama

Peebles, P J E *Physicist, Educator*
%Princeton University, Physics Dept, Princeton, NJ 08544

Peerce, Larry *Movie Director*
7731 Firenze Ave, Los Angeles, CA 90046

Peete, Calvin *Golfer*
Rt 21, Box 81, Tarpon Way, North Fort Myers, FL 33903

Peeters, Pete *Hockey Player*
%Boston Bruins, 150 Causeway St, Boston, MA 02114

Pei, I M *Architect*
%Pei Cobb Freed Partners, 600 Madison Ave, New York, NY 10022

Peierls, Rudolf E *Mathematical Physicist*
2-B Northmoor Rd, Flat B, Oxford OX2 6UP, England

Peladeau, Pierre *Editor*
%Le Journal de Montreal, 155 Quest Port Royal, Montreal PQ H3L 2B1, Canada

Pele (Edison Arantes do Nascimento) *Soccer Player*
%Warner Communications, 75 Rockefeller Plz, New York, NY 10019

Pelen, Perrine *Skier*
31 Ave de l'Eygala, 38700 Corens Mont Fleury, France

Pell, Claiborne *Senator, RI*
Ledge Rd, Newport, RI 02840

Pell, Wilbur F, Jr *Judge*
%US Courthouse, 219 S Dearborn St, Chicago, IL 60604

Pellegrini, Bob *Football Player*
342 W Quail Dr, Mamora, NJ 08223

Pelletier, Joseph A *Businessman*
%Pacific Resources Inc, PO Box 3379, Honolulu, HI 96842

Pelli, Cesar *Architect*
1056 Chapel St, New Haven, CT 06510

Pelosi, Nancy *Representative, CA*
%House of Representatives, Washington, DC 20515

Peltason, Jack W *Educator*
%University of California, Chancellor's Office, Irvine, CA 92717

Pemberton, Brian *Businessman*
%Cable & Wireless PLC, Mercury House, Theobald's Rd, London WC1, England

Pena, Alejandro *Baseball Player*
1713 Germain Dr, Montebello, CA 90640

Pena, Elizabeth *Actress*
%STE Representation, 9301 Wilshire Blvd, #312, Beverly Hills, CA 90210

Pena, Federico *Mayor*
%Mayor's Office, City Hall, 1437 Bannock St, Denver, CO 80202

Pender, Mel *Track Athlete*
4910 Karl's Gate Dr, Marietta, GA 30062

Penderecki, Krzysztof *Composer, Conductor*
Ul Cisowa 22, 30-229 Cracow, Poland

Pendergrass, Henry P *Physician, Educator*
1621 21st Ave S, Nashville, TN 37232

Pendergrass, Teddy *Singer*
1505 Flat Rock Rd, Narberth, PA 19072

Penders, Tom *Basketball Coach*
%University of Texas, Athletic Dept, Austin, TX 78713

Pendleton, Moses *Dancer, Choreographer*
%Momix, PO Box 35, Washington, CT 06793

Pendleton, Terry *Baseball Player*
%Atlanta Braves, PO Box 4064, Atlanta, GA 30302

Penisten, Glenn E *Businessman*
%American Microsystems Inc, 3800 Homestead Ave, Santa Clara, CA 95051

Penn & Teller *Comedians-Illusionists*
%Earth's Center, PO Box 1196, New York, NY 10185

Penn, Arthur *Movie Director*
124 W 60th, New York, NY 10023

Penn, Christopher *Actor*
6728 Zumirez Dr, Malibu, CA 90265

Penn, Irving *Photographer*
89 5th Ave, New York, NY 10011

Penn, Sean *Actor*
PO Box 2630, Malibu, CA 90265

Pennario, Leonard *Concert Pianist*
1140 Calle Vista Dr, Beverly Hills, CA 90210

Pennel, John *Track Athlete*
%Adidas USA, PO Box 4137, Westlake Village, CA 91359

Penney, Alexandra *Editor*
%Self Magazine, 350 Madison Ave, New York, NY 10017

Pennington, Weldon J *Publisher*
%Seattle Times, 1120 John St, Seattle, WA 98111

Pennington, William N *Businessman*
%Circus Circus Enterprises, 2880 Las Vegas Blvd S, Las Vegas, NV 89109

Pennock of Norton, Baron *Businessman*
%BICC, 21 Bloomsbury St, London WC1B 3QN, England

Penny, Joe *Actor*
%Viacom Productions, 100 Universal City Plz, Universal City, CA 91608

Penny, Timothy J (Tim) *Representative, MN*
%House of Representatives, Washington, DC 20515

Penske, Roger *Auto Racing Driver, Builder*
%Penske Corp, 176 Riverside Ave, Red Bank, NJ 07701

Penzias, Arno A *Nobel Physics Laureate*
%Bell Laboratories, Radiophysics Research Dept, Holmdel, NJ 07733

Pep, Willie *Boxer*
36 Wayland St, Hartford, CT 06114

Pepitone, Joe *Baseball Player*
667 E 79th St, Brooklyn, NY 11236

Pepper, John E *Businessman*
%Procter & Gamble Co, 1 Procter & Gamble Plz, Cincinnati, OH 45202

Pepper, Louis H *Financier*
%Washington Mutual Savings Bank, 1101 2nd Ave, Seattle, WA 98101

Peppler, Mary Jo *Volleyball Player*
1103 NW 36th Ave, Gainesville, FL 32609

Perahia, Murray *Concert Pianist*
%Frank Salomon Assoc, 201 W 54th St, #4-C, New York, NY 10019

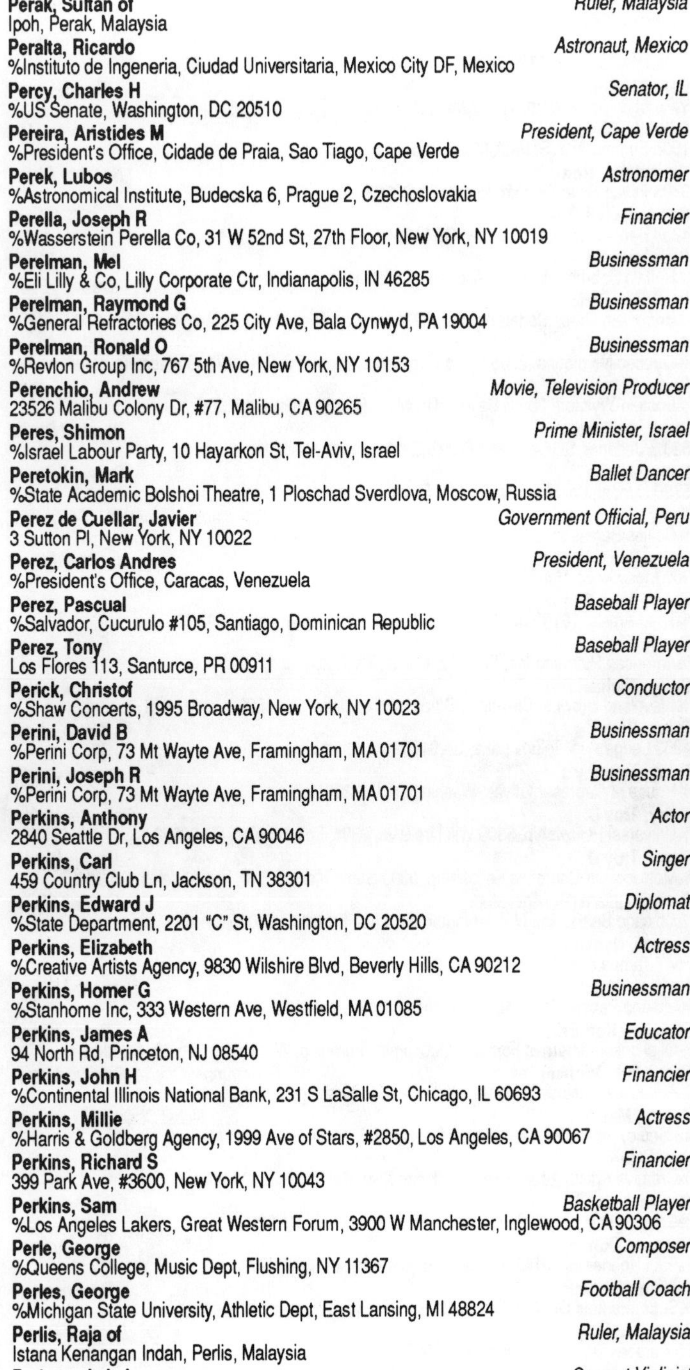

Perak, Sultan of — *Ruler, Malaysia*
Ipoh, Perak, Malaysia

Peralta, Ricardo — *Astronaut, Mexico*
%Instituto de Ingeneria, Ciudad Universitaria, Mexico City DF, Mexico

Percy, Charles H — *Senator, IL*
%US Senate, Washington, DC 20510

Pereira, Aristides M — *President, Cape Verde*
%President's Office, Cidade de Praia, Sao Tiago, Cape Verde

Perek, Lubos — *Astronomer*
%Astronomical Institute, Budecska 6, Prague 2, Czechoslovakia

Perella, Joseph R — *Financier*
%Wasserstein Perella Co, 31 W 52nd St, 27th Floor, New York, NY 10019

Perelman, Mel — *Businessman*
%Eli Lilly & Co, Lilly Corporate Ctr, Indianapolis, IN 46285

Perelman, Raymond G — *Businessman*
%General Refractories Co, 225 City Ave, Bala Cynwyd, PA 19004

Perelman, Ronald O — *Businessman*
%Revlon Group Inc, 767 5th Ave, New York, NY 10153

Perenchio, Andrew — *Movie, Television Producer*
23526 Malibu Colony Dr, #77, Malibu, CA 90265

Peres, Shimon — *Prime Minister, Israel*
%Israel Labour Party, 10 Hayarkon St, Tel-Aviv, Israel

Peretokin, Mark — *Ballet Dancer*
%State Academic Bolshoi Theatre, 1 Ploschad Sverdlova, Moscow, Russia

Perez de Cuellar, Javier — *Government Official, Peru*
3 Sutton Pl, New York, NY 10022

Perez, Carlos Andres — *President, Venezuela*
%President's Office, Caracas, Venezuela

Perez, Pascual — *Baseball Player*
%Salvador, Cucurulo #105, Santiago, Dominican Republic

Perez, Tony — *Baseball Player*
Los Flores 113, Santurce, PR 00911

Perick, Christof — *Conductor*
%Shaw Concerts, 1995 Broadway, New York, NY 10023

Perini, David B — *Businessman*
%Perini Corp, 73 Mt Wayte Ave, Framingham, MA 01701

Perini, Joseph R — *Businessman*
%Perini Corp, 73 Mt Wayte Ave, Framingham, MA 01701

Perkins, Anthony — *Actor*
2840 Seattle Dr, Los Angeles, CA 90046

Perkins, Carl — *Singer*
459 Country Club Ln, Jackson, TN 38301

Perkins, Edward J — *Diplomat*
%State Department, 2201 "C" St, Washington, DC 20520

Perkins, Elizabeth — *Actress*
%Creative Artists Agency, 9830 Wilshire Blvd, Beverly Hills, CA 90212

Perkins, Homer G — *Businessman*
%Stanhome Inc, 333 Western Ave, Westfield, MA 01085

Perkins, James A — *Educator*
94 North Rd, Princeton, NJ 08540

Perkins, John H — *Financier*
%Continental Illinois National Bank, 231 S LaSalle St, Chicago, IL 60693

Perkins, Millie — *Actress*
%Harris & Goldberg Agency, 1999 Ave of Stars, #2850, Los Angeles, CA 90067

Perkins, Richard S — *Financier*
399 Park Ave, #3600, New York, NY 10043

Perkins, Sam — *Basketball Player*
%Los Angeles Lakers, Great Western Forum, 3900 W Manchester, Inglewood, CA 90306

Perle, George — *Composer*
%Queens College, Music Dept, Flushing, NY 11367

Perles, George — *Football Coach*
%Michigan State University, Athletic Dept, East Lansing, MI 48824

Perlis, Raja of — *Ruler, Malaysia*
Istana Kenangan Indah, Perlis, Malaysia

Perlman, Itzhak — *Concert Violinist*
%International Creative Mgmt, 40 W 57th St, New York, NY 10019

P

Perlman, Rhea *Actress*
PO Box 27365, Los Angeles, CA 90027

Perlman, Ron *Actor*
%Badgley Connor, 9229 Sunset Blvd, #607, Los Angeles, CA 90069

Perot, H Ross *Businessman*
%Perot Systems Corp, 12377 Merit Dr, #1600, Dallas, TX 75251

Perpich, Rudy *Governor, MN*
1006 Summit Ave, St Paul, MN 55105

Perranoski, Ron *Baseball Player*
3805 Indian River Dr, Vero Beach, FL 32963

Perreau, Gigi *Actress*
4258 Beeman Ave, Studio City, CA 91604

Perreault, Gil *Hockey Player*
%Buffalo Sabres, Memorial Auditorium, Buffalo, NY 14202

Perrine, Valerie *Actress*
%Borinstein Oreck Bogart Agency, 8271 Melrose Ave, #110, Los Angeles, CA 90046

Perron, Jean *Hockey Coach*
%Quebec Nordiques, 2205 Ave du Colisee, Quebec PQ G1L 4W7, Canada

Perry, Felton *Actor*
%Epstein-Wyckoff, 280 S Beverly Dr, #400, Beverly Hills, CA 90212

Perry, Gaylord *Baseball Player*
320 E Jefferies St, Gaffney, SC 29342

Perry, Jim *Baseball Player*
5720 Duncan Ln, Minneapolis, MN 55436

Perry, Joe *Rock Guitarist (Aerosmith), Songwriter*
%Collins/Barasso Mgmt, 215 1st St, Cambridge, MA 02142

Perry, Joe (Fletcher) *Football Player*
350 Moscow St, San Francisco, CA 94112

Perry, John Bennett *Actor*
%Triad Artists, 10100 Santa Monica Blvd, #1600, Los Angeles, CA 90067

Perry, Ken *Businessman*
%American Petrofina Inc, Fina Plz, Dallas, TX 75206

Perry, Michael Dean *Football Player*
%Cleveland Browns, Cleveland Stadium, Cleveland, OH 45202

Perry, Roger *Actor*
4363 Ledge Ave, Toluca Lake, CA 91602

Perry, Timothy J *Representative, MN*
%House of Representatives, Washington, DC 20515

Perry, Troy D *Religious Leader*
%Universal Fellowship, 5300 Wilshire Blvd, #304, Los Angeles, CA 90029

Perry, Troy D *Religious Leader*
%Metropolitan Churches Fellowship, 5300 Santa Monica Blvd, Los Angeles, CA 90029

Perry, William (Refrigerator) *Football Player*
%Chicago Bears, 250 N Washington Rd, Lake Forest, IL 60045

Persoff, Nehemiah *Actor*
5847 Tampa Ave, Tarzana, CA 91356

Person, Chuck *Basketball Player*
%Indiana Pacers, 30 E Market St, Indianapolis, IN 46204

Persson, Karl-Erik *Businessman*
%Oljekonsumenternas Forbund Eleonomisk Forening, Warfvinges Vag 25, Sweden

Pertschuk, Michael *Government Official, Political Activist*
%Advocacy Institute, 1730 "M" St NW, #600, Washington, DC 20036

Perutz, Max F *Nobel Chemistry Laureate*
42 Sedley Taylor Rd, Cambridge, England

Pesci, Joe *Actor*
%Creative Artists Agency, 9830 Wilshire Blvd, Beverly Hills, CA 90212

Pescia, Lisa *Actress*
%Craig Agency, 8485 Melrose Ave, #E, Los Angeles, CA 90069

Pescow, Donna *Actress*
%Paul Kohner Inc, 9169 Sunset Blvd, Los Angeles, CA 90069

Peskin, Kenneth *Businessman*
%Supermarkets General Corp, 301 Blair Rd, Woodbridge, NJ 07095

Pesky, Johnny *Baseball Player*
25 Parsons Dr, Swampscott, MA 01907

Peter, Valentine J *Religious Leader, Educator*
%Father Flanagan's Boys Home, Boys Town, NE 68010

P

Peterdi, Gabor *Artist*
108 Highland Ave, Rowayton, CT 06853

Peters, Bernadette *Singer, Actress*
277 West End Ave, New York, NY 10023

Peters, Brock *Actor*
PO Box 8156, North Hollywood, CA 91602

Peters, Charles *Editor*
%Washington Monthly, 1711 Connecticut Ave NW, Washington, DC 20009

Peters, Floyd *Football Player, Coach*
%Tampa Bay Buccaneers, 1 Buccaneer Pl, Tampa, FL 33607

Peters, Gary *Baseball Player*
2626 Espanola Ave, Sarasota, FL 33580

Peters, Jean *Actress*
507 N Palm Dr, Beverly Hills, CA 90210

Peters, Jon *Movie Producer*
%Columbia Pictures, 10202 W Washington Blvd, Culver City, CA 90230

Peters, Mary *Track Athlete*
Willowtree Cottage, River Rd, Dunmurray, Belfast, Northern Ireland

Peters, Mike *Editorial Cartoonist (Grimmy)*
%Peters Creative Grp, PO Box 35357, Sarasota, FL 34242

Peters, Roberta *Opera Singer*
64 Garden Rd, Scarsdale, NY 10583

Peters, Tom *Management Consultant, Writer*
%Tom Peters Grp, 505 Hamilton Ave, Palo Alto, CA 94301

Peters, Tony *Football Player*
13408 Sandrock Ct, Chantilly, VA 22021

Petersen, Donald E *Businessman*
%Ford Motor Co, American Rd, Dearborn, MI 48121

Petersen, Forrest S *Test Pilot, Navy Admiral*
%Petersen Baldwin Enterprises, 1217 Evermay Ct, McLean, VA 22101

Petersen, Howard C *Financier*
%Fidelity Bank, Board & Walnut, Philadelphia, PA 19109

Petersen, Raymond J *Publisher*
%Hearst Inc, 958 8th Ave, New York, NY 10019

Petersen, Robert E *Publisher*
%Petersen Publishing Co, 8490 Sunset Blvd, Los Angeles, CA 90069

Petersen, Wolfgang *Movie Director*
%Chasin Agency, 190 N Canon Dr, #201, Beverly Hills, CA 90210

Peterson, Ben *Wrestler*
%Camp of Champs, PO Box 438, Watertown, WI 53094

Peterson, Bruce *Test Pilot*
43665 21st W, Lancaster, CA 93534

Peterson, Chase N *Educator*
%University of Utah, President's Office, Salt Lake City, UT 84112

Peterson, Collin C *Representative, MN*
%House of Representatives, Washington, DC 20515

Peterson, Dave *Photographer*
%Des Moines Register, PO Box 957, Des Moines, IA 50304

Peterson, Dave *Hockey Coach*
%US Hockey Team, 1750 E Boulder St, Colorado Springs, CO 80909

Peterson, Donald H *Astronaut*
427 Pebblebrook, Seabrook, TX 77586

Peterson, Elly *Women's Activist*
1515 "M" St NW, Washington, DC 20005

Peterson, Esther *Consumer Advocate*
7714 13th St NW, Washington, DC 20022

Peterson, Fritz *Baseball Player*
PO Box 1337, Jupiter, FL 33468

Peterson, James R *Businessman*
%Parker Pen Co, 1 Parker Pl, Janesville, WI 53545

Peterson, Oscar *Jazz Pianist, Composer*
%Regal Recordings Ltd, 2421 Hammond Rd, Mississauga ON L5K 1T3, Canada

Peterson, Pete *Representative, FL*
%House of Representatives, Washington, DC 20515

Peterson, Richard H *Businessman*
%Pacific Gas & Electric Co, 77 Beale St, San Francisco, CA 94106

P

Peterson – Pettit

Peterson, Roger Tory — *Ornithologist, Artist*
Neck Rd, Old Lymne, CT 06371

Peterson, Rudolph A — *Financier*
86 Sea View Ave, Piedmont, CA 94611

Peterson, Russell W — *Governor, DE*
1613 N Broom St, Wilmington, DE 19806

Peterson, Sidney R — *Businessman*
%Getty Oil Co, 3810 Wilshire Blvd, Los Angeles, CA 90010

Peterson, Thomas R — *Educator*
%Seton Hall University, President's Office, South Orange, NJ 07079

Peterson, Walter R — *Governor, NH; Educator*
19 East Mountain Rd, Peterborough, NH 03458

Petherbridge, Edward — *Actor*
%Duncan Heath, 162/70 Wardour St, London W1V 5A7, England

Petibon, Richie — *Football Player, Coach*
%Washington Redskins, Dulles Airport, Box 17247, Washington, DC 20041

Petit, Philippe — *Tight Rope Walker*
%Cathedral of Saint John the Devine, 1047 Amsterdam Ave, New York, NY 10025

Petit, Roland — *Ballet Dancer, Choreographer*
%Ballet National Marseille, Pl Auguste-Carli, 13001 Marseilles, France

Petraglia, Johnny — *Bowler*
%Professional Bowlers Assn, 1720 Merriman Rd, Akron, OH 44313

Petranoff, Tom — *Track Athlete*
%Anheuser-Busch Inc, PO Box 2113, Los Angeles, CA 90051

Petrassi, Goffredo — *Composer*
Via Ferdinando di Savoia 3, 00196 Rome, Italy

Petri, Thomas E — *Representative, WI*
%House of Representatives, Washington, DC 20515

Petrie, Daniel, Sr — *Movie, Theatre Director*
8457 Melrose Pl, #200, Los Angeles, CA 90069

Petrie, Geoff — *Basketball Player*
%Portland Trail Blazers, 700 NE Multnomah St, Portland, OR 97232

Petrie, George O — *Actor*
%Gage Group, 9255 Sunset Blvd, #515, Los Angeles, CA 90069

Petrie, Milton — *Businessman*
%Petrie Stores Corp, 70 Enterprise Corp, Secaucus, NJ 07904

Petrocelli, Rico — *Baseball Player*
19 Townsend Rd, Lynnfield, MA 01940

Petrone, Rocco A — *Missile Engineer*
1329 Grandvia Altamira, Palos Verdes Estates, CA 90274

Petrosian, Tigran — *Chess Player*
%Physical Culture & Sports Committee, Skaterny Pereulok, Moscow, Russia

Petrov, Vasily — *Army Marshal, Russia*
%Ministry of Defense, 34 Naberezhnaya M Thoreza, Moscow, Russia

Petrovics, Emil — *Composer*
Naprafprgp Utca 9/A, 1021 Budapest, Hungary

Petry, Dan — *Baseball Player*
1808 Cartlen Dr, Placentia, CA 92670

Petry, Thomas E — *Businessman*
%Eagle-Picher Industries, 580 Walnut St, Cincinnati, OH 45202

Pett, Joe — *Editorial Cartoonist*
%Lexington Herald-Leader, Main & Midland, Lexington, KY 40507

Pettet, Joanna — *Actress*
%Gores/Fields Agency, 10100 Santa Monica Blvd, #700, Los Angeles, CA 90067

Pettigrew, L Eudora — *Educator*
%State University of New York, President's Office, Old Westbury, NY 11568

Pettijohn, Francis J — *Geologist*
512 Woodbine Ave, Towson, MD 21204

Pettinga, Cornelius W — *Businessman*
%Eli Lilly & Co, Lilly Corporate Ctr, Indianapolis, IN 46285

Pettingill, Gordon H — *Space Scientist*
%Massachusetts Institute of Technology, Space Research Ctr, Cambridge, MA 02139

Pettit, Bob (Robert L, Jr) — *Basketball Player*
1837 Longwood Dr, Baton Rouge, LA 70808

Pettit, Joseph M — *Educator*
%Georgia Insitute of Technology, President's Office, Atlanta, GA 30332

Petty, Kyle *Auto Racing Driver*
%Vandercook Co, Smith Tower, #400, Hwy 29, Harrisburg, NC 28075

Petty, Richard *Auto Racing Driver*
Rt 3, Box 631, Randleman, NC 27317

Petty, Tom *Singer*
%Tom Petty & the Heartbreakers, PO Box 833, San Francisco, CA 94101

Petty, Travis H *Businessman*
%El Paso Natural Gas Co, 1 Paul Kayser Ctr, El Paso, TX 79978

Peyser, Penny *Actress*
%J Michael Bloom Ltd, 9200 Sunset Blvd, #710, Los Angeles, CA 90069

Pezzano, Chuck *Bowling Writer*
%Professional Bowlers Assn, 1720 Merriman Rd, Akron, OH 44313

Pfaffmann, Carl *Physiological Psychologist*
1 Gracie Terr, New York, NY 10028

Pfann, George R *Football Player*
120 Warwick Pl, Ithaca, NY 14850

Pfeifer, Friedl *Skier*
6430 E Hummingbird Ln, Paradise Valley, AZ 85253

Pfeiffer, Carl E *Businessman*
%Quanex Corp, 1900 W Loop S, Houston, TX 77027

Pfeiffer, Doug *Ski Instructor, Editor*
PO Box 1806, Big Bear Lake, CA 92315

Pfeiffer, Eckhard *Businessman*
%Compaq Computer Corp, 20333 FM 149, Houston, TX 77070

Pfeiffer, Michelle *Actress*
%International Creative Mgmt, 8899 Beverly Blvd, Los Angeles, CA 90048

Pfeiffer, Norman *Architect*
%Hardy Holzman Pfeiffer, 811 W 7th St, Los Angeles, CA 90017

Pfeiffer, Robert J *Businessman*
%Alexander & Baldwin Inc, 822 Bishop St, Honolulu, HI 96801

Pflimlin, Pierre *Prime Minister, France*
24 Ave de la Paix, 67000 Strasbourg, France

Pflug, Jo Ann *Actress*
200 Jungle Rd, Palm Beach, FL 33480

Phelan, John J *Businessman*
%Stride Rite Corp, 5 Cambridge Ctr, Cambridge, MA 02142

Phelps, Ashton, Jr *Publisher*
%New Orleans Times-Picayune, 3800 Howard Ave, New Orleans, LA 70140

Phelps, Edwin F *Businessman*
%Crane Co, 757 3rd Ave, New York, NY 10017

Phelps, Gordon (Babe) *Baseball Player*
1417 Hale St, Odenton, MD 21113

Philbin, Regis *Entertainer*
955 Park Ave, New York, NY 10028

Philbrick, Herbert *Writer, Counter Spy*
%General Delivery, North Hampton, NH 03862

Philip *Crown Prince, England*
Buckingham Palace, London SW1, England

Philip (Saliba), Primate *Religious Leader*
%Antiochian Orthodox Christian Church, 358 Mountain Rd, Englewood, NJ 07631

Philips, Jesse *Businessman*
%Philips Industries, 4801 Springfield St, Dayton, OH 45401

Phillip, Andy *Basketball Player*
PO Box 385, Rancho Mirage, CA 92270

Phillips, Carol *Businesswoman, Editor*
%Clinique Laboratories Inc, 767 5th Ave, New York, NY 10022

Phillips, Chynna *Singer, Actress*
%International Creative Mgmt, 8899 Beverly Blvd, Los Angeles, CA 90048

Phillips, Edward E *Businessman*
%New England Mutual Life Insurance, 501 Boylston St, Boston, MA 02117

Phillips, Graham *Businessman*
%Ogilvy & Mather Worldwide, 2 E 48th St, New York, NY 10017

Phillips, Harry *Judge*
2809 Wimbledon Rd, Nashville, TN 37215

Phillips, Harry J, Sr *Businessman*
%Browning-Ferris Industries, 14701 St Mary's, Houston, TX 77079

Phillips, Harvey *Concert Tuba Player*
%TubaRanch, 4769 S Harrell Rd, Bloomington, IN 47401

Phillips, Howard *Public Policy Anaylst*
%Conservative Caucus, 47 West St, Boston, MA 02115

Phillips, James D, Jr *Judge*
%US Court of Appeals, PO Box 3617, Durham, NC 27702

Phillips, John *Singer (Mamas & Papas), Songwriter*
Marmont, Langham HS, 302 Regent St, London W1, England

Phillips, John G *Businessman*
%Louisiana Land & Exploration Co, 225 Baronne St, New Orleans, LA 70112

Phillips, Julianne *Actress*
%Gersh Agency, 232 N Canon Dr, Beverly Hills, CA 90210

Phillips, Kristie *Gymnast*
%Karolyi's World Gym, 17203 Bamwood Dr, Houston, TX 77090

Phillips, Lawrence S *Businessman*
%Phillips-Van Heusen Corp, 1290 Ave of Americas, New York, NY 10104

Phillips, Lou Diamond *Actor*
%Harris & Goldberg Agency, 1999 Ave of Stars, #2850, Los Angeles, CA 90067

Phillips, Mackenzie *Actress*
%Baker & McKenzie, 805 3rd Ave, New York, NY 10022

Phillips, Michelle *Actress, Singer (Mamas & Papas)*
PO Box 396, Reseda, CA 91337

Phillips, Norma *Social Activist*
%Mothers Against Drunk Driving, PO Box 819100, Dallas, TX 75381

Phillips, Robert M *Businessman*
%Chesebrough-Pond's Inc, Westport, CT 06881

Phillips, Robert W *Astronaut*
%MATSCO, 1050 Bay Area Blvd, Houston, TX 77058

Phillips, Sian *Actress*
%Saraband Agency, 153 Petherton Rd, Highbury, London N5, England

Phillips, Stone *Commentator*
%NBC-TV, News Dept, 30 Rockefeller Plz, New York, Ny 10020

Phillips, Thomas L *Businessman*
%Raytheon Co, 141 Spring St, Lexington, MA 02173

Phillips, Warren H *Businessman*
%Dow Jones Co, 200 Liberty St, New York, NY 10281

Phillips, Wendy *Actress*
%STE Representation, 9301 Wilshire Blvd, #312, Beverly Hills, CA 90210

Phillips, William *Editor, Writer*
%Partisan Review, 121 Bay State Rd, Boston, MA 02215

Phillips, William E *Businessman*
%Ogilvy Group, Inc, 2 E 48th St, New York, NY 10017

Phipps, Ogden M *Financier, Thoroughbred Racing Executive*
%Belmont Park, PO Box 90, Jamaica, NY 11417

Phoenix, River *Actor*
1450 Belfast Dr, Los Angeles, CA 90069

Phomvihane, Kaysone *Prime Minister, Laos*
%Prime Minister's Office, Vietiane, Laos

Phoumi Vongvichit *President, Laos*
%President's Office, Vientiane, Laos

Piaget, Jean *Psychologist*
%Geneva University, Psychology & Education Dept, Geneva, Switzerland

Piazza, Marguerite *Opera Singer*
6018 River Oaks Rd, Memphis, TN 38138

Picachy, Lawrence Cardinal *Religious Leader*
%Archbishop's House, 32 Park St, Calcutta 700016, India

Picard, Dennis J *Businessman*
%Raytheon Co, 141 Spring St, Lexington, MA 02173

Picard, Henry *Golfer*
13 Formosa Dr, Charleston, SC 29407

Picardo, Robert *Actor*
%"Wonder Years" Show, ABC-TV, 2040 Ave of Stars, Los Angeles, CA 90067

Picasso, Paloma *Jewelry Designer*
%Tiffany Co, 727 5th Ave, New York, NY 10022

Piccard, Franck *Skier*
%Olympic Committee, 23 Rue d'Anjou, 75008 Paris, France

Piccard, Jacques *Underwater Scientist*
19 Ave de l'Avenir, 1012 Lausanne, Switzerland

Piccone, Robin *Fashion Designer*
%Piccone Apparel Corp, 1424 Washington Blvd, Venice, CA 90291

Picerni, Paul *Actor*
19119 Wells Dr, Tarzana, CA 91356

Pichler, Joseph A *Businessman*
%Kroger Co, 1014 Vine St, Cincinnati, OH 45202

Pickel, Bill *Football Player*
%Los Angeles Raiders, 332 Center St, El Segundo, CA 90245

Pickens, T Boone, Jr *Businessman*
%Mesa Limited Partnership, 1 Mesa Sq, Amarillo, TX 79189

Pickering, Thomas R *Diplomat*
%Department of State, 2201 "C" St NW, Washington, DC 20520

Pickering, William H *Scientist, Educator*
292 St Katherine Dr, Flintridge, CA 91011

Pickett, Bobby (Boris) *Singer*
%WPLJ-FM Radio, 2 Penn Plz, New York, NY 10121

Pickett, Cindy *Actress*
%William Morris Agency, 151 El Camino, Beverly Hills, CA 90212

Pickett, Owen B *Representative, VA*
%House of Representatives, Washington, DC 20515

Pickle, J J *Representative, TX*
%House of Representatives, Washington, DC 20515

Pickles, Christina *Actress*
137 S Westgate Ave, Los Angeles, CA 90049

Picon, Molly *Actress*
1 Lincoln Plz, #35-E, New York, NY 10023

Piel, Gerard *Editor, Publisher*
%Scientific American Magazine, 415 Madison Ave, New York, NY 10017

Piel, Jonathan *Editor*
%Scientific American Magazine, 415 Madison Ave, New York, NY 10017

Pierce, Billy *Baseball Player*
9000 S Francisco, Evergreen Park, IL 60642

Pierce, James R *Publisher*
27 Bulkridge Dr, Amherst, NH 03031

Pierce, John R *Electrical Engineer*
931 Canon Dr, Pasadena, CA 91106

Pierce, Lawrence W *Judge*
%US Court of Appeals, US Courthouse, Foley Sq, New York, NY 10007

Pierce, Rickey *Basketball Player*
%Seattle SuperSonics, 190 Queen Ave N, Seattle, WA 98109

Pierce, Scott *Businessman*
%E F Hutton Grp, 1 Battery Park Plz, New York, NY 10004

Piergallini, Alfred A *Businessman*
%Gerber Products Co, 445 State St, Fremont, MI 49412

Pieroni, Leonard *Businessman*
%Parsons Corp, 100 W Walnut St, Pasadena, CA 91124

Pierpoint, Robert *Commentator*
%CBS-TV, News Dept, 2020 "M" St NW, Washington, DC 20036

Pierson, Jean *Businessman*
%Airbus-Industrie, 5 Ave de Villiers, 75017 Paris, France

Pierson, Markus *Sculptor*
%OutWest, 7216-F Washington NE, Albuquerque, NM 87109

Pierson, Robert D *Financier*
%Carteret Savings & Loan, 200 South St, Morristown, NJ 07960

Pietrangeli, Nicola *Tennis Player*
Via Eustachio Manfredi 15, Rome, Italy

Pietruski, John M *Businessman*
%Sterling Drug Inc, 90 Park Ave, New York, NY 10016

Pifer, Alan *Foundation Executive*
311 Greens Farms Rd, Greens Farms, CT 06436

Pigford, Robert L *Chemical Engineer*
300 Wilson Rd, Newark, DE 19711

Piggott, Lester *Thoroughbred Racing Jockey*
Florizel, Newmarket, Suffolk, England

P

Pigott Smith, Tim *Actor*
%Michael Whitehall, 125 Gloucester Rd, London SW7, England

Pigott, Charles M *Businessman*
%Paccar Inc, 777 106th Ave NE, Bellevue, WA 98004

Pigott, John A *Businessman*
%Anixter Bros Inc, 4711 Golf Rd, Skokie, IL 60076

Pigott, Richard J *Businessman*
%Beatrice Companies, 2 N LaSalle St, Chicago, IL 60602

Pihos, Pete *Football Player*
%Regal Home Improvement Co, 1600 Altamont Ave, Richmond, VA 23230

Pilarczyk, Daniel *Religious Leader*
%National Conference of Catholic Bishops, 3211 4th St, Washington, DC 20017

Pilkington, Alastir *Glass Engineer, Businessman*
%Pilkington Brothers, Prescot Rd, Merseyside WA10 8DH, England

Pillard, Charles H *Labor Leader*
%Electrical Workers Union, 1125 15th St NW, Washington, DC 20005

Pilliod, Charles J, Jr *Businessman, Diplomat*
%US Embassy, Paseo de la Reforma 305, Mexico City DF, Mexico

Pillsbury, Edward P *Museum Director*
%Kimbell Art Museum, 3333 Camp Bowie Blvd, Fort Worth, TX 76107

Pilous, Rudy *Hockey Coach, Executive*
%Toronto Maple Leafs, 60 Carlton St, Toronto ON M5B 1L1, Canada

Pilson, Neal H *Television Executive*
%CBS-TV, Sports Dept, 51 W 52nd St, New York, NY 10019

Pimenta, Simon Ignatius Cardinal *Religious Leader*
Archbishop's House, 21 N Parekh Marg, Bombay 400 039, India

Pinchot, Bronson *Actor*
%STE Representation, 9301 Wilshire Blvd, #312, Beverly Hills, CA 90210

Pinckney, Ed *Basketball Player*
%Boston Celtics, 151 Merrimac St, Boston, MA 02115

Pincus, Lionel I *Financier*
%E M Warburg, Pincus & Co, 277 Park Ave, New York, NY 10017

Pindling, Lynden Oscar *Prime Minister, Bahamas*
%Prime Minister's Office, PO Box N-7147, Nassau, Bahamas

Pine, Robert *Actor*
3975 Van Noord Ave, Studio City, CA 91604

Pineau-Valencienne, Didier *Businessman*
%Schneider, 42 Rue d'Anjou, 75008 Paris, France

Pinera, Mike *Singer*
812 Briny Ave, #12-D, Pompano Beach, FL 33062

Pinero, Miguel *Playwright, Poet*
%Neal Gantcher, 1370 Ave of Americas, New York, NY 10019

Ping, Charles J *Educator*
%Ohio University, President's Office, Athens, OH 45701

Pingel, John *Football Player*
582 Peach Tree Ln, Grosse Pointe Woods, MI 48236

Pingree, David *Educator*
%Brown University, History of Math Dept, Providence, RI 02912

Piniella, Lou *Baseball Player, Manager*
103 MacIntyre Ln, Allendale, NJ 07401

Pinkett, Allen *Football Player*
%New Orleans Saints, 6928 Saints Dr, Metairie, LA 70003

Pinkham, Mary Ellen *Writer, Columnist*
4264 Cambridge St, Saint Louis Park, MN 48236

Pinnock, Trevor *Conductor*
35 Gloucester Crescent, London NW1 7DL, England

Pinochet Ugarte, Augusto *President, Chile*
%Palacio de la Moneda, Santiago, Chile

Pinson, Vada *Baseball Player*
710 31st St, Oakland, CA 94609

Pintasilgo, Maria de Lourdes *Premier, Portugal*
Almeda Santo Antonio dos Capuchos 4-5, 1100 Lisbon, Portugal

Pintauro, Danny *Actor*
%Agency for Performing Arts, 9000 Sunset Blvd, #1200, Los Angeles, CA 90069

Pinter, Harold *Playwright*
%ACTAC, 16 Cadogan Ln, London SW1, England 33403

Piore, Emanuel R *Physicist*
115 Central Park West, New York, NY 10023

Piper, John *Artist, Writer*
Fawley Bottom Farmhouse, Henley-on Thames, Oxon, England

Pippen, Scottie *Basketball Player*
%Chicago Bulls, 980 N Michigan Ave, Chicago, IL 60611

Piraro, Dan *Cartoonist (Bizarro)*
%Chronicle Features, 870 Market St, San Francisco, CA 94102

Pires de Miranda, Pedro *Businessman*
%Petroleos de Portugal, R Flores 7, 1200 Lisbon, Portugal

Pires, Pedro *Prime Minister, Cape Verde*
%Prime Minister's Office, Praia, Cape Verde

Pirie, Robert S *Financier*
%Rothschild Inc, 1 Rockefeller Plz, New York, NY 10020

Pironio, Eduardo Cardinal *Religious Leader*
Piazza del S Uffizio 11, 00193 Rome, Italy

Piscopo, Joe *Actor*
%William Morris Agency, 151 El Camino, Beverly Hills, CA 90212

Pisier, Marie-France *Actress*
19 Rue Servandoni 75006 Paris, France

Pistner, Stephen L *Businessman*
%McCrory Corp, 888 7th St, New York, NY 10019

Pistor, Charles H, Jr *Financier*
%NorthPark National Bank, 1300 N Park Center, Dallas, TX 75225

Pitino, Rick *Basketball Coach*
%University of Kentucky, Athletic Dept, Lexington, KY 40536

Pitman, Charles H *Marine Corps General*
%Deputy Chief Staff Aviation, Marine Corps Headquarters, Washington, DC 20380

Pitney, Gene *Singer*
%David McGrath, 6046 37th Ave, Kenosha, WI 53142

Pitou Zimmerman, Penny *Skier*
%Penny Pitou Travel, 55 Canal St, Laconia, NH 03246

Pitt, Earle W *Businessman*
%Foxboro Co, Bristol Park, Foxboro, MA 02035

Pittendrigh, Colin S *Biologist*
26240 Jeanette Rd, Salinas, CA 93908

Pittman, R F *Publisher*
%Tampa Tribune, 202 S Parker St, Tampa, FL 33601

Pittman, Richard A *Vietnam War Marine Corps Hero (CMH)*
216 Rancho Del Oro Dr, #4, Oceanside, CA 92057

Pittman, Robert *Television Executive*
%Time Warner Enterprises, 75 Rockefeller Plz, New York, NY 10019

Pitts, Tyrone S *Religious Leader*
%Progressive National Baptist Convention, 601 50th St NE, Washington, DC 20019

Pitzer, Kenneth S *Chemist*
12 Eagle Hill, Berkeley, CA 94707

Place, B C Godfrey *WW II Royal Navy Hero (VC), Admiral*
Old Bakery, Corton Denham, Sherbourne, Dorset DT9 4LR, England

Place, Mary Kay *Actress*
2739 Motor Ave, Los Angeles, CA 90064

Plager, S Jay *Judge*
%US Court of Appeals, 7171 Madison Pl NW, Washington, DC 20439

Plaidy, Jean *Writer*
%G P Putnam's Sons, 200 Madison Ave, New York, NY 10166

Plain, Belva *Writer*
%Delacorte Press, 666 5th Ave, New York, NY 10103

Planchon, Roger *Theatre Director, Playwright*
8 Rue Michel-Servet, 69100 Villeurbanne, France

Planinc, Milka *Prime Minister, Yugoslavia*
%Federal Executive Council, Bul Lenjina 2, 11075 Novi Belgrad, Yugoslavia

Plano, Richard J *Physicist*
PO Box 306, Middlebush, NJ 08873

Plant, Robert *Singer, Composer*
484 Kings Rd, London SW10 0LF, England

Plante, William M *Commentator*
%CBS-TV, News Dept, 2020 "M" St NW, Washington, DC 20036

Platini, Michel *Soccer Player*
%Michel Platini Sports Ctr, St Cyprien, France

Platon, Nicolas *Archaeologist*
Leof Alexandras 126, Athens 704, Greece

Platt, Howard *Businessman*
%United States Shoe Corp, 1 Eastwood Dr, Cincinnati, OH 45227

Platts, John H *Businessman*
%Whirlpool Corp, 2000 US 33 N, Benton Harbor, MI 49022

Playten, Alice *Actress*
33 5th Ave, New York, NY 10003

Pleasence, Donald *Actor*
7 W Eton Pl, Mews, London W1, England

Pleau, Larry *Hockey Coach*
%Hartford Whalers, 1 Civic Center Plz, Hartford, CT 06103

Pleshette, Suzanne *Actress*
PO Box 1492, Beverly Hills, CA 90213

Pletcher, Eldon *Editorial Cartoonist*
%Times-Picayune/States-Item, 3800 Howard Ave, New Orleans, LA 70140

Plettner, Bernhard *Businessman*
%Siemens A G, Wittelsbacherplatz 2, 8000 Munich 2, Germany

Plettner, Helmut *Businessman*
%Bosch-Siemens Hausgerate, Hochstrasse 17, 8000 Munich 80, Germany

Pleven, Rene *Prime Minister, France*
12 Rue Chateaubriand, Dinan, Cotes-du-Nord, France

Plimpton, Calvin H *Physician*
%Downstate Medical Ctr, 450 Clarkson Ave, Brooklyn, NY 11203

Plimpton, George *Writer*
541 E 72nd St, New York, NY 10021

Plimpton, Martha *Actress*
%International Creative Mgmt, 8899 Beverly Blvd, Los Angeles, CA 90048

Plisetskaya, Maiya *Ballerina*
%State Academic Bolshoi Theatre, 1 Ploshchad Sverdlova, Moscow, Russia

Pliska, Paul *Opera Singer*
%Metropolitan Opera Assn, Lincoln Ctr, New York, NY 10023

Plotkin, Stanley A *Medical Virologist*
3940 Delancey St, Philadelphia, PA 19104

Plowright, Joan *Actress*
70 Roebuck House, Palace St, London SW1, England

Plumb, Eve *Actress*
%Marshak-Wyckoff Assoc, 280 S Beverly Dr, #400, Beverly Hills, CA 90212

Plummer, Amanda *Actress*
49 Wampum Hill Rd, Weston, CT 06883

Plummer, Christopher *Actor*
49 Wampum Hill Rd, Weston, CT 06883

Plunkett, Hugh V, Jr *Businessman*
%Mutual of Omaha Life Insurance, Mutual of Omaha Plz, Omaha, NE 68175

Plunkett, Jim (James W, Jr) *Football Player*
51 Kilroy Way, Atherton, CA 94025

Pocklington, Peter *Hockey Executive*
%Edmonton Oilers, Northlands Coliseum, Edmonton AB T5B 4M9, Canada

Podhoretz, Norman *Editor, Writer*
%Commentary Magazine, 165 E 56th St, New York, NY 10022

Podres, Johnny *Baseball Player*
1 Colonial Ct, Glen Falls, NY 12801

Pogorelich, Ivo *Concert Pianist*
%Kantor Concert Mgmt, 30 Weymouth St, London W1N 3FA, England

Pogrebin, Letty Cottin *Editor, Writer*
33 W 67th St, New York, NY 10023

Pogue, Mack *Businessman*
%Lincoln Property Co, 2 Turtle Creek, #1800, Dallas, TX 75219

Pogue, William R *Astronaut*
%William R Pogue Assoc, 1101 S Old Missouri Rd, #30, Springdale, AR 72764

Pohl, Dan *Golfer*
11609 S Tusaye Ct, Phoenix, AZ 85044

Pohlad, Carl R *Baseball Executive*
%Minnesota Twins, 501 Chicago Ave S, Minneapolis, MN 55415

Poile, N A (Bud) *Hockey Executive*
%International Hockey League, 3850 Priority Way S Dr, Indianapolis, IN 46240

Poitier, Sidney *Actor*
1007 Cove Way, Beverly Hills, CA 90210

Polanyi, John C *Nobel Chemistry Laureate*
%University of Toronto, Chemistry Dept, Toronto ON M5S 1A1, Canada

Poletti, Ugo Cardinal *Religious Leader*
Vicario di Roma, Piazza S Giovanni in Laterano 6, 00184 Rome, Italy

Poling, Harold A *Businessman*
%Ford Motor Co, American Rd, Dearborn, MI 48121

Politz, Henry A *Judge*
%US Court of Appeals, 500 Fannin St, Shreveport, LA 71101

Polk, George *Businessman*
%Alberto-Culver Co, 2525 Armitage Ave, Melrose Beach, FL 60160

Poll, Sylvia *Swimmer*
Telefono 32-19-81, Apartado 7368, San Jose, Costa Rica

Polla, Dennis L *Microbiotics Engineer*
%University of Minnesota, Electrical Engineering Dept, Minneapolis, MN 55455

Pollack, Daniel *Concert Pianist*
1323 Sierra Alta Way, Los Angeles, CA 90069

Pollack, Jim *Actor*
%Erika Wain Agency, 1418 N Highland Ave, #102, Los Angeles, CA 90028

Pollack, Joseph *Labor Leader*
%Insurance Workers Union, 1017 12th St NW, Washington, DC 20005

Pollack, Milton *Judge*
%US District Court, US Courthouse, Foley Sq, New York, NY 10007

Pollak, Cheryl A *Actress*
%Gersh Agency, 232 N Canon Dr, Beverly Hills, CA 90210

Pollan, Tracy *Actress*
3960 Laurel Canyon Blvd, Studio City, CA 91604

Pollard, C William *Businessman*
%ServiceMaster Industries, 2300 Warrenville Rd, Downers Grove, IL 60515

Pollard, Carl F *Businessman*
%Humana Inc, 500 W Main St, Louisville, KY 40201

Pollard, Jim (James C) *Basketball Player*
7400 NW 16th St, Plantation, FL 33313

Pollard, La Tanya *Basketball Player*
%California State University, Athletic Dept, Long Beach, CA 90840

Pollard, Michael J *Actor*
%Yvette Bikoff Agency, 8721 Santa Monica Blvd, #21, West Hollywood, CA 90067

Pollin, Abe *Basketball, Hockey Executive*
%Centre Grp, Capital Centre, 1 Harry Truman Dr, Landover, MD 20785

Pollock, John T *Businessman*
%Dorsey Corp, 400 W 45th St, Chattanooga, TN 37401

Pollock, Michael *Admiral of the Fleet, England*
Ivy House, Churchstoke, Montgomery, Powys SY15 6DU, Wales

Pollock, Thomas *Entertainment Executive*
%Universal Pictures, 100 Universal City Plz, Universal City, CA 91608

Polyakov, Valery *Cosmonaut*
141 160 Svyosdny Gorodok, Moskovskoi Oblasti, Potchta Kosmonavtov, Russia

Polynice, Olden *Basketball Player*
%Los Angeles Clippers, Sports Arena, 3939 S Figueroa St, Los Angeles, CA 90037

Pomeroy, Wardell B *Psychotherapist*
1611 Vallejo St, San Francisco, CA 94123

Pomodora, Arnaldo *Sculptor*
Via Vigevano 5, 20144 Milan, Italy

Ponazecki, Joe *Actor*
%Don Buchwald Assoc, 10 E 44th St, New York, NY 10017

Ponce Enrile, Juan *Government Official, Philippines*
2305 Morado St, Dasmarinas Village, Makati, Metro Manila, Philippines

Pond, Norman H *Businessman*
%Varian Assoc, 611 Hansen Way, Palo Alto, CA 94303

Ponder, Henry *Educator*
%Fisk University, President's Office, Nashville, TN 37208

Ponnamperuma, Cyril A *Chemist*
%University of Maryland, Chemical Evolution Laboratory, College Park, MD 20742

P

Pons – Porter

Pons, B Stanley *Chemist*
%University of Utah, Chemistry Dept, Eyring Bldg, Salt Lake City, UT 84112

Pons, Juan *Opera Singer*
%Columbia Artists Mgmt Inc, 165 W 57th St, New York, NY 10019

Pont, Johnny *Football Coach*
%Equitable Assurance Society, 3900 Carew Tower, Cincinnati, OH 45202

Ponti, Carlo *Movie Producer*
71 Ave George V, 75006 Paris, France

Ponti, Michael *Concert Pianist*
Heubergstrasse 32, 8716 Eschenlohe, Germany

Pontikes, Kenneth N *Businessman*
%Comdisco Inc, 6400 Shafer Ct, Rosemont, IL 60018

Ponzini, Anthony *Actor*
%Harry Gold Assoc, 3500 W Olive Ave, #1400, Burbank, CA 91505

Pool, John L *Cancer Surgeon*
560 Belden Hill Rd, Wilton, CT 06897

Poole, Barney *Football Player*
111 Saratoga Cir, Hattisburg, MS 39401

Poole, Cecil F *Judge*
%US Court of Appeals, Court Bldg, San Francisco, CA 94101

Poole, William *Government Official, Economist*
%Council of Economic Advisers, Old Executive Office Bldg, Washington, DC 20500

Pooley, Don *Golfer*
PO Box 35352, Tucson, AZ 85740

Poons, Larry *Artist*
831 Broadway, New York, NY 10003

Pope, Edwin *Sportswriter*
%Miami Herald, 1 Herald Plz, Miami, FL 33101

Pope, Everett P *WW II Marine Corps Hero (CMH)*
4 Water Oak, Fern Beach, FL 32034

Pope, Paula Jean Myers *Diver*
415 Del Norte Rd, Ojai, CA 93023

Pope, Peter T *Businessman*
%Pope & Talbot Inc, 1500 SW 1st Ave, Portland, OR 97201

Pope-Hennessy, John W *Museum Director, Historian*
1130 Park Ave, New York, NY 10028

Popejoy, William J *Financier*
%Financial Corp of America, 18401 Von Karman Ave, Irvine, CA 92715

Popoff, Frank *Businessman*
%Dow Chemical Co, 2030 William H Dow Ctr, Midland, MI 48674

Popov, Leonid *Cosmonaut*
141 160 Svyosdny Gorodok, Moskovskoi Oblasti, Potchta Kosmonavtov, Russia

Popov, Oleg *Actor*
%Organization of State Circuses, 15 Neglinnaya Ul, Moscow, Russia

Popovich, Pavel R *Cosmonaut*
141 160 Svyosdny Gorodok, Moskovskoi Oblasti, Potchta Kosmonavtov, Russia

Poppa, Ryal R *Businessman*
%StorageTek, 2270 S 88th St, Louisville, CO 80028

Popper, Karl *Philosopher*
136 Welcomes Rd, Kenley, Surrey CR2 5HH, England

Popwell, Albert *Actor*
1830 N Bronson Ave, Los Angeles, CA 90028

Pordy, Leon *Businessman*
%Chock Full o' Nuts Corp, 425 Lexington Ave, New York, NY 10017

Porizkova, Paulina *Model, Actress*
%Elite Model Mgmt, 111 E 22nd St, New York, NY 10010

Porsche, Ferdinand *Businessman*
%Porsche Dr Ing HCF, Porschenstrasse 42, 7000 Stutthart 40, Germany

Porteous, Patrick A *WW II British Army Hero (VC)*
Christmas Cottage, Church Ln, Funtington, West Sussex PO 18 9LQ, England

Porter, David H *Educator*
%Skidmore College, President's Office, Saratoga Springs, NY 12866

Porter, Don *Actor*
%William Morris Agency, 151 El Camino, Beverly Hills, CA 90212

Porter, Eric *Actor*
%London Mgmt, 235/241 Regent St, London W1A 2JT, England

Porter, George *Nobel Chemistry Laureate*
%Imperial College, Photomolecular Sciences Center, London SW7 2BB, England

Porter, John E *Representative, IL*
%House of Representatives, Washington, DC 20515

Porter, Keith R *Cytologist, Educator*
%University of Colorado, Molecular Cellular Dept, Boulder, CO 80309

Porter, Milton *Businessman*
%L B Foster Co, 415 Holiday Dr, Pittsburgh, PA 15220

Porter, Richard J *Financier*
%Great Lakes Federal Savings & Loan, 401 E Liberty, Ann Arbor, MI 48107

Porter, Richard W *Electrical Engineer*
164 Cat Rock Rd, Cos Cob, CT 06807

Porter, Terry *Basketball Player*
%Portland Trail Blazers, 700 NE Multnomah St, Portland, OR 97232

Portis, Charles *Writer*
7417 Kingwood, Little Rock, AR 77207

Portman, John C, Jr *Architect*
225 Peachtree St NE, #1800, Atlanta, GA 30303

Posner, Richard A *Judge*
%US Court of Appeals, 219 Dearborn St, Chicago, IL 60604

Posner, Steven *Businessman*
%NVF Co, Yorklyn Rd, Yorklyn, DE 19736

Posner, Victor *Financier*
%Victoria Plz, 6917 Collins Ave, 17th Floor, Miami Beach, FL 33141

Posnick, Adolph *Businessman*
%Ferro Corp, 1 Erieview Plz, Cleveland, OH 44114

Post, Markie *Actress*
%William Morris Agency, 151 El Camino, Beverly Hills, CA 90212

Post, Mike *Composer*
%Mike Post Productions, 1007 W Olive, Burbank, CA 91506

Post, Sandra *Golfer*
%Ladies Professional Golf Assn, 2570 Volusia Ave, #B, Daytona Beach, FL 32114

Poster, Steve *Cinematographer*
%Smith/Gosnell/Nicholson, 1515 Palisades Dr, #N, Pacific Palisades, CA 90272

Postlewait, Kathy *Golfer*
%Ladies Professional Golf Assn, 2570 Volusia Ave, #B, Daytona Beach, FL 32114

Poston, Tom *Actor*
%International Creative Mgmt, 8899 Beverly Blvd, Los Angeles, CA 90048

Posvar, Wesley W *Educator*
%University of Pittsburgh, President's Office, Pittsburgh, PA 15260

Potila, Antii *Businessman*
%Rauma-Repola Oy, PL 203, Snellmaninkatu 13, 00170 Helsinki 17, Finland

Potok, Chaim *Writer, Artist*
20 Berwick Rd, Merion, PA 19131

Potter, Cynthia *Diver, Sportscaster*
6500 N Tierra Catalinas, #86, Tucson, AZ 85718

Potter, Dan M *Religious Leader*
PO Box 1342, Albany, NY 12201

Potter, Dennis *Writer*
Morecambe Lodge, Duxmere, Roos-on-Wye, Herefordshire, England

Potter, Philip A *Religious Leader*
%World Council of Churches, 150 Rt de Ferney 1211, Geneva 20, Switzerland

Potter, Robert J *Businessman*
%Datapoint Corp, 9725 Datapoint Dr, San Antonio, TX 78284

Potts, Annie *Actress*
%Erwin Stoff, 9128 Sunset Blvd, Los Angeles, CA 90069

Potts, Cliff *Actor*
%David Shapira Assoc, 15301 Ventura Blvd, #345, Sherman Oaks, CA 91403

Potvin, Denis *Hockey Player*
%David Cogan Mgmt, Empire State Bldg, New York, NY 10118

Poulin, Dave *Hockey Player*
%Philadelphia Flyers, Spectrum, Pattison Pl, Philadelphia, PA 19148

Poulos, Michael J *Businessman*
%American General Corp, 29292 Allen Pkwy, Houston, TX 77019

Pouncey, Peter R *Educator*
%Amherst College, President's Office, Amherst, MA 01002

Pound, Dick *Olympics Official*
%Canadian Olympic Assn, 1600 Naismith Dr, Ottawa ON K1B 5N4, Canada

Pound, Robert V *Physicist*
87 Pinehurst Rd, Belmont, MA 02178

Poungui, Ange E *Prime Minister, Congo*
%Prime Minister's Office, Brazzaville, Congo

Pountain, Eric J *Businessman*
%Tarmac, Ettingshall, Wolverhampton, London WV4 6JP, England

Poupard, Paul Cardinal *Religious Leader*
%Pontificium Consilium Pro Dialogo, 00120 Vatican City, Rome, Italy

Pousette, Lisa *Actress*
%Atkins Assoc, 303 S Crescent Heights Blvd, Los Angeles, CA 90024

Pousette-Dart, Richard *Artist*
286 Haverstraw Rd, Suffern, NY 10901

Poussaint, Alvin F *Psychiatrist, Educator*
%Judge Baker Guidance Ctr, 295 Longwood Ave, Boston, MA 02115

Povich, Maury *Commentator, Entertainer*
1 W 72nd St, New York, NY 10023

Povich, Shirley *Sportswriter*
%Washington Post, 1150 15th St NW, Washington, DC 20071

Powell, Anthony *Writer*
The Chantry Near Frome, Somerset BA11 3LJ, England

Powell, Boog (John W) *Baseball Player*
%US Anglers Marine, Key West, FL 33040

Powell, C Robert *Businessman*
%Reichhold Chemicals, 525 N Broadway, White Plains, NY 10603

Powell, Colin L *Army General*
%Office of Chairman, Joint Chiefs of Staff, Pentagon, Washington, DC 20301

Powell, Earl A, III *Museum Director*
%Los Angeles County Museum of Art, 5905 Wilshire Blvd, Los Angeles, CA 90036

Powell, George E, Jr *Businessman*
%Yellow Freight System Inc, 10990 Roe Ave, Overland Park, KS 66207

Powell, J Enoch *Government Official, England*
33 S Eaton Pl, London SW1, England

Powell, Jane *Singer, Actress*
230 W 55th St, #14-B, New York, NY 10019

Powell, Jody *Government Official, Journalist*
%Ogilvy & Mather Public Relations, 1901 "L" St NW, Washington, DC 20036

Powell, John *Track Athlete*
%John Powell Assoc, 10445 Mary Ave, Cupertino, CA 95014

Powell, Lewis F, Jr *Supreme Court Justice*
%US Supreme Court, 1 1st St NE, Washington, DC 20543

Powell, Mel *Composer*
%California School of Arts, Music Dept, Valencia, CA 91355

Powell, William A *Businessman*
%Mid-America Dairymen Inc, PO Box 1837, Springfield, MO 65805

Powers, J F *Writer*
%Alfred Knopf Inc, 201 E 50th St, New York, NY 10022

Powers, James B *Religious Leader*
%American Baptist Assn, 4605 N State Line, Texarkana, TX 75503

Powers, Mala *Actress*
10543 Valley Spring Ln, North Hollywood, CA 91602

Powers, Robert M *Businessman*
%Staley Continental Inc, 1701 Golf Rd, Rolling Meadows, IL 60008

Powers, Stefanie *Actress*
2661 Hutton Dr, Beverly Hills, CA 90210

Pownall, Thomas G *Businessman*
%Martin Marietta Corp, 6801 Rockledge Dr, Bethesda, MD 20817

Pozsgay, Imre *Government Leader, Hungary*
%Hungarian Socialist Party, Budapest, Hungary

Pramoj, Mom Rachawongse Seni *Prime Minister, Thailand*
219 Egamai Rd, Bangkok, Thailand

Pratt, Edmund T, Jr *Businessman*
%Pfizer Inc, 235 E 42nd St, New York, NY 10017

Pratt, George C *Judge*
%US Court of Appeals, Uniondale Ave & Hempstead Trnpk, Uniondale, NY 11553

Precourt, Charles J *Astronaut*
%NASA, Johnson Space Center, Houston, TX 77058

Pregerson, Harry *Judge*
%US Court of Appeals, 21800 Oxnard St, Woodland Hills, CA 91367

Pregulman, Merv *Football Player*
%Siskin Steel & Supply Co, PO Box 1191, Chattanooga, TN 37401

Prelog, Vladimir *Nobel Chemistry Laureate*
Bellariastrasse 33, 8002 Zurich, Switzerland

Premadasa, Ranasinghe *President, Sri Lanka*
%President's Office, Colombo, Sri Lanka

Premauer, Werner *Financier*
%Bayerische Vereinsbank, 8000 Munich 2, Germany

Prentiss, Paula *Actress, Comedienne*
719 N Foothill Rd, Beverly Hills, CA 90210

Presle, Micheline *Actress*
%S Vatiney, 41 Rue Temple, 75004 Paris, France

Presley, Priscilla *Actress*
1167 Summit Dr, Beverly Hills, CA 90210

Press, Frank *Geophysicist*
%National Academy of Sciences, 2101 Constitution Ave, Washington, DC 20418

Pressburger, Emeric *Movie Producer*
Shoemaker's Cottage, Aspall, Stowmarket, Suffolk, England

Pressey, Paul *Basketball Player*
%San Antonio Spurs, 600 E Market St, San Antonio, TX 78205

Pressler, H Paul *Judge*
2133 Pine Valley Dr, Houston, TX 77019

Pressler, Larry *Senator, SD*
%US Senate, Washington, DC 20510

Pressman, Edward R *Movie Producer*
%Edward R Pressman Films, 445 N Bedford Dr, #PH, Beverly Hills, CA 90210

Pressman, Lawrence *Actor*
15033 Encanto Dr, Sherman Oaks, CA 91403

Preston, Billy *Singer, Songwriter*
%DePasse-Jones Mgmt, 6255 Sunset Blvd, Los Angeles, CA 90028

Preston, James E *Businessman*
%Avon Products Inc, 9 W 57th St, New York, NY 10019

Preston, Mike *Actor*
%Artists Group, 1930 Century Park West, #403, Los Angeles, CA 90067

Preston, Seymour S, III *Businessman*
%Pennwalt Corp, 3 Pkwy, Philadelphia, PA 19102

Pretre, Georges *Conductor*
Chateau de Vaudricourt, A Naves, Par Castres 81100, France

Preus, David W *Religious Leader*
%American Lutheran Church, 422 S 5th St, Minneapolis, MN 55415

Preus, J A O *Religious Leader, Educator*
400 N 4th St, #1502, St Louis, MO 63102

Previn, Andre *Conductor, Composer*
304 S Bedford Dr, Beverly Hills, CA 90212

Previn, Dory *Singer, Songwriter*
2533 Zorada Dr, Los Angeles, CA 90046

Prew, William A *Swimmer, Businessman*
1920 S Ocean Blvd, #A, Delray Beach, FL 33483

Prey, Hermann *Opera, Concert Singer*
Fichtenstrasse 14, 8033 Krailling vor Munich, Germany

Price, Charles H, II *Diplomat*
%US Embassy, Grosvenor Sq, London, England

Price, Don K *Educator*
984 Memi Dr, Cambridge, MA 02138

Price, Frank *Entertainment Executive*
%Price Entertainment, Sony, 10202 W Washington Blvd, Culver City, CA 90232

Price, Frederick K C *Religious Leader*
%Crenshaw Christian Church, 7901 S Vermont Ave, Los Angeles, CA 90044

Price, George *Cartoonist*
81 Westervelt Ave, Tenafly, NJ 07670

Price, K M *Businessman*
%Morrison Knudsen Corp, Morrison Knudsen Plz, Boise, ID 83707

Price, Kenneth *Artist*
PO Box 1356, Taos, NM 87571

Price, Larry C *Photographer*
%Philadelphia Inquirer, 400 N Broad St, Philadelphia, PA 19101

Price, Leontyne *Opera Singer*
%Columbia Artists Mgmt Inc, 165 W 57th St, New York, NY 10019

Price, Margaret *Opera Singer*
%Harrison/Parrott Ltd, 12 Penzance Pl, London W11 4PA, England

Price, Mark *Basketball Player*
%Cleveland Cavaliers, 2923 Statesboro Rd, Richfield, OH 44286

Price, Mark *Basketball Player*
%Cleveland Cavaliers, PO Box 5000, Richfield, OH 44286

Price, Mark S *Businessman*
%Equitas Group, 3029 N Alma School Rd, Chandler, AZ 85205

Price, Paul E *Businessman*
%Quaker Oats Co, Merchandize Mart Plz, Chicago, IL 60654

Price, Ray *Singer*
PO Box 1986, Mt Pleasant, TX 75230

Price, Reynolds *Writer*
4813 Duke Station, Durham, NC 27706

Price, Robert E *Businessman*
%Price Co, 2657 Ariane Dr, San Diego, CA 92117

Price, Robert M *Businessman*
%Control Data Corp, 8100 34th Ave S, Minneapolis, MN 55440

Price, S H *Publisher*
%Newsweek Inc, 444 Madison Ave, New York, NY 10022

Price, Sol *Businessman*
%Price Co, 2657 Ariane Dr, San Diego, CA 92117

Price, Vincent *Actor*
9255 Swallow Dr, Los Angeles, CA 90069

Price, Willard D *Explorer*
814-N Via Alhambra, Laguna Hills, CA 92653

Prichard, Peter S *Editor*
%USA Today, 1000 Wilson Blvd, Arlington, VA 22209

Pride, Charlie *Singer*
3198 Royal Ln, #204, Dallas, TX 75229

Priesand, Sally J *Clergywoman*
10 Wedgewood Cir, Eatontown, NJ 07724

Prigogine, Ilya *Nobel Chemistry Laureate*
67 Ave Fond'Roy, 1180 Brussels, Belgium

Primatesta, Raul Francisco Cardinal *Religious Leader*
Arzobispado, Ave H Irigoyen 98, 5000 Cordoba, Argentina

Primis, Lance R *Publisher*
%New York Times, 229 W 43rd St, New York, NY 10036

Prince *Singer*
9401 Kiowa Trl, Chanhassen, MN 55317

Prince, Gregory S, Jr *Educator*
%Hampshire College, President's Office, Amherst, MA 01002

Prince, Harold S *Theatre Producer*
%Harold Prince Organization, 10 Rockefeller Plz, #1009, New York, NY 10020

Prince, William *Actor*
%Twentieth Century Artists, 3800 Barham Blvd, Los Angeles, CA 90068

Principal, Victoria *Actress*
%Triad Artists, 10100 Santa Monica Blvd, #1600, Los Angeles, CA 90067

Prine, Andrew *Actor*
3264 Longridge Ave, Sherman Oaks, CA 91403

Prine, John *Singer, Songwriter*
%Al Bunetta Mgmt, 4121 Wilshire Blvd, #215, Los Angeles, CA 90010

Prine, Malcolm M *Businessman, Baseball Executive*
%Ryan Homes Inc, 100 Ryan Ct, Pittsburgh, PA 15205

Pringle, Joan *Actress*
23938 Hamlin St, Canoga Park, CA 91307

Prinz, Dianne *Astronaut*
%US Naval Research Laboratory, Washington, DC 20375

Prinz, Gerhard *Businessman*
%Daimler-Benz AG 7, Stuttgart 60, Germany

Pritchett, James *Actor*
53 W 74th St, New York, NY 10023
Pritchett, Matt *Cartoonist (Matt)*
%London Daily Telegraph, 181 Marsh Wall, London E14 9SR, England
Pritchett, Victor S *Writer*
12 Regents Park Terr, London NW1, England
Pritkin, Roland I *Eye Surgeon*
3505 Highcrest Rd, Rockford, IL 61101
Pritzker, Jay A *Businessman*
%Marmon Grp, 39 S LaSalle St, Chicago, IL 60603
Pritzker, Robert A *Businessman*
%Marmon Grp, 39 S LaSalle St, Chicago, IL 60603
Prix, Wolf *Architect*
%Coop Himmelblau, 2497 Armacost Ave, Los Angeles, CA 90064
Probert, Bob *Hockey Player*
%Detroit Red Wings, 600 Civic Center Dr, Detroit, MI 48226
Probst, Walter F *Businessman*
706 Shelter Cove Dr, Lake Arrowhead, CA 92352
Prochnow, Herbert V *Financier*
2950 Harrison St, Evanston, IL 60201
Prochnow, Jurgen *Actor*
%International Creative Mgmt, 8899 Beverly Blvd, Los Angeles, CA 90048
Procknow, Donald E *Businessman*
%Western Electric Co, 222 Broadway, New York, NY 10038
Proctor, Charles N *Skier*
6 Oak Rd, Santa Cruz, CA 95060
Proctor, David *Businessman*
%Ashton-Tate Corp, 20101 Hamilton Ave, Torrance, CA 90502
Prodi, Romano *Businessman*
%Istituto Ricostruzione Industriale, Via Veneto 89, 00187, Rome, Italy
Profumo, John D *Government Official, England*
28 Commercial St, London E1 6LS, England
Prokhorov, Aleksandr M *Nobel Physics Laureate*
%Lebedev Institute of Physics, 53 Leninsky Prospekt, Moscow, Russia
Prokosch, Frederic *Writer*
Ma Trouvaille, 06 Plan de Grasse, France
Prophet, Elizabeth Clare *Religious Leader*
%Church Universal & Triumphant, Box A, Livingston, MT 59047
Propp, Brian *Hockey Player*
%Philadelphia Flyers, Spectrum, Pattison Pl, Philadelphia, PA 19148
Prosky, Robert *Actor*
%Susan Smith Assoc, 121 N San Vicente Blvd, Beverly Hills, CA 90211
Prosser, Robert *Religious Leader*
%Cumberland Presbyterian Church, 1978 Union Ave, Memphis, TN 38104
Prost, Alain *Racing Car Driver*
%Star Racing Promotion, 2 Rue Neuve, 1450 Sainte-Croix, France
Protopopov, Oleg *Figure Skater*
Chalet Hubel, 3818 Grindelwald, Switzerland
Prowse, David *Actor*
%David Prowse Fitness Centre, 12 Marshalsea Rd, London SE1 4YB, England
Prowse, Juliet *Dancer, Actress*
343 S Beverly Glen, Los Angeles, CA 90024
Proxmire, William *Senator, WI*
%US Senate, Washington, DC 20510
Prudhomme, Paul *Chef*
406 Chartes St, #2, New Orleans, LA 70130
Pruett, Jeanne *Singer*
1300 Division St, #201, Nashville, TN 37203
Pruitt, Basil A *Burn Surgeon*
%US Army Institute of Surgical Research, Fort Sam Houston, TX 78234
Pruitt, Greg *Football Player*
24306 Stonehedge Dr, Westlake, OH 44145
Pruitt, James E *Businessman*
%Harris Graphics Corp, 200 Seminole Ave, Melbourne, FL 32901
Pruitt, Peter *Businessman*
%Frank B Hall Co, 549 Pleasantville Rd, Briarcliff Manor, NY 10510

Prussia, Leland S *Financier*
%BankAmerica Corp, Bank of America Ctr, San Francisco, CA 94104
Pruyn, William J *Businessman*
%Eastern Enterprises, 1 Beacon St, Boston, MA 02108
Pryor, David H *Senator/Governor, AR*
%US Senate, Washington, DC 20510
Pryor, Hubert *Editor, Publisher*
3560 S Ocean Blvd, #607, South Palm Beach, FL 33480
Pryor, Nicholas *Actor*
%Century Artists, 9744 Wilshire Blvd, #308, Beverly Hills, CA 90212
Pryor, Peter P *Editor*
%Daily Variety, 5700 Wilshire Blvd, Los Angeles, CA 90036
Pryor, Richard *Comedian*
1115 Moraga Dr, Los Angeles, CA 90049
Pryor, Thomas M *Editor*
%Daily Variety, 1400 N Cahuenga Blvd, Los Angeles, CA 90028
Ptashne, Mark S *Molecular Biologist*
%Harvard University, Biochemistry Dept, Cambridge, MA 02138
Puapua, Tomasi *Prime Minister, Tuvalu*
%Prime Minister's Office, Funafuti, Tuvalu
Pucci, Bert *Publisher*
%Los Angeles Magazine, 1888 Century Park East, Los Angeles, CA 90067
Pucci, Emilio (Marchese di Barsento) *Couturier*
Palazzo Pucci, 6 Via dei Pucci, Florence, Italy
Puck, Theodore T *Biophysicist*
10 S Albion St, Denver, CO 80222
Puck, Wolfgang *Chef*
%Spago Restaurant, 8795 W Sunset Blvd, Los Angeles, CA 90069
Puckett, Allen E *Businessman*
%Hughes Aircraft Co, 7200 Hughes Terr, Los Angeles, CA 90045
Puckett, Gary *Singer*
7817 Backer Rd, San Diego, CA 92126
Puckett, Kirby *Baseball Player*
8924 Ashley Terr, Brooklyn Park, MN 55443
Puente, John G *Businessman*
%M/A-COM Inc, 7 New England Executive Park, Burlington, MA 01803
Puente, Tito *Orchestra Leader*
200 W 51st St, #1410, New York, NY 10019
Puett, Clay *Thoroughbred Racing Gate Inventor*
%Clay Puett True Center Gate Co, 2211 E Hartford, Phoenix, AZ 85022
Pugh, Lawrence R *Businessman*
%VF Corp, 1047 N Park Rd, Wyomissing, PA 19610
Pugsley, Don *Actor*
%Lee Miller Agency, 5000 Lankershim Blvd, North Hollywood, CA 91601
Puica, Maricica *Track Athlete*
%Olympic Committee, Str Vasile Conta 16, Bucarest, Romania
Pulitzer, Joseph, Jr *Publisher*
%St Louis Post-Dispatch, 1133 Franklin Ave, St Louis, MO 63101
Pulliam, Eugene S *Publisher*
%Indianapolis Star, 307 N Pennsylvania St, Indianapolis, IN 46204
Pullin, Charles R *Businessman*
%Koppers Co, Koppers Bldg, Pittsburgh, PA 15219
Pulte, William J *Businessman*
%Pulte Home Corp, 6400 Farmington Rd, West Bloomfield, MI 48033
Pulver, Liselotte *Actress*
%Mrs L M Gibbs, 16 Ave Calas, 1206 Geneva, Switzerland
Pund, Henry R (Peter) *Football Player*
Toreneke Trl, Darien, CT 06820
Punsley, Bernard *Actor*
1415 Granvia Altemeia, Rancho Palos Verdes, CA 90274
Puppa, Daren *Hockey Player*
%Buffalo Sabres, Memorial Auditorium, Buffalo, NY 14202
Purcell, Edward M *Nobel Physics Laureate*
5 Wright St, Cambridge, MA 02138
Purcell, John R *Businessman*
%SFN Companies, 1900 E Lake Ave, Glenview, IL 60025

Purcell, Patrick *Publisher*
%Boston Herald, 300 Harrison St, Boston, MA 02106

Purcell, Philip J *Businessman*
%Dean Witter Financial Services Grp, 130 Liberty St, New York, NY 10006

Purcell, Sarah *Actress*
%International Creative Mgmt, 8899 Beverly Blvd, Los Angeles, CA 90048

Purdum, Robert L *Businessman*
%Armco Corp, 177 Madison Ave, Morristown, NJ 07960

Purdy, James *Writer*
236 Henry St, Brooklyn, NY 11201

Purim, Flora *Singer*
%MPM Mgmt, 518 N La Cienega Blvd, Los Angeles, CA 90048

Purkey, Robert *Baseball Player*
5767 King School Rd, Bethel Park, PA 15102

Purl, Linda *Actress*
%David Shapira Assoc, 15301 Ventura Blvd, #345, Sherman Oaks, CA 91403

Pursell, Carl D *Representative, MI*
%House of Representatives, Washington, DC 20515

Pusey, Nathan M *Educator*
200 E 66th St, New York, NY 10021

Putnam, Ashley *Opera Singer*
%Colbert Artists Mgmt, 111 W 57th St, New York, NY 10019

Puttnam, David *Movie Producer*
%Enigma Productions, 11/15 Queens Gate Place Mew, London SW7 5BG, England

Puzo, Mario *Writer*
866 Manor Ln, Bay Shore, NY 11706

Pye, A Kenneth *Educator*
%Southern Methodist University, President's Office, Dallas, TX 75275

Pyle, Denver *Actor*
10614 Whipple St, North Hollywood, CA 91602

Pym, Francis *Government Official, England*
Everton Park, Sandy, Beds, England

Pynchon, Thomas *Writer*
%J B Lippincott Co, E Washington Sq, Philadelphia, PA 19105

Pyne, Stephen J *Historian*
%University of Iowa, History Dept, Iowa City, IA 52242

Qaboos Bin Said *Sultan, Oman*
%The Palace, Muscat, Sultanate of Oman

Qasimi, Sheikh Saqr bin Muhammad al- *Ruler, Ras al Khaimah*
%Royal Palace, Ras al Khaimah, United Arab Emirates

Qasimi, Sheikh Sultan bin Muhammad Al- *Ruler, Sharjah*
%Royal Palace, Sharjah, United Arab Emirates

Qin Jiwei *Army General, China*
%Defense Minister's Office, Communist Party, Beijing, China

Quackenbush, Bill (H Q) *Hockey Player*
18 Washington St, Rocky Hill, NJ 08553

Quade, John *Actor*
%Alex Brewis Agency, 12429 Laurel Terrace Dr, Studio City, CA 91604

Quadros, Janio *President, Brazil*
%Mayor's Office, Sao Paulo, Brazil

Quaid, Dennis *Actor*
%Gersh Agency, 232 N Canon Dr, Beverly Hills, CA 90210

Quaid, Randy *Actor*
%Bresler Kelly Kipperman, 15760 Ventura Blvd, #1730, Encino, CA 91436

Quant, Mary *Fashion Designer*
%Mary Quant Ltd, 3 Ives St, London SW3 2NE, England

Quarrie, Don *Track Athlete*
1867 Rainbow Terrace Ln, Montebello, CA 90640

Quarry, Jerry *Boxer*
11382 Orange Park Blvd, Orange, CA 92669

Quastel, J Hirsch *Biochemist*
4585 Langara Ave, Vancouver BC V6R 1C9, Canada

Quayle, J Daniel *Vice President*
%Vice President's Office, Executive Office Building, Washington, DC 20501

Queler, Eve *Conductor*
%Opera Orchestra of New York, 239 W 72nd St, #2-R, New York, NY 10023

Quennell, Peter *Writer*
26 Cheyne Row, London SW3, England

Questel, Mae *Actress*
27 E 65th St, New York, NY 10021

Quick, Diana *Actress*
39 Seymour Walk, London SW10, England

Quick, Mike *Football Player*
%Philadelphia Eagles, Veterans Stadium, Philadelphia, PA 19148

Quick, Richard *Swimming Coach*
%Stanford University, Athletic Dept, Stanford, CA 94305

Quie, Albert H *Governor, MN*
Rt 5, Box 231-A, Faribault, MN 55021

Quillen, James H *Representative, TN*
1601 Fairidge Pl, Kingsport, TN 37664

Quine, Willard V O *Philosopher*
38 Chestnut St, Boston, MA 02108

Quinlan, Kathleen *Actress*
PO Box 2465, Malibu, CA 90265

Quinlan, Michael R *Businessman*
%McDonald's Corp, McDonald's Plz, Oak Brook, IL 60521

Quinn, Aidan *Actor*
PO Box 2149, Santa Monica, CA 90406

Quinn, Anthony *Actor*
60 East End Ave, New York, NY 10028

Quinn, Bill *Actor*
%Abrams Artists, 9200 Sunset Blvd, #625, Los Angeles, CA 90069

Quinn, Carmel *Singer*
456 Park Ave, Leonia, NJ 07025

Quinn, John C *Editor*
%Gannett Foundation, 1101 Wilson Blvd, Arlington, VA 22209

Quinn, John J *Educator*
%University of Tennessee, President's Office, Knoxville, TN 37996

Quinn, Martha *Entertainer*
1440 S Sepulveda Blvd, #118, Los Angeles, CA 90024

Quinn, Pat *Hockey Executive*
%Vancouver Canucks, 100 N Renfrew St, Vancouver BC V5K 3N7, Canada

Quinn, Sally *Journalist*
3014 "N" St NW, Washington, DC 20007

Quinn, William F *Governor, HI*
1365 Laukahi St, Honolulu, HI 96821

Quinn, William J *Businessman*
1420 Sheridan Rd, #4-D, Wilmette, IL 60091

Quintero, Jose *Theatre Director*
%Stage Directors & Choreographers Society, 1501 Broadway, New York, NY 10021

Quiroga, Elena *Writer*
%Real Academia de la Historia, Leon 21, Madrid 14, Spain

Quisenberry, Dan *Baseball Player*
12208 Buena Vista, Leawood, KS 66209

Quittmeyer, Robert T *Businessman*
%Amatar Corp, 1251 Ave of Americas, New York, NY 10020

Quivar, Florence *Opera Singer*
%Metropolitan Opera Assn, Lincoln Center Plz, New York, NY 10023

R

Raab – Rahal

Raab, G Kirk *Businessman*
272 Otis Rd, Barrington Hills, IL 60010

Raab, Walter F *Businessman*
%AMP Inc, 470 Friendship Rd, Harrisburg, PA 17109

Raaum, Gustav *Skier*
PO Box 700, Mercer Island, WA 98040

Rabb, Irvin W *Businessman*
%Stop & Shop Companies, PO Box 369, Boston, MA 02101

Rabb, Maxwell M *Diplomat*
1025 5th Ave, New York, NY 10028

Rabb, Norman S *Businessman*
%Stop & Shop Companies, PO Box 369, Boston, MA 02101

Rabb, Sidney R *Businessman*
%Stop & Shop Companies, PO Box 369, Boston, MA 02101

Rabbitt, Eddie *Singer*
%Scotti Bros, 2128 W Pico Blvd, Santa Monica, CA 90405

Rabin, Itzhak *Prime Minister, Israel*
%Knesset, Jerusalem, Israel

Rabin, Stanley A *Businessman*
%Commercial Metals Co, 7800 Stemmons Fwy, Dallas, TX 75247

Rabinow, Jacob *Electrical Engineer*
6920 Selkirk Dr, Bethesda, MD 20234

Raboy, S Caesar *Businessman*
%Connecticut Mutual Life Insurance, 140 Garden St, Hartford, CT 06154

Rabsztyn, Grazyna *Track Athlete*
%Olympic Committee, Rue Frascati 4, 00483 Varsovie, Poland

Raburn, W B *Businessman*
%Snap-on Tools Corp, 2801 80th St, Kenosha, WI 53141

Rachins, Alan *Actor*
1124 N Larrabee St, Los Angeles, CA 90069

Racimo, Victoria *Actress*
%Lantz Office, 888 7th Ave, #2500, New York, NY 10106

Racine, Georges *Businessman*
%Mobile Oil Francaise, 20 Ave Andre Prothin, 92081 Paris, France

Radatz, Dick *Baseball Player*
%Atlantic Container, PO Box 348, Braintree, MA 02184

Rader, Andrew I *Businessman*
%Allen-Bradley Co, 1201 S 2nd St, Milwaukee, WI 53204

Rader, Doug *Baseball Manager*
2114 Oakwood Dr, Bakersfield, CA 93304

Rader, Randall R *Judge*
%US Claims Court, 717 Madison Pl NW, Washington, DC 20005

Radford, Michael *Movie Director*
3-B Rickering Mews, London W2 5AD, England

Radojevic, Danilo *Ballet Dancer*
%American Ballet Theatre, 890 Broadway, New York, NY 10003

Radwanski, George *Editor*
%Toronto Star, 1 Yonge St, Toronto ON M5E 1E6, Canada

Rae, Charlotte *ACtress*
1413 Allenford, Los Angeles, CA 90049

Rafelson, Bob *Movie Director*
822 Marymont Ln, Los Angeles, CA 90069

Rafferty, Tim *Football Player*
%Dallas Cowboys, 1 Cowboys Pkwy, Irving, TX 75063

Raffi (Cavoukian) *Vocalist*
%Jensen Communications, 120 S Victory Blvd, #201, Burbank, CA 91502

Raffin, Deborah *Actress*
2630 Eden Pl, Beverly Hills, CA 90210

Rafsanjani, Hojatolislam Hashemi *Government Official, Iran*
%Parliament, Teheran, Iran

Raftery, S Frank *Labor Leader*
%Painters & Allied Trades Union, 1750 New York Ave NW, Washington, DC 20006

Ragin, John S *Actor*
5708 Briarcliff Rd, Los Angeles, CA 90068

Rahal, Bobby *Auto Racing Driver*
PO Box 1128, Dublin, OH 43017

Rahall, Nick Joe, II *Representative, WV*
%House of Representatives, Washington, DC 20515

Rahn, Hermann *Physiologist*
75 Windsor Ave, Buffalo, NY 14209

Raidl, Claus J *Businessman*
%Chemie Linz, St Peter Strasse 25, A-4021 Linz, Austria

Railsback, Steve *Actor*
PO Box 1308, Los Angeles, CA 90078

Railsback, Thomas F *Representative, IL*
%House of Representatives, Washington, DC 20515

Raimond, Jean-Bernard *Government Official, France*
203 Ave Daumesnil, 75012 Paris, France

Raine, Kathleen *Poet*
47 Paultons Sq, London SW3, England

Rainer, Luise *Actress*
%Knittel, Vico Morcote, 6911 Lugano, Switzerland

Raines, Cristina *Actress*
%David Shapira Assoc, 15301 Ventura Blvd, #345, Sherman Oaks, CA 91403

Raines, Franklin D *Financier*
%Lazzard Freres, 1 Rockefeller Plz, New York, NY 10020

Raines, Tim *Baseball Player*
2316 Airport Blvd, Sanford, FL 32771

Rainey, Ford *Actor*
3821 Carbon Canyon Rd, Malibu, CA 90265

Rainey, Wayne *Motorcyle Racing Rider*
%International Racers, 1633 E 4th St, #132, Santa Ana, CA 92701

Rainier III *Prince, Monaco*
Palais de Monaco, 98015 Monte Carlo 518, Monaco

Rainwater, Gregg *Actor*
PO Box 291836, Los Angeles, CA 90029

Raisian, John *Educator*
%Hoover Institution, Stanford University, Stanford, CA 94305

Raitt, Bonnie *Singer*
7323 Woodrow Wilson Dr, Los Angeles, CA 90046

Raitt, John *Singer, Actor*
%Lew Sherrell Agency, 1354 Los Robles, Palm Springs, CA 92262

Rakich, Robert T *Businessman*
%Capital Holding Corp, 680 4th Ave, Louisville, KY 40232

Rakowski, Mieczyslaw *Premier, Poland*
%Central Committee, Ul Nowy Swiat 6, 00-497 Warsaw, Poland

Rall, David P *Toxicologist*
%National Institute of Envrionmental Health, Triangle Park, NC 27709

Rallis, George J *Prime Minister, Greece*
4 Kanari St, Athens, Greece

Ralph, Sheryl Lee *Actress*
%Michael Schlesinger Assoc, 8730 Sunset Blvd, #220, Los Angeles, CA 90069

Ralston, Dennis *Tennis Player*
%US Tennis Assn, 1212 Ave of Americas, New York, NY 10036

Ralston, Esther *Actress*
35 Heather Way, Ventura, CA 93003

Ralston, Vera Hruba *Actress*
4121 Crescienta Dr, Santa Barbara, CA 93110

Ramage, Rob *Hockey Player*
%Calgary Flames, PO Box 1540, Station M, Calgary AB T2P 3B9, Canada

Ramahatra, Victor *Prime Minister, Madagascar*
%Prime Minister's Office, Antananarivo, Madgascar

Rambahadur Limbu *Vietnam War Sarawak Army Hero (VC)*
Box 420, Bandar Seri Begawan, Negara Brunei Darussalam, Brunei

Rambis, Kurt *Basketball Player*
%Phoenix Suns, 2910 N Central, Phoenix, AZ 85012

Rambo, Dack *Actor*
Rambo Horse Farm, Earlimart, CA 93219

Rambo, David L *Religious Leader*
%Christian & Missionary Alliance, PO Box 35000, Colorado Springs, CO 80935

Ramey, Samuel *Opera Singer*
320 Central Park West, New York, NY 10025

R

Ramgoolam – Randolph

Ramgoolam, Seewosagur — *Prime Minister, Mauritius*
85 Desforges St, Port Louis, Mauritius

Ramirez Vazquez, Pedro — *Architect*
Ave de la Fuentes 170, Mexico City 20 DF, Mexico

Ramirez, Raul — *Tennis Player*
Avenida Ruiz, 65 Sur Ensenada, Baja California, Mexico

Ramis, Harold — *Actor, Screenwriter, Director*
456 15th St, Santa Monica, CA 90402

Ramo, Simon — *Businessman*
%TRW Inc, 1 Space Park, Redondo Beach, CA 90278

Ramos, Fidel V — *Army General, Philippines*
%Ministry of Defense, Camp Aguinaldo, Quezon City, Philippines

Ramos, Mando — *Boxer*
13765 Cedar St, #1, Westminster, CA 92683

Ramos, Mel — *Artist*
5941 Ocean View Dr, Oakland, CA 94618

Rampal, Jean-Pierre — *Concert Flutist*
15 Ave Mozart, 75016 Paris, France

Rampton, Calvin L — *Governor, UT*
2492 S 2300 E, Salt Lake City, UT 84115

Ramsay, Garrard (Buster) — *Football Player*
RR 4, Maryville, TN 37801

Ramsay, Jack — *Basketball Coach, Executive*
%Indiana Pacers, 2 W Washington St, Indianapolis, IN 46204

Ramsey, Frank — *Basketball Player*
Buckner Ridge Ln, Box 363, Madisonville, KY 42431

Ramsey, Logan — *Actor*
%Henderson/Hogan Agency, 247 S Beverly Dr, #102, Beverly Hills, CA 90210

Ramsey, Mike — *Hockey Player*
%Buffalo Sabres, Memorial Auditorium, Buffalo, NY 14202

Ramsey, Norman F, Jr — *Nobel Physics Laureate*
21 Monmouth Ct, Brookline, MA 02146

Ramsey, William — *Singer, Songwriter*
Biebricher Allee 37, 62 Wiesbaden, Germany

Ramstad, Jim — *Representative, MN*
%House of Representatives, Washington, DC 20515

Rand, Robert W — *Neurosurgeon, Educator*
%University of California, Neuropsychiatric Institute, Los Angeles, CA 90024

Randall, Bo (W D, Jr) — *Knife Maker*
%Randall Made Knives, PO Box 1988, Orlando, FL 32802

Randall, Claire — *Religious Leader*
%National Council of Churches, 475 Riverside Dr, New York, NY 10115

Randall, James R — *Businessman*
%Archer Daniels Midland Co, 4666 Faries Pkwy, Decatur, IL 62525

Randall, Tony — *Actor, Comedian*
145 Central Park West, #6-C, New York, NY 10012

Randi, James — *Illusionist*
51 Lunnox Ave, Runsen, NJ 07760

Randle, Roger — *Mayor*
%Mayor's Office, City Hall, 200 Civic Center, Tulsa, OK 74103

Randolph, A Raymond — *Judge*
%US Court of Appeals, 3rd & Constitution Ave NW, Washington, DC 20001

Randolph, Boots — *Jazz Saxophonist*
4798 Licton Pike, Whites Creek, TN 37189

Randolph, Jennings — *Senator, WV*
300 3rd St, Elkins, WV 26241

Randolph, John — *Actor*
561 W 163rd St, New York, NY 10032

Randolph, Joyce — *Actress*
295 Central Park W, #18-A, New York, NY 10024

Randolph, Judson G — *Pediatric Surgeon*
111 Michigan Ave NW, Washington, DC 20010

Randolph, Leo — *Boxer*
2012 S "K" St, Tacoma, WA 95128

Randolph, Willie — *Baseball Player*
648 Juniper Pl, Franklin Lakes, NJ 07417

Randrup, Michael *Test Pilot*
10 Fairlawn Rd, Lytham, Lanc, England

Rands, Bernard *Composer*
301 Sunset Dr, Encinitas, CA 92024

Rangel, Charles B *Representative, NY*
74 W 132nd St, New York, NY 10037

Ranieri, Lewis S *Financier*
%Salomon Bros, 1 New York Plz, New York, NY 10004

Rankin, Judy *Golfer*
%Kingsmill-on-the-James Golf Course, Williamsburg, VA 23185

Rankin, Kenny *Singer*
8033 Sunset Blvd, #1037, Los Angeles, CA 90046

Ransey, Kelvin *Basketball Player*
%New Jersey Nets, Meadowlands Arena, East Rutherford, NJ 07073

Ransohoff, Joseph *Neurosurgeon*
%New York University, Medical School, 560 1st St, New York, NY 10016

Ransohoff, Martin *Movie Producer*
%Martin Ransohoff Productions, Lorimar Plz, Burbank, CA 91505

Rao, P V Narasimha *Prime Minister, India*
%Prime Minister's Office, 1 Safdarjung Rd, New Delhi 11011, India

Raoul, Alfred *Prime Minister, Congo*
%Embassy of Congo, 16 Ave F D Roosevelt, 1050 Brussels, Belgium

Raper, Kenneth B *Bacteriologist*
4110 Chippewa Dr, Madison, WI 53711

Raphael, Sally Jessy *Entertainer*
%MultiMedia Entertainment, 8 Elm St, New Haven, CT 06510

Rappuoli, Rino *Medical Researcher*
%Sclavo Research Center, Via Fiorentina 1, 53100, Siena, Italy

Rapson, Ralph *Architect*
1 Seymour Ave, Minneapolis, MN 55404

Rarick, Cindy *Golfer*
%Ladies Professional Golf Assn, 2570 Volusia Ave, #B, Daytona Beach, FL 32114

Rasche, David *Actor*
%Gersh Agency, 232 N Canon Dr, Beverly Hills, CA 90210

Rashad, Phylicia *Actress*
%Bret Adams, 448 W 44th St, New York, NY 10036

Raskin, Abraham H *Editor*
136 E 64th St, New York, NY 10021

Raskin, David *Composer*
6519 Aldea Ave, Van Nuys, CA 91406

Rasmus, Robert N *Businessman*
%Masonite Corp, 29 N Wacker Dr, Chicago, IL 60606

Rasmussen, Norman C *Nuclear Engineer*
77 Massachusetts Ave, Cambridge, MA 02139

Ratchford, William R *Representative, CT*
2 Johnson Dr, Danbury, CT 06810

Ratcliffe, John A *Radio Astronomer*
193 Huntingdon Rd, Cambridge CB3 0DL, England

Ratelle, Jean *Hockey Player*
%Boston Bruins, 150 Causeway St, Boston, MA 02114

Rathbone, Perry T *Museum Director*
151 Coolidge Hill, Cambridge, MA 02138

Rather, Dan *Commentator*
%CBS-TV, 524 W 57th St, New York, NY 10019

Rathmann, Jim *Auto Racing Driver*
3950 N Riverside Dr, Indialantic, FL 32903

Ratican, Peter J *Businessman*
%Maxicare Health Plans, 5200 W Century Blvd, Los Angeles, CA 90045

Ratigan, William *Writer*
223 Park Ave, Charlevoix, MI 49720

Ratjen, Karl G *Businessman*
%Volkswagenwerk, 3180 Wolfsburg 1, Germany

Ratsiraka, Didier *President, Madagascar*
%President's Office, Antananarivo, Madagascar

Rattle, Simon *Conductor*
%Harold Holt Ltd, 31 Sinclair Rd, London W14 ONS, England

R

Ratushinskaya – Rayfield

Ratushinskaya, Irina *Poet*
15 Crothall Close, Palmers Green, London N13, England

Raty, Seppo *Track Athlete*
%Finnish Olympic Committee, Radiokatu 12, SF-00240 Helsinki 25, Finland

Ratzenberger, John *Actor*
10445 Valley Spring Ln, North Hollywood, CA 91602

Ratzinger, Joseph Cardinal *Religious Leader*
Piazza del Santuffizio 11, 00120 Vatican City, Rome, Italy

Rau, Johannes *Government Official, West Germany*
Katernbergerstrasse 171, 5600 Wuppertal 1, Germany

Rau, Santha Rama *Writer*
D/10 Mafatlal Park, Bhulabhai Desai Rd, Bombay 26, India

Rauch, Johnny *Football Player, Coach*
30 Tads Trl, Oldsmar, FL 34677

Rauch, Philip *Businessman*
%Parker Hannifin Corp, 17325 Euclid Ave, Cleveland, OH 44112

Raum, Arnold *Judge*
%US Tax Court, 400 2nd St NW, Washington, DC 20217

Rauschenberg, Robert *Artist*
%Leo Castelli Gallery, 420 W Broadway, New York, NY 10012

Rauth, J Donald *Businessman*
%Martin Marietta Corp, 6801 Rockledge Dr, Bethesda, MD 20817

Raveling, George H *Basketball Coach*
%University of Southern California, Heritage Hall, Los Angeles, CA 90089

Raven, Robert D *Attorney*
%Morrison & Forester, 345 California St, 35th Fl, San Francisco, CA 94104

Rawl, Lawrence G *Businessman*
%Exxon Corp, 1251 Ave of Americas, New York, NY 10020

Rawling, Hunter R, III *Educator*
%University of Kansas, President's Office, Lawrence, KS 66045

Rawlings, Jerry J *President, Ghana*
%Ministry of Defense, Accra, Ghana

Rawlings, Keith *Businessman*
%Artic Trading Co, Eskimo Point, Northwest Territory, Canada

Rawls, Betsy *Golfer*
%Ladies Professional Golf Assn, 2570 Volusia Ave, #B, Daytona Beach, FL 32114

Rawls, Lou *Singer*
109 Fremont Pl W, Los Angeles, CA 90005

Rawson, Merle R *Businessman*
%Hoover Co, 101 Maple St E, North Canton, OH 44720

Ray, Dixy Lee *Governor, WA*
Foxtrot Farm, 600 3rd Ave, Fox Island, WA 98333

Ray, Donald P *Political Economist, Editor*
1505 28th St S, Arlington, VA 22206

Ray, Gene Anthony *Actor*
104-60 Queens Blvd, #1-D, Forest Hills, NY 11375

Ray, Michael L *Educator*
%Stanford University, Business School, Stanford, CA 94305

Ray, Richard *Representative, GA*
%House of Representatives, Washington, DC 20515

Ray, Robert D *Governor, IA*
%Blue Cross/Blue Shield of Iowa, 636 Grand, Des Moines, IA 50309

Ray, Ronald E *Vietnam War Army Hero (CMH)*
%Veterans Administration, Human Res/Admin, 810 Vermont NW, Washington, DC 20420

Ray, Russell L, Jr *Businessman*
%Pan American Corp, 200 Park Ave, New York, NY 10166

Ray, Satyajit *Movie Director*
1/1 Bishop Lefroy Rd, #8, Calcutta 20, India

Rayburn, Gene *Entertainer*
Seaview Ave, Osterville, ME 02655

Rayburn, William B *Businessman*
%Snap-on Tools Corp, 2801 80th St, Kenosha, WI 53141

Raye, Martha *Comedienne*
1153 Roscomare Rd, Los Angeles, CA 90024

Rayfield, Allan L *Businessman*
%GTE Corp, 1 Stamford Forum, Stamford, CT 06904

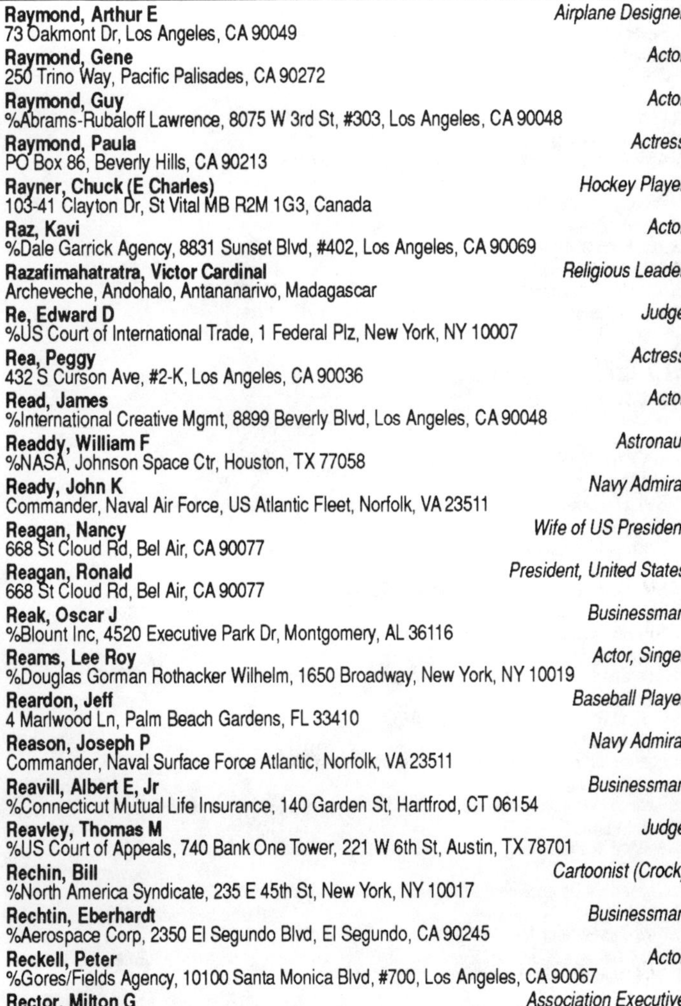

Raymond, Arthur E — *Airplane Designer*
73 Oakmont Dr, Los Angeles, CA 90049

Raymond, Gene — *Actor*
250 Trino Way, Pacific Palisades, CA 90272

Raymond, Guy — *Actor*
%Abrams-Rubaloff Lawrence, 8075 W 3rd St, #303, Los Angeles, CA 90048

Raymond, Paula — *Actress*
PO Box 86, Beverly Hills, CA 90213

Rayner, Chuck (E Charles) — *Hockey Player*
103-41 Clayton Dr, St Vital MB R2M 1G3, Canada

Raz, Kavi — *Actor*
%Dale Garrick Agency, 8831 Sunset Blvd, #402, Los Angeles, CA 90069

Razafimahatratra, Victor Cardinal — *Religious Leader*
Archeveche, Andohalo, Antananarivo, Madagascar

Re, Edward D — *Judge*
%US Court of International Trade, 1 Federal Plz, New York, NY 10007

Rea, Peggy — *Actress*
432 S Curson Ave, #2-K, Los Angeles, CA 90036

Read, James — *Actor*
%International Creative Mgmt, 8899 Beverly Blvd, Los Angeles, CA 90048

Readdy, William F — *Astronaut*
%NASA, Johnson Space Ctr, Houston, TX 77058

Ready, John K — *Navy Admiral*
Commander, Naval Air Force, US Atlantic Fleet, Norfolk, VA 23511

Reagan, Nancy — *Wife of US President*
668 St Cloud Rd, Bel Air, CA 90077

Reagan, Ronald — *President, United States*
668 St Cloud Rd, Bel Air, CA 90077

Reak, Oscar J — *Businessman*
%Blount Inc, 4520 Executive Park Dr, Montgomery, AL 36116

Reams, Lee Roy — *Actor, Singer*
%Douglas Gorman Rothacker Wilhelm, 1650 Broadway, New York, NY 10019

Reardon, Jeff — *Baseball Player*
4 Marlwood Ln, Palm Beach Gardens, FL 33410

Reason, Joseph P — *Navy Admiral*
Commander, Naval Surface Force Atlantic, Norfolk, VA 23511

Reavill, Albert E, Jr — *Businessman*
%Connecticut Mutual Life Insurance, 140 Garden St, Hartfrod, CT 06154

Reavley, Thomas M — *Judge*
%US Court of Appeals, 740 Bank One Tower, 221 W 6th St, Austin, TX 78701

Rechin, Bill — *Cartoonist (Crock)*
%North America Syndicate, 235 E 45th St, New York, NY 10017

Rechtin, Eberhardt — *Businessman*
%Aerospace Corp, 2350 El Segundo Blvd, El Segundo, CA 90245

Reckell, Peter — *Actor*
%Gores/Fields Agency, 10100 Santa Monica Blvd, #700, Los Angeles, CA 90067

Rector, Milton G — *Association Executive*
%National Council on Crime & Delinquency, 288 Monroe, River Edge, NJ 07661

Redbone, Leon — *Singer*
%Handler, 179 Aquetong Rd, New Hope, PA 18938

Redd, Thomas C — *Publisher*
%Family Circle Magazine, 488 Madison Ave, New York, NY 10022

Redding Hutner, Juli — *Actress*
115 N Carolwood Dr, Los Angeles, CA 90024

Reddy, D Raj — *Computer Scientist*
%Robotics Institute, Carnegie-Mellon University, Pittsburgh, PA 15213

Reddy, Helen — *Singer*
820 Stanford St, Santa Monica, CA 90403

Redenbacher, Orville — *Businessman*
1780 Avenida del Mondo, #704, Coronado, CA 92118

Redfern, John D — *Businessman*
%Lafarge Corp, 12700 Park Central Pl, Dallas, TX 75251

Redford, Robert — *Actor*
PO Box 837, Provo, UT 84601

Redgrave, Lynn — *Actress*
21342 Colina Dr, Box 1207, Topanga, CA 90290

Redgrave, Vanessa *Actress*
1 Ravenscourt Rd, London W6, England
Redington, Joe, Sr *Dog Sled Racer*
%Joe Redington Sled Dog Institute, HC 30, Box 5460, Wasilla, AK 99687
Redman, James *Businessman*
%Redman Industries, 2550 Walnut Hill Ln, Dallas, TX 75229
Redmond, Marge *Actress*
%Abrams Artists, 9200 Sunset Blvd, #625, Los Angeles, CA 90069
Redmond, Walter T *Businessman*
%Kellogg Co, 235 Porter St, Battle Creek, MI 49016
Redpath, Jean *Singer*
Sunny Knowe, The Promenade, Leven, Fife, Scotland
Redstone, Sumner M *Theater Executive*
%National Amusements Inc, 31 St James Ave, Boston, MA 02116
Reed, Ishmael *Writer*
1446 6th St, #C, Berkeley, CA 94710
Reed, Jerry *Singer*
45 Music Square W, Nashville, TN 37203
Reed, John F *Representative, RI*
%House of Representatives, Washington, DC 20515
Reed, John H *Governor, ME*
410 "O" St SW, Washington, DC 20024
Reed, John S *Businessman*
%Santa Fe Southern Pacific Corp, 224 S Michigan Ave, Chicago, IL 60604
Reed, John S *Financier*
%Citicorp, 399 Park Ave, New York, NY 10043
Reed, Lawrence A *Businessman*
%Dow Corning Corp, 2200 W Salzburg Rd, Auburn, MI 48611
Reed, Lou *Singer, Songwriter*
%Sire Records, 75 Rockefeller Plz, New York, NY 10019
Reed, Mark A *Physicist*
%Yale University, Electrical Engineering Dept, PO Box 2157, New Haven, CT 06520
Reed, Rex *Entertainment Critic*
1 W 72nd St, #86, New York, NY 10023
Reed, Robert *Actor*
%Agency for Performing Arts, 9000 Sunset Blvd, #1200, Los Angeles, CA 90069
Reed, Robert G, III *Businessman*
%Pacific Resources Inc, PO Box 3379, Honolulu, HI 96842
Reed, Shanna *Actress*
%Agency for Performing Arts, 9000 Sunset Blvd, #1200, Los Angeles, CA 90069
Reed, Thomas C *Government Official*
%Quaker Hill Development Corp, 530 "D" St, San Rafael, CA 94901
Reed, Willis *Basketball Player, Coach, Executive*
%New Jersey Nets, Meadowlands Arena, East Rutherford, NJ 07073
Reedy, George E, Jr *Educator, Journalist*
2307 E Newberry Blvd, Milwaukee, WI 53211
Rees, Clifford H, Jr *Air Force General*
Vice Commander-in-Chief, US Air Force Europe, APO, AE 09094
Rees, Mina *Mathematician, Educator*
301 E 66th St, New York, NY 10021
Rees, Norma *Educator*
%California State University, President's Office, Hayward, CA 94542
Rees, Roger *Actor*
%International Creative Mgmt, 8899 Beverly Blvd, Los Angeles, CA 90048
Reese, Della *Singer*
1910 Bel Air Rd, Los Angeles, CA 90024
Reese, Eddie *Swimming Coach*
%University of Texas, Athletic Dept, Austin, TX 78712
Reese, Jimmie *Baseball Coach*
%California Angels, PO Box 2000, Anaheim, CA 92803
Reese, Mason *Actor*
3575 Cahuenga Blvd W, #470, Los Angeles, CA 90068
Reese, Pee Wee (Harold) *Baseball Player*
3211 Beals Branch Rd, Louisville, KY 40206
Reeve, Christopher *Actor*
%International Creative Mgmt, 40 W 57th St, New York, NY 10019

Reeves, Dan *Football Player, Coach*
%Denver Broncos, 13655 E Dove Valley Pkwy, Englewood, CO 80112

Reeves, Del *Singer, Songwriter*
991 Hwy 100, Centerville, TN 37033

Reeves, Keanu *Actor*
7920 Sunset Blvd, #350, Los Angeles, CA 90046

Reeves, Richard *Columnist*
%Universal Press Syndicate, 4900 Main St, Kansas City, M0 64112

Reeves, Steve *Actor*
%Classic Images Enterprises, PO Box 807, Valley Center, CA 92082

Regalbuto, Joe *Actor*
%Bauman Hiller Assoc, 5750 Wilshire Blvd, #512, Los Angeles, CA 90036

Regan, Donald T *Secretary, Treasury; Financier*
%William Morris Agency, 151 El Camino, Beverly Hills, CA 90212

Regazzoni, Clay *Auto Racing Driver*
Via Monzoni 13, CH-6900 Lugano, Switzerland

Regehr, Duncan *Actor*
%David Shapira Assoc, 15301 Ventura Blvd, #345, Sherman Oaks, CA 91403

Reggiani, Serge *Singer, Actor*
Le Redon, 06370 Mouans-Sartoux, France

Reghanti, Thomas J *Businessman*
%Fruehauf Corp, 10900 Harper Ave, Detroit, MI 48213

Regula, Ralph *Representative, OH*
%House of Representatives, Washington, DC 20515

Rehm, Jack D *Publisher*
%Meredith Corp, 1716 Locust St, Des Moines, IA 50336

Rehnquist, William H *Supreme Court Chief Justice*
%US Supreme Court, 1 1st St NE, Washington, DC 20543

Reich, Jack E *Businessman*
%American United Life Insurance, 1 American Sq, Indianapolis, IN 46206

Reich, John *Theater Director*
724 Bohemia Pkwy, Sayville, NY 11782

Reich, Robert B *Economist*
%Harvard University, School of Government, Cambridge, MA 02138

Reich, Steve *Composer*
%Lynn Garon Mgmt, 1199 Park Ave, New York, NY 10028

Reichardt, Carl E *Financier*
%Wells Fargo Co, 420 Montgomery St, San Francisco, CA 94163

Reichert, Jack F *Businessman*
%Brunswick Corp, 1 Brunswick Plz, Skokie, IL 60077

Reichman, Fred *Artist*
1235 Stanyan St, San Francisco, CA 94117

Reichman, Paul *Businessman*
%Olympia & York Develop, 2 First Canadian Pl, Toronto ON M5X 1B5, Canada

Reichstein, Tadeus *Nobel Medicine Laureate*
Weissensteinstrasse 22, CH-4059 Basel, Switzerland

Reid, Frances *Actress*
%Brooke Dunn Oliver Agency, 9165 Sunset Blvd, #202, Los Angeles, CA 90069

Reid, Harry *Senator, NV*
%US Senate, Washington, DC 20510

Reid, J R *Basketball Player*
%Charlotte Hornets, 2 First Union Ctr, #2600, Charlotte, NC 28282

Reid, James S, Jr *Businessman*
%Standard Products Co, 2130 W 110th St, Cleveland, OH 44102

Reid, Ogden R *Journalist, Diplomat*
Ophir Hill, Purchase, NY 10577

Reid, Robert *Basketball Player*
%Charlotte Hornets, 2 First Union Ctr, #2600, Charlotte, NC 28202

Reid, Robert *Skier*
%Dixfield Health Care Ctr, Dixfield, ME 04224

Reid, Steve (Stephen E) *Football Player, Physician*
262 Graemere, Northfield, IL 60093

Reid, Tim *Actor*
16540 Adlon Rd, Encino, CA 91436

Reid, William R *WW II British Royal Air Force Hero (VC)*
Cranford, Ferntower Pl, Crieff, Perthshire PH7 3DD, Scotland

Reif, Louis R *Businessman*
%National Fuel Gas Co, 30 Rockefeller Plz, New York, NY 10112

Reig Rodriguez, Joaquin *Businessman*
Compania Espanola de Petroleas, Avenida de America 32, Madrid 2, Spain

Reightler, Kenneth S, Jr *Astronaut*
%NASA, Johnson Space Ctr, Houston, TX 77058

Reilly, Charles Nelson *Actor*
2341 Gloaming Way, Beverly Hills, CA 90210

Reilly, John *Actor*
%Harris Goldberg Agency, 1999 Ave of Stars, #2850, Los Angeles, CA 90067

Reilly, Robert F *Businessman*
%Phillips-Van Heusen Corp, 1290 Ave of Americas, New York, NY 10104

Reilly, William K *Government Official*
%Environmental Protection Agency, 401 "M" St SW, Washington, DC 20460

Reimer, Dennis J *Army General*
Vice Chief of Staff, Hq USA, Washington, DC 20310

Reimer, Roland *Religious Leader*
%Mennonite Brethren Churches General Conference, 8000 W 21st, Wichita, KS 67212

Reiner, Carl *Actor, Writer, Director*
714 N Rodeo Dr, Beverly Hills, CA 90210

Reiner, Rob *Actor, Movie Director*
9161 Hazen Dr, Beverly Hills, CA 90210

Reines, Frederick *Physicist*
2655 Basswood St, Newport Beach, CA 92660

Reinhardt, John E *Diplomat*
6801 Laverock Ct, Bethesda, MD 20817

Reinhardt, Max *Publisher*
16 Pelham Cres, London SW7 2NR, England

Reinhardt, Stephen *Judge*
%US Court of Appeals, 312 N Spring St, Los Angeles, CA 90012

Reinhart, Andrew J *Businessman*
%Grolier Inc, Sherman Turnpike, Danbury, CT 06816

Reinhold, Judge *Actor, Director*
%International Creative Mgmt, 8899 Beverly Blvd, Los Angeles, CA 90048

Reinisch, June M *Association Executive*
%Kinsey Institute, Morrison Hall, Bloomington, IN 47405

Reinking, Ann *Actress, Dancer*
80 Central Park West, #7-G, New York, NY 10023

Reinsdorf, Jerry M *Baseball Executive*
%Chicago White Sox, 333 W 35th St, Chicago, IL 60616

Reiser, Paul *Actor*
%William Morris Agency, 151 El Camino, Beverly Hills, CA 90212

Reitz, Bruce *Surgeon*
%Johns Hopkins Hospital, 600 N Wolfe St, Baltimore, MD 21205

Reitz, Elmer A *Businessman*
%Greif Bros Corp, 621 Pennsylvania Ave, Delaware, OH 43015

Relman, Arnold *Editor, Physician*
%New England Journal of Medicine, 1440 Main St, Waltham, MA 02554

Remigino, Lindy *Track Athlete*
22 Paris Ln, Newington, CT 06111

Remsen, Bert *Actor*
5722 Mammoth Ave, Van Nuys, CA 91401

Remy, Jerry *Baseball Player*
5 Dennis Dr, Westport, MA 02790

Renaud, Line *Singer*
%Folklore, 1671 Appian Way, Santa Monica, CA 90401

Renchard, William S *Financier*
%Chemical Bank, 30 Rockefeller Plz, New York, NY 10112

Rendell, Ed *Mayor*
%Mayor's Office, City Hall, 23 N Juniper St, Philadelphia, PA 19107

Rendell, Ruth *Writer*
Nussteads, Polstead, Suffolk, Colchester CO6 5DN, England

Rene, Albert *President, Seychelles*
%State House, Victoria, Mahe, Seychelles

Renier, James J *Businessman*
%Honeywell Inc, Honeywell Plz, Minneapolis, MN 55408

Renko, Steve *Baseball Player*
3408 W 35th St, Leawood, KS 68209

Rennebohm, J Fred *Religious Leader*
%Congregational Christian Churches National Assn, Box 1620, Oak Creek, MI 53154

Renner, William B *Businessman*
%Aluminum Co of America, 1501 Alcoa Bldg, Pittsburgh, PA 15219

Rennert, Wolfgang *Conductor*
Holbeinstrasse 58, 100 Berlin 45, Germany

Reno, William H *Army General*
Dept Chief of Staff for Personnel, Hq USA, Washington, DC 20310

Rens, A N *Businessman*
%Esso N V, Frankrijklei 101, 2000 Antwerp, Belgium

Rensch, Joseph R *Businessman*
%Pacific Lighting Corp, 810 S Flower St, Los Angeles, CA 90017

Rense, Paige *Editor*
1288 Angelo Dr, Beverly Hills, CA 90210

Rensi, Edward H *Businessman*
%McDonald's Corp, McDonald's Plz, Oak Brook, IL 60521

Rentmeester, Co *Photographer*
4479 Douglas Ave, Bronx, NY 10971

Rentschler, Frederick B *Businessman*
%Northwest Airlines Inc, Minneapolis-St Paul Airport, St Paul, MN 55111

Rescigno, Nicola *Conductor*
61 W 62nd St, #6-F, New York, NY 10023

Reshevsky, Samuel H *Chess Player*
5 Hadassah Ln, Spring Valley, NY 10977

Resnais, Alain *Movie Director*
70 Rue Des Plantes, 75014 Paris, France

Resnick, Milton *Artist*
80 Forsyth St, New York, NY 10002

Resnik, Regina *Opera Singer*
50 W 56th St, New York, NY 10019

Restani, Jane A *Judge*
%US Court of International Trade, 1 Federal Plz, New York, NY 10007

Reston, James *Columnist*
1804 Kallorama Sq NW, Washington, DC 20008

Retton, Mary Lou *Gymnast*
RR 9, Box 493, Fairmont, WV 26554

Retzlaff, Pete *Football Player*
%Sports Film, 511 Old Lancaster Pike, Berwyn, PA 19312

Reuben, David R *Psychiatrist, Writer*
%Scott Meredith, 845 3rd Ave, New York, NY 10022

Reuschel, Rick *Baseball Player*
1403 Picadilly Cir, Mount Prospect, IL 60056

Reuss, Jerry *Baseball Player*
%ESPN, Sports Dept, ESPN Plaza, 935 Middle St, Bristol, CT 06010

Reuss, Lloyd E *Businessman*
%General Motors Corp, 3044 W Grand Blvd, Detroit, MI 48202

Reuter, Edzard *Businessman*
%Daimler-Benz AG, Postfach 202, 7000 Stuttgart 60, Germany

Reutter, Hermann *Concert Pianist*
%Elfenstrasse 107, Stuttgart-Mohringen, Germany

Revel, Jean-Francois *Writer*
55 Quai de Bourbon, 75004 Paris, France

Reviglio, Franco *Businessman*
%Ente Nazionale Indrocarburi, Piazzala Enrico Mattei 1, 00144 Rome, Italy

Revill, Clive *Actor*
%Judy Schoen Assoc, 606 N Larchmont Blvd, #206, Los Angeles, CA 90004

Revollo Bravo, Mario Cardinal *Religious Leader*
Arzobispado, Carrera 7a N 10-20, Bogota DE, Colombia

Rey, Fernando *Actor*
Orense 62, Madrid 20, Spain

Reynolds Booth, Nancy *Skier*
3197 Padaro Ln, Carpinteria, CA 93013

Reynolds, A William *Businessman*
%GenCorp Inc, 175 Ghent Rd, Akron, OH 44313

R

Reynolds – Rhodes

Reynolds, Albert *Prime Minister, Ireland*
%Prime Minister's Office, Parliament, Dublin, Ireland

Reynolds, Allie *Baseball Player*
2709 Cashion Pl, Oklahoma City, OK 73112

Reynolds, Anna *Opera Singer*
37 Chelwood Gdns, Richmond, Surrey TW9 4JG, England

Reynolds, Burt *Actor*
1001 Indiantown Rd, Jupiter, FL 33458

Reynolds, Butch *Track Athlete*
%Advantage International, 1025 Thomas Jefferson St NW, Washington, DC 20007

Reynolds, David P *Businessman*
%Reynolds Metals Co, 6601 Broad Street Rd, Richmond, VA 23261

Reynolds, Dean *Commentator*
%ABC-TV, News Dept, 1717 De Sales St NW, Washington, DC 20036

Reynolds, Debbie *Actress, Singer*
11595 La Maida, North Hollywood, CA 91602

Reynolds, Donald W *Publisher*
%Donrey House, 920 Rogers Ave, Fort Smith, AR 72902

Reynolds, Frank *Commentator*
1124 Connecticut Ave NW, Washington, DC 20036

Reynolds, Gene *Actor*
2034 Castillian Dr, Los Angeles, CA 90068

Reynolds, Gordon E *Businessman*
%Sealed Power Corp, 100 Terrace Plz, Muskegon, MI 49443

Reynolds, Herbert H *Educator*
%Baylor University, President's Office, Waco, TX 76798

Reynolds, J Guy *Navy Admiral*
Director, Test/Evaluation/Technology, Navy Department, Washington, DC 20350

Reynolds, J Louis *Businessman*
5511 Cary Street Rd, Richmond, VA 23226

Reynolds, Jerry *Basketball Coach*
%Sacramento Kings, 1515 Sports Dr, Sacramento, CA 95834

Reynolds, John H *Physicist, Educator*
%University of California, Physics Dept, Berkeley, CA 94720

Reynolds, John W *Governor, WI; Judge*
%US District Court, 517 E Wisconsin Ave, Milwaukee, WI 53202

Reynolds, Peter William John *Businessman*
%Ranks Hovis Mcdougall, Alma Rd, Windsor, Berks SL4 3ST, England

Reynolds, Randolph N *Businessman*
%Reynolds Metals Co, 6601 Broad St, Richmond, VA 23261

Reynolds, Robert O *Football Player*
11661 San Vicente Blvd, #306, Los Angeles, CA 90049

Reynolds, Thomas A, Jr *Attorney*
%Winston & Strawn, 1 First National Plz, Chicago, IL 60603

Reynolds, William C, Jr *Businessman*
%Foster Wheeler Corp, 110 S Orange Ave, Livingston, NJ 07039

Rhoades, Barbara *Actress*
12366 Ridge Cir, Los Angeles, CA 90049

Rhoads, George *Sculptor*
1478 Mecklenburg Rd, Ithaca, NY 14850

Rhoads, James B *Archivist*
%Rhoads Assoc, 6502 Cipriano Rd, Lanham, MD 20706

Rhoden, Rick *Baseball Player*
235 SW 12th Ave, Boynton Beach, FL 33435

Rhodes, Donnelly *Actor*
%Century Artists, 9744 Wilshire Blvd, #308, Beverly Hills, CA 90212

Rhodes, Frank H T *Educator*
%Cornell University, President's Office, Ithaca, NY 14853

Rhodes, James A *Governor, OH*
2375 Tremont Rd, Columbus, OH 43221

Rhodes, John J *Representative, AZ*
1114 N Cherry, Mesa, AZ 85201

Rhodes, John J, III *Representative, AZ*
%House of Representatives, Washington, DC 20515

Rhodes, William R *Financier*
%Citicorp, 399 Park Ave, New York, NY 10013

Rhodes, Zhandra *Fashion Designer*
85/87 Richford St, Hammersmith, London W6 7HJ, England

Rhome, Jerry *Football Player, Coach*
%Phoenix Cardinals, PO Box 888, Phoenix, AZ 85001

Rhue, Madlyn *Actress*
%Harry Gold Assoc, 3500 W Olive, #1400, Burbank, CA 91505

Rhys-Davies, John *Actor*
%The Agency, 10351 Santa Monica Blvd, #211, Los Angeles, CA 90025

Riady, Mochtar *Financier*
%Bank Central Asia, 25/26 Jalan Asemka, Jakarta Barat 01, Indonesia

Ribbs, Willy T *Auto Racing Driver*
%International Motor Sports Assn, PO Box 3465, Bridgeport, CT 06605

Ribeiro, Antonio Cardinal *Religious Leader*
Campo Martires da Patria 45, 1198 Lisbon Codex, Portugal

Ribicoff, Abraham *Secretary, Health Education & Welfare*
%Kaye Scholer Fierman Hays Handler, 425 Park Ave, New York, NY 10022

Riboud, Antoine *Businessman*
%Boussois-Souchon-Neuvese, 7 Rue de Teheran, 75381 Paris Cedex 08, France

Ricardo-Campbell, Rita *Economist*
26915 Alejandro Dr, Los Altos Hills, CA 94022

Riccardo, John J *Businessman*
2243 Tottenham, Birmingham, MI 10172

Ricci, Franco Maria *Publisher*
Via Cino Del Duca 8, 20122 Milan, Italy

Ricci, Ruggiero *Concert Violinist*
2930 E Delhi Rd, Ann Arbor, MI 48103

Ricciardi, Franc M *Businessman*
%Richton International Corp, 1345 Ave of Americas, New York, NY 10105

Rice, Donald B *Government Official*
%Secretary's Office, Department of Air Force, Pentagon, Washington, DC 20330

Rice, Donna *Actress*
%Erickson Agency, 1483 Chain Bridge Rd, McLean, VA 22101

Rice, Emmett J *Financier*
%Federal Reserve, 20th & Constitution NW, Washington, DC 20551

Rice, Gene D *Religious Leader*
%Church of God, PO Box 2430, Cleveland, TN 37320

Rice, Gene E *Financier*
%First Federal Savings & Loan, 3003 N Central Ave, Phoenix, AZ 85012

Rice, Glen *Basketball Player*
%Miami Heat, 100 Chopin Plz, Miami, FL 33131

Rice, Jerry *Football Player*
%San Francisco 49ers, 4949 Centennial Blvd, Santa Clara, CA 95054

Rice, Jim *Baseball Player*
135 Woden Wy, Winter Haven, FL 33880

Rice, Joseph A *Financier*
%Irving Bank Corp, 1 Wall St, New York, NY 10005

Rice, Norm *Mayor*
%Mayor's Office, City Hall, 600 4th Ave, Seattle, WA 98104

Rice, Stuart A *Chemist*
5421 Greenwood Ave, Chicago, IL 60615

Rice, Tim *Lyricist*
196 Shaftesbury Ave, London WC2, England

Rich, Adam *Actor*
1450 Belfast Dr, Los Angeles, CA 90069

Rich, Adrienne *Poet*
%Stanford University, English Dept, Stanford, CA 94305

Rich, Alexander *Molecular Biologist*
2 Walnut Ave, Cambridge, MA 02140

Rich, Allan *Actor*
225 E 57th St, New York, NY 10022

Rich, Ben R *Aeronautical Engineer, Designer*
%Lockheed Aeronautical System, 2550 N Hollywood Way, Burbank, CA 91510

Rich, Frank H *Drama Critic*
%New York Times, 229 W 43rd St, New York, NY 10036

Rich, Giles S *Judge*
%US Court of Appeals, 717 Madison Pl NW, Washington, DC 20439

R

Rich – Richardson

Rich, Harry E *Businessman*
%Brown Grp, 8400 Maryland Ave, St Louis, MO 63105

Rich, Lee *Entertainment Executive*
%Lee Rich Productions, Warner Communs, 75 Rockefeller Plz, New York, NY 10019

Rich, Marc *Businessman*
%Marc Rich Co AG, Zug, Switzerland

Rich, Patrick *Businessman*
%BOC Group, Hammersmith House, London W6, England

Richard, Cliff *Singer*
%Gormley Mgmt, PO Box 46-C, Esher, Surrey KY10 9AF, England

Richard, Harold *Businessman*
%AGRI Industries, PO Box 4887, Des Moines, IA 50306

Richard, Henri *Hockey Player*
%Brasserie Henri Richard, 3461 Park, Montreal PQ H2X 2X6, Canada

Richard, J R *Baseball Player*
10235 Sagedale, Houston, TX 77089

Richard, Maurice *Hockey Player*
10950 Peloquin, Montreal PQ H2C 2K8, Canada

Richards, Ann W *Governor, TX*
%Governor's Office, State Capitol, PO Box 12428, Austin, TX 78711

Richards, Beah *Actress*
1308 S New Hampshire Ave, Los Angeles, CA 90019

Richards, Bob *Track Athlete*
%Chatham Corp, 1853 Zanzibar Ln, Minneapolis, MN 55441

Richards, Frank *Actor*
%William Carroll Agency, 120 S Victory Blvd, #104, Burbank, CA 91501

Richards, Frederic M *Biochemist*
69 Andrews Rd, Guilford, CT 06437

Richards, Keith *Musician*
Redlands, W Wittering, Chichester, Sussex, England

Richards, Lloyd *Theatre Director*
90 York Sq, New Haven, CT 06511

Richards, Mark *Surfer*
755 Hunter St, Newcastle NSW 2302, Australia

Richards, Paul G *Theoretical Seismologist*
%Columbia University, Geological Sciences Dept, New York, NY 10027

Richards, Reuben F *Businessman*
%Inspiration Resources Corp, 250 Park Ave, New York, NY 10177

Richards, Richard N *Astronaut*
%NASA, Johnson Space Ctr, Houston, TX 77058

Richardson of Duntisbourne, William H *Financier*
%Bank of England, London EC2R 8AH, England

Richardson of Lee, John S *Physician*
Windcutter, Lee, North Devon, England

Richardson, Ashley *Model*
%Ford Model Agency, 344 E 59th St, New York, NY 10022

Richardson, Bill *Representative, NM*
%House of Representatives, Washington, DC 20515

Richardson, Bobby *Baseball Player*
47 Adams, Sumter, SC 29150

Richardson, D Kenneth *Businessman*
%Hughes Aircraft Co, 200 N Sepulveda Blvd, El Segundo, CA 90245

Richardson, Elliot L *Secretary, Defense & HEW*
%Milbank Tweed Hadley McCloy, 1825 "I" St NW, Washington, DC 20006

Richardson, F C *Educator*
%State University of New York, President's Office, Buffalo, NY 14222

Richardson, Frank H *Businessman*
%Shell Oil Co, 1 Shell Plz, Houston, TX 77002

Richardson, Gordon W H *Financier*
%Bank of England, London EC2R 8AH, England

Richardson, Hamilton *Tennis Player*
920 Park Ave, New York, NY 10028

Richardson, Howard *Playwright*
207 Columbus Ave, New York, NY 10023

Richardson, Ian *Actor*
131 Lavender Sweep, London SW 11, England

Richardson, John T *Educator*
%DePaul University, Chancellor's Office, Chicago, IL 60604

Richardson, Midge *Editor*
%Seventeen Magazine, 850 3rd Ave, New York, NY 10022

Richardson, Nolan *Basketball Coach*
%University of Arkansas, Broyles Athletic Complex, Fayetteville, AR 72701

Richardson, Pooh *Basketball Player*
%Minnesota Timberwolves, 500 City Pl, 730 Hennepin Ave, Minneapolis, MN 55403

Richardson, S Smith, Jr *Businessman*
%Richardson-Vicks Inc, 10 Westport Rd, Wilton, CT 06897

Richardson, Sam *Sculptor*
4121 Sequoyah Rd, Oakland, CA 94605

Richardson, Susan *Actress*
%Joseph/Knight Agency, 1680 N Vine St, #726, Los Angeles, CA 90028

Richardson, W Franklyn *Religious Leader*
%National Baptist Convention, 52 S 6th Ave, Mt Vernon, NY 10550

Richer, Stephane *Hockey Player*
%Montreal Canadiens, 2313 St Catherine St W, Montreal PQ H3H 1N2, Canada

Richey, Ronald K *Businessman*
%Torchmark Corp, 2001 3rd Ave S, Birmingham, AL 35233

Richie, Lionel *Singer, Songwriter*
%Kragen & Co, 1112 N Sherbourne Dr, Los Angeles, CA 90069

Richler, Mordecai *Writer*
1321 Sherbroke St W, #80-C, Montreal PQ H3Y 1J4, Canada

Richley, Robert D *Financier*
%First City BankCorp, 1001 Fannin St, #400, Houston, TX 77002

Richman, Caryn *Actress*
%Paul Kohner Inc, 9169 Sunset Blvd, Los Angeles, CA 90069

Richman, Herbert J *Businessman*
%Data General Corp, 4400 Computer Dr, Westboro, MA 01580

Richman, Peter Mark *Actor*
5114 Del Moreno Dr, Woodland Hills, CA 91364

Richmond, Mitch *Basketball Player*
%Sacramento Kings, 1 Sports Dr, Sacramento, CA 95834

Richter, Annegret *Track Athlete*
Benninghofer Strasse 47, 4600 Dortmund-Horde, Germany

Richter, Burton *Nobel Physics Laureate*
%Stanford University, Linear Accelerator Ctr, PO Box 4349, Stanford, CA 94305

Richter, E E *Businessman*
%Modine Manufacturing Co, 1500 DeKoven Ave, Racine, WI 53401

Richter, Gerhard *Artist*
%Marian Goodman Gallery, 24 W 57th St, New York, NY 10019

Richter, Hans W *Writer*
Flossmannstrasse 13, 8 Munich 60, Germany

Richter, Les *Football Player*
%NASCAR, 1801 Speedway Blvd, Daytona Beach, FL 32015

Richter, Pat *Football Player, Administrator*
%University of Wisconsin, Athletic Dept, 1440 Monroe St, Madison, WI 53711

Richter, Sviatoslav *Concert Pianist*
%Moscow State Philharmonic Society, 31 Ul Gorkogo, Moscow, Russia

Richter, Ulrike *Swimmer*
Goethestrasse 65, 9417 Zwonitz, Germany

Rick, Charles M, Jr *Geneticist*
8 Parkside Dr, Davis, CA 95616

Rickards, L M *Businessman*
%Phillips Petroleum Co, Phillips Bldg, Bartlesville, OK 74004

Ricken, Norman *Businessman*
%Toys "R" Us Inc, 395 W Passiac St, Rochelle Park, NJ 07662

Ricker, Robert S *Religious Leader*
%Baptist General Conference, 2002 S A Heights Rd, Arlinghton Heights, IL 60005

Rickershauser, Charles E, Jr *Financier*
%Pacific Stock Exchange, 233 S Beaudry Ave, Los Angeles, CA 90012

Rickey, George W *Sculptor*
Rt 2, Box 235, East Chatham, NY 12060

Rickles, Don *Comedian*
925 N Alpine Dr, Beverly Hills, CA 90210

Rickman, Alan *Actor*
%InterTalent Agency, 131 S Rodeo Dr, #300, Beverly Hills, CA 90212

Ridder, Anthony *Publisher*
%Knight-Ridder Newspapers, 1 Herald Plz, Miami, FL 33101

Ridder, Bernard H, Jr *Publisher*
%Knight-Ridder Newspapers, 1 Herald Plz, Miami, FL 33101

Ridder, P Anthony *Publisher*
%San Jose Mercury News, 750 Ridder Park Dr, San Jose, CA 95190

Riddick, Steve *Track Athlete*
7601 Crittenden, #F-2, Philadelphia, PA 19118

Riddles, Libby *Dog Sled Racer*
%General Delivery, Teller, AK 99778

Ride, Sally K *Astronaut*
%California Space Institute, Univ of California, MS-0221, La Jolla, CA 92093

Ridge, Tom *Representative, PA*
%House of Representatives, Washington, DC 20515

Ridgeway, Matthew B *Army General*
918 W Waldheim Rd, Pittsburgh, PA 15215

Ridgley, Bob *Actor*
%Twentieth Century Artists, 3800 Barham Blvd, Los Angeles, CA 90068

Ridgway, Brunilde S *Archaeologist*
%Bryn Mawr College, Archaeology Dept, Bryn Mawr, PA 19010

Riedy, John K *Businessman*
%Interco Inc, PO Box 8777, St Louis, MO 63102

Riefenstahl, Leni *Movie Director*
Tengstrasse 20, 8000 Munich 40, Germany

Riegle, Donald W, Jr *Senator, MI*
%US Senate, Washington, DC 20515

Rienstra, John *Football Player*
%Cleveland Browns, Cleveland Stadium, Cleveland, OH 44114

Riessen, Marty *Tennis Player*
%US Tennis Assn, 1212 Ave of Americas, New York, NY 10036

Rietz, Robert A *Businessman*
%A O Smith Corp, 11270 W Park Pl, Milwaukee, WI 53224

Rifkin, Jeremy *Writer, Social Activist*
%Economic Trends Foundation, 1130 17th St NW, #630, Washington, DC 20036

Rifkin, Ron *Actor*
%Triad Artists, 10100 Santa Monica Blvd, #1600, Los Angeles, CA 90067

Rigby McCoy, Cathy *Gymnast*
%Cathy Rigby Gym, 18948 Persimmon St, Fountain Valley, CA 92708

Rigg, Diana *Actress*
%London Mgmt, 235-241 Regent St, London W1A 2JT, England

Riggin Soule, Aileen *Diver*
2943 Kalakaua Ave, #1007, Honolulu, HI 96815

Riggin, Paul *Hockey Player*
%Washington Capitals, Capital Ctr, 1 Truman Dr, Landover, MD 20785

Riggins, Gerald *Football Player*
%Washington Redskins, Dulles Airport, Box 17247, Washington, DC 20041

Riggs, Bobby *Tennis Player*
508 "E" Ave, Coronado, CA 92118

Riggs, Frank *Representative, CA*
%House of Representatives, Washington, DC 20515

Riggs, Gerald *Football Player*
%Washington Redskins, Dulles Airport, Box 17247, Washington, DC 20041

Riggs, Henry F *Educator*
%Harvey Mudd College, President's Office, Claremont, CA 91711

Riggs, Lorrin A *Psychologist*
Brown University, Psychology Laboratory, Providence, RI 02912

Riggs, Robert O *Educator*
%Austin Peay State University, President's Office, Clarkesville, TN 37044

Righetti, Dave *Baseball Player*
1574 Koch Ln, San Jose, CA 95125

Righi-Lambertini, Egano Cardinal *Religious Leader*
Piazza della Citta Leonina 9, 00193 Rome, Italy

Rights, Graham H *Religious Leader*
%Moravian Church Southern Province, 459 S Church St, Winston-Salem, NC 27108

Rigney, Bill *Baseball Manager*
3136 Round Hill Rd, Alamo, CA 94507

Riha, Bohumil *Writer*
Belohorska 137, Prague 6 169 00, Czechoslovakia

Riker, Albert J *Plant Pathologist*
2760 E 8th St, Tucson, AZ 85716

Riklis, Meshulam *Businessman*
%Rapid-American Corp, 888 7th Ave, New York, NY 10106

Riles, Wilson *Educator*
%California Department of Education, 721 Capitol Mall, Sacramento, CA 95814

Riley, Bridget *Artist*
%Juda Rowan Gallery, 11 Tottenham Mews, London W1P 9PJ, England

Riley, Gary *Actor*
%Harry Gold Assoc, 3500 W Olive Ave, #1400, Burbank, CA 91505

Riley, Jack *Actor*
%Artists Agency, 10000 Santa Monica Blvd, #305, Los Angeles, CA 90067

Riley, Jack *Hockey Coach*
%US Military Academy, Athletic Dept, West Point, NY 10996

Riley, Jeannie C *Singer*
%J R Monaghan, PO Box 454, Brentwood, TN 37027

Riley, Pat *Basketball Player, Coach*
%New York Knicks, Madison Square Grdn, 4 Pennsylvania Plz, New York, NY 10001

Riley, Richard A *Businessman*
%Firestone Tire & Rubber Co, 1200 Firestone Pkwy, Akron, OH 44317

Riley, Terry M *Composer, Musician*
%Shri Moonshine Ranch, 13699 Moonshine Rd, Camptonville, CA 95922

Rimington, Dave *Football Player*
%Philadelphia Eagles, Veterans Stadium, Philadelphia, PA 19148

Rimmel, James E *Religious Leader*
%Evangelical Presbyterian Church, 26049 Five Mile Rd, Detroit, MI 48239

Rinaldi, Kathy *Tennis Player*
%Advantage International, 1025 Thomas Jefferson St NW, Washington, DC 20007

Rinaldo, Benjamin *Skier*
%The Ski World, 3680 Buena Park Dr, North Hollywood, CA 91604

Rinaldo, Matthew J *Representative, NJ*
142 Headley Terr, Union, NJ 07083

Rinearson, Peter M *Journalist*
Seattle Times, Fairview & John, Seattle, WA 98111

Rinehart, Kenneth *Chemist*
%University of Illinois, Chemistry Dept, Urbana, IL 61801

Ringeon, Richard M *Businessman*
%Ball Corp, 345 S High St, Muncie, IN 47302

Ringer, Robert J *Writer, Publisher*
%Stratford Press, 9606 Santa Monica Blvd, #40, Beverly Hills, CA 90210

Ringo, Jim *Football Player*
%Buffalo Bills, 1 Bills Dr, Orchard Park, NY 14127

Ringwald, Molly *Actress*
%International Creative Mgmt, 8899 Beverly Blvd, Los Angeles, CA 90048

Riopelle, Jean-Paul *Artist*
11 Rue Fremincourt, 75015 Paris, France

Riordan, James Q *Businessman*
%Mobil Corp, 150 E 42nd St, New York, NY 10017

Riordan, Mike *Basketball Player*
%Riordan's Saloon, 26 Market Space, Annapolis, MD 21401

Rios Montt, Efrain *President, Guatemala*
%President's Office, Guatemala City, Guatemala

Rios, Alberto *Poet*
%Arizona State University, English Dept, Tempe, AZ 85287

Ripken, Cal, Jr *Baseball Player*
410 Clover St, Aberdeen, MD 21001

Ripken, Cal, Sr *Baseball Manager*
410 Clover St, Aberdeen, MD 21001

Ripley, Alexandra *Writer*
%William Morris Agency, 151 El Camino, Beverly Hills, CA 90212

Ripley, S Dillon *Museum Director, Zoologist*
2324 Massachusetts Ave NW, Washington, DC 20008

R

Rippey – Roach

Rippey, Rodney Allan *Actor*
%Dorothy Day Otis, 6430 Sunset Blvd, Los Angeles, CA 90028

Ripple, Kenneth F *Judge*
%US Court of Appeals, 204 S Main St, South Bend, IN 46601

RisCassi, Robert W *Army General*
CINC, UN Cmd/Cbd Fcs, Cmd/US Forces Korea, EUSA, APO, AP 96205

Risebrough, Doug *Hockey Coach*
%Calgary Flames, PO Box 1540, Calgary AL T2P 3B9, Canada

Risien, Cody *Football Player*
%Cleveland Browns, Cleveland Stadium, Cleveland, OH 44114

Risk, Thomas N *Financier*
10 Bedford Pl, Edinburgh EH4 3DH, Scotland

Rison, Andre *Football Player*
%Atlanta Falcons, Suwanee Rd, Suwanee, GA 30174

Risse, Klaus H *Businessman*
%Miles Laboratories, 1127 Myrtle St, Elkhart, IN 46515

Ritcher, Jim *Football Player*
%Buffalo Bills, 1 Bills Dr, Orchard Park, NY 14127

Ritchey, S Donley *Businessman*
%Lucky Stores, 6300 Clark Ave, Dublin, CA 94568

Ritchie, Daniel L *Television Executive*
%Westinghouse Broadcasting Co, 888 7th Ave, New York, NY 10106

Ritchie, Michael *Movie Director, Producer*
%Miracle Pictures, 22 Miller Ave, Mill Valley, CA 94941

Ritchie-Calder, Peter *Writer*
Philipstoun House, Linlithgow, West Lothian, EH4 97NB, Scotland

Ritenour, Lee *Singer*
PO Box 6774, Malibu, CA 90265

Ritger, Dick *Bowler*
%Professional Bowlers Assn, 1720 Merriman Rd, Akron, OH 44313

Ritmeester van de Kamp, J E *Businessman*
%Royal Pkg Industries Van Leer, Anserdanseweg 26, Amsterdam, Netherlands

Ritter, Donald L *Representative, PA*
%House of Representatives, Washington, DC 20515

Ritter, John *Actor*
236 Tigertail Rd, Los Angeles, CA 90049

Rittereiser, Robert P *Businessman*
%E F Hutton Grp, 1 Battery Park Plz, New York, NY 10004

Rivera, Chita *Actress, Singer, Dancer*
99 S Greenbush, Blauvelt, NY 10913

Rivera, Geraldo *Entertainer*
311 W 43rd St, New York, NY 10036

Rivera, Ron *Football Player*
%Chicago Bears, 250 N Washington Rd, Lake Forest, IL 60045

Rivers, Doc *Basketball Player*
%Los Angeles Clippers, Sports Arena, 3939 S Figueroa St, Los Angeles, CA 90037

Rivers, Joan *Entertainer*
1 E 62nd St, New York, NY 10021

Rivers, Johnny *Singer*
3141 Coldwater Canyon Ln, Beverly Hills, CA 90210

Rivers, Larry *Artist*
92 Little Plains Rd, Southampton, NY 11968

Rivers, Mickey *Baseball Player*
350 NW 48th St, Miami, FL 33127

Rivette, Jacques *Movie Director*
20 Blvd de la Bastille, 75012 Paris, France

Rivlin, Alice M *Government Official, Environmentalist*
2842 Chesterfield Pl, Washington, DC 20008

Rizzuto, Phil *Baseball Player, Sportscaster*
912 Westminster Ave, Hillside, NJ 07205

Roach, Hal *Movie Producer*
1231 Lago Vista Dr, Beverly Hills, CA 90210

Roach, John R *Religious Leader*
226 Summit Ave, St Paul, MN 55102

Roach, John V *Businessman*
%Tandy Corp, 1800 One Tandy Ctr, Fort Worth, TX 76102

Roach, Max *Jazz Percussionist*
415 Central Park West, New York, NY 10025

Roark, Terry P *Educator*
%University of Wyoming, President's Office, Laramie, WY 82071

Robards, Jason *Actor*
%International Creative Mgmt, 8899 Beverly Blvd, Los Angeles, CA 90048

Robb, Charles S *Governor/Senator, VA*
%US Senate, Washington, DC 20510

Robbe-Grillet, Alain *Movie Director*
18 Blvd Maillot, 92200 Neuilly-sur-Seine, France

Robbins, D Walter, Jr *Businessman*
%W R Grace Co, 1114 Ave of Americas, New York, NY 10036

Robbins, Frederick C *Nobel Medicine Laureate*
7021 Oak Forest Ln, Bethesda, MD 20817

Robbins, Harold *Writer*
990 N Patencio Rd, Palm Springs, CA 92262

Robbins, Jerome *Choreographer, Director*
117 E 81st St, New York, NY 10028

Robbins, Marty *Singer*
713 18th Ave, Nashville, TN 37203

Robbins, Tim *Actor*
%International Creative Mgmt, 8899 Beverly Blvd, Los Angeles, CA 90048

Robbins, Tom *Writer*
PO Box 338, La Conner, WA 98257

Robens of Woldingham, Baron *Government Official, England*
%Johnson Matthey, 78 Hatton Gdn, London EC1N 8JF, England

Roberto Colin, Oswaldo *Financier*
%Banco do Brasil, Caixa Postal 562, 70 000 Brasilia DF, Brazil

Roberts, Barbara *Governor, OR*
%Governor's Office, State Capitol, #254, Salem, OR 97310

Roberts, Bert C, Jr *Businessman*
%MCI Communications Corp, 1133 19th St NW, Washington, DC 20036

Roberts, Burnell R *Businessman*
%Mead Corp, Courthouse Plz NE, Dayton, OH 45463

Roberts, Chalmers M *Journalist*
6699 MacArthur Blvd, Bethesda, MD 20816

Roberts, Charles C *Businessman*
%DeKalb AgResearch Inc, 3100 Sycamore Rd, DeKalb, IL 60115

Roberts, Doris *Actress*
6225 Quebec Dr, Los Angeles, CA 90068

Roberts, Eric *Actor*
853 7th Ave, #9-A, New York, NY 10019

Roberts, Eugene, Jr *Editor*
%Philadelphia Inquirer, 400 N Broad St, Philadelphia, PA 19101

Roberts, George A *Businessman*
%Teledyne Inc, 1901 Ave of Stars, Los Angeles, CA 90067

Roberts, George R *Financier*
%Kohlberg Kravis Roberts Co, 3 Embarcadero Ctr, San Francisco, CA 94111

Roberts, Henry R *Businessman*
171 Bloomfield Ave, Hartford, CT 06105

Roberts, John D *Chemist*
%California Institute of Technology, Chemistry Dept, Pasadena, CA 91125

Roberts, Julia *Actress*
%International Creative Mgmt, 8899 Beverly Blvd, Los Angeles, CA 90048

Roberts, Kenneth L *Financier*
%First American Corp, First American Ctr, Nashville, TN 37268

Roberts, Kenny *Motorcycle Racing Rider*
%Gary Howard, International Racers, 1633 E 4th St, #132, Santa Ana, CA 92701

Roberts, Larry *Football Player*
%San Francisco 49ers, 4949 Centennial Blvd, Santa Clara, CA 95054

Roberts, Oral *Evangelist*
%Oral Roberts University, 7777 S Lewis Ave, Tulsa, OK 74171

Roberts, Pat *Representative, KS*
%House of Representatives, Washington, DC 20515

Roberts, Pernell *Actor*
20395 Seaboard Rd, Malibu, CA 90265

Roberts, Robin *Baseball Player*
504 Terrace Hill Rd, Temple Terrace, FL 33617

Roberts, Robin *Sportscaster*
%ESPN-TV, Sports Dept, ESPN Center, 935 Middle St, Bristol, CT 06010

Roberts, Tanya *Actress*
%Agency for Performing Arts, 9000 Sunset Blvd, #1200, Los Angeles, CA 90069

Roberts, Thomas H, Jr *Businessman*
%DeKalb AgResearch Inc, 3100 Sycamore Rd, DeKalb, IL 60115

Roberts, Tony *Actor*
970 Park Ave, #8-N, New York, NY 10028

Roberts, Xavier *Businessman*
%Original Appalachian Artworks, Hwy 75, Cleveland, GA 30528

Robertson, Alvin *Basketball Player*
%Milwaukee Bucks, 1001 N 4th St, Milwaukee, WI 53203

Robertson, Cliff *Actor*
325 Dunemere Dr, La Jolla, CA 92037

Robertson, Dale *Actor*
13263 Ventura Blvd, #4, Studio City, CA 91604

Robertson, James D *Anatomist*
132 Oak Dr, Durham, NC 27707

Robertson, M G (Pat) *Evangelist*
%Christian Broadcasting Network, CBN Ctr, Virginia Beach, VA 23463

Robertson, Oscar *Basketball Player*
%Basketball Hall of Fame, PO Box 179, Springfield, MA 01101

Robertson, Robbie *Vocalist, Songwriter, Guitarist*
%Geffen Records, Warner Bros, 9130 Sunset Blvd, Los Angeles, CA 90069

Robertson, T Wayne *Businessman*
%Sports Marketing Enterprises, RJR-Nabisco, 9 W 57th St, New York, NY 10010

Robes, Ernest C (Bill) *Ski Jumper*
3 Mile Rd, Etna, NH 03750

Robie, Carl *Swimmer*
2828 S Tamiami Trl, Sarastota, FL 33579

Robinowitz, Joe *Editor, Publisher*
%TV Guide Magazine, 100 Matsonford Rd, Radnor, PA 19088

Robinowitz, Joseph *Editor*
%Boston Herald, 300 Harrison St, Boston, MA 02106

Robins, E Claiborne, Jr *Businessman*
%A H Robins Co, 1407 Cummings Dr, Richmond, VA 23261

Robinson of Woolwich, John *Religious Leader*
%Trinity College, Cambridge CB2 1TQ, England

Robinson, A N Raymond *Prime Minister, Trinidad & Tobago*
%Prime Minister's Office, St Ann's, Trinidad & Tobago

Robinson, Andrew *Actor*
%STE Representation, 9301 Wilshire Blvd, #312, Beverly Hills, CA 90210

Robinson, Arnie *Track Athlete*
5930 Albemarle, San Diego, CA 92139

Robinson, Arthur H *Cartographer*
101 Burr Oak Ln, Mount Horeb, WI 53572

Robinson, Brooks *Baseball Player*
1506 Sherbrook Rd, Lutherville, MD 21093

Robinson, Charles Knox *Actor*
%BDP Assoc, 10637 Burbank Blvd, North Hollywood, CA 91601

Robinson, Chip *Auto Racing Driver*
PO Box 476, Oldwick, NJ 08858

Robinson, Chris *Actor*
PO Box 85007, Los Angeles, CA 90072

Robinson, Cleveland *Labor Leader*
%Distributive Workers of America, 13 Astor Pl, New York, NY 10003

Robinson, Cliff *Basketball Player*
%Philadelphia 76ers, PO Box 25040, Veterans Stadium, Philadelphia, PA 19147

Robinson, Dave *Football Player*
406 S Rose Blvd, Akron, OH 44320

Robinson, David *Basketball Player*
%San Antonio Spurs, 600 E Market St, San Antonio, TX 78205

Robinson, Eddie G *Football Coach*
%Grambling State University, Athletic Dept, Grambling, LA 71245

Robinson, Frank *Baseball Player, Manager*
15557 Aqua Verde Dr, Los Angeles, CA 90077

Robinson, Gerald *Football Player*
%Minnesota Vikings, 9520 Vikings Dr, Eden Prairie, MN 55344

Robinson, Holly *Actress*
%Dolores Robinson Mgmt, 335 N Maple Dr, #250, Beverly Hills, CA 90210

Robinson, James D, III *Businessman*
%American Express Co, 1 American Express Plz, New York, NY 10004

Robinson, Jerry *Football Player*
%Los Angeles Raiders, 332 Center St, El Segundo, CA 90245

Robinson, Larry *Hockey Player*
%Los Angeles Kings, Great Western Forum, 3900 W Manchester, Inglewood, CA 90306

Robinson, Laura *Actress*
1933 Monon St, Los Angeles, CA 90027

Robinson, Mary *President, Ireland*
%President's Office, Baile Atha Cliath 8, Dublin, Ireland

Robinson, Paul Heron, Jr *Financier, Diplomat*
%American Embassy, 100 Wellington St, Ottawa ON K1P 5T1, Canada

Robinson, Rumeal *Basketball Player*
%Atlanta Hawks, 100 Techwood Dr NW, Atlanta, GA 30303

Robinson, Smokey *Singer, Songwriter*
631 N Oakhurst Dr, Beverly Hills, CA 90210

Robinson, Spottswood W, III *Judge*
%US Court of Appeals, 3rd & Constitution NW, Washington, DC 20001

Robinson, Wilkes C *Judge*
%US Claims Court, 717 Madison Pl NW, Washington, DC 20005

Robison, Paula *Concert Flutist*
%Kazuko Hillyer International, 250 W 57th St, New York, NY 10019

Robitaille, Luc *Hockey Player*
%Los Angeles Kings, Great Western Forum, 3900 W Manchester, Inglewood, CA 90306

Robustelli, Andy *Football Player*
%Robustelli World Travel, 30 Spring St, Stamford, CT 06901

Roby, Reggie *Football Player*
%Miami Dolphins, 2269 NW 199th St, Miami, FL 33056

Rocard, Michel *Premier, France*
72 Rue de Varenne, 75700 Paris, France

Rocco, Alex *Actor*
1755 Ocean Oaks Rd, Carpinteria, CA 93013

Rocco, Louis R *Vietnam War Army Hero (CMH)*
3918 San Isidro NW, Albuquerque, NM 87107

Rochberg, George *Composer*
285 Aronimink Dr, Newton Square, PA 19073

Roche, Anthony D (Tony) *Tennis Player*
5 Kapiti St, St Ives NSW 2075, Australia

Roche, Eugene *Actor*
451 1/2 Kelton Ave, Los Angeles, CA 90024

Roche, James M *Businessman*
425 Dunston Rd, Bloomfield Hills, MI 48013

Roche, John P *Political Scientist*
15 Bay State Rd, Weston, MA 02193

Roche, Kevin *Architect*
20 Davis St, Hamden, CT 06517

Rock, Arthur *Businessman*
%Arthur Rock Co, 1635 Russ Bldg, San Francisco, CA 94104

Rock, Doug *Businessman*
%Smith International Inc, 4490 Von Karman Ave, Newport Beach, CA 92660

Rockefeller, David *Financier*
1 Chase Manhattan Plz, New York, NY 10015

Rockefeller, John D (Jay), IV *Senator/Governor, WV*
%US Senate, Washington, DC 20510

Rockefeller, Laurance S *Businessman*
%Rockefeller Bros Fund, 30 Rockefeller Plz, New York, NY 10112

Rockwell, Martha *Skier, Coach*
%Dartmouth College, Box 9, Hanover, NH 03755

Rockwell, Willard F, Jr *Businessman*
%Rockwell International Corp, 600 Grant St, Pittsburgh, PA 15219

R

Rodberg – Rogers

Rodberg, Lawrence L *Businessman*
%Air Express International Corp, 151 Harvard Ave, Stamford, CT 06902

Rodd, Marcia *Actress*
251 W 71st St, New York, NY 10023

Roddey, Otha C *Businessman*
%Parsons Corp, 100 W Walnut St, Pasadena, CA 91124

Roderick, David M *Businessman*
%USX Corp, 600 Grant St, Pittsburgh, PA 15230

Rodgers, Bill *Marathon Runner*
372 Chestnut Hill Ave, Boston, MA 02146

Rodgers, Jimmy *Basketball Coach*
%Minnesota Timberwolves, 500 City Place, 730 Hennepin Ave, Minneapolis, MN 55403

Rodgers, John *Geologist*
%Yale University, Geology Dept, New Haven, CT 06520

Rodgers, Johnny *Football Player*
2925 Hamilton, Omaha, NE 68131

Rodgers, T J *Businessman*
%Cypress Semiconductor, 3901 N 1st St, San Jose, CA 95134

Rodino, Peter W, Jr *Representative, NJ*
970 Broad St, Newark, NJ 07102

Rodman, Dennis *Basketball Player*
%Detroit Pistons, Palace, 1 Championship Dr, Auburn Hills, MI 48057

Rodrigue, George *Journalist*
%Dallas News, Communications Ctr, Dallas, TX 75265

Rodriguez Castella, Luis *Businessman*
%Empresa Nacional Siderurgica SA, Velazquez #134, Madrid 6, Spain

Rodriguez, Andres *President, Paraguay*
%Casa Presidencial, Ave Mariscal Lopez, Asuncion, Paraguay

Rodriguez, Chi Chi (Juan) *Golfer*
%Professional Golfers Assn, PO Box 12458, Palm Beach Gardens, FL 33410

Rodriguez, Johnny *Singer*
PO Box 488, Sabinal, TX 78881

Rodriguez, Joseph C *Korean War Army Hero (CMH)*
1736 Tommy Aaron Dr, El Paso, TX 79936

Rodriguez, Larry *Religious Leader*
%Metropolitan Churches Fellowship, 5300 Santa Monica Blvd, Los Angeles, CA 90029

Rodriguez, Paul *Actor*
%KMEX, 5420 Melrose Ave, Los Angeles, CA 90038

Rodriguez, Raul *Float Designer*
%Fiesta Floats, 9362 Lower Azusa Rd, Temple City, CA 91780

Roe, John H *Businessman*
%Bemis Company Inc, 800 Northstar Ctr, Minneapolis, MN 55402

Roe, Robert A *Representative, NJ*
%House of Representatives, Washington, DC 20515

Roebling, Mary G *Financier*
777 W State St, Trenton, NJ 08605

Roedel, Paul R *Businessman*
%Carpenter Technology Corp, 101 W Bern St, Reading, PA 19603

Roeder, Kenneth D *Physiologist*
454 Monument St, Concord, MA 01742

Roeg, Nicolas *Movie Director*
2 Oxford & Cambridge Mansions, Old Marylebone Rd, London NW1, England

Roemer, Charles (Buddy) *Governor, LA*
%Governor's Office, State Capitol Bldg, Baton Rouge, LA 70804

Roemer, Timothy J *Representative, IN*
%House of Representatives, Washington, DC 20515

Roenicke, Gary *Baseball Player*
10800 Mills Springs Dr, Nevada City, CA 95959

Roessner, Gilbert G *Financier*
%CityFed Financial Corp, Rt 202-206, Bedminster, NJ 07921

Roff, J Hugh, Jr *Businessman*
%United Energy Resources, 700 Milam, Houston, TX 77002

Rogers, Bill *Golfer*
%International Management Grp, 1 Erieview Plz, Cleveland, OH 44114

Rogers, Charles (Buddy) *Actor*
1147 Pickfair Way, Beverly Hills, CA 90210

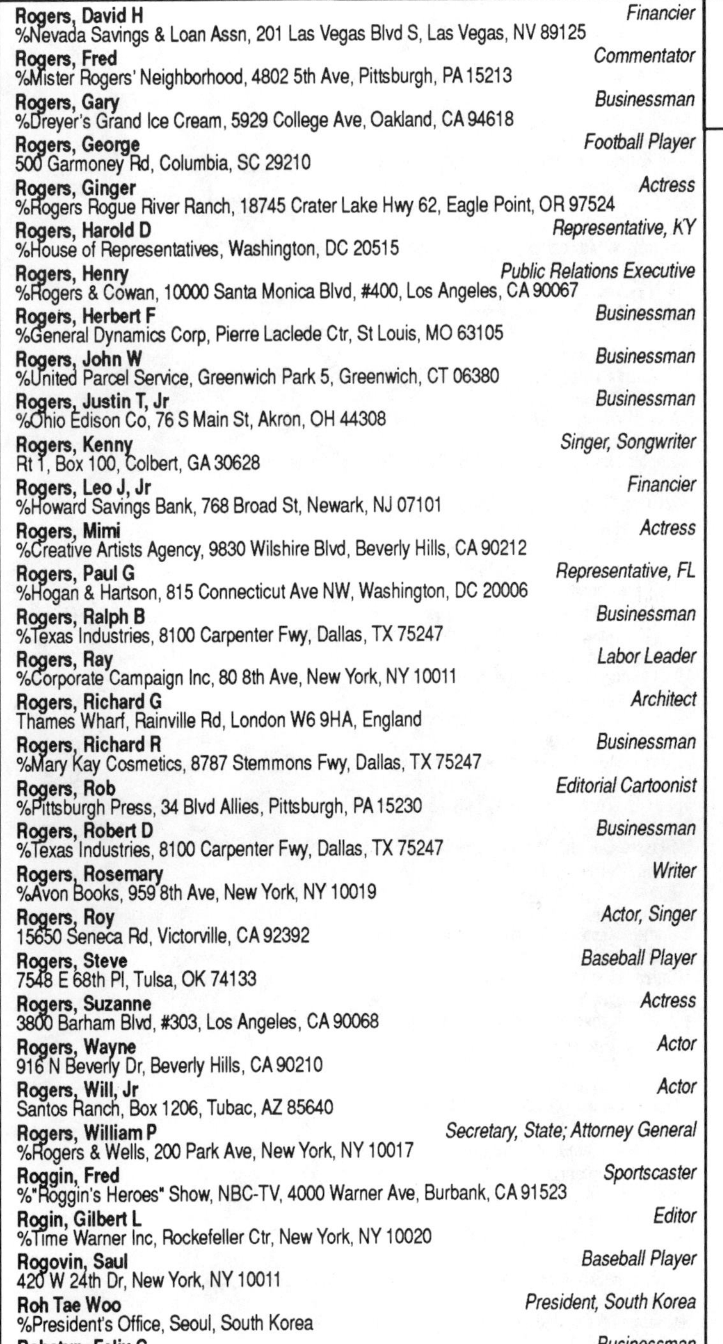

Rogers, David H *Financier*
%Nevada Savings & Loan Assn, 201 Las Vegas Blvd S, Las Vegas, NV 89125

Rogers, Fred *Commentator*
%Mister Rogers' Neighborhood, 4802 5th Ave, Pittsburgh, PA 15213

Rogers, Gary *Businessman*
%Dreyer's Grand Ice Cream, 5929 College Ave, Oakland, CA 94618

Rogers, George *Football Player*
500 Garmoney Rd, Columbia, SC 29210

Rogers, Ginger *Actress*
%Rogers Rogue River Ranch, 18745 Crater Lake Hwy 62, Eagle Point, OR 97524

Rogers, Harold D *Representative, KY*
%House of Representatives, Washington, DC 20515

Rogers, Henry *Public Relations Executive*
%Rogers & Cowan, 10000 Santa Monica Blvd, #400, Los Angeles, CA 90067

Rogers, Herbert F *Businessman*
%General Dynamics Corp, Pierre Laclede Ctr, St Louis, MO 63105

Rogers, John W *Businessman*
%United Parcel Service, Greenwich Park 5, Greenwich, CT 06380

Rogers, Justin T, Jr *Businessman*
%Ohio Edison Co, 76 S Main St, Akron, OH 44308

Rogers, Kenny *Singer, Songwriter*
Rt 1, Box 100, Colbert, GA 30628

Rogers, Leo J, Jr *Financier*
%Howard Savings Bank, 768 Broad St, Newark, NJ 07101

Rogers, Mimi *Actress*
%Creative Artists Agency, 9830 Wilshire Blvd, Beverly Hills, CA 90212

Rogers, Paul G *Representative, FL*
%Hogan & Hartson, 815 Connecticut Ave NW, Washington, DC 20006

Rogers, Ralph B *Businessman*
%Texas Industries, 8100 Carpenter Fwy, Dallas, TX 75247

Rogers, Ray *Labor Leader*
%Corporate Campaign Inc, 80 8th Ave, New York, NY 10011

Rogers, Richard G *Architect*
Thames Wharf, Rainville Rd, London W6 9HA, England

Rogers, Richard R *Businessman*
%Mary Kay Cosmetics, 8787 Stemmons Fwy, Dallas, TX 75247

Rogers, Rob *Editorial Cartoonist*
%Pittsburgh Press, 34 Blvd Allies, Pittsburgh, PA 15230

Rogers, Robert D *Businessman*
%Texas Industries, 8100 Carpenter Fwy, Dallas, TX 75247

Rogers, Rosemary *Writer*
%Avon Books, 959 8th Ave, New York, NY 10019

Rogers, Roy *Actor, Singer*
15650 Seneca Rd, Victorville, CA 92392

Rogers, Steve *Baseball Player*
7548 E 68th Pl, Tulsa, OK 74133

Rogers, Suzanne *Actress*
3800 Barham Blvd, #303, Los Angeles, CA 90068

Rogers, Wayne *Actor*
916 N Beverly Dr, Beverly Hills, CA 90210

Rogers, Will, Jr *Actor*
Santos Ranch, Box 1206, Tubac, AZ 85640

Rogers, William P *Secretary, State; Attorney General*
%Rogers & Wells, 200 Park Ave, New York, NY 10017

Roggin, Fred *Sportscaster*
%"Roggin's Heroes" Show, NBC-TV, 4000 Warner Ave, Burbank, CA 91523

Rogin, Gilbert L *Editor*
%Time Warner Inc, Rockefeller Ctr, New York, NY 10020

Rogovin, Saul *Baseball Player*
420 W 24th Dr, New York, NY 10011

Roh Tae Woo *President, South Korea*
%President's Office, Seoul, South Korea

Rohatyn, Felix G *Businessman*
%Lazard Freres Co, 1 Rockefeller Plz, New York, NY 10020

Rohda, Rodney R *Businessman*
%Home Life Insurance, 253 Broadway, New York, NY 10007

Rohmer, Eric *Movie Director*
26 Ave Pierre-ler-de-Serbie, 75116 Paris, France

Rohnstedt, Albert N *Financier*
%Lomas & Nettleton Financial Corp, 2001 Bryan Tower, Dallas, TX 75201

Rohrer, Heinrich *Nobel Physics Laureate*
%IBM Research Laboratory, CH-8803 Ruschlikon, Switzerland

Rohrmann, Gunter *Businessman*
%Air Express International Corp, 151 Harvard Ave, Stamford, CT 06902

Roizman, Owen *Cinematographer*
%Murray Neidorf, 315 S Beverly Dr, #211, Beverly Hills, CA 90212

Rojas, Francisco *Businessman*
%Petroleos Mexicanos, Av Marina Nacional 329, Mexico City 11311 DF, Mexico

Roland, Gilbert *Actor*
518 N Roxbury Dr, Beverly Hills, CA 90210

Roland, Gyl *Actress*
%Howard Love Agency, 4244 Berryman Ave, Los Angeles, CA 90066

Roland, Johnny *Football Player, Coach*
%Chicago Bears, 250 N Washington Rd, Lake Forest, IL 60045

Rolandi, Gianna *Opera Singer*
%New York City Opera, Lincoln Ctr, New York, NY 10023

Rolland, Ian M *Businessman*
%Lincoln National Corp, 1300 S Clinton St, Fort Wayne, IN 46801

Rolle, Esther *Actress*
4421 Don Felipe Dr, Los Angeles, CA 90008

Rollins, H Moak *Businessman*
%Smith International, 4490 Von Karman Ave, Newport Beach, CA 92660

Rollins, Howard E *Actor*
%Michael Thomas Agency, 305 Madison Ave, New York, NY 10017

Rollins, Orville W *Businessman*
%Rollins Inc, 2170 Piedmont Rd NE, Atlanta, GA 30324

Rollins, Reed C *Botanist*
19 Chauncy St, Cambridge, MA 02138

Rollins, Sonny *Jazz Saxophonist*
Route 9-G, Germantown, NY 12526

Rollwagen, John A *Businessman*
%Cray Research, 608 2nd Ave, Minneapolis, MN 55420

Roman, Herschel L *Geneticist*
5619 NE 77th St, Seattle, WA 98115

Roman, Joseph *Labor Leader*
%Glass & Ceramic Workers Union, 556 E Town St, Columbus, OH 43215

Roman, Kenneth, Jr *Businessman*
%American Express, World Financial Ctr, New York, NY 10285

Roman, Petre *Prime Minister, Romania*
%Prime Minister's Office, Bucharest, Romania

Roman, Ruth *Actress*
%Curtis Roberts Enterprises, 9056 Santa Monica Blvd, Los Angeles, CA 90069

Romanenko, Yuri *Cosmonaut*
141 160 Svyosdny Gorodok, Moskovskoi Oblasti, Potchta Kosmonavtov, Russia

Romano, Umberto *Artist*
162 E 83rd St, New York, NY 10028

Romanos, Jack *Publisher*
%Pocket Books, 1230 Ave of Americas, New York, NY 10021

Romans, Donald B *Businessman*
%Bally Manufacturing Corp, 8700 W Bryn Mawr Ave, Chicago, IL 60631

Romansky, Monroe J *Physician*
6609 32nd Pl NW, Washington, DC 20015

Romberg, Bert *Businessman*
%Commercial Metals Co, 7800 Stemmons Fwy, Dallas, TX 75247

Romberg, Paul F *Educator*
%California State University, President's Office, San Francisco, CA 94132

Rome, Harold *Composer*
%Chappell & Co, 810 7th Ave, New York, NY 10019

Romelfanger, Charles *Labor Leader*
%Pattern Makers League, 501 15th St, #204, Moline, IL 61265

Romeo, Robin *Bowler*
%Ladies Professional Bowlers Assn, 7171 Cherryvale Blvd, Rockford, IL 61112

Romer, Roy *Governor, CO*
%Governor's Office, State Capitol Bldg, #136, Denver, CO 80203

Romero, Cesar *Actor*
12115 San Vicente Blvd, #302, Los Angeles, CA 90049

Romero, Ned *Actor*
19438 Lassen Ave, Northridge, CA 91324

Romero, Pepe *Concert Guitarist*
%Columbia Artists Mgmt Inc, 165 W 57th St, New York, NY 10019

Romero-Barcelo, Carlos A *Governor, PR*
%Royal Bank Ctr, #807, Hato Rey, PR 00918

Romig, Joe *Football Player*
5475 Western Ave, Boulder, CO 80301

Romiti, Cesare *Businessman*
%Fiat SpA, Corso Marconi 10, Torino, Italy

Romney, George *Secretary, Housing & Urban Development*
1840 East Valley Rd, Bloomfield Hills, MI 48013

Ronan, William J *Railway Engineer*
655 Park Ave, New York, NY 10021

Ronet, Maurice *Actor*
1 Bis Ave de Lowendal, 75007 Paris, France

Roney, Paul H *Judge*
%US Court of Appeals, Federal Bldg, 144 1st Ave S, St Petersburg, FL 33701

Ronk, Glenn E *Businessman*
%General Signal Corp, High Ridge Park, Stamford, CT 06904

Rono, Peter *Track Athlete*
%Mount Saint Mary's College, Athletic Dept, Emmitsburg, MD 21727

Ronstadt, Linda *Singer*
%Peter Asher Mgmt, 644 N Doheny Dr, Los Angeles, CA 90069

Rook, Susan *Commentator*
%Cable News Network, 1 CNN Center, PO Box 105366, Atlanta, GA 30348

Rooker, George S *Businessman*
%Dorchester Gas Corp, 5735 Pineland Dr, Dallas, TX 75231

Rooney, Andy *Commentator*
254 Rowayton Ave, Rowayton, CT 06853

Rooney, Dan *Football Executive*
%Pittsburgh Steelers, Three Rivers Stadium, Pittsburgh, PA 15212

Rooney, Francis C, Jr *Businessman*
%Melville Corp, 3000 Westchester Ave, Harrison, NY 10528

Rooney, Mickey *Actor*
%Ruth Webb Enterprises, 7500 Devista Dr, Los Angeles, CA 90046

Roosa, Robert V *Financier, Government Official*
30 Woodlands Rd, Harrison, NY 10528

Roosa, Stuart A *Astronaut*
%Gulf Coast Coors, 13360 Industrial Seaway Blvd, Gulfport, MS 39505

Roots, Melvin H *Labor Leader*
%Plasters & Cement Workers Union, 1125 17th St NW, Washington, DC 20036

Rorem, Ned *Composer, Writer*
%Boosey & Hawkes, 30 W 57th St, New York, NY 10019

Rorty, Richard M *Philosopher*
%Princeton University, Philosophy Dept, Princeton, NJ 08544

Ros-Lehtinen, Ileana *Representative, FL*
%House of Representatives, Washington, DC 20515

Rosato, Genesia *Ballerina*
%Royal Ballet, Convent Garden, Bow St, London WL2E 7Q4, England

Rosberg, Keke *Auto Racing Driver*
39 Ave Princess Grace, Monte Carlo, Monaco

Roschkov, Victor *Editorial Cartoonist*
1 Yonge St, Toronto ON, Canada 90068

Rose Marie *Actress*
6918 Chisholm Ave, Van Nuys, CA 91406

Rose, Charles G, III *Representative, NC*
%House of Representatives, Washington, DC 20515

Rose, Charlie *Commentator*
%WNET-TV, News Dept, 356 W 58th St, New York, NY 10019

Rose, Jamie *Actress*
13268 Mulholland Dr, Beverly Hills, CA 90210

Rose, Judd *Commentator*
%ABC-TV, News Dept, 1330 Ave of Americas, New York, NY 10019

Rose, Lee *Basketball Coach*
%University of South Florida, Athletic Dept, Tampa, FL 33620

Rose, Michael D *Businessman*
%Holiday Corp, 1023 Cherry Rd, Memphis, TN 38117

Rose, Murray *Swimmer*
3305 Carse Dr, Los Angeles, CA 90028

Rose, Pete *Baseball Player*
10415 Stonebridge Blvd, Boca Raton, FL 33498

Rosellini, Albert D *Governor, WA*
5936 6th Ave S, Seattle, WA 98108

Roseman, Saul *Biochemist*
8206 Cranwood Ct, Baltimore, MD 21208

Rosen, Al *Baseball Player, Executive*
%San Francisco Giants, Candlestick Park, San Francisco, CA 94124

Rosen, Benjamin M *Businessman*
%Compaq Computer Corp, 20333 FM 149, Houston, TX 77070

Rosen, Charles *Concert Pianist*
101 W 78th St, New York, NY 10024

Rosen, Martin M *Financier*
2115 Paul Spring Rd, Alexandria, VA 22307

Rosen, Milton W *Engineer, Physicist*
5610 Alta Vista Rd, Bethesda, MD 20034

Rosen, Nathaniel *Concert Cellist*
%Columbia Artists Mgmt Inc, 165 W 57th St, New York, NY 10019

Rosenbaum, Edward E *Physician*
333 NW 23rd St, Portland, OR 97210

Rosenberg, Henry A, Jr *Businessman*
%Crown Central Petroleum Corp, 1 N Charles, Baltimore, MD 21201

Rosenberg, Howard *Television Critic*
%Los Angeles Times, Times Mirror Sq, Los Angeles, CA 90053

Rosenberg, Richard M *Financier*
%BankAmerica Corp, Bank of America Ctr, San Francisco, CA 94104

Rosenberg, Steven A *Cancer Researcher, Surgeon*
9015 Honeybee Ln, Bethesda, MD 20014

Rosenberg, Stuart *Movie Director*
1984 Coldwater Canyon Dr, Beverly Hills, CA 90210

Rosenblatt, Roger *Editor*
%Time Warner Co, Time & Life Bldg, New York, NY 10020

Rosenblith, Walter A *Scientist*
164 Mason Terr, Brookline, MA 02146

Rosenbluth, Leonard *Basketball Player*
12251 SW 95th, Coral Gables, FL 33186

Rosenburg, Saul A *Oncologist*
%Stanford University, Oncology Division, Stanford, CA 94305

Rosenfeld, Arnold *Editor*
%Cox Newspapers, 1400 Lake Hearn Dr NE, Atlanta, GA 30319

Rosenfield, James *Television Executive*
%CBS-TV Network, 51 W 52nd St, New York, NY 10019

Rosenman, Leonard *Composer*
%Gorfaine-Schwartz Agency, 3815 Olive Ave, #201, Burbank, CA 91505

Rosenn, Max *Judge*
%US Courthouse, 197 S Main St, Wilkes-Barre, PA 18701

Rosenquist, James *Artist*
PO Box 4, 420 Broadway, Aripeka, FL 33502

Rosenson, Jay H *Businessman*
%Firestone Tire & Rubber Co, 1200 Firestone Pkwy, Akron, OH 44317

Rosenstein, Samuel M *Judge*
2200 S Ocean Ln, #1508, Ft Lauderdale, FL 33316

Rosenthal, A M *Editor*
%New York Times, 229 W 43rd St, New York, NY 10036

Rosenthal, Bernard J *Artist*
1482 York Ave, #4-D, New York, NY 10021

Rosenthal, Dick *Sports Official*
%University of Notre Dame, Athletic Dept, Notre Dame, IN 46556

Rosenthal, Richard *Businessman*
%Citizens Utilities Co, High Ridge Park, Stamford, CT 06905
Rosenwald, E John *Financier*
%Bear Stearns Co, 55 Water St, New York, NY 10041
Rosenzweig, Barney *Television Producer*
%Orion Television, 2630 Lacy St, Los Angeles, CA 90031
Rosewall, Ken *Tennis Player*
%Assn of Tennis Pros, 200 Tournament Players Rd, Ponte Vedra Beach, FL 32082
Rosin, Walter L *Religious Leader*
%Lutheran Church Missouri Synod, 1333 S Kirkwood, St Louis, MO 63122
Ross Fairbanks, Anne *Swimmer*
10 Grandview Ave, Troy, NY 12180
Ross, Al *Cartoonist*
2185 Bolton St, Bronx, NY 10462
Ross, Betsy *Sportscaster*
%Madison Square Grdn Network, Sports Dept, 4 Pennsylania Plz, New York, NY 10001
Ross, Bobby *Football Coach*
%San Diego Chargers, 9449 Friars Rd, San Diego, CA 92120
Ross, Charlotte *Actress*
%Abrams Artists, 9200 Sunset Blvd, #625, Los Angeles, CA 90069
Ross, Clarence A *Swimmer*
13 Elston Rd, Upper Montclair, NJ 07043
Ross, David A *Museum Director*
%Whitney Museum of American Art, 945 Madison Ave, New York, NY 10021
Ross, Donald K *Businessman*
%New York Life Insurance, 51 Madison Ave, New York, NY 10010
Ross, Donald K *WW II Navy Hero (CMH)*
Rokalu Ranch, 15871 Glenwood Rd SW, Port Orchard, WA 98366
Ross, Donald R *Judge*
%US Court of Appeals, Federal Bldg, PO Box 307, Omaha, NE 68101
Ross, Douglas T *Computer Scientist*
%Softech Inc, 460 Totten Pond Rd, Waltham, MA 92254
Ross, Elisabeth Kubler *Physician*
Shanti Nilaya, PO Box 2396, Escondido, CA 92025
Ross, Herbert *Movie Director*
30900 Broad Beach Rd, Malibu, CA 90265
Ross, Ian M *Electrical Engineer, Businessman*
%Bell Laboratories, 600 Mountain Ave, Murray Hill, NJ 07974
Ross, Jerry L *Astronaut*
%NASA, Johnson Space Ctr, Houston, TX 77058
Ross, Jimmy D *Army General*
Deputy Chief of Staff for Logistics, Army Department, Washington, DC 20310
Ross, Karie *Sportscaster*
%ESPN, Sports Dept, ESPN Plz, 935 Middle St, Bristol, CT 06010
Ross, Katherine *Actress*
33050 Pacific Coast Hwy, Malibu, CA 90265
Ross, Marion *Actress*
14159 Riverside Dr, #101, Sherman Oaks, CA 91423
Ross, Steven J *Businessman*
%Time Warner Inc, 75 Rockefeller Plz, New York, NY 10019
Ross, Wilburn K *WW II Army Hero (CMH)*
Box 12, 8199 Haskell St, Dupont, WA 98327
Rosse, James N *Publisher*
%Freedom Newspapers Inc, PO Box 19549, Irvine, CA 92713
Rossellini, Isabella *Model, Actress*
%Click Model Mgmt, 881 7th Ave, New York, NY 10019
Rossen, Carol *Actress*
14238 Sunset Blvd, Pacific Palisades, CA 90272
Rosser, James M *Educator*
%California State University, President's Office, Los Angeles, CA 90032
Rosser, James M *Educator*
%California State University, President's Office, Los Angeles, CA 90032
Rosser, Ronald E *WW II Army Hero (CMH)*
36 James St, Roseville, OH 43777
Rosset, Barnet L, Jr *Publisher*
%Grove Press, 196 W Houston St, New York, NY 10014

R

Rossi – Rothermere of Hemsted

Rossi, Agnelo Cardinal *Religious Leader*
Collegio Urbano di Propaganda Fide, Via Urbano 8, 00165 Rome, Italy

Rossi, Bruno *Physicist*
221 Mt Auburn St, Cambridge, MA 02138

Rossi, Giorgio *Businessman*
%SNIA BPD, Via Borgonuovo 14, 20121 Milan, Italy

Rossi, Opilio Cardinal *Religious Leader*
Via Della Scrofa 70, 00186 Rome, Italy

Rossi, Ralph L *Businessman*
%United States Tobacco Co, 100 W Putnam Ave, Greenwich, CT 06830

Rossini, Frederick D *Chemist*
605 S Highway 1, #T-900, Juno Beach, FL 33408

Rossner, Judith *Writer*
%Julian Bach Agency, 747 3rd Ave, New York, NY 10017

Rosten, Irwin *Writer, Producer, Director*
2217 Chelan Dr, Los Angeles, CA 90068

Rostenkowski, Dan *Representative, IL*
1372 W Evergreen St, Chicago, IL 60622

Rostow, Eugene V *Economist*
208 S Ronan St, New Haven, CT 06511

Rostow, Walt W *Economist, Government Official*
1 Wildwind Pt, Austin, TX 78746

Rostropovich, Mstislav *Concert Cellist, Conductor*
%National Symphony, Kennedy Ctr, Washington, DC 20566

Rostvold, Gerhard N *Economist*
19712 Oceanaire, Huntington Beach, CA 92649

Roszak, Theodore *Historian*
%California State University, History Dept, Hayward, CA 94542

Rotberg, Eugene H *Financier*
7211 Brickyard Rd, Potomac, MD 20854

Rote, Kyle *Football Player*
1175 York Ave, New York, NY 10021

Rote, Tobin *Football Player*
1644 Leadbury Dr, Bloomfield Hills, MI 48013

Roth, Ann *Costume Designer*
%United Scenic Artists, 1540 Broadway, New York, NY 10036

Roth, Arnold *Cartoonist*
%National Cartoonists Society, 9 Ebony Ct, Brooklyn, NY 11229

Roth, David Lee *Singer*
3960 Laurel Canyon Blvd, #430, Studio City, CA 91604

Roth, Dick *Swimmer*
Big Spring Ranch, Wells, NV 89835

Roth, Henry *Writer*
%Jewish Publication Society, 1930 Chestnut St, Philadelphia, PA 19103

Roth, Jesse *Endocrinologist*
%National Institute of Arthritis, 9000 Rockville Pike, Bethesda, MD 20205

Roth, Mark *Bowler*
%International Artists & Athletes Mgmt, 515 Madison Ave, New York, NY 10022

Roth, Philip *Writer*
%Farrar Straus & Giroux, 19 Union Sq W, New York, NY 10003

Roth, Toby *Representative, WI*
%House of Representatives, Washington, DC 20515

Roth, William G *Businessman*
%Dravo Corp, 1 Oliver Plz, Pittsburgh, PA 15222

Roth, William V, Jr *Senator, DE*
%US Senate, Washington, DC 20510

Rothell, George E *Financier*
%First Interstae Bank of Utah, 175 S Main St, Salt Lake City, UT 84111

Rothenberg, Alan J *Soccer, Basketball Executive*
%U S Soccer Federation, 1750 E Boulder St, Colorado Springs, CO 80909

Rothenberg, Susan *Artist*
%Willard Gallery, 29 E 72nd St, New York, NY 10021

Rothenberger, Anneliese *Opera Singer*
8268 Salenstein Am Untersee, Switzerland

Rothermere of Hemsted, Viscount *Publisher*
New Carmelite House, Carmelite St, London EC4, England

Rothman, Frank *Entertainment Executive*
10555 Rocca Pl, Los Angeles, CA 90077

Rothmeier, Steven G *Businessman*
%Capital Grp, 333 S Hope St, Los Angeles, CA 90071

Rothschild, Elie R de *Financier*
%Time & Life Bldg, 17 Ave Matignon, 75428 Paris, France

Rothschild, Guy E A P de *Financier*
2 Rue St Louis en l'Ile, 75004 Paris, France

Rothschild, Miriam *Naturalist*
%Ashton World, Peterborough, Northants, England

Rothstein, Ron *Basketball Coach*
%Miami Heat, Miami Arena, Miami, FL 33136

Roubos, Gary L *Businessman*
%Dover Corp, 277 Park Ave, New York, NY 10172

Roukema, Margaret S *Representative, NJ*
%House of Representatives, Washington, DC 20515

Roundfield, Dan *Basketball Player*
%Washington Bullets, Capital Ctr, 1 Truman Dr, Landover, MD 20785

Roundtree, Richard *Actor*
8383 Wilshire Blvd, #1018, Beverly Hills, CA 90212

Rourke, Mickey *Actor*
%Creative Artists Agency, 9830 Wilshire Blvd, Beverly Hills, CA 90212

Rouse, Irving *Anthropologist*
12 Ridgewood Terr, North Haven, CT 06520

Rouse, James W *Businessman*
%Enterprise Development Co, 610 American City Building, Columbia, MD 21044

Rouse, Jeff *Swimmer*
%Stanford University, Athletic Dept, Stanford, CA 94305

Rowan, Robert D *Businessman*
%Fruehauf Corp, 10900 Harper Ave, Detroit, MI 48213

Rowe, James W *Businessman*
%Great Atlantic & Pacific Tea Co, 2 Paragon Dr, Montvale, NJ 07645

Rowe, Misty *Actress*
%Exclusive Artists Agency, 2501 W Burbank Blvd, Burbank, CA 91505

Rowell, Lester John, Jr *Businessman*
%Provident Mutual Life Insurance, 1600 Market St, Philadelphia, PA 19103

Rowland, F Sherwood *Chemist*
4807 Dorchester Rd, Corona del Mar, CA 92625

Rowland, J Roy *Representative, GA*
%House of Representatives, Washington, DC 20515

Rowland, James A *Businessman*
%Safeway Stores, 4th & Jackson, Oakland, CA 94660

Rowland, John W *Labor Leader*
%Amalgamated Transit Union, 5025 Wisconsin Ave NW, Washington, DC 20016

Rowland, Landon H *Businessman*
%Kansas City Southern Industries, 114 W 11th, Kansas City, MO 64105

Rowland, Robert A *Government Official*
%Occupational Safety Commission, 1825 "K" St NW, Washington, DC 20006

Rowland, Roland W (Tiny) *Businessman*
%Lorrho Ltd, Cheapside House, 138 Cheapside, London EC2V 6BL, England

Rowlands, Gena *Actress*
7917 Woodrow Wilson Dr, Los Angeles, CA 90046

Rowling, Wallace E *Prime Minister, New Zealand*
%Parliament Bldgs, Wellington, New Zealand

Roy, Patrick *Hockey Player*
%Montreal Canadiens, 2313 St Catherine St W, Montreal PQ H3H 1N2, Canada

Roy, Vesta M *Governor, NH*
%State Senate, State House, Concord, NH 03301

Royal, Darrell K *Football Coach*
10507 La Costa Dr, Austin, TX 78747

Roybal, Edward R *Representative, CA*
%House of Representatives, Washington, DC 20515

Royer, Charles *Mayor*
%Mayor's Office, City Hall, 600 4th Ave, Seattle, WA 98104

Royko, Mike *Columnist*
%Chicago Tribune, 435 N Michigan Ave, Chicago, IL 60611

Royster, Vermont *Editor*
2425 Springmoor Cir, Raleigh, NC 27615
Rozelle, Pete *Football Executive*
%National Football League, 410 Park Ave, New York, NY 10022
Rozhdestvensky, Gennady *Conductor*
%Victor Hochhauser Ltd, 4 Holland Park Ave, London W11, England
Rozhdestvensky, Valery *Cosmonaut*
141 160 Syvosdny Gorodok, Moskovskoi Oblasti, Potchta Kosmonavtov, Russia
Rozier, Mike *Football Player*
%Atlanta Falcons, Suwanee Rd, Suwanee, GA 30174
Rubbia, Carlo *Nobel Physics Laureate*
%Harvard University, Physics Dept, Cambridge, MA 20138
Rubeli, Paul E *Businessman*
%Aztar Corp, 3838 E Van Buren St, Phoenix, AZ 85008
Ruben, William *Businessman*
%Bonwit Teller Inc, 1120 Ave of Americas, New York, NY 10036
Rubenstein, Ann *Commentator*
%NBC-TV, News Dept, 30 Rockefeller Plz, New York, NY 10112
Rubicam, Raymond *Businessman*
87 Mountain Shadows, Scottsdale, AZ 85253
Rubik, Erno *Inventor (Rubik Cube)*
Magyar Iparmuveszeti Foiskola, Zugligeti Ut 11/25, 1121 Budapest, Hungary
Rubin, Harry *Biologist*
%University of California, Molecular Biology Dept, Berkeley, CA 94720
Rubin, Jennifer *Actress*
%Triad Artists, 10100 Santa Monica Blvd, #1600, Los Angeles, CA 90067
Rubin, Jerry *Political Activist*
%M Evans & Co, 216 E 49th St, New York, NY 10017
Rubin, Robert *Medical Researcher*
%Massachusetts General Hospital, 32 Fruit St, Boston, MA 02114
Rubin, Stephen *Publisher*
%Doubleday Co, 245 Park Ave, New York, NY 10167
Rubin, Theodore I *Psychiatrist*
18 E 78th St, New York, NY 10021
Rubin, Vera *Astronomer*
%Carnegie Institute, 524 Broad Branch Rd NW, Washington, DC 20015
Rubin, William *Museum Curator*
%Museum of Modern Art, 11 W 53rd St, New York, NY 10019
Rubinstein, John *Actor*
10420 Scenario Ln, Los Angeles, CA 90024
Ruckelshaus, William D *Government Official, Businessman*
%Browning-Ferris Industries, 14701 St Mary's, Houston, TX 77079
Rudd, Eldon *Representative, AZ*
6900 E Camelback Rd, #315, Scottsdale, AZ 85251
Rudd, Hughes *Commentator*
%NBC-TV, News Dept, 1330 Ave of Americas, New York, NY 10019
Rudd, Ricky *Auto Racing Driver*
%NASCAR, 1801 Volusia Ave, Daytona Beach, FL 32015
Rudel, Julius *Conductor*
%Metropolitan Opera Assn, Lincoln Center Plz, New York, NY 10036
Rudenstine, Neil *Educator*
%Harvard University, President's Office, Cambridge, MA 02138
Ruder, David S *Government Official, Educator*
%Baker & McKenzie, 2800 Prudential Plz, Chicago, IL 60601
Rudi, Joe *Baseball Player*
RR 1, Box 66, Baker, OR 97814
Rudie, Evelyn *Actress*
%Santa Monica Playhouse, 1211 4th St, Santa Monica, CA 90401
Ruding, H Onno *Financier*
Wilhelminaplein 5, 2243 HE Wassenaar, Netherlands
Rudman, Warren *Senator, NH*
41 Indian Rock Rd, Nashua, NH 03060
Rudolf, Max *Conductor*
220 W Rittenhouse Sq, Philadelphia, PA 19103
Rudolph, Alan *Movie Director*
1020 S Carmelina Ave, Los Angeles, CA 90049

Rudolph, Donald E *WW II Army Hero (CMH)*
497 Shamrock Dr, Bovey, MN 55709

Rudolph, Paul M *Architect*
54 W 57th St, New York, NY 10019

Rue. Sara *Actress*
%Harris & Goldberg Agency, 1999 Ave of Stars, #2850, Los Angeles, CA 90067

Ruebhausen, Oscar M *Businessman*
%National Starch & Chemical Corp, Finderne Ave, Bridgewater, NJ 08807

Ruether, Rosemary *Theologian*
1426 Hinman Ave, Evanston, IN 60201

Ruettgers, Ken *Football Player*
%Green Bay Packers, 1265 Lombardi Ave, Green Bay, WI 54303

Ruff, Howard J *Fiscal Analyst, Writer*
PO Box 31, Springfield, UT 84663

Ruffle, John F *Financier*
%J P Morgan Co, 23 Wall St, New York, NY 10015

Rugambwa, Laurian Cardinal *Religious Leader*
St Joseph, PO Box 167, Dar es Salaam, Tanzania

Ruge, John A *Cartoonist*
240 Bronxville Rd, #B-4, Bronxville, NY 10708

Ruhnau, Heinz *Businessman*
%Deutsche Lufthansa, Von Gablenzstrasse 2-6, 5000 Koeln, Germany

Ruiz, Alejandro R *WW II Army Hero (CMH)*
32146 Road 124, Visalia, CA 93291

Rukavishnikov, Nikolai *Cosmonaut*
141 160 Svyosdny Gorodok, Moskovskoi Oblasti, Potchta Kosmonavtov, Russia

Rukeyser, Louis R *Commentator*
%"Wall Street Week" Show, Maryland Public Television, Owings Mill, MD 21117

Rukeyser, William S *Publisher*
%Whittle Books, 505 Market, Knoxville, TN 37902

Ruland, Jeff *Basketball Player*
%Philadelphia 76ers, PO Box 25040, Veterans Stadium, Philadelphia, PA 19147

Rule, Elton H *Television Executive*
706 N Linden Dr, Beverly Hills, CA 90210

Rule, Janice *Actress*
3681 Empire Dr, Los Angeles, CA 90034

Rummelsburg, Al S *Businessman*
%Farberware, 1500 Bassett Ave, Bronx, NY 10461

Rumsfeld, Donald *Secretary, Defense; Businessman*
%William Blair Co, 135 S LaSalle St, Chicago, IL 60603

Runcie, Robert A K *Archbishop, Canterbury*
%Lambeth Palace, London SE1 9JU, England

Runco, Mario, Jr *Astronaut*
%NASA, Johnson Space Ctr, Houston, TX 77058

Rundgren, Todd *Singer*
%Panacea Entertainment, 2705 Glendower Rd, Los Angeles, CA 90027

Runge, Donald E *Businessman*
%Farm House Foods Corp, 111 E Wisconsin Ave, Milwaukee, WI 53202

Runge, Ed *Baseball Umpire*
4949 Cresita Dr, San Diego, CA 92115

Runnells, Charles *Educator*
%Pepperdine University, Chancellor's Office, Malibu, CA 90265

Runyan, Joe *Dog Sled Racer*
%Rt 1, 314.5 Parks Hwy, Nenana, AK 99760

Runyon, Edwin *Religious Leader*
%General Assn of General Baptists, 100 Stinson Dr, Popular Bluff, MO 63901

Rupert, John E *Financier*
%Broadview Financial Corp, 6000 Rockside Woods Blvd, Cleveland, OH 44131

Rupert, Michael *Actor*
%Writers & Artists Agency, 11726 San Vicente Blvd, #300, Los Angeles, CA 90049

Rupp, George *Educator*
%Rice University, President's Office, Houston, TX 77251

Ruscha, Edward *Artist*
1024 3/4 N Western Ave, Los Angeles, CA 90029

Rush, Barbara *Actress*
1708 Tropical Ave, Beverly Hills, CA 90210

R

Rush – Rutherford

Rush, Jennifer *Singer*
%Epic Records, Sony Music, 1801 Century Park West, Los Angeles, CA 90067

Rush, Kenneth *Government Official*
3147 "O" St NW, Washington, DC 20007

Rush, Richard *Movie Director, Producer*
821 Stradella Rd, Los Angeles, CA 90077

Rushworth, Robert A *Test Pilot, Air Force General*
1027 Garrido Dr, Camarillo, CA 93010

Rusk, Dean *Secretary, State*
1 Lafayette Sq, 620 Hill St, Athens, GA 30601

Ruskin, Uzi *Businessman*
%United Merchants & Manufacturers Inc, 1407 Broadway, New York, NY 10018

Russ, William *Actor*
%Bresler Kelly Assoc, 15760 Ventura Blvd, #1730, Encino, CA 91436

Russell, Betsy *Actress*
%Media Artists Grp, 6255 Sunset Blvd, #627, Los Angeles, CA 90028

Russell, Bill *Basketball Player, Coach*
PO Box 58, Mercer Island, WA 98040

Russell, Charles T *Businessman*
%Visa International, PO Box 26673, San Francisco, CA 94126

Russell, Donald J *Businessman*
2298 Pacific Ave, San Francisco, CA 94115

Russell, Donald Stuart *Governor/Senator, SC; Judge*
%US Court of Appeals, PO Box 1985, Spartanburg, SC 29301

Russell, Fred *Sportswriter*
3804 Brighton Rd, Nashville, TN 37205

Russell, George *Jazz Drummer, Pianist; Composer*
%New England Conservatory of Music, 33 Gainsborough St, Boston, MA 02115

Russell, Harold *Actor, Government Official*
34 Old Town Rd, Hyannis, MA 02601

Russell, James S *Navy Admiral, Hero*
7734 Walnut Ave NW, Tacoma, WA 98498

Russell, Jane *Actress*
2935 Torrito Rd, Montecito, CA 93108

Russell, Ken *Movie Director*
7 Bellmont Wood Ln, Watford, Herts, England

Russell, Kurt *Actor*
229 E Gainsborough Rd, Thousand Oaks, CA 91360

Russell, Leon *Singer, Songwriter*
PO Box 1006, Hendersonville, TN 37077

Russell, Mark *Comedian*
2828 Wisconsin Ave NW, Washington, DC 20007

Russell, Marybeth *Publisher*
%Elle Magazine, 551 5th Ave, New York, NY 10176

Russell, Nipsy *Comedian*
353 W 57th St, New York, NY 10021

Russell, Theresa *Actress*
%Gersh Agency, 232 N Canon Dr, Beverly Hills, CA 90210

Russell, Thomas F *Businessman*
%Federal-Mogul Corp, 26555 Northwestern Pkwy, Southfield, MI 48034

Russell, William L *Geneticist*
130 Tabor Rd, Oak Ridge, TN 37830

Russo, Martin *Representative, IL*
%House of Representatives, Washington, DC 20515

Russo, Thomas J *Businessman*
%Ponderosa Inc, PO Box 578, Dayton, OH 45401

Rutan, Burt *Airplane Designer*
%Scaled Composites, Mojave Airport, Hangar 78, Mojave, CA 93501

Rutan, Richard G *Experimental Airplane Pilot, Designer*
%Voyager Aircraft Inc, Mojave Airport, Hangar 77, Mojave, CA 93501

Ruth, Mike *Football Player*
%New England Patriots, Sullivan Stadium, Foxboro, MA 02035

Ruthenberg, Donald B *Educator*
%Columbia College, President's Office, Columbia, MO 65216

Rutherford, Ann *Actress*
826 Greenway Dr, Beverly Hills, CA 90210

Rutherford, Ira *Businessman*
%Associated Milk Producers, 6609 Blanco Rd, San Antonio, TX 78216

Rutherford, Jack D *Businessman*
%International Harvester Co, 401 N Michigan Ave, Chicago, IL 60611

Rutherford, Johnny *Auto Racing Driver*
4919 Black Oak Ln, Fort Worth, TX 76114

Rutherford, Robert L *Air Force General*
Vice Commander in Chief, Material Air Command, Scott Air Force Base, IL 62225

Rutigliano, Sam *Football Coach*
%Liberty University, Athletic Dept, Lynchburg, VA 24506

Rutledge, John *Economist*
%Claremont Economics Institute, Claremont, CA 91711

Rutledge, W A *Businessman*
%Emerson Electric Co, 8000 W Florissant Ave, St Louis, MO 63136

Rutledge, William P *Businessman*
%Teledyne Inc, 1901 Ave of Stars, Los Angeles, CA 90067

Rutstein, David Davis *Educator, Physician*
98 Winthrop St, Cambridge, MA 02138

Ruttan, Susan *Actresss*
%J Michael Bloom Ltd, 9200 Sunset Blvd, #710, Los Angeles, CA 90069

Ruttenberg, Joseph *Cinematographer*
132 Spalding Dr, Beverly Hills, CA 90212

Ruud, Birger *Nordic Skier*
Munstersvei 20, 3600 Kongsberg, Norway

Ruud, Sigmund *Skier, Ski Jumper*
Kirkeveien 57, Oslo 3, Norway

Ruuska Percy, Sylvia *Swimmer*
4216 College View Way, Carmichael, CA 95608

Ruutel, Arnold *Chairman, Estonia*
%Supreme Council, Talliin, Estonia

Ruuttu, Christian *Hockey Player*
%Buffalo Sabres, Memorial Auditorium, Buffalo, NY 14202

Ruwe, Robert P *Judge*
%US Tax Court, 400 2nd St NW, Washington, DC 20217

Ruyak, Beth *Sportscaster*
%ABC-TV, Sports Dept, 47 W 66th St, New York, NY 10023

Ryan, Arthur F *Financier*
%Chase Manhattan Corp, 1 Chase Manhattan Plz, New York, NY 10081

Ryan, Buddy *Football Coach*
%Cable News Network, Sports Dept, 1 CNN Ctr, PO Box 105366, Atlanta, GA 30348

Ryan, Debbie *Basketball Coach*
%University of Virginia, Athletic Dept, PO Box 3785, Charlottesville, VA 22903

Ryan, Fran *Actress*
4204 Woodland Ave, Burbank, CA 91505

Ryan, Frank J *Businessman*
%Air Products & Chemicals Inc, PO Box 538, Allentown, PA 18105

Ryan, James L *Judge*
%US Court of Appeals, US Courthouse, 231 W Lafayette Blvd, Detroit, MI 48226

Ryan, James P *Businessman*
%Ryland Grp, 10221 Wincopin Cir, Columbia, MD 21044

Ryan, John D *Businessman*
%Wetterau Inc, 8920 Pershall Rd, Hazelwood, MO 63042

Ryan, John T, Jr *Businessman*
%Mine Safety Appliances, 600 Penn Center Blvd, Pittsburgh, PA 15235

Ryan, Kent *Football Player*
5550 W University Blvd, Dallas, TX 75209

Ryan, Martin J, Jr *Air Force General*
Commander, 8th Air Force, Barksdale Air Force Base, LA 71110

Ryan, Meg *Actress*
3466 La Sombra Dr, Los Angeles, CA 90068

Ryan, Meg *Actress*
%International Creative Mgmt, 8899 Beverly Blvd, Los Angeles, CA 90048

Ryan, Michael M *Actor*
48 E 3rd St, New York, NY 10003

Ryan, Mitchell *Actor*
9744 Wilshire Blvd, #206, Beverly Hills, CA 90212

R

Ryan, Nolan — *Baseball Player*
719 Dezzo Dr, Alvin, TX 77511

Ryan, Patrick G — *Businessman*
%Combined International Corp, 222 N Dearborn St, Chicago, IL 60601

Ryan, Richard L — *Businessman*
%Allied Van Lines, 2120 S 25th St, Broadview, IL 60153

Ryan, Tim — *Sportscaster*
%CBS-TV, Sports Dept, 51 W 52nd St, New York, NY 10019

Ryan, Tim — *Football Player*
%Chicago Bears, 250 N Washington Rd, Lake Forest, IL 60045

Ryan, Tom K — *Cartoonist (Tumbleweeds)*
%North America Syndicate, 235 E 45th St, New York, NY 10017

Rydell, Bobby — *Singer*
917 Bryn Mawr Ave, Narbeth, PA 19072

Rydell, Mark — *Movie Director*
1 Topsail St, Marina del Rey, CA 90292

Ryder, Winona — *Actress*
1636 N Beverly Dr, Beverly Hills, CA 90210

Rykiel, Sonia — *Fashion Designer*
6 Rue de Grenelle, 75006 Paris, France

Ryman, Robert — *Artist*
17 W 16th St, New York, NY 10011

Rymer, Pamela Ann — *Judge*
%US Court of Appeals, 125 S Grand Ave, Pasadena, CA 91109

Rymer, S Bradford, Jr — *Businessman*
%Magic Chef Inc, 740 King Edward Ave SE, Cleveland, TN 37311

Rypien, Mark — *Football Player*
%Washington Redskins, Dulles Airport, Box 17247, Washington, DC 20041

Rysanek, Leonie — *Opera Singer*
8201 Neubeuren, Germany

Ryumin, Valery — *Cosmonaut*
141 160 Svyosdny Gorodok, Moskovskoi Oblasti, Potchta Kosmonavtov, Russia

Ryun, Jim — *Track Athlete*
Rt 3, Box 62-B, Lawrence, KS 66044

Saam, Byrum *Sportscaster*
%Philadelphia Phillies, PO Box 7575, Philadelphia, PA 19101
Saar, Bettye *Artist*
8074 Willow Glen Rd, Los Angeles, CA 90046
Saari, Roy *Swimmer*
PO Box 7086, Mammoth Lakes, CA 95346
Saatchi, Charles *Businessman*
%Saatchi & Saatchi Co, 80 Charlotte St, London W1, England
Saatchi, Maurice *Businessman*
%Saatchi & Saatchi Co, 80 Charlotte St, London W1, England
Sabah, Sheikh al-Ahmad al-Jaber al- *Amir, Kuwait*
%Sief Palace, Amiry Diwan, Kuwait
Sabah, Sheikh Ali Al Khalifah Al- *Businessman*
%Kuwait Petroleum Corp, PO Box 26565, Safat, Kuwait
Sabah, Sheikh Saad al-Abdullah al-Salem *Prime Minister, Kuwait*
%Prime Minister's Office, Kuwait City, Kuwait
Sabatini, Gabriela *Tennis Player*
Ap Int 14, Suc 27, 1427 Buenos Aires, Argentina
Sabato, Ernesto *Writer*
Severino Langeri 3135, Santos Lugares, Argentina
Sabattani, Aurelio Cardinal *Religious Leader*
Piazza S Marta, 00120 Vatican City, Rome, Italy
Saberhagen, Bret *Baseball Player*
19229 Arminta St, Reseda, CA 91335
Sabin, Albert B *Physician, Scientist*
715 Knotty Pine Rd, Charleston, SC 29412
Sabo, Martin O *Representative, MN*
%House of Representatives, Washington, DC 20515
Sacco, Michael *Labor Leader*
%Seafarers International Union, 5201 Auth Wy, Camp Springs, MO 20746
Sachar, Abram L *Educator*
66 Beaumont Ave, Newtonville, MA 02160
Sachs, Gloria *Fashion Designer*
%Gloria Sachs Designs Ltd, 550 7th Ave, New York, NY 10018
Sachs, Robert G *Physicist*
5490 South Shore Dr, Chicago, IL 60615
Sack, Steve *Cartoonist (Professor Doodle's)*
%Tribune Media Services, 34 E Concord St, Orlando, FL 32801
Sacks, Oliver *Physician, Neurologist*
%Einstein College of Medicine, 119 Horton St, Bronx, NY 10464
Sadat, Jehan El- *Social Activist*
%International Development Ctr, University of Maryland, College Park, MD 20742
Saddler, Donald E *Theater Choreographer, Dancer*
%Coleman-Rosenberg Agency, 667 Madison Ave, New York, NY 10021
Saddler, Sandy *Boxer*
%National Maritime Union, Phys Ed Dept, 346 W 17th, New York, NY 10011
Sade (Abu) *Singer*
237 Madison Ave, New York, NY 10016
Sadecki, Ray *Baseball Player*
7710 Everett, Kansas City, KS 66112
Sadiq Al Mahedi *Prime Minister, Sudan*
%Prime Minister's Office, Khartoum, Sudan
Sadler, Carl L *Businessman*
%Rohr Industries, PO Box 878, Chula Vista, CA 92012
Sadler, David G *Businessman*
%Savin Corp, Columbus Ave, Valhalla, NY 10595
Sadoon Kubbu *Financier*
%Rafidain Bank, New Banks' St, Massarif, Baghdad, Iraq
Saeki, Akira *Businessman*
%Sharp Corp, 22-22 Nagaikecho, Abenoku, Osaka 543, Japan
Saeki, Takashi *Businessman*
%Nisshin Flour Milling Co, 19-12 Nihonbasi-Komamicho, Tokyo 103, Japan
Saenger, Theordore J *Businessman*
%Pacific Telesis Grp, 140 New Montgomery St, San Francisco, CA 94105
Safdie, Moshe *Architect*
2 Faneuil Hall, Marketplace, Boston, MA 02109

S

Safer – Sakic

Safer, Morley *Commentator*
%CBS-TV, New Dept, 524 W 57th St, New York, NY 10019

Saffiotti, Umberto *Pathologist*
5114 Wissioming Rd, Bethesda, MD 20816

Safire, William *Journalist, Author*
%New York Times, 1627 "I" St NW, Washington, DC 20006

Sagal, Katey *Actress*
%Progressive Artists Agency, 400 S Beverly Dr, #216, Beverly Hills, CA 90212

Sagan, Carl E *Astronomer, Educator*
%Cornell University, Laboratory for Planetary Studies, Ithaca, NY 14853

Sagan, Francoise *Writer*
25 Rue d'Alesia, 75014 Paris, France

Sagansky, Jeff *Entertainment Executive*
%CBS-Entertainment, 51 W 57th St, New York, NY 10019

Sagdeev, Roald *Physicist*
%Institute of Space Research, Profsoyuznaya 88, Moscow, Russia

Sagendorf, Forrest C (Bud) *Cartoonist (Popeye)*
%King Features Syndicate, 235 E 45th St, New York, NY 10017

Sager, Carole Bayer *Singer, Songwriter*
1465 Donhill Dr, Beverly Hills, CA 90210

Sager, Ruth *Geneticist*
%Sidney Farber Cancer Institute, 44 Binney St, Boston, MA 02115

Saget, Bob *Actor*
%Leading Artists, 445 N Bedford Dr, #PH, Beverly Hills, CA 90210

Sahl, Mort *Comedian*
2325 San Ysidro Dr, Beverly Hills, CA 90210

Said Mohamed Djohar *President, Comoros Islands*
%President's Office, Moroni, Comoros Islands

Said, Edward W *Educator*
%Columbia University, English Dept, Hamilton Hall, New York, NY 10027

Saiki, Patricia *Representative, HI; Government Official*
%Small Business Administration, 1441 "L" St NW, Washington, DC 20416

Sailer, Toni *Skier*
%General Delivery, Kitzbuhel, Austria

Sain, Johnny *Baseball Player*
2 S 707 Ave Latour, Oakbrook, IL 60521

Saint James, Susan *Actress*
%Marlene Fait, 854 N Genesee Ave, Los Angeles, CA 90046

Saint Laurent, Yves *Fashion Designer*
5 Ave Marceau, 75116 Paris, France

Saint, Crosbie E *Army General*
CinC, US Army Europe & 7th Army, APO, AE 09014

Saint, Eva Marie *Actress*
%Paul Kohner Inc, 9169 Sunset Blvd, Los Angeles, CA 90069

Saint-Subber, Arnold *Theater Producer*
116 E 64th St, New York, NY 10021

Sainte-Marie, Buffy *Singer, Songwriter*
RR 1, Box 368, Kapaa, Kauai, HI 96746

Saito, Eishiro *Businessman*
%Nippon Steel Corp, 2-6-3 Otemachi, Chiyodaku, Tokyo, Japan

Saito, Kiyoshi *Artist*
1-23-14 Nishimikado, Kamakura City, Japan

Saito, Shigeyoshi *Businessman*
%Daishowa Paper Manufacturing Co, 133 Imai, Fuji City 417, Japan

Sajak, Pat *Entertainer*
%"Wheel of Fortune" Show, 3400 Riverside Dr, 2nd Fl, Burbank, CA 91505

Sakabe, Takeo *Businessman*
%Ashai Glass Co, 2-1-1 Marunouchi, Chiyodaku, Tokyo 100, Japan

Sakamoto, Isamu *Businessman*
2-5-3 Fujoshiroda, Suita City, Japan

Sakamoto, Soichi *Swimming Coach*
768 McCully St, Honolulu, HI 96826

Sakamura, Ken *Computer Inventor*
%University of Tokyo, Information Science Dept, Tokyo, Japan

Sakic, Joe *Hockey Player*
%Quebec Nordiques, 2205 Ave du Colisee, Quebec PQ G1L 4W7, Canada

Sakmann, Bert *Nobel Medicine Laureate*
%Max Planck Institute for Medical Research, D-6900 Heidelberg, Germany
Salam, Abdus *Nobel Physics Laureate*
%Imperial College of Science, Prince Consort Rd, London SW7, England
Salam, Saeb *Prime Minister, Lebanon*
Rue Moussaitbe, BP 3147, Beirut, Lebanon
Salan, Raoul *Army General, France*
41 Blvd Raspail, 75007 Paris, France
Salans, Lester B *Physician*
%National Arthritis Institute, 9000 Rockville Pike, Bethesda, MD 20205
Salant, Richard S *Television Executive*
%Columbia Broadcasting System, 30 Rockefeller Plz, New York, NY 10020
Salazar, Alberto *Marathon Runner*
%Athletics West, 3968 W 13th Ave, Eugene, OR 97402
Salbaing, Pierre A *Businessman*
%Liquid Air Corp, 1 Embarcadero Ctr, San Francisco, CA 94111
Saldana, Theresa *Actress*
%BDP Assoc, 10637 Burbank Blvd, North Hollywood, CA 91601
Saldich, Robert J *Businessman*
%Raychem Corp, 300 Constitution Dr, Menlo Park, CA 94025
Saleh, Ali Abdullah *President, Yemen Arab Republic*
%President's Office, Sana'a, Yemen Arab Republic
Salenger, Meredith *Actress*
%William Morris Agency, 151 El Camino, Beverly Hills, CA 90212
Salerno-Sonnenberg, Nadja *Concert Violinist*
%Columbia Artists Mgmt Inc, 165 W 57th St, New York, NY 10019
Sales, Eugenio de Araujo Cardinal *Religious Leader*
Palacio Sao Joaquim, Rua da Gloria 446, 20000 Rio de Janeiro RJ, Brazil
Sales, Soupy *Comedian*
245 E 35th St, New York, NY 10016
Saliba, Jacob *Businessman*
%Katy Industries, 853 Dundee Ave, Elgin, IL 60120
Saligman, Harvey *Businessman*
%Interco Inc, 10 Broadway, St Louis, MO 63102
Salii, Lazarus *President, Palau*
%President's Office, Koror, Palau
Salinas de Gortari, Carlos *President, Mexico*
%Palacio de Gobierno, Mexico City DF, Mexico
Salinger, J D *Writer*
%Harold Ober Assoc, 40 W 49th St, New York, NY 10017
Salinger, Pierre *Senator, CA; Journalist*
%ABC-TV, News Dept, 8 Carburton St, London W1P 7DT, England
Salisbury, Harrison E *Journalist*
%New York Times, 229 W 43rd St, New York, NY 10036
Salizzoni, Frank L *Businessman*
%Trans World Corp, 605 3rd Ave, New York, NY 10158
Salk, Jonas E *Physician, Scientist*
2444 Ellentown Rd, La Jolla, CA 92037
Salle, David *Artist*
%Larry Gagosian Gallery, 980 Madison Ave, #PH, New York, NY 10021
Salley, John *Basketball Player*
%Detroit Pistons, Palace, 1 Championship Dr, Auburn Hills, MI 48057
Salminen, Matti *Opera Singer*
%Mariedi Anders Artists Mgmt, 535 El Camino del Mar, San Francisco, CA 94121
Salming, Borje *Hockey Player*
%Detroit Red Wings, 600 Civic Center Dr, Detroit, MI 48226
Salmon, Thomas P *Governor, VT*
%Salmon & Nostrand, Centennial Arcade, #300, Bellows Falls, VT 05101
Salomon, Leon E *Army General*
DCG, TRADOC for Combined Arms Support, Fort Lee, VA 23801
Salomon, Richard *Educator*
1516 Riverbank Rd, Stamford, CT 06903
Salonen, Esa-Pekka *Conductor*
%Los Angeles Philharmonic, Music Ctr, 135 N Grand, Los Angeles, CA 90012
Saltpeter, Edwin E *Physicist*
116 Westbourne Ln, Ithaca, NY 14850

Saltzman, Charles E *Financier*
30 E 62nd St, New York, NY 10021

Saltzman, Harry *Movie, Theater Producer*
%Mike Beck, 729 7th Ave, New York, NY 10019

Salvagni, Carlos A *Businessman*
%Upjohn Co, 7000 Portage Rd, Kalamazoo, MI 49001

Salvatori, Henry *Businessman*
1901 Ave of Stars, #1130, Los Angeles, CA 90067

Salvino, Carmen *Bowler*
2658 N New England, Chicago, IL 60635

Salzman, Sheldon R *Businessman*
%Uniroyal Inc, World Headquarters, Middlebury, CT 06749

Sam the Sham (Domingo S Samudio) *Singer*
3667 Tutwiler Ave, Memphis, TN 38122

Samaranch Torello, Juan Antonio *International Olympic Official*
Avda Pau Casals 24, 08021 Barcelona 6, Spain

Samaras, Lucas *Sculptor, Photographer*
%Pace Gallery, 32 E 57th St, New York, NY 10023

Samborn, J Warren *Businessman*
%GATX Corp, 120 S Riverside Plz, Chicago, IL 60606

Sambrook, Roy *Businessman*
%Chesebrough-Pond's Inc, Westport, CT 06881

Samford, Frank P *Businessman*
%Torchmark Corp, 2001 3rd Ave S, Birmingham, AL 35233

Samford, John S P *Businessman*
%Liberty National Life Insurance, 2001 3rd Ave S, Birmingham, AL 35233

Sammet, Rolf *Businessman*
%Hoechst, Postfach 80 03 20, Frankfurt/Main 80, Germany

Sammons, James H *Association Executive*
%American Medical Assn, 535 N Dearborn St, Chicago, IL 60610

Samms, Emma *Actress*
10401 Wyton Dr, Los Angeles, CA 90024

Samois, Nicholas P *Science Administrator*
%Brookhaven National Laboratory, Director's Office, Upton, Long Island, NY 11973

Sample, Steven B *Educator*
%University of Southern California, President's Office, Los Angeles, CA 90089

Sampras, Pete *Tennis Player*
6816 Verde Ridge Rd, Rancho Palos Verdes, CA 90274

Sampson, Patsy H *Educator*
%Stephens College, President's Office, Columbia, MO 65215

Sampson, Robert *Actor*
%Gores/Fields Agency, 10100 Santa Monica Blvd, #700, Los Angeles, CA 90067

Samuel, Primate Mar-Athanasius Y *Religious Leader*
%Syrian Orthodox Church of Antioch, 45 Fairmount Ave, Hackensack, NJ 07601

Samuelson, C A *Businessman*
%Arla Ekonomisk Forening, 104 46 Stockholm, Sweden

Samuelson, Don *Governor, ID*
Rt 3, Box 300, Sandpoint, ID 83864

Samuelson, Paul A *Nobel Economics Laureate*
94 Somerset St, Belmont, MA 02178

Samuelsson, Bengt *Physician*
%Karolinska Institute, Chemistry Dept, 10401 Stockholm, Sweden

Samuelsson, Kjell *Hockey Player*
%Philadelphia Flyers, Spectrum, Pattison Pl, Philadelphia, PA 19148

Samuelsson, Ulf *Hockey Player*
%Hartford Whalers, 1 Civic Center Plz, Hartford, CT 06103

San Giacomo, Laura *Actress*
%Writers & Artists Agency, 11726 San Vicente Blvd, #300, Los Angeles, CA 90049

Sanborn, David *Jazz Saxophonist*
%Warner Bros Records, 3300 Warner Blvd, Burbank, CA 91505

Sanchez del Campo, Alberto *Prime Minister, Peru*
%Prime Minister's Office, Lima, Peru

Sanchez Hernandez, Fidel *President, El Salvador*
Calle Arce 1128, San Salvador, El Salvador

Sanchez Vicario, Arantxa *Tennis Player*
%International Management Group, 22 E 71st St, New York, NY 10021

Sanchez, Emilio *Artist*
333 E 30th St, New York, NY 10016

Sanchez, Jose Cardinal *Religious Leader*
%Congregation for Evangelization of Peoples, Vatican City, Rome, Italy

Sanchez, Joseph J *Businessman*
%General Motors do Brasil, Ave Goias 1805, Sao Caetano do Sul SP, Brazil

Sand, Paul *Actor*
%STE Representation, 9301 Wilshire Blvd, #312, Beverly Hills, CA 90210

Sanda, Dominique *Actress*
38 Rue de Lisbonne, 75008 Paris, France

Sandage, Allan R *Astronomer*
%Hale Observatories, 813 Santa Barbara St, Pasadena, CA 91101

Sandberg, Michael G R *Financier*
%Hongkong & Shanghai Banking Corp, 1 Queen's Rd Central, Hong Kong

Sandberg, Ryne *Baseball Player*
2357 Iroquois Dr, Glenview, IL 60025

Sander, Anne *Golfer*
%Stephen Sander, 1219 Parkside Dr E, Seattle, WA 98112

Sanderling, Kurt *Conductor*
%Mariedi Anders Artists Mgmt, 535 El Camino del Mar St, San Francisco, CA 94121

Sanders, Barry *Football Player*
%Detroit Lions, Silverdome, 1200 Featherstone Rd, Pontiac, MI 48057

Sanders, Bernard *Representative, VT*
%House of Representatives, Washington, DC 20515

Sanders, Carl E *Governor, GA*
1400 Candler Bldg, Atlanta, GA 30043

Sanders, Charles A *Businessman*
%Squibb Corp, PO Box 4000, Princeton, NJ 08540

Sanders, Deion *Football Player*
%Atlanta Falcons, Suwanee Rd, Suwanee, GA 30174

Sanders, Doug *Golfer*
8828 Sandingham, Houston, TX 77024

Sanders, James C *Government Official*
%Small Business Administration, 1441 "C" St NW, Washington, DC 20416

Sanders, Jon *Yachtsman*
28 Portland St, Redlands 6009 WA, Australia

Sanders, Lawrence *Writer*
%G P Putnam's Sons, 200 Madison Ave, New York, NY 10016

Sanders, Marlene *Commentator*
%WNET-TV, News Dept, 356 W 58th St, New York, NY 10019

Sanders, Richard *Actor*
4954 Strohm Ave, North Hollywood, CA 91601

Sanders, Summer *Swimmer*
%Stanford University, Athletic Dept, Stanford, CA 94305

Sanders, W J (Jerry), III *Businessman*
%Advanced Micro Devices, 901 Thompson Pl, Sunnyvale, CA 94088

Sanders, Wayne R *Businessman*
%Kimberly-Clark Corp, PO Box 619100, Dallas, TX 75261

Sanderson, Tessa *Track Athlete*
%Olympic Assn, 1 Wandsworth Plain, London SW18 1EH, England

Sanderson, William *Actor*
%Stone Manners Agency, 9113 Sunset Blvd, Los Angeles, CA 90069

Sanderson, Wimp *Basketball Coach*
%University of Alabama, Athletic Dept, University, AL 35486

Sandler, Herbert M *Financier*
%Golden West Financial Corp, 1901 Harrison St, Oakland, CA 94612

Sandler, Marion O *Financier*
%Golden West Financial Corp, 1901 Harrison St, Oakland, CA 94612

Sandlund, Debra *Actress*
%Harris & Goldberg Agency, 1999 Ave of Stars, #2850, Los Angeles, CA 90067

Sandness, Claire *Businessman*
%Land O'Lakes Inc, 4001 Lexington Ave N, Arden Hills, MN 55112

Sandrich, Jay H *Television Director*
1 Northstar, #205, Marina del Rey, CA 90292

Sands, Don W *Businessman*
%Gold Kist Inc, 244 Perimeter Center Pkwy NE, Atlanta, GA 30301

S

Sands – Sapsowitz

Sands, Julian *Actor*
%Writers & Artists Agency, 11726 San Vicente Blvd, #300, Los Angeles, CA 90049

Sands, Thomas E *Businessman*
%Big Three Industries, 3535 W 12th St, Houston, TX 77008

Sands, Tommy *Singer*
4785 N Dino Blvd, Kissionmee, FL 32741

Sandstrom, Tomas *Hockey Player*
%Los Angeles Kings, Great Western Forum, 3900 W Manchester, Inglewood, CA 90306

Sandy, Gary *Actor*
12810 Waddell St, North Hollywood, CA 91607

Sandygren, E W *Businessman*
%Pacific Gamble Robinson Co, 10829 NE 68th St, Kirkland, WA 98033

Saneyev, Viktor *Track Athlete*
%Light Athletic Federation, Skatertnyi per 4, Moscow G 69, Russia

Sanford, Carl M, Jr *Financier*
%Bankers Trust New York Corp, 16 Wall St, New York, NY 10005

Sanford, Charles S, Jr *Financier*
%Bankers Trust New York Corp, 16 Wall St, New York, NY 10005

Sanford, Isabel *Actress*
%Agency for Performing Arts, 9000 Sunset Blvd, #1200, Los Angeles, CA 90069

Sanford, Terry *Governor/Senator, NC; Educator*
1508 Pinecrest Rd, Durham, NC 27705

Sang, Samantha *Singer*
200 W 51st St, #1410, New York, NY 10019

Sanger, Frederick *Nobel Chemistry Laureate*
%Medical Research Council Laboratory, Hills Rd, Cambridge CB2 2QH, England

Sangster, Robert E *Businessman*
%Vernons Organization, The Nunnery, Douglas, Isle of Man, England

Sanguinetti Cairolo, Julio Maria *President, Uruguay*
%President's Office, Montevideo, Uruguay

Sano, Fukujiro *Businessman*
%TDK Corp, 1-13-1 Nihonbashi, Chuoku, Tokyo 103, Japan

Sansom, Chip *Cartoonist (Born Losers)*
1050 Erie Cliff Dr, Cleveland, OH 44107

Santamaria, Mongo *Congo Drummer*
%Hooke, 78-08 223rd St, Bayside, NY 11364

Santana, Carlos *Guitarist*
%Bill Graham Productions, 201 11th St, San Francisco, CA 94103

Santana, Manuel *Tennis Player*
%International Tennis Hall of Fame, 194 Bellevue Ave, Newport, RI 02840

Santer, Jacques *Premier, Luxembourg*
%Premier's Office, Luxembourg, Luxembourg

Santiago, Benito *Baseball Player*
Urba Villa Jauca, #B-21, Santa Isabel, PR 00757

Santmyer, Helen Hoover *Social Worker*
%Hospitality Home East, N Monroe Dr, Xenia, OH 45385

Santo, Ron *Baseball Player*
1303 Somerset, Glenview, IL 60025

Santorini, Paul E *Physicist, Engineer*
PO Box 49, Athens, Greece

Santoro, Carmelo *Businessman*
%Ashton-Tate Corp, 20101 Hamilton Ave, Torrance, CA 90502

Santorum, Rick *Representative, PA*
%House of Representatives, Washington, DC 20515

Santos, Alexandre J M Dos Cardinal *Religious Leader*
Paco Arquiepiscopal, Avenida Eduardo Mondlane 1448, CP Maputo, Mozambique

Santos, Joe *Actor*
%Gores/Fields Agency, 10100 Santa Monica Blvd, #700, Los Angeles, CA 90067

Santry, Arthur J, Jr *Businessman*
%Combustion Engineering Inc, 900 Long Ridge Rd, Stamford, CT 06902

Santucci, John *Actor*
%Ed Adler, 12424 Wilshire Blvd, Los Angeles, CA 90025

Sappenfield, Richard W *Businessman*
%Murray Ohio Manufacturing Co, Franklin Rd, Brentwood, TN 37027

Sapsowitz, Sidney H *Businessman*
%MGM/UA Entertainment Co, 10202 W Washington Blvd, Culver City, CA 90230

Sara, Mia *Actress*
%Gersh Agency, 232 N Canon Dr, Beverly Hills, CA 90210

Sarafanov, Gennady *Cosmonaut*
141 160 Svyosdny Gorodok, Moskovskoi Oblasti, Potchta Kosmonavtov, Russia

Sarafian, Armen *Educator*
1950 3rd St, La Verne, CA 91750

Sarandon, Chris *Actor*
%Susan Smith Assoc, 121 N San Vicente Blvd, Beverly Hills, CA 90211

Sarandon, Susan *Actress*
%International Creative Mgmt, 8899 Beverly Blvd, Los Angeles, CA 90048

Sarasin, A E *Financier*
Freiestrasse 107, CH-4002 Basel, Switzerland

Sarazen, Gene *Golfer*
%Emerald Beach Apts, PO Box 667, Marco Island, FL 33937

Sarbanes, Paul S *Senator, MD*
%US Senate, Washington, DC 20510

Sardegna, Carl J *Businessman*
%Union Mutual Life Insurance, 2211 Congress St, Portland, ME 04122

Sardi, Maurice C *Businessman*
%Westinghouse Electric Corp, Gateway Ctr, Pittsburgh, PA 15222

Sardi, Vincent, Jr *Restauranteur*
%Sardi's Restaurant, 234 W 44th St, New York, NY 10036

Sargent, Ben *Editorial Cartoonist*
%Austin American-Statesman, 166 E Riverside Dr, Austin, TX 78767

Sargent, Dick *Actor*
7422 Palo Vista Dr, Los Angeles, CA 90046

Sargent, Francis W *Governor, MA*
Farm St, Dover, MA 02030

Sargent, Joseph *Movie Producer, Director*
33740 Pacific Coast Hwy, Malibu, CA 90265

Sarni, Vincent A *Businessman*
%PPG Industries, 1 PPG Pl, Pittsburgh, PA 15272

Sarnoff, William *Publisher*
%Warner Publishing Inc, 75 Rockefeller Plz, New York, NY 10019

Sarosi, Imre *Swimming Coach*
1033 Bp Harrer Dal u 4, Hungary

Sarraute, Nathalie *Writer*
12 Ave Pierre 1 de Serbie, 75116 Paris, France

Sarrazin, Michael *Actor*
9920 Beverly Grove Dr, Beverly Hills, CA 90201

Sarton, May *Author, Poet*
PO Box 99, York, ME 03909

Sartzetakis, Christos *President, Greece*
%President's Office, Athens, Greece

Sasaki, Kunihiko *Financier*
%Fuji Bank, 1-5-5 Otemachi, Chiyodaku, Tokyo 100, Japan

Sasaki, Sadamichi *Businessman*
%Fuji Heavy Industries, 1-7-2 Nishi-Shinjuku, Shinjukuku, Tokyo 160, Japan

Sasaki, Satoshi *Financier*
%Shoko Chukin Bank, 2-10-17 Yaesu, Chuoku, Tokyo 104, Japan

Sasaki, Takanobu *Businessman*
%Nippon Mining Co, 2-10-1 Toranomon, Minatoku, Tokyo 105, Japan

Sass, Sylvia *Opera Singer*
%Dido Senger Artists, The Garden, 103 Randolph Ave, London W9 1DL, England

Sasser, Clarence E *Vietnam War Army Hero (CMH)*
13414 FM 521, Rosharon, TX 77583

Sasser, James R *Senator, TN*
%US Senate, Washington, DC 20510

Sassmannshausen, Gunther *Businessman*
%Preussag, Leibnizufer 9, 3000 Hanover, Germany

Sassoon, Vidal *Hair Stylist*
2049 Century Park East, #3900, Los Angeles, CA 90067

Sassou-Nguesso, Denis *President, Congo People's Republic*
%President's Office, Brazzaville, Congo People's Republic

Sather, Glen *Hockey Coach, Executive*
%Edmonton Oilers, Northlands Coliseum, Edmonton AL T5B 4M9, Canada

S

Sato, Eric *Volleyball Player*
%US Volleyball Team, National Training Center, PO Box 24219, San Diego, CA 92124

Satowaki, Joseph Cardinal *Religious Leader*
%Archbishop's House, Minamiyametecho 5-3, Nagasaki, Japan

Saudners, Ernest W *Businessman*
%Arthur Guinness & Sons, 10 Albermarle St, London W1X 4AJ, England

Sauer, George H, Sr *Football Player, Coach*
3625 MacArthur Dr, Waco, TX 76708

Sauer, Hank *Baseball Player*
207 Vallejo Ct, Millbrae, CA 94030

Saul, Ralph S *Businessman*
%Connecticut General & INA Corp, 1600 Arch St, Philadelphia, PA 19101

Sauls, Don *Religious Leader*
%Pentecostal Free Will Baptist Church, PO Box 1568, Dunn, NC 28334

Saunders, Cicely *Hospice Movement Founder*
%St Christopher's Hospice, 51-53 Lawreie Park Rd, Sydenham 6DZ, England

Saunders, George L, Jr *Attorney*
179 E Lake Shore Dr, Chicago, IL 60611

Saura, Carlos *Movie Director*
%Direccion General del Libro, Paseo De la Casrellana 109, Madrid 16, Spain

Sauter, Van Gordon *Television Executive*
%Variety Magazine, 5700 Wilshire Blvd, Los Angeles, CA 90036

Sauvan, Henri L *Businessman*
1 Sq Max Hymans, 75757 Paris Cedex 15, France

Sauve, Bob *Hockey Player*
%New Jersey Devils, Meadowlands Arena, East Rutherford, NJ 07073

Savage, Elizabeth *Actress*
%Ambrosio/Mortimer Assoc, 301 N Canon Dr, #305, Beverly Hills, CA 90210

Savage, Fred *Actor*
PO Box 869, Tarzana, CA 91357

Savage, Gus *Representative, IL*
%House of Representatives, Washington, DC 20515

Savage, Randy (Macho Man) *Wrestler*
%World Wrestling Federation, 1055 Summer St, Greenwich, CT 06905

Savalas, Telly *Actor*
%Sheraton Universal Hotel, 333 Universal City Plz, Universal City, CA 91608

Savard, Denis *Hockey Player*
%Montreal Canadiens, 2313 St Catherine St W, Montreal PQ H3H 1N2, Canada

Savard, Serge *Hockey Player, Executive*
%Montreal Canadiens, 2313 St Catherine St W, Montreal PQ H3H 1N2, Canada

Saville, Curtis *Long Distance Rower, Explorer*
RFD Box 44, West Charleston, VT 05872

Saville, Kathleen *Long Distance Rower, Explorer*
RFD Box 44, West Charleston, VT 05872

Savimbi, Jonas *Political Leader, Angola*
%Black Manafort Stone Kelly, 1111 N Fairfax St, Alexandria, VA 22314

Savinykh, Viktor *Cosmonaut*
141 160 Svyosdny Gorodok, Moskovskoi Oblasti, Potchta Kosmonavtov, Russia

Savio, Mario *Student Activist*
%San Francisco State University, Physics Dept, San Francisco, CA 94132

Savitskaya, Svetlana *Cosmonaut*
141 160 Svyosdny Gorodok, Moskovskoi Oblasti, Potchta Kosmonavtov, Russia

Savitt, Richard *Tennis Player*
19 E 80th St, New York, NY 10021

Sawallisch, Wolfgang *Conductor*
%Bayerische Staatsoper, Postfach 745, D-8000 Munich 1, Germany

Sawhill, John C *Government, Association Official*
%Nature Conservancy, 1815 N Lynn St, Arlington, VA 22209

Sawyer, Diane *Commentator*
%ABC-TV, News Dept, 77 W 66th St, New York, NY 10023

Sawyer, Forrest *Commentator*
%ABC-TV, New Dept, 1330 Ave of Americas, New York, NY 10019

Sawyer, Grant *Governor, PA*
Lionel Sawyer Collins, Valley Bank Plz, #1700, 300 S 4th St, Las Vegas, NV 89101

Sawyer, James L *Labor Leader*
%Leather Workers Union, 11 Peabody Sq, Peabody, MA 01960

Sax, Steve *Baseball Player*
%Chicago White Sox, 324 W 35th St, Chicago, IL 60616

Saxbe, William H *Attorney General; Senator, OH*
Rt 2, Mechanicsburg, OH 43044

Saxon, John *Actor*
2432 Banyan Dr, Los Angeles, CA 90049

Saxton, H James *Representative, NJ*
%House of Representatives, Washington, DC 20515

Sayers, E Roger *Educator*
%University of Alabama, President's Office, Tuscaloosa, AL 35487

Sayers, Gale *Football Player*
624 Buck Rd, Northbrook, IL 60062

Sayles, John *Movie Director*
555 W 57th St, #1230, New York, NY 10019

Scaasi, Arnold *Fashion Designer*
681 5th Ave, New York, NY 10022

Scacchi, Greta *Actress*
%Heath, Paramount House, 162-170 Wardour St, London W1V 3AT, England

Scaggs, Boz (William R) *Singer*
%Frontline Mgmt, 345 N Maple Dr, #235, Beverly Hills, CA 90210

Scales, Charles W, Jr *Financier*
%First Federal Savings & Loan, 301 College St, Greenville, SC 29602

Scalfaro, Oscar L *Government Official, Italy*
%Chamber of Deputies, Piazza Montecitorio, 00100 Rome, Italy

Scali, John A *Government Official, Journalist*
%ABC-TV, 1717 DeSales St NW, Washington, DC 20036

Scalia, Antonin *Supreme Court Justice*
%US Supreme Court, 1 1st St NE, Washington, DC 20543

Scalia, Jack *Actor*
%Wallack Assoc, 1717 N Highland Ave, #701, Los Angeles, CA 90028

Scammon, Richard M *Political Scientist*
5508 Greystone St, Chevy Chase, MD 20815

Scancarelli, Jim *Cartoonist (Gasoline Alley)*
%Tribune Media Services, 34 E Concord St, Orlando, FL 32801

Scandling, William F *Businessman*
%Saga Corp, 1 Saga Ln, Menlo Park, CA 94025

Scanga, Italo *Artist*
7127 Olivetas, La Jolla, CA 92037

Scarabelli, Michele *Actress*
%Henderson/Hogan Agency, 247 S Beverly Dr, #102, Beverly Hills, CA 90210

Scarbath, Jack *Football Player*
736 Calvert Rd, Rising Sun, MD 21911

Scarbrough, W Carl *Labor Leader*
%Furniture Workers Union, 1910 Airlane Dr, Nashville, TN 37210

Scardino, Albert *Journalist*
%Georgia Gazette, PO Box 9925, Savannah, GA 31412

Scarfe, Gerald A *Cartoonist*
10 Cheyne Walk, London SW3, England

Scargill, Arthur *Labor Leader*
%National Union of Mineworkers, 2 Huddersfield Rd, Barnsley, England

Scarwid, Diana *Actress*
PO Box 3614, Savannah, GA 31404

Scates, Al *Volleyball Coach*
%University of California, Athletic Dept, Los Angeles, CA 90024

Scavullo, Francesco *Photographer*
212 E 63rd St, New York, NY 10021

Schaal, Richard *Actor*
%Atkins Assoc, 303 S Crescent Heights Blvd, Los Angeles, CA 90024

Schachman, Howard K *Molecular Biochemist*
%University of California, Molecular Biology Dept, Berkeley, CA 94720

Schacht, Henry B *Businessman*
%Cummins Engineering Co, 1000 5th St, Columbus, IN 47201

Schachter, Norm *Football Referee*
7716 Westlawn Ave, Los Angeles, CA 90045

Schaeberle, Robert M *Businessman*
%Nabisco Brands Inc, River Rd, East Hanover, NJ 07936

S

Schaefer – Schell

Schaefer, Daniel L — *Representative, CO*
%House of Representatives, Washington, DC 20515

Schaefer, Ernst J — *Medical Researcher*
%Tufts University, Nutrition Research Ctr, Medford, MA 02155

Schaefer, George — *Movie Director*
1040 Woodland Dr, Beverly Hills, CA 90210

Schaefer, John F — *Businessman*
%Baker International Corp, 500 City Pkwy W, Orange, CA 92668

Schaefer, Vincent J — *Research Physicist*
%Atmospheric Research Ctr, 100 Fuller Rd, Albany, NY 12203

Schaefer, William D — *Governor, MD*
%Governor's Office, State Capitol, Annapolis, MD 21401

Schaeffer, Susan F — *Writer*
%Alfred A Knopf Inc, 201 E 50th St, New York, NY 10022

Schaeffler, Johann — *Businessman*
%Airbus-Industrie, 5 Ave de Villiers, 75017 Paris, France

Schaeneman, Lewis G, Jr — *Businessman*
%Stop & Shop Companies, PO Box 369, Boston, MA 02101

Schafer, Otto — *Businessman*
%FAG Kugelfischer Georg Schafer, 8720 Schweinfurt 1, Germany

Schairer, George S — *Aerospace Design Engineer*
4242 Hunts Point Rd, Bellevue, WA 90402

Schaller, George B — *Zoologist*
%Animal Research Ctr, New York Zoological Society, Bronx Park, NY 10460

Schallert, William — *Actor*
14920 Ramos Pl, Pacific Palisades, CA 90272

Schally, Andrew V — *Nobel Medicine Laureate*
%Veterans Administration Hospital, 1601 Perdido St, New Orleans, LA 70146

Schanberg, Sydney H — *Journalist*
%New York Newsday, 2 Park Ave, New York, NY 10016

Schanck, J Thomas — *Businessman*
%Signode Corp, 3600 W Lake Ave, Glenview, IL 60025

Schank, Roger C — *Computer Scientist, Psychologist*
%Yale University, Computer Science Dept, 10 Hillhouse Ave, New Haven, CT 06520

Scharffenberger, George T — *Businessman*
%City Investing Co, 59 Maiden Ln, New York, NY 10038

Scharffenberger, William J — *Businessman*
%Wheeling-Pittsburgh Steel Corp, 4 Gateway Ctr, Pittsburgh, PA 15230

Schauer, Henry — *WW II Army Hero (CMH)*
840 Madrona Ave S, Salem, OR 97302

Schaufuss, Peter — *Ballet Dancer, Artistic Director*
%National Ballet of Canada, 157 King St E, Toronto ON MSC 169, Canada

Schawlow, Arthur L — *Nobel Physics Laureate*
849 Esplanada Way, Stanford, CA 94305

Schayes, Adolph — *Basketball Player*
5 Northridge Dr, DeWitt, NY 13214

Schayes, Dan — *Basketball Player*
%Milwaukee Bucks, 1001 N 4th St, Milwaukee, WI 53203

Schedeen, Anne — *Actress*
%Metropolitan Talent Agency, 9320 Wilshire Blvd, #300, Beverly Hills, CA 90212

Scheel, Paul J — *Businessman*
%USF&G Corp, 100 Light St, Baltimore, MD 21202

Scheel, Walter — *President, West Germany*
Lindenstrasse 22, 5000 Cologne-Marienburg, Germany

Scheffler, Steve — *Basketball Player*
%Purdue University, Athletic Dept, West Lafayette, IN 47907

Scheibel, Arnold B — *Medical Researcher*
1621 Morrison St, Encino, CA 91316

Scheider, Roy — *Actor*
11 E 73rd St, #2-B, New York, NY 10021

Scheider, Wilhelm — *Businessman*
%Freid Krupp GmbH, Altendorferstrass 103, 4300 Essen, Germany

Schein, Philip S — *Physician*
6212 Robinwood Rd, Bethesda, MD 20034

Schell, Maria — *Actress*
Bei Wasserburg/Inn, 8094 Heberthal, Germany

Schell, Maximilian *Actor*
Keplestrasse 2, 8000 Munich 80, Germany

Schembechler, Glenn E (Bo) *Football Coach*
870 Arlington Blvd, Ann Arbor, MI 48106

Schenk, Boyd F *Businessman*
%IC Industries, 111 E Wacker Dr, Chicago, IL 60601

Schenkel, Chris *Sportscaster*
%ABC-TV, Sports Dept, 1330 Ave of Americas, New York, NY 10019

Schepisi, Fred *Movie Director*
%Wald Organization, 1964 Westwood Blvd, #405, Los Angeles, CA 90025

Scheraga, Harold A *Chemist*
212 Homestead Terr, Ithaca, NY 14850

Scherer, Alfredo Vicente Cardinal *Religious Leader*
%Residencia Arquiepiscopal, Rue Espirito Santo 95, Porto Alegre, Brazil

Scherer, Robert W *Businessman*
%Georgia Power Co, 333 Piedmont Ave NW, Atlanta, GA 30308

Scherpenhuijsen Rom, W E *Financier*
%Nederlandsche Middenstandsbank, PO Box 1800, Amsterdam, Netherlands

Scherrer, Jean-Louis *Fashion Designer*
51 Ave du Montaigne, 75008 Paris, France

Scheuer, James H *Representative, NY*
%House of Representatives, Washington, DC 20515

Scheuer, Paul J *Chemist*
3271 Melemele Pl, Honolulu, HI 96822

Schey, Ralph *Businessman*
%Scott & Fetzer Co, 28800 Clemens Rd, Westlake, OH 44145

Schiavelli, Vincent *Actor*
%J Michael Bloom Ltd, 9200 Sunset Blvd, #710, Los Angeles, CA 90069

Schickele, Peter *Composer, Comedian*
%Vanguard Records, 71 W 23rd St, New York, NY 10010

Schieffer, Bob *Commentator*
%CBS-TV, News Dept, 2020 "M" St NW, Washington, DC 20036

Schieri, Paul J *Businessman*
%Fort Howard Paper Co, 1919 S Broadway, Green Bay, WI 54304

Schiff, Steven H *Representative, NM*
%US House of Representatives, Washington, DC 20515

Schiffer, Claudia *Model*
112 Central Park South, New York, NY 10019

Schiffer, Menahem M *Mathematician*
3748 Laguna Ave, Palo Alto, CA 94306

Schifrin, Lalo *Composer*
710 N Hillcrest Rd, Beverly Hills, CA 90210

Schillebeeckx, Edward *Theologian*
%Crossroad Publishing Co, 575 Lexington Ave, New York, NY 10022

Schiller, Harvey W *Sports Executive*
%US Olympic Committee, 1750 E Boulder St, Colorado Springs, CO 80909

Schiller, Karl *Government Official, West Germany*
Reindorferstrasse 84, 2112 Jesteburg, Germany

Schiller, Lawrence J *Television Director*
17137 Addison St, Encino, CA 91316

Schimberni, Mario *Businessman*
%Motedison, Foro Buonaparte 31, 20121 Milan, Italy

Schimmel, Paul R *Biochemist*
%Massachusetts Institute of Technology, Biology Dept, Cambridge, MA 02139

Schindler, Alexander M *Religious Leader*
%Union of American Hebrew Congregations, 838 5th Ave, New York, NY 10021

Schine, G David *Businessman*
626 S Hudson Ave, Los Angeles, CA 90005

Schirra, Walter M, Jr *Astronaut*
16834 Via de Santa Fe, PO Box 73, Rancho Santa Fe, CA 92067

Schisgal, Murray *Playwright*
%Writer's Guild, 55 W 57th St, New York, NY 10019

Schlafly, Phyllis *Women's Activist*
68 Fairmount, Alton, IL 62002

Schlegel, John P *Educator*
%University of San Francisco, President's Office, San Francisco, CA 94117

Schlesinger, Arthur M, Jr — *Writer, Educator*
%City University of New York, 33 W 42nd St, New York, NY 10036

Schlesinger, James R — *Secretary, Defense & Energy*
%Georgetown University, 1800 "K" St NW, Washington, DC 20006

Schlesinger, John R — *Movie, Theater Director*
1896 Rising Glen, Los Angeles, CA 90069

Schloemer, Paul G — *Businessman*
%Parker Hannifin Corp, 17325 Euclid Ave, Cleveland, OH 44112

Schlondorff, Volker — *Movie Director*
Obermaierstrasse 1, 8000 Munich 22, Germany

Schloredt, Bob — *Football Player*
%Nestle-Beich, 1827 N 167th, Seattle, WA 98133

Schlosberg, Richard T, III — *Publisher*
%Los Angeles Times, Times Mirror Sq, Los Angeles, CA 90053

Schlumberger, Jean — *Jewelry Designer*
%Tiffany's, 727 5th Ave, New York, NY 10022

Schluter, Poul — *Prime Minister, Denmark*
%Prime Minister's Office, Prins Jorgens Gaard 11, 1218 Copenhagen, Denmark

Schmeling, Max — *Boxer*
2114 Hallenstedt, Hamburg, Germany

Schmidheiny, Max — *Financier*
%Holderbank Financiere Glarus, Hauptstrasse 44, 8750 Glarus, Switzerland

Schmidheiny, Thomas — *Financier*
%Holderbank Financiere Glarus, Hauptstrasse 44, 8750 Glarus, Switzerland

Schmidt, Benno C, Jr — *Educator*
%Yale University, President's Office, New Haven, CT 06520

Schmidt, Carl F — *Pharmacologist, Physiologist*
%Thomas Wynne Apartments, #1/3-B, Wynne, PA 19096

Schmidt, Chauncey E — *Financier*
%Bank of California, 400 California St, San Francisco, CA 94104

Schmidt, Ernest J — *Basketball Player*
216 Broadway, Goodland, KS 67735

Schmidt, Helmut — *Chancellor, West Germany*
%Die Zeit, Speersport 1, 2000 Hamburg 1, Germany

Schmidt, James C — *Financier*
%Great American First Savings Bank, 600 "B" St, San Diego, CA 92183

Schmidt, Joe — *Football Player*
29600 Northwestern Hwy, Southfield, MI 48037

Schmidt, Kate — *Track Athlete*
1422 Armadale, Eagle Rock, CA 90042

Schmidt, Maarten — *Astronomer*
%California Institute of Technology, Astronomy Dept, Pasadena, CA 91125

Schmidt, Mike — *Baseball Player*
24 Lakewood Dr, Media, PA 19063

Schmidt, Milt — *Hockey Player*
%Boston Bruins, 150 Causeway St, Boston, MA 02114

Schmidt, Richard — *Orthopedic Surgeon*
%University of Pennsylvania Hospital, 3400 Spruce St, Philadelphia, PA 19104

Schmidt, Wolfgang — *Track Athlete*
Birheckenstrasse 116-B, 7000 Stuttgart 70, Germany

Schmidt-Nielsen, Knut — *Physiologist*
%Duke University, Zoology Dept, Durham, NC 27706

Schmidtke, Fredy — *Cyclist*
%General Delivery, 5000 Koln-Worringen, Germany

Schmiege, Robert W — *Businessman*
%CNW Corp, 165 North Canal, 1 North Western Ctr, Chicago, IL 60606

Schmitt, Francis O — *Neurobiologist*
72 Byron Rd, Weston, MA 02193

Schmitt, Harrison H — *Senator, NM; Astronaut*
PO Box 14338, Albuquerque, NM 87191

Schmitt, Roland W — *Educator*
%Rensselaer Polytechnic Institute, President's Office, Troy, NY 12180

Schmoke, Kurt — *Mayor*
%Mayor's Office, City Hall, 100 Holliday St, Baltimore, MD 21202

Schnabel, Julian — *Artist*
%Mary Boone Gallery, 420 W Broadway, New York, NY 10012

Schnabel, Karl Ulrich *Concert Pianist*
305 West End Ave, New York, NY 10023

Schnackenberg, Roy *Artist*
1919 N Orchard, Chicago, IL 60614

Schnarre, Monika *Model*
%Ford Model Agency, 344 E 59th St, New York, NY 10022

Schneerson, Menachem Mendel *Religious Leader*
%Lubavitch Habsidim, 770 Eastern Pkwy, Brooklyn, NY 11213

Schneider, Andrew *Journalist*
%Pittsburgh Press, 34 Blvd of Allies, Pittsburgh, PA 15230

Schneider, Claudine *Representative, RI*
%Harvard University, Kennedy School of Government, Cambridge, MA 02138

Schneider, Frederick W *Businessman*
%Public Service Enterprise Grp, 80 Park Plz, Newark, NJ 07101

Schneider, John *Actor*
%Trails End Productions, PO Box 1726, Mechanicsburg, PA 17055

Schneider, Stephen H *Climatologist*
%National Ctr for Atmospheric Research, Box 3000, Boulder, CO 80307

Schneider, Vreni *Skier*
8767 Elm, Switzerland

Schneider, William G *Physical Chemist*
%National Research Council, Ottawa ON K1A 0R6, Canada

Schneiderhan, Wolfgang *Concert Violinist*
Kaasgrabengasse 98-A, 1190 Vienna, Austria

Schnelldorfer, Manfred *Figure Skater*
Seydlitz Strasse 55, 8000 Munich 80, Germany

Schnellenberger, Howard *Football Coach*
%University of Louisville, Athletic Dept, Louisville, KY 40292

Schochet, Bob *Cartoonist*
Sunset Rd, Highland Mills, NY 10930

Schoellkopf, Caroline Rose *Businesswoman*
%Rosewood Resources, 100 Crescent Ct, Dallas, TX 75205

Schoemehl, Vincent C *Mayor*
%Mayor's Office, 1200 Market St, #200, St Louis, MO 63103

Schoendienst, Al (Red) *Baseball Player, Manager*
331 Ladue Woods Ct, Creve Coeur, MO 63141

Schoenfeld, Gerald *Theater Producer*
%Shubert Organization Inc, 225 W 44th St, New York, NY 10036

Schoenfield, Al *Swimming Administrator*
6502 Verde Ridge Rd, Rancho Palos Verdes, CA 90274

Schoenthal, Robert *Financier*
%L F Rothschild Unterberg Tobin, 55 Water St, New York, NY 10041

Schofield, George H *Businessman*
%Zurn Industries, 1 Zurn Pl, Erie, PA 16505

Schofield, Seth E *Businessman*
%USAir Inc, 2345 Crystal Dr, Arlington, VA 22227

Scholder, Fritz *Artist*
118 Cattletrack Rd, Scottsdale, AZ 85251

Scholes, Clarke *Swimmer*
1360 Somerset, Grosse Pointe Park, MI 48230

Scholes, Myron *Economist*
%Stanford University, Graduate Business School, Stanford, CA 94305

Scholz, Rupert *Government Official, West Germany*
Bundesministerium de Verteidigung, Handthohe, 5300 Bonn, Germany

Schonberg, Claude-Michel *Composer*
%Theater Royal Drury Lane, Catherine St, London WC2, England

Schonberg, Harold C *Music Critic*
118 Riverside Dr, New York, NY 10024

Schoneman, John A *Businessman*
%Wausau Insurance Companies, 2000 Westwood Dr, Wausau, WI 54401

Schonzeler, Hans-Hubert *Conductor*
%Savage Club, 9 Fitzmaurice Pl, London W1, England

Schoolnik, Gary *Medical Researcher*
%Stanford University Medical School, Microbiology Dept, Stanford, CA 94305

Schorer, Jane *Journalist*
%Des Moines Register, Box 957, Des Moines, IA 50304

S

Schork – Schroeter

Schork, John E — *Businessman*
%Research-Cottrell Inc, PO Box 1500, Somerville, NJ 08876

Schorr, Bill — *Cartoonist (Phoebe's Place)*
%Los Angeles Times Syndicate, Times-Mirror Sq, Los Angeles, CA 90053

Schorr, Daniel — *Journalist, Author*
3113 Woodley Rd, Washington, DC 20008

Schorsch, Ismar — *Educator*
%Jewish Theological Seminary, Chancellor's Office, New York, NY 10027

Schott, Marge — *Baseball Executive*
%Cincinnati Reds, 100 Riverfront Stadium, Cincinnati, OH 45202

Schottenheimer, Marty — *Football Coach*
%Kansas City Chiefs, 1 Arrowhead Dr, Kansas City, MO 64129

Schou, Mogens — *Psychiatrist*
%Aarhus University, Institute of Psychiatry, Aarhus, Denmark

Schowalter, Edward R, Jr — *Korean War Army Hero (CMH)*
913 Bibb Ave, Auburn, AL 36830

Schrader, Ken — *Auto Racing Driver*
PO Box 599, Licking, MO 65542

Schrader, Paul — *Movie Director, Screenwriter*
908 Malcolm Ave, Los Angeles, CA 90024

Schraer, Rosemary S J — *Educator*
%University of California, Chancellor's Office, Riverside, CA 92521

Schrag, Karl — *Artist*
127 E 95th St, New York, NY 10028

Schramm, David N — *Astrophysicist*
4923 S Kimbark Ave, Chicago, IL 60615

Schramm, Tex — *Football Executive*
9355 Sunny Brook, Dallas, TX 75220

Schramm, Wilbur — *Educator*
1650 Ala Moana, #3009, Honolulu, CA 96815

Schreiber, Avery — *Actor*
4420 Los Feliz Blvd, #201, Los Angeles, CA 90027

Schreiber, Martin J — *Governor, WI*
2013 N Hi Mount Blvd, Milwaukee, WI 53208

Schreier, Peter — *Opera Singer*
%Mariedi Anders Mgmt, 535 El Camino del Mar, San Francisco, CA 94121

Schreyer, Edward R — *Government Official, Canada*
%Government House, Rideau Hall, Ottawa ON K1A 0A1, Canada

Schreyer, William A — *Businessman*
%Merrill Lynch Co, 1 Liberty Plz, 165 Broadway, New York, NY 10080

Schrieffer, John R — *Nobel Physics Laureate*
1009 Las Palmas Dr, Santa Barbara, CA 93110

Schriesheim, Alan — *Applied Chemist*
%Director's Office, Argonne National Laboratory, Argonne, IL 60439

Schriever, Bernard A — *Air Force General*
4501 Dexter St NW, Washington, DC 20007

Schrimshaw, Nevin S — *Nutritionist*
Sandwich Notch Farm, Thornton, NH 03223

Schroder, Rick — *Actor*
9 Sandy Ln, Greenwich, CT 06830

Schroeder, Barbet — *Movie Director*
%Citrin Cooperman Co, 342 Madison Ave, New York, NY 10173

Schroeder, John H, Jr — *Educator*
%University of Wisconsin-Milwaukee, President's Office, Milwaukee, WI 53201

Schroeder, Mary M — *Judge*
%US Court of Appeals, 230 N 1st Ave, Phoenix, AZ 85025

Schroeder, Patricia — *Representative, CO*
%House of Representatives, Washington, DC 20515

Schroeder, Ted (Frederick R, Jr) — *Tennis Player*
1010 W Muirlands Dr, La Jolla, CA 92037

Schroeder, Terry — *Water Polo Player, Coach*
%Pepperdine University, Athletic Dept, Malibu, CA 90265

Schroer, Edmund A — *Businessman*
%Northern Indiana Public Service Co, 5265 Hohman Ave, Hammond, IN 46320

Schroeter, Louis C — *Businessman*
%Upjohn Co, 7000 Portage Rd, Kalamazoo, MI 49001

Schrom, Ken *Baseball Player*
713 Roisante, El Paso, TX 79922
Schrontz, Frank *Businessman*
%Boeing Co, 7755 E Marginal Way S, Seattle, WA 98108
Schruefer, John J *Physician*
%Georgetown University Hospital, Ob-Gyn Dept, Washington, DC 20007
Schubert, Mark *Swimming Coach*
%University of Texas, Athletic Dept, Austin, TX 78712
Schuck, John *Actor*
%Badgley Connor, 9229 Sunset Blvd, #607, Los Angeles, CA 90069
Schueler, Jon R *Artist*
40 W 22nd St, New York, NY 10010
Schuenke, Donald J *Businessman*
%Northwestern Mutual Life Insurance, 720 E Wisconsin, Milwaukee, WI 53202
Schulberg, Budd *Writer*
Brookside, Box 707, Westhampton Beach, NY 11978
Schuller, Grete *Sculptor*
8 Barstow Rd, #7-G, Great Neck, NY 11021
Schuller, Gunther *Composer*
167 Dudley Rd, Newton Centre, MA 02159
Schuller, Robert H *Evangelist*
464 S Esplanade, Orange, CA 92669
Schultes, Richard E *Ethnobotanist*
%Harvard University Botanical Museum, Oxford St, Cambridge, MA 02138
Schultz, Dave *Wrestler*
4338 Upland Dr, Madison, WI 53705
Schultz, Dick *Association Executive*
%National Collegiate Athletic Assn, PO Box 1906, Shawnee Mission, KS 66222
Schultz, Dwight *Actor*
2824 Nichols Canyon Dr, Los Angeles, CA 90046
Schultz, Frederick H *Government Official*
%Federal Reserve System, 20th & Constitution NW, Washington, DC 20551
Schultz, Gerald E *Businessman*
%Bell & Howell Co, 5215 Old Orchard Rd, Skokie, IL 60077
Schultz, Ken *Mayor*
%Mayor's Office, City Hall, 400 Marquette Ave NW, Albuquerque, NM 87102
Schultz, Peter G *Chemist*
%University of California, Chemistry Dept, Berkeley, CA 94720
Schultz, Robert J *Businessman*
%General Motors Corp, 3044 W Grand Blvd, Detroit, MI 48202
Schultz, Theodore W *Nobel Economics Laureate*
5620 S Kimbark Ave, Chicago, IL 60637
Schultze, Charles L *Government Official*
5826 Nevada Ave NW, Washington, DC 20015
Schulz, Charles *Cartoonist (Peanuts)*
1 Snoopy Pl, Santa Rosa, CA 95401
Schulz, William F *Religious Leader*
%Unitarian Universalist Assn, 25 Beacon St, Boston, MA 02108
Schulze, Erwin E *Businessman*
%Ceco Industries, 1400 Kensington Rd, Oak Brook, IL 60521
Schulze, Richard T *Representative, PA*
525 Morris Ln, Berwyn, PA 19312
Schumacher, Robert A *Businessman*
%Georgia-Pacific Corp, 133 Peachtree St NE, Atlanta, GA 30303
Schuman, William H *Composer*
88 Richmond Hill Rd, Greenwich, CT 06830
Schumann, Maurice *Government Official, France*
53 Ave Marechal-Lyautey, 75016 Paris, France
Schumer, Charles E *Representative, NY*
%House of Representatives, Washington, DC 20515
Schumm, Joseph J *Businessman*
%AnnTaylor Stores Corp, 3 E 57th, New York, NY 10022
Schurmann, Petra *Swimmer*
Max-Emanuel-Strasse 7, 8130 Starnberg, Germany
Schussler Fiorenza, Elisabeth *Writer, Educator*
%Notre Dame University, Theology Dept, Notre Dame, IN 46556

S

Schutz – Schwery

Schutz, Stephen *Graphic Artist*
%Blue Mountain Arts Inc, 1645 Broadway, Boulder, CO 80302

Schutz, Susan Polis *Poet*
%Blue Mountain Arts Inc, 1645 Broadway, Boulder, CO 80302

Schuur, Diane *Singer*
PO Box 955, Auburn, WA 98071

Schwab, Charles *Financier*
%Charles Schwab Co, 101 Montgomery St, San Francisco, CA 94104

Schwab, Martin J *Businessman*
%United Merchants & Manufacturers Inc, 1407 Broadway, New York, NY 10018

Schwantner, Joseph *Composer*
%Eastman School of Music, 26 Gibbs St, Rochester, NY 14604

Schwartz, Bernard L *Businessman*
%Loral Corp, 600 3rd Ave, New York, NY 10016

Schwartz, David *Businessman*
%Rent-A-Wreck of America, 1100 Glendon Ave, #1250, Los Angeles, CA 90024

Schwartz, Linda *Sociologist*
%University of Washington, Sociology Dept, Seattle, WA 98195

Schwartz, Melvin *Nobel Physics Laureate*
%Digital Pathways, 201 Ravendale Dr, Mountain View, CA 94043

Schwartz, Michael *Educator*
%Kent State University, President's Office, Kent, OH 44242

Schwartz, Richard J *Businessman*
%Jonathan Logan Inc, 50 Terminal Rd, Secaucus, NJ 07094

Schwartz, Robert G *Businessman*
%Metropolitan Life Insurance, 1 Madison Ave, New York, NY 10010

Schwartz, Stephen L *Composer, Lyricist*
%Paramuse Assoc, 1414 Ave of Americas, New York, NY 10019

Schwartz, Tony *Communications Specialist*
455 W 56th St, New York, NY 10019

Schwartz, William A *Broadcast Executive*
%Cox Enterprises, 1400 Lake Hearn Dr NE, Atlanta, GA 30319

Schwartzberg, Howard *Judge*
%Courthouse, 111 Grove St, White Plains, NY 10601

Schwarz, Gerard *Conductor*
575 West End Ave, #4-B, New York, NY 10024

Schwarz, John H *Physicist*
%California Institute of Technology, Physics Dept, Pasadena, CA 91125

Schwarz, Rudolf *Conductor*
24 Wildcroft Manor, London SW 15, England

Schwarz, Wolfgang *Figure Skater*
Program Zeitschriftenverlag, Parkring 12, Stiege 9/9, 1010 Vienna, Austria

Schwarzenegger, Arnold *Body Builder, Actor*
PO Box 1234, Santa Monica, CA 90406

Schwarzkopf, Elisabeth *Opera Singer*
Rebhusstrasse 29, 8126 Zunnikon, Zurich, Switzerland

Schwarzkopf, H Norman *Army General*
%International Creative Mgmt, 8899 Beverly Blvd, Los Angeles, CA 90048

Schwarzschild, Martin *Astronomer*
12 Ober Rd, Princeton, NJ 08540

Schwebel, Stephen M *Judge*
1917 23rd St NW, Washington, DC 20008

Schweickart, Russell L *Astronaut*
67 Issaquah Dock, Waldo Point Harbor, Sausalito, CA 94965

Schweiker, Richard S *Secretary, Health & Human Services*
600 Arch St, Philadelphia, PA 19106

Schweikert, J E *Religious Leader*
%North American Old Roman Catholic Church, 4200 N Kedvale, Chicago, IL 60641

Schweikher, Paul *Architect*
580 Skyline Dr, High Tor, Sedona, AZ 86336

Schweitzer, M Peter *Businessman*
%Caesars World, 1801 Century Park East, Los Angeles, CA 90067

Schweitzer, Pierre-Paul *Financier*
19 Rue de Valois, 75001 Paris, France

Schwery, Henri Cardinal *Religious Leader*
Bishoporic of Sion, CP 2068, 1950 Sion 2, Switzerland

Schwinden, Ted *Governor, MT*
1335 Highland St, Helena, MT 59601
Schwinger, Julian S *Nobel Physics Laureate*
%University of California, Physics Dept, Los Angeles, CA 90024
Scirica, Anthony J *Judge*
%US Court of Appeals, US Courthouse, 601 Market St, Philadelphia, PA 19106
Sciutti, Graziella *Opera Singer*
%RCA Records, 1133 Ave of Americas, New York, NY 10036
Scofield, Dino *Actor*
3330 Barham Blvd, #103, Los Angeles, CA 90068
Scofield, Paul *Actor*
The Gables, Balcombe, Sussex, England
Scoggins, Tracy *Actress*
PO Box 2121, Malibu, CA 90265
Scolari, Peter *Actor*
%William Morris Agency, 151 El Camino, Beverly Hills, CA 90212
Scolnick, Edward *Cancer Researcher*
%Merck & Co, Research & Development, PO Box 2000, Rahway, NJ 07065
Score, Herb *Baseball Player, Sportscaster*
%WWWE, Sports Dept, 13th & Superior Sts, Cleveland, OH 44144
Scorsese, Martin *Movie Director, Writer*
%Creative Artists Agency, 9830 Wilshire Blvd, Beverly Hills, CA 90212
Scott, Byron *Basketball Player*
%Los Angeles Lakers, Great Western Forum, 3900 W Manchester, Inglewood, CA 90306
Scott, Clyde L (Smackover) *Football Player*
12840 Rivercrest Dr, Little Rock, AR 72212
Scott, Dave *Triathlete*
2121-A 2nd St, #104, Davis, CA 95616
Scott, David C *Businessman*
%Allis-Chalmers Corp, 1205 S 70th St, West Allis, WI 53214
Scott, David R *Astronaut*
%SST Inc, 11444 W Olympic Blvd, 10th Fl, Los Angeles, CA 90064
Scott, Debralee *Actress*
%Fifi Oscard Assoc, 19 W 44th St, New York, NY 10036
Scott, Dennis *Basketball Player*
%Orlando Magic, 1 Magic Pl, Orlando, FL 32801
Scott, Dick *Football Player*
9606 Falls Rd, Potomac, MD 20854
Scott, Donovan *Actor*
%Harry Gold Assoc, 3500 W Olive Ave, #1400, Burbank, CA 91505
Scott, Frank E *Financier*
%First Western Financial Corp, 2700 W Sahara Ave, Las Vegas, NV 89102
Scott, Fred *Actor*
1716 Camino Parocela, Palm Springs, CA 92262
Scott, George *Baseball Player*
1316 Goodrich St, Greenville, MS 38701
Scott, George C *Actor*
%Jane Deacy Agency, 181 Revolutionary Dr, Scarsborough, NY 10510
Scott, Hugh D, Jr *Senator, PA*
3014 Woodland Dr NW, Washington, DC 20008
Scott, Irene F *Judge*
%US Tax Court, 400 2nd St NW, Washington, DC 20217
Scott, Isadore M *Businessman*
%Tosco Corp, 2401 Colorado Ave, Santa Monica, CA 90406
Scott, Jacqueline *Actress*
PO Box 69405, Los Angeles, CA 90069
Scott, Jane *Jazz Critic*
%Cleveland Plain Dealer, 1801 Superior Ave, Cleveland, OH 44114
Scott, Jerry *Cartoonist (Baby Blues)*
%Creators Syndicate, 5777 W Century Blvd, #700, Los Angeles, CA 90045
Scott, John A *Publisher*
%Playboy Enterprises, 680 N Lake Shore Dr, Chicago, IL 60611
Scott, John S *Businessman*
%Richardson-Vicks Inc, 10 Westport Rd, Wilton, CT 06897
Scott, Jonathan L *Businessman*
%American Stores Co, 709 E South Temple, Salt Lake City, UT 84102

S

Scott – Scully-Power

Scott, Judson *Actor*
1650 Broadway, #302, New York, NY 10019

Scott, Lizabeth *Actress*
PO Box 5522, Beverly Hills, CA 90210

Scott, Martha *Actress*
14054 Chandler Blvd, Van Nuys, CA 91401

Scott, Melody Thomas *Actress*
%Save the Earth, 4881 Topanga Canyon Blvd, #201, Woodland Hills, CA 91364

Scott, Mike *Baseball Player*
5417 W 134th Pl, Hawthorne, CA 90250

Scott, Paul *Writer*
33 Drumsheugh Gdns, Edinburgh, Scotland

Scott, Peter F *Businessman*
%Di Giorgio Corp, 1 Maritime Plz, San Francisco, CA 94111

Scott, Peter L *Businessman*
%Black & Decker Corp, 701 Joppa Rd, Towson, MD 21204

Scott, Pippa *Actress*
%STE Representation, 9301 Wilshire Blvd, #312, Beverly Hills, CA 90210

Scott, Robert S *WW II Army Hero (CMH)*
312 Camino Encatado, Santa Fe, NM 87501

Scott, Robert W *Governor, NC; Educator*
%North Carolina Community College System, 200 W Jones St, Raleigh, NC 27603

Scott, Ronnie *Musician*
47 Firth St, London W1V 5TE, England

Scott, Spencer *Financier*
%Citadel Holding Corp, 600 N Brand Blvd, Glendale, CA 91203

Scott, Steve *Track Athlete*
1428 Eolus St, Leucadia, CA 92024

Scott, Thomas C *Football Player*
215 Lexington Ave, New York, NY 10016

Scott, Tony *Movie Director*
%Bill Unger, 422 N Hayworth Ave, Los Angeles, CA 90048

Scott, Walter C *Businessman*
%Savannah Foods & Industries, PO Box 339, Savannah, GA 31402

Scott, Walter D *Businessman*
%GrandMet USA Inc, 100 Paragon Dr, Montvale, NJ 07645

Scott, Willard *Entertainer*
%NBC-TV, News Dept, 30 Rockefeller Plz, New York, NY 10020

Scott, William L *Senator, VA*
3930 West Ox Rd, Fairfax County, VA 22030

Scott, Wilton E *Businessman*
107 Glynn Way Dr, Houston, TX 77056

Scotti, Vito *Actor*
5456 Vanalden Ave, Tarzana, CA 91356

Scotto, Renata *Opera Singer*
%Robert J Lombardo, 30 W 60th St, New York, NY 10023

Scovil, Samuel K *Businessman*
%Cleveland-Cliffs Co, Huntington Bldg, Cleveland, OH 44115

Scowcroft, Brent *Air Force General, Government Official*
%National Security Affairs, White House, 1600 Pennsylvania, Washington, DC 20500

Scranton, William W *Governor, PA; Ambassador to UN*
%Northeastern National Bank Bldg, #231, Penn & Spruce, Scranton, PA 18503

Scribner, Charles, Jr *Publisher*
%Charles Scribner's Sons, 597 5th Ave, New York, NY 10017

Scripps, Charles E *Publisher*
10 Grandin Ln, Cincinnati, OH 45208

Scruggs, Earl *Singer, Banjoist*
201 Donna Dr, Box 66, Madison, TN 37115

Scudamore, Peter *Thoroughbred Racing Jockey*
Mucky Cottage, Grangehill, Naunton, Cheltenham, Glos GL54 3AY, England

Sculley, John *Businessman*
%Apple Computer, 20525 Mariani Ave, Cupertino, CA 95014

Scully, Vin *Sportscaster*
1555 Capri Dr, Pacific Palisades, CA 90272

Scully-Power, Paul D *Astronaut*
%Naval Underwater Systems Ctr, New London, CT 06320

Seaborg, Glenn T *Nobel Chemistry Laureate*
%University of California, Lawrence Laboratory, Cyclotron Rd, Berkeley, CA 94720

Seaforth-Hayes, Susan *Actress*
4528 Beck Ave, North Hollywood, CA 91602

Seaga, Edward P G *Prime Minister, Jamaica*
Vale Royal, Kingston, Jamaica

Seagal, Steven *Actor*
Box 727, Los Olivos, CA 93441

Seagren, Bob *Track Athlete, Actor*
120 S Thurston Ave, Los Angeles, CA 90049

Seagrove, Jenny *Actress*
%J Michael Bloom Ltd, 9200 Sunset Blvd, #710, Los Angeles, CA 90069

Seale, Bobby *Social Activist*
%Cafe Society, 302 W Chelton Ave, Philadelphia, PA 19144

Seale, John *Cinematographer*
%Smith/Gosnell/Nicholson, 1515 Palisades Dr, #N, Pacific Palisades, CA 90272

Seals, Dan *Singer*
PO Box 1770, Hendersonville, TN 37077

Seals, Son *Singer*
%Alligator Productions, PO Box 60234, Chicago, IL 60660

Sealy, Malik *Basketball Player*
%St John's University, Athletic Dept, Jamaica, NY 11439

Seamans, Robert C, Jr *Engineer*
%Massachusetts Institute of Technology, Engineering Dept, Cambridge, MA 02139

Searle, John *Philosopher*
109 Yosemite Rd, Berkeley, CA 94707

Searle, Ronald *Artist*
%John Locke Studio, 15 E 76th St, New York, NY 10021

Searock, Charles J, Jr *Air Force General*
Vice Commander, Logistics Command, Wright-Patterson Air Force Base, OH 45433

Sears, Ernest R *Geneticist*
2009 Mob Hill, Columbia, MO 65201

Sears, Vic *Football Player*
181 Ross Ln, Eugene, OR 97404

Seaton, W B *Businessman*
%American President Companies, 1800 Harrison St, Oakland, CA 94612

Seaton, William R *Businessman*
%Ashland Oil, Ashland Dr, Russell, KY 41169

Seau, Junior *Football Player*
%San Diego Chargers, 9449 Friars Rd, San Diego, CA 92120

Seaver, Tom *Baseball Player*
Larkspur Ln, Greenwich, CT 06830

Seavey, David *Editorial Cartoonist*
%USA Today, PO Box 500, Washington, DC 20044

Seawell, William T *Businessman*
340 Palmetto Point, John's Island, Vero Beach, FL 32960

Sebastian, John *Singer, Songwriter*
%Warner Bros Records, 3300 Warner Blvd, Burbank, CA 91510

Sebastiani, Sam *Businessman*
%Sebastiani Winnery, 389 4th St E, Sonoma, CA 95476

Secchia, Peter *Diplomat*
%US Embassy, Via Veneto 1119-A, Rome, Italy

Secombe, Harry *Actor*
46 St James Pl, London SW1, England

Sedaka, Neil *Singer, Songwriter*
%Neil Sedaka Music, 330 W 58th St, #4-A, New York, NY 10019

Seddon, Margaret Rhea *Astronaut*
%NASA, Johnson Space Ctr, Houston, TX 77058

Sedelmaier, Joe *Movie, Television Director*
610 Fairbanks Ct, Chicago, IL 60611

Sedgman, Frank A *Tennis Player*
26 Bolton Ave, Hampton, Vic 3188, Australia

Sedgwick, Kyra *Actress*
%Creative Artists Agency, 9830 Wilshire Blvd, Beverly Hills, CA 90212

Sedney, Jules *Prime Minister, Suriname*
Pernardstrasse 1, Paramaribo, Suriname

S

Sedykh, Yuri *Track Athlete*
%USSR Sports Council, 4 Skatertny Pereulok, Moscow, Russia

See, Carolyn *Writer*
PO Box 107, Topanga, CA 90290

Seefelder, Matthias *Businessman*
%BASF, Carl-Bosch-Str 38, D-6700 Ludwigshafen, Germany

Seeger, Pete *Singer, Songwriter*
Dutchess Junction, Beacon, NY 12508

Seegers, Paul R *Businessman*
%Centex Corp, 4600 RepublicBank Tower, Dallas, TX 75201

Seely, Jeannie *Singer*
Rt 2, Box 448, Hendersonville, TN 37075

Sega, Ronald M *Astronaut*
%NASA, Johnson Space Center, Houston, TX 77058

Segal, Erich *Writer*
%Lazarow, 119 W 57th St, #1106, New York, NY 10019

Segal, Fred *Fashion Designer*
%Fred Segal Jeans, 8100 Melrose Ave, Los Angeles, CA 90046

Segal, George *Sculptor*
Davidson Mill Rd, New Brunswick, NJ 08901

Segal, George *Actor*
%Wallin Simon Black, 1350 Ave of Americas, New York, NY 10019

Segall, Joel *Educator*
%City University of New York, President's Office, New York, NY 10010

Segall, Maurice *Businessman*
%Zayre Corp, 770 Cochituate Rd, Framingham, MA 01701

Sege, Thomas D *Businessman*
%Varian Assoc, 611 Hansen Way, Palo Alto, CA 94303

Segelstein, Irwin S *Television Executive*
%National Broadcasting Co, 30 Rockfeller Plz, New York, NY 10020

Seger, Bob *Singer, Songwriter*
%Punch Enterprises, 567 Purdy St, Birmingham, MI 48009

Segerstrom, Henry *Businessman, Philanthropist*
%C J Segerstrom & Sons, 3315 Fairview Rd, Costa Mesa, CA 92626

Segnar, Sam F *Businessman*
%HNG/InterNorth Inc, 2223 Dodge St, Omaha, NE 68102

Segui, Diego *Baseball Player*
13421 Leavenworth Rd, Kansas City, KS 66109

Segura, Francisco (Pancho) *Tennis Player*
%La Costa Resort Hotel & Spa, Costa del Mar Rd, Carlsbad, CA 92009

Seguso, Robert *Tennis Player*
%Advantage International, 1025 Thomas Jefferson St NW, Washington, DC 20007

Seiberling, John F *Representative, OH*
2 S Main St, Akron, OH 44308

Seibert, Donald V *Businessman*
%J C Penney Co, 1301 Ave of Americas, New York, NY 10019

Seibert, Peter *Skier*
PO Box 1016, Edwards, CO 81632

Seibou, Ali *President, Military Council of Niger*
%Supreme Military Council, Niamey, Niger

Seidelman, Susan *Movie Director*
%International Creative Mgmt, 40 W 57th St, New York, NY 10019

Seidman, L William *Government Official, Businessman*
%BDO Seidman, 1430 Broadway, New York, NY 10018

Seifert, George *Football Coach*
%San Francisco 49ers, 4949 Centennial Blvd, Santa Clara, CA 95054

Seigel, Daniel A *Businessman*
%Thrifty Corp, 5051 Rodeo Rd, Los Angeles, CA 90016

Seigenthaler, John L *Publisher*
%The Tennessean, 1100 Broadway, Nashville, TN 37203

Seikaly, Ron *Basketball Player*
%Miami Heat, Miami Arena, Miami, FL 33136

Seinfeld, Jerry *Comedian*
%Jonas Public Relations, 417 S Beverly Dr, Beverly Hills, CA 90212

Seitz, Collins J *Judge*
%US Court of Appeals, 844 King St, Wilmington, DE 19801

Seitz, Frederick *Physicist*
%Rockefeller University, 66th & York, New York, NY 10021

Seixas, E Victor (Vic), Jr *Tennis Player*
716 N Beau Chene Dr, Mandeville, LA 70448

Seki, Mashiko *Financier*
%Mitsui Bank, 1-1-2 Yurakucho, Chiyodaku, Tokyo 100, Japan

Sekimoto, Tadahiro *Businessman*
%NEC Corp, 5-33-1 Shiba, Minatoku, Tokyo 108, Japan

Selangor, Sultan of *Ruler, Selangor*
Shah Alam, Selangor, Malaysia

Selbrede, Herbert *Businessman*
%Wisconsin Dairies Cooperative, Rt 3, Baraboo, WI 53913

Selby, John Douglas *Businessman*
%Consumers Power Co, 212 W Michigan Ave, Jackson, MI 49203

Seldes, George *Writer*
RFD 1, Box 127, Windsor, VT 05089

Selecman, Charles E *Businessman*
3433 Southwestern Blvd, Dallas, TX 75225

Seles, Monica B *Tennis Player*
%Women's Tennis Assn, 133 1st St NE, St Petersburg, FL 33701

Selig, Allan H (Bud) *Baseball Executive*
%Milwaukee Brewers, County Stadium, 201 S 46th St, Milwaukee, WI 53214

Seligman, Henry *Atomic Scientist*
Scherpegasse 8/VI/3, 1190 Vienna, Austria

Seligman, Martin E P *Psychologist*
%University of Pennsylvania, Psychology Dept, Philadelphia, PA 19104

Selikoff, Irving J *Physician*
%Mount Sinai Medical Ctr, 10 E 102nd St, New York, NY 10029

Selinger, Frank *Businessman*
%Joseph Schlitz Brewing Co, 235 W Galena St, Milwaukee, WI 53212

Sell, Henry *Editor*
%Harper's Bazaar Magazine, 320 E 57th St, New York, NY 10022

Sella, George J, Jr *Businessman*
%American Cyanamid Co, 1 Cyanamid Plz, Wayne, NJ 07470

Sellecca, Connie *Actress*
%William Morris Agency, 151 El Camino, Beverly Hills, CA 90212

Selleck, Tom *Actor*
10560 Wilshire Blvd, #1606, Los Angeles, CA 90024

Seller, Peg *Sychronized Swimmer, Coach*
72 Monkswood Cres, Newmarket ON L3Y 2K1, Canada

Sellers, Brad *Basketball Player*
%Chicago Bulls, 980 N Michigan Ave, Chicago, IL 60611

Sellers, Franklin *Religious Leader*
%Reformed Episcopal Church, 2001 Frederick Rd, Baltimore, MD 21228

Sellin, Thorsten *Sociologist*
%General Delivery, Gilmantown, NH 03237

Sells, Boake A *Businessman*
%Revco D S Inc, 1925 Enterprise Pkwy, Twinsburg, OH 44087

Sells, Harold E *Businessman*
%Woolworth Corp, 233 Broadway, New York, NY 10279

Selmon, Leroy *Football Player*
%Tampa Bay Buccaneers, 1 Buccaneer Pl, Tampa, FL 33607

Selmon, Lucious *Football Player, Coach*
%University of Oklahoma, Athletic Dept, Norman, OK 73019

Selya, Bruce M *Judge*
%US Court of Appeals, US Courthouse, Providence, RI 02903

Selzer, Milton *Actor*
%LA Artists Talent Agency, 2566 Overland Ave, #600, Los Angeles, CA 90064

Semak, Michael *Photographer*
1796 Spruce Hill Rd, Pickering ON L1V 1S4, Canada

Sembler, Melvin F *Diplomat*
%US Embassy, Moomah Pl, Canberra, Australia

Semel, Terry S *Movie Executive*
%Warner Bros Inc, 4000 Warner Blvd, Burbank, CA 91522

Semelsberger, Kenneth J *Businessman*
%Scott & Fetzer Co, 28000 Clemens Rd, Westlake, OH 44145

S

Semenyaka – Seven

Semenyaka, Lyudmila *Ballerina*
%State Academic Bolshoi Theatre, 1 Ploshchad Sverdlova, Moscow, Russia

Semerena, Pierre *Businessman*
%American Motors Corp, 27777 Franklin Rd, Southfield, MI 48034

Semkow, Jerzy *Conductor*
%Rochester Philharmonic, 108 East Ave, Rochester, NY 14604

Semler, Jerry D *Businessman*
%American United Life Insurance, 1 American Sq, Indianapolis, IN 46206

Sendak, Maurice B *Writer, Illustrator*
200 Chestnut Hill Rd, Ridgefield, CT 06877

Senff, Nida *Swimmer*
%D W Couturier-Senff, Praam 122, 1186-TL Amstelveen, Netherlands

Senghor, Leopold Sedar *President, Senegal; Poet*
1 Sq de Tocqueville, 75015 Paris, France

Sengoku, Jo *Businessman*
%Kuraray Co, 12-39 Umeda, Kitaku, Osaka 530, Japan

Sengstacke, John H *Publisher*
%Sengstacke Newspapers, 2400 S Michigan Ave, Chicago, IL 60616

Senna, Ayrton *Auto Racing Driver*
%Houston Palace, 7 Ave Princess Grace, Monte Carlo, Monaco

Sensenbrenner, F James, Jr *Representative, WI*
%House of Representatives, Washington, DC 20515

Sensi, Giuseppe Cardinal *Religious Leader*
16 Piazza S Calisto, 00153 Rome, Italy

Sentelle, David B *Judge*
%US Court of Appeals, 3rd & Constitution Ave NW, Washington, DC 20001

Seraphim, His Beatitude Archbishop *Religious Leader*
%Holy Synod of Church of Greece, Athens, Greece

Serber, Robert *Physicist*
450 Riverside Dr, New York, NY 10027

Sere, Jouko *Businessman*
%Rauma-Repola Oy, PL 203, Snellmaninkatu 13, 00170 Helsinki 17, Finland

Serebrov, Alexander S *Cosmonaut*
141 160 Svyosdny Gorodok, Moskovskoi Oblasti, Potchta Kosmonavtov, Russia

Sereni, Mario *Opera Singer*
%Eric Semon Assoc, 111 W 57th St, New York, NY 10019

Sergeyev, Konstantin *Ballet Director*
2 Gogol St, #13, St Petersburg 191065, Russia

Serkin, Peter *Concert Pianist*
RFD 3, Brattleboro, VT 05301

Serlemitsos, Peter J *Astronomer*
%BBXRT Project, Goddard Space Flight Ctr, Greenbelt, MD 20771

Serra, Richard *Sculptor*
%Leo Castelli Gallery, 420 W Broadway, New York, NY 10013

Serrano, Jose *Representative, NY*
%House of Representatives, Washington, DC 20515

Servan-Schreiber, Jean-Claude *Journalist*
147 Bis Rue d'Alesia, 75014 Paris, France

SerVass, Cory J *Editor*
%Saturday Evening Post Magazine, 1100 Waterway Blvd, Indianapolis, IN 46206

Sessions, William S *Judge, Law Enforcement Official*
%Federal Bureau of Investigation, 9th & Pennsylvania NW, Washington, DC 20535

Seth, Oliver *Judge*
%US Court of Appeals, PO Drawer 1, Santa Fe, NM 87504

Sethna, Homi N *Engineer*
Old Yacht Club, Chatrapati Shrivaji Maharaj, Bombay 400 038, India

Sethness, Charles O *Financier*
131 Shore Rd, Old Greenwich, CT 06870

Setlow, Richard B *Biophysicist*
4 Beachland Ave, East Quogue, NY 11942

Sevareid, Eric *Commentator*
%CBS-TV, News Dept, 2020 "M" St NW, Washington, DC 20036

Sevastyanov, Vitayl *Cosmonaut*
141 160 Svyosdny Gorodok, Moskovskoi Oblasti, Potchta Kosmonavtov, Russia

Seven, Johnny *Actor*
11024 Balboa Blvd, Granada Hills, CA 91344

Severance, Joan *Model*
%Elite Model Mgmt, 111 E 22nd St, New York, NY 10010
Severeid, Susanne *Actress*
%Barry Freed Co, 9255 Sunset Blvd, #603, Los Angeles, CA 90069
Severino, John C *Television Executive*
%Prime Ticket Network, 401 S Prairie St, Inglewood, CA 90301
Severinsen, Doc (Carl H) *Jazz Trumpeter, Band Leader*
2807 Nicholas Canyon, Los Angeles, CA 90046
Seybold, Jonathan *Businessman*
%Seybold Seminars, 6922 Wildlife Rd, Malibu, CA 90265
Seymour, Carolyn *Actress*
%Ambrosio/Mortimer Assoc, 301 N Canon Dr, #305, Beverly Hills, CA 90210
Seymour, Jane *Actress*
St Catherine's Ct, Batheaston, Bath, Avon, England
Seymour, John *Senator, CA*
%US Senate, Washington, DC 20510
Seymour, Lynn *Ballerina*
%S A Gorlinsky Ltd, 35 Dover St, London W1X 4NJ, England
Seymour, Stephanie *Model*
%Elite Model Mgmt, 111 E 22nd St, New York, NY 10010
Seymour, Stephanie K *Judge*
%US Court of Appeals, US Courthouse, 333 W 4th St, Tulsa, OK 74103
Sgnnergren, Stig *Businessman*
%Stora Kopparbergs Bergstags AB, Fack 791 01 Falun, Sweden
Shaara, Michael *Writer*
2074 Robinhood Dr, Melbourne, FL 32935
Shabat, Oscar *Educator*
%City Colleges of Chicago, Chancellor's Office, Chicago, IL 60601
Shackelford, Ted *Actor*
%International Creative Mgmt, 8899 Beverly Blvd, Los Angeles, CA 90048
Shad, John S R *Businessman, Government Official*
%Drexel Burnham Lambert Inc, 60 Broad St, New York, NY 10004
Shafer, R Donald *Religious Leader*
%Brethren in Christ Church, PO Box 245, Upland, CA 91785
Shafer, Raymond P *Governor, PA*
%Dunaway & Cross, 1146 19th St, Washington, DC 20036
Shaffer, C Elwood *Businessman*
%Super Food Services, Kettering Box 2323, Dayton, OH 45429
Shaffer, Peter *Playwright*
173 Riverside Dr, New York, NY 10024
Shaffer, Raymond F *Businessman*
%Greyhound Corp, Greyhound Tower, Phoenix, AZ 85077
Shafto, Robert *Businessman*
%New England Mutual Life Insurance, 501 Boylston St, Boston, MA 02117
Shagan, Steve *Writer*
%Myron Slobedien, 10100 Santa Monica Blvd, Los Angeles, CA 90067
Shah Reza Pahlavi II *Crown Prince, Iran*
Kubbeh Palace, Heliopolis, Cairo, Egypt
Shah, Idries *Writer*
%A P Watt Ltd, 26/28 Bedford Row, London WC1R 4HL, England
Shahabuddin Ahmed *President, Judge, Bangladesh*
%Supreme Court, Office of Chief Justice, Dhaka, Bangladesh
Shakespeare, Frank J, Jr *Television Executive, Diplomat*
%US Embassy, Holy See, Vatican City, Rome, Italy
Shaklee, Forrest C, Jr *Businessman*
%Shaklee Corp, 444 Market St, San Francisco, CA 94111
Shaklee, Raleigh L *Businessman*
%Shaklee Corp, 444 Market St, San Francisco, CA 94111
Shalala, Donna E *Educator*
%University of Wisconsin, Chancellor's Office, Madison, WI 53706
Shales, Tom *Journalist*
%Washington Post, 1150 15th St NW, Washington, DC 20071
Shalikashvili, John M *Army General*
Asst to Chairman, Joint Chiefs of Staff, Washington, DC 20301
Shalit, Gene *Movie Critic*
225 E 79th St, New York, NY 10021

S

Shamir – Sharman

Shamir, Yitzhak *Prime Minister, Israel*
%Prime Minister's Office, Knesset, Jerusalem, Israel

Shanagher, Anthony D *Businessman*
%Allegheny International, 2 Oliver Plz, Pittsburgh, PA 15230

Shanahan, Mike *Football Coach*
%San Francisco 49ers, 4949 Centennial Blvd, Santa Clara, CA 95054

Shandling, Garry *Comedian*
825 N San Vicente, Los Angeles, CA 90069

Shane, Bob *Singer (Kingston Trio)*
28 Milton Ave, Alpharetta, GA 30201

Shane, Leonard *Financier*
%Mercury Savings & Loan, 7812 Edinger Ave, Huntington Beach, CA 92647

Shank, Bud *Jazz Musician*
PO Box 948, Port Townsend, WA 98368

Shank, Roger C *Computer Scientist*
%Northwestern University, Institute for Learning Sciences, Evanston, IL 60201

Shankar, Ramsewak *President, Suriname*
%President's Office, Paramaribo, Suriname

Shankar, Ravi *Sitar Player*
%Basil Douglas Artists, 8 St George's Terr, London W1, England

Shanker, Albert *Labor Leader*
%American Federation of Teachers, 555 New Jersey NW, Washington, DC 20001

Shanks, Michael *Economist*
703 Mountjoy, Barbicon, London EC2, England

Shannon, Claude E *Applied Mathematician*
5 Cambridge St, Winchester, MA 01890

Shannon, E L, Jr *Businessman*
%Santa Fe International Corp, PO Box 4000, Alhambra, CA 91802

Shannon, James A *Medical Research Administrator*
8302 SW Homewood St, Portland, OR 97225

Shantz, Bobby *Baseball Player*
152 Mount Pleasant Ave, Ambler, PA 19002

Shapell, Nathan *Businessman*
%Shapell Industries, 8383 Wilshire Blvd, #700, Beverly Hills, CA 90211

Shapiro, Ascher H *Mechanical Engineer*
111 Perkins St, Jamaica Plain, MA 02174

Shapiro, Debbie *Actress*
%Agency for Performing Arts, 9000 Sunset Blvd, #1200, Los Angeles, CA 90069

Shapiro, Eli *Economist*
180 Beacon St, Boston, MA 02116

Shapiro, Harold T *Educator*
%Princeton University, President's Office, Princeton, NJ 08544

Shapiro, Irving S *Businessman*
%Skadden Arps Slate Meagher Flom, 919 3rd Ave, New York, NY 10003

Shapiro, Karl *Poet*
3 Linden Pl, Woodland, CA 95695

Shapiro, Marc J *Financier*
%Texas Commerce Bancshares, 600 Travis St, Houston, TX 77002

Shapiro, Mary L *Government Official*
%Securities & Exchange Commission, 450 5th St NW, Washington, DC 20549

Shapiro, Moses *Businessman*
%General Instrument Corp, 767 5th Ave, New York, NY 10153

Shapleigh, Warren M *Businessman*
%Ralston Purina Co, Checkerboard Sq, St Louis, MO 63164

Sharif, Nawaz *Prime Minister, Pakistan*
%Prime Minister's Office, Islamabad, Pakistan

Sharif, Omar *Actor*
%William Morris Agency, 31/32 Soho Sq, London W1V 5O6, England

Sharkey, Jack *Boxer*
Pleasant St, PO Box 242, Epping, NH 03042

Sharkey, Ray *Actor*
%Moress-Nanas-Golden, 12424 Wilshire Blvd, #840, Los Angeles, CA 90025

Sharma, Rakesh *Cosmonaut, India*
%HAL Nasik Division, Ojhar Township PO, Distt Nasik 422207, India

Sharman, Bill *Basketball Player, Coach, Executive*
%Los Angeles Lakers, Great Western Forum, 3900 W Manchester, Inglewood, CA 90308

Sharon, Ariel *Government Official, Israel*
%Knesset, Jerusalem, Israel

Sharp, Eric *Businessman*
%Cable & Wireless PLC, Mercury House, Theobalds Rd, London WC1, England

Sharp, Linda *Basketball Coach*
%Southwest Texas State University, Athletic Dept, San Marcos, TX 78666

Sharp, Mitchell W *Government Official, Canada*
Varette Bldg, 130 Albert St, Ottawa ON K1P 5G4, Canada

Sharp, Philip R *Representative, IN*
%House of Representatives, Washington, DC 20515

Sharp, Phillip A *Molecular Biologist*
119 Grasmere St, Newton, MA 02158

Sharpe, Luis *Football Player*
%Phoenix Cardinals, PO Box 888, Phoenix, AZ 81001

Sharpe, Sterling *Football Player*
%Green Bay Packers, 1265 Lombardi Ave, Green Bay, WI 54303

Sharpe, Tom *Writer*
%Richard Scott Simon Ltd, 43 Doughty St, London WC1N 2LF, England

Sharpe, William F *Nobel Economics Laureate*
%Stanford University, Graduate School of Business, Stanford, CA 94305

Sharqi, Sheikh Hamad bin Muhammad al- *Ruler, Fujairah*
%Royal Palace, Fujairah, United Arab Emirates

Shatalov, Valdimir A *Cosmonaut*
141 160 Svyosdny Gorodok, Moskovskoi Oblasti, Potchta Kosmonavtov, Russia

Shatner, William *Actor*
3674 Berry Ave, Studio City, CA 91604

Shaub, Harold A *Businessman*
1250 Country Club Rd, Gladwyne, PA 19035

Shavelson, Melville *Producer, Writer*
11947 Sunshine Terr, North Hollywood, CA 91604

Shaver, Helen *Actress*
%Litke/Gale, 10390 Santa Monica Blvd, #300, Los Angeles, CA 90025

Shaw, Artie *Jazz Clarinetist*
2127 W Palos Ct, Newbury Park, CA 91320

Shaw, Bella *Commentator*
%Cable News Network, News Dept, 1 CNN Center, PO Box 105366, Atlanta, GA 30348

Shaw, Bernard *Commentator*
%Cable News Network, News Dept, 111 Massachusetts Ave NW, Washington, DC 20001

Shaw, Bob *Baseball Player*
31 Saddle Back Rd, Jupiter, FL 33458

Shaw, Brewster H, Jr *Astronaut*
%NASA/KSC, Mail Code MK, Kennedy Space Center, FL 32899

Shaw, Brian *Basketball Player*
%Miami Heat, 100 Chopin Plz, Miami, FL 33131

Shaw, Carolyn Hagner *Publisher*
%Social Register, 2620 "P" St NW, Washington, DC 20007

Shaw, David *Journalist*
%Los Angeles Times, Times-Mirror Sq, Los Angeles, CA 90053

Shaw, E Clay, Jr *Representative, FL*
609 Coral Way, Fort Lauderdale, FL 33301

Shaw, George *Football Player*
%June S Jones Co, 225 SW Broadway, Portland, OR 97205

Shaw, Harry A, III *Businessman*
%Huffy Corp, 7701 Byers Rd, Miamisburg, OH 45342

Shaw, J C *Businessman*
%Shaw Industries, 616 E Walnut Ave, Dalton, GA 30722

Shaw, John S, Jr *Businessman*
%Sonat Inc, First National-Southern Natural Bldg, Birmingham, AL 35203

Shaw, Robert E *Businessman*
%Shaw Industries, 616 E Walnut Ave, Dalton, GA 30722

Shaw, Robert L *Conductor*
%Atlanta Symphony, 1280 Peachtree St NE, Atlanta, GA 30309

Shaw, Run Run *Movie Producer*
Shaw House, Lot 220 Clearwater Bay Rd, Kowloon, Hong Kong

Shaw, Scott *Photographer*
%Odessa American, 222 E 4th, Odessa, TX 79760

Shaw, Stan *Actor*
%Harris & Goldberg Agency, 1999 Ave of Stars, #2850, Los Angeles, CA 90067

Shaw, Tim *Swimmer, Water Poloist*
%California State University, Athletic Dept, Long Beach, CA 90840

Shaw, Walter B *Businessman*
%Turner Corp, 633 3rd Ave, New York, NY 10017

Shawcross of Friston, H William *Judge; Government Official, England*
Friston Pl, Sussex, England

Shawn, Wallace *Actor*
%Triad Artists, 10100 Santa Monica Blvd, #1600, Los Angeles, CA 90067

Shawn, William *Editor*
%New Yorker Magazine, 25 W 43rd St, New York, NY 10028

Shayne, Robert *Actor*
555 Laurie Ln, #J-7, Thousand Oaks, CA 91360

Shea, Charles W *WW II Army Hero (CMH)*
85 S Lincoln Rd, Plainview, NY 11803

Shea, Jack *Speed Skater*
General Delivery, Town of North Elba, Lake Placid, NY 12946

Shea, James J, Jr *Businessman*
%Milton Bradley Co, 1500 Main St, Springfield, MA 01101

Shea, John *Actor*
%International Creative Mgmt, 40 W 57th St, New York, NY 10019

Shea, Joseph F *Space Scientist*
15 Dogwood Rd, Weston, MA 02193

Shear, Rhonda *Comedienne*
%"Up All Night" Show, USA Network, 2049 Century Park East, Los Angeles, CA 90067

Shearing, George *Jazz Pianist, Composer*
PO Box 2120, Toluca Lake, CA 91602

Sheed, Wilfrid *Writer*
%General Delivery, Sag Harbor, NY 11963

Sheedy, Ally *Actress*
PO Box 6327, Malibu, CA 90265

Sheehan, Jeremiah J *Businessman*
%Reynolds Metals Co, 6601 Broad St, Richmond, VA 23261

Sheehan, John C *Organic Chemist*
10 Moon Hill Rd, Lexington, MA 33149

Sheehan, Neil *Journalist*
4505 Klingle St NW, Washington, DC 20016

Sheehan, Patty *Golfer*
%RLG ProImage, PO Box 11675, Reno, NV 89510

Sheehan, Susan *Writer*
%Houghton-Mifflin Co, 52 Vanderbilt Ave, New York, NY 10017

Sheehy, Gail *Writer*
%William Morrow, 105 Madison Ave, New York, NY 10016

Sheehy, Patrick *Businessman*
%BAT Industries, Windsor House, 50 Victoria St, London SW1H 0NL, England

Sheen, Charlie *Actor*
1845 Olivera Dr, Agoura Hills, CA 91301

Sheen, Martin *Actor*
6916 Dune Dr, Malibu, CA 90265

Sheffield, William *Governor, AK*
2412 Hialeah Dr, Anchorage, AK 99503

Sheikh Ali Al Khalifah Al Sabah *Businessman*
%Kuwait Petroleum Corp, PO Box 26565, Safat, Kuwait

Sheikh Salem Ahmed Bin Mahfouz *Financier*
%National Commercial Bank, PO Box 3555, Jeddah 21481, Saudi Arabia

Sheinberg, Sidney J *Entertainment Executive*
%MCA Inc, 100 Universal City Plz, Universal City, CA 91608

Sheiner, David *Actor*
351 S Fuller Ave, #12-F, Los Angeles, CA 90036

Sheinfeld, David *Composer*
1458 24th Ave, San Francisco, CA 94122

Sheinkman, Jack *Labor Leader*
%Amalgamated Clothing & Textile Workers Union, 15 Union Sq, New York, NY 10003

Sheinwold, Alfred *Bridge Expert, Columnist*
2625 Angelo Dr, Los Angeles, CA 90017

Shekhar, Chandra *Prime Minister, India*
%Prime Minister's Office, New Delhi 110011, India
Shelbourne, Philip *Businessman*
%Britoil, 150 St Vincent St, Glasgow G2 5LJ, Scotland
Shelby, Carroll *Auto Racing Driver, Builder*
%Shelby Industries, 19021 S Figueroa, Gardena, CA 90248
Shelby, Richard C *Senator, AL*
66 High Forest, Tuscaloosa, AL 35406
Sheldon, Sidney *Writer*
10250 W Sunset Blvd, Los Angeles, CA 90077
Shell, Art *Football Player, Coach*
%Los Angeles Raiders, 332 Center St, El Segundo, CA 90245
Shell, Donnie *Football Player*
307 Torwood Dr, Columbia, SC 29203
Shelley, R Gene *Businessman*
%Raytheon Co, 141 Spring St, Lexington, MA 02173
Shelton, Larry B *Businessman*
%Genesco Inc, Genesco Park, Nashville, TN 37202
Shelton, Lonnie *Basketball Player*
%Cleveland Cavaliers, 2923 Statesboro Rd, Richfield, OH 44286
Shelton, Wayne *Businessman*
%Planning Research Corp, 1500 Planning Research Dr, McLean, VA 22102
Shepard, Alan B, Jr *Astronaut; Navy Admiral*
%Seven Fourteen Enterprises, 3203 Mercer St, #200, Houston, TX 77027
Shepard, Jean *Singer*
%Tessier, 204 Old Hickory Blvd, Madison, TN 38104
Shepard, Sam *Actor*
%Martha Luttrell, 8898 Beverly Blvd, Los Angeles, CA 90048
Shephard, Stephen B *Editor*
%Business Week Magazine, 1221 Ave of Americas, New York, NY 10020
Shepherd, Cybill *Model, Actress*
16037 Royal Oak Rd, Encino, CA 91436
Shepherd, Mark, Jr *Businessman*
%Texas Instruments, 13500 N Central Expressway, Dallas, TX 75265
Shepherd, Sherrie *Cartoonist (Francie)*
%United Feature Syndicate, 200 Park Ave, New York, NY 10166
Shepherd, William M *Astronaut*
%NASA, Johnson Space Ctr, Houston, TX 77058
Sheppard, Jonathan *Steeplechase Racing Trainer*
Ashwell Stables, 297 Lamborntown Rd, West Grove, PA 19390
Shepperd, Alfred J *Businessman*
%Wellcome Foundation Ltd, 103 Euston Rd, London NW1 2BP, England
Shera, Mark *Actor*
%Agency for Performing Arts, 9000 Sunset Blvd, #1200, Los Angeles, CA 90069
Sheridan, Jamey *Actor*
%Sames/Rollnick Assoc, 250 W 57th St, New York, NY 10107
Sheridan, Nicollette *Actress*
PO Box 25578, Los Angeles, CA 90025
Sherlock, Nancy J *Astronaut*
%NASA, Johnson Space Center, Houston, TX 77058
Sherman, Cindy *Photographer*
%Metro Pictures, 150 Greene St, New York, NY 10012
Sherman, Paddy *Publisher*
%The Citizen, Box 5020, Ottawa ON K2C 3M4, Canada
Sherman, Richard M *Composer, Lyricist*
1032 Hilldale Ave, Los Angeles, CA 90069
Sherman, Robert B *Songwriter, Writer*
1032 Hilldale Ave, Los Angeles, CA 90069
Sherman, Vincent *Movie Director*
6355 Sycamore Meadows Dr, Malibu, CA 90265
Sherman, William *Religious Leader*
%Woodmont Baptist Church, 2100 Woodmont Blvd, Nashville, TN 37215
Shernoff, William M *Attorney*
600 S Indian Hill, Claremont, CA 91711
Sherrard, Mike *Football Player*
%San Francisco 49ers, 4949 Centennial Blvd, Santa Clara, CA 95054

Sherrill, Jackie *Football Coach*
%Mississippi State University, Athletic Dept, Mississippi State, MS 39762

Sherrod, Blackie *Sportswriter*
%Dallas Morning News, Communications Ctr, Dallas, TX 75265

Sherrod, Robert L *Writer*
4000 Cathedral Ave NW, Washington, DC 20016

Sherwood, David J *Businessman*
%Prudential Insurance Co, Prudential Plz, Newark, NJ 07101

Sherwood, Madeline Thornton *Actress*
32 Leroy St, New York, NY 10014

Sherwood, P Louis *Businessman*
%Great Atlantic & Pacific Tea Co, 2 Paragon Dr, Montvale, NJ 07645

Shettles, Landrum B *Obstetrician, Gynecologist*
2380 Rochelle Ave, Las Vegas, NV 89109

Shevchenko, Arkady N *Government Official, Russia*
%Alfred A Knopf Inc, 201 E 50th St, New York, NY 10022

Shewmaker, Jack *Businessman*
%Wal-Mart Stores, 702 SW 8th St, Bentonville, AK 72712

Shields, Brooke *Model, Actress*
PO Box 147, Harrington Park, NJ 07640

Shields, Perry *Judge*
%US Tax Court, 400 2nd St NW, Washington, DC 20217

Shields, Robert *Mime (Shields & Yarnell)*
%International Creative Mgmt, 8899 Beverly Blvd, Los Angeles, CA 90048

Shigeta, James *Actor*
8917 Cynthia St, #1, Los Angeles, CA 90069

Shikler, Aaron *Artist*
44 W 77th St, New York, NY 10024

Shima, Masahiko *Businessman*
%Maruzen Oil Co, 6-1-20 Akasaka, Minatoku, Tokyo 107, Japan

Shimamura, Seizo *Businessman*
%Meiji Milk Products, 2-3-6 Kyobashi, Chuoku, Tokyo 104, Japan

Shimkus, Joanna *Actress*
9350 Wilshire Blvd, #310, Beverly Hills, CA 90212

Shimono, Sab *Actor*
3332 Descanso Dr, Los Angeles, CA 90026

Shindo, Sadakazu *Businessman*
%Mitsubishi Electric Corp, 2-2-3 Marunouchi, Chiyodaku, Tokyo 100, Japan

Shinn, George L *Financier*
%First Boston Inc, Park Avenue Plz, New York, NY 10055

Shinn, Richard R *Businessman*
31 Lindsay Dr, Greenwich, CT 06830

Shino, Kotaro *Businessman*
%Shionogi Co, 12 Doshomachi Sanchome, Higashiku, Osaka 541, Japan

Shinohara, Akira *Businessman*
%Denki Kagaku Kogyo, 1-4 Yurakucho, Chiyodaku, Tokyo 100, Japan

Shiotani, Tadau *Financier*
%Taiyo Kobe Bank, 56 Naniwa, Chuoku, Kobe 650, Japan

Shipler, David K *Journalist*
%New York Times, 229 W 43rd St, New York, NY 10036

Shipley, Walter V *Financier*
%Chemical Banking Corp, 277 Park Ave, New York, NY 10172

Shipp, John Wesley *Actor*
%Gersh Agency, 232 N Canon Dr, Beverly Hills, CA 90210

Shippey, William L *Businessman*
%Millipore Corp, 80 Ashby Rd, Bedford, MA 01730

Shire, David L *Composer*
14820 Valley Vista, Sherman Oaks, CA 91403

Shire, Talia *Actress*
10730 Bellagio Rd, Los Angeles, CA 90077

Shirer, William L *Commentator, Writer*
Box 487, 34 Sunset Ave, Lenox, MA 01240

Shirley, Alesia *Actress*
%Michael Wallach Mgmt, 9200 Sunset Blvd, Los Angeles, CA 90069

Shirley, Don *Jazz Pianist*
%Carnegie Hall, #130, 150 W 57th St, New York, NY 10019

Shirley, George *Opera Singer*
%New School for Arts, 176 N Fullerton, Montclair, NJ 07042

Shirley, J Dallas *Basketball Referee*
1620 Valencia Way, Reston, VA 22090

Shirley-Quirk, John *Opera Singer*
White House, 82 Heath End Rd, Flackwell, Heath, Bucks HP10 9ES, England

Shively, Donald G *Businessman*
%Cincinnati Milacron Inc, 4701 Marburg Ave, Cincinnati, OH 45209

Shnayerson, Robert B *Editor*
118 Riverside Dr, New York, NY 10024

Shobert, Bubba *Motorcycle Racing Rider*
PO Box 1726, Carmel Valley, CA 93924

Shock, Ernest F *Labor Leader*
%United Steelworkers Uphostery Division, 25 N 4th St, Philadelphia, PA 19106

Shocked, Michelle *Singer*
%Mercury/Polygram Records, 3800 W Alameda Ave, Burbank, CA 91505

Shoda, Hidesaburo *Businessman*
%Nisshin Flour Milling Co, 91-12 Nihonbashi-Koamicho, Tokyo 103, Japan

Shoda, Tatsuo *Financier*
%Nippon Credit Bank, 13-10 Kudankita, Chiyodaku, Tokyo 102, Japan

Shoecraft, John A *Balloonist*
%Shoecraft Contracting Co, 7430 E Stetson Dr, Scottsdale, AZ 85251

Shoemaker, Alvin V *Financier*
%First Boston Inc, Park Avenue Plz, New York, NY 10055

Shoemaker, Willie *Thoroughbred Racing Jockey, Trainer*
2545 Fairfield Pl, San Marino, CA 91108

Shoffner, Wilson A *Army General*
Deputy Commanding General, TRADOC for Combined Arms, Fort Leavenworth, KS 66027

Shonin, Georgi S *Cosmonaut*
141 160 Syvosdny Gorodok, Moskovskoi Oblasti, Potchta Kosmonavtov, Russia

Shore, Dinah *Singer*
916 Oxford Way, Beverly Hills, CA 90210

Shorenstein, Walter H *Businessman*
%Milton Meyer Co, 1 California, San Francisco, CA 94111

Short, Alonzo E, Jr *Army General*
Director, Defense Communications Agency, Washington, DC 20305

Short, Bobby *Musician, Actor*
205 W 57th St, New York, NY 10019

Short, L N, Jr *Businessman*
%Mine Safety Appliances Co, 600 Penn Center Blvd, Pittsburgh, PA 15235

Short, Martin *Comedian*
%William Morris Agency, 151 El Camino, Beverly Hills, CA 90212

Short, Robert H *Businessman*
%Portland General Electric Co, 121 SW Salmon St, Portland, OR 97204

Shorter, Frank *Marathon Runner*
%Frank Shorter Sports Wear, 89-D Willowbrook Rd, Boulder, CO 80301

Shortley, George M *Businessman*
%PS Group Inc, 3225 N Harbor Dr, San Diego, CA 92101

Shortridge, Steve *Actor*
%Stan Kamens Mgmt, 7772 Torreyson Dr, Los Angeles, CA 90046

Shortway, Richard H *Publisher*
%Vogue Magazine, 350 Madison Ave, New York, NY 10017

Shostakovich, Maxim *Conductor*
309 Florida Hill Rd, Ridgefield, CT 06877

Shoup, Michael G *Businessman*
%Kaneb Services, 1 Sugar Creek Pl, Sugar Land, TX 77478

Shower, Kathy *Actress*
%Schiowitz/Clay/Rose, 8228 Sunset Blvd, #212, Los Angeles, CA 90046

Shrimpton, Jean *Model, Actress*
Abbey Hotel, Penzance, Cornwall, England

Shriver, Donald W, Jr *Educator*
%Union Theological Seminary, President's Office, New York, NY 10027

Shriver, Loren J *Astronaut*
%NASA, Johnson Space Ctr, Houston, TX 77058

Shriver, Maria *Commentator*
321 Hampton Dr, #203, Venice, CA 90291

S

Shriver – Sidi Mohammed

Shriver, R Sargent, Jr *Government Official*
Fried Frank Harris Shriver Jacobson, 1350 New Hampshire NW, Washington, DC 20036

Shrontz, Frank A *Businessman*
%Boeing Co, 7755 E Marginal Way S, Seattle, WA 98108

Shuart, James M *Educator*
%Hofstra University, President's Office, Hempstead, NY 11550

Shubin, Neil H *Biologist*
%Harvard University, Biology Dept, Cambridge, MA 02138

Shue, Elisabeth *Actress*
76 S Orange Ave, South Orange, NJ 07079

Shugart, Alan F *Computer Disc Drive Inventor*
%Seagate Technologies, 920 Disc Dr, Scotts Valley, CA 95066

Shugdermidijn Gurraggchaa *Cosmonaut, Mongolia*
Ljotschik Kosmonaut MNR, Ulan Bator, Mongolia

Shugrue, Martin R, Jr *Businessman*
%Eastern Airlines, Miami International Airport, Miami, FL 33148

Shula, Don *Football Coach*
16620 W Prestwick Pl, Miami Lakes, FL 33014

Shuler, Ellie G, Jr *Air Force General*
Commander, 8th Air Force, Barksdale Air Force Base, LA 71110

Shuler, Mickey *Football Player*
%New York Jets, 598 Madison Ave, New York, NY 10022

Shull, Harrison *Educator, Chemist*
%University of Colorado, Chancellor's Office, Boulder, CO 80309

Shull, Richard B *Actor*
%J Carter Gibson Agency, 9000 Sunset Blvd, #801, Los Angeles, CA 90069

Shulman, Irving *Writer*
%William E Stein, 9454 Wilshire Blvd, #801, Beverly Hills, CA 90212

Shulman, Mark *Businessman*
%Henri Brendel Inc, 10 W 57th St, New York, NY 10019

Shulman, Marshall *Political Scientist*
450 Riverside Dr, New York, NY 10027

Shultz, George P *Secretary, Treasury & Labor*
776 Dolores St, Stanford, CA 94305

Shumate, John *Basketball Player, Coach*
%Southern Methodist University, Athletic Dept, Dallas, TX 75275

Shumsky, Oscar *Concert Violinist*
%Maxim Gershunoff Attractions, 502 Park Ave, New York, NY 10022

Shumway, F Ritter *Figure Skater*
1777 E Henrietta Rd, Rochester, NY 14623

Shumway, Forrest N *Businessman*
11255 N Torrey Pines Rd, La Jolla, CA 92037

Shumway, Norman E *Heart Surgeon*
%Stanford University, Medical Ctr, Stanford, CA 94305

Shushkevich, Stanislav *President, Belarus*
%President's Office, Parliament, Minsk, Belarus, Russia

Shuster, E G (Bud) *Representative, PA*
%House of Representatives, Washington, DC 20515

Shutt, Edwin H, Jr *Businessman*
%Tambrands Inc, 10 Delaware Dr, Lake Success, NY 11042

Shyer, Charles R *Television Writer, Director*
4040 Stansburg Ave, Sherman Oaks, CA 91423

Siart, William *Financier*
%First Interstate Bancorp, 707 Wilshire Blvd, Los Angeles, CA 90017

Sias, John B *Publisher*
%Capital Cities Communications, 24 E 51st St, New York, NY 10022

Sibbett, Jane *Actress*
%Susan Smith Assoc, 121 N San Vicente Blvd, Beverly Hills, CA 90211

Sibley, Antoinette *Ballerina*
%Royal Ballet, Covent Gdn, Bow St, London WL2E 7QA, England

Sider, Harvey R *Religious Leader*
%Brethren in Christ Church, PO Box 245, Upland, CA 91785

Sidey, Hugh *Journalist*
888 16th St NW, Washington, DC 20006

Sidi Mohammed *Crown Prince, Morocco*
%Royal Palace, Rabat, Morocco

Sidney, George *Movie Director*
910 N Rexford Dr, Beverly Hills, CA 90210

Sidney, Sylvia *Actress*
%Century Artists, 9744 Wilshire Blvd, #308, Beverly Hills, CA 90212

Siebert, Sonny *Baseball Player*
2583 Brush Creek, St Louis, MO 63129

Siegal, Calvin *Businessman*
%Palm Beach Inc, 400 Pike St, Cincinnati, OH 45202

Siegbahn, Kai M B *Nobel Physics Laureate*
%University of Uppsala, Physics Institute, Uppsala, Sweden

Siegel, Herbert J *Businessman*
%Chris-Craft Industries, 600 Madison Ave, New York, NY 10022

Siegel, Janis *Musician*
%Manhattan Transfer, AVNET, 3815 W Olive Ave, Burbank, CA 91505

Siegel, Martin A *Financier*
%Kidder Peabody Co, 10 Hanover Sq, New York, NY 10005

Siegel, Milton P *International Official*
2833 Sackett, Houston, TX 77098

Siegel, Morris J *Businessman*
%Celestial Seasonings Herb Tea Co, 1780 55th St, Boulder, CO 80301

Siegel, Robert *Commentator*
%National Public Radio, News Dept, 2025 "M" Sst NW, Washington, DC 20036

Siegfried & Roy *Animal Trainers, Illusionists*
%Beyond Belief, 1639 N Valley Dr, Las Vegas, NV 89108

Siemens, Peter Von *Businessman*
%Wittelsbacherplatz 2, 8 Munich 2, Germany

Siemon, Jeff *Football Player*
5401 Londonderry, Edina, MN 55435

Siepi, Cesare *Opera Singer*
12095 Brookfield Club Dr, Roswell, GA 30075

Sierens, Gayle *Sportscaster*
%NBC-TV, Sports Dept, 30 Rockefeller Plz, New York, NY 10020

Sievers, Roy *Baseball Player*
11505 Bellefontaine Rd, Spanish Lake, MO 63138

Sifford, Charlie *Golfer*
%Professional Golfers Assn, PO Box 109601, Palm Beach Gardens, FL 33410

Sigiura, Binsuke *Financier*
%Long-Term Credit Bank of Japan, 1-2-4 Otemachi, Tokyo 100, Japan

Sigler, Andrew C *Businessman*
%Champion International Corp, 1 Champion Plz, Stamford, CT 06921

Sigler, Franklin E *WW II Marine Corps Hero (CMH)*
RR 4, Box 4080, Newton, NJ 07860

Sigman, Carl *Songwriter*
1036 NE 203rd Ln, North Miami Beach, FL 33179

Sigoloff, Sanford C *Businessman*
%Wickes Companies, 3340 Ocean Park Blvd, Santa Monica, CA 90405

Siguler, George W *Businessman*
%Monarch Capital Corp, 1 Financial Plz, Springfield, MA 01102

Sigwart, Ulrich *Heart Surgeon*
%Centre Hospitalier Universitaire Vaudois, Lausanne, Switzerland

Siilasvuo, Ensio *Army General, Finland*
Castrenikatu 6A18, 00530 Helsinki 53, Finland

Sikahema, Val *Football Player*
%Green Bay Packers, 1265 Lombardi Ave, Green Bay, WI 54304

Sikes, Alfred C *Government Official*
%Federal Communications Commission, 1919 "M" St NW, Washington, DC 20554

Sikes, Cynthia *Actress*
2595 Basil Ln, Los Angeles, CA 90077

Sikes, Robert L F *Representative, FL*
%Robert L F Sikes Public Library, Crestview, FL 32536

Sikking, James B *Actor*
258 S Carmelina Ave, Los Angeles, CA 90049

Sikma, Jack *Basketball Player*
%Milwaukee Bucks, 901 N 4th St, Milwaukee, WI 53203

Sikorski, Gerry *Representative, MN*
%House of Representatives, Washington, DC 20515

S

Silas – Silvia

Silas, C J (Pete) *Businessman*
%Phillips Petroleum Co, Phillips Bldg, Bartlesville, OK 74004

Silber, John *Educator*
132 Carlton St, Brookline, MA 02146

Silberman, Charles *Writer*
535 E 86th St, New York, NY 10028

Silberman, Laurence H *Judge*
%US Court of Appeals, 3rd & Constitution NW, Washington, DC 20001

Silhava, Zdanka *Track Athlete*
%Olympic Committee, Narodni Trida 33, 11293 Prague, Czechoslovakia

Silk, George *Photographer*
Owenoke Park, Westport, CT 06880

Silk, Leonard S *Economist, Columnist*
115 S Fullerton Ave, Montclair, NJ 07042

Silkert, Robert *Businessman*
%Reckitt & Coleman North American Grp, 1 Mustard St, Rochester, NY 14692

Silletto, C David *Businessman*
%Lincoln National Corp, 1300 S Clinton St, Fort Wayne, IN 46801

Sillin, Lelan F, Jr *Businessman*
%Northeast Utilities Co, Selden St, Berlin, CT 06037

Sillitoe, Alan *Writer*
21 The Street, Wittersham, Kent, England

Sills, Beverly *Opera Singer, Director*
211 Central Park West, New York, NY 10024

Silva Henriquez, Raul Cardinal *Religious Leader*
Palacio Arzobispal, Casilla 30-D, Santiago, Chile

Silva, Henry *Actor*
%Harris & Goldberg Agency, 1999 Ave of Stars, #2850, Los Angeles, CA 90067

Silva, Jackie *Volleyball Player*
%Marcia Esposito, PO Box 931416, Los Angeles, CA 90093

Silva, Ozires *Businessman*
%Petrobras, 65 Ave Republica do Chile, Rio de Janeiro, Brazil

Silver, Edward J *Religious Leader*
%Bible Way Church, 5118 Clarendon Rd, Brooklyn, NY 11226

Silver, Horace *Jazz Pianist*
%Bridge Mgmt, 106 Fort Greene Pl, Brooklyn, NY 11217

Silver, Joel *Movie Producer*
%Silver Pictures, 4000 Warner Blvd, Burbank, CA 91522

Silver, Julius *Businessman*
%Polaroid Corp, 549 Technology Sq, Cambridge, MA 02139

Silver, Robert S *Mechanical Engineer*
Oakbank, Breadalbane St, Tobermory, Isle of Mull, Scotland

Silver, Ron *Actor*
3855 Woodcliffe Rd, Sherman Oaks, CA 91403

Silverman, Al *Publisher*
%Book-of-the-Month Club Inc, Rockefeller Ctr, New York, NY 10020

Silverman, Fred *Television Executive*
%MGM Studios, 10202 W Washington Blvd, Culver City, CA 90230

Silverman, Jonathan *Actor*
%International Creative Mgmt, 8899 Beverly Blvd, Los Angeles, CA 90048

Silverman, Syd *Publisher*
%Variety, 154 W 46th St, New York, NY 10046

Silvers, Robert J *Publisher*
%Saturday Evening Post Magazine, 1100 Waterway Blvd, Indianapolis, IN 46202

Silverstein, Abe *Aeronautical Engineer*
21160 Seabury Ave, Fairview Park, OH 44126

Silverstein, Elliott *Movie Director*
%Director's Guild, 7950 Sunset Blvd, Los Angeles, CA 90046

Silverstein, Joseph *Conductor*
%Utah Symphony Orchestra, 123 W South Temple, Salt Lake City, UT 84101

Silverstein, Shel *Cartoonist*
%Harper & Row, 10 E 53rd St, New York, NY 10022

Silvia *Queen, Sweden*
%Royal Palace, Stockholm, Sweden

Silvia, Charles *Swimming Contributor*
1974 Allen St, Springfield, MA 01118

Sime, Dave *Track Athlete, Physician*
240 Harbor Dr, Key Biscayne, FL 33149

Simeoni, Sara *Track Athlete*
Via Castello Rivoli Veronese, 37010 Verona, Italy

Simes, Dimitri K *Political Scientist*
4430 Vacation Ln, Arlington, VA 22207

Simic, Charles *Poet*
PO Box 192, Strafford, NH 03884

Simkin, William E *Labor Mediator*
5210 N Nina Dr, Tucson, AZ 85704

Simmonds, Kennedy A *Prime Minister, St Christopher & Nevis*
%Prime Minister's Office, Basseterre, St Christopher & Nevis

Simmons, Adele S *Educator, Association Executive*
%MacArthur Foundation, 140 S Dearborn St, Chicago, IL 60603

Simmons, Harold *Businessman*
%NL Industries, 1230 Ave of Americas, New York, NY 10020

Simmons, Harold C *Businessman*
%Amalgamated Sugar Co, First Security Bank Bldg, Ogden, UT 84401

Simmons, Jean *Actress*
636 Adelaide Way, Santa Monica, CA 90402

Simmons, Joseph *Singer (Run-DMC)*
%Rush Productions, 1133 Broadway, New York, NY 10010

Simmons, Lionel *Basketball Player*
%Sacramento Kings, 1 Sports Dr, Sacramento, CA 95834

Simmons, Myron P *Businessman*
%CertainTeed Corp, PO Box 860, Valley Forge, PA 19482

Simmons, Richard *Exercise Host*
PO Box 5403, Beverly Hills, CA 90209

Simmons, Richard D *Publisher*
%Washington Post Co, 1150 15th St NW, Washington, DC 20071

Simmons, Richard P *Businessman*
%Allegheny Ludlum Industries, 2 Oliver Plz, Pittsburgh, PA 15222

Simmons, Richard S *Financier*
%Chemical New York Corp, 277 Park Ave, New York, NY 10172

Simmons, Ted *Baseball Player*
PO Box 26, Chesterfield, MO 63017

Simmons, Ted D *Businessman*
%Mutual Benefit Life Insurance, 520 Broad St, Newark, NJ 07101

Simms, Ginny *Singer*
1578 Murray Canyon Dr, Palm Springs, CA 92262

Simms, Larry *Actor*
PO Box 55, Grays River, WA 98621

Simms, Phil *Football Player*
%New York Giants, Giants Stadium, East Rutherford, NJ 07073

Simms, Primate George Otto *Religious Leader*
62 Cypress Grove Rd, Dublin 6, Ireland

Simon, Bob *Commentator*
%CBS-TV, News Dept, 2020 "M" St NW, Washington, DC 20036

Simon, Carly *Singer*
130 W 57th St, #12-B, New York, NY 10019

Simon, Claude *Nobel Literature Laureate*
Pl Vieille, Salses, 66600 Rivesaltes, France

Simon, Edward R, Jr *Businessman*
%Herman Miller Inc, 8500 Byron Rd, Zeeland, MI 49464

Simon, George W *Astronaut*
%Air Force Geophysics Lab, Sacramento Peak Observatory, Sunspot, NM 88349

Simon, Herbert A *Nobel Economics Laureate*
%Carnegie-Mellon University, Psychology Dept, Pittsburgh, PA 15213

Simon, John *Movie, Drama Critic*
%New York Magazine, 755 2nd Ave, New York, NY 10017

Simon, Norton *Businessman*
22400 Pacific Coast Hwy, Malibu, CA 90265

Simon, Paul *Senator, IL*
%US Senate, Washington, DC 20510

Simon, Paul *Singer, Songwriter*
1619 Broadway, #500, New York, NY 10019

S

Simon, Peter E — *Businessman*
%Prime Motor Inns Inc, 700 Rt 46 E, Fairfield, NJ 07006
Simon, Roger M — *Columnist*
%Chicago Sun-Times, 401 N Wabash Ave, Chicago, IL 60611
Simon, Simone — *Actress*
5 Rue De Tilsitt, 75008 Paris, France
Simon, William E — *Secretary, Treasury*
%Wesray Corp, 330 South St, Morristown, NJ 07960
Simone, Albert J — *Educator*
%University of Hawaii, Chancellor's Office, Honolulu, HI 96822
Simone, Nina — *Singer, Songwriter*
%Andy Stroud, 383 Central Park West, New York, NY 10025
Simonis, Adrianus J Cardinal — *Religious Leader*
Aartsbisdom, BP 14019, 3508 SB Utrecht, Netherlands
Simonov, Yuriy I — *Conductor*
%Bolshoi State Academic Theatre, 1 Ploshchad Sverdlova, Moscow, Russia
Simons, Laurence B — *Government Official*
%Housing & Urban Development Department, 451 7th SW, Washington, DC 20410
Simonsen, Renee — *Model*
%Ford Model Agency, 344 E 59th St, New York, NY 10022
Simpkins, Ron — *Football Player*
%Cincinnati Bengals, 200 Riverfront Stadium, Cincinnati, OH 45202
Simplot, John R — *Businessman*
%J R Simplot Co, 999 Main St, Boise, ID 83701
Simpson Stern, Carol — *Labor Leader*
%American Assn of University Professors, 1012 14th St NW, Washington, DC 20005
Simpson, Adele — *Fashion Designer*
530 7th Ave, New York, NY 10018
Simpson, Alan K — *Senator, WY*
%US Senate, Washington, DC 20510
Simpson, David — *Businessman*
%Gould Inc, 10 Gould Ctr, Rolling Meadows, IL 60008
Simpson, Don — *Movie Producer*
9472 Cherokee Ln, Beverly Hills, CA 90210
Simpson, John R — *Law Enforcement Official*
%US Secret Service, 1800 "G" St NW, Washington, DC 20223
Simpson, Lee C — *Businessman*
%Louisiana-Pacific Corp, 111 SW 5th Ave, Portland, OR 97204
Simpson, Louis — *Writer*
PO Box 91, Port Jefferson, NY 11777
Simpson, Louis A — *Businessman*
%Geico Corp, 5260 Western Ave NW, Washington, DC 20076
Simpson, Milward L — *Governor, WY*
901 Simpson Ave, Cody, WY 82414
Simpson, O J — *Football Player, Actor, Sportscaster*
360 N Rockingham Ave, Los Angeles, CA 90049
Simpson, Ralph — *Basketball Player*
%Metropolitan State College, Athletic Dept, Denver, CO 80204
Simpson, Scott — *Golfer*
%Cornerstone Sports, 2515 McKinney, #940, Dallas, TX 75201
Simpson, Terry — *Hockey Coach*
%New York Islanders, Nassau Coliseum, Uniondale, NY 11553
Simpson, Tim — *Golfer*
%Jack P Simpson, 3031 Mornington Dr NW, Atlanta, GA 30327
Simpson, Valerie — *Singer (Ashford & Simpson)*
%George Sciffer, 1155 N La Cienega Blvd, Los Angeles, CA 90069
Simpson, Wayne — *Baseball Player*
330 Collamer Dr, Carson, CA 90744
Sims, Frank M — *Businessman*
%Clark Equipment Co, 100 N Michigan St, South Bend, IN 46634
Sims, Joan — *Actress, Comedienne*
17 Esmond Ct, Thackery St, London W8, England
Sims, Naomi — *Businesswoman, Model*
%Naomi Sims Collection, 48 E 21st St, New York, NY 10010
Sin, Jaime L Cardinal — *Religious Leader*
121 Arzobispo St, Entramuros, PO Box 132, Manila, Philippines

Sinatra, Frank *Singer, Actor*
70588 Frank Sinatra Dr, Rancho Mirage, CA 92270
Sinatra, Frank, Jr *Singer*
2211 Florian Pl, Beverly Hills, CA 90210
Sinatra, Nancy *Singer*
9817 Hythe Ct, Beverly Hills, CA 90210
SinBad *Actor*
%Agency for Performing Arts, 9000 Sunset Blvd, #1200, Los Angeles, CA 90069
Sinclair, Clive M *Businessman*
Stone House, 3 Madingley Rd, Cambridge CB3 0EE, England
Sindelar, Joey *Golfer*
213 Prospect Hill Rd, Horseheads, NY 14845
Sinden, Harry *Hockey Player*
%Boston Bruins, 150 Causeway St, Boston, MA 02114
Singer, Bill *Baseball Player*
1712 Antigua Wy, Newport Beach, CA 92660
Singer, Isadore M *Mathematician*
%University of California, Mathematics Dept, Berkeley, CA 94720
Singer, Marc *Actor*
%David Shapira Assoc, 15301 Ventura Blvd, #345, Sherman Oaks, CA 91403
Singer, S Fred *Geophysicist*
428 N Gordon St, Alexandria, VA 22304
Singh, Dinesh *Government Official, India*
Raj Bhawan, Kalakankar, Dist Pratapgarh UP 230203, India
Singh, Swaran *Government Official, India*
7 Hastings Rd, New Delhi, India
Singh, Vishwanath Pratap *Prime Minister, India*
%Prime Minister's Office, South Block, New Delhi 110001, India
Singlaub, John K *Army General*
PO Box 6335, Alexandria, VA 22306
Singletary, Mike *Football Player*
%Chicago Bears, 250 N Washington Rd, Lake Forest, IL 60045
Singleton, Chris *Football Player*
%New England Patriots, Sullivan Stadium, Foxboro, MA 02036
Singleton, Henry E *Businessman*
%Teledyne Inc, 1901 Ave of Stars, Los Angeles, CA 90067
Singleton, Kenny *Baseball Player*
5 Tremblant Ct, Lutherville, MD 21093
Singleton, Penny *Actress*
13419 Riverside Dr, #C, Sherman Oaks, CA 91423
Singleton, William D *Publisher*
%Houston Post, 4747 Southwest Frwy, Houston, TX 77001
Sington, Fred *Football Player*
2017 5th Ave N, Birmingham, AL 35203
Sinner, George A *Governor, ND*
%Governor's Office, State Capitol, Bismarck, ND 58505
Sinopoli, Giuseppe *Conductor, Composer*
%Deutsche Grammophon, PolyGram Records, 810 7th Ave, New York, NY 10019
Sinton, Nell *Artist*
1020 Francisco St, San Francisco, CA 94109
Sippel, Heinz *Financier*
%Hessische Landesbank-Girozentrale, 6000 Frankfurt am Main, Germany
Siri Singh Sahib *Religious Leader*
%Sikh, 1649 S Robertson Blvd, Los Angeles, CA 90035
Sirica, John J *Judge*
5069 Overlook Rd NW, Washington, DC 20016
Sirtis, Marina *Actress*
%Ambrosio/Mortimer Assoc, 301 N Canon Dr, #305, Beverly Hills, CA 90210
Sisco, Joseph J *Educator, Government Official*
4982 Sentinal Dr, Sumner, MD 20016
Sishido, Fukushige *Businessman*
%Fuji Electric Co, 1-1 Tanabeshinden, Kawasakiku, Kawasaki 210, Japan
Sisisky, Norman *Representative, VA*
%House of Representatives, Washington, DC 20515
Siskel, Gene *Movie Critic*
%Chicago Tribune, 435 N Michigan Ave, Chicago, IL 60611

S

Sisson – Skoronski

Sisson, C H *Writer*
Moorfield Cottage, The Hill, Langport, Somerset TA10 9PU, England

Sister Max *Fashion Designer*
%Mount Everest Centre for Buddhist Studies, Katmandu, Nepal

Sites, James W *Publisher*
%American Legion Magazine, 700 N Pennsylvania St, Indianapolis, IN 46206

Sithole, Ndabaningi *Political Leader, Zimbabwe*
%ZANU Party, PO Box UA 525, Harare, Zimbabwe

Sitkovetsky, Dmitry *Concert Violinist*
%Columbia Artists Mgmt Inc, 165 W 57th St, New York, NY 10019

Sitter, Carl L *Korean War Marine Corps Hero (CMH)*
3307 Quail Hill Dr, Midlothian, VA 23112

Sizova, Alla Ivanova *Ballerina*
%State Kirov Academic Ballet, Ploschad Iskusstv 1, St Petersburg, Russia

Sjoberg, Patrik *Track Athlete*
%Olympic Committee, Idrottens Hus, 12387 Farsta, Sweden

Sjoberg, Sigurd A *Space Scientist*
%NASA, Johnson Space Ctr, Houston, TX 77058

Sjoman, Volgot *Movie Director*
PO Box 27126, 10251 Stockholm, Sweden

Skaggs, David *Representative, CO*
%House of Representatives, Washington, DC 20515

Skaggs, L S (Sam) *Businessman*
%American Stores Co, 709 E South Temple, Salt Lake City, UT 84102

Skala, Lilia *Actress*
42-02 Layton St, Elmhurst, NY 11373

Skates, Ronald L *Businessman*
%Data General Corp, 4400 Computer Dr, Westboro, MA 01580

Skeen, Joseph R *Representative, NM*
PO Box 67, Pichacho, NM 88343

Skeggs, Leonard T, Jr *Biochemist*
10212 Blair Ln, Kirtland, OH 44094

Skelton, Byron G *Judge*
%US Court of Appeals, Federal Bldg, Temple, TX 76501

Skelton, Ike (Isaac Newton, IV) *Representative, MO*
1615 Franklin Ave, Lexington, MO 64067

Skelton, Red *Comedian*
37801 Thompson Rd, Rancho Mirage, CA 92270

Skerritt, Tom *Actor*
%Triad Artists, 10100 Santa Monica Blvd, #1600, Los Angeles, CA 90067

Skibbie, Lawrence F *Army General*
%American Defense Preparedness Assn, 1625 "I" St NW, Washington, DC 20006

Skilling, Hugh H *Electrical Engineer*
672 Mirada Rd, Stanford, CA 94305

Skinner, Jonty *Swimmer, Coach*
%University of Alabama, Athletic Dept, Tuscaloosa, AL 35487

Skinner, Samuel K *Secretary, Transportation*
%White House, 1600 Pennsylvania Ave NW, Washington, DC 20500

Skinner, Stanley T *Businessman*
%Pacific Gas & Electric Co, 77 Beale St, San Francisco, CA 94106

Skjvorecky, Josef *Writer*
%Erindale College, English Dept, Toronto ON M5S 1A5, Canada

Sklenar, Herbert A *Businessman*
%Vulcan Materials Co, 1 Metroplex Dr, Birmingham, AL 35209

Skoblikova, Lydia *Speed Skater*
B Chernizovskaya St 6-2-43, Moscow, Russia

Skold, Per *Businessman*
%Sventskt Stal, PO Box 16344, 103 26 Stockholm, Sweden

Skolimowski, Jerzy *Movie Director*
%Film Polski, Ul Mazowiecka 6/8, 00-048 Warsaw, Poland

Skoludek, Horst *Businessman*
%Carl-Zeiss-Stiftung, Postfach 1369, 7982 Oberkochen, Germany

Skopil, Otto R, Jr *Judge*
%US Court of Appeals, Pioneer Courthouse, 555 SW Yamhill St, Portland, OR 97204

Skoronski, Bob *Football Player*
N-8597 Fire Lane 9, Menasha, WI 54952

Skrebneski *Photographer*
1350 N LaSalle Dr, Chicago, IL 60610

Skrowaczewski, Stanislaw *Conductor, Composer*
PO Box 700, Wayzata, MN 55391

Skrypnyk, Metropolitan Mstyslav S *Religious Leader*
%Ukranian Orthodox Church, PO Box 495, South Bound Brook, NJ 08880

Skutt, Thomas J *Businessman*
%United of Omaha Life Insurance, Mutual of Omaha Plz, Omaha, NE 68175

Skutt, V J *Businessman*
%United of Omaha Life Insurance, Mutual of Omaha Plz, Omaha, NE 68175

Skye, Ione *Actress*
%The Agency, 10351 Santa Monica Blvd, #211, Los Angeles, CA 90025

Slack, Edward J *Businessman*
%PPG Industries, 1 PPG Pl, Pittsburgh, PA 15272

Slade, Bernard N *Playwright*
345 N Saltair Ave, Los Angeles, CA 90049

Slade, Mark *Actor*
2247 Linda Flora Dr, Los Angeles, CA 90077

Slade, Roy *Museum Director*
500 Lone Pine Rd, Bloomfield Hills, MI 48013

Sladkevicius, Vicentas Cardinal *Religious Leader*
R Carno 31, 234230 Kaisiadorys, Lietuva, Lithuania

Slagle, James R *Computer Scientist*
2117 W Hoyt Ave, St Paul, MN 55108

Slate, Jeremy *Actor*
%Artists Group, 1930 Century Park West, #403, Los Angeles, CA 90067

Slater, Christian *Actor*
%Creative Artists Agency, 9830 Wilshire Blvd, Beverly Hills, CA 90212

Slater, Helen *Actress*
%William Morris Agency, 151 El Camino, Beverly Hills, CA 90212

Slater, Jackie *Football Player*
%Los Angeles Rams, 2327 W Lincoln Ave, Anaheim, CA 92801

Slater, Joseph E *Educator*
%Aspen Institute for Humanistic Studies, 1000 N 3rd St, Aspen, CO 81611

Slatkin, Leonard *Conductor*
%St Louis Symphony, Powell Symphony Hall, 718 N Grand Blvd, St Louis, MO 63103

Slaton, Tony *Football Player*
%Dallas Cowboys, 1 Cowboys Pkwy, Irving, TX 75063

Slattery, Jim *Representative, KS*
%House of Representatives, Washington, DC 20515

Slattvik, Simon *Nordic Skier*
%General Delivery, 2600 Lillehammer, Norway

Slaughter, Enos *Baseball Player*
RR 2, Box 159, Roxboro, NC 27573

Slaughter, Frank *Writer*
PO Box 14, Ortega Station, Jacksonville, FL 32210

Slaughter, John B *Educator*
%Occidental College, President's Office, Los Angeles, CA 90041

Slaughter, Louise M *Representative, NY*
%House of Representatives, Washington, DC 20515

Slaughter, Webster *Football Player*
%Cleveland Browns, Cleveland Stadium, Cleveland, OH 44114

Slayton, Donald K (Deke) *Astronaut*
%Space Services Inc, 7015 Gulf Fwy, #140, Houston, TX 77087

Sleet, Moneta, Jr *Photographer*
%Ebony Magazine, 820 S Michigan Ave, Chicago, IL 60605

Slezak, Erika *Actress*
%International Creative Mgmt, 40 W 57th St, New York, NY 10019

Slichter, Charles P *Physicist*
61 Chestnut Ct, Champaign, IL 61821

Slick, Grace *Singer*
%Starship Inc, 1319 Bridgeway, Sausalito, CA 94965

Sliger, Bernard F *Educator*
%Florida State University, President's Office, Tallahassee, FL 32306

Sliwa, Curtis *Founder, Guardian Angels*
%Guardian Angels, 982 E 89th St, Brooklyn, NY 11236

Sliwa, Lisa *National Director, Guardian Angels*
%Guardian Angels, 982 E 89th St, Brooklyn, NY 11236

Sloan, Albert F *Businessman*
%Lance Inc, 8600 South Blvd, Charlotte, NC 28210

Sloan, Alexander M *Air Force General*
Surgeon General, Hq USAF, Bolling Air Force Base, Washington, DC 20332

Sloan, Jerry *Basketball Player, Coach*
%Utah Jazz, Salt Palace, 100 SW Temple, Salt Lake City, UT 84101

Sloan, Norm *Basketball Coach*
%University of Florida, Athletic Dept, Gainesville, FL 32611

Sloan, Steve *Football Coach*
%Duke University, Athletic Dept, Durham, NC 27706

Slocum, George S *Businessman*
%Transco Energy Co, 2800 Post Oak Blvd, Houston, TX 77056

Slocum, R C *Football Coach*
%Texas A&M University, Athletic Dept, College Station, TX 77843

Sloneker, John G *Businessman*
%Ohio Casualty Corp, 136 N 3rd St, Hamilton, OH 45025

Slonimsky, Nicolas *Composer*
10847 3/4 Wilshire Blvd, Los Angeles, CA 90024

Slotnick, Bernard *Publisher*
%DC Comics Grp, 355 Lexington Ave, New York, NY 10017

Slotnick, Mortimer *Artist*
43 Amherst Dr, Rochelle, NY 10804

Slotnick, R Nathan *Surgeon (Fetal-to-Fetal Transplant)*
%University of California Medical School, Prenatal Genetics, Davis, CA 95616

Slovin, Bruce *Businessman*
%Revlon Group Inc, 767 5th Ave, New York, NY 10153

Sloviter, Dolores Korman *Judge*
%US Court of Appeals, US Courthouse, 601 Market St, Philadelphia, PA 19106

Sloyan, James *Actor*
3709 Longview Valley Rd, Sherman Oaks, CA 91423

Sluman, Jeff *Golfer*
%Professional Golfers Assn, PO Box 109601, Palm Beach Gardens, FL 33410

Slusarski, Tadeusz *Track Athlete*
Ul Atenska 2 m 154, 03-978 Warsaw, Poland

Smagorinsky, Joseph *Meteorologist*
%Princeton University, Geology & Geophysics Dept, Princeton, NJ 08544

Smale, Stephen *Mathematician*
68 Highgate Rd, Berkeley, CA 94720

Small, Lawrence M *Financier*
%Federal National Mortgage Assn, 3900 Wisconsin Ave NW, Washington, DC 20016

Small, William J *Television Executive*
%National Broadcasting Co, 30 Rockefeller Plz, New York, NY 10020

Small, William N *Navy Admiral*
%Navy Department, Pentagon, Washington, DC 20350

Smalley, Richard E *Chemist*
%Rice University, Chemistry Dept, PO Box 1892, Houston, TX 77251

Smalley, Roy *Baseball Player*
534 W Arbor Vitae, Inglewood, CA 90301

Smallpeice, Basil *Businessman*
Bridge House, Leigh Hill Rd, Cobham, Surrey, England

Smarr, Larry L *Physicist*
%University of Illinois, Supercomputing Applications Ctr, Champaign, IL 61820

Smart, Jean *Actress*
%William Morris Agency, 151 El Camino, Beverly Hills, CA 90212

Smart, L Edwin *Businessman*
%Trans World Corp, 605 3rd Ave, New York, NY 10158

Smathers, George A *Senator, FL*
Alfred I du Pont Bldg, Miami, FL 33131

Smeal, Eleanor *Women's Activist*
425 13th St NW, Washington, DC 20004

Smerlas, Fred *Football Player*
%New England Patriots, Sullivan Stadium, Foxboro, MA 02035

Smigel, Irwin *Dentist*
%Smigel Research 635 Madison Ave, New York, NY 10022

Smiley, Jane *Writer*
%Iowa State University, English Dept, Ames, IA 50011
Smiley, John *Baseball Player*
208 W 3rd Ave, Trappe, PA 19426
Smirnoff, Yakov *Comedian*
%Comrade in America, 1427 N Kings Rd, Los Angeles, CA 90069
Smith Court, Margaret *Tennis Player*
53 Watkins Rd, Claremont, Perth WA 5010, Australia
Smith Osborne, Madolyn *Actress*
%InterTalent Agency, 131 S Rodeo Dr, #300, Beverly Hills, CA 90212
Smith, Albert C *Biologist*
%University of Hawaii, Botany Dept, Honolulu, HI 96822
Smith, Albert K *Businessman*
%Big Three Industries, 3535 W 12th St, Houston, TX 77008
Smith, Albert L, Jr *Representative, AL*
%House of Representatives, Washington, DC 20515
Smith, Alexis *Actress*
%International Creative Mgmt, 8899 Beverly Blvd, Los Angeles, CA 90048
Smith, Alfred J *Labor Leader*
%Mechanics Educational Society, 15300 E Seven Mile Rd, Detroit, MI 48205
Smith, Anne Mollegen *Editor*
%McCall's Magazine, 230 Park Ave, New York, NY 10169
Smith, Anthony *Football Player*
%Los Angeles Raiders, 332 Center St, El Segundo, CA 90245
Smith, Ben *Football Player*
%Philadelphia Eagles, Veterans Stadium, Philadelphia, PA 19148
Smith, Bill *Swimmer*
46-450 Holokaa St, Kaneohe, HI 96744
Smith, Billy *Hockey Player*
%New York Islanders, Nassau Veterans Coliseum, Uniondale, NY 11553
Smith, Billy Ray, Jr *Football Player*
%San Diego Chargers, 9449 Friars Rd, San Diego, CA 92108
Smith, Bruce *Football Player*
%Buffalo Bills, 1 Bills Dr, Orchard Park, NY 14127
Smith, Bubba *Football Player, Actor*
5178 Sunlight Pl, Los Angeles, CA 90016
Smith, Buffalo Bob *Actor*
Big Lake, Princeton, ME 04619
Smith, Calvert H *Educator*
%Morris Brown College, President's Office, Atlanta, GA 30314
Smith, Calvin *Track Athlete*
2628 Colonial Dr NE, Tuscaloosa, AL 35404
Smith, Carl G *Businessman*
%Gerber Products Co, 445 State St, Fremont, MI 49412
Smith, Carleton *Foundation Executive, Art Expert*
Chalet le Stop, 1882 Gryon, Switzerland
Smith, Charles *Basketball Player*
%Los Angeles Clippers, Sports Arena, 3939 Figueroa St, Los Angeles, CA 90037
Smith, Charles Martin *Actor*
146 N Almont Dr, #8, Los Angeles, CA 90048
Smith, Chesterfield *Attorney*
5915 Ponce de Leon Blvd, #63, Coral Gables, FL 33146
Smith, Christopher *Representative, NJ*
%House of Representatives, Washington, DC 20515
Smith, Connie *Singer*
1300 Division St, #103, Nashville, TN 37203
Smith, Cotter *Actor*
%Gersh Agency, 232 N Canon Dr, Beverly Hills, CA 90210
Smith, Cyril S *Metallurgist, Historian*
31 Madison St, Cambridge, MA 02138
Smith, D E *Businessman*
%A O Smith Corp, 3533 N 27th St, Milwaukee, WI 53216
Smith, Darwin E *Businessman*
%Kimberly-Clark Corp, PO Box 619100, Dallas, TX 75261
Smith, Dean *Basketball Coach*
%University of North Carolina, PO Box 2126, Chapel Hill, NC 27514

Smith, Denny *Representative, OR*
%House of Representatives, Washington, DC 20515

Smith, Derek *Basketball Player*
%Sacramento Kings, 1515 Sports Dr, Sacramento, CA 95834

Smith, Dick *Diving Coach*
PO Box 304, Woodlands, TX 77313

Smith, Doug *Football Player*
%Los Angeles Rams, 2327 W Lincoln Ave, Anaheim, CA 92801

Smith, Doug *Basketball Player*
%Dallas Mavericks, Reunion Arena, 777 Sports St, Dallas, TX 75207

Smith, Edward S *Judge*
%US Court of Appeals, US Courthouse, 1729 5th Ave N, Birmingham, AL 35203

Smith, Emil L *Biochemist, Biophysicist*
%University of California, Medical School, Los Angeles, CA 90024

Smith, Emmitt *Football Player*
%Dallas Cowboys, 1 Cowboys Pkwy, Irving, TX 75063

Smith, Ernest A (Smoky) *WW II Canadian Army Hero (VC)*
%Smith Travel Centre, 1067 Howe St, Vancouver BC V6Z 1P6, Canada

Smith, Frederick W *Businessman*
%Federal Express Corp, 2990 Airways Blvd, Memphis, TN 38194

Smith, Gerard *Publisher, Tennis Executive*
%World Tennis Assn, 133 1st St NE, St Petersburg, FL 33701

Smith, Gerard C *Government Official*
2425 Tracy Pl NW, Washington, DC 20008

Smith, H Russell *Businessman*
%Avery International, 150 N Orange Grove Blvd, Pasadena, CA 91103

Smith, Hal *Actor*
%Joseph Heldfond Rix, 1717 N Highland Ave, #414, Los Angeles, CA 90028

Smith, Hamilton O *Nobel Medicine Laureate*
8222 Carrbridge Cir, Baltimore, MD 21204

Smith, Harold B, Jr *Businessman*
%Illinois Tool Works, 8501 W Higgins Rd, Chicago, IL 60631

Smith, Harry *Commentator*
%CBS-News, 524 W 57th St, New York, NY 10019

Smith, Harry *Bowler*
%Professional Bowlers Assn, 1720 Merriman Rd, Akron, OH 44313

Smith, Harry E *Football Player*
805 Leawood Terr, Columbia, MO 65203

Smith, Harry K *Businessman*
%Big Three Industries, 3535 W 12th St, Houston, TX 77008

Smith, Hedrick *Journalist*
4204 Rosemary St, Chevy Chase, MD 20015

Smith, Henry N *Educator*
2550 Dana St, #9-D, Berkeley, CA 94704

Smith, Hoke L *Educator*
%Towson State University, President's Office, Towson, MD 21204

Smith, Howard G *Publisher*
%Newsweek Magazine, 444 Madison Ave, New York, NY 10022

Smith, Howard K *Commentator*
6450 Brooks Ln, Washington, DC 20016

Smith, Hulett C *Governor, WV*
2105 Harper Rd, Beckley, WV 25801

Smith, Ian *Prime Minister, Rhodesia*
Gwenoro Farm, Selukwe, Zimbabwe

Smith, J Henry *Businessman*
36 N Crescent, Maplewood, NJ 07040

Smith, J Stanford *Businessman*
77 W 45th St, New York, NY 10036

Smith, J T *Football Player*
%Phoenix Cardinals, PO Box 888, Phoenix, AZ 85100

Smith, Jabbo *Jazz Trumpeter*
%Lorraine Gordon, 2 Charlton St, New York, NY 10014

Smith, Jack *Journalist, Author*
4251 Camino Real, Los Angeles, CA 90065

Smith, Jaclyn *Actress*
773 Stradella Rd, Los Angeles, CA 90077

S

Smith, James (Bonecrusher) *Boxer*
PO Box 1385, Littleton, NC 27546

Smith, James F *Businessman*
%Crown Central Petroleum Corp, 1 N Charles, Baltimore, MD 21201

Smith, James F, Jr *Financier*
%First American Corp, First American Ctr, Nashville, TN 37268

Smith, Jay *Publisher*
%Atlanta Journal-Constitution, 72 Marietta St, Atlanta, GA 30303

Smith, Jeff *Writer, Food Expert*
%Frugal Gourmet, 88 Virginia Ave, #2, Seattle, WA 98101

Smith, Jerry E *Judge*
%US Court of Appeals, 515 Rusk Ave, Houston, TX 77002

Smith, Jimmy *Jazz Organist*
11921 Miwok Ct, Wilton, CA 95693

Smith, John *Track Athlete*
%University of California, Athletic Dept, Los Angeles, CA 90024

Smith, John B *Businessman*
%Mayflower Corp, 9998 N Michigan Rd, Carmel, IN 46032

Smith, John Coventry *Religious Leader*
%World Council of Churches, 150 Rt de Ferbey, 1211 Geneva 20, Switzerland

Smith, John F, Jr *Businessman*
%General Motors Corp, 3044 W Grand Blvd, Detroit, MI 48202

Smith, Kathy *Physical Fitness Expert*
9690 Heather Rd, Beverly Hills, CA 90210

Smith, Kenny *Basketball Player*
%Atlanta Hawks, 100 Techwood Dr NW, Atlanta, GA 30303

Smith, Lamar *Representative, TX*
%House of Representatives, Washington, DC 20515

Smith, Lane *Actor*
%Harris & Goldberg Agency, 1999 Ave of Stars, #2850, Los Angeles, CA 90067

Smith, Larry *Representative, FL*
%House of Representatives, Washington, DC 20515

Smith, Larry *Football Coach*
%University of Southern California, Heritage Hall, Los Angeles, CA 90089

Smith, Larry *Basketball Player*
%Golden State Warriors, Oakland Coliseum, Oakland, CA 94621

Smith, Lawrence Leighton *Conductor*
%San Antonio Symphony, 109 Lexington Ave, San Antonio, TX 78205

Smith, Leighton W, Jr *Navy Admiral*
Deputy CNO, Plans/Policy/Operations, Navy Department, Washington, DC 20350

Smith, Leo W, II *Air Force General*
Vice CINC, Strategic Air Command, Hq SAC, Offutt Air Force Base, NE 68113

Smith, Leonard *Football Player*
%Phoenix Cardinals, PO Box 888, Phoenix, AZ 85001

Smith, Leslie *Businessman*
%BOC Grp, Hammersmith House, Hammersmith W6 9DX, England

Smith, Liz *Columnist*
160 E 38th St, New York, NY 10016

Smith, Lloyd B *Businessman*
%A O Smith Corp, 11270 W Park Pl, Milwaukee, WI 53224

Smith, Lonnie M *Businessman*
%Hillenbrand Industries, Hwy 46, Batesville, IN 47006

Smith, Loren A *Judge*
%US Claims Court, 717 Madison Pl NW, Washington, DC 20005

Smith, Maggie *Actress*
%International Creative Mgmt, 388-396 Oxford St, London W1, England

Smith, Margaret Chase *Senator, ME*
PO Box 366, Norridgewock Ave, Skowhegan, ME 04976

Smith, Marshall *Businessman*
%Commodore International, 3330 Scott Blvd, Santa Clara, CA 95050

Smith, Martha *Actress*
9690 Heather Rd, Beverly Hills, CA 90210

Smith, Martin Cruz *Writer*
%Knox Burger Assoc, 391 Washington Sq S, New York, NY 10012

Smith, Mary Louise *Government Official*
654 59th St, Des Moines, IA 50312

S

Smith – Smith

Smith, Moishe — *Artist*
%Utah State University, Art Dept, Logan, UT 84322

Smith, Morris — *Financier*
%Magellan Fund, 82 Devonshire St, Boston, MA 02109

Smith, Neal E — *Representative, IA*
RFD 1, Altoona, IA 50009

Smith, Norman R — *Educator*
%Wagner College, President's Office, Staten Island, NY 10301

Smith, O C — *Singer*
14621 Leadwell St, Van Nuys, CA 91405

Smith, Oliver — *Theatrical Designer*
%Ballet Theatre Foundation, 890 Broadway, New York, NY 10003

Smith, Orin R — *Businessman*
%Engelhard Corp, Menlo Park, Edison, NJ 08818

Smith, Page — *Educator*
235 Pine Flat Rd, Santa Cruz, CA 95060

Smith, Patti — *Singer*
%Arista Records, 6 W 57th St, New York, NY 10019

Smith, Philip L — *Businessman*
%Pillsbury Co, 200 S 6th St, Minneapolis, MN 55402

Smith, Preston E — *Governor, TX*
3400 50th St, Lubbock, TX 79413

Smith, R Jackson — *Diver*
15 Sylvan Ln, Greenwich, CT 06870

Smith, Rankin M — *Football Executive*
%Atlanta Falcons, Suwanee Rd, Suwanee, GA 30174

Smith, Ray E — *Religious Leader*
%Open Bible Standard Churches, 2020 Bell Ave, Des Moines, IA 50315

Smith, Raymond W — *Businessman*
%Bell Atlantic Corp, 1600 Market St, Philadelphia, PA 19103

Smith, Reggie — *Baseball Player*
11764 Doral Ave, Northridge, CA 91326

Smith, Rex — *Actor*
%Agency for Performing Arts, 9000 Sunset Blvd, #1200, Los Angeles, CA 90069

Smith, Richard A — *Entertainment Executive*
%General Cinema Corp, 27 Boylston St, Chestnut Hill, MA 02176

Smith, Richard M — *Editor*
%Newsweek Magazine, 444 Madison Ave, New York, NY 10022

Smith, Richard S — *Businessman*
%National Intergroup Inc, 20 Stanwix St, Pittsburgh, PA 15222

Smith, Riley — *Football Player*
PO Box 6152, Mobile, AL 36606

Smith, Robert C — *Editor*
%TV Guide Magazine, 100 Matsonford Rd, Radnor, PA 19087

Smith, Robert F — *Representative, OR*
%House of Representatives, Washington, DC 20515

Smith, Robert Gray (Graysmith) — *Editorial Cartoonist*
%San Francisco Chronicle, 901 Mission St, San Francisco, CA 94103

Smith, Robert H — *Financier*
%Security Pacific Corp, 333 S Hope St, Los Angeles, CA 90071

Smith, Robert I — *Businessman*
%Public Service Electric & Gas Co, 80 Park Plz, Newark, NJ 07101

Smith, Robyn — *Thoroughbred Racing Jockey*
1155 San Ysidro Dr, Beverly Hills, CA 90210

Smith, Roger — *Actor*
2707 Benedict Canyon, Beverly Hills, CA 90210

Smith, Rolland — *Commentator*
%CBS-TV, News Dept, 524 W 57th St, New York, NY 10019

Smith, Samuel H — *Educator*
%Washington State University, President's Office, Pullman, WA 99164

Smith, Shelley — *Model, Actress*
%Artists Agency, 10000 Santa Monica Blvd, #305, Los Angeles, CA 90067

Smith, Sherwood H, Jr — *Businessman*
%Carolina Power & Light Co, 411 Fayetteville St, Raleigh, NC 27602

Smith, Sinjin — *Volleyball Player*
%Smithers, 2523 Santa Monica Blvd, Santa Monica, CA 90403

Smith, Stan *Tennis Player*
%Assn of Tennis Pros, 200 Tournament Players Rd, Ponte Vedra Beach, FL 32082

Smith, Steve *Basketball Player*
%Miami Heat, Miami Arena, Miami, FL 33136

Smith, Steven J *Businessman*
%Ryan Homes Inc, 100 Ryan Ct, Pittsburgh, PA 15205

Smith, Stewart W, Jr *Businessman*
%Union Electric Co, 1901 Gratiot St, St Louis, MO 63103

Smith, Tom E *Businessman*
%Food Lion Inc, Harrison Rd, Salisbury, NC 28145

Smith, Tommie *Track Athlete*
%Santa Monica College, Athletic Dept, Santa Monica, CA 90405

Smith, Tony *Artist*
%Pace Gallery, 32 E 57th St, New York, NY 10022

Smith, Vernon S (Catfish) *Football Player*
PO Box 724, La Jolla, CA 92038

Smith, Virginia B *Educator*
%Mills College, President's Office, Oakland, CA 94613

Smith, Virginia D *Representative, NE*
General Delivery, Chappell, NE 69129

Smith, W Keith *Financier*
%Mellon Bank Corp, 1 Mellon Bank Ctr, Pittsburgh, PA 15258

Smith, Wallace B *Religious Leader*
%Reorganized Church of Latter Day Saints, Box 1059, Independence, MO 64051

Smith, Ward *Businessman*
%White Consolidated Industries, 11770 Berea Rd, Cleveland, OH 44111

Smith, Wayman F, Jr *Businessman*
%Pabst Brewing Co, 1000 Market St, Milwaukee, WI 53201

Smith, William *Actor*
%Don Gerler Assoc, 3349 Cahuenga Blvd, #2, Los Angeles, CA 90068

Smith, William D *Navy Admiral*
US Representative to NATO Military Committee, APO, AE 09667

Smith, William Jay *Writer*
1675 York Ave, #20-K, New York, NY 10028

Smith, William T *Businessman*
%Champlin Petroleum Co, 5301 Camp Bowie Blvd, Forth Worth, TX 76107

Smith, William Terry *Businessman*
%Savin Corp, Columbus Ave, Valhalla, NY 10595

Smith, Willie *Football Player*
%Cleveland Browns, Cleveland Stadium, Cleveland, OH 44114

Smithburg, William D *Businessman*
%Quaker Oats Co, 345 Merchandise Mart Plz, Chicago, IL 60654

Smithers, Jan *Actress*
2401 Colorado Ave, #160, Santa Monica, CA 90404

Smithers, William *Actor*
11664 Laurelcrest Dr, Studio City, CA 91604

Smitrovich, Bill *Actor*
%"Life Goes On" Show, ABC-TV, 2040 Ave of Stars, Los Angeles, CA 90067

Smits, Jimmy *Actor*
%Creative Artists Agency, 9830 Wilshire Blvd, Beverly Hills, CA 90212

Smits, Rik *Basketball Player*
%Indiana Pacers, 2 W Washington St, Indianapolis, IN 46204

Smolan, Rick *Photographer*
%Collins SF, 50 Osgood Pl, #400, San Francisco, CA 94133

Smotherman, G Cromer *Businessman*
%Murray Ohio Manufacturing Co, Franklin Rd, Brentwood, TN 37027

Smothers, Dick *Comedian (Smothers Brothers)*
%SmoBro Productions, 8489 W 3rd St, #1078, Los Angeles, CA 90048

Smothers, Tom *Comedian (Smothers Brothers)*
%SmoBro Productions, 8489 W 3rd St, #1078, Los Angeles, CA 90048

Smurfit, Michael W J *Businessman*
%Jefferson Smurfit Corp, 401 Alton St, Alton, IL 62002

Smylie, Robert E *Governor, ID*
117 Locust St, Boise, ID 83712

Smyth, Charles P *Physical Chemist*
245 Prospect Ave, Princeton, NJ 08540

S

Smyth – Snyder

Smyth, Craig H *Art Historian*
Villa I Tatti, Via di Vincigliata, 50135 Florence, Italy

Smyth, Randy *Yachtsman*
%Sails by Smyth, 15640 Graham St, Huntington Beach, CA 92649

Smythe, Quenton G M *WW II South African Army Hero (VC)*
54 Seadoone Rd, Amanzimtoti 4126, Natal, South Africa

Smythe, Reg *Cartoonist (Andy Capp)*
Whitegates, 96 Caledonian Rd, Hartlepool, Cleveland, England

Snead, J C (Jesse Caryle) *Golfer*
PO Box 1152, Ponte Verde Beach, FL 32082

Snead, Norm *Football Player*
104 James Landing, Newport News, VA 23606

Snead, Sam *Golfer*
PO Box 544, Hot Springs, VA 24445

Sneath, William S *Businessman*
%Union Carbide Corp, 39 Old Ridgbury Rd, Danbury, CT 06817

Snedaker, Robert H, Jr *Businessman*
%United Telecommunications, 2330 Johnson Dr, Westwood, KS 66205

Snedeker, Robert D *Businessman*
%Texas Air Corp, 333 Clay St, Houston, TX 77002

Sneed, Joseph T *Judge*
%US Court of Appeals, Court Bldg, San Francisco, CA 94101

Sneider, Richard L *Diplomat*
211 Central Park West, New York, NY 10024

Snell, Esmond E *Biochemist*
5001 Greystone Dr, Austin, TX 78731

Snell, George D *Nobel Medicine Laureate*
21 Atlantic Ave, Bar Harbor, ME 04609

Snell, Peter *Track Athlete*
%University of Texas Health Science Ctr, Physiology Dept, Dallas, TX 75235

Snell, Richard *Businessman*
%Aztar Corp, 3838 E Van Buren St, Phoenix, AZ 85008

Sneva, Tom *Auto Racing Driver*
3301 E Valley Vista Ln, Paradise Valley, AZ 85253

Snider, Edward M *Hockey Executive*
1804 Rittenhouse Sq, Philadelphia, PA 19103

Snider, Edwin (Duke) *Baseball Player*
3037 Lakemont Dr, Fallbrook, CA 92028

Snider, R Michael *Medical Researcher (Substance P)*
%Pfizer Pharmaceuticals, Eastern Point Rd, Groton, CT 06340

Snipes, Wesley *Actor*
%Gersh Agency, 232 N Canon Dr, Beverly Hills, CA 90210

Snipstead, Richard *Religious Leader*
%Free Lutheran Congregations Assn, 402 W 11th St, Canton, SD 57013

Snodgrass, William D *Poet*
%University of Delaware, English Dept, Newark, DE 19711

Snodgress, Carrie *Actress*
16650 Schoenborn, Sepulveda, CA 91343

Snow, Hank *Singer*
PO Box 1084, Nashville, TN 37202

Snow, Jack *Football Player*
401 Purdue Cir, Seal Beach, CA 90740

Snow, John W *Businessman*
%CSX Corp, 901 E Cary St, Richmond, VA 23219

Snow, Percy *Football Player*
%Kansas City Chiefs, 1 Arrowhead Dr, Kansas City, MO 64129

Snow, Phoebe *Singer, Songwriter*
%Bernstein, 505 Park Ave, New York, NY 10022

Snowdon, Earl of *Photographer*
22 Launceston Pl, London W8 5RL, England

Snowe, Olympia J *Representative, ME*
%House of Representatives, Washington, DC 20515

Snyder, Bruce *Football Coach*
%Arizona State University, Athletic Dept, Tempe, AZ 85287

Snyder, Donald *Air Force General*
Vice Commander, Tactical Air Command, Langley Air Force Base, VA 23665

Snyder, Gary *Poet*
18442 Macnab Cypress Rd, Nevada City, CA 95959

Snyder, Jimmy (The Greek) *Oddsmaker, Journalist*
%News America Syndicate, 1703 Kaiser Ave, Irvine, CA 92714

Snyder, Laurence H *Educator*
2885 Oahu Ave, Honolulu, HI 96822

Snyder, Richard E *Publisher*
%Simon & Schuster, 1230 Ave of Americas, New York, NY 10020

Snyder, Robert C *Businessman*
%Quanex Corp, 1900 West Loop S, Houston, TX 77027

Snyder, Solomon H *Psychiatrist, Pharmacologist*
2300 W Rogers Ave, Baltimore, MD 21209

Snyder, Tom *Commentator*
2801 Hutton Dr, Beverly Hills, CA 90210

Snyder, William B *Businessman*
%GEICO Corp, 5260 Western Ave NW, Washington, DC 20076

Soames of Fletching, A Christopher J *Government Official, England*
%White's Club, St James's St, London SW1, England

Soares, Mario *President, Portugal*
R Dr Joao Soares, #2-3, 1700 Lisbon, Portugal

Soble, Ron *Actor*
%BDP Assoc, 10637 Burbank Blvd, North Hollywood, CA 91601

Socks, Laverne J *Businessman*
%Briggs & Stratton Corp, 12301 W Wirth St, Wauwatosa, WI 53222

Sockwell, Oliver R *Businessman*
%Student Loan Marketing Assn, 1050 Thomas Jefferson, Washington, DC 20007

Sodano, Angelo Cardinal *Religious Leader*
%Office of Secretary of State, 00120 Vatican City, Rome, Italy

Soderbergh, Steven *Movie Director*
%United Talent, 9560 Wilshire Blvd, #501, Beverly Hills, CA 90212

Soderstrom, Elisabeth *Opera Singer*
19 Hersbyvagen, 181 42 Lidingo, Sweden

Sohn Kee Chung *Marathon Runner*
%Korean Olympic Committee, International PO Box 1106, Seoul, South Korea

Sohn, John P *Businessman*
%Arvin Industries, 1531 13th St, Columbus, IN 47201

Sokolov, Gregory *Concert Pianist*
%Yolanta Skura, Opus 3, 420 W 24th St, New York, NY

Sokolove, James G *Attorney*
1 Boston Pl, Boston, MA 02108

Sokolow, Anna *Dancer, Choreographer*
%Julliard School of Dance, Lincoln Ctr, New York, NY 10023

Sokomanu, George *President, Vanuatu*
%President's Office, Vila, Vanuatu

Solandt, Ormond M *Physiologist, Educator*
Wolfe Den, RR 1, Bolton ON L0P 1A0, Canada

Solarz, Stephen J *Representative, NY*
241 Dover St, Brooklyn, NY 11235

Solberg, Magnar *Biathlete*
Stabellvn 60, 7000 Trondheim, Norway

Soleri, Paolo *Architect*
%Cosanti Foundation, 6433 Doubletree Rd, Scottsdale, AZ 85253

Soles, P J *Actress*
%Gores/Fields Agency, 10100 Santa Monica Blvd, #700, Los Angeles, CA 90067

Solh, Rashid *Prime Minister, Lebanon*
%Chambre of Deputes, Place de l'Etoile, Beirut, Lebanon

Solheim, Karsten *Businessman*
%Karsten Manufacturing Corp, 2201 W Desert Cove Ave, Phoenix, AZ 85029

Solomon, Anthony M *Financier*
%Federal Reserve Bank, Federal Reserve PO Station, New York, NY 10045

Solomon, Arthur K *Biophysicist*
27 Cragie St, Cambridge, MA 02138

Solomon, Ezra *Educator*
775 Santa Ynez, Stanford, CA 94305

Solomon, Gerald *Representative, NY*
23 North Rd, Queensbury Glens Falls, NY 12801

S

Solomon – Sorel

Solomon, Harold *Tennis Player*
1500 S Ocean Blvd, Pompano Beach, FL 33062

Solomon, Michael J *Television Executive*
%Lorimar-Telepictures, 10202 W Washington Blvd, Culver City, CA 90230

Solomon, Richard L *Psychologist*
3815 Walnut St, Philadelphia, PA 19174

Solomon, Robert *Economist*
8502 W Howell Rd, Bethesda, MD 20817

Solomon, Yonty *Concert Pianist*
43 Belsize Park Gdns, London NW3 4JJ, England

Solovyev, Anatoly *Cosmonaut*
141 160 Svyosdny Gorodok, Moskovskoi Oblasti, Potchta Kosmonavtov, Russia

Solovyev, Vladimir *Cosmonaut*
141 160 Svyosdny Gorodok, Moskovskoi Oblasti, Potchta Kosmonavtov, Russia

Solow, Robert M *Nobel Economics Laureate*
528 Lewis Wharf, Boston, MA 02110

Solt, Ron *Football Player*
%Indianapolis Colts, 7001 W 56th St, Indianapolis, IN 46254

Solti, Georg *Conductor*
Chalet Haut Pre, Villars sur Ollons, Vaud, Switzerland

Solvay, Jacques *Businessman*
%Solvay & Cie, Rue du Prince Albert 33, 1050 Brussels, Belgium

Solzhenitsyn, Aleksandr *Nobel Literature Laureate*
%Harper & Row, 10 E 53rd St, New York, NY 10022

Somare, Michael T *Prime Minister, Papua New Guinea*
Karan, Murik Lakes, East Sepik, Papua New Guinea

Sombrotto, Vincent R *Labor Leader*
%National Letter Carriers Assn, 100 Indiana Ave NW, Washington, DC 20001

Somers, Brett *Actress*
1650 Broadway, #406, New York, NY 10019

Somers, Suzanne *Actress*
10342 Mississippi Ave, Los Angeles, CA 90025

Sommars, Julie *Actress*
12959 Woodbridge, Studio City, CA 91604

Sommaruga, Cornelio *International Official, Switzerland*
%International Red Cross, 12 Grand-Mezel Pl, 1204 Geneva, Switzerland

Sommer, Charles H *Businessman*
942 Tirrill Farms Rd, St Louis, MO 63124

Sommer, Elke *Actress*
540 N Beverly Glen, Los Angeles, CA 90024

Sommerfelt, Christiaan *Businessman*
%Elkem, PO Box 5430, Maj Middelthunsgt 27, Oslo 3, Norway

Sommers, Gordon H *Religious Leader*
%Moravian Church, PO Box 1245, Bethlehem, PA 18016

Somogi, Judith *Conductor*
%Herbert Barrett Mgmt, 1860 Broadway, New York, NY 10023

Somogyi, Jozsef *Sculptor*
Marton Ut 3/5, 1038 Budapest, Hungary

Sondheim, Stephen J *Composer, Lyricist*
246 E 49th St, New York, NY 10017

Sonnenfeldt, Helmut *Government Official*
4105 Thornapple St, Chevy Chase, MD 20815

Sonsini, Larry *Attorney*
%Wilson Sonsini Goodrich Rosati, 2 Palo Alto Sq, #900, Palo Alto, CA 94306

Sontag, Susan *Writer*
%Farrar Straus & Giroux, 19 Union Sq W, New York, NY 10003

Soose, Billy *Boxer*
Box 127, Tafton, PA 18464

Sophia *Queen, Spain*
%Palacio de la Zarzuela, Madrid, Spain

Sorato, Bruno F *Businessman*
%AluSuisse, Feldeggstrasse 4, 8034 Zurich 8, Switzerland

Sorel, Edward *Artist*
Rt 301, Carmel, NY 10512

Sorel, Louise *Actress*
%Gage Grp, 1650 Broadway, New York, NY 10019

Sorensen, Jacki 19420 Merridy St, Northridge, CA 91324	*Physical Fitness Expert*
Sorensen, Robert H %Perkin-Elmer Corp, 761 Main Ave, Norwalk, CT 06859	*Businessman*
Sorensen, Theodore C 345 Park Ave, New York, NY 10022	*Government Official*
Sorenson, Richard K 3393 Skyline Blvd, Reno, NV 89509	*WW II Marine Corps Hero (CMH)*
Sorlie, Don 15315 SE 44th Pl, Bellevue, WA 98006	*Test Pilot*
Soros, George %Soros Fund Mgmt, 10 Columbus Cir, New York, NY 10019	*Financier*
Sorsa, Kalevi Valtioneuvoston Kanslia, Aleksanteninkatu 3D, 00170 Helsinki 17, Finland	*Prime Minister, Finland*
Sorvino, Paul %Charter Mgmt, 9000 Sunset Blvd, #1112, Los Angeles, CA 90069	*Actor*
Sothern, Ann PO Box 2285, Ketchum, ID 83340	*Actress*
Soto, Jock %New York City Ballet, Lincoln Center Plz, New York, NY 10023	*Ballet Dancer*
Soto, Mario Joachs-Lachaustegui #42, Sur-Bani, Dominican Republic	*Baseball Player*
Soto, Talisa %Flick East/West Talents, 6671 Sunset Blvd, Los Angeles, CA 90028	*Model, Actress*
Sotomayor, Antonio 3 Le Roy Pl, San Francisco, CA 94109	*Artist*
Sottsass, Ettore, Jr Via Manzoni 14, 20121 Milan, Italy	*Industrial Designer*
Soul, David 2001 Hillcrest Rd, Los Angeles, CA 90068	*Actor*
Soul, Louise %Gage Group, 9255 Sunset Blvd, #515, Los Angeles, CA 90069	*Actress*
Soulages, Pierre 18 Rue des Trois-Portes, 75005 Paris, France	*Artist*
Sourrouille, Juan %Ministry of Economics, Buenos Aires, Argentina	*Government Official, Argentina*
Soutar, Dave %Professional Bowlers Assn, 1720 Merriman Rd, Akron, OH 44313	*Bowler*
Soutendijk, Renee %Lantz 888 7th Ave, #2500, New York, NY 10106	*Actress*
Souter, David H %US Supreme Court, 1 1st St NE, Washington, DC 20543	*Supreme Court Justice*
Southard, Frank A, Jr 4620 North Park Ave, Chevy Chase, MD 20015	*Economist*
Southern, Terry RFD, East Canaan, CT 06024	*Writer*
Souza, Francis Newton 148 W 67th St, New York, NY 10022	*Artist*
Souzay, Gerard 26 Rue Freycinet, 75116 Paris, France	*Singer*
Sovern, Michael I %Columbia University, President's Office, New York, NY 10027	*Educator*
Sowell, Arnold 651 Parkview Cir, Pacifica, CA 94404	*Track Athlete*
Sowell, Thomas %Hoover Institute, Stanford University, Stanford, CA 94305	*Economist*
Soyinka, Wole %University of Ife, Dramatic Arts Dept, Ile-Ife, Nigeria	*Nobel Literature Laureate*
Soyster, Harry E Director, Defense Intelligency Agency, Washington, DC 20301	*Army General*
Spacek, Sissy %Creative Artists Agency, 9830 Wilshire Blvd, Beverly Hills, CA 90212	*Actress*
Spacey, Kevin %Creative Artists Agency, 9830 Wilshire Blvd, Beverly Hills, CA 90212	*Actor*
Spader, James %International Creative Mgmt, 8899 Beverly Blvd, Los Angeles, CA 90048	*Actor*

S

Spaght – Spencer

Spaght, Monroe E *Businessman*
2 Lyall Mews, Belgravia, London SW1X 8DJ, England

Spahn, Warren *Baseball Player*
RR 2, Hartshorne, OK 74547

Spahr, Charles E *Businessman*
24075 Lyman Blvd, Shaker Heights, OH 44122

Spalti, Peter *Businessman*
%Sulzer Brothers Ltd, 8401 Winterhur, Switzerland

Spanarkel, Jim *Basketball Player*
1934 Harmon Cove Towers, Secaucus, NJ 07094

Spano, Joe *Actor*
%Susan Smith Assoc, 121 N San Vicente Blvd, Beverly Hills, CA 90211

Sparberg, L F W *Businessman*
%IBM Deutschland, Pascalstrasse 100, 7000 Stuttgart 80, Germany

Spark, Muriel *Writer*
%Harold Ober Agency, 40 E 49th St, New York, NY 10017

Sparks, Jack D *Businessman*
%Whirlpool Corp, 2000 US 33 N, Benton Harbor, MI 49022

Sparlis, Al *Football Player*
13206 Mindanao Way, Marina del Rey, CA 90292

Sparv, Camilla *Actress*
%Tisherman Agency, 6767 Forest Lawn Dr, #115, Los Angeles, CA 90068

Spassky, Boris *Chess Player*
%State Committee for Sports, Skatertny Pereulok 4, Moscow, Russia

Spear, Laurinda *Architect*
%Arquitectonica International, 2151 LeJeune Rd, Coral Gables, FL 33134

Spears, William D *Football Player*
202 Fairy Trl, Lookout Mountain, TN 37350

Specter, Arlen *Senator, PA*
3417 Warden Dr, Philadelphia, PA 19129

Spector, Elisabeth (Lisa) *Government Official*
%Resolution Trust Corp, 801 17th St NW, Washington, DC 20434

Spector, Phil *Record Company Executive*
%Phil Spector Intl, 686 S Arroyo Pkwy, #PH, Pasadena, CA 91105

Spedding, Frank H *Chemist, Physicist*
520 Oliver Cir, Ames, IA 50011

Speedie, Mac *Football Player*
2158-D Via Mariposa E, Laguna Hills, CA 92653

Speier, Chris *Baseball Player*
6114 E Montecito, Scottsdale, AZ 85251

Speight, Francis *Artist*
508 E 9th St, Greenville, NC 27834

Spelling, Aaron *Movie, Television Producer*
111 N Mapleton Dr, Los Angeles, CA 90024

Spellman, John D *Governor, WA*
%Carney Stephenson Badley Smith, 2300 Columbia Ctr, Seattle, WA 98104

Spence, Dave *Labor Leader*
%Horseshoers Union, Rt 2, Box 71-C, Englishtown, NJ 07726

Spence, Floyd D *Representative, SC*
PO Box 869, Lexington, SC 29072

Spence, Roger F *Religious Leader*
%Reformed Episcopal Church, 2001 Frederick Rd, Baltimore, MD 21228

Spence, Wallace *Swimmer*
20121 NE 15th Ave, Miami, FL 33179

Spencer, Donald C *Mathematician*
943 County Rd 204, Durango, CO 81301

Spencer, Edson W *Businessman*
%Honeywell Inc, Honeywell Plz, Minneapolis, MN 55408

Spencer, Elizabeth *Writer*
2300 St Mathieu, Montreal PQ, Canada

Spencer, F Gilman *Editor*
%Denver Post, 650 15th St, Denver, CO 80202

Spencer, Frank Cole *Surgeon, Educator*
560 1st Ave, New York, NY 10016

Spencer, John *Actor*
%"LA Law" Show, 20th Century Fox Studios, PO Box 900, Beverly Hills, CA 90213

Spencer, Melvin J *Religious Leader*
%Free Methodist Church, PO Box 535002, Winona Lake, IN 46590

Spencer, Susan *Commentator*
%CBS-TV, News Dept, 2020 "M" St NW, Washington, DC 20036

Spencer, Tim *Football Player*
%San Diego Chargers, 9449 Friars Rd, San Diego, CA 92108

Spencer, William I *Financier*
12 Beekman Pl, New York, NY 10022

Spencer-Devlin, Muffin *Golfer*
1561 S Congress Ave, #141, Delray Beach, FL 33455

Spender, Percy C *Judge*
Headingley House, 11 Wellington St, Woolhara, Sydney NSW 2025, Australia

Spender, Stephen *Writer*
15 Loudoun Rd, London NW8, England

Sperlich, Peter W *Political Scientist*
39 Adeline Dr, Walnut Creek, CA 94596

Sperry, Roger W *Nobel Medicine Laureate*
3625 Lombardy Rd, Pasadena, CA 91107

Spethmann, Dieter *Businessman*
Thyssen AG, Kaiser-Wilhelm-strasse 100, 4100 Duisburg 11, Germany

Spicer, William E, III *Physicist*
785 Mayfield Rd, Stanford, CA 94305

Spiegel, Abraham *Financier*
%Columbia Savings & Loan, 8840 Wilshire Blvd, Beverly Hills, CA 90211

Spiegel, Modie *Businessman*
%Spiegel Co, 175 E Delaware Pl, Chicago, IL 60611

Spielberg, David *Actor*
%Artists Agency, 10000 Santa Monica Blvd, #305, Los Angeles, CA 90067

Spielberg, Steven *Movie Director*
%Amblin Entertainment, 100 Universal City Plz, #477, Universal City, CA 91608

Spielman, Chris *Football Player*
%Detroit Lions, Silverdome, 1200 Featherstone Rd, Pontiac, MI 48057

Spielvogel, Carl *Businessman*
%Backer & Spielvogel Inc, 11 W 42nd St, New York, NY 10036

Spier, Peter *Artist*
Warden Cliff Rd, PO Box 210, Shoreham, NY 11786

Spigelmire, Michael F *Army General*
Commanding General, VIII Corps, US Army Europe/7th Army, APO, AE 09107

Spilhaus, Athelstan F *Meteorologist, Oceanographer*
PO Box 1063, Middlesburg, VA 22117

Spillane, Mickey *Writer*
%General Delivery, Murrells Inlet, SC 29576

Spiller, Robert J *Financier*
%Boston Five Cents Savings Bank, 10 School St, Boston, MA 02108

Spilman, Robert H *Businessman*
%Bassett Furniture Industries, PO Box 626, Bassett, VA 24055

Spindler, Marc *Football Player*
%Detroit Lions, Silverdome, 1200 Featherstone Rd, Pontiac, MI 48057

Spinetti, Victor *Actor*
52 Manchester St, London W1, England

Spinks, Leon *Boxer*
%Ditka's Restaurant, 223 W Ontario, Chicago, IL 60610

Spinks, Michael *Boxer*
%Centerville Rd, Wilmington, DE 19808

Spinola, Antonio S R de *President, Portugal*
%Ministerio de Defesa, Lisbon, Portugal

Spitz, Mark *Swimmer*
9171 Wilshire Blvd, #530, Beverly Hills, CA 90212

Spitzer, Lyman, Jr *Astronomer*
659 Lake Dr, Princeton, NJ 08540

Spivak, Lawrence *Broadcast Producer, Commentator*
Wardman Towers, 2600 Woodley Rd NW, Washington, DC 20008

Spivakovsky, Tossy *Concert Violinist*
29 Burnham Hill, Westport, CT 06880

Splittorff, Paul *Baseball Player*
4204 Hickory Ln, Blue Spring, MO 64015

S

Spock – St Laurent

Spock, Benjamin *Physician, Social Activist*
General Delivery, Camden, ME 04843

Spoehr, Alexander *Anthropologist*
2548 Makiki Heights Dr, Honolulu, HI 96822

Spohr, Arnold Theodore *Ballet Director*
%Royal Winnipeg Ballet, 289 Portage Ave, Winnipeg MA R3B 2B4, Canada

Spooner, John *Writer, Stockbroker*
%Houghton-Mifflin Co, 666 3rd Ave, New York, NY 10017

Spoor, William H *Businessman*
%Pillsbury Co, 200 S 6th St, Minneapolis, MN 55402

Sporck, Charles E *Businessman*
%National Semiconductor Corp, 2900 Semiconductor Dr, Santa Clara, CA 95051

Spradlin, G D *Actor*
%Gersh Agency, 232 N Canon Dr, Beverly Hills, CA 90210

Sprague, E Russell *Businessman*
%Tambrands Inc, 10 Delaware Dr, Lake Success, NY 11042

Sprague, George F *Research Agronomist*
2212 S Lynn, Urbana, IL 61801

Sprague, Peter J *Businessman*
%National Semiconductor Corp, 2900 Semiconductor Dr, Santa Clara, CA 95052

Sprague, William W, Jr *Businessman*
%Savannah Foods & Industries, PO Box 339, Savannah, GA 31402

Spratt, John M, Jr *Representative, SC*
%House of Representatives, Washington, DC 20515

Spring, Sherwood C *Astronaut*
%ASPO, DAMO/FDX, 2810 Old Lee Hwy, Fairfax, VA 22031

Springer, Neil A *Businessman*
%International Harvester Co, 401 N Michigan Ave, Chicago, IL 60611

Springer, Robert C *Astronaut*
%Boeing Aerospace/Electronics, MS JRO5, 499 Boeing Blvd, Huntsville, AL 35824

Springer, William H *Businessman*
%Ameritek Corp, 225 W Randolph St, Chicago, IL 60606

Springer, William L *Representative, IL*
900 W Park, Champaign, IL 61820

Springfield, Rick *Actor, Singer*
15456 Cabrito Rd, Van Nuys, CA 91406

Springsteen, Bruce *Singer*
2227 Mandeville Canyon, Los Angeles, CA 90049

Sprinkel, Beryl W *Government Official*
1705 Brookwood Dr, Flossmoor, IL 60422

Sprouse, James M *Judge*
%US Court of Appeals, PO Box 401, Lewisburg, WV 24901

Spurrier, Steve *Football Player, Coach*
%University of Florida, Athletic Dept, PO Box 14485, Gainesville, FL 32604

Squier, Billy *Singer*
145 Central Park West, New York, NY 10023

Squires, John *Computer Disc Drive Engineer*
%Conner Peripherals, 3081 Zanker Rd, San Jose, CA 95134

Sri Chinmoy *Religious Leader*
%Peace Concert, PO Box 20380, New York, NY 10017

St Cyr, Lili *Exotic Dancer*
624 N Plymouth Blvd, #7, Los Angeles, CA 90004

St George, Nicholas *Businessman*
%Oakwood Homes Corp, 2225 S Holden Rd, Greensboro, NC 27407

St George, William R *Navy Admiral*
862 San Antonio Pl, San Diego, CA 92106

St Germain, Fernand J *Representative, RI*
121 Woodland Rd, Woonsocket, RI 02895

St James, Lyn *Auto Racing Driver*
%MotorSports, 175 SW 20th Way, Dania, FL 33004

St John, Bill D *Businessman*
%Dresser Industries, 1505 Elm St, Dallas, TX 75221

St Juan, Olga *Actress*
%O'Brien, 12100 Sunset Blvd, #2, Los Angeles, CA 90025

St Laurent, Yves *Fashion Designer*
5 Ave du Marceau, 75016 Paris, France

Staats, Elmer B — *Government Official*
5011 Overlook Rd NW, Washington, DC 20016

Stabler, Kenny — *Football Player*
%Kenny Stabler Sporting Goods Co, PO Box 382, Selma, AL 36701

Stack, Allen M — *Swimmer*
PO Box 76, Honolulu, HI 96810

Stack, Robert — *Actor*
321 St Pierre Rd, Los Angeles, CA 90024

Stacy, Hollis — *Golfer*
%Ladies Professional Golf Assn, 2570 Volusia Ave, #B, Daytona Beach, FL 32114

Stadler, Craig — *Golfer*
%Professional Golfers Assn, PO Box 109601, Palm Beach Gardens, FL 33410

Stadtman, Earl R — *Biochemist*
16907 Redland-Derwood Rd, Derwood, MD 20855

Stafford, Harrison — *Football Player*
Rt 1, Box 216-H, Edna, TX 77957

Stafford, Jo — *Singer*
2339 Century Hill, Los Angeles, CA 90067

Stafford, John M — *Businessman*
%Pillsbury Co, 200 S 6th St, Minneapolis, MN 55402

Stafford, Nancy — *Actress*
%Harris & Goldberg Agency, 1999 Ave of Stars, #2850, Los Angeles, CA 90067

Stafford, Robert T — *Governor/Senator, VT*
64 Litchfield Ave, Rutland, VT 05701

Stafford, Thomas P — *Astronaut, Air Force General*
Stafford Burke Hecker, 1006 Cameron St, Alexandria, VA 22314

Stager, Gus — *Swimming Coach*
%University of Michigan, Athletic Dept, Ann Arbor, MI 48104

Stahl, Lesley — *Commentator*
%CBS-TV, News Dept, 51 W 52nd St, New York, NY 10019

Stahle, Hans — *Businessman*
%Alfa-Laval, PO Box 12150, 102 24, Stockhom, Sweden

Stahr, Elvis J, Jr — *Conservationist*
Martin Dale, Greenwich, CT 06830

Staley, Dawn — *Basketball Player*
%University of Virginia, Athletic Dept, Charlottesville, VA 22906

Staley, Delbert C — *Businessman*
%NYNEX Corp, 335 Madison Ave, New York, NY 10017

Stallings, Gene — *Football Coach*
%University of Alabama, Athletic Dept, Tuscaloosa, AL 35487

Stallings, George — *Religious Leader*
%African American Catholic Congregation, 1134 11th St NW, Washington, DC 20001

Stallings, Richard — *Representative, ID*
%House of Representatives, Washington, DC 20515

Stallone, Sylvester — *Actor, Director*
%White Eagle Enterprises, 8800 Sunset Blvd, Los Angeles, CA 90067

Stallworth, John — *Football Player*
%General Delivery, Brownsboro, AL 35741

Stalman, Ria — *Track Athlete*
%Olympic Committee, Surinamestrasse 33, 2585 La Harve, Netherlands

Stamos, Theodoros — *Artist*
37 W 83rd St, New York, NY 10024

Stamp, Terence — *Actor*
%Plant & Froggatt, 4 Windmill St, London W1, England

Stamper, Malcolm T — *Businessman, Aviation Engineer*
%Boeing Co, 7755 E Marginal Way S, Seattle, WA 98108

Stander, Lionel — *Actor*
13176 Boca de Canon Ln, Los Angeles, CA 90049

Stanfel, Dick — *Football Player, Coach*
%Chicago Bears, 250 N Washington Rd, Lake Forest, IL 60045

Stanfill, Bill — *Football Player*
2307 Tara Dr, Albany, GA 31707

Stanfill, Dennis C — *Entertainment Executive*
%MGM-Pathe Communications, 10202 W Washington Blvd, Culver City, CA 90230

Staniar, Burton B — *Businessman*
%Westinghouse Broadcasting Co, 90 Park Ave, New York, NY 10016

S

Stankovic – Starr

Stankovic, Borislav *Basketball Executive*
%FIBA, 19 Rugendasstrasse, 8000 Munich 71, Germany

Stanky, Eddie *Baseball Manager*
2100 Spring Hill Rd, Mobile, AL 36607

Stanley, Allan H *Hockey Player*
%Allan Stanley Hockey Camp, 15 Four Winds Dr, Toronto ON, Canada

Stanley, David *Businessman*
%Payless Cashways Inc, 2301 Main, Kansas City, MO 64141

Stanley, Florence *Actress*
%Artists Agency, 10000 Santa Monica Blvd, #305, Los Angeles, CA 90067

Stanley, Frank *Cinematographer*
PO Box 2230, Los Angeles, CA 90078

Stanley, Kim *Actress*
888 7th Ave, #2500, New York, NY 10106

Stanley, Marianne Crawford *Basketball Coach*
%University of Southern California, Heritage Hall, Los Angeles, CA 90089

Stanley, Ralph *Bluegrass Guitarist*
380 Lexington Ave, #119, New York, NY 10017

Stanley, Steven M *Paleobiologist*
1110 Bellemore Rd, Baltimore, MD 21210

Stanley, Walter *Football Player*
%Washington Redskins, Dulles Airport, PO Box 17247, Washington, DC 20041

Stans, Maurice H *Secretary, Commerce*
211 S Orange Grove Ave, Pasadena, CA 91105

Stantis, Scott *Editorial Cartoonist*
%Memphis Commerical-Appeal, 495 Union Ave, Memphis, TN 38101

Stanton, Donald S *Educator*
%Oglethorpe University, President's Office, Atlanta, GA 30319

Stanton, Frank *Broadcast Executive*
10 E 56th St, New York, NY 10022

Stanton, Harry Dean *Actor*
14527 Mulholland Dr, Los Angeles, CA 90024

Stanton, Jeff *Motorcycle Racing Rider*
1137 Athens Rd, Sherwood, MI 49089

Stapleton, Jean *Actress*
635 Perugia Way, Los Angeles, CA 90024

Stapleton, Maureen *Actress*
15 W 70th St, New York, NY 10023

Stapleton, Walter K *Judge*
%US Court of Appeals, Lockbox 33, 844 King St, Wilmington, DE 19801

Stapp, John P *Aerospace Scientist*
%New Mexico Research Institute, PO Box 553, Alamogordo, NM 88310

Starbuck, Jo Jo *Figure Skater*
%Leonard Glusman, 1925 Century Park East, #800, Los Angeles, CA 90067

Stargell, Willie *Baseball Player*
113 Ashley Pl, Stone Mountain, GA 30083

Stark, Fortney H (Pete) *Representative, CA*
%House of Representatives, Washington, DC 20515

Stark, Jack L *Educator*
%Claremont McKenna College, President's Office, Claremont, CA 91711

Stark, Jurgen K *Religious Leader*
%Church of Christ Scientist, 175 Huntington Ave, Boston, MA 02115

Stark, Ray *Movie Producer*
232 S Mapleton Dr, Los Angeles, CA 90024

Stark, Rohn *Football Player*
%Indianapolis Colts, 7001 W 56th St, Indianapolis, IN 46254

Starker, Janos *Concert Cellist*
1241 Winfield Rd, Bloomington, IN 47401

Starling, James D *Army General*
DCinC, US Transportation Command, Scott Air Force Base, IL 62225

Starnes, Vaughn A *Surgeon*
%Stanford Univ Medical Ctr, Heart-Lung Transplant Program, Stanford, CA 94305

Starr, Albert *Cardiac Surgeon*
5050 SW Patton Rd, Portland, OR 97221

Starr, Bart *Football Player*
%Real Asset Management Grp, 143 Union Blvd, #900, Lakewood, CO 80228

Starr, Blaze *Exotic Dancer*
%Carrolltown Mall, Eldersburg, MD 21784
Starr, Isaac *Medical Scientist*
%University Hospital, 36th & Spence, Philadelphia, PA 19104
Starr, Kay *Singer*
223 Ashdale Ave, Los Angeles, CA 90077
Starr, Kenneth W *Government Official, Judge*
%Solictor General's Office, Justice Department, Washington, DC 20530
Starr, Leonard *Cartoonist (Annie, Kelly Green)*
46 Post Rd E, Westport, CT 06880
Starr, Ringo *Singer (Beatles), Actor*
"Rocca Bella," 24 Ave Princess Grace, Monte Carlo, Monaco
Starzl, Thomas E *Physician*
%University of Pittsburgh, Medical School, Pittsburgh, PA 15261
Stassen, Harold E *Governor, MN*
431 E Haskell St, #1, West St Paul, MN 55118
Stastny, Anton *Hockey Player*
%Quebec Nordiques, 2205 Ave du Colisee, Charlesbourg PQ G1L 4W7, Canada
Stastny, Peter *Hockey Player*
%New Jersey Devils, Meadowlands Arena, East Rutherford, NJ 07073
Stata, Ray *Businessman*
%Analog Devices Inc, Rt 1, Industrial Park, Norwood, MA 02062
Station, Larry *Football Player*
%Pittsburgh Steelers, Three Rivers Stadium, Pittsburgh, PA 15212
Stattin, Eric *Financier*
%Florida Federal Savings & Loan, PO Box 1509, St Petersburg, FL 33731
Staub, Rusty *Baseball Player*
1271 3rd Ave, New York, NY 10021
Staubach, Roger *Football Player*
%Staubach Co, 6750 LBJ Fwy, #1100, Dallas, TX 75240
Stautner, Ernest A *Football Player; Coach*
%Denver Broncos, 13655 E Dove Valley Pkwy, Englewood, CO 80112
Stayskal, Wayne *Editorial Cartoonist*
%Chicago Tribune, 435 N Michigan Ave, Chicago, IL 60611
Stead, Jerre L *Businessman*
%AT&T Communications, 295 N Maple Ave, Basking Ridge, NJ 07920
Steadman, J Richard *Orthopedic Surgeon*
1139 2nd, South Lake Tahoe, CA 95706
Stearns, H Myrl *Businessman*
%Varian Assoc, 611 Hansen Way, Palo Alto, CA 94303
Stebbins, George L *Geneticist*
1009 Ovejas Ave, Davis, CA 95616
Steber, Eleanor *Opera Singer*
PO Box 342, Port Jefferson, NY 11777
Stecher, Theodore P *Astronomer*
%UIT Project, Goddard Space Flight Ctr, Greenbelt, MD 20771
Steegmuller, Francis *Writer*
200 E 66th St, New York, NY 10021
Steel, Danielle *Writer*
PO Box 1637, Murray Hill Station, New York, NY 10156
Steel, David M S *Government Official, England*
Cherry Dene, Ettrick Bridge, Selkirkshire, Scotland
Steel, Dawn *Movie Producer*
%Walt Disney Studios, 500 S Buena Vista St, Burbank, CA 91521
Steele, Charles G *Businessman*
%Deloitte Touche Co, 1114 Ave of Americas, New York, NY 10036
Steele, Danielle *Writer*
%Morton Janklow Assoc, 598 Madison Ave, New York, NY 10022
Steele, Richard *Boxing Referee*
5009 Long View Dr, Las Vegas, NV 89120
Steele, Roderick M *Businessman*
%Potlatch Corp, 1 Maritime Plz, San Francisco, CA 94111
Steele, Tommy *Singer, Actor*
%International Creative Mgmt, 388-98 Oxford St, London W1N 9HE, England
Steen, Thomas *Hockey Player*
%Winnipeg Jets, 15-1430 Maroons Rd, Winnipeg MB R3G 0L5, Canada

S

Steenburgen – Steinkraus

Steenburgen, Mary — *Actress*
%International Creative Mgmt, 8899 Beverly Blvd, Los Angeles, CA 90048

Steere, William C — *Businessman*
%Pfizer Inc, 235 E 42nd St, New York, NY 10017

Stefanich, Jim — *Bowler*
%Professional Bowlers Assn, 1720 Merriman Rd, Akron, OH 44313

Steffy, Joe — *Football Player*
%Broadway Buick, 259 Broadway, Newburgh, NY 12550

Stegemeier, Richard J — *Businessman*
%Unocal Corp, 1201 W 5th St, Los Angeles, CA 90051

Steger, Joseph A — *Educator*
%University of Cincinnati, President's Office, Cincinnati, OH 45221

Steger, Will — *Arctic Explorer*
%Think South, PO Box 4097, St Paul, MN 55104

Stegner, Wallace — *Writer*
13456 S Fork Ln, Los Altos, CA 94022

Steig, William — *Writer, Artist*
Rt 1, Box KH-2, Kent, CT 06757

Steiger, Rod — *Actor*
%Gersh Agency, 232 N Canon Dr, Beverly Hills, CA 90210

Steigerwalt, Gary — *Concert Pianist*
%Pro Musicis Foundation, 1351 Ocean Front Walk, #203, Santa Monica, CA 90401

Stein, Herbert — *Government Official, Economist*
2500 Virginia Ave NW, Washington, DC 20037

Stein, Horst — *Conductor*
%Mariedi Anders Mgmt, 535 El Camino Del Mar, San Francisco, CA 94121

Stein, Howard — *Financier*
%Dreyfuss Corp, 767 5th Ave, New York, NY 10022

Stein, Joseph — *Playwright*
1130 Park Ave, New York, NY 10028

Stein, Robert — *Editor*
%McCall's Magazine, 230 Park Ave, New York, NY 10169

Steinbach, Alice — *Journalist*
%Baltimore Sun, 501 N Calvert St, Baltimore, MD 21278

Steinberg, David — *Comedian*
4539 Gloria Ave, Encino, CA 91346

Steinberg, Leigh — *Sports Attorney*
2727 Dunleer Pl, Los Angeles, CA 90064

Steinberg, Leo — *Art Critic*
%University of Pennsylvania, Art History Dept, Philadelphia, PA 19104

Steinberg, Robert M — *Businessman*
%Reliance Insurance, 919 3rd Ave, New York, NY 10022

Steinberg, Saul — *Artist, Cartoonist*
%New Yorker Magazine, 25 W 43rd St, New York, NY 10036

Steinberg, Saul P — *Businessman*
%Reliance Group Holdings, 55 E 52nd St, New York, NY 10055

Steinberg, William R — *Labor Leader*
%American Radio Assn, 26 Journal Sq, #1501, Jersey City, NJ 07306

Steinberger, Jack — *Nobel Physics Laureate*
21 Chemin des Merles, 1213 Ouex, Geneva, Switzerland

Steinbrenner, George M, III — *Baseball Executive*
512 Florida Ave, Tampa, FL 33601

Steinem, Gloria — *Social Activist, Editor*
%Ms Magazine, 230 Park Ave, New York, NY 10169

Steiner, George — *Writer*
32 Barrow Rd, Cambridge, England

Steiner, Jeffrey J — *Businessman*
%Fairchild Corp, 3800 W Service Blvd, Chantilly, VA 22021

Steinhardt, Michael — *Financier*
%Steinhardt Partners, 605 3rd Ave, New York, NY 10158

Steinhardt, Richard — *Biologist*
%University of California, Biology Dept, Berkeley, CA 94720

Steinhart, Ronald G — *Financier*
%InterFirst Corp, 1201 Elm St, Dallas, TX 75202

Steinkraus, Bill — *Equestrian Rider*
PO Box 3038, Noroton, CT 06820

Steinkuhler, Dean *Football Player*
%Houston Oilers, 6910 Fannin St, Houston, TX 77030

Steinsaltz, Adin *Religious Leader*
%Israel Institute for Talmudic Publications, Box 1458, Jerusalem, Israel

Steinseifer, Carrie *Swimmer*
11859 N 80th Pl, Scottsdale, AZ 85260

Stella, Frank *Artist*
17 Jones St, New York, NY 10021

Stempel, Ernest E *Businessman*
%American International Grp, 70 Pine St, New York, NY 10270

Stempel, Robert C *Businessman*
%General Motors Corp, 3044 W Grand Blvd, Detroit, MI 48202

Stenerud, Jan *Football Player*
%Howard Needles Tammen Bergendoff, 9200 Ward Pkwy, Kansas City, MO 64141

Stengel, Louis C, Jr *Businessman*
%Manhattan Industries, 1155 Ave of Americas, New York, NY 10036

Stenholm, Charles W *Representative, TX*
%House of Representatives, Washington, DC 20515

Stenmark, Ingemar *Skier*
%Skiing Magazine, 1 Park Ave, New York, NY 10016

Stennis, John C *Senator, MS*
%General Delivery, DeKalb, MS 39328

Stenzel, Edwin L *Businessman*
%BASF Corp, 9 Campus Dr, Parsippany, NJ 07054

Stepanian, Ian *Financier*
%Bank of Boston Corp, 100 Federal St, Boston, MA 02110

Stepanova-Prozumenshikova, Galina *Swimmer*
%Olympic Committee, Luzhnetzkaya Nab 8, Moscow, Russia

Stephan, George P *Businessman*
%Kollmorgen Corp, 10 Mill Pond Ln, Simsbury, CT 06070

Stephanie *Princess, Monaco*
%Palace Princier, Monaco-Ville, Monaco

Stephens, Helen *Track Athlete*
11 Thacker Ct, Florissant, MO 63031

Stephens, James M *Government Official*
%National Labor Relations Board, 1717 Pennsylvania NW, Washington, DC 20570

Stephens, Olin James, II *Naval Architect, Yacht Designer*
%Sparkman & Stephens, 79 Madison Ave, New York, NY 10016

Stephens, Robert *Actor*
%Film Rights Ltd, 113 Wardour St, London W1, England

Stephens, Sanford (Sandy) *Football Player*
1930 E 86th St, #111, Bloomington, MN 55420

Stephens, Stanley *Governor, MT*
%Governor's Office, State Capitol, Helena, MT 59620

Stephens, W Thomas *Businessman*
%Manville Corp, Ken-Caryl Ranch, Denver, CO 80217

Stephens, Woody *Thoroughbred Racing Trainer*
98 Scherer Blvd, Franklin Square, NY 11010

Stephenson, Jan *Golfer*
6300 Ridglea Pl, #1118, Fort Worth, TX 76116

Steppling, John *Playwright*
%William Morris Agency, 151 El Camino, Beverly Hills, CA 90212

Sterban, Richard *Singer (Oak Ridge Boys)*
%Oak Ridge Boys, 329 Rockland Rd, Hendersonville, TN 37075

Sterkel, Jill *Swimmer*
%Indiana University, Athletic Dept, Bloomington, IN 47405

Sterling, Philip *Actor*
4114 Benedict Canyon Dr, Sherman Oaks, CA 91423

Sterling, Robert *Actor*
121 S Bentley Ave, Los Angeles, CA 90049

Stern, David H *Basketball Executive*
%National Basketball Assn, Olympic Tower, 645 5th Ave, New York, NY 10022

Stern, Ernest *Financier*
%International Reconstruction Bank, 2323 Wyoming Ave NW, Washington, DC 20008

Stern, Gary *Financier*
%Federal Reserve Bank, 250 Marquette Ave, Minneapolis, MN 55480

Stern, Howard *Entertainer*
%WXRK-FM Radio, 600 Madison Ave, New York, NY 10022
Stern, Isaac *Concert Violinist*
211 Central Park West, New York, NY 10024
Stern, Leonard B *Television, Movie Producer*
1709 Angelo Dr, Beverly Hills, CA 90210
Stern, Leonard N *Businessman*
%Hartz Mountain Industries, 700 S 4th St, Harrison, NJ 07029
Stern, Lillibet *Actress*
8322 Beverly Blvd, #202, Los Angeles, CA 90048
Stern, Richard *Writer*
%University of Chicago, English Dept, Chicago, IL 60637
Stern, Robert A M *Architect*
211 W 61st St, New York, NY 10023
Sternbach, Leo H *Medical Chemist*
10 Woodmont Rd, Upper Montclair, NJ 07043
Sternecky, Neal *Cartoonist (Pogo)*
%Los Angeles Times Syndicate, Times Mirror Sq, Los Angeles, CA 90053
Sternhagen, Frances *Actress*
152 Sutton Manor Rd, New Rochelle, NY 10805
Steuber, Robert J *Football Player*
2 Barrett Woods Dr, RR 1, Manchester, MO 63011
Stevens, Allen L *Businessman*
%McLean Industries, 660 Madison Ave, New York, NY 10021
Stevens, Andrew *Actor*
9612 Arby Dr, Beverly Hills, CA 90210
Stevens, Cat (Yusef Islam) *Singer, Songwriter*
27 Curzon St, London W1, England
Stevens, Connie *Actress*
9551 Cherokee Ln, Beverly Hills, CA 90210
Stevens, Craig *Actor*
1308 N Flores St, Los Angeles, CA 90069
Stevens, Dorit *Actress, Model*
11524 Amanda Dr, Studio City, CA 91604
Stevens, Fisher *Actor*
%Triad Artists, 10100 Santa Monica Blvd, #1600, Los Angeles, CA 90067
Stevens, George, Jr *Movie Producer*
%New Liberty Productions, Kennedy Center, Washington, DC 20566
Stevens, Gordon K G *Businessman*
%Lever Brothers Co, 390 Park Ave, New York, NY 10022
Stevens, John Paul *Supreme Court Justice*
%US Supreme Court, 1 1st St NE, Washington, DC 20543
Stevens, Joseph *Businessman*
%Whittaker Corp, 12838 Saticoy St, North Hollywood, CA 91605
Stevens, Kaye *Singer, Actress*
145 N Almont Dr, Los Angeles, CA 90048
Stevens, Ray *Singer, Songwriter*
%Ahab Music, 1708 Grand Ave, Nashville, TN 37212
Stevens, Rise *Opera Singer*
930 5th Ave, New York, NY 10021
Stevens, Roger L *Theatre Producer*
1686 34th St NW, Washington, DC 20007
Stevens, Scott *Hockey Player*
%New Jersey Devils, Meadowlands Arena, East Rutherford, NJ 07073
Stevens, Shadoe *Actor*
%Agency for Performing Arts, 9000 Sunset Blvd, #1200, Los Angeles, CA 90069
Stevens, Stella *Actress*
2180 Coldwater Canyon Rd, Beverly Hills, CA 90210
Stevens, Theodore F *Senator, AK*
PO Box 879, Anchorage, AK 99510
Stevens, Warren *Actor*
14324 Killion St, Van Nuys, CA 91401
Stevens, Whitney *Businessman*
%J P Stevens Co, 1185 Ave of Americas, New York, NY 10036
Stevens, William E *Businessman*
%Black & Decker Manufacturing Co, 701 E Joppa Rd, Towson, MD 21204

Stevenson, Adlai E, III *Senator, IL*
%Mayer Brown Platt, 231 S LaSalle St, Chicago, IL 60604
Stevenson, McLean *Actor*
%William Morris Agency, 151 El Camino, Beverly Hills, CA 90212
Stevenson, Parker *Actor*
4875 Louis Ave, Encino, CA 91316
Stevenson, Teofilo *Boxer*
%Olympic Committee, Zona Postale 4, Calle 13, #601, Havana, Cuba
Stever, H Guyford *Aeronautical, Space Engineer*
1528 33rd St NW, Washington, DC 20007
Steward, H Leighton *Businessman*
%Louisiana Land & Exploration Co, 225 Baronne St, New Orleans, LA 70112
Stewart of Fulham, R Michael M *Government Official, England*
Combe, Newbury, Berks, England
Stewart, Catherine Mary *Actress*
%Gage Group, 9255 Sunset Blvd, #515, Los Angeles, CA 90069
Stewart, Charles E *Businessman*
%Maxus Energy Corp, 717 N Harwood St, Dallas, TX 75201
Stewart, Dave *Baseball Player*
817 Manchester Ct, Claremont, CA 91711
Stewart, Donald W *Senator, AL*
9003 Teddy Rae Ct, Springfield, VA 22152
Stewart, Douglas Day *Screenwriter*
%Writer's Guild, 8955 Sunset Blvd, Los Angeles, CA 90048
Stewart, Elaine *Actress*
1011 N Roxbury Dr, Beverly Hills, CA 90210
Stewart, Gary *Singer*
PO Box 25371, Charlotte, NC 28212
Stewart, Jackie *Auto Racing Driver*
24 Rte de Divonne, 1260 Nyon, Switzerland
Stewart, James E *Businessman*
%Lone Star Industries, 1 Greenwich Plz, Greenwich, CT 06836
Stewart, Jimmy *Actor*
918 N Roxbury Dr, Beverly Hills, CA 90210
Stewart, Martha *Writer*
%General Delivery, Westport, CT 06881
Stewart, Mary *Writer*
79 Moringside Park, Edinburgh EH10 5EZ, Scotland
Stewart, Melvin, Jr *Swimmer*
1311 Lake Lauden, Knoxville, TN 37916
Stewart, Norm *Basketball Coach*
%University of Missouri, Athletic Dept, Columbia, MO 65211
Stewart, Patrick *Actor*
%Boyack, 9 Cork St, London W1, England
Stewart, Payne *Golfer*
%Leader Enterprises, 390 N Orange Ave, #2600, Orlando, FL 32801
Stewart, Peggy *Actress*
11139 Hortense St, North Hollywood, CA 91602
Stewart, Raymond A, Jr *Businessman*
%Yellow Freight System of Delaware, 10990 Roe Ave, Overland Park, KS 66207
Stewart, Redd *Songwriter, Singer*
%Tessier, 264 Old Hickory Blvd, Madison, TN 37115
Stewart, Robert F *Businessman*
%IC Industries, 111 E Wacker Dr, Chicago, IL 60601
Stewart, Robert L *Astronaut, Army General*
%Hq US Space Command, Code SPJ5, Peterson Air Force Base, CO 80914
Stewart, Robert W *Businessman*
%Primark Corp, 8251 Greensboro Dr, McLean, VA 22102
Stewart, Rod *Singer, Songwriter*
12824 Evanston St, Los Angeles, CA 90049
Stewart, Russell L *Financier*
%Home Federal Bank of Florida, 1901 Central Ave, St Petersburg, FL 33713
Stewart, Thomas *Opera Singer*
%Columbia Artists Mgmt Inc, 165 W 57th St, New York, NY 10019
Stewart, Thomas D *Physical Anthropologist*
1191 Crest Ln, McLean, VA 22101

Stibitz, George R *Computer Scientist*
Rt 3, Box 552, Lymne, NH 03768

Stich, Michael *Tennis Player*
850 Jahre, Elmshorn, Germany

Stich, Otto *President, Switzerland*
%President's Office, Bern, Switzerland

Sticht, J Paul *Businessman*
%RJR Nabisco Inc, Reynolds Blvd, Winston-Salem, NC 27102

Stickel, Fred A *Publisher*
%Portland Oregonian, 1320 SW Broadway, Portland, OR 97201

Stickney, Dorothy *Actress*
13 E 94th St, New York, NY 10023

Stieb, Dave *Baseball Player*
1960 Jeannie Ln, Gilroy, CA 95020

Stieber, Tamar *Journalist*
%Albuquerque Journal, 717 Silver Ave SW, Albuquerque, NM 87103

Stiers, David Ogden *Actor*
3827 Rhonda Vista, Los Angeles, CA 90027

Stigwood, Robert *Movie, Theater, Music Producer*
146 Central Park South, New York, NY 10019

Stilgoe, Richard *Lyricist*
%Noel Gray Artists, 24 Denmark St, London WC2H 8NJ, England

Still, Eric *Football Player*
%Houston Oilers, PO Box 1516, Houston, TX 77030

Stiller, Jerry *Comedian*
118 Riverside Dr, #5-A, New York, NY 10024

Stillings, Floyd *Rodeo Performer*
2118 S Baldwin Ave, Arcadia, CA 91006

Stillwell, Bermar S *Businessman*
%Gates Learjet Corp, 1255 E Aero Park Blvd, Tucson, AZ 85734

Stilwell, Richard *Opera Singer*
1969 Rockingham, McLean, VA 22101

Stine, Jack W *Businessman*
%Northern Indiana Public Service Co, 5265 Hohman Ave, Hammond, IN 46320

Stine, Richard *Editorial Cartoonist*
PO Box 4699, Rolling Bay, WA 98061

Stiner, Carl W *Army General*
CinC, US Special Operations Command, MacDill Air Force Base, FL 33608

Sting (Gordon Summer) *Singer, Actor*
2 The Grove, Highgate Village, London N16, England

Stingley, Darryl *Football Player*
%New England Patriots, Sullivan Stadium, Foxboro, MA 02035

Stinson, George A *Businessman*
420 Oliver Rd, Sewickley, PA 15143

Stiritz, William P *Businessman*
%Ralston Purina Co, Checkerboard Sq, St Louis, MO 63164

Stirling, David *WW II Army Commando Hero*
22 S Audley St, London W1, England

Stirling, Linda *Actress*
3760 Wrightwood, North Hollywood, CA 91604

Stitzlein, Lorraine *Bowling Executive*
%Professional Bowlers Assn, 1720 Merriman Rd, Akron, OH 44313

Stock, Barbara *Actress*
13421 Cheltenham Dr, Sherman Oaks, CA 91423

Stock, V N *Businessman*
%Canadian Packers, 95 St Clair Ave W, Toronto ON M4V 1P2, Canada

Stockdale, James B *Vietnam War Navy Hero (CMH), Admiral*
%Stanford University, Hoover Institute, Stanford, CA 94305

Stockhausen, Karlheinz *Composer*
%Studio fur Elektronische Musik, Wallrafplatz 5, Cologne, Germany

Stockman, David A *Government Official, Financier*
%Salomon Brothers, 1 New York Plz, New York, NY 10004

Stockton, Dave *Golfer*
%Casa de Golf, 4812 Lakeview Canyon Rd, Westlake Village, CA 91361

Stockton, Dick *Sportscaster*
%CBS TV, Sports Dept, 51 W 52nd St, New York, NY 10019

Stockton, John *Basketball Player*
%Utah Jazz, 5 Triad Ctr, Salt Lake City, UT 84180

Stockton, Richard L *Tennis Player*
%US Tennis Assn, 1212 Ave of Americas, New York, NY 10036

Stockwell, Dean *Actor*
%Susan Smith Assoc, 121 N San Vicente Blvd, Beverly Hills, CA 90211

Stockwell, Guy *Actor*
%Dade/Rosen/Schultz Agency, 11846 Ventura Blvd, #100, Studio City, CA 91604

Stoddard, Brandon *Television Executive*
%ABC Entertainment, 2040 Ave of Stars, Los Angeles, CA 90067

Stokely, William B, III *Businessman*
%Stokely-Van Camp Inc, 941 N Meridan St, Indianapolis, IN 46206

Stokes of Leyland, Donald G *Businessman*
7 Egerton Pl, London SW3 2EF, England

Stokes, Carl B *Mayor*
%Stokes & Green, Leader Bldg, #620, Cleveland, OH 44114

Stokes, Colin *Businessman*
2701 Reynolds Dr, Winston-Salem, NC 27104

Stokes, Dewey R *Labor Leader*
%Fraternal Order of Police, 2100 Gardner Ln, Louisville, KY 40205

Stokes, Louis *Representative, OH*
%House of Representatives, Washington, DC 20515

Stokkan, Bill *Auto Racing Executive*
%Champion Auto Racing Teams, 390 Enterprise Ct, Bloomfield Hills, MI 48302

Stolle, Frederick S *Tennis Player*
%Turnberry Isle Yacht & Racquet Club, 19735 Turnberry Way, North Miami, FL 33180

Stolley, Richard B *Editor*
%Time Inc, Rockefeller Ctr, New York, NY 10020

Stolojan, Theodor *Prime Minister, Romania*
%Prime Minister's Office, Bucharest, Romania

Stoltenberg, Gerhard *Government Official, West Germany*
Grauheindorferstrasse 108, 5300 Bonn 1, Germany

Stoltz, Eric *Actor*
5200 Lankershim Blvd, #260, North Hollywood, CA 91601

Stoltzman, Richard *Concert Clarinetist*
2001 Hoover Ave, Oakland, CA 94602

Stone, Albert L *Thoroughbred Racing Executive*
700 Central Ave, PO Box 8427, Louisville, KY 40208

Stone, Andrew L *Movie Director*
10478 Wyton Dr, Los Angeles, CA 90024

Stone, Christopher *Actor*
23035 Cumorah Crest Dr, Woodland Hills, CA 91364

Stone, Donald C *Government Official, Educator*
3955 Bigelow Blvd, Pittsburgh, PA 15213

Stone, Donald J *Businessman*
%Federated Department Stores, 7 W 7th St, Cincinnati, OH 45202

Stone, Edward C, Jr *Space Physicist*
%California Institute of Technology, Physics Dept, Pasadena, CA 91125

Stone, Ezra *Actor*
Stone Meadows Farm, Box D, Newtown, PA 18940

Stone, Irving I *Businessman*
%American Greetings Corp, 10500 American Rd, Cleveland, OH 44144

Stone, Jack *Religious Leader*
%Church of Nazarene, 6401 The Paseo, Kansas City, MO 64131

Stone, Jesse, Jr *Educator*
%Southern University, President's Office, Baton Rouge, LA 70813

Stone, Lawrence *Historian*
266 Moore St, Princeton, NJ 08540

Stone, Leonard *Actor*
%Amaral Talent Agency, 10000 Riverside Dr, Toluca Lake, CA 91602

Stone, Martin *Businessman*
1299 Ocean Ave, Santa Monica, CA 90401

Stone, Marvin L *Editor*
6368 Waterway Dr, Lake Barcroft, Falls Church, VA 22044

Stone, Michael P W *Government Official*
%Secretary's Office, Department of Army, Pentagon, Washington, DC 20310

Stone, Morris S *Businessman*
%American Greetings Corp, 10500 American Rd, Cleveland, OH 44144

Stone, Oliver *Movie Director, Screenwriter*
%Ixtlan Corp, 321 Hampton Dr, #105, Venice, CA 90291

Stone, Peter H *Playwright, Scenarist*
160 E 71st St, New York, NY 10021

Stone, Richard *Nobel Economics Laureate*
13 Millington Rd, Cambridge, England

Stone, Robert *Writer*
%Alfred A Knopf, 201 E 50th St, New York, NY 10022

Stone, Roger D *Political Consultant*
34 W 88th St, New York, NY 10024

Stone, Roger W *Businessman*
%Stone Container Corp, 360 N Michigan Ave, Chicago, IL 60601

Stone, Sharon *Actress*
%Dorothy Stone, PO Box 252, West Springfield, PA 16443

Stone, Steve *Baseball Player*
%Baltimore Orioles, Memorial Stadium, Baltimore, MD 21218

Stone, W Clement *Businessman*
%Combined International Corp, 222 N Dearborn St, Chicago, IL 60601

Stonecipher, Harry C *Businessman*
%Sundstrand Corp, 4751 Harrison Ave, Rockford, IL 61125

Stookey, John H *Businessman*
%National Distillers & Chemical Corp, 99 Park Ave, New York, NY 10016

Stookey, Paul *Singer (Peter, Paul & Mary), Songwriter*
Newworld, Rt 175, South Blue Hill, ME 04615

Stoph, Willi *Head of State, East Germany*
Kolsterstrasse 47, 102 Berlin, Germany

Stoppard, Tom *Playwright*
Iver Grove, Iver, Bucks, England

Storaro, Vittorio *Cinematographer*
Via Divino Amore 2, Frattecchie, Merino, Italy

Storch, Larry *Actor*
336 West End St, #17-F, New York, NY 10023

Storer, Peter *Broadcast Executive*
%Storer Broadcasting Co, 1177 Kane Concourse, Miami Beach, FL 33154

Storey, David M *Playwright*
2 Lyndhurst Gdns, London NW3, England

Storey, Will M *Businessman*
%Federated Department Stores, 7 W 7th St, Cincinnati, OH 45202

Storhoff, Don *Businessman*
%Wisconsin Dairies Cooperative, Rt 3, Baraboo, WI 53913

Stork, Gilbert *Chemist*
459 Next Day Hill Dr, Englewood, NJ 07631

Storm, Gale *Actress*
308 N Sycamore Ave, #104, Los Angeles, CA 90036

Storm, Hannah *Sportscaster*
%Cable News Network, Sports Dept, 1 CNN Ctr, PO Box 105366, Atlanta, GA 30348

Storrs, Thomas I *Financier*
%NCNB Corp, 1 NCNB Plz, Charlotte, NC 28255

Story, Ralph *Commentator*
3425 Wonderview Dr, Los Angeles, CA 90068

Stossels, John *Commentator*
%ABC-TV, News Dept, 153 Columbus Cir, New York, NY 10023

Stottlemyre, Mel *Baseball Player*
9 S 3rd St, Yakima, WA 98901

Stout, Don B *Financier*
%Georgia Federal Bank, 20 Marietta St NW, Atlanta, GA 30303

Stoutland, Frederick A *Businessman*
%Provident Life & Accident Insurance, Fountain Sq, Chattanooga, TN 37402

Stover Irwin Russ, Juno *Diver*
601 Beachcomber Blvd, #370, Lake Havasu City, AZ 86403

Stover, James R *Businessman*
%Eaton Corp, Eaton Ctr, 1111 Superior Ave, Cleveland, OH 44114

Stover, William R *Businessman*
%Old Republic International Corp, 307 N Michigan Ave, Chicago, IL 60601

Stowe, Leland *Journalist*
801 Greenhills Dr, Ann Arbor, MI 48105

Stowe, Madeleine *Actress*
%InterTalent Agency, 121 S Rodeo Dr, #300, Beverly Hills, CA 90212

Stowers, James E *Financier*
%Twentieth Century Investors, 605 W 47th St, Kansas City, MO 64141

Stoyanov, Krassimir *Cosmonaut, Bulgaria*
141 160 Svyosdny Gorodok, Moskovskoi Oblasti, Potchta Kosmonavtov, Russia

Strachan, Rod *Swimmer*
13812 Glenmere Dr, Santa Ana, CA 92705

Straetz, Robert P *Businessman*
%Textron Inc, 40 Westminster St, Providence, RI 02903

Straight, Beatrice *Actress*
156 E 62nd St, New York, NY 10021

Strait, George *Singer*
%Erv Woolsey Mgmt, 1000 18th Ave S, Nashville, TN 37212

Stram, Hank *Football Coach, Sportscaster*
194 Belle Terre Blvd, Covington, LA 70433

Stranahan, Robert A, Jr *Businessman*
%Champion Spark Plug Co, 900 Upton Ave, Toldeo, OH 43661

Strand, Curt R *Businessman*
%Hilton International Co, 301 Park Ave, New York, NY 10022

Strand, Mark *Poet*
%Poet Laureate's Office, Library of Congress, 10 1st St SE, Washington, DC 20540

Strand, Robin *Actor*
%Gersh Agency, 232 N Canon Dr, Beverly Hills, CA 90210

Strang, Charles D *Businessman*
%Outboard Marine Corp, 100 Sea-Horse Dr, Waukegan, IL 60085

Strange, Curtis *Golfer*
%Kingsmill Golf Club, Williamsburg, VA 23186

Strasberg, Susan *Actress*
%William Morris Agency, 151 El Camino, Beverly Hills, CA 90212

Strasser, Robin *Actress*
%STE Representation, 9301 Wilshire Blvd, #312, Beverly Hills, CA 90210

Strassman, Marcia *Actress*
%Gersh Agency, 232 N Canon Dr, Beverly Hills, CA 90210

Stratas, Teresa *Opera Singer*
%Metropolitan Opera Assn, Lincoln Ctr, New York, NY 10023

Stratton, Frederick P, Jr *Businessman*
%Briggs & Stratton Corp, 12301 W Wirth St, Wauwatosa, WI 53222

Stratton, Julius A *Physicist*
100 Memorial Dr, Cambridge, MA 02142

Stratton, William B *Governor, IL*
%Chicago Bank of Commerce, 200 E Randolph Dr, Chicago, IL 60601

Straub, Peter *Writer*
53 W 85th St, New York, NY 10026

Straub, Robert W *Governor, OR*
2087 Orchard Heights Rd NW, Salem, OR 97304

Straus, Leonard H *Businessman*
%Thrifty Corp, 5051 Rodeo Rd, Los Angeles, CA 90016

Straus, William L, Jr *Physical Anthropologist*
7111 Park Heights Ave, #506, Baltimore, MD 21215

Strauss, Peter *Actor*
10736 Le Conte Ave, Los Angeles, CA 90024

Strauss, Robert S *Political Leader*
%Republic Bank Bldg, #2800, Dallas, TX 75201

Strauss, Willis A *Businessman*
%HNG/InterNorth Inc, 2223 Dodge St, Omaha, NE 68102

Strausz-Hupe, Robert *Diplomat*
%American Embassy, Ataturk Bulvari 110, Ankara, Turkey

Strawberry, Darryl *Baseball Player*
1419 Red Bluff Ct, San Dimas, CA 91773

Strawser, Neil *Commentator*
130 "E" St SE, Washington, DC 20003

Streeter, Donald V *Financier*
%Atlantic Federal Savings & Loan, 1750 E Sunrise, Fort Lauderdale, FL 33304

S

Streetman – Strub

Streetman, Ben G *Electrical Engineer*
2901 Rolling Acres Dr, Champaign, IL 61820

Strehler, Giorgio *Theatre Director*
%Theatre of Europe, 1 Pl Paul Claudel, 75006 Paris, France

Streich, Rita *Opera Singer*
Karntnerstrasse 23, Vienna I, Austria

Streisand, Barbra *Singer, Actress, Director*
307 N Carolwood, Los Angeles, CA 90077

Streisinger, George *Biologist*
%University of Oregon, Molecular Biology Institute, Eugene, OR 97403

Streit, Clarence K *Journalist*
2853 Ontario Rd NW, Washington, DC 20009

Streitwieser, Andrew, Jr *Chemist*
%University of California, Chemistry Dept, Berkeley, CA 94720

Strekalov, Gennady *Cosmonaut*
141 160 Svyosdny Gorodok, Moskovskoi Oblasti, Potchta Kosmonavtov, Russia

Strenger, Hermann J *Businessman*
%Bayer AG, 5090 Leverkusen, Germany

Stretton, Ross *Ballet Dancer*
%American Ballet Theatre, 890 Broadway, New York, NY 10003

Strickland de la Hunty, Shirley *Track Athlete*
22 Fraser Rd, Applecross WA 6153, Australia

Strickland, Amzie *Actress*
%Mishkin Agency, 2355 Benedict Canyon, Beverly Hills, CA 90210

Strickland, Gail *Actress*
%Harris & Goldberg Agency, 1999 Ave of Stars, #2850, Los Angeles, CA 90067

Strickland, Robert L *Businessman*
%Loew's Companies, PO Box 1111, North Wilkesboro, NC 28656

Strickland, Rod *Basketball Player*
%San Antonio Spurs, 600 E Market St, San Antonio, TX 78205

Strickler, Ivan *Businessman*
%Mid-America Dairymen, PO Box 1837, Springfield, MO 65805

Stricklyn, Ray *Actor*
852 N Genesee Ave, Los Angeles, CA 90046

Strider, Marjorie *Artist*
7 Worth St, New York, NY 10013

Stringer, Howard *Television Executive*
%CBS Broadcast Group, 51 W 52nd St, New York, NY 10019

Stringer, Vivian *Basketball Coach*
%University of Iowa, Athletic Dept, Iowa City, IA 52242

Stritch, Elaine *Singer, Actress*
%Felix de Woolfe, 1 Robert St, London WC2, England

Strode, Woody *Actor*
PO Box 1553, Glendora, CA 91740

Stroh, Peter W *Businessman*
%Stroh Brewery Co, 1 Stroh Dr, Detroit, MI 48226

Strolz, Hubert *Skier*
%Olympic Committee, Prinz-Eugen-Strasse 12, 1040 Vienna, Austria

Strom, Brock *Football Player*
4301 W 110th St, Leawood, KS 66211

Strom, Earl *Basketball Referee*
1437 Shaner Dr, Pottstown, PA 19464

Stromberg, Arthur H *Businessman*
%URS Corp, 155 Bovet Rd, San Mateo, CA 94402

Strong, Leonell C *Cancer Research Scientist*
8533 Sugarman Dr, La Jolla, CA 92037

Strong, Maurice F *Government Official, Canada*
%ISI Development Services, 32 St James St, London SW1A 1HD, England

Stroud, Don *Actor*
%David Shapira Assoc, 15301 Ventura Blvd, #345, Sherman Oaks, CA 91403

Stroud, Joe H *Editor*
%Detroit Free Press, 321 W Lafayette Blvd, Detroit, MI 48231

Strouse, Charles *Composer*
171 W 57th St, New York, NY 10019

Strub, Robert P *Thoroughbred Race Track Owner*
%Santa Anita Race Track, 285 W Huntington Dr, Arcadia, CA 91006

Strube, Juergen F *Businessman*
%BASF Corp, 9 Campus Dr, Parsippany, NJ 07054

Struchkova, Raisa *Ballerina*
%State Academic Bolshoi Theatre, 1 Ploshchad Sverdlova, Moscow, Russia

Strudler, Robert J *Businessman*
%US Home Corp, 1800 West Loop S, Houston, TX 77027

Struever, Stuart M *Anthropologist*
2000 Sheridan Rd, Evanston, IL 60201

Strugnell, John *Theologian*
%Harvard University, Divinity School, 45 Francis Ave, Cambridge, MA 02138

Struthers, Sally *Actress*
%Cunningham-Escott-Dipene, 261 S Robertson Blvd, Beverly Hills, CA 90211

Stuart, Barbara *Actress*
%Artists Group, 1930 Century Park West, #403, Los Angeles, CA 90067

Stuart, Gloria *Actress*
884 S Bundy Dr, Los Angeles, CA 90049

Stuart, Lyle *Publisher*
120 Enterprise Ave, Secaucus, NJ 07094

Stuart, Mary *Actress*
30 E 68th St, New York, NY 10001

Stuart, Maxine *Actress*
%Century Artists, 9744 Wilshire Blvd, #308, Beverly Hills, CA 90212

Stuart, Robert D, Jr *Businessman*
%Quaker Oats Co, Merchandise Mart Plz, Chicago, IL 60654

Studds, Gerry E *Representative, MA*
16 Black Horse Ln, Cohesset, MA 02025

Studenroth, Carl W *Labor Leader*
%Molders & Allied Workers Union, 1225 E McMillan St, Cincinnati, OH 45206

Stukel, James J *Educator*
%University of Illinois at Chicago, President's Office, Chicago, IL 60680

Stump, Bob *Representative, AZ*
PO Box 5, Tolleson, AZ 85353

Sturdivant, John N *Labor Leader*
%American Government Employees Federation, 80 "F" St NW, Washington, DC 20001

Sturdivant, Tom *Baseball Player*
825 SW 113th St, Oklahoma City, OK 73170

Sturges, John *Movie Director*
726 Upham, San Luis Obispo, CA 93401

Sturman, Eugene *Sculptor*
1108 W Washington Blvd, Venice, CA 90291

Sturzenegger, Otto *Businessman*
%Ciba-Geigy Corp, 444 Saw Mill Rd, Ardsley, NY 10502

Stutz, Geraldine *Businesswoman, Publisher*
%Panache Press, Random House Inc, 201 E 50th St, New York, Ny 10022

Stuzin, Charles B *Financier*
%Citizens Savings Financial Corp, 999 Brickell Ave, Miami, FL 33131

Styne, Jule *Composer, Producer*
237 W 51st St, New York, NY 10019

Styron, William *Writer*
RFD, Roxbury, CT 06783

Suad, Anthony *Photographer*
%Denver Post, PO Box 1709, Denver, CO 80201

Suarez Gondalez, Adolfo *Prime Minister, Spain*
Sagasta, 33 Madrid 4, Spain

Suarez, Xavier *Mayor*
%Mayor's Office, City Hall, 3500 Pan American Dr, Miami, FL 33133

Subotnick, Morton *Composer*
%Theodore Presser Publishing, Bryn Mawr, PA 19010

Suchet, David *Actor*
169 Queen's Gate, #8, London SW7 5EH, England

Suchon, Eugen *Composer*
Bradlanska Ul, 11 Bratislava, 80100 Czechoslovakia

Suck Won Yu *Businessman*
%Sunkyong Ltd, 5-3 2-Ka Namdaemunro, Chungku, Seoul, South Korea

Sudarmono, Pratiwi *Astronaut, Indonesia*
Jalan Pegangsaan, Timut 16, Jarkarta, Indonesia

Sudersham, Ennackel — *Theoretical Physicist*
%University of Texas, Physics Dept, Austin, TX 78713

Sudol, Ed — *Baseball Umpire*
415 Rivilo Blvd, Daytona Beach, FL 32014

Suenaga, Soichiro — *Businessman*
%Mitsubishi Heavy Industries, 5-1 Marubouchi, Chiyodaku, Tokyo, Japan

Sues, Alan — *Actor*
%Bret Adams Ltd, 448 W 44th St, New York, NY 10036

Suess, Hans E — *Geochemist*
%University of California, Chemistry Dept, La Jolla, CA 92093

Sugar, Bert Randolph — *Writer, Editor*
6 Southview Rd, Chappaqua, NY 10514

Sugar, Leo — *Football Player*
816 Coutant, Flushing, MI 48433

Sugarman, Burt — *Actor*
400 Trousdale Pl, Beverly Hills, CA 90210

Suggs, Louise — *Golfer*
%Ladies Professional Golf Assn, 2570 Volusia Ave, #B, Daytona Beach, FL 32114

Sugiura, Hideo — *Businessman*
%Honda Motor Co, 27-8-6 Jingumae, Shibuyaku, Tokyo 150, Japan

Suhara, Akira — *Businessman*
%Honshu Paper Co, 5-12-8 Ginza, Chuoku, Tokyo 104, Japan

Suharto — *President, Indonesia*
%President's Office, 15 Jalan Merdeka Utara, Jakarta, Indonesia

Suhor, Yvonne — *Actress*
%J Michael Bloom Ltd, 9200 Sunset Blvd, #710, Los Angeles, CA 90069

Suhr, Gus — *Baseball Player*
341 Hazel Ave, Millbrae, CA 94030

Suhrheinrich, Richard F — *Judge*
%US Court of Appeals, Federal Bldg, 231 W Lafayette Blvd, Detroit, MI 48226

Suitner, Otmar — *Conductor*
Platanestrasse 13, Berlin-Niederschonhausen, Germany

Sukova, Helen — *Tennis Player*
%Women's Tennis Assn, 133 1st St NE, St Petersburg, FL 33701

Sulaiman, Jose — *Boxing Official*
%World Boxing Council, Apartado 75-254, Mexico City 14 DF, Mexico

Suleymanoglu, Naim — *Weightlifter*
%Olympic Committee, Sisli, Buyukdere Cad 18 Tankaya, Istanbul, Turkey

Suliotis, Elena — *Opera Singer*
Villa il Poderino, Via Incontri 38, Florence, Italy

Sulkin, Sidney — *Editor*
%Changing Times Magazine, 220 E 42nd St, New York, NY 10017

Sullivan, Barry — *Actor*
14687 Round Valley Dr, Sherman Oaks, CA 91403

Sullivan, Barry F — *Financier*
%First Chicago Corp, 1 First National Plz, Chicago, IL 60670

Sullivan, Billy — *Football Executive*
%New England Patriots, Foxboro Stadium, Foxboro, MA 02035

Sullivan, Brendan — *Attorney*
%Williams & Connolly, Hill Bldg, 839 17th St NW, Washington, DC 20006

Sullivan, Danny — *Auto Racing Driver*
2811 Arizona Ave, Santa Monica, CA 90404

Sullivan, Eugene J J — *Businessman*
%Borden Inc, 277 Park Ave, New York, NY 10172

Sullivan, Frank E — *Businessman*
%Mutual Benefit Life Insurance, 520 Broad St, Newark, NJ 07101

Sullivan, Fred R — *Businessman*
%Kidde Inc, Park 80 W, Plaza Two, Saddle Brook, NJ 07662

Sullivan, Gordon R — *Army General*
Chief of Staff, Hdqs, US Army, Washington, DC 20310

Sullivan, Joe — *Businessman*
%Sound Seventy Corp, 210 25th Ave N, Nashville, TN 37203

Sullivan, Kathleen — *Commentator*
%NBC-TV, Sports Dept, 30 Rockefeller Plaza, New York, NY 10020

Sullivan, Kathryn D — *Astronaut*
%NASA, Johnson Space Ctr, Houston, TX 77058

Sullivan, Leon H *Religious Leader*
%Zion Baptist Church, 3600 N Broad St, Philadelphia, PA 19140
Sullivan, Louis W *Secretary, Health & Human Services*
%Health & Human Services Department, 200 Independence SW, Washington, DC 20201
Sullivan, Mike *Governor, WY*
%Governor's Office, State Capitol Bldg, Cheyenne, WY 82002
Sullivan, Pat *Football Player, Coach*
%Texas Christian University, Athletic Dept, Fort Worth, TX 76129
Sullivan, Richard P *Businessman*
%Easco Corp, 201 N Charles St, Baltimore, MD 21201
Sullivan, Robert E *Businessman*
%Harris Graphics Corp, 200 Seminole Ave, Melbourne, FL 32901
Sullivan, Susan *Actress*
%STE Representation, 9301 Wilshire Blvd, #312, Beverly Hills, CA 90210
Sullivan, Walter S *Journalist*
%New York Times, 229 W 43rd St, New York, NY 10036
Sullivan, William J *Educator*
%Seattle University, President's Office, Seattle, WA 98122
Sultan Salman Al-Saud *Astronaut, Saudi Arabia*
PO Box 18368, Riyadh, Saudi Arabia
Sultan, Donald *Artist*
%Andrew Dierken Fine Arts Gallery, 8563 1/2 Cashio, Los Angeles, CA 90035
Sulzberger, Arthur Ochs, Jr *Publisher*
%New York Times, 229 W 43rd St, New York, NY 10036
Sulzberger, Cyrus Leo *Writer*
General Delivery, Spetsais, Greece
Summer, Donna *Singer*
%Camden ITG, 822 S Robertson Blvd, #200, Los Angeles, CA 90035
Summerall, Pat *Sportscaster*
12536 Marsh Creek Dr, Ponte Vedra, FL 32082
Summers, Carol *Artist*
133 Prospect Ct, Santa Cruz, CA 95065
Summers, Dana *Cartoonist (Lug Nuts)*
%Orlando Sentinel, 633 N Orange Ave, Orlando, FL 32801
Summers, William K *Medical Researcher*
%University of California, Medical Ctr, Los Angeles, CA 90024
Summitt, Pat Head *Basketball Coach*
%University of Tennessee, Athletic Dept, Knoxville, TN 37996
Sumners, Rosalynn *Figure Skater*
%Barbara Kindness, 9912 225th Pl SW, Edmonds, WA 98020
Sun Yun-Suan *Prime Minister, Taiwan*
1 Chung Hsiao E Rd, Taipei 110, Taiwan
Sundance, Robert *Social Activist*
%Indian Alcoholism Commission of California, 225 W 8th, Los Angeles, CA 90014
Sunderland, Harry D *Businessman*
%Safeway Stores, 4th & Jackson, Oakland, CA 94660
Sundlun, Bruce G *Governor, RI*
%Governor's Office, 222 State House, Providence, RI 02903
Sundquist, Don *Representative, TN*
%House of Representatives, Washington, DC 20515
Sundquist, Ulf *Businessman*
Neste Oy, Keilaniemi, SF-02150 Espoo 15, Finland
Sundvold, Jon *Basketball Player*
%Miami Heat, Miami Arena, Miami, FL 33136
Sununu, John H *Governor, NH; Government Official*
%White House, 1600 Pennsylvania Ave NW, Washington, DC 20500
Suquia Goicoechea, Angel Cardinal *Religious Leader*
El Cardenal Arxobispo, San Justo 2, 28074 Madrid, Spain
Surdam, Robert M *Financier*
%NBD Bancorp, 611 Woodward Ave, Detroit, MI 48226
Surtees, John *Auto Racing Driver*
%Team Surtees, Station Rd, Edenbridge, Kent TN8 6HL, England
Susa, Conrad *Composer*
%E C Schirmer Co, 112 South St, Boston, MA 02111
Susi, Carol Ann *Actress*
846 N Sweetzer Ave, Los Angeles, CA 90069

S

Susman – Svendsen

Susman, Todd *Actor*
10340 Keokuk Ave, Chatsworth, CA 91311

Sutcliffe, Rick *Baseball Player*
313 NW North Shore Dr, Parkville, MO 64151

Suter, Albert E *Businessman*
%Whirlpool Corp, 2000 US N, Benton Harbor, MI 49022

Suter, Gary *Hockey Player*
%Calgary Flames, PO Box 1540, Station M, Calgary AB T2P 3B9, Canada

Sutherland, Joan *Opera Singer*
%Ingpen & Williams, 14 Kensington Ct, London W8, England

Sutherland, Kiefer *Actor*
%InterTalent Agency, 131 S Rodeo Dr, #300, Beverly Hills, CA 90212

Sutherland, Robert *Businessman*
%Smith International Inc, 4490 Von Karman Ave, Newport Beach, CA 92660

Sutter, Brent *Hockey Player*
%Chicago Blackhawks, 1800 W Madison St, Chicago, IL 60612

Sutter, Brian *Hockey Player, Coach*
%St Louis Blues, 5700 Oakland Ave, St Louis, MO 63110

Sutter, Bruce *Baseball Player*
1368 Hamilton Rd, Kennesaw, GA 30144

Sutter, Ron *Hockey Player*
%St Louis Blues, 57 Oakland Ave, St Louis, MO 63110

Sutton, Don *Baseball Player, Sportscaster*
3390 Vandiver Dr, Marietta, GA 30066

Sutton, Donald C *Businessman*
%Pacific Mutual Life Insurance, 700 Newport Center Dr, Newport Beach, CA 92660

Sutton, Eddie *Basketball Coach*
%Oklahoma State University, Athletic Dept, Stillwater, OK 74078

Sutton, George P *Aeronautical Engineer*
725 Barrington Ave, #110, Los Angeles, CA 90049

Sutton, Grady *Comedian*
1207 N Orange Dr, Los Angeles, CA 90038

Sutton, Hal *Golfer*
6917 Avondale, Shreveport, LA 71107

Sutton, Thomas C *Businessman*
%Dover Corp, 277 Park Ave, New York, NY 10172

Suzman, Janet *Actress*
%William Morris Agency, 147-149 Wardour St, London W1V 3TB, England

Suzuki, Eiji *Businessman*
%Mitsubishi Chemical Industries, 2-5-2 Marunouchi, Tokyo 100, Japan

Suzuki, Haruo *Businessman*
%Showa Denko, 1-13-9 Shiba Daimon, Minatoku, Tokyo, Japan

Suzuki, Hisaaki *Businessman*
%Yokohama Rubber Co, 5-36-11 Shimbashi, Minatoku, Tokyo 105, Japan

Suzuki, Osami *Businessman*
%Suzuki Motor Co, 300 Takatsuka, Kamimura, Hamanagun, Japan

Suzuki, Robert *Educator*
%California Polytechnic University, President's Office, Pomona, CA 91768

Suzuki, Saburosuke *Businessman*
%Ajinomoto Co, 1-5-8 Kyobashi, Chuoku, Tokyo 104, Japan

Suzuki, Seiji *Businessman*
%Mitsubishi Chemical Industries, 2-5-2 Marunouchi, Tokyo 100, Japan

Suzuku, Kazuo *Businessman*
%Toppan Printing Co, 1-5-1 Taito, Taitoku, Tokyo 100, Japan

Suzy (Aileen Mehle) *Columnist*
%Milton Fenster Assoc, 540 Madison Ave, New York, NY 10022

Svan, Gunde *Nordic Skier*
%General Delivery, Vansbro, Sweden

Svanholm, Poul J *Businessman*
%United Breweries, Vesterfaelledvej 100, DK-1799 Copenhagen, Denmark

Svedberg, Bjorn *Businessman*
%L M Ericsson Telephone, Telefonplan, 126 25 Stockholm, Sweden

Svendsen, George *Football Player*
2100 Mary Hills Dr, Golden Valley, MN 55422

Svendsen, Louise Averill *Museum Curator*
%Guggenheim Museum, 1071 5th Ave, New York, NY 10028

Svenson, Bo *Actor*
801 Greentree Rd, Pacific Palisades, CA 90272

Svetlanov, Yevgeni *Conductor*
%Russian State Symphony, Ul Gertzena 13, Moscow K-9, Russia

Swados, Elizabeth *Writer, Composer*
112 Waverly Pl, New York, NY 10011

Swaggart, Jimmy *Evangelist*
PO Box 2550, Baton Rouge, LA 70821

Swaggert, H Patrick *Educator*
%State University of New York, President's Office, Albany, NY 12222

Swain, Donald C *Educator*
%University of Louisville, President's Office, Louisville, KY 40292

Swainson, John B *Governor, MI*
10301 Hogan Rd, Manchester, MI 48158

Swales, William E *Businessman*
%Marathon Petroleum Co, 539 S Main St, Findlay, OH 45840

Swan, Annalyn *Editor*
%Savvy Magazine, 111 8th Ave, New York, NY 10011

Swan, Henry, II *Physician*
6700 W Lakeridge Rd, Lakewood, CO 80227

Swanberg, William A *Writer*
Taunton Ln, Rt 3, Newton, CT 06470

Swanljung, Kurt *Businessman*
%Kymmene-Stromberg Corp, PO Box 300, 00131 Helsinki, Finland

Swann, Donald *Comedian, Composer*
13 Albert Bridge Rd, London SW11 4PX, England

Swann, Lynn *Football Player, Sportscaster*
%Artists Agency, 10000 Santa Monica Blvd, #305, Los Angeles, CA 90067

Swanson, Dennis *Television Executive*
%ABC-Sports, 47 W 66th St, New York, NY 10023

Swanson, Kristy *Actress*
%Agency for Performing Arts, 9000 Sunset Blvd, #1200, Los Angeles, CA 90069

Swarthout, Glendon *Writer*
5045 Tamanar Way, Scottsdale, AZ 85253

Swartz, W John *Businessman*
%Santa Fe Southern Pacific Corp, 224 S Michigan Ave, Chicago, IL 60604

Swayze, John Cameron *Commentator*
491 Riversville Rd, Greenwich, CT 06830

Swayze, Patrick *Actor*
%Lemond/Zetter Inc, 8370 Wilshire Blvd, Beverly Hills, CA 90211

Swearingen, John E, Jr *Businessman*
Amoco Building, 200 E Randolph Dr, Chicago, IL 60601

Sweeney, John J *Labor Leader*
%Service Employees International Union, 1313 "L" St NW, Washington, DC 20005

Sweeney, Mac *Representative, TX*
%House of Representatives, Washington, DC 20515

Sweeney, Robert J *Businessman*
%Murphy Oil Corp, 200 Peach St, El Dorado, AK 71730

Sweet, Bernard *Businessman*
%Republic Airlines, 7500 Airline Dr, Minneapolis, MN 55450

Sweger, John B *Financier*
%Fortune Financial Grp, 2120 US 19 S, Clearwater, FL 33546

Swenson, Inga *Actress*
%STE Representation, 9301 Wilshire Blvd, #312, Beverly Hills, CA 90210

Swenson, Rick *Dog Sled Racer*
%Trot-A-Long Kennel, Manley, AK 99756

Swenson, Swen *Actor, Dancer*
16 Minetta Ln, New York, NY 10012

Swensson, Earl S *Architect*
%Earl Swensson Assoc, Vanderbilt Plz, Nashville, TN 37212

Swett, Dick *Representative, NH*
%House of Representatives, Washington, DC 20515

Swett, James E *WW II Marine Corps Hero (CMH)*
PO Box 327, Trinity Center, CA 96091

Swift, A Dean *Businessman*
%Sears Roebuck & Co, Sears Tower, Chicago, IL 60684

S

Swift – Szoke Arpadomjan

Swift, Al *Representative, WA*
%House of Representatives, Washington, DC 20515

Swift, Stephen J *Judge*
%US Tax Court, 400 2nd St NW, Washington, DC 20217

Swiggett, Robert L *Businessman*
%Kollmorgen Corp, 10 Mill Pond Ln, Simsbury, CT 06070

Swinburne, Nora *Actress*
%Edmund Knight, 35 Bywater St, Chelsea, London SW3, England

Swindall, Pat *Representative, GA*
%House of Representatives, Washington, DC 20515

Swindells, William, Jr *Businessman*
%Willamette Industries, 3800 First Interstate Tower, Portland, OR 97201

Swindoll, Charles R *Evangelist, Writer*
%Insight for Living, 211 E Imperial Hwy, Fullerton, CA 92635

Swink, Jim *Football Player*
1201 8th Ave, Fort Worth, TX 76104

Swit, Loretta *Actress*
%Agency for Performing Arts, 9000 Sunset Blvd, #1200, Los Angeles, CA 90069

Switzer, Barry *Football Coach*
%University of Oklahoma, Athletic Dept, 180 W Brooks, Norman, OK 73019

Swofford, Ken *Actor*
%Stone Manners Agency, 9113 Sunset Blvd, Los Angeles, CA 90069

Syberberg, Hans-Jurgen *Movie Director*
German Film Productions, Langenbeckstrasse 9, 6200 Wiesbaden, Germany

Sydnor, Charles W, Jr *Educator*
%Emory & Henry College, President's Office, Emory, VA 24327

Sykora, Don D *Businessman*
%Houston Industries, 611 Walker Ave, Houston, TX 77002

Sylvia *Queen, Sweden*
%Royal Palace, Stockholm, Sweden

Sylvia *Singer*
12424 Wilshire Blvd, #830, Los Angeles, CA 90025

Symington, Fife *Governor, AZ*
%Governor's Office, State Capitol, 1700 W Washington, Phoenix, AZ 85007

Symms, Steven D *Senator, ID*
%US Senate, Washington, DC 20510

Syms, Sylvia *Actress*
%Marmont Mgmt, Langhom House, 302 Regent St, London W1R 5AL, England

Synar, Michael L *Representative, OK*
503 1/2 N 15th St, Muskogee, OK 74401

Synge, Henry Millington *Businessman*
%Union International, 13-16 West Smithfield, London EC1A 9JN, England

Synge, Richard L M *Nobel Chemistry Laureate*
19 Meadow Rise Rd, Norwich NR2 3QE, England

Sytsma, John F *Labor Leader*
%Locomotive Engineers Brotherhood, 1370 Ontario Ave, Cleveland, OH 44114

Szabo, Gabor *Jazz Guitarist*
%Impulse Records, 70 Universal Plz, Universal City, CA

Szasz, Thomas S *Psychiatrist*
4739 Limberlost Ln, Manlius, NY 13104

Szekely, Eva *Swimmer*
Szepvolgyi Ut 4/B, 1025 Budapest, Hungary

Szekessy, Karen *Photographer*
Haynstrasse 2, 2000 Hamburg 20, Germany

Szigmond, Vilmos *Cinematographer*
PO Box 2230, Los Angeles, CA 90078

Szoka, Edmund C Cardinal *Religious Leader*
%Prefecture for Economic Affairs, Vatican City, Rome, Italy

Szoke Arpadomjan, Katalin *Swimmer*
9283 Swallow Dr, Los Angeles, CA 90069

Tabackin, Lew *Jazz Flutist*
38 W 94th St, New York, NY 10025
Tabai, Ieremia T *President, Kiribati*
%President's Office, Tarawa, Kiribati
Taber, Carol A *Publisher*
%Lang Communications, 342 Madison Ave, 22nd Fl, New York, NY 10173
Tabitha 'Masentle *Princess, Lesotho*
%Royal Palace, PO Box 524, Maseru, Lesotho
Tabone, Censu *President, Malta*
%President's Office, Valletta, Malta
Tabori, Kristoffer *Actor*
%The Agency, 10351 Santa Monica Blvd, #211, Los Angeles, CA 90025
Tabori, Laszlo *Track Athlete*
13656 Burbank Blvd, Van Nuys, CA 91401
Tacha, Deanell R *Judge*
%US Court of Appeals, 4830 W 15th St, Lawrence, KS 66049
Tacke, David R *Businessman*
%E-Systems Inc, 6250 LBJ Fwy, Dallas, TX 75266
Taddei, Giuseppe *Opera Singer*
%Metropolitan Opera Assn, Lincoln Center Plz, New York, NY 10023
Taft, Dudley S *Broadcast Executive*
%Taft Broadcasting Co, 1718 Young St, Cincinnati, OH 45210
Taft, Robert A, Jr *Senator, OH*
4300 Drake Rd, Cincinnati, OH 45243
Tagliabue, Paul *Football Executive*
%National Football League, 410 Park Ave, New York, NY 10022
Taguchi, Nobutaka *Swimmer*
%Kanoya P E College, Swimming Dept, Kanoya-City, Kagoshima, Japan
Tahara, Hishashi *Businessman*
%Honshu Paper Co, 5-12-8 Ginza, Chuoku, Tokyo 104, Japan
Tait, John E *Businessman*
%Penn Mutual Life Insurance, Independence Sq, Philadelphia, PA 19172
Taj Mahal *Singer*
%Folklore Productions, 1671 Appian Way, Santa Monica, CA 90401
Taji, Kazutoshi *Businessman*
%Nippon Light Metal Co, 7-2 Otemachi, Chiyodaku, Tokyo 100, Japan
Tajo, Italo *Opera Singer*
5541 Penway Ct, Cincinnati, OH 45239
Takada, Ryoichi *Businessman*
%Hino Motors, 3-1-1 Hinodai, Hino City, Tokyo 191, Japan
Takahashi, Kokichi *Businessman*
%Kobe Steel, 1-3-18 Wakinohamacho, Chuoko, Kobe 651, Japan
Takahashi, Michiaki *Immunologist*
%Osaka University, Microbial Diseases Research Institute, Osaka, Japan
Takahashi, Yusaku *Businessman*
%Showa Sangyo Co, 2-1 Uchi Kanda, Chiyodaku, Tokyo, Japan
Takasaki, Yoshiro *Businessman*
%Toyo Seikan Kaisha Ltd, 1-3-1 Uchisaiwaicho, Chiyodaku, Tokyo 100, Japan
Takashima, Setsuo *Businessman*
%Mitsui Mining & Smelting, 2-1-1 Nihonbashi-Muromachi, Tokyo 103, Japan
Takeda, Yutaka *Businessman*
%Nippon Steel Corp, 2-6-3 Otemachi, Chiyodaku, Tokyo 100, Japan
Takei, George *Actor*
4368 W 8th St, Los Angeles, CA 90005
Takeshita, Noboru *Prime Minister, Japan*
%Liberal Democratic Party, Diet, Tokyo, Japan
Tal, Josef *Composer*
3 Dvira Haneviyah St, Jerusalem, Israel
Talbert, William F (Billy) *Tennis Player*
%US Banknote Co, 345 Hudson St, New York, NY 10014
Talbot, Don *Swimming Coach*
%Canadian Sports Fed, 333 River Rd, Vanier, Ottawa ON K1L 8B9, Canada
Talbot, Matthew J *Businessman*
%Tosco Corp, 2401 Colorado Ave, Santa Monica, CA 90406
Talbot, Nita *Actress*
3420 Merrimac Rd, Los Angeles, CA 90049

Talbott, John H *Physician*
Commodore Club, 177 Ocean Lane Dr, Key Biscayne, FL 33149

Talese, Gay *Writer*
154 E Atlantic Blvd, Ocean City, NJ 08226

Taliaferro, George *Football Player*
3013 Stratfield Dr, Bloomington, IN 47401

Tallchief, Maria *Ballerina*
%Chicago City Ballet, 223 W Erie St, Chicago, IL 60610

Talley, Darryl *Football Player*
%Buffalo Bills, 1 Bills Dr, Orchard Park, NY 14127

Tallman, Patricia *Actress*
%Julie Nathenson, 9229 Sunset Blvd, Los Angeles, CA 90069

Tallon, Robin *Representative, SC*
%House of Representatives, Washington, DC 20515

Talmadge, Herman E *Governor/Senator, GA*
%Barnett & Alagia, 15 Circle Dr, Hampton, GA 30228

Tam, Reuben *Artist*
PO Box 831, Kapaa, HI 96746

Tamaki, Masakazu *Businessman*
%Chiyoda Chemical Engineering, 21-1 Tsurmi Chuo, Yokohama 230, Japan

Tamayo Mendez, Arnaldo *Cosmonaut, Cuba*
5-A Ave 1210, Esq A 14, Miramar, Ciudad La Habana, Cuba

Tamblyn, Russ *Actor*
2316 6th St, #2, Santa Monica, CA 90405

Tambor, Jeffrey *Actor*
4443 St Clair Ave, Studio City, CA 91604

Tamburello, Ben *Football Player*
%Philadelphia Eagles, Veterans Stadium, Philadelphia, PA 19148

Tamm, Igor E *Nobel Physics Laureate*
%Rockefeller Institute, 1230 York Ave, New York, NY 10021

Tamm, Peter *Publisher*
%Axel Springer Verlag, Kochstrasse 50, 1000 Berlin 61, Germany

Tan, Amy *Writer*
%G P Putnam's Sons, 200 Madison Ave, New York, NY 10016

Tanaka, Fumio *Businessman*
%Oji Paper Co, 4-7-5 Ginza, Chuoku, Tokyo 104, Japan

Tanaka, Kakuei *Prime Minister, Japan*
12-19-12 Mezirodai, Bunkyoku, Tokyo, Japan

Tanaka, Shoji *Research Scientist*
%University of Tokyo, Physics Dept, Tokyo, Japan

Tanana, Frank *Baseball Player*
28492 S Harwick, Farmington Hills, MI 48018

Tandon, Sirjang Lal *Businessman*
%Tandon Corp, 20320 Prairie St, Chatsworth, CA 91311

Tanen, Ned *Entertainment Executive*
%Paramount Pictures Corp, 5555 Melrose Ave, Los Angeles, CA 90038

Tanenbaum, Marc H *Religious Leader*
%American Jewish Committee, 165 E 56th St, New York, NY 10022

Tanford, Charles *Physiologist*
1430 Mangum St, Durham, NC 27701

Tang, Thomas *Judge*
%US Court of Appeals, 230 N 1st Ave, Phoenix, AZ 85025

Tange, Kenzo *Architect*
7-2-21 Akasaka, Minato-ku, Tokyo, Japan

Taniguchi, Tadatsugu *Molecular Biologist*
%University of Osaka, Molecular & Cellular Biology Dept, Osaka, Japan

Tanii, Akio *Businessman*
%Matsushita Electrical Industrial, 1006 Kadoma City, Osaka 571, Japan

Tankersley, G J *Businessman*
%Consolidated Natural Gas Co, 4 Gateway Ctr, Pittsburgh, PA 15222

Tanksley, Steven D *Plant Geneticist*
%Cornell University, Plant Genetics Dept, Ithaca, NY 14853

Tannen, Alain *Movie Director*
Rue du Point-du-Jour 12, 1202 Geneva, Switzerland

Tannenwald, Theodore, Jr *Judge*
%US Tax Court, 400 2nd St NW, Washington, DC 20217

Tanner Nahrgang, Elaine *Swimmer*
107-101 E 29th St, North Vancouver BC V7N 1C5, Canada

Tanner, Chuck *Baseball Manager*
34 Maitland Ln E, New Castle, PA 16101

Tanner, Roscoe *Tennis Player*
1109 Gnome Trl, Lookout Mountain, TN 37350

Tannowa, Naritada *Businessman*
%Mitsui Petrochemical Industries, 2-5 Kasumigaseki, Tokyo 100, Japan

Taofinu'u, Pio Cardinal *Religious Leader*
%Cardinal's Office, PO Box 532, Apia, Western Samoa

Tape, Gerald F *Physicist*
6717 Tulip Hill Terr, Bethesda, MD 20816

Taper, S Mark *Financier*
%First Charter Financial Corp, 9465 Wilshire Blvd, Beverly Hills, CA 90212

Tappan, David S, Jr *Businessman*
%Fluor Corp, 3333 Michelson Dr, Irvine, CA 92730

Tarbell, Dean S *Chemist*
6033 Sherwood Dr, Nashville, TN 37215

Tarbox, Frank K *Businessman*
%Penn Mutual Life Insurance, Independence Sq, Philadelphia, PA 19172

Tari, Le *Actor*
%Twentieth Century Artists, 3800 Barham Blvd, Los Angeles, CA 90068

Tariq Al-Tuckmachi *Financier*
%Rafidain Bank, New Banks St, Massarif, Baghdad, Iraq

Tarkanian, Jerry *Basketball Coach*
%University of Nevada, Athletic Dept, Las Vegas, NV 89153

Tarkenton, Fran *Football Player, Businessman*
%Tarkenton & Co, 3340 Peachtree Rd NE, #444, Atlanta, GA 30326

Tarnow, Robert L *Businessman*
%Goulds Pumps Inc, 240 Fall St, Seneca Falls, NY 13148

Tarr, Curtis W *Government Official*
3701 39th St, Moline, IL 61265

Tarr, Jeffrey *Financier*
%Junction Partners, 437 Madison Ave, New York, NY 10022

Tarr, Robert J, Jr *Businessman*
%General Cinema Corp, 27 Boylston St, Chestnut Hill, MA 02176

Tarski, Alfred *Mathematician*
462 Michigan Ave, Berkeley, CA 94707

Tartabull, Dan *Baseball Player*
4105 NW 185th St, Coral City, FL 33055

Tartikoff, Brandon *Television Executive*
%Paramount Pictures, 1 Gulf+Western Plz, New York, NY 10023

Tarver, Jackson W *Publisher*
%Atlanta Journal-Constitution, 72 Marietta St, Atlanta, GA 30303

Tashiro, Takeshi *Financier*
%Sumitomo Trust & Banking Ltd, 5-15 Kitahama, Osaka 540, Japan

Tata, J R D *Businessman*
The Cairn, Altamount Rd, Bombay 400 026, India

Tate, Albert, Jr *Judge*
%US Court of Appeals, 600 Camp St, New Orleans, LA 70130

Tate, Frank *Boxer*
%Houston Boxing Assn, 5470 Newcastle, Houston, TX 77027

Tate, Jeffrey P *Conductor*
%Royal Opera House, Convent Gdn, London WC2E 7QA, England

Taub, Henry *Businessman*
%Automatic Data Processing, 1 ADP Blvd, Roseland, NJ 07068

Taub, Melvin S *Businessman*
%Prime Motor Inns Inc, 700 Rt 46 E, Fairfield, NJ 07006

Taube, Henry *Nobel Chemistry Laureate*
441 Gerona Rd, Stanford, CA 94305

Taubman, Alfred *Businessman*
%Taubman Co, 3270 W Big Beaver Rd, #300, Troy, MI 48084

Taufa'ahau Tupou IV *King, Tonga*
%The Palace, PO Box 6, Nuku'alofa, Tonga

Tauke, Thomas J *Representative, IA*
1715 Glen Oak, Dubuque, IA 52001

T

Taulbee – Taylor

Taulbee, John E *Businessman*
%Central & South West Corp, 2121 San Jacinto St, Dallas, TX 75266

Taupin, Bernie *Lyricist*
1320 N Doheny Dr, Los Angeles, CA 90049

Tauzin, W J (Billy) *Representative, LA*
%House of Representatives, Washington, DC 20515

Tavener, John *Football Player*
197 N Main, Johnstown, OH 43031

Taverner, Sonia *Ballerina*
PO Box 129, Stony Plain AB, Canada

Tavernier, Bertrand *Movie Director*
66 Blvd Malesherbes, 75008 Paris, France

Tavoulareas, William P *Businessman*
%Mobil Corp, 150 E 42nd St, New York, NY 10017

Taya, Sid Ahmed Ould *President, Mauritania*
%President's Office, Nouakchott, Mauritania

Taylor, Arthur R *Businessman*
30 Rockefeller Plz, #4300, New York, NY 10112

Taylor, Billy *Jazz Pianist, Composer*
555 Kappock St, Bronx, NY 16463

Taylor, Charles (Chuck) *Football Player, Coach*
242 Oak Grove Ave, Atherton, CA 94025

Taylor, Charles H *Representative, NC*
%House of Representatives, Washington, DC 20515

Taylor, Charley *Football Player, Executive*
%Washington Redskins, Dulles Airport, Box 17247, Washington, DC 20041

Taylor, Dave *Hockey Player*
%Los Angeles Kings, Great Western Forum, 3900 W Manchester, Inglewood, CA 90306

Taylor, Delores *Actress*
12953 Marlboro St, Los Angeles, CA 90049

Taylor, Don *Movie Director*
1111 San Vicente Blvd, Santa Monica, CA 90402

Taylor, Donald *Businessman*
%Rexnord, 350 N Sunny Slope Rd, Brookfield, WI 53005

Taylor, Dub *Actor*
21417 Gaona St, Woodland Hills, CA 91364

Taylor, Elizabeth *Actress*
700 Nimes Rd, Los Angeles, CA 90024

Taylor, Eric *Artist*
13 Tredgold Ave, Branhope Near Leeds, W Yorkshire LS16 9BS, England

Taylor, Ernest-Frank *Actor*
3857 Tracy St, Los Angeles, CA 90027

Taylor, Gene *Representative, MI*
%House of Representatives, Washington, DC 20515

Taylor, Gene *Representative, MS*
%House of Representatives, Washington, DC 20515

Taylor, George *Botanist*
Belhaven House, Dunbar, East Lothian EH42 1NS, England

Taylor, Henry S *Poet*
PO Box 85, Lincoln, VA 22078

Taylor, Horace G *Army General*
Commanding General, III Corps & Fort Hood, Fort Hood, TX 76544

Taylor, James *Singer, Songwriter*
%Peter Asher Mgmt, 644 N Doheny Dr, Los Angeles, CA 90069

Taylor, James A *Vietnam War Army Hero (CMH)*
793 Hagemann Dr, Livermore, CA 94550

Taylor, Jim *Football Player*
8069 Summa Ave, #A, Baton Rouge, LA 70809

Taylor, John R *Financier*
%Bankers Life Co, 711 High St, Des Moines, IA 50307

Taylor, Joseph H, Jr *Radio Astronomer*
272 Hartley St, Princeton, NJ 08544

Taylor, Kenneth N *Publisher*
1515 E Forest Ave, Wheaton, IL 60187

Taylor, Lauriston S *Physicist*
7407 Denton Rd, Bethesda, MD 20014

Taylor, Lawrence *Football Player*
%New York Giants, Giants Stadium, East Rutherford, NJ 07073
Taylor, Lawrence E *Columnist*
1000 Jefferson Dr, #228, Washington, DC 20568
Taylor, Lionel *Football Player, Coach*
%Texas Southern University, Athletic Dept, Houston, TX 77004
Taylor, Mark L *Actor*
7919 W Norton Ave, Los Angeles, CA 90046
Taylor, Meshach *Actor*
%David Shapira Assoc, 15301 Ventura Blvd, #345, Sherman Oaks, CA 91403
Taylor, Paul B *Dancer, Choreographer*
%Yesselman, 550 Broadway, New York, NY 10012
Taylor, Paul S *Economist*
1163 Euclid Ave, Berkeley, CA 94708
Taylor, Peter *Writer*
1841 Wayside Pl, Charlottesville, VA 22903
Taylor, R G *Financier*
%First Western Financial Corp, 2700 W Sahara Ave, Las Vegas, NV 89102
Taylor, R Lee, II *Businessman*
%Federal Co, PO Box 17236, Memphis, TN 38187
Taylor, Richard E *Nobel Physics Laureate*
%Stanford Linear Accelerator Ctr, PO Box 4349, Stanford, CA 94305
Taylor, Rip *Comedian*
1608 Sombrero Dr, Las Vegas, NV 89109
Taylor, Robert Lewis *Writer*
Bulb Bridge Rd, South Kent, CT 06785
Taylor, Rod *Actor*
2375 Bowmont Dr, Beverly Hills, CA 90210
Taylor, Ruth *Actress*
1575 Via Norte, Palm Springs, CA 92262
Taylor, Samuel A *Playwright*
%General Delivery, East Blue Hill, ME 04629
Taylor, Steven *Musician (Aerosmith)*
%Collins/Barasso Mgmt, 215 1st St, Cambridge, MA 02142
Taylor, Telford *Attorney, Writer*
54 Morningside Dr, New York, NY 10025
Taylor, William *Government Official, Financier*
%Federal Deposit Insurance Corp, 550 17th St NW, Washington, DC 20429
Taylor, William O *Publisher*
%Affiliated Publications, 135 Morrissey Blvd, Boston, MA 02107
Taylor, Wilson H *Businessman*
%Cigna Corp, 1 Logan Sq, Philadelphia, PA 19103
Taylor-Young, Leigh *Actress*
%The Agency, 10351 Santa Monica Blvd, #211, Los Angeles, CA 90025
Tcherina, Ludmila *Ballerina*
42 Cours Albert 1er, 75008 Paris, France
Tcherkassky, Marianna *Ballerina*
%American Ballet Theater, 890 Broadway, New York, NY 10003
Tchoungi, Simon Pierre *Prime Minister, Cameroon*
BP 1057, Yaounde, Cameroon
Te Kanawa, Kiri *Opera Singer*
%Basil Horsfield, Estoril 3, 31 Ave Princess Grace, Monte Carlo, Monaco
Teaff, Grant *Football Coach*
8265 Forest Ridge, Waco, TX 76710
Teagle, Terry *Basketball Player*
%Golden State Warriors, Oakland Coliseum, Oakland, CA 94621
Teague, Bertha *Basketball Coach*
117 E 17th St, Ada, OK 74820
Teal, David J *Air Force General*
Vice Comdr, USAF Systems Command, Andrews Air Force Base, Washington, DC 20334
Teale, Edwin Way *Writer*
Trail Wood, Hampton, CT 06247
Tear, Robert *Opera Singer*
11 Ravenscourt Ct, London W6, England
Teasdale, Joseph *Governor, MO*
800 W 47th St, Kansas City, MO 64112

T

Teasley, Harry E *Businessman*
%Coca-Cola Foods Division, 310 North Ave NW, Atlanta, GA 30313

Tebaldi, Renata *Opera Singer*
Piazzetta della Guastella 1, 20122 Milan, Italy

Tebbetts, Birdie *Baseball Player, Manager*
229 Oak Ave, Anna Maria, FL 33501

Tebbitt, Norman *Government Official, England*
%House of Commons, London SW1, England

Tebbutt, Arthur R *Statistician*
1511 Pelican Point Dr, Sarasota, FL 33581

Tedrow, Irene *Actress*
5763 Corteen Pl, North Hollywood, CA 91602

Teets, John W *Businessman*
%Greyhound Corp, Greyhound Tower, Phoenix, AZ 85077

Teichner, Helmut *Skier*
4250 Marine Dr, #2101, Chicago, IL 60654

Teitell, Conrad L *Attorney*
44 Binney Ln, Old Greenwich, CT 06870

Tekulve, Kent *Baseball Player*
1531 Sequoia, Pittsburgh, PA 15241

Telegdi, Valentine L *Physicist*
%University of Chicago, Physics Dept, Chicago, IL 60637

Tellep, Daniel M *Businessman*
%Lockheed Corp, 4500 Park Granada Blvd, Burbank, CA 91399

Teller, Edward *Physicist*
%University of California, PO Box 808, Livermore, CA 94550

Telling, Edward R *Businessman*
%Sears Roebuck & Co, Sears Tower, Chicago, IL 60684

Telnack, John J (Jack) *Automobile Designer*
%Ford Motor Co, American Rd, Dearborn, MI 48121

Teltscher, Eliot *Tennis Player*
%Pepperdine University, Athletic Dept, Malibu, CA 90265

Temesvari, Andrea *Tennis Player*
%ProServ, 888 17th St NW, #1200, Washington, DC 20006

Temianka, Henri *Conductor*
2915 Patricia Ave, Los Angeles, CA 90064

Temin, Howard M *Nobel Medicine Laureate*
%University of Wisconsin, McArdle Laboratory, Madison, WI 53706

Temirkanov, Yuri *Conductor*
%St Petersburg Philharmonic, 1 Ploshchad Iskusstv, St Petersburg, Russia

Temko, Allan *Journalist*
%San Francisco Chronicle, 901 Misson St, San Francisco, CA 94103

Temple, Arthur *Businessman*
%Temple-Inland Inc, 303 S Temple Dr, Diboll, TX 75941

Temple, Edward S *Track Coach*
%Tennessee State University, Athletic Dept, Nashville, TN 37203

Templeton, Garry *Baseball Player*
13552 Del Pomonte Rd, Poway, CA 92064

Templeton, John M *Financier*
%Lyford Cay Club, Box N-7776, Nassau, Bahamas

Tenace, Gene *Baseball Player*
15368 Marker Rd, Poway, CA 92064

Tenenbaum, Michael *Businessman*
%Inland Steel Co, 30 W Monroe St, Chicago, IL 60603

Tennant, Samuel M *Businessman*
%Aerospace Corp, 2350 El Segundo Blvd, El Segundo, CA 90245

Tennant, Veronica *Ballerina*
%National Ballet of Canada, 157 King St E, Toronto ON M5C 1G9, Canada

Tennant, Victoria *Actress*
PO Box 929, Beverly Hills, CA 90213

Tenney, Jon *Actor*
%Agency for Performing Arts, 9000 Sunset Blvd, #1200, Los Angeles, CA 90069

Tennille, Toni *Singer (Captain & Tennille)*
%Triad Artists, 10100 Santa Monica Blvd, #1600, Los Angeles, CA 90067

Tenorio, Pedro *Governor, CM*
%Governor's Office, Capitol Hill, Saipan, CM 96950

Ter Horst, Jerald *Government Official, Journalist*
7815 Evening Ln, Alexandria, VA 22306

Teraoka, Masami *Artist*
%Space Gallery, 6015 Santa Monica Blvd, Los Angeles, CA 90028

Teresa, Mother *Nobel Peace Laureate*
Missionaries of Charity, 5-A Chandra Bose Rd, Calcutta 700016, India

Tereshkova, Valentina V *Cosmonaut*
%Soviet Woman's Committee, 6 Nemirovich-Danchenko, Moscow 103009, Russia

Terra, Daniel J *Businessman, Art Patron*
528 Roslyn Rd, Kenilowrth, IL 60043

Terracciano, Anthony P *Financier*
%Chase Manhattan Corp, 1 Chase Manhattan Plz, New York, NY 10081

Terracciano, Frank P *Financier*
%Mellon Bank Corp, 1 Mellon Bank Ctr, Pittsburgh, PA 15258

Terry, Hilda *Cartoonist (Teena)*
8 Henderson Pl, New York, NY 10028

Terry, Megan *Playwright*
2309 Hanscom Blvd, Omaha, NE 68105

Terry, Walter *Dance Critic*
%Saturday Review Magazine, 1290 Ave of Americas, New York, NY 10019

Tesch, Emmanuel *Businessman*
%ARBED, Ave de la Liberte, 2930 Luxembourg

Tesh, John *Entertainer*
%"Entertainment Tonight" Show, Paramount-TV, 555 Melrose, Los Angeles, CA 90038

Tesich, Steve *Writer*
40 W 57th St, New York, NY 10019

Testaverde, Vinny *Football Player*
%Tampa Bay Buccaneers, 1 Buccaneer Pl, Tampa, FL 33607

Testi, Fabio *Actor*
%M Pietravalle, Viale Buozzi 5, 00197 Rome, Italy

Teti, Alfred L *Financier*
%CenTrust Savings Bank, 101 E Flagler St, Miami, FL 33131

Tetley, Glen *Ballet Director, Choreographer*
15 W 9th St, New York, NY 10011

Tewes, Lauren *Actress*
%Borinstein Oreck Bogart, 8271 Melrose Ave, #110, Los Angeles, CA 90046

Thagard, Norman E *Astronaut*
%NASA, Johnson Space Ctr, Houston, TX 77058

Thalheimer, Richard *Businessman*
%Sharper Image, 680 Davis St, San Francisco, CA 94111

Thani, Sheikh Khalifa ibn Hamad al- *Emir, Qatar*
%Royal Palace, Doha, Qatar

Tharp, Twyla *Dancer, Choreographer*
%Twyla Tharp Dance Foundation, 38 Walker St, New York, NY 10013

Thatcher, Margaret H *Prime Minister, England*
%House of Commons, London SW1A 0AA, England

Thaves, Bob *Cartoonist (Frank & Earnest)*
PO Box 67, Manhattan Beach, CA 90266

Thaxter, Phyllis *Actress*
716 Riomar Dr, Vero Beach, FL 32963

Thayer, James M *Financier*
%Gibraltar Financial Corp, 9111 Wilshire Blvd, Beverly Hills, CA 90210

Thayer, W Paul *Businessman, Government Official*
10200 Hollow Way, Dallas, TX 75229

Theile, David *Swimmer*
84 Woodville St, Hendea, Brisbane 4011, Australia

Theismann, Joe *Football Player*
150 Branch Rd SE, Vienna, VA 22180

Theobald, Thomas C *Financier*
%Continental Illinois Corp, 231 S LaSalle St, Chicago, IL 60697

Theodorakis, Mikis *Composer*
111 Rue Notre-Dame-des-Champs, 75006 Paris, France

Theodosius, Primate Metropolitan *Religious Leader*
%Orthodox Church in America, PO Box 675, Syosset, NY 11791

Theroux, Paul *Writer*
35 Elsynge Rd, London SW18 2NR, England

Thesiger, Wilfred P *Explorer*
15 Shelley Ct, Tite St, London SW3 4JB, England

Theus, Reggie *Basketball Player*
%New Jersey Nets, Meadowlands Arena, East Rutherford, NJ 07073

Thiandoum, Hyacinthe Cardinal *Religious Leader*
Archeveche, BP 1908, Dakar, Senegal

Thibaudet, Jean-Yves *Concert Pianist*
%IMG Artists, 22 E 71st St, New York, NY 10021

Thibiant, Aida *Fashion Expert*
%Institut de Beaute, 449 N Canon Dr, Beverly Hills, CA 90210

Thicke, Alan *Actor*
%Fred Lawrence Assoc, 9044 Melrose Ave, #300, Los Angeles, CA 90069

Thiebaud, Wayne *Artist*
1617 17th Ave, Sacramento, CA 95818

Thier, Samuel O *Physician*
8 Spector Rd, Woodbridge, CT 06525

Thieriot, Richard T *Publisher*
%San Francisco Chronicle, 901 Mission St, San Francisco, CA 94103

Thierry, Jacques *Financier*
%Banque Bruxelles Lambert, 24 Ave Marnix, 1050 Brussels, Belgium

Thiess, Ursula *Actress*
1940 Bel Air Rd, Los Angeles, CA 90077

Thimann, Kenneth V *Biologist*
36 Pasatiempo Dr, Santa Cruz, CA 95060

Thimmesch, Nicholas *Journalist*
6301 Broad Branch Rd, Chevy Chase, MD 20015

Thinnes, Roy *Actor*
2641 Nichols Canyon Rd, Los Angeles, CA 90046

Thirdkill, David *Basketball Player*
%Boston Celtics, 151 Merrimac St, Boston, MA 02114

Thirkettle, Jim *Auto Racing Driver*
%NASCAR, 1801 Volusia Ave, Daytona Beach, FL 32015

Thirsk, Bob *Astronaut, Canada*
%National Research Council, Montreal Rd, Ottawa ON K1A 0R6, Canada

Thode, Henry G *Chemist*
%McMaster University, Nuclear Research Bldg, Hamilton ON L8S 4K1, Canada

Thoma, Georg *Nordic Skier*
Bisten 6, 7824 Hinterzarten, Germany

Thomas of Swynnerton, Hugh *Historian*
29 Ladbroke Grove, London W11, England

Thomas, B J *Singer*
%Starbound, 128 Volunteer Dr, Hendersonville, TN 37075

Thomas, Barbara S *Government Official*
%Securities & Exchange Commission, 450 5th St NW, Washington, DC 20549

Thomas, Bert L *Businessman*
%Winn-Dixie Stores, 5050 Edgewood Ct, Jacksonville, FL 33203

Thomas, Betty *Actress*
%International Creative Mgmt, 8899 Beverly Blvd, Los Angeles, CA 90048

Thomas, Blair *Football Player*
%New York Jets, 598 Madison Ave, New York, NY 10022

Thomas, Charles F *Basketball Executive*
%Houston Rockets, Summit, Greenway Plz, #10, Houston, TX 77046

Thomas, Clarence *Supreme Court Justice*
%US Supreme Court, 1 1st St NE, Washington, DC 20543

Thomas, Craig *Representative, WY*
%House of Representatives, Washington, DC 20515

Thomas, D M *Writer, Poet*
Coach House, Rashleigh Vale, Tregolls Rd, Truro, Cornwall TR1 1TJ, England

Thomas, Debi *Figure Skater*
%Stanford University, Athletic Dept, Stanford, CA 94305

Thomas, Derrick *Football Player*
%Kansas City Chiefs, 1 Arrowhead Dr, Kansas City, MO 64129

Thomas, Dominic R *Religious Leader*
%Church of Jesus Christ, 6th & Lincoln Sts, Monongahela, PA 15063

Thomas, Donald A *Astronaut*
%NASA, Johnson Space Center, Houston, TX 77058

Thomas, E Donnall *Nobel Medicine Laureate*
%Hutchinson Cancer Research Center, 1124 Columbia St, Seattle, WA 98104

Thomas, Frank *Baseball Player*
118 Doray Dr, Pittsburgh, PA 15237

Thomas, Franklin A *Foundation Executive*
%Ford Foundation, 230 E 43rd St, New York, NY 10017

Thomas, Gorman *Baseball Player*
5102 W Bluemound Rd, Milwaukee, WI 53208

Thomas, Helen *Journalist*
1400 "I" St NW, Washington, DC 20004

Thomas, Isiah *Basketball Player*
%Detroit Pistons, Palace, 1 Championship Dr, Auburn Hills, MI 48057

Thomas, Joab L *Educator*
%Pennsylvania State University, President's Office, University Park, PA 16802

Thomas, Kurt *Gymnast*
%George Wallach, 1400 Braeridge Dr, Beverly Hills, CA 90210

Thomas, L C *Businessman*
%Sohio Pipe Line Co, Midland Bldg, Cleveland, OH 44115

Thomas, Lee J *Businessman*
%Sterling Drugs Inc, 90 Park Ave, New York, NY 10016

Thomas, Lee M *Government Official*
%Enviromental Protection Agency, 401 "M" St SW, Washington, DC 20460

Thomas, Lewis *Physician, Educator*
333 E 68th St, New York, NY 10021

Thomas, Lindsay *Representative, GA*
%House of Representatives, Washington, DC 20515

Thomas, Llewellyn H *Theoretical Physicist*
3012 Wycliff Rd, Raleigh, NC 27607

Thomas, Michael Tilson *Conductor*
%Carson Office, 119 W 57th St, New York, NY 10019

Thomas, Milton H *Financier*
%Dallas Federal Financial Corp, 8333 Douglas Ave, Dallas, TX 75225

Thomas, Philip Michael *Actor*
%Exclusive Artists Agency, 2501 W Burbank Blvd, Burbank, CA 91505

Thomas, Pinklon *Boxer*
%Angelo Dundee, 1505 NW 167th St, #405, Miami, FL 33169

Thomas, R David *Businessman*
%Wendy's International, 4288 W Dublin Granville Rd, Dublin, OH 43017

Thomas, Ralph S *Businessman*
%Robertshaw Controls Co, 1701 Byrd Ave, Richmond, VA 23261

Thomas, Rene *Financier*
%Banque Nationale de Paris, 16 Blvd des Italiens, 75009 Paris, France

Thomas, Richard *Actor*
5261 Cleon Ave, North Hollywood, CA 91601

Thomas, Richard L *Financier*
%First Chicago Corp, 1 First National Plz, Chicago, IL 60670

Thomas, Robert E *Businessman*
%Mapco Inc, 1800 Baltimore, Tulsa, OK 74119

Thomas, Ross *Writer*
28124 Pacific Coast Hwy, Malibu, CA 90265

Thomas, Scott *Football Player*
%US Air Force Academy, Athletic Dept, Air Force Academy, CO 80804

Thomas, Thurman *Football Player*
%Buffalo Bills, 1 Bills Dr, Orchard Park, NY 14127

Thomas, Tracy Y *Mathematician*
249 N Glenroy Ave, Los Angeles, CA 90049

Thomas, W Bruce *Businessman*
%USX Corp, 600 Grant St, Pittsburgh, PA 15230

Thomas, William M *Representative, CA*
1830 Truxton Ave, Bakersfield, CA 93301

Thomopoulos, Anthony *Television Executive*
%ABC-Entertainment, 1330 Ave of Americas, New York, NY 10019

Thompson, Anthony *Football Player*
%Phoenix Cardinals, PO Box 888, Phoenix, AZ 85100

Thompson, Bill M *Businessman*
%Phillips Petroleum Co, Phillips Bldg, Bartlesville, OK 74004

T

Thompson – Thompson

Thompson, Carlos *Actor*
Villa La Loma, Goldingen, Switzerland

Thompson, Daley *Track Athlete*
%Olympic Assn, 1 Wadsworth Plain, London SW18 1EH, England

Thompson, Darrell *Football Player*
%Green Bay Packers, 1265 Lombardi Ave, Green Bay, WI 54303

Thompson, David *Basketball Player*
4380 S Syracuse St, #304, Denver, CO 80237

Thompson, David C *Coast Guard Admiral*
%US Coast Guard, Atlantic, Governors Island, New York, NY 10004

Thompson, David R *Judge*
%US Court of Appeals, 940 Front St, San Diego, CA 92189

Thompson, Edward K *Editor*
%Smithsonian Magazine, 900 Jefferson Dr, Washington, DC 20560

Thompson, Edward T *Editor*
%Reader's Digest Assn, Pleasantville, NY 10570

Thompson, Emma *Actress*
%Renaissance Theatre, 56 King's Rd, Kingston-upon-Thames KT2 5H8, England

Thompson, G Ralph *Religious Leader*
%Seventh-day Adventists, 12501 Old Columbia Pike, Silver Spring, MD 20904

Thompson, Homer A *Archaeologist*
134 Mercer St, Princeton, NJ 08540

Thompson, Hugh *Educator*
%Washburn University, President's Office, Topeka, KS 66621

Thompson, Hunter *Journalist, Writer*
PO Box 220, Woody Creek, CO 81656

Thompson, J Lee *Movie Director*
%Cannon Films, 640 San Vicente Blvd, Los Angeles, CA 90048

Thompson, James B, Jr *Geologist*
20 Richmond Rd, Belmont, MA 02178

Thompson, James R, Jr *Space Administrator*
%Marshall Space Flight Ctr, Director's Office, Huntsville, AL 35812

Thompson, Jere W *Businessman*
%Southland Corp, 2828 N Haskell Ave, Dallas, TX 75204

Thompson, John A *Businessman*
2-A High Point Rd, Westport, CT 06880

Thompson, John B *Basketball Coach*
%Georgetown University, Athletic Dept, Washington, DC 20057

Thompson, John M, Jr *Businessman*
%National Gypsum Co, 4500 Lincoln Plz, Dallas, TX 75201

Thompson, John P *Businessman*
%Southland Corp, 2828 N Haskell Ave, Dallas, TX 75204

Thompson, John W *Financier*
%AmeriWest Financial Corp, 6400 Uptown Blvd NE, Albuquerque, NM 87110

Thompson, Kay *Singer, Actress*
300 E 57th St, New York, NY 10022

Thompson, Kenneth L *Computer Scientist*
18 Ridge Way, Fanwood, NJ 07023

Thompson, LaSalle *Basketball Player*
%Sacramento Kings, 1515 Sports Dr, Sacramento, CA 95834

Thompson, Lea *Actress*
7966 Woodrow Wilson Dr, Los Angeles, CA 90046

Thompson, Linda *Actress*
%Artists Group, 1930 Century Park West, #403, Los Angeles, CA 90067

Thompson, Max *WW II Army Hero (CMH)*
Rt 3, Box 56, Canton, NC 28716

Thompson, Milton *Test Pilot*
1640 W Ave L-12, Lancaster, CA 93534

Thompson, Paul H *Educator*
%Weber State University, President's Office, Ogden, UT 84408

Thompson, R Patrick *Financier*
%New York Mercantile Exchange, 4 World Trade Ctr, New York, NY 10048

Thompson, Richard C *Publisher*
%US News & World Report Magazine, 2400 "N" St NW, Washington, DC 20037

Thompson, Robert G K *Army General, England*
Pitcott House, Winsford Minehead, Som, England

Thompson, Sada *Actress*
PO Box 490, Southbury, CT 06488

Thompson, Starley L *Climatologist*
%National Ctr for Atmospheric Research, PO Box 3000, Boulder, CO 80307

Thompson, Tommy *Football Player*
PO Box 366, Calico Rock, AR 72519

Thompson, Tommy G *Governor, WI*
%Governor's Office, State Capitol, PO Box 7863, Madison, WI 53707

Thompson, W Reid *Businessman*
%Potomac Electric Power Co, 1900 Pennsylvania NW, Washington, DC 20068

Thompson, William P *Religious Leader*
%World Council of Churches, 475 Riverside Dr, New York, NY 10115

Thompson, Willis H, Jr *Businessman*
%MAPCO Inc, 1800 S Baltimore Ave, Tulsa, OK 74119

Thomsen, Ib *Businessman*
%Goodyear Tire & Rubber Co, 1144 E Market St, Akron, OH 44316

Thomson of Fleet, Kenneth R *Publisher*
8 Kensington Palace Gdns, London W8, England

Thomson, Bobby *Baseball Player*
122 Sunlit Dr, Watchung, NJ 07060

Thomson, Gordon *Actor*
%Edrick/Rich Mgmt, 8957 Norma Pl, Los Angeles, CA 90069

Thomson, H C (Hank) *Harness Racing Official*
PO Box 38, Mullett Lake, MI 49761

Thomson, James A *Foundation Executive*
%Rand Corp, 1700 Main St, Santa Monica, CA 90406

Thomson, June *Commentator*
%KNBC-TV, News Dept, 3000 W Alameda Ave, Burbank, CA 91523

Thomson, Kenneth *Publisher*
%Thomson Newspapers, 65 Queen St W, Toronto ON M5H 2MB, Canada

Thomson, Meldrim, Jr *Governor, NH*
Mt Cube Farm, Orford, NH 03773

Thomson, Peter W *Golfer*
Malvern, Vic 3141, Australia

Thon, William *Artist*
%General Delivery, Port Clyde, ME 04855

Thone, Charles *Governor, NE*
%Erickson & Sederstrom, 301 S 13th St, #400, Lincoln, NE 68508

Thoni, Gustav *Skier, Coach*
39026 Prato Allo Stelvio-Prao BZ, Italy

Thorn, George W *Physician*
%Harvard Medical School, 45 Shattuck St, Boston, MA 02115

Thornberry, W Homer *Judge*
%US Circuit Court, 200 W 8th St, Austin, TX 78701

Thorne, Oakleigh B *Businessman*
%Commerce Clearing House, 4025 W Peterson Ave, Chicago, IL 60646

Thorne-Smith, Courtney *Actress*
%STE Representation, 9301 Wilshire Blvd, Beverly Hills, CA 90210

Thorneycroft of Dunston, Peter *Government Official, England*
%House of Lords, London SW1, England

Thornhill, Arthur H, Jr *Publisher*
%Little Brown & Co, Rockefeller Ctr, New York, NY 10020

Thornton, Andre *Baseball Player*
Box 395, Chagrin Falls, OH 44022

Thornton, John V *Businessman*
%Consolidated Edison Co, 4 Irving Pl, New York, NY 10003

Thornton, Kathryn C *Astronaut*
%NASA, Johnson Space Ctr, Houston, TX 77058

Thornton, Ray *Representative, AR*
%House of Representatives, Washington, DC 20515

Thornton, William E *Astronaut*
%NASA, Johnson Space Ctr, Houston, TX 77058

Thornton-Sherwood, Madeleine *Actress*
32 Leroy St, New York, NY 10014

Thorp, Willard L *Economist*
9 Harkness Rd, Amherst, MA 01002

Thorpe, James *Library, Art Gallery Director*
%Huntington Library, 1650 Orlando Rd, San Marino, CA 91108
Thorpe, Jeremy *Government Official, England*
2 Orme Sq, Bayswater, London W2, England
Thorpe, Jim *Golfer*
%Professional Golfers Assn, PO Box 109601, Palm Beach Gardens, FL 33410
Thorpe, Otis *Basketball Player*
%Houston Rockets, Summit, Greenway Plaza, #10, Houston, TX 77046
Thorsen, Howard B *Coast Guard Admiral*
Commander, Atlantic Area, US Coast Guard, Governors Island, New York, NY 10004
Thorsness, Leo K *Vietnam Air Force Hero (CMH)*
9640 Rainier Ave S, Seattle, WA 98110
Threlkeld, Richard *Commentator*
%CBS-TV, News Dept, 51 W 52nd St, New York, NY 10019
Threshie, R David, Jr *Publisher*
%Orange County Register, 625 N Grand Ave, Santa Ana, CA 92711
Throne, Malachi *Actor*
13067 Greenleaf St, Studio City, CA 91604
Throneberry, Marv *Baseball Player*
12102 Macon Rd, Collierville, TN 38017
Thulin, Ingrid *Actress*
Kevingestrand 7-B, 18231 Danderyd, Sweden
Thumer, Petra *Swimmer*
Robert-Siebert-Strasse 76, Karl-Marx-Stadt 9047, Germany
Thunholm, Lars-Erik *Businessman*
%Swedish Match, PO Box 16100, 103 22 Stockholm, Sweden
Thuot, Pierre J *Astronaut*
%NASA, Johnson Space Ctr, Houston, TX 77058
Thurman, Uma *Actress*
%Flick East-West Talents, 1608 Las Palmas Ave, Los Angeles, CA 90028
Thurmond, J Strom *Senator/Governor, SC*
PO Box 981, Aiken, SC 29801
Thurmond, Nate *Basketball Player*
%Golden State Warriors, Oakland Coliseum, Oakland, CA 94621
Thurow, Lester C *Educator*
%Massachusetts Institute of Technology, Economics Dept, Cambridge, MA 02139
Thurston, Frederick (Fuzzy) *Football Player*
572 Danz Ave, Green Bay, WI 54302
Thwaits, James A *Businessman*
%Minnesota Mining & Manufacturing Co, 3-M Ctr, St Paul, MN 55144
Thygerson, Kenneth J *Financier*
%Imperial Corp of America, 401 W "A" St, San Diego, CA 92101
Thyssen-Bornenisza, Hans-Heinrich *Businessman, Art Collector*
Villa Favorita, 6976 Castagnola di Lugano, Switzerland
Tiainen, Juha *Track Athlete*
%Olympic Committee, Topeliuksenkatu 41 a A, Helsinki 25, Finland
Tian Jiyun *Government Official, China*
%Vice Premier's Office, Communist Party, Beijing, China
Tibbets, Paul W *WW II Army Air Corps Hero*
5574 Knollwood Dr, Columbus, OH 43232
Tibbetts, Hubert M *Businessman*
%Thomas J Lipton Inc, 800 Sylvan Ave, Englewood Cliffs, NJ 07632
Tice, George A *Photographer*
323 Gill Ln, #9-B, Iselin, NJ 08830
Tichnor, Alan *Religious Leader*
%United Synagogue of America, 155 5th Ave, New York, NY 10010
Tickner, Charlie *Figure Skater*
5410 Sunset Dr, Littleton, CO 80123
Tidbury, Charles Henderson *Businessman*
%Whitebread & Co Brewery, Chiswell St, London EC14 4SD, England
Tidwell, Moody R, III *Judge*
%US Claims Court, 717 Madison Pl NW, Washington, DC 20005
Tiegs, Cheryl *Model*
7060 Hollywood Blvd, #1010, Los Angeles, CA 90028
Tiemann, Norbert T *Governor, NE*
%Henningson Durham Richardson, 12700 Hillcrest Rd, #125, Dallas, TX 75230

T

Tien, Chang-Lin *Educator*
%University of California, Chancellor's Office, Berkeley, CA 94720

Tierney, Lawrence *Actor*
%Don Gerler Assoc, 3349 Cahuenga Blvd, #2, Los Angeles, CA 90068

Tietjens, Norman O *Judge*
3509 Overlook Ln, Washington, DC 20016

Tietz, William J, Jr *Educator*
%Montana State University, President's Office, Bozeman, MT 59717

Tiffany (Renee Darwish) *Singer*
13659 Victory Blvd, #550, Van Nuys, CA 91401

Tiffin, Pamela *Actress*
15 W 67th St, New York, NY 10023

Tigar, Kenneth *Actor*
%Michael Schlesinger Assoc, 8730 Sunset Blvd, #220, Los Angeles, CA 90069

Tiger, Lionel *Social Scientist*
RD 2, Millbrook, NY 12545

Tiivola, Mika *Businessman*
%Nokia Grp, Mikonkatu 15 A, SF-00101 Helsinki 10, Finland

Tikkanen, Esa *Hockey Player*
%Edmonton Oilers, Northlands Coliseum, Edmonton AL T5B 4M9, Canada

Tilberis, Elizabeth *Editor*
%Harper's Bazaar Magazine, 1900 Broadway, New York, NY 10019

Tiller, Nadja *Actress*
Via Tamporiva 26, 6976 Castagnola, Switzerland

Tillinghast, Charles C, Jr *Businessman*
25 John St, Providence, RI 02906

Tillis, Mel *Singer*
809 18th Ave S, Nashville, TN 37203

Tillis, Pam *Singer*
PO Box 25304, Nashville, TN 37202

Tilston, Frederick A *WW II Canadian Army Hero (VC)*
RR 1, Kettleby ON L0G 1J0, Canada

Tilton, Charlene *Actress*
4634 Azalia Dr, Tarzana, CA 91356

Tilton, David L *Businessman*
%Financial Corp of Santa Barbara, 3908 State St, Santa Barbara, CA 93105

Tilton, Martha *Singer*
2257 Mandeville Canyon Rd, Los Angeles, CA 90049

Timbers, William H *Judge*
915 Lafayette Blvd, Bridgeport, CT 06604

Timerman, Jacobo *Publisher*
%Alfred Knopf Inc, 201 E 50th St, New York, NY 10022

Timken, W R *Businessman*
%Timken Co, 1835 Dueber Ave SW, Canton, OH 44706

Timken, W T, Jr *Businessman*
%Timken Co, 1835 Dueber Ave SW, Canton, OH 44706

Timme, Robert *Architect*
%Taft Architects, 807 Peden St, Houston, TX 77006

Timmermann, Ulf *Track Athlete*
Conrad Blenkle Strasse 34, 1055 Berlin, Germany

Timmons, Steve *Volleyball Player*
%RedSand, 720 Gateway Center Dr, San Diego, CA 92101

Timofeyeva, Nina *Ballerina*
%State Academic Bolshoi Theater, 1 Ploshchad Sverdlova, Moscow, Russia

Tinbergen, Jan *Nobel Economics Laureate*
Haviklaan 31, 2566XD The Hague, Netherlands

Tincher, William R *Businessman*
%Purex Corp, 5101 Clark Ave, Lakewood, CA 90712

Tindemans, Leo *Prime Minister, Belgium*
Jan Verbertlei 24, 2520 Edegem, Belgium

Ting, Samuel C C *Nobel Physics Laureate*
15 Moon Hill Rd, Lexington, MA 02173

Ting, Walasse *Artist*
100 W 25th St, New York, NY 10001

Tingay, Lance *Tennis Player*
10 Hill Ct, Wimbledon Hill Rd, London SW19 7PD, England

T

Tinker – Tobin

Tinker, Grant *Television Executive*
760 Lausanne Rd, Los Angeles, CA 90024

Tinkham, Michael *Physicist*
98 Rutledge Rd, Belmont, MA 02178

Tinsley, Bruce *Editorial Cartoonist*
%USA Today, 1000 Wilson Blvd, Arlington, VA 22209

Tinsley, Jack *Editor*
%Fort Worth Star-Telegram, 400 W 7th St, Fort Worth, TX 76102

Tiny Tim *Singer*
%Hotel Olcott, 27 W 72nd St, New York, NY 10023

Tippett, Andre *Football Player*
%New England Patriots, Sullivan Stadium, Foxboro, MA 02035

Tippett, Michael K *Composer, Conductor*
%Schott & Co, 48 Great Marlborough St, London W1V 2BN, England

Tippett, W Paul *Businessman*
%Springs Industries, 205 N White St, Fort Hill, SC 29715

Tippett, W Paul, Jr *Businessman*
%American Motors Corp, 27777 Franklin Rd, Southfield, MI 48034

Tipton, Daniel *Religious Leader*
%Churches of Christ in Christian Union, Box 30, Circleville, OH 43113

Tipton, Eric *Football Player*
125 Nina Ln, Williamsburg, VA 23185

Tiriac, Ion *Tennis Player*
%Estoril, 31 Ave Princess Grace, Monte Carlo, Monaco

Tisch, Laurence A *Businessman*
%CBS Inc, 51 W 52nd St, New York, NY 10019

Tisch, Preston R *Government Official*
%US Postal Service, 475 L'Enfant Plz West SW, Washington, DC 20260

Tisch, Steve *Screenwriter*
%Steve Tisch Co, 3819 Hughes Ave, Culver City, CA 90232

Tisdale, Wayman *Basketball Player*
%Sacramento Kings, 1515 Sports Dr, Sacramento, CA 95834

Titov, Gherman S *Cosmonaut*
141 160 Svyosdny Gorodok, Moskovskoi Oblasti, Potchta Kosmonavtov, Russia

Titov, Vladimir *Cosmonaut*
141 160 Svyosdny Gorodok, Moskovskoi Oblasti, Potchta Kosmonavtov, Russia

Tittle, Y A *Football Player*
310 S Lafayette St, Marshall, TX 75670

Titus-Carmel, Gerard *Artist*
La Grand Maison, 02210 Oulchy Le Chateau, France

Tjoflat, Gerald B *Judge*
%US Court of Appeals, 311 Monroe St W, Jacksonville, FL 32202

Tkaczuk, Ivan *Religious Leader*
%Ukrainian Orthodox Church, 90-34 139th St, Jamaica, NY 11435

To Huu *Government Official, Vietnam*
%Central Committee, Rue Hoang Van Thu, #1-C, Hanoi, Vietnam

Toback, James *Movie Director*
11 E 87th St, New York, NY 10028

Tober, Barbara *Editor*
%Bride Magazine, 350 Madison Ave, New York, NY 10017

Tobey, David *Basketball Referee*
740 Dearborn St, Teaneck, NJ 07666

Tobey, Kenneth *Actor*
14155 Magnolia Blvd, #34, Sherman Oaks, CA 91423

Tobian, Gary *Diver*
1330 Daily Circle Dr, Glendale, CA 91208

Tobias, Andrew *Writer*
%Micro Education Corp of America, 285 Riverside Ave, Westport, CT 06880

Tobias, Randall L *Businessman*
%American Telephone & Telegraph Co, 550 Madison Ave, New York, NY 10022

Tobias, Robert M *Labor Leader*
%Treasury Employees Union, 1730 "K" St NW, Washington, DC 20006

Tobiasse, Theo *Artist*
3 Quai Rauba Coupa, 06 Nice, France

Tobin, Don *Cartoonist (The Little Woman)*
1320 Temple Hills, Laguna Beach, CA 92651

Tobin, James 117 Alden Ave, New Haven, CT 06515	*Nobel Economics Laureate*
Tobin, Robert G %Stop & Shop Companies, PO Box 369, Boston, MA 02101	*Businessman*
Tocchet, Rick %Philadelphia Flyers, Spectrum, Pattison Pl, Philadelphia, PA 19148	*Hockey Player*
Toda, Kengo %Nippondenso, 1-1 Showamachi, Kariya City 448, Japan	*Businessman*
Todd of Trumpington, Baron Alexander R %Christ's College, Cambridge CB2 3BU, England	*Nobel Chemistry Laureate*
Todd, Ann Seagrove Cottage, Walkerswick, Suffolk, England 06515	*Actress*
Todd, Harry W %Rohr Industries, Foot of "H" St, Chula Vista, CA 92012	*Businessman*
Todd, Mark PO Box 507, Cambridge, New Zealand	*Equestrian*
Todd, Richard Chinham Farm, Faringdon, Oxon, England	*Actor*
Todorov, Stanko Narodno Sobranie, Sofia, Bulgaria	*Prime Minister, Bulgaria*
Toennies, Jan Peter Ewaldstrasse 7, 3400 Gottingen, Germany	*Physicist*
Tofani, Loretta %Washington Post, 1150 15th St NW, Washington, DC 20071	*Journalist*
Tognini, Michel %Centre d'Essais en Vol, BP 16, Cazaux, 33260 La Teste, France	*Spatinaut, France*
Tokusuye, Tomoo %Teijin Ltd, 11 Minamihonmachi, Higashiku, Osaka 541, Japan	*Businessman*
Tolan, Bobby 4145 Olympic Blvd, Los Angeles, CA 90043	*Baseball Player*
Toland, John 1 Long Ridge Rd, Danbury, CT 06810	*Writer*
Tolbert, Berlinda %Borinstein Oreck Bogart Agency, 8271 Melrose Ave, #110, Los Angeles, CA 90046	*Actress*
Toles, Tom %Buffalo News, 1 News Plaza, Buffalo, NY 14240	*Editorial Cartoonist*
Tolkan, James %Gores/Fields Agency, 10100 Santa Monica Blvd, #700, Los Angeles, CA 90067	*Actor*
Tollett, Leland E %Tyson Foods Inc, 2210 W Oaklawn, Springdale, AK 72764	*Businessman*
Tolsky, Susan 10815 Acama St, North Hollywood, CA 91602	*Actress*
Tomasek, Frantisek Cardinal Hradcanske Namesti 16, 119 02 Prague 1, Czechoslovakia	*Religious Leader*
Tomasson, Helgi %San Francisco Ballet, 455 Franklin St, San Francisco, CA 94102	*Ballet Dancer, Artistic Director*
Tomba, Albert %Olympic Committee, Forco Italico, Rome, Italy	*Skier*
Tombaugh, Clyde W PO Box 306, Mesilla Park, NM 88047	*Astronomer*
Tomei, Concetta %International Creative Mgmt, 8899 Beverly Blvd, Los Angeles, CA 90048	*Actress*
Tomfohrde, Heinn F %GAF Corp, 1361 Alps Rd, Wayne, NJ 07470	*Businessman*
Tominac, John J 3234 Taylor Rd, Carmel, CA 93923	*WW II Army Hero (CMH)*
Tomioka, Hiroshi %Konishiroku Photo Industry, 1-26-2 Nishi-Shinjuku, Tokyo 160, Japan	*Businessman*
Tomita, Stan 1344 15th Ave, Honolulu, HI 96816	*Photographer*
Tomjanovich, Rudy %Houston Rockets, Summit, Greenway Plz, #10, Houston, TX 77046	*Basketball Player*
Tomko, Jozef Cardinal Villa Betania, Via Urbano VIII-16, 00165 Rome, Italy	*Religious Leader*
Tomlin, Lily %Omnipotent Theatricalz, PO Box 27700, Los Angeles, CA 90027	*Comedienne, Actress*

T

Tomlinson - Torrissen

Tomlinson, Charles *Writer*
%Bristol University, English Dept, Bristol BS8 1TH, England

Tomlinson, David *Actor*
Brook Cottage, Mursley, Bucks, England

Tomlinson, John *Opera Singer*
%Angel Records, 1370 Ave of Americas, New York, NY 10019

Tomowa-Sintow, Anna *Opera Singer*
%Columbia Artists Management Inc, 165 W 57th St, New York, NY 10019

Tompkins, Angel *Actress*
PO Box 5069, Beverly Hills, CA 90210

Tonegawa, Susumu *Geneticist*
%Massachusetts Institute of Technology, Genetics Dept, Cambridge, MA 02139

Tonelli, John *Hockey Player*
%Chicago Blackhawks, 1800 W Madison St, Chicago, IL 60612

Toney, Andrew *Basketball Player*
%Philadelphia 76ers, Veterans Stadium, PO Box 25040, Philadelphia, PA 19147

Tonnemaker, Clayton *Football Player*
5113 Balmoral Ln, Bloomington, MN 55437

Tonsmeire, Arthur, Jr *Financier*
%First Southern Federal Savings & Loan, 851 S Beltline Hwy, Mobile, AL 36606

Tooker, Gary L *Businessman*
%Motorola Inc, 1303 E Algonquin Rd, Schaumburg, IL 60196

Tooker, George *Artist*
RR 1, Box 237, Hartland, VT 05048

Toomey, Bill *Track Athlete*
%US Olympic Committee, 1750 E Boulder St, Colorado Springs, CO 80909

Toon, Al *Football Player*
%New York Jets, 598 Madison Ave, New York, NY 10022

Toon, Malcolm *Diplomat*
5809 Marbury Rd, Bethesda, MD 20034

Toot, Joseph F, Jr *Businessman*
%Timken Co, 1835 Dueber Ave SW, Canton, OH 44706

Topol *Actor*
3 Dov Hoz St, Tel-Aviv, Israel

Topol, Sidney *Businessman*
%Scientific-Atlanta Inc, 1 Technology Pkwy, Atlanta, GA 30348

Topper, J Ray *Businessman*
%Anchor Hocking Corp, 109 N Broad St, Lancaster, OH 43132

Topping, Seymour *Editor*
%New York Times, 229 W 43rd St, New York, NY 10036

Torbert, Carl A, Jr *Businessman*
%Dravo Corp, 1 Oliver Plz, Pittsburgh, PA 15222

Torborg, Jeff *Baseball Player, Manager*
1375 Chapel Hill, Mountainside, NJ 07092

Torma, Julius *Boxer*
U Libenskeho Pivovaru 15, 170 00 Prague 7, Czechoslovakia

Torme, Mel *Singer*
%International Ventures, 1734 Coldwater Canyon, Beverly Hills, CA 90210

Torn, Rip *Actor*
435 W 22nd St, New York, NY 10011

Torre, Joe *Baseball Player, Manager*
3088 Greenfield Dr, Marietta, GA 30067

Torrence, Dean *Singer (Jan & Dean)*
6310 Rodgerton Dr, Los Angeles, CA 90068

Torres, Esteban E *Representative, CA*
%House of Representatives, Washington, DC 20515

Torres, Jose *Boxer*
%NY State Athletic Commission, 270 Broadway, New York, NY 10007

Torres, Liz *Singer, Actress*
%Atkins Assoc, 303 S Crescent Heights Blvd, Los Angeles, CA 90048

Torrey, Rich *Cartoonist (Hartland)*
%King Features Syndicate, 235 E 45th St, New York, NY 10017

Torricelli, Robert G *Representative, NJ*
%House of Representatives, Washington, DC 20515

Torrissen, Birger *Nordic Skier*
PO Box 216, Lakeville, CT 06039

Torruella, Juan R *Judge*
%US Court of Appeals, PO Box 3671, San Juan, PR 00904
Tose, Leonard *Football Executive*
%Philadelphia Eagles, Veterans Stadium, Philadelphia, PA 19148
Toski, Bob *Golfer*
160 Essex St, Newark, OH 43055
Totenberg, Nina *Commentator*
%National Public Radio, News Dept, 2025 "M" St NW, Washington, DC 20036
Totter, Audrey *Actress*
1945 Glendon Ave, #301, Los Angeles, CA 90025
Toups, John M *Businessman*
%Planning Research Corp, 1500 Planning Research Dr, McLean, VA 22102
Tournier, Michel *Writer*
Le Presbytere, Choisel, 78460 Chevreuse, France
Tousey, Richard *Physicist*
7725 Oxon Hill Rd, Oxon Hill, MD 20745
Toussaint, Allen *Composer, Jazz Pianist*
%Sea Saint Recording Studio, 3809 Clematis Ave, New Orleans, LA 70122
Towbin, A Robert *Financier*
1010 5th Ave, New York, NY 10028
Tower, H L *Businessman*
%Stanhome Inc, 333 Western Ave, Westfield, MA 01085
Tower, Raymond C *Businessman*
%FMC Corp, 200 E Randolph Dr, Chicago, IL 60601
Towers, Constance *Actress*
2415 Century Hill, Los Angeles, CA 90067
Towers, John *Businessman*
%AMAX Inc, AMAX Ctr, Greenwich, CT 06836
Towers, Kenneth *Editor*
%Chicago Sun-Times, 401 N Wabash, Chicago, IL 60611
Towers, Thomas R *Businessman*
%Universal Leaf Tobacco Co, Hamilton & Broad, Richmond, VA 23230
Towne, Robert *Movie Director*
25036 Malibu Rd, Malibu, CA 90265
Townes, Charles H *Nobel Physics Laureate*
%University of California, Physics Dept, Berkeley, CA 94720
Townes, Harry *Actor*
2476 Horseshoe Canyon Rd, Los Angeles, CA 90046
Towns, Edolphus *Representative, NY*
94 N Corona Ave, Valley Stream, NY 11580
Townsend, Andre *Football Player*
1930-F S Helena, Aurora, CO 80013
Townsend, Colleen *Actress*
%National Presbyterian Church, 4101 Nebraska Ave NW, Washington, DC 20006
Townsend, Greg *Football Player*
%Los Angeles Raiders, 332 Center St, El Segundo, CA 90245
Townsend, M Wilbur *Businessman*
%Handy & Harman, 850 3rd Ave, New York, NY 10022
Townsend, Robert *Actor*
%Tinsel Townsend Productions, 8033 Sunset Blvd, #890, Los Angeles, CA 90046
Townsend, Roscoe *Religious Leader*
%Evangelical Friends, 2018 Maple, Wichita, KS 67213
Townshend, Peter *Singer*
The Boathouse, Ranelagh Dr, Twickenham, Middlesex TW1 1QZ, England
Toy, Sam *Businessman*
%Ford Motor, Eagle Way, Brentwood, Essex CM13 3BW, England
Toyada, Eiji *Businessman*
%Toyota Motor Co, 1 Toyotacho, Toyota City 471, Japan
Toye, Wendy *Choreographer, Ballerina*
%David Watson, Simpson Fox, 52 Shaftesbury Ave, London W1V 7DE, England
Toyoda, Minoru *Businessman*
%Aisin Seiki Co, 2-1 Asahimachi, Kariya 448, Japan
Toyoda, Shoichiro *Businessman*
%Toyota Motor Corp, 1 Toyotacho, Toyota City, Aichi Prefecture 471, Japan
Toyoda, Yoshitoshi *Businessman*
%Toyoda Automatic Loom Works, 2-1 Toyodacho, Kariya City 448, Japan

Toyonaga, Kozo *Businessman*
%Jujo Paper Co, 1-12-1 Yurakucho, Chiyodaku, Tokyo 100, Japan

Tozzi, Giorgio *Opera Singer*
6263 Ebbtide Way, Malibu, CA 90265

Trabert, Tony *Tennis Player*
2 Trojan Ct, Rancho Mirage, CA 92270

Tracey, Margaret *Ballerina*
%New York City Ballet, Lincoln Center Plz, New York, NY 10023

Trachtenberg, Stephen J *Educator*
%George Washington University, President's Office, Washington, DC 20052

Tracy, Arthur *Singer*
350 W 57th St, New York, NY 10021

Tracy, David M *Businessman*
%J P Stevens Co, 1185 Ave of Americas, New York, NY 10036

Traficant, James *Representative, OH*
%House of Representatives, Washington, DC 20515

Trafton, Roland M *Businessman*
%SAFECO Corp, SAFECO Plz, Seattle, WA 98185

Trager, Milton *Physical Thearpist*
%Trager Institute, 10 Old Mill St, Mill Valley, CA 94941

Train, Harry D, II *Navy Admiral*
465 Dillingham Rd, Norfolk, VA 23511

Train, Russell E *Government Official, Environmentalist*
%World Wildlife Fund, 1601 Connecticut Ave NW, Washington, DC 20009

Trainor, Bernard E *Marine Corps General*
%Marine Corps Headquarters, Washington, DC 20380

Tramiel, Jack *Businessman*
%Atari Corp, 1265 Borregas Ave, Sunnyvale, CA 94086

Trammell, Alan *Baseball Player*
7346 Sandy Creek Ln, Battle Creek, MI 48010

Trani, Eugene P *Educator*
%Virginia Commonwealth University, President's Office, Richmond, VA 23284

Traub, Charles *Photographer*
39 E 10th St, New York, NY 10013

Trautlein, Donald H *Businessman*
%Bethlehem Steel Corp, 701 E 3rd St, Bethlehem, PA 18016

Trautman, Gerald H *Businessman*
501 W Puget, Phoenix, AZ 85021

Trautwig, Al *Sportscaster*
%ABC-TV, Sports Dept, 1330 Ave of Americas, New York, NY 10019

Travanti, Daniel J *Actor*
14205 Sunset Blvd, Pacific Palisades, CA 90272

Travelena, Fred *Actor*
PO Box 171, Encino, CA 91316

Travell, Janet G *Physician*
4525 Cathedral Ave NW, Washington, DC 20016

Travers, Bill *Actor*
8 Chelsea Manor, Flood St, London SW3, England

Travers, Oliver S, Jr *Businessman*
%Allegheny International, 2 Oliver Plaza, Pittsburgh, PA 15230

Travis, Cecil *Baseball Player*
2260 Highway 138, Riverdale, GA 30296

Travis, Nancy *Actress*
%Gersh Agency, 232 N Canon Dr, Beverly Hills, CA 90210

Travis, Randy *Singer*
%Lib Hatcher Agency, PO Box 121712, Nashville, TN 37213

Travis, Richard *Actor*
914 S Barrington Ave, Los Angeles, CA 90024

Travolta, Ellen *Actress*
5832 Nagle Ave, Van Nuys, CA 91401

Travolta, John *Actor*
Rancho Tajiguas, Sunburst Farms, Highway 101, Goleta, CA 93017

Traxler, Bob *Representative, MI*
%House of Representatives, Washington, DC 20515

Treadway, Edward A *Labor Leader*
%Elevator Constructors Union, 5565 Sterret Pl, Columbia, MD 21044

Treadway, James C, Jr *Government Official*
%Securities & Exchange Commission, 450 5th Ave NW, Washington, DC 20549
Treadway, Kenneth *Swimming Contributor*
%Phillips Petroleum Co, Adams Bldg, Bartlesville, OK 74003
Treas, Terri *Actress*
%Agency for Performing Arts, 9000 Sunset Blvd, #1200, Los Angeles, CA 90069
Trebek, Alex *Entertainer*
2666 Carmer Dr, Los Angeles, CA 90046
Treen, David C *Governor, LA*
%Deutsch Kerrigan Stile, 755 Magazine, New Orleans, LA 70130
Tregurtha, Paul R *Businessman*
%Moore McCormack Resources, 1 Landmark Sq, Stamford, CT 06901
Treiman, Sam B *Physicist*
60 McCosh Cir, Princeton, NJ 08540
Trejos Fernandez, Jose J *President, Costa Rica*
Apartado 10096, 1000 San Jose, Costa Rica
Trelford, Donald *Editor*
%London Observer, 8 St Andrew's Hill, London EC4V 5JA, England
Tremayne, Les *Actor*
901 S Barrington Ave, Los Angeles, CA 90049
Tremont, Ray C *Religious Leader*
%Volunteers of America, 3813 N Causeway Blvd, Metairie, LA 70002
Trenet, Charles *Singer, Songwriter*
2 Rue Anatole-France, 11100 Narbonne, France
Trengganu *Sultan, Malaysia*
Istana Badariah, Kuala Trengganu, Trengganu, Malaysia
Tretyak, Ivan *Army General, Russia*
%Ministry of Defense, 34 Nanerezhnaya M Thoreza, Moscow, Russia
Tretyak, Vladislav *Hockey Player*
%Olympic Committee, Luzhnetskaya Nab 8, Moscow, Russia
Trevelyan, Edward N *Sailor*
1515 Laguna, #3, Santa Barbara, CA 93101
Trever, John *Editorial Cartoonist*
%Albuquerque Journal, 717 Silver Ave SW, Albuquerque, NM 87103
Trevino, Lee *Golfer*
1221 Abrams Rd, #327, Richardson, TX 75081
Trevor, Claire *Actress*
%Pierce Hotel, 2 E 61st St, New York, NY 10022
Trevor-Roper, H R *Historian*
Master's Lodge, Peterhouse College, Cambridge, England
Treybig, James G *Businessman*
%Tandem Computers, 19333 Vallco Pkwy, Cupertino, CA 95014
Tribbitt, Sherman W *Governor, DE*
39 Hazel Rd, Dover, DE 19901
Tribe, Laurence H *Attorney, Educator*
%Harvard University, Law School, Griswold Hall, Cambridge, MA 02138
Trickle, Dick *Auto Racing Driver*
%Victoria Enterprises, 8520 Arbor Ln, Wisconsin Rapids, WI 54494
Triffin, Robert *Economist*
125 High St, New Haven, CT 06520
Trigere, Pauline *Fashion Designer*
550 7th Ave, New York, NY 10018
Trillin, Calvin *Writer*
%New Yorker Magazine, 20 W 43rd St, New York, NY 10036
Trimble, Vance *Editor*
1013 Sunset Ave, Kenton Hills, KY 41011
Trinh, Eugene *Astronaut*
%Jet Propulsion Laboratory, 4800 Oak Grove Dr, Pasadena, CA 91109
Trippi, Charles L *Football Player*
125 Riverhill Ct, Athens, GA 30601
Tripucka, Kelly *Basketball Player*
%Charlotte Hornets, 2 First Union Ctr, #2600, Charlotte, NC 28202
Tritt, Travis *Singer*
PO Box 440099, Kennesaw, GA 30144
Trott, Stephen S *Judge*
%US Court of Appeals, US Courthouse, 550 W Fort St, Boise, ID 93724

T

Trottier – Tsoucalas

Trottier, Bryan — *Hockey Player*
%New York Islanders, Nassau Coliseum, Uniondale, NY 11558

Trouillot, Ertha Pascal — *President, Haiti*
%Presidential Palace, Port-au-Prince, Haiti

Troup, Bobby — *Musician, Actor*
16074 Royal Oak St, Encino, CA 91316

Troupe, Tom — *Actor*
8829 Ashcroft Ave, Los Angeles, CA 90048

Troutman, William M — *Businessman*
%Lone Star Industries, 1 Greenwich Plz, Greenwich, CT 06836

Troutt, William E — *Educator*
%Belmont College, Chancellor's Office, Nashville, TN 37212

Trowbridge, Alexander B — *Secretary, Commerce*
700 New Hampshire Ave NW, Washington, DC 20037

Troy, Mike — *Swimmer*
141 Shady Ln, Walnut Creek, CA 94596

Troyanos, Tatiana — *Opera Singer*
%Columbia Artists Mgmt Inc, 165 W 57th St, New York, NY 10019

Trubshaw, Brian — *Test Pilot, Businessman*
%British Aerospace, Filton, Bristol, England

Trucks, Virgil (Fire) — *Baseball Player*
2156 Grayson Valley Dr, Birmingham, AL 35235

Trudeau, Garry — *Cartoonist (Doonesbury)*
%Universal Press Syndicate, 4900 Main St, Kansas City, MO 64112

Trudeau, Jack — *Football Player*
%Indianapolis Colts, 7001 W 56th St, Indianapolis, IN 46254

Trudeau, Pierre — *Prime Minister, Canada*
%Hennan Blaikie Assoc, 1001 de Maisonneuve, Montreal PQ H3A 1M4, Canada

Trueschler, Bernard C — *Businessman*
%Baltimore Gas & Electric Co, Gas & Electric Bldg, Baltimore, MD 21203

Truesdell, Donald F — *Nicaragan Campaign Marine Hero (CMH)*
Rt 1, Box 77, Lugoff, SC 29078

Truly, Richard H — *Astronaut, Space Administrator, Admiral*
%NASA Hdqs, Code A, Washington, DC 20546

Truman, David B — *Political Scientist*
Tory Hill Rd, Box 308, Hillsdale, NY 12529

Truman, Margaret — *Writer*
%William Morrow Co, 105 Madison Ave, New York, NY 10016

Trumka, Richard — *Labor Leader*
%United Mine Workers, 900 15th St NW, Washington, DC 20005

Trump, Donald J — *Businessman*
%Trump Organization, 725 5th Ave, New York, NY 10022

Trump, Ivana — *Businesswoman*
%The Plaza, 5th Ave & Central Park S, New York, NY 10019

Trundy, Natalie — *Actress*
713 N Beverly Dr, Beverly Hills, CA 90210

Trusel, Lisa — *Actress*
%Abrams Artists, 9200 Sunset Blvd, #625, Los Angeles, CA 90069

Trusheim, H Edwin — *Businessman*
%General American Life Insurance, PO Box 396, St Louis, MO 63166

Tryggvason, Bjarni — *Astronaut, Canada*
%National Research Council, Montreal Rd, Ottawa ON K1A OR6, Canada

Tryoshnikov, Alexey F — *Explorer*
%Geographical Society, Grivtzov St 10, 190000 St Petersburg, Russia

Trzaskoma, Richard J — *Air Force General*
Commander, 22nd Air Force, Travis Air Force, CA 94535

Tsai, Gerald, Jr — *Businessman*
%Primerica Corp, PO Box 3610, Greenwich, CT 06838

Tsao, I Fu — *Chemical Engineer*
%University of Michigan, Chemical Engineering Dept, Ann Arbor, MI 48109

Tschudi, Hans-Peter — *President, Switzerland*
%International Committee de la Croix-Rouge, 1211 Geneva, Switzerland

Tsongas, Paul E — *Senator, MA*
%Foley Hoag Eliot, 1 Post Office Sq, Boston, MA 02109

Tsoucalas, Nicholas — *Judge*
%US Court of International Trade, 1 Federal Plz, New York, NY 10007

Tsuchiya, Masao *Businessman*
%Fuji Kosan Co, 4-3 Nagatcho, Chiyodaku, Tokyo 100, Japan

Tu'ipelahake, Prince Fatafehi *Prime Minister, Tonga*
%Prime Minister's Office, Nuku'alofa, Tonga

Tubbs, Billy *Basketball Coach*
%University of Oklahoma, Athletic Dept, Norman, OK 73019

Tubbs, Tony *Boxer*
%Carl King, 32 E 69th St, New York, NY 10021

Tuchman, Maurice *Museum Curator*
%Los Angeles Museum of Art, 5905 Wilshire Blvd, Los Angeles, CA 90036

Tuck, James L *Physicist*
2502 35th St, Los Alamos, NM 87544

Tuck, Leighton B *Financier*
%First Interstate Bancorp, 707 Wilshire Blvd, Los Angeles, CA 90017

Tucker, Marcia *Museum Official*
%New Museum of Contemporary Art, 583 Broadway, New York, NY 10012

Tucker, Michael *Actor*
%STE Representation, 9301 Wilshire Blvd, #312, Beverly Hills, CA 90210

Tucker, Tanya *Singer*
PO Box 15245, Nashville, TN 37215

Tucker, William E *Educator*
%Texas Christian University, Chancellor's Office, Fort Worth, TX 76129

Tuckwell, Barry *Concert French Hornist*
%Athenaeum Club, Pall Mall, London SW1, England

Tudor, John *Baseball Player*
14 Forest St, Peabody, MA 01960

Tuke, Anthony *Businessman*
%Rio Tinto-Zinc, 6 St James's Sq, London SW1Y 4LD, England

Tukey, John W *Statistician*
115 Arreton Rd, Princeton, NJ 08540

Tully, Alice *Philanthropist, Music Patron*
%Alice Tully Hall, 1941 Broadway, New York, NY 10023

Tully, Daniel P *Businessman*
%Merrill Lynch Co, 165 Broadway, New York NY 10080

Tully, Darrow *Publisher*
%Arizona Republic, PO Box 1950, Phoenix, AZ 85001

Tumi, Christian W Cardinal *Religious Leader*
Archveche, BP 272, Garoua, Cameroon

Tune, Tommy *Dancer, Actor*
1501 Broadway, #1508, New York, NY 10036

Tunney, Jim *Football Referee*
%National Football League, 350 Park Ave, New York, NY 10022

Tunney, John V *Senator, CA*
106 Esparta Way, Santa Monica, CA 90402

Tupouto'a *Crown Prince, Tonga*
%The Palace, PO Box 6, Nuku'alofa, Tonga

Tupper, C John *Physician, Educator*
PO Box 2007, El Macera, CA 95618

Tupua Tamasese Lealofi IV *Prime Minister, Western Samoa*
%Prime Minister's Office, Apia, Western Samoa

Turco, Richard P *Atmospheric Scientist*
%R & D Assoc, 4640 Admiralty Way, Marina del Rey, CA 90292

Turcol, Thomas *Journalist*
%Virginian Pilot-Ledger Star, 150 W Brambleton Ave, Norfolk, VA 23510

Tureck, Rosalyn *Concert Pianist*
%Tureck Bach Institute, 215 E 68th St, New York, NY 10021

Turgeon, Pierre *Hockey Player*
%New York Islanders, Nassau Coliseum, Uniondale, NY 11553

Turgeon, Sylvain *Hockey Player*
%Hartford Whalers, 1 Civic Center Plz, Hartford, CT 06103

Turkel, Ann *Actress*
9877 Beverly Grove, Beverly Hills, CA 90210

Turkevich, Anthony L *Chemist*
175 Briarwood Loop, Briarwood Lakes, Oak Brook, IL 60521

Turley, Bob *Baseball Player*
PO Box 786, Marco Island, FL 33937

T

Turley – Turner

Turley, Joseph F *Businessman*
%Gillette Co, Prudential Tower Bldg, Boston, MA 02199

Turley, Keith L *Businessman*
%AZP Grp, 411 N Central Ave, Phoenix, AZ 85004

Turley, Stewart *Businessman*
%Jack Eckerd Corp, 8333 Bryan Dairy Rd, Largo, FL 33543

Turlington, Cindy *Model*
%Ford Model Agency, 344 E 59th St, New York, NY 10022

Turman, Glynn *Actor*
%Agency for Performing Arts, 9000 Sunset Blvd, #1200, Los Angeles, CA 90069

Turnbull, David *Physicist*
77 Summer St, Weston, MA 02193

Turnbull, Renaldo *Football Player*
%New Orleans Saints, 6928 Saints Dr, Metairie, LA 70003

Turnbull, William *Architect*
Pier 1 1/2, The Embarcadero, San Francisco, CA 94111

Turner, Clyde (Bulldog) *Football Player*
%Pro Football Hall of Fame, 2121 George Halas Dr, Canton, OH 44708

Turner, Edwin L *Astrophysicist*
%Princeton University, Astrophysical Sciences Dept, Princeton, NJ 08544

Turner, Francis J *Geologist*
2525 Hill Ct, Berkeley, CA 94708

Turner, Fred L *Businessman*
%McDonald's Corp, McDonald's Plz, Oak Brook, IL 60521

Turner, Gene *Figure Skater*
763 Blossom Way, #11, Hayward, CA 94541

Turner, Glenn W *Businessman*
PO Box 52, Rt 1, Maitland, FL 32751

Turner, Grant *Broadcaster*
PO Box 414, Brentwood, TN 37207

Turner, Ike *Singer*
2360 Jupiter Dr, Los Angeles, CA 90043

Turner, James C *Labor Leader*
%Operating Engineers Union, 1125 17th St NW, Washington, DC 20036

Turner, James R *Baseball Player*
1004 Woodmont Blvd, Nashville, TN 37204

Turner, James T *Judge*
%US Claims Court, 717 Madison Pl NW, Washington, DC 20005

Turner, Janine *Actress*
%Gage Group, 9255 Sunset Blvd, #515, Los Angeles, CA 90069

Turner, John G *Businessman*
%Northwestern National Life Insurance, 20 Washington S, Minneapolis, MN 55440

Turner, John N *Prime Minister, Canada*
%House of Commons, Ottawa ON K1A 0AG, Canada

Turner, Kathleen *Actress*
%Gersh Agency, 232 N Canon Dr, Beverly Hills, CA 90210

Turner, Lana *Actress*
%Gores/Fields Agency, 10100 Santa Monica Blvd, #700, Los Angeles, CA 90067

Turner, R Gerald *Educator*
%University of Mississippi, President's Office, University, MS 38677

Turner, Ross James *Businessman*
%Genstar Corp, 1177 W Hastings St, Vancouver BC, Canada

Turner, Sherri *Golfer*
%Ladies Professional Golf Assn, 2570 Volusia Ave, #B, Daytona Beach, FL 32114

Turner, Stacey *Actress*
%Diamond Artists, 9200 Sunset Blvd, #909, Los Angeles, CA 90069

Turner, Stansfield *Navy Admiral, Government Official*
1320 Skipwith Rd, McLean, VA 22101

Turner, Ted *Communications, Sports Executive*
1050 Techwood Dr, Atlanta, GA 30318

Turner, Tina *Singer*
%Roger Davies Mgmt, 3575 Cahuenga Blvd W, Los Angeles, CA 90068

Turner, William H *Financier*
%Chemical Banking Corp, 277 Park Ave, New York, NY 10172

Turner, William J *Businessman*
%Automatic Data Processing, 1 ADP Blvd, Roseland, NJ 07068

Turnley, David C *Photographer*
%Detroit Free Press, 321 W Lafayette Blvd, Detroit, MI 48231

Turow, Scott *Writer*
8000 Sears Tower, Chicago, IL 60606

Turpin, Melvin *Basketball Player*
%Washington Bullets, Capital Center, 1 Truman Dr, Landover, MD 20785

Turrell, James *Artist*
%Skystone Foundation, PO Box 725, Flagstaff, AZ 86002

Turturro, John *Actor*
%Gersh Agenncy, 232 N Canon Dr, Beverly Hills, CA 90210

Tushingham, Rita *Actress*
%London Mgmt, 235-241 Regent St, London W1A 2JT, England

Tutone, Tommy *Singer, Dancer*
%International Creative Mgmt, 40 W 57th St, New York, NY 10019

Tutt, William Thayer *Hockey Executive*
2621 Spring Grove Terr, Colorado Springs, CO 80906

Tuttle, Edwin E *Businessman*
%Pennwalt Corp, 3 Parkway, Philadelphia, PA 19102

Tuttle, Elbert P *Judge*
56 Forsyth St NW, Atlanta, GA 30303

Tuttle, O Frank *Geochemist*
PO Box 16, Greer, AZ 85927

Tuttle, Perry *Football Player*
506 Regency Wood II NE, Atlanta, GA 30319

Tuttle, Robert D *Businessman*
%Sealed Power Corp, 100 Terrace Plz, Muskegon, MI 49443

Tuttle, William G T, Jr *Army General*
CG, USA Material Command, 5001 Eisenhower Ave, Alexandria, VA 22333

Tutu, Desmond M *Nobel Peace Laureate, Religious Leader*
Bishopscourt, Claremont Cape 7700, South Africa

Tway, Bob *Golfer*
%Professional Golfers Assn, PO Box 109601, Palm Beach Gardens, FL 33410

Tweed, John N *Religious Leader*
%Reformed Presbyterian Church, 1117 E Devonshire, Phoenix, AZ 85014

Tweed, Shannon *Model, Actress*
3800 Barham Blvd, #105, Los Angeles, CA 90068

Twiggy (Leslie Lawson) *Model, Actress*
1920 Los Encinos Ave, Glendale, CA 91203

Twilley, Howard *Football Player*
4526 S Columbia, Tulsa, OK 74105

Twitty, Conway *Singer*
1 Music Village Blvd, Henderson, TN 37075

Twombly, Cy *Artist*
%Leo Castelli Gallery, 420 W Broadway, New York, NY 10013

Twomey, David M *Marine Corps General*
%Marine Corps Headquarters, Washington, DC 20380

Twomey, William P *Businessman*
%Itel Corp, 1 Embarcadero Ctr, San Francisco, CA 94111

Twyman, Jack *Businessman, Basketball Player*
%Super Food Services Inc, Kettering Box 2323, Dayton, OH 45429

Tydings, Joseph D *Senator, MD*
5320 27th St, Washington, DC 20016

Tyler, Anne *Writer*
222 Turnbridge Rd, Baltimore, MD 21212

Tyler, Bonnie *Singer*
%International Creative Mgmt, 8899 Beverly Blvd, Los Angeles, CA 90048

Tyler, Harold R, Jr *Attorney*
%Patterson Belknap Webb Tyler, 30 Rockefeller Plz, New York, NY 10020

Tyler, Steve *Singer (Aerosmith)*
%Collins/Barasso Mgmt, 215 1st St, Cambridge, MA 02142

Tyner, Charles *Actor*
%Dade/Rosen/Schultz Agency, 11846 Ventura Blvd, #100, Studio City, CA 91604

Tyner, McCoy *Jazz Pianist, Composer*
%Walker, 420 Clinton Ave, Brooklyn, NY 11238

Tyrrell, Susan *Actress*
826 Amoroso Pl, Venice, CA 90291

Tyson, Charles R *Businessman*
%Penn Mutual Life Insurance, Independence Sq, Philadelphia, PA 19172

Tyson, Cicely *Actress*
315 W 70th St, New York, NY 10023

Tyson, Don *Businessman*
%Tyson Foods Inc, 2210 W Oaklawn, Springdale, AK 72764

Tyson, Graham *Businessman*
%Dataproducts Corp, 6200 Canoga Ave, Woodland Hills, CA 91365

Tyson, Mike *Boxer*
%Don King, 968 Pinehurst Dr, Las Vegas, NV 89109

Tyson, Richard *Actor*
%Triad Artists, 10100 Santa Monica Blvd, #1600, Los Angeles, CA 90067

Tyus, Wyomia *Track Athlete*
1101 Kensington Ave, Los Angeles, CA 90019

Ubouj, Herman J *Businessman*
%Arkansas Best Corp, 1000 S 21st St, Fort Smith, AK 72901
Ubriaco, Gene *Hockey Coach*
%Pittsburgh Penguins, Civic Arena, Pittsburgh, PA 15219
Ubukata, Taiji *Businessman*
%Ishikawajima-Harima Heavy Industries, 2-1 Otemachi, Tokyo 100, Japan
Uchida, Mitsuko *Concert Pianist*
%Shaw Concerts, 1900 Broadway, New York, NY 10023
Udall, Morris K *Representative, AZ*
142 S Calle Chaparita, Tucson, AZ 85716
Udall, Stewart L *Secretary, Interior*
%Hill Christopher Phillips, 1900 "M" St NW, Washington, DC 20036
Udell, Rochelle *Editor*
%Conde Nast Publications Inc, 350 Madison Ave, New York, NY 10017
Udenhout, Wim *Prime Minister, Suriname*
%Prime Minister's Office, Paramaribo, Suriname
Udouj, Herman J *Businessman*
%Arkansas Best Corp, 1000 S 21st St, Fort Smith. AR 72901
Udvari, Frank *Hockey Referee*
2-40S Glasgow, Kitchener ON N2M 2N1, Canada
Ueberroth, Peter V *Baseball Executive; Olympics Official*
61 Emerald Bay, Laguna Beach, CA 92651
Uecker, Bob *Baseball Player, Actor*
15734 Hawthorne Dr, Menomonee Falls, WI 53051
Uehling, Barbara S *Educator*
%University of California, Chancellor's Office, Santa Barbara, CA 93106
Ueki, Shigeaki *Businessman*
%Petrobras-Petroleo, Caixa Postal 809, 20 035 Rio de Janeiro, Brazil
Uelses, John *Track Athlete*
4760 Holly Ave, Fairfax, VA 22030
Uemura, Ko *Financier*
%Fuji Bank & Trust Co, 1 World Trade Ctr, New York, NY 10048
Ueno, Taichi *Businessman*
%Kurarau Co, 12-39 Umeda, Kitaku, Osaka 530, Japan
Uggams, Leslie *Singer, Actress*
%William Morris Agency, 151 El Camino, Beverly Hills, CA 90212
Uhl, Edward G *Businessman*
%Fairchild Industries, 300 W Service Rd, Chantilly, VA 22021
Ukropina, James R *Businessman*
%Pacific Lighting Corp, 810 S Flower St, Los Angeles, CA 90017
Ulanova, Galina *Ballerina*
%State Academic Bolshoi Theatre, 1 Ploshchad Sverdlova, Moscow, Russia
Ulene, Arthur L *Physician, Entertainer*
10810 Via Verona, Los Angeles, CA 90024
Ulland, Olav *Skier*
2664 West Lake Sammamish Pkwy SE, Bellevue, WA 98008
Ullman, Norman *Hockey Player*
19 Averdon Crest, Don Mills ON M3A 1P4, Canada
Ullman, Tracy *Comedienne*
%Gracie Films, 10201 W Pico Blvd, #9, Los Angeles, CA 90035
Ullmann, Liv *Actress*
Hafrs Fjordsgate #7, Oslo 2, Norway
Ulloa Elias, Manuel *Prime Minister, Peru*
Ave Alvarez Calderon, 605-Piso 5, Lima 27, Peru
Ullsten, Ola *Prime Minister, Sweden*
%Folkpartiet, PO Box 6508, 113 83 Stockholm, Sweden
Ulrich, Laurel T *Historian*
%University of New Hampshire, History Dept, Durham, NH 03824
Ultmann, John E *Physician*
5632 S Harper St, Chicago, IL 60637
Ulvaeus, Bjorn *Singer (ABBA), Composer*
%ABBA, PO Box 260725, 10041 Stockholm, Sweden
Umedo, Zenji *Businessman*
%Kawasaki Heavy Industries, 2-1-18 Nakamachidori, Chuoku, Kobe 650, Japan
Underhill, Jacob B *Businessman*
%New York Life Insurance, 51 Madison Ave, New York, NY 10010

U

Underwood – Urvin

Underwood, Benton J — *Psychologist*
1745 Stevens Dr, Glenview, IL 60025

Underwood, Blair — *Actor*
PO Box 349, Petersburg, VA 23805

Underwood, Cecil H — *Governor, WV*
609 13th Ave, Huntingdon, WV 25701

Ungaro, Emanuel — *Fashion Designer*
25 Rue de Fbg St Honore, 75008 Paris, France

Unger, Jim — *Cartoonist (Herman)*
%Universal Press Syndicate, 4900 Main St, Kansas City, MO 64112

Unger, Kay — *Fashion Designer*
%St Gillian Sportswear, 498 7th Ave, New York, NY 10018

Unger, Leonard — *Diplomat*
31 Amherst Rd, Belmont, MA 02178

Unitas, Johnny — *Football Player*
%National Circuits, 4820 Seton Dr, Baltimore, MD 21215

Uno, Osamu — *Businessman*
%Toyoba Co, 2-2-8 Dojimahama, Kitaku, Osaka 53, Japan

Unruh, James A — *Businessman*
%Unisys Corp, 1 Burroughs Pl, Detroit, MI 48232

Unruh, Jerry L — *Navy Admiral*
Commander, 3rd Fleet, FPO, AP 96601

Unseld, Wes — *Basketball Player, Coach*
%Washington Bullets, Capital Centre, 1 Truman Dr, Landover, MD 20785

Unser, Al — *Auto Racing Driver*
7625 Central NW, Albuquerque, NM 87105

Unser, Al, Jr — *Auto Racing Driver*
%Championship Auto Racing Teams, 390 Enterprise Ct, Bloomfield Hills, MI 48302

Unterberg, Thomas I — *Financier*
%L F Rothschild Unterberg Towbin, 55 Water St, New York, NY 10041

Updike, John — *Writer*
%General Delivery, Beverly Farms, MA 01915

Upham, Charles H — *WW II New Zealand Army Hero (VC and Bar)*
Landsdowne, Parnassus R D, Hundalee, North Canterbury, New Zealand

Upshaw, Dawn — *Opera Singer*
%Columbia Artists Mgmt Inc, 165 W 57th St, New York, NY 10019

Upshaw, Gene — *Football Player, Union Leader*
%Professional Athlete's Union, 1300 Connecticut Ave NW, Washington, DC 20036

Upson, Stuart B — *Businessman*
%Dancer Fitzgerald Sample Dorland, 405 Lexington Ave, New York, NY 10017

Upton, Fred — *Representative, MI*
%House of Representatives, Washington, DC 20515

Urakawa, Hiroshi — *Businessman*
%Nissan Shatai Co, 10-1 Amanuma, Hiratsuka City 254, Japan

Urban, Thomas N — *Businessman*
%Pioneer Hi-Bred International, 400 Locust, Des Moines, IA 50309

Urbanchek, Jon — *Swimming Coach*
%University of Michigan, Athletic Dept, Ann Arbor, MI 48109

Urich, Robert — *Actor*
15930 Woodvale Rd, Encino, CA 91436

Uris, Leon — *Writer*
PO Box 1559, Aspen, CO 81612

Urist, Marshall R — *Orthopedic Surgeon*
%University of California Medical Ctr, Ortho/Bone Lab, Los Angeles, CA 90024

Urmson, Claire — *Model*
%Ford Model Agency, 344 E 59th St, New York, NY 10022

Urquhart, Brian E — *Diplomat*
131 E 66th St, New York, NY 10021

Urquhart, Lawrence M — *Businessman*
%Burma Oil, Burmah House, Pipers Way, Swindon, Wilts SN3 1RE, England

Urshan, Nathaniel A — *Religious Leader*
%United Pentecostal Church International, 8855 Dunn Rd, Hazelwood, MO 63042

Ursi, Corrado Cardinal — *Religious Leader*
Largo Donnaregina 23-80134, Naples, Italy

Urvin, Tinsley H — *Businessman*
%Alexander & Alexander Services, 1211 Ave of Americas, New York, NY 10036

Usery, William J, Jr *Secretary, Labor*
2400 Virginia Ave, Washington, DC 20037

Ustinov, Peter *Actor*
11 Rue de Silly, 92100 Boulogne, France

Ut, Nick *Photographer*
%Associated Press, Photo Dept, 221 S Figueroa St, #300, Los Angeles, CA 90012

Utada, Katsuhiro *Businessman*
%Ajinomoto Co, 1-5-8 Kyobashi Chuoku, Tokyo 104, Japan

Utiger, Ronald E *Businessman*
%Tube Investments, Five Ways, Birminhgam BI6 8SQ, England

Utley, Edwin E *Businessman*
%Carolina Power & Light, 411 Fayetteville St, Raleigh, NC 27602

Utley, Garrick *Commentator*
%NBC-TV, News Dept, 4001 Nebraska Ave NW, Washington, DC 20016

Utzon, Jorn *Architect*
%General Delivery, 3150 Hellebaek, Denmark

Uys, Jacobus J *Movie Director*
108 Palm St, Northcliff Ext 6, Johannesburg 2195, South Africa

V

Vaccaro – Valo

Vaccaro, Brenda *Actress*
%Cunningham-Escott-Dipene, 261 S Robertson Blvd, Beverly Hills, CA 90211

Vaccaro, John (Sonny) *Businessman*
%Nike Inc, 3900 SW Murray Blvd, Beaverton, OR 97005

Vachon, Louis-Albert Cardinal *Religious Leader*
%Le Seminaire de Quebec, Case Postale 460, Quebec PQ G1R 4R7, Canada

Vachon, Rogie *Hockey Player, Executive*
%Los Angeles Kings, Great Western Forum, 3900 W Manchester, Inglewood, CA 90306

Vachss, Andrew H *Writer*
299 Broadway, 1800, New York, NY 10007

Vadim, Roger *Movie Director*
2429 Beverly Ave, Santa Monica, CA 90406

Vagelos, P Roy *Businessman*
%Merck & Co, PO Box 2000, Rahway, NJ 07065

Vail, Thomas *Editor*
%Cleveland Plain Dealer, 1801 Superior Ave, Cleveland, OH 44114

Vaillaud, Michel *Businessman*
%Schlumberger Ltd, 277 Park Ave, New York, NY 10172

Vajna, Andrew *Movie Producer*
%Cinergi Productions, 414 N Camden Dr, #1000, Beverly Hills, CA 90210

Valar, Paul *Skier*
PO Box 906, Franconia, NH 03580

Valdez, Luis *Playwright*
%El Teatro Capesino, 705 4th St, San Juan Bautista, CA 95045

Valdiserri, C L *Businessman*
%Weirton Steel Corp, 400 Three Springs Dr, Weirton, WV 26062

Vale, Jerry *Singer*
621 N Palm Dr, Beverly Hills, CA 90210

Valen, Nancy *Actress*
%Artists Agency, 10000 Santa Monica Blvd, #305, Los Angeles, CA 90067

Valente, Benita *Opera Singer*
%Anthony Checchia, 135 S 18th St, Philadelphia, PA 19103

Valente, Catarina *Singer*
Via ai Ronci 12, CH-6816 Bissone, Switzerland

Valenti, Carl M *Publisher*
%Information Services Grp, Dow Jones Co, 22 Cortlandt, New York, NY 10007

Valenti, Jack *Movie Executive*
%Motion Picture Assn, 1600 "I" St NW, Washington, DC 20006

Valentin, Barbara *Actress*
Stollbergstrasse 11, 8000 Munich 22, Germany

Valentine, Bobby *Baseball Player, Manager*
2113 Greta Ln, Fort Worth, TX 76112

Valentine, DeWain *Artist*
69 Market St, Venice, CA 90291

Valentine, I Tim *Representative, NC*
%House of Representatives, Washington, DC 20515

Valentine, Karen *Actress*
145 W 67th St, #42-H, New York, NY 10023

Valentine, Raymond C *Agronomist*
%University of California, Plant Growth Laboratory, Davis, CA 95616

Valentini Terrani, Lucia *Opera Singer*
Piazza Cavour 4, 35100 Padora, Italy

Valentino (Garavani) *Fashion Designer*
Palazzo Mignanelli, Piazza Mignanelli 22, 00187 Rome, Italy

Valenzuela, Fernando *Baseball Player*
3004 N Beachwood Dr, Los Angeles, CA 90068

Valeriani, Richard *Commentator*
%Shearson Lehman Hutton, 2 World Trade Ctr, New York, NY 10048

Vallee, Bert L *Biochemist, Physician*
56 Browne St, Brookline, MA 02146

Valli, Frankie *Singer*
%Curb Records, MCA, 70 Universal City Plz, Universal City, CA 91608

Vallone, Raf *Actor*
%Anne Alvares, Correa Panis, 18 Rue Troyon, 75017 Paris, France

Valo, Elmer *Baseball Player*
571 Columbia Ave, Palmerton, PA 18071

Valtman, Edmund *Editorial Cartoonist*
41 Foothills Way, Bloomfield, CT 06002

Valvano, Jim *Basketball Coach; Sportscaster*
%ABC-TV, Sports Dept, 1330 Ave of Americas, New York, NY 10019

Van Allan, Richard *Opera Singer*
18 Octavia St, London SW11 3DN, England

Van Allen, James A *Physicist*
5 Woodland Mounds Rd, RFD 6, Iowa City, IA 52240

Van Amerongen, Jerry *Cartoonist (The Neighborhood)*
2329 Newton Ave S, Minneapolis, MN 55405

Van Andel, Jay *Businessman*
7186 Windy Hill Rd, Grand Rapids, MI 49506

Van Ark, Joan *Actress*
10950 Alta View Dr, Studio City, CA 91604

Van Arsdale, Dick *Basketball Player*
3930 E Camelback Rd, Phoenix, AZ 85018

Van Arsdale, Tom *Basketball Player*
3930 E Camelback Rd, Phoenix, AZ 85018

Van Auken, John A *Tennis Contributor*
%Canadian Tennis Technology Ltd, PO Box 1538, Sydney NS B1P 6R7, Canada

Van Breda Kolff, Bill (Butch) *Basketball Coach*
%Hofstra University, Athletic Dept, Hempstead, NY 11550

Van Brunt, Edward E, Jr *Businessman*
%AZP Grp, 411 N Central Ave, Phoenix, AZ 85004

Van Buren, Abigail (Pauline Phillips) *Columnist (Dear Abby)*
%Universal Press Syndicate, 4900 Main St, Kansas City, MO 62114

Van Buren, Robert *Financier*
%Midlantic Corp, PO Box 600, Edison, NJ 08818

Van Buren, Steve *Football Player*
2305 Ann St, Philadelphia, PA 19134

Van Damme, Jean Claude *Actor*
PO Box 4149, Chatsworth, CA 91313

Van de Ven, Monique *Actress*
%Marion Rosenberg, 8428 Melrose Pl, #C, Los Angeles, CA 90069

Van de Wetering, John E *Educator*
%State University of New York, President's Office, Brockport, NY 14420

Van den Berg, Lodewijk *Astronaut*
%EG&G Corp, 130 Robin Hill Rd, Goleta, CA 93117

Van den Haag, Ernest *Psychoanalyst, Writer*
118 W 79th St, New York, NY 10024

Van Der Grinten, W C L *Businessman*
%DSM, Naamloze Vennootschap, PO Box 65, Heerlen, Netherlands

Van der Klugt, Cor J *Businessman*
%Philips' Gloeilampenfabrieken, 5621 CT Eindhoven, Netherlands

Van der Meer, Simon *Nobel Physics Laureate*
%Center for Nuclear Research, 1211 Geneva 23, Switzerland

Van Deventer, Neill *Publisher*
%Cleveland Plain Dealer, 1801 Superior Ave, Cleveland, OH 44114

Van Devere, Trish *Actress*
3211 Retreat Ct, Malibu, CA 90265

Van Doren, Mamie *Actress*
428 31st St, Newport Beach, CA 92663

Van Dreelen, John *Actor*
%Paul Kohner Inc, 9169 Sunset Blvd, Los Angeles, CA 90069

Van Driel, G H *Businessman*
%Koninklijke Wessanen, 1180 Ak Amsterdam, Netherlands

Van Duivenbooden, F G *Businessman*
%Esso Bederland, Zuid Hollandlaan 7, The Hague, Netherlands

Van Dusen, Granville *Actor*
2161 Ridgemont Dr, Los Angeles, CA 90046

Van Dyke, Dick *Actor, Comedian*
%William Morris Agency, 151 El Camino, Beverly Hills, CA 90212

Van Ekris, Anthonie C *Businessman*
%Kay Corp, 320 King St, Alexandria, VA 22314

Van Fleet, James A *Army General*
5210 Van Fleet Rd, Polk City, FL 33868

V

Van Fleet – Vanbiesbrouck

Van Fleet, Jo *Actress*
54 Riverside Dr, New York, NY 10024

Van Gennip, Yvonne *Speed Skater*
%Ice Productions, Capsheuvel 95, 2517 KA The Hague, Netherlands

Van Graafeiland, Ellsworth A *Judge*
%Federal Bldg, 100 State St, Rochester, NY 14614

Van Halen, Eddie *Singer*
%Van Halen, 10100 Santa Monica Blvd, #2460, Los Angeles, CA 90067

Van Hamel, Martine *Ballerina*
%Peter S Diggins Assoc, 133 W 71st St, New York, NY 10023

Van Hellmond, Andy *Hockey Referee*
75 International Blvd, #300, Rexdale ON M9W 6L9, Canada

Van Hoften, James D A *Astronaut*
%Bechtel National, Defense & Space Org, 50 Beale St, San Francisco, CA 94119

Van Horn, Richard L *Educator*
%University of Oklahoma, President's Office, Norman, OK 73019

Van Horne, Keith *Football Player*
%Chicago Bears, 250 N Washington Rd, Lake Forest, IL 60045

Van Leuven, Arthur E *Businessman*
%Transamerica Corp, 600 Montgomery St, San Francisco, CA 94111

Van Orsdel, Ralph A *Businessman*
%Amfac Inc, 44 Montgomery St, San Francisco, CA 94120

Van Pallandt, Nina *Actress, Singer*
845 E 6th St, Los Angeles, CA 90021

Van Patten, Dick *Actor*
13920 Magnolia Blvd, Sherman Oaks, CA 91423

Van Patten, Jimmy *Actor*
3151 Cahuenga Blvd, #310, Los Angeles, CA 90068

Van Patten, Joyce *Actress*
1321 N Hayworth, #C, Los Angeles, CA 90046

Van Patten, Nels *Actor*
3151 Cahuenga Blvd, #310, Los Angeles, CA 90068

Van Patten, Timothy *Actor*
%Progressive Artists Agency, 400 S Beverly Dr, #216, Beverly Hills, CA 90212

Van Patten, Vincent *Actor*
%Light Co, 901 Bringham Ave, Los Angeles, CA 90049

Van Peebles, Mario *Actor*
%International Creative Mgmt, 8899 Beverly Blvd, Los Angeles, CA 90048

Van Riemsdijk, H A C *Businessman*
%Phillip Gloeilampenfabrieken, 5621 CT Eindhoven, Netherlands

Van Roden, Donald *Businessman*
%SmithKline Beckman Corp, 1 Franklin Plz, Philadelphia, PA 19101

Van Runkle, Theodora *Fashion Designer*
38300 Highway 1, Gualala, CA 95445

Van Ryn, John *Tennis Player*
350 Coconut Row, #2-B, Palm Beach, FL 33480

Van Sant, R William *Businessman*
%Lukens Inc, 50 S 1st Ave, Coatesville, PA 19320

Van Schaik, Gerard *Businessman*
%Heineken, 2-E Weteringplanatsoen 21, 1017-ZD Amsterdam, Netherlands

Van Staveren, Petra *Swimmer*
%Olympic Committee, Surinamestraar 33, 2585 Le Harve, Netherlands

Van Tamelen, Eugene Earl *Chemist*
1 Smugglers' Cove, Cap Estate, Castries, St Lucia

Van Tuyle, Robert *Businessman*
%Beverly Enterprises, 873 S Fair Oaks Ave, Pasadena, CA 91105

Van Valkenburgh, Deborah *Actress*
%Gersh Agency, 232 N Canon Dr, Beverly Hills, CA 90210

Van Wachem, Loedwijk C *Businessman*
%Royal Dutch/Shell Grp, 30 Carel van Bylandtaan, The Hague, Netherlands

Van Wagner, Bruce *Businessman*
%Anixter Bros, 4711 Golf Rd, Skokie, IL 60076

Van Zant, Steve *Singer, Songwriter*
322 W 57th St, New York, NY 10019

Vanbiesbrouck, John *Hockey Player*
%New York Rangers, Madison Square Grdn, 4 Pennsylvania Plz, New York, NY 10001

Vance, Cyrus R *Secretary, State*
%Simpson Thacher Bartlett, 1 Battery Park Plz, New York, NY 10004

Vance, Robert S *Judge*
%US Court of Appeals, 1800 5th Ave N, Birmingham, AL 35203

Vandenburgh, Jane *Writer*
%North Point Press, PO Box 6275, Albany, CA 94706

Vander Jagt, Guy *Representative, MI*
%House of Representatives, Washington, DC 20515

Vanderberg Shaw, Helen *Synchronized Swimming Coach*
%Heaven's Fitness, 301 14th St NW, Calgary AL T2N 2A1, Canada

Vanderbilt, Oliver D *Financier*
133 Old Gulph Rd, Wynnewood, PA 19096

Vanderhoof, John D *Governor, CO*
%Club Twenty, 845 Grand, Grand Junction, CO 81502

VanderMeer, Johnny *Baseball Player*
4005 Leona Ave, Tampa, FL 33606

Vandermeersch, Bernard *Antropologist*
%University of Bordeaux, Antropology Dept, Bordeaux, France

Vanderveen, Loet *Sculptor*
Lime Creek 5, Big Sur, CA 93920

VanDerveer, Tara *Basketball Coach*
%Stanford University, Athletic Dept, Stanford, CA 94305

Vandeweghe, Ernie *Basketball Player, Physician*
211 N Prairie Ave, Inglewood, CA 90301

Vandeweghe, Kiki *Basketball Player*
%New York Knicks, Madison Square Grdn, 4 Pennsylvania Plz, New York, NY 10001

Vandiver, S Ernest *Governor, GA*
109 Hartwell Dr, Lasvonia, GA 30553

Vandross, Luther *Singer*
1200 Chanruss Pl, Beverly Hills, CA 90210

Vane, John R *Nobel Medicine Laureate*
White Angles, 7 Beech Dell, Keston, Kent BR2 6EP, England

Vanek, John *Basketball Referee*
9th St, RD 1, Nesquehoning, PA 18240

Vaness, Carol *Opera Singer*
%Herbert Breslin Agency, 119 W 57th St, New York, NY 10019

Vanilla Ice (Robby Van Winkle) *Singer*
%SBK Records, 1290 Ave of Americas, New York, NY 10104

Vanity *Singer, Actress*
%William Morris Agency, 151 El Camino Dr, Beverly Hills, CA 90212

Vannelli, Gino *Singer*
31220 La Baya Dr, #110, Westlake Village, CA 91362

Vanocer, Sander *Commentator*
%ABC-TV, News Dept, 1330 Ave of Americas, New York, NY 10019

Varady, Julia *Opera Singer*
%Metropolitan Opera Assn, Lincoln Center Plz, New York, NY 10023

Varda, Agnes *Movie Director*
86 Rue Daguerre, 75014 Paris, France

Varda, Chryssa *Artist*
15 E 88th St, New York, NY 10028

Varga, Imre *Sculptor*
Bartha-Utca 1, Budapest XII, Hungary

Vargas Llosa, Mario *Writer*
%PEN, 62-63 Glebe Pl, London SW3, England

Vargas, Jay R *Vietnam War Marine Air Corps Hero (CMH)*
COMNAVSURPAC, Code 30, Naval Amphibious Base Coronado, San Diego, CA 92155

Varinoyannis, V J *Businessman*
%Motor Oil Corinth Refineries, 2 Karageorgi Servias, Athens 10562, Greece

Varmus, Harold E *Nobel Medicine Laureate*
%University of California, Microbiology-Immmunolgy Dept, San Francisco, CA 94143

Varnay, Astrid *Opera Singer*
%Metropolitan Opera Assn, Lincoln Center Plz, New York, NY 10023

Vasarely, Victor *Artist*
83 Rue Aux Reliques, Annet-sur-Marne, 77410 Claye Souilly, France

Vasary, Tamas *Concert Pianist*
9 Village Rd, London N3, England

Vasiliyev, Vladimir *Ballet Dancer*
%State Academic Bolshoi Theatre, 1 Ploshchad Sverdlova, Moscow, Russia

Vasquez Rana, Mario *Publisher*
%El Sol de Mexico, Guillermo Prieto 7, Mexico City DF, Mexico

Vassiliou, George *President, Cyprus*
%President's Office, Nicosia, Cyprus

Vassos, John *Artist*
Comstock Hill Rd, Norfolk, CT 06850

Vasyuchenko, Yuri *Ballet Dancer*
%State Academic Bolshoi Theatre, 1 Ploschad Sverdlova, Moscow, Russia

Vasyutin, Vladimir *Cosmonaut*
141 160 Svyosdny Gorodok, Moskovskoi Oblasti, Potchta Kosmonavtov, Russia

Vaughn, Robert *Actor*
162 Old West Mountain Rd, Ridgefield, CT 06877

Vaught, John *Football Coach*
Hwy North 6 W, Oxford, MS 38655

Veach, Charles L *Astronaut*
%NASA, Johnson Space Ctr, Houston, TX 77058

Veale, Tinkham, II *Businessman*
%Alco Standard Corp, PO Box 834, Valley Forge, PA 19482

Veasey, Craig *Football Player*
%Pittsburgh Steelers, Three Rivers Stadium, Pittsburgh, PA 15212

Veasey, Josephine *Opera Singer*
Pound Cottage, St Mary Vourne, Andover, Hants, England

Vee, Bobby *Singer*
PO Box 41, Sauk Rapids, MN 56379

Vega, Suzanne *Singer*
1500 Broadway, #1703, New York, NY 10036

Veil, Simone *Government Official, France*
11 Pl Vauban, 75007 Paris, France

Velasquez, Jorge *Thoroughbred Racing Jockey*
770 Allerton Ave, Bronx, NY 10467

Velazco, Sheila K *Labor Leader*
%National Federal Employees Federation, 1016 16th St NW, Washington, DC 20036

Velikhov, Yevgeny P *Physicist*
%M V Lononosov University, Leninskie Gorky, Moscow 119808, USSR

Veljohnson, Reginald *Actor*
%Badgley McQueeney Connor, 9229 Sunset Blvd, #607, Los Angeles, CA 90069

Vendela *Model*
%Eileen Ford Agency, 344 E 59th St, New York, NY 10022

Vendler, Helen *Educator*
16-A Still St, Brookline, MA 02146

Veneman, Gerard E *Businessman*
%Great Northern Nekoosa Corp, 75 Prospect St, Stamford, CT 06904

Venet, Philippe *Fashion Designer*
62 Rue Francois 1er, 75008 Paris, France

Venkataraman, Ramaswamy *President, India*
%President's Office, New Delhi, India

Vento, Bruce F *Representative, MN*
%House of Representatives, Washington, DC 20515

Ventres, R J *Businessman*
%Borden Inc, 277 Park Ave, New York, NY 10172

Venturi, Ken *Golfer*
%Professional Golfers Assn, PO Box 109601, Palm Beach Gardens, FL 33410

Venturi, Robert *Architect*
%Venturi Rauch & Scott, 4236 Main St, Philadelphia, PA 19127

Venuta, Benay *Singer, Actress*
50 E 79th St, New York, NY 10021

Venza, Jack *Broadcast Executive*
%WNET-TV, 356 W 58th St, New York, NY 10019

Vera, Billy *Singer*
%Progressive Artists Agency, 400 S Beverly Blvd, #216, Beverly Hills, CA 90212

Verdeur, Joe *Swimmer*
15 Bryn Mawr Ave, Bala-Cynwyd, PA 19004

Verdi, Bob *Sportswriter*
%Chicago Tribune, 435 N Michigan Ave, Chicago, IL 60611

Verdon, Gwen *Dancer, Actress*
91 Central Park West, New York, NY 10023
Verdy, Violette *Ballerina*
44 W 62nd St, #25-C, New York, NY 10023
Vereen, Ben *Actor*
8730 Sunset Blvd, #600, Los Angeles, CA 90069
Verhoeven, Paul *Movie Director*
%Riverside Pictures, 1075 AA Amsterdam, Netherlands
Verhoogen, John *Geophysicist*
2100 Marin Ave, Berkeley, CA 94707
Verkuil, Paul R *Educator*
%College of William & Mary, President's Office, Williamsburg, VA 23185
Vermeil, Dick *Football Coach, Sportscaster*
%CBS-TV, Sports Dept, 51 W 52nd St, New York, NY 10019
Verne, Richard *Radio Executive*
%NBC Radio, 30 Rockefeller Plz, New York, NY 10020
Vernier-Palliez, Bernard *Diplomat, France*
%French Embassy, 2535 Belmont Rd NW, Washington, DC 20008
Vernon, Glen *Actor*
12016 Moorpark St, #3, Studio City, CA 91604
Vernon, John *Actor*
15125 Mulholland Dr, Los Angeles, CA 90024
Vernon, Mickey *Baseball Player*
100 E Rose Valley Rd, Wallingford, PA 19086
Vernon, Mike *Hockey Player*
%Calgary Flames, PO Box 1540, Station M, Calgary AB T2P 3B9, Canada
Veronis, John J *Publisher*
%JJV Publishing Co, 660 Madison Ave, New York, NY 10021
Versace, Dick *Basketball Coach*
%Turner Broadcast System, Sports Dept, 1050 Techwood Dr, Atlanta, GA 30318
Versace, Gianni *Fashion Designer*
%Gianni Versace Inc, Via San Pietro all'Orto, Milan, Italy
Versalles, Zoilo *Baseball Player*
8645 Fremont S, Bloomington, MN 55420
Vessels, Billy *Football Player*
4701 Santa Maria St, Coral Gables, FL 33146
Vessey, John W, Jr *Army General*
Star Rt, Box 136-A, Garrison, MN 56450
Vest, Charles M *Educator*
%Massachusetts Institute of Technology, President's Office, Cambridge, MA 02138
Vest, George S *Diplomat*
%US Mission, 40 Blvd du Regent, Brussels 1000, Belgium
Vest, Jake *Cartoonist (That's Jake)*
1709 Carol Woods Dr, Apopka, FL 32703
Vest, R Lamar *Religious Leader*
%Church of God, PO Box 2430, Cleveland, TN 37320
Vetrov, Aleksandr *Ballet Dancer*
%State Academic Bolshoi Theatre, 1 Ploschad Sverdlova, Moscow, Russia
Vettrus, Richard *Religious Leader*
%Church of Lutheran Brethren, 707 Crestview Dr W, Union, IA 52175
Viccellio, Henry, Jr *Air Force General*
Director, Joint Staff, Joint Chiefs of Staff, Washington, DC 20318
Vickers, Jon *Opera Singer*
%Metropolitan Opera Assn, Lincoln Center Plz, New York, NY 10023
Viclosky, Peter *Representative, IN*
%House of Representatives, Washington, DC 20515
Victor, Paul-Emile *Explorer, Civil Engineer*
%Polar Expeditions, 47 Ave de Marechal Fayolle, 75116 Paris, France
Vida, J D *Test Pilot (SR-71)*
%OL Det 6, 2762LS/FT, Edwards Air Force Base, CA 93523
Vidal, Gore *Writer*
2562 Outpost Dr, Los Angeles, CA 90068
Vidmar, Peter *Gymnast*
%Wally Wolf, 3956 Overland Ave, #205, Culver City, CA 90230
Vieillard, Roger *Artist*
7 Rue de l'Estrapade, 75005 Paris, France

V

Vieira – Virolainen

Vieira, Joao Bernardo *Head of State, Guinea-Bissau*
Conselho de Estado, Bissau, Guinea-Bissau

Vieira, Meredith *Commentator*
%CBS-TV, News Dept, 524 W 57th St, New York, NY 10019

Viereck, Peter *Poet, Historian*
12 Silver St, South Hadley, MA 01075

Vigoda, Abe *Actor*
1215 Beverly View Dr, Beverly Hills, CA 90210

Viguerie, Richard A *Political Leader*
7777 Leesburg Pike, Falls Church, VA 22043

Viktorenko, Alexander *Cosmonaut*
141 160 Svyosdny Gorodok, Moskovskoi Oblasti, Potchta Kosmonavtov, Russia

Vilas, Guillermo *Tennis Player*
%Guy Cromwell Betz, Pembroke One Bldg, #525, Virginia Beach, VA 23462

Vilenkin, Alex *Physicist, Astronomer*
%Tufts University, Physics & Astronomy Dept, Medford, MA 02155

Villa, Carlos *Artist*
1664 Grove St, San Francisco, CA 94117

Villas Boas, Orlando *Anthropologist, Explorer*
Parque Nacional do Xingu, Rua Capital Federal 309, 01259 Sao Paulo, Brazil

Villechaize, Herve *Actor*
PO Box 1305, Burbank, CA 91507

Villella, Edward *Ballet Dancer, Choreographer*
%Prodigal Productions, 129 W 69th St, New York, NY 10023

Villoria, Richard *Educator*
%World Future Society, 4916 St Elmo Ave, Bethesda, MD 20814

Vincent, Francis T (Fay), Jr *Baseball Executive*
%Baseball Commissioner's Office, 350 Park Ave, New York, NY 10022

Vincent, Helen *Editor*
%True Story Magazine, 215 Lexington Ave, New York, NY 10016

Vincent, James *Businessman*
%Biogen Inc, 14 Cambridge Ctr, Cambridge, MA 02142

Vincent, Jan-Michael *Actor*
PO Box 7000, Redondo Beach, CA 90277

Vincent, Jay *Basketball Player*
%Washington Bullets, Capital Ctr, 1 Truman Dr, Landover, MD 20785

Vincent, Sam *Basketball Player*
%Orlando Magic, Box 76, 1 Dupont Cir, Orlando, FL 32802

Vines, H Ellsworth *Tennis Player*
%La Quinta Golf Club, PO Box 821, La Quinta, CA 92253

Vines, Jerry *Religious Leader*
%First Baptist Church, 124 W Ashley St, Jacksonville, FL 32202

Vines, William *Financier*
%Australia & New Zealand Banking Group, 55 Collins, Melbourne, Australia

Vink, Pieter Carel *Businessman*
%North American Philips Corp, 100 E 42nd St, New York, NY 10017

Vinogradov, Oleg *Ballet Director*
%Kirov Ballet Theatre, 1 Ploshchad Iskusstr, St Petersburg, Russia

Vinson, James S *Educator*
%University of Evansville, President's Office, Evansville, IN 47722

Vint, Jesse *Actor*
%BDP Assoc, 10637 Burbank Blvd, North Hollywood, CA 91601

Vinton, Bobby *Singer*
%Rexford Productions, PO Box 906, Malibu, CA 90265

Vinton, Will *Animator*
%Will Vinton Productions, 2580 NW Upshur, Portland, OR 97210

Viola, Frank *Baseball Player*
844 Sweetwater Island Cir, Longwood, FL 32779

Virata, Cesar E *Prime Minister, Philippines*
63 E Maya Dr, Quezon City, Philippines

Virdon, Bill *Baseball Manager*
1311 River Rd, Springfield, MO 65804

Viren, Lasse *Track Athlete*
Suomen Urheilulitto, Box 25202, 00250 Helsinki 25, Finland

Virolainen, Johannes *Prime Minister, Finland*
Kirkniemi, Lohja, Finland

Visciosky, Peter J *Representative, IN*
%House of Representatives, Washington, DC 20515
Viscuso, Sal *Actor*
6491 Ivarene Ave, Los Angeles, CA 90068
Vise, David A *Journalist*
%Washington Post, 1150 15th St NW, Washington, DC 20071
Vishnevskaya, Galina *Opera Singer*
%State Academic Bolshoi Theatre, 1 Ploshchad Sverdlova, Moscow, Russia
Viso, Michel *Spatinaut, France*
%CNES, 129 R Universite 7e, 75007 Paris, France
Visscher, Maurice B *Physiologist*
120 Melbourne Ave SE, Minneapolis, MN 55414
Visser, Lesley *Sportscaster*
%CBS-TV, Sports Dept, 51 W 52nd St, New York, NY 10019
Vitale, Dick *Sportscaster*
%ESPN, Sports Dept, ESPN Plz, 935 Middle St, Bristol, CT 06010
Vititoe, William P *Businessman*
%Michigan Bell Telephone Co, 444 Michigan Ave, Detroit, MI 48226
Vitti, Monica *Actress*
Via Vicenzo Tiberio 18, Rome, Italy
Vlug, Dirk J *WW II Army Hero (CMH)*
1464 Seymour Ave NW, Grand Rapids, MI 49504
Vo Nguyen Giap *Army General, Vietnam*
Dang Cong San Vietnam, 1-C Blvd Hoang Van Thu, Hanoi, Vietnam
Vo Van Kiet *Prime Minister, Vietnam*
%Prime Minister's Office, Council of Ministers, Hanoi, Vietnam
Vogel, Hans-Jochen *Government Official, West Germany*
%Bundeshaus, 5300 Bonn 1, Germany
Vogel, Wolfgang *Attorney, Spy Expert*
Reilerstrasse 4, Berlin, Germany
Vogels, H C *Businessman*
%Messerschmitt-Bolkew-Blohm, 8000 Munich 80, Germany
Vogelstein, Bert *Cancer Researcher*
%Johns Hopkins University, School of Medicine, Oncology Ctr, Baltimore, MD 21218
Vogt, Peter K *Virologist*
2011 Zonal Ave, Los Angeles, CA 90033
Voight, Jon *Actor*
13340 Galewood Dr, Sherman Oaks, CA 91423
Voinovich, George V *Governor, OH*
%Governor's Office, State House, 77 S High St, Columbus, OH 43215
Voiselle, Bill *Baseball Player*
RR 2, Box 318, Ninety Six, SC 29666
Voisinet, James R *Businessman*
%National Gypsum Co, 4500 Lincoln Plz, Dallas, TX 75201
Volberding, Paul *Cancer Researcher*
%S F General Hospital, AIDS Activities Div, 995 Potrero, San Francisco, CA 94110
Volcker, Paul A *Government Official*
%James D Wolfensohn Inc, 425 Park Ave, New York, NY 10022
Volk, Harry J *Financier*
%Union Bank, 1900 Ave of Stars, #210, Los Angeles, CA 90067
Volk, Igor *Cosmonaut*
140 161 Svyosdny Gorodok, Moskovskoi Oblasti, Potchta Kosmonavtov, Russia
Volkmer, Harold L *Representative, MO*
%House of Representatives, Washington, DC 20515
Volkov, Alexander *Cosmonaut*
141 160 Svyosdny Gorodok, Moskovskoi Oblasti, Potchta Kosmonavtov, Russia
Vollenweider, Andreas *Concert Harpist*
%CBS Records, 51 W 52nd St, New York, NY 10019
Volpe, John A *Secretary, Transportation; Governor, MA*
15 Tudo Rd, Nahant, MA 01908
Volynov, Boris V *Cosmonaut*
141 160 Svyosdny Gorodok, Moskovskoi Oblasti, Potchta Kosmonavtov, Russia
Volz, Nedra *Actress*
615 Tulare Way, Upland, CA 91786
Von Aroldingen, Karin *Ballerina*
%New York City Ballet, Lincoln Ctr, New York, NY 10023

V

Von Arx – Vucanovich

Von Arx, Dolph W *Businessman*
%Thomas J Lipton Inc, 800 Sylvan Ave, Englewood Cliffs, NJ 07632

Von Dohnanyi, Christoph *Conductor*
Hamburgische Staatsoper, Gr Theaterstrasse 34, 2 Hamburg 36, Germany

Von Frisch, Karl *Nobel Medicine Laureate*
10 Uber der Klause, Munich 90, Germany

Von Furstenberg, Betsy *Actress*
%Baekel & Jennings Agency, 427 N Canon Dr, #205, Beverly Hills, CA 90210

Von Furstenberg, Diane *Fashion Designer*
745 5th Ave, New York, NY 10151

Von Furstenberg, Egon *Fashion Designer*
50 E 72nd St, New York, NY 10021

Von Hapsburg-Lothringem, Otto *Government Official, West Germany*
Hindenburgstrasse 14, 8134 Pocking-Starnberg, Germany

Von Hartz, Maria del Carmen *Model*
%Ford Model Agency, 344 E 59th St, New York, NY 10022

Von Klitzing, Klaus *Nobel Physics Laureate*
%Max Planck Solid State Research Institute, Stuttgart, Germany

Von Kuenheim, Eberhard *Businessman*
%Bayerische Motorenwerke, Mauerkirchenstrasse 105, 8000 Munich, Germany

Von Otter, Anne Sofie *Opera Singer*
%Columbia Artists Mgmt Inc, 165 W 57th St, New York, NY 10019

Von Runkle, Theodora *Costume Designer*
8805 Lookout Mountain Rd, Los Angeles, CA 90046

Von Saltza Olmstead, Chris *Swimmer*
7060 Fairway Pl, Carmel, CA 93921

Von Stade, Frederica *Opera Singer*
%Columbia Artists Mgmt Inc, 165 W 57th St, New York, NY 10019

Von Sydow, Max *Actor*
Strandvegen B, S-11456 Stockholm, Sweden

Von Tobel, Paul, III *Businessman*
%Hardware Wholesalers Inc, Box 868, Fort Wayne, IN 46801

Von Weizsacker, Carl-Friedrich *Philosopher*
Alpenstrasse 15, 8131 Starnberg-Socking, Germany

Von Weizsacker, Richard *President, West Germany*
Villa Hammerschmidt, Bonn, Germany

Von Wening, Eugene, Jr *Businessman*
%Turner Corp, 633 3rd Ave, New York, NY 10017

VonBerg, William G *Businessman*
%Sybron Corp, 1100 Midtown Tower, Rochester, NY 14604

Vonnegut, Kurt, Jr *Writer*
Scudder's Ln, West Barnstable, MA 02668

Voorhees, John J *Dermatologist*
%University of Michigan Medical Ctr, Outpatient Bldg, Ann Arbor, MI 48109

Vos Savant, Marilyn *Writer*
124 W 60th St, New York, NY 10023

Vosler, Forrest L *WW II Army Air Corps Hero (CMH)*
1611 Old Rt 31, Memphis, NY 13112

Voss, James S *Astronaut*
%NASA, Johnson Space Ctr, Houston, TX 77058

Voss, Janice E *Astronaut*
%NASA, Johnson Space Ctr, Houston, TX 77058

Voulkos, Peter *Artist*
1306 3rd St, Berkeley, CA 94710

Voute, William J *Financier*
%Salomon Bros, 1 New York Plz, New York, NY 10004

Voznesensky, Andrei A *Poet*
Kotelnicheskaya Nab 1/15, Bl W, #62, Moscow 109 240, Russia

Vranitzky, Franz *Chancellor, Austria*
%Chancellor's Office, Ballhausplatz 2, 1014 Vienna, Austria

Vreeland, Eleanor P *Educator*
%Katherine Gibbs School, President's Office, New York, NY 10017

Vuarnet, Jean *Skier*
Chalet Squaw Peak, 74110 Auoriaz, France

Vucanovich, Barbara F *Representative, NV*
%House of Representatives, Washington, DC 20515

Vuitton, Henri-Louis *Fashion Designer*
78 Bis Ave Marceau, 75000 Paris, France

Vuono, Carl E *Army General*
%Office of Chief of Staff, US Army, Pentagon, Washington, DC 20310

Vyent, Louise *Model*
%Pauline's Model Mgmt, 379 W Broadway, New York, NY 10012

Wachner, Linda *Businesswoman*
%Warnaco Inc, 350 Lafayette St, Bridgeport, CT 06601
Wachtel, Christine *Track Athlete*
Neubrandenburg 2, Germany
Wachter, Anita *Skier*
Gantschierstrasse 579, 6780 Schruns, Austria
Wachter, Eberhard *Opera Singer*
46 Felix-Mottlstrasse, Vienna XIX, Austria
Wacker, Jim *Football Coach*
%University of Minnesota, Athletic Dept, Minneapolis, MN 55455
Waddell, John C *Businessman*
%Arrow Electronics Inc, 767 5th Ave, New York, NY 10153
Waddell, John Henry *Artist*
Star Route 2273, Oak Creek Village Rd, Cornville, AZ 86325
Waddington, Miriam *Writer*
32 Yewfield Cres, Don Mills ON M5C 2Y6, Canada
Wade, Edgar L *Religious Leader*
%Christian Methodist Episcopal Church, PO Box 3403, Memphis, TN 38101
Wade, L Margaret *Basketball Coach*
%Basketball Hall of Fame, PO Box 179, Springfield, MA 01101
Wade, Ormand J *Businessman*
%Ameritek Inc, 225 W Randolph St, Chicago, IL 60606
Wade, Virginia *Tennis Player*
Sharstead Ct, Sittingbourne, Kent, England
Wadkins, Bobby *Golfer*
%Pros Inc, PO Box 673, Richmond, VA 23206
Wadkins, Lanny *Golfer*
%Pros Inc, PO Box 673, Richmond, VA 23206
Wadsworth, Charles *Chamber Musician*
%Chamber Music Society, Alice Tully Hall, Lincoln Ctr, New York, NY 10023
Wages, Robert E *Labor Leader*
%Oil Chemical Atomic Workers Int'l Union, PO Box 2812, Denver, CO 80201
Wagg, Peter *Television Producer*
%Lorimar-Telepictures, 10202 W Washington Blvd, Culver City, CA 90230
Waggoner, Lyle *Actor*
4450 Balboa Ave, Encino, CA 91316
Wagner, Chuck *Actor*
44 Floyd Rd, Verona, NJ 07044
Wagner, Gerrit A *Businessman*
%Royal Dutch/Shell Grp, 30 Carel Van Bylandtlaan, The Hague, Netherlands
Wagner, Lindsay *Actress*
%International Creative Mgmt, 8899 Beverly Blvd, Los Angeles, CA 90048
Wagner, Lisa *Bowler*
%Ladies Pro Bowlers Tour, 7171 Cherryvale Blvd, Rockford, IL 61112
Wagner, Robert *Actor*
1500 Old Oak Rd, Los Angeles, CA 90077
Wagner, Robert T *Educator*
%South Dakota State University, President's Office, Brookings, SD 57007
Wagner, Robin *Stage, Set Designer*
%Robin Wagner Studio, 890 Broadway, New York, NY 10003
Wagner, Roger *Choral Director*
5930 Penfield Ave, Woodland Hills, CA 91367
Wagner, Wolfgang M M *Opera Director*
Festspielhugel Nr 3, 8580 Bayreuth, Germany
Wagoner, Harold E *Architect*
331 Lindsey Dr, Berwyn, PA 19312
Wagoner, Porter *Singer, Songwriter*
PO Box 121089, Nashville, TN 37212
Wahl, Ken *Actor*
%Terry Newton, 1950 Sawtelle Blvd, #250, Los Angeles, CA 90025
Wahlgren, Olof G C *Editor*
Nicoloviusgatan 5-B, 217-57 Malmo, Sweden
Wahlstrom, Jarl H *Religious Leader*
%Salvation Army International, 101 Queen Victoria St, London EC4, England
Waihee, John *Governor, HI*
%Governor's Office, State Capitol Bldg, #500, Honolulu, HI 96813

Wain, John B *Writer*
%Macmillan & Co, Little Essex St, London WC2 3LF, England

Wainer, Stanley A *Businessman*
%Wyle Laboratories, 128 Maryland St, El Segundo, CA 90245

Wainwright, Bill C *Financier*
%Georgia Federal Bank, 20 Marietta St NW, Atlanta, GA 30303

Wainwright, James *Actor*
%Lew Sherrell Agency, 1354 Los Robles, Palm Springs, CA 92262

Waite, Ralph *Actor*
8060 Mulholland Dr, Los Angeles, CA 90046

Waite, Ric *Cinematographer*
%Smith/Gosnell/Nicholson, 1515 Palisades Dr, #N, Pacific Palisades, CA 90272

Waits, Tom *Singer*
%Island Records, 444 Madison Ave, New York, NY 10022

Waitz, Grete *Track Athlete*
%Bjoken School, Oslo, Norway

Wajda, Andrzej *Movie Director*
Ul Haukego 14, 01-540 Warsaw, Poland

Wakeman, Rick *Jazz Musician, Composer*
Bajonor House, 2 Bridge St, Peel, Isle of Man

Walcott, Gregory *Actor*
%Associated Talent International, 1320 Armacost Ave, #2, Los Angeles, CA 90025

Walcott, Jersey Joe *Boxer*
1500 Baird Ave, Camden, NJ 08103

Wald, George *Nobel Medicine Laureate*
21 Lakeview Ave, Cambridge, MA 02138

Wald, Jeff *Talent Agent*
9291 Burton Way, Beverly Hills, CA 90210

Wald, Patricia M *Judge*
%US Court of Appeals, 3rd & Constitution NW, Washington, DC 20001

Wald, Richard C *Television Executive*
35 Orchard Rd, Larchmont, NY 10538

Waldbaum, Ira *Businessman*
%Waldbaum Inc, Hemlock & Boulevard, Central Islip, NY 11722

Waldbaum, Julia *Businesswoman*
%Waldbaum Inc, Hemlock & Boulevard, Central Islip, NY 11722

Walden, Robert *Actor*
1450 Arroyo View Dr, Pasadena, CA 91103

Waldheim, Kurt *President, Austria*
Ballhausplatz 2, 1010 Vienna, Austria

Waldo, Carolyn *Synchronized Swimmer*
%International Management Grp, 150 Bloor St W, Toronto ON M5S 2X9, Canada

Waldron, Hicks B *Businessman*
%Avon Products, 9 W 57th St, New York, NY 10019

Walenberg, Alan *Publisher*
%Redbook Magazine, 224 W 57th St, New York, NY 10019

Walesa, Lech *Nobel Peace Laureate*
Ul Pilotow 17 D/3, Gdansk-Zaspa, Poland

Walgreen, Charles R, III *Businessman*
%Walgreen Co, 200 Wilmot Rd, Deerfield, IL 60015

Walgren, Doug *Representative, PA*
%House of Representatives, Washington, DC 20515

Walk, Igor *Cosmonaut*
141 160 Svyosdny Gorodok, Moskovskoi Oblasti, Potchta Kosmonavtov, Russia

Walken, Christopher *Actor*
142 Cedar Rd, Wilton, CT 06897

Walker, Alan *Anthropologist*
%Johns Hopkins Medical School, Cell Biology & Anatomy Dept, Baltimore, MD 21205

Walker, Alice *Social Activist, Writer*
720 Steiner St, San Francisco, CA 94117

Walker, Ardis M *Poet*
PO Box 37, Kernville, CA 93238

Walker, Charles D *Astronaut*
%McDonnell Douglas Astronautics, St Louis Airport, St Louis, MO 92647

Walker, Charles Edward *Economist*
10120 Chapel Rd, Potomac, MD 20854

Walker, Clint *Actor*
%David Shapira Assoc, 15301 Ventura Blvd, #345, Sherman Oaks, CA 91403

Walker, Colleen *Golfer*
%Ladies Professional Golf Assn, 2570 Volusia Ave, #B, Daytona Beach, FL 32114

Walker, David M *Astronaut*
%NASA, Johnson Space Ctr, Houston, TX 77058

Walker, Doak *Football Player*
PO Box TT, Steamboat Springs, CO 80477

Walker, E Cardon *Movie Executive*
%Walt Disney Productions, 500 S Buena Vista St, Burbank, CA 91521

Walker, Edward B, III *Businessman*
%Gulf Oil Corp, PO Box 4523, Houston, TX 77210

Walker, Henry A, Jr *Businessman*
%Amfac Inc, 44 Montgomery St, San Francisco, CA 94120

Walker, Herschel *Football Player*
%Minnesota Vikings, 9520 Viking Dr, Eden Prairie, MN 55344

Walker, James C *Businessman*
%Warnaco Inc, 350 Lafayette St, Bridgeport, CT 06601

Walker, James E *Educator*
%Middle Tennessee State University, President's Office, Murfreesboro, TN 37132

Walker, James L *Labor Leader*
%Fireman & Oilers Brotherhood, 1100 Circle 75 Pkwy, Atlanta, GA 30339

Walker, Jimmy (J J) *Comedian*
%Gersh Agency, 232 N Canon Dr, Beverly Hills, CA 90210

Walker, John *Track Athlete*
Jeffs Rd, RD Papatoetoe, New Zealand

Walker, John *Museum Curator*
%National Gallery of Art, 1729 "H" St NW, Washington, DC 20006

Walker, John C *Plant Pathologist*
10045 Royal Oak Rd, #45, Sun City, AZ 85351

Walker, John M, Jr *Judge*
%US Court of Appeals, US Courthouse, Foley Sq, New York, NY 10007

Walker, Kenny *Basketball Player*
%New York Knicks, Madison Square Grdn, 4 Pennsylvania Plz, New York, NY 10001

Walker, LeRoy *Track Coach*
1208 Red Oak Ave, Durham, NC 27707

Walker, Marcy *Actress*
%David Shapira Assoc, 15301 Ventura Blvd, #345, Sherman Oaks, CA 91403

Walker, Marcy *Actress*
4403 Ckybourn Ave, North Hollywood, CA 91602

Walker, Martin D *Businessman*
%Rockwell International Corp, 600 Grant St, Pittsburgh, PA 15219

Walker, Melvin *Track Athlete*
932 E 55th St, Chicago, IL 60615

Walker, Mort *Cartoonist (Beetle Bailey, Sarge)*
61 Studio Ct, Stamford, CT 06903

Walker, Nancy *Actress*
3702 Eureka Dr, Studio City, CA 91604

Walker, Peter E *Government Official, England*
Deer Park, Droitwich, Worcs, England

Walker, Robert *Actor*
%TOPS, 23410 Civic Center Way, Malibu, CA 90265

Walker, Robert S *Representative, PA*
6065 Parkridge Dr, East Petersburg, PA 17520

Walker, Ronald F *Businessman*
%United Brands Co, 1271 Ave of Americas, New York, NY 10020

Walker, Ronald Frederick *Financier*
%American Financial Corp, 1 E 4th St, Cincinnati, OH 45202

Walker, Wesley *Football Player*
%New York Jets, 598 Madison Ave, New York, NY 10022

Walker, Wilbert A *Businessman*
220 Bellview Blvd, Belleair, FL 33516

Walker, Winston W *Businessman*
%Provident Mutual Life Insurance, 1600 Market St, Philadelphia, PA 19103

Walkup, William E *Businessman*
1140 Brooklawn Dr, Los Angeles, CA 90024

Wall, Akure *Model*
%Elite Model Mgmt, 111 E 22nd St, New York, NY 10010

Wall, Art *Golfer*
%Professional Golfers Assn, PO Box 109601, Palm Beach Gardens, FL 33410

Wall, Brian *Sculptor*
1824 Grant Ave, San Francisco, CA 94133

Wall, David *Ballet Dancer*
%Royal Ballet, Convent Gdn, Bow St, London WC2E 7QA, England

Wall, Frederick T *Physical Chemist*
2468 Via Viesta, La Jolla, CA 92037

Wall, Shannon J *Labor Leader*
%National Maritime Union, 346 W 17th St, New York, NY 10011

Wall, William E *Businessman*
%Kansas Power & Light Co, 818 Kansas Ave, Topeka, KS 66612

Wallace Stone, Dee *Actress*
23035 Cumorah Crest Dr, Woodland Hills, CA 91364

Wallace, Bruce *Geneticist*
940 McBryde Dr, Blacksburg, VA 24060

Wallace, Craig K *Physician*
%National Institutes of Health, 9000 Rockville Pike, Bethesda, MD 20205

Wallace, David W *Businessman*
%Todd Shipyards, 1 State Street Plz, New York, NY 10004

Wallace, George C *Governor, AL*
%Troy State University, Drawer 4419, Montgomery, AL 36195

Wallace, J Clifford *Judge*
%US Court of Appeals, 940 Front St, San Diego, CA 92189

Wallace, Marcia *Actress*
8937 Appian Way, Los Angeles, CA 90046

Wallace, Mike *Commentator*
%CBS-TV, News Dept, 524 W 57th St, New York, NY 10019

Wallace, W Ray *Businessman*
%Trinity Industries, 2525 Stemmons Fwy, Dallas, TX 75207

Wallace, William F *Football Player*
Rt 1, Box 145, Lake Arthur, LA 70549

Wallach, Eli *Actor*
90 Riverside Dr, New York, NY 10024

Wallach, Tim *Baseball Player*
10762 Holly Dr, Garden Grove, CA 92640

Wallechinsky, David *Writer*
%William Morrow Co, 105 Madison Ave, New York, NY 10016

Wallenberg, Peter *Businessman*
%SKF AB, Hornsgatan 1, 1415 50, Goteborg, Sweden

Waller, Michael *Editor*
%Kansas City Star-Times, 1729 Grand Ave, Kansas City, MO 64108

Waller, William L *Governor, MS*
220 S President, Jackson, MS 39201

Wallgren, Sven *Businessman*
%Esselte AB, Box 1371, 171 27 Stockholm-Solna, Sweden

Wallin, Winston R *Businessman*
%Medtronic Inc, 7000 Central Ave NE, Minneapolis, MN 55432

Walling, Cheves *Chemist*
2784 Blue Spruce Dr, Salt Lake City, UT 84117

Wallis, Gordon T *Financier*
%Irving Bank Corp, 1 Wall St, New York, NY 10005

Wallis, Shani *Actress*
%Robert Cosden Enterprises, 7080 Hollywood Blvd, Los Angeles, CA 90028

Walliser, Maria *Skier*
%Olympic Committee, Case Postale, 1814 La Tour-de-Peilz, Switzerland

Walls, Everson *Football Player*
%New York Giants, Giants Stadium, East Rutherford, NJ 07073

Walmsley, Jon *Actor*
%Bobby Ball Talent Agency, 6290 Sunset Blvd, Los Angeles, CA 90028

Walsh, Bill *Football Coach*
%Stanford University, Athletic Dept, Stanford, CA 94305

Walsh, Don *Underwater Explorer*
1337 Via Zumaya, Palos Verdes Estates, CA 90274

W

Walsh, James A *Businessman*
%Armstrong Rubber Co, 500 Sargent Dr, New Haven, CT 06536

Walsh, James S *Businessman*
%Beech Aircraft Corp, 9709 E Central, Wichita, KS 67201

Walsh, John *Moderator*
%"Most Wanted" Show, Fox Television, 5151 Wisconsin Ave NW, Washington, DC 20016

Walsh, John A *Editor*
135 E 50th St, New York, NY 10022

Walsh, John, Jr *Museum Curator*
%J Paul Getty Art Museum, 17985 Pacific Coast Hwy, Malibu, CA 90265

Walsh, Kenneth A *WW II Marine Air Corps Hero (CMH)*
1008 Riviera Dr, Santa Ana, CA 92706

Walsh, Lawrence E *Government Official, Attorney*
1902 Bedford St, Oklahoma City, OK 73116

Walsh, Leo M, Jr *Businessman*
%Equitable Life Assurance Society, 787 7th Ave, New York, NY 10019

Walsh, M Emmet *Actor*
%Gersh Agency, 232 N Canon Dr, Beverly Hills, CA 90210

Walsh, Michael H *Businessman*
%Tenneco Inc, Tenneco Bldg, PO Box 2511, Houston, TX 77002

Walsh, Patrick C *Urologist*
%Johns Hopkins Hospital, Brady Urological Institute, Baltimore, MD 21205

Walsh, Steve *Football Player*
%New Orleans Saints, 6928 Saints Dr, Metairie, LA 70003

Walsh, Sydney *Actress*
%Gersh Agency, 232 N Canon Dr, Beverly Hills, CA 90210

Walsh, William B *Medical Administrator*
%Project HOPE, Health Sciences Education Ctr, Millwood, VA 22646

Walston, Ray *Actor*
%Harry Gold Assoc, 3500 W Olive Ave, #1400, Burbank, CA 91505

Walter, Henry G, Jr *Businessman*
%International Flavors & Fragrances, 521 W 57th St, New York, NY 10019

Walter, James W *Businessman*
%Jim Walter Corp, 1500 N Dale Mabry Hwy, Tampa, FL 33607

Walter, Jessica *Actress*
10530 Strathmore Dr, Los Angeles, CA 90024

Walter, John R *Businessman*
%R R Donnelley & Sons Co, 2223 Martin Luther King Dr, Chicago, IL 60616

Walter, Paul H L *Labor Leader*
%University Professors Assn, 1012 14th St, Washington, DC 20005

Walters, Barbara *Commentator*
33 W 60th St, New York, NY 10023

Walters, Charles *Movie Director*
23922-A De Ville Way, Malibu, CA 90265

Walters, David *Governor, OK*
%Governor's Office, State Capitol Bldg, #212, Oklahoma City, OK 73105

Walters, Harry N *Government Official*
%Veterans Administration, 810 Vermont Ave NW, Washington, DC 20420

Walters, Peter *Businessman*
%British Petroleum, Britannic House, Moor Ln, London EC2Y 9BU, England

Walters, Vernon A *Government Official, General*
%US Delegation, 799 UN Plz, New York, NY 10017

Walton, Ernest T S *Nobel Physics Laureate*
26 St Kebin's Park, Dantry Rd, Dublin 6, Ireland

Walton, Meredith *Religious Leader*
%Friends General Conference, 1520-B Race St, Philadelphia, PA 19102

Walton, S Robson *Businessman*
%Wal-Mart Stores, 702 SW 8th St, Bentonville, AK 72712

Walton, Sam M *Businessman*
%Wal-Mart Stores, 702 SW 8th St, Bentonville, AK 72716

Waltrip, Darrell *Auto Racing Driver*
PO Box 855, Franklin, TN 37065

Waltrip, William H *Businessman*
%IU International Corp, 1500 Walnut St, Philadelphia, PA 19102

Walworth, Arthur *Writer*
%Graduates Club, 155 Elm St, New Haven, CT 06508

Waly, Carl E %NASA, Johnson Space Center, Houston, TX 77058	*Astronaut*
Wambaugh, Joseph 30 Linda Isle, Newport Beach, CA 92660	*Writer*
Wan Li %State Council, Beijing, China	*Government Official, China*
Wanamaker, Sam 354 N Croft Ave, Los Angeles, CA 90048	*Actor*
Wang Zhen %State Council, Beijing, China	*Government Official, China*
Wang, Frederick A %Wang Laboratories, 1 Industrial Ave, Lowell, MA 01851	*Businessman*
Wang, Henry Y %University of Michigan, Chemical Engineering Dept, Ann Arbor, MI 48109	*Chemical Engineer*
Wang, Lorraine %Wang Laboratories, 1 Industrial Ave, Lowell, MA 01851	*Businesswoman*
Wang, Taylor %Jet Propulsion Laboratory, 4800 Oak Grove Dr, Pasadena, CA 91109	*Astronaut, Physicist*
Wang, Y C %Formosa Plastics Corp, 39 Chung Shang 3rd Rd, Kaohsiung, Taiwan	*Businessman*
Wangchuk, Jigme Singye %Royal Palace, Thimphu, Bhutan	*King, Bhutan*
Wantland, Earl %Tektronix Inc, PO Box 500, Beaverton, OR 97077	*Businessman*
Wanzer, Bobby %St John Fisher College, Athletic Dept, Rochester, NY 14618	*Basketball Player*
Wapner, Joseph A %"People's Court" Show, 1717 N Highland Ave, Los Angeles, CA 90028	*Judge, Actor*
Ward, Benjamin %New York Police Commissioner' Office, 1 Police Plz, New York, NY 10038	*Law Enforcement Official*
Ward, Bob (Robert R) 8031 Telegraph Rd, Severn, MD 21144	*Football Player*
Ward, Burt 1559 Pacific Coast Hwy, #815, Hermosa Beach, CA 90254	*Actor*
Ward, David 1 Kennedy Cres, Lake Wanaka, New Zealand	*Opera Singer*
Ward, Douglas Turner %Negro Ensemble Co, 1540 Broadway, New York, NY 10036	*Actor, Playwright*
Ward, Elmer L, Jr %Palm Beach Inc, 400 Pike St, Cincinnati, OH 45202	*Businessman*
Ward, Fred %STE Representation, 9301 Wilshire Blvd, #712, Beverly Hills, CA 90210	*Actor*
Ward, Harvie %Grand Cyprus Golf Club, 1 N Jacaranda, Orlando, FL 32822	*Golfer*
Ward, James (Skip) PO Box 755, Beverly Hills, CA 90213	*Actor*
Ward, Milton H %Freeport-McMoRan Inc, 1615 Poydras St, New Orleans, LA 70161	*Businessman*
Ward, Ralph E, Jr %Chesebrough-Pond's Inc, Westport, CT 06881	*Businessman*
Ward, Rev Sterling %Brethren Church, 524 College Ave, Ashland, OH 44805	*Religious Leader*
Ward, Richard H %Del Monte Corp, 1 Market Plz, San Francisco, CA 94105	*Businessman*
Ward, Robert 308 Montecito Ave, Durham, NC 27707	*Composer*
Ward, Rodger %Vintage Racing, PO Box 7000-728, Redondo Beach, CA 90277	*Auto Racing Driver*
Ward, Sela %International Creative Mgmt, 8899 Beverly Blvd, Los Angeles, CA 90048	*Actress*
Ward, Simon %IFA Ltd, 11-12 Hanover St, London W1, England	*Actor*
Ward, Thomas W %House of Representatives, Washington, DC 20515	*Representative, IN*
Wardeberg, George E %Whirlpool Corp, 2000 US 33 N, Benton Harbor, MI 49022	*Businessman*

W

Warden - Washburn

Warden, Jack *Actor*
23604 Malibu Colony Rd, Malibu, CA 90265

Ware, Andre *Football Player*
%Detroit Lions, Silverdome, 1200 Featherstone Rd, Pontiac, MI 48057

Ware, Herta *Actress*
%Selected Artists Agency, 13111 Ventura Blvd, Studio City, CA 91604

Ware, Karl E *Businessman*
%White Consolidated Industries, 11770 Berea Rd, Cleveland, OH 44111

Warfield, Marsha *Actress*
%International Creative Mgmt, 8899 Beverly Blvd, Los Angeles, CA 90048

Warfield, William *Opera Singer*
%University of Illinois, Music Dept, Urbana, IL 61801

Waring, Todd *Actor*
%Artists Agency, 10000 Santa Monica Blvd, #305, Los Angeles, CA 90067

Warioba, Joseph *Prime Minister, Tanzania*
%Prime Minister's Office, Dar-es-Salaam, Tanzania

Wark, Robert *Museum Curator*
%Huntington Library & Art Gallery, 1151 Oxford Rd, San Marino, CA 91108

Warlock, Billy *Actor*
%Abrams Artists, 9200 Sunset Blvd, #625, Los Angeles, CA 90069

Warmerdam, Cornelius (Dutch) *Track Athlete*
3976 N 1st St, Fresno, CA 93726

Warnecke, John Carl *Architect*
300 Broadway, San Francisco, CA 94133

Warner, David *Actor*
%Leading Artists Ltd, 60 St James's St, London SW1, England

Warner, Douglas A, III *Financier*
%J P Morgan & Co, 23 Wall St, New York, NY 10015

Warner, John Christian *Educator, Physical Chemist*
%St Barnabas Village, #411-A, 5850 Meridian Rd, Gibsonia, PA 15044

Warner, John W *Senator, VA*
Atoka Farm, Middleburg, VA 22117

Warner, Karl *Track Athlete*
167 Heritage Rd, Rochester, NY 14617

Warner, Malcolm-Jamal *Actor*
%Artists First, 8230 Beverly Blvd, #23, Los Angeles, CA 90048

Warner, Philip G *Editor*
%Houston Chronicle, 801 Texas Ave, Houston, TX 77002

Warner, Todd *Artist*
159-B NW 11th St, Boca Raton, FL 33432

Warner, William W *Writer*
2243 47th St NW, Washington, DC 20003

Warnes, Jennifer *Singer*
%Triad Artists, 10100 Santa Monica Blvd, #1600, Los Angeles, CA 90067

Warnke, Paul C *Government Official*
5037 Garfield St NW, Washington, DC 20016

Warren, Jennifer *Actress*
1675 Old Oak Rd, Los Angeles, CA 90049

Warren, L D *Editorial Cartoonist*
1815 William Howard Taft Rd, #203, Cincinnati, OH 45206

Warren, Lesley Ann *Actress*
3619 Meadville, Sherman Oaks, CA 91403

Warren, Michael *Actor*
1141 Stearns Dr, Los Angeles, CA 90035

Warren, Robert *Businessman*
%Premier Industrial Corp, 4500 Euclid Ave, Cleveland, OH 44103

Warren, Tom *Triathlete*
2393 La Marque, Pacific Beach, CA 92109

Warrick, Ruth *Actress*
903 Park Ave, New York, NY 10021

Warwick, Dionne *Singer*
%Triad Artists, 10100 Santa Monica Blvd, #1600, Los Angeles, CA 90067

Washburn, Barbara *Mapologist*
220 Somerset St, Belmont, MA 02114

Washburn, Beverly *Actress*
%Cavaleri Assoc, 6605 Hollywood Blvd, #220, Los Angeles, CA 90028

Washburn, H Bradford, Jr *Museum Official, Explorer*
220 Somerset St, Belmont, MA 02114

Washburn, Sherwood L *Anthropologist*
2797 Shasta Rd, Berkeley, CA 94708

Washington, Claudell *Baseball Player*
12 Charles Hill Rd, Orinda, CA 94563

Washington, Craig A *Representative, TX*
%House of Representatives, Washington, DC 20515

Washington, Denzel *Actor*
4604 Placida Ave, Toluca Lake, CA 91602

Washington, Gene A *Football Player*
1177 California St, #1131, San Francisco, CA 94108

Washington, Grover, Jr *Jazz Saxophonist*
%Zane Mgmt, 700 Three Penn Ctr, Philadelphia, PA 19102

Washington, Joe *Football Player*
%Atlanta Falcons, Suwanee Rd, Suwanee, GA 30174

Washington, Pearl (Dewayne) *Basketball Player*
%New Jersey Nets, Meadowlands Arena, East Rutherford, NJ 07073

Washington, Walter *Educator*
%Alcorn State University, President's Office, Loman, MS 39096

Washington, Walter E *Mayor*
1025 15th St NW, Washington, DC 20005

Washio, Hideo *Businessman*
%Niigata Engineering Co, 1-4-1 Kasumigaseki, Chiyodaku, Tokyo 100, Japan

Wasiak, Stan *Baseball Manager*
%Vero Beach Dodgers, Dodgertown, PO Box 2887, Vero Beach, FL 32961

Wass, Ted *Actor*
7667 Seattle Pl, Los Angeles, CA 90046

Wasserburg, Gerald J *Geophysicist*
4100 Pinecrest Dr, Altadena, CA 91001

Wasserman, Bert W *Businessman*
%Time Warner Inc, 75 Rockefeller Plz, New York, NY 10019

Wasserman, Dale *Playwright*
%Maurice Spanbock, 1345 Ave of Americas, New York, NY 10019

Wasserman, Dan *Editorial Cartoonist*
%Boston Globe, 135 Morrissey Blvd, Boston, MA 02107

Wasserman, Lew R *Entertainment Executive*
%MCA Inc, 100 Universal City Plz, Universal City, CA 91608

Wasserstein, Bruce *Financier*
%Wasserstein Perella Co, 31 W 52nd St, #2700, New York, NY 10019

Wasserstein, Wendy *Playwright*
%Fred Nathan Co, 1650 Broadway, #501, New York, NY 10019

Watanabe, Milio *Computer Scientist*
%Nippon Electric Co, Computer Labs, 5-33-1 Shiba, Tokyo, Japan

Watanabe, Moriyuki *Businessman*
%Mazda Motor Corp, 3-1 Shinchi, Fuchucho, Akigun, Hiroshima 730-91, Japan

Watanabe, Takeo *Businessman*
%Mitsubishi Oil Co, 1-2-4 Toranomon, Minatoku, Tokyo 100, Japan

Watanabe, Yasushi *Financier*
%Bank of Tokyo, 1-63 Nihonbashi Hongokucho, Chuoku, Tokyo 103, Japan

Waterman, Felicity *Actress*
%Harry Gold Assoc, 3500 W Olive, #1400, Burbank, CA 91505

Waters, Bunny *Actress*
903 N Bedford Dr, Beverly Hills, CA 90210

Waters, Frank *Writer*
PO Box 1127, Taos, NM 87571

Waters, John *Movie Director*
2601 Madison Ave, #704, Baltimore, MD 21217

Waters, Lou *Commentator*
%Cable News Network, 1 CNN Center, PO Box 105366, Atlanta, GA 30348

Waters, Maxine *Representative, CA*
%House of Representatives, Washington, DC 20515

Waters, Muddy *Singer*
%Cameron Organization, 320 S Waiola Ave, La Grange, IL 60525

Waters, Richard *Publisher*
%Sporting News, 1212 N Lindbergh Blvd, St Louis, MO 63166

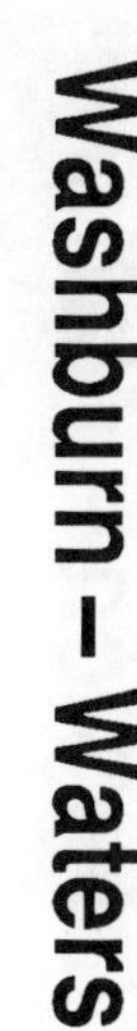

Waterston, Sam *Actor*
RR Box 197, East St, West Cornwall, CT 06796

Wathen, Thomas W *Businessman*
%California Plant Protection Inc, 6727 Odessa, Van Nuys, CA 91406

Watkins, Hays T *Businessman*
%CSX Corp, 901 E Cary St, Richmond, VA 23219

Watkins, James D *Secretary, Energy; Navy Admiral*
%Department of Energy, 1000 Independence Ave SW, Washington, DC 20585

Watkins, Tasker *WW II British Army Hero (VC), Judge*
5 Pump Ct, Middle Temple, London EC4, England

Watkins, Wesley W *Representative, OK*
521 S Broadway St, Ada, OK 74820

Watrous, Bill *Jazz Trombonist*
%Willard Alexander Inc, 660 Madison Ave, New York, NY 10021

Watson Richardson, Pokey *Swimmer*
4960 Maunalani Cir, Honolulu, HI 96816

Watson, A J *Auto Racing Engineer*
5420 Crawfordsville Rd, Speedway City, IN 46224

Watson, Alberta *Actress*
%Triad Artists, 10100 Santa Monica Blvd, #1600, Los Angeles, CA 90067

Watson, Arthel (Doc) *Singer*
%Folklore Productions, 1671 Appian Way, Santa Monica, CA 90401

Watson, Bobs *Actor*
2700 Montrose Ave, Montrose, CA 91020

Watson, Cecil James *Physician*
%Abbott Northwestern Hospital, 2727 Chicago Ave, Minneapolis, MN 55407

Watson, James D *Nobel Medicine Laureate*
Bungtown Rd, Cold Spring Harbor, NY 11724

Watson, James L *Judge*
%US Court of International Trade, 1 Federal Plz, New York, NY 10007

Watson, Martha *Track Athlete*
2291 Sabrosa St, Las Vegas, NV 89115

Watson, Mills *Actor*
2824 Dell Ave, Venice, CA 90291

Watson, Mills *Actor*
%Artists Group, 1930 Century Park West, #403, Los Angeles, CA 90067

Watson, Raymond L *Entertainment Executive*
900 Cagney Ln, Newport Beach, CA 92663

Watson, Thomas A *Businessman*
%Lincoln National Corp, 1300 S Clinton St, Fort Wayne, IN 46801

Watson, Thomas J, Jr *Businessman, Ambassador*
Meadowcraft Ln, Greenwich, CT 06836

Watson, Tom *Golfer*
Commerce Tower, #1313, 911 Main, Kansas City, MO 64105

Watson, Wilson D *WW II Marine Corps Hero (CMH)*
PO Box 433, Clarkesville, AR 72830

Watt, James G *Secretary, Interior*
9950 E Grand Ave, Englewood, CO 80110

Watt, Ray *Businessman*
%Watt Industries, 2716 Ocean Park Blvd, Santa Monica, CA 90406

Watt, Tom *Hockey Coach*
%Toronto Maple Leafs, 60 Carlton St, Toronto ON M5B 1L1, Canada

Wattenberg, Ben J *Demographer*
%American Enterprise Institute, 1150 17th St NW, Washington, DC 20036

Watterson, Bill *Cartoonist (Calvin & Hobbes)*
%General Delivery, Hudson, OH 44236

Watterson, Brett *Astronaut*
%HQ Space Division, PO Box 92960, Worldway Postal Ctr, Los Angeles, CA 90009

Watts, Andre *Concert Pianist*
%Columbia Artists Mgmt Inc, 165 W 57th St, New York, NY 10019

Watts, Ernie *Art Director, Stage Designer*
%International Creative Mgmt, 40 W 57th St, New York, NY 10019

Watts, Glenn E *Labor Leader*
%Communications Workers of America, 1925 "K" St NW, Washington, DC 20006

Watts, Heather *Ballerina*
%New York City Ballet, Lincoln Center Plz, New York, NY 10023

Watts, Helen *Opera Singer*
Rock House, Wallis, Ambleston, Haverford-West, Dyfed SA62 5RA, Wales
Watts, Stan *Basketball Coach*
205 E 2950 North St, Provo, UT 84604
Watts, William E *Businessman*
%General Nutrition Inc, 921 Penn Ave, Pittsburgh, PA 15222
Waugh, Auberon *Writer*
%Literary Review, 51 Beak St, London W1R 3LF, England
Waugh, Irving *Businessman*
1086 Lynwood Blvd, Nashville, TN 37215
Wax, Edward L *Businessman*
%Compton Advertising, 767 5th Ave, New York, NY 10022
Waxman, Al *Actor*
%Harris & Goldberg Agency, 1999 Ave of Stars, #2850, Los Angeles, CA 90067
Waxman, Henry A *Representative, CA*
%House of Representatives, Washington, DC 20515
Way, Alva O *Businessman*
%Travelers Corp, 1 Tower Sq, Hartford, CT 06115
Wayland, Len *Actor*
%Brooke Dunn Oliver, 9165 Sunset Blvd, #202, Los Angeles, CA 90069
Waymer, Dave *Football Player*
%San Francisco 49ers, 4949 Centennial Blvd, Santa Clara, CA 95054
Wayne, David *Actor*
868 Napoli Dr, Pacific Palisades, CA 90272
Wayne, June *Artist*
1108 N Tamarind Ave, Los Angeles, CA 90038
Wayne, Marshall *Diver*
Rt 1, Box 824, Hiawassee, GA 30546
Wayne, Patrick *Actor*
10502 Whipple St, North Hollywood, CA 91602
Wazzan, Chafic al- *Prime Minister, Lebanon*
%Council of Ministers, Pl de l'Etoile, Beirut, Lebanon
Wearly, William L *Businessman*
%Ingersoll-Rand Co, 200 Chestnut Ridge Rd, Woodcliff Lake, NJ 07675
Wearn, Wilson C *Businessman, Publisher*
%Multimedia Inc, 305 S Main St, Greenville, SC 29601
Wearstier, Earl Ford *Businessman*
%Diebold Inc, 5995 Mayfair Rd, North Canton, OH 44720
Weatherly, Shawn *Actress*
%Gordon-Rossen Agency, 12700 Ventura Blvd, #340, Studio City, CA 91604
Weathers, Carl *Actor*
%Rogers & Cowan Agency, 10000 Santa Monica Blvd, #400, Los Angeles, CA 90067
Weatherspoon, Clarence *Basketball Player*
%University of Southern Mississippi, Athletic Dept, Hattiesburg, MS 39408
Weatherstone, Dennis *Financier*
%J P Morgan Co, 23 Wall St, New York, NY 10015
Weaver, C R *Businessman*
%Clorox Co, 1221 Broadway, Oakland, CA 94612
Weaver, Dennis *Actor*
PO Box 983, Malibu, CA 90265
Weaver, Earl *Baseball Manager*
19016 W Lake Dr, Hialeah, FL 33015
Weaver, Fritz *Actor*
161 W 75th St, New York, NY 10023
Weaver, Galbraith McF *Businessman*
%Southland Royalty Co, 200 InterFirst Tower, Fort Worth, TX 76102
Weaver, James *Cartoonist*
%Art Room Inc, 3145 N Meridian St, Indianapolis, IN 46208
Weaver, Monte *Baseball Player*
826 S Lake Adair Blvd, Orlando, FL 32804
Weaver, Robby *Actor*
%Artists Group, 1930 Century Park West, #403, Los Angeles, CA 90067
Weaver, Robert C *Secretary, Housing & Urban Development*
215 E 68th St, New York, NY 10021
Weaver, Sigourney *Actress*
12 W 72nd St, New York, NY 10023

Weaver, Sylvester L (Pat), Jr *Television Executive*
818 Deerpath Rd, Santa Barbara, CA 93108

Weaver, Warren E *Chemist*
7607 Horsepen Rd, Richmond, VA 23229

Webb, B A *Businessman*
%Gulf Oil Ltd, Imperial Sq, Cheltenham, Glos GL50 1TF, England

Webb, Chloe *Actress*
%International Creative Mgmt, 8899 Beverly Blvd, Los Angeles, CA 90048

Webb, James A, Jr *Financier*
%Nashville City Bank, 315 Union St, Nashville, TN 37201

Webb, James E *Government Official*
2800 36th St NW, Washington, DC 20007

Webb, Jimmy *Songwriter*
1560 N Laurel Ave, #109, Los Angeles, CA 90046

Webb, Lucy *Comedienne*
%International Creative Mgmt, 8899 Beverly Blvd, Los Angeles, CA 90048

Webb, Richard *Actor*
13330 Chandler Blvd, Sherman Oaks, CA 91401

Webb, Richmond *Football Player*
%Miami Dolphins, Robbie Stadium, 2269 NW 199th, Miami, FL 33056

Webb, Spud *Basketball Player*
%Sacramento Kings, 1 Sports Dr, Sacramento, CA 95834

Weber, Arnold R *Educator*
%Northwestern University, President's Office, Evanston, IL 60208

Weber, Dick *Bowler*
1305 Arlington Dr, Florissant, MO 63033

Weber, Donald W *Businessman*
%Continental Telecom Inc, 245 Perimeter Center Pkwy, Atlanta, GA 30346

Weber, Eugen *Historian*
11579 Sunset Blvd, Los Angeles, CA 90049

Weber, Pete *Bowler*
1305 Arlington Dr, Florissant, MO 63033

Weber, Robert M *Cartoonist*
%New Yorker Magazine, 20 W 43rd St, New York, NY 10036

Weber, Roy E *Financier*
%Great Lakes Federal Savings & Loan, 401 E Liberty St, Ann Arbor, MI 48107

Weber, Stephen *Educator*
%State University of New York, President's Office, Oswego, NY 13126

Weber, Steven *Actor*
%International Creative Mgmt, 8899 Beverly Blvd, Los Angeles, CA 90048

Weber, Vin *Representative, MN*
%House of Representatives, Washington, DC 20515

Webster, Alex *Football Player*
16 Shady Ln, Tequesta, FL 33458

Webster, George *Football Player*
%Pittsburgh Steelers, Three Rivers Stadium, Pittsburgh, PA 15212

Webster, Marvin *Basketball Player*
%Milwaukee Bucks, 901 N 4th St, Milwaukee, WI 53203

Webster, Mike *Football Player, Coach*
%Kansas City Chiefs, 1 Arrowhead Dr, Kansas City, MO 64129

Webster, R Howard *Publisher, Baseball Executive*
%Toronto Globe & Mail, 444 Front St W, Toronto ON M5V 2S9, Canada

Webster, Robert *Diver*
%University of Alabama, Athletic Dept, University, AL 35486

Webster, Tom *Hockey Coach*
%Los Angeles Kings, Great Western Forum, 3900 W Manchester, Inglewood, CA 90306

Wechsler, Raymond *Businessman*
%United Press International, 800 Broadway, Cincinnati, OH 45202

Weddington, Sarah *Attorney*
709 W 14th St, Austin, TX 78701

Wedemeyer, Herman *Football Player*
%Servco Pacific Inc, 900 Fort Street Mall, #500, Honolulu, HI 96813

Wedgeworth, Ann *Actress*
70 Riverside Dr, New York, NY 10024

Wedgwood, Veronica *Historian*
%University College, History Dept, London WC1, England

Wedman, Scott *Basketball Player*
%Boston Celtics, 151 Merrimac St, Boston, MA 02114
Wee Kim Yew *President, Singapore*
%President's Office, St Andrew's Rd, Singapore 0617, Singapore
Weed, Maurice James *Composer*
RR 1, Box 641, Timberlane Rd, Waynesville, NC 28786
Weege, Reinhold *Television Producer*
4131 Longridge Ave, Sherman Oaks, CA 91423
Weekly, John W *Businessman*
%United of Omaha Life Insurance, Mutual of Omaha Plz, Omaha, NE 68175
Weems, Katharine L *Artist*
PO Box 126, Manchester, MA 01944
Weese, Harry M *Architect*
314 W Willow St, Chicago, IL 60610
Wefald, Jon *Educator*
%Kansas State University, President's Office, Manhattan, KS 66506
Wegner, Hans *Furniture Designer*
Tinglevej 17, 2820 Gentof'tte, Denmark
Weibel, Robert *Pediatrician*
%University of Pennsylvania, Medical School, Philadelphia, PA 19104
Weibring, D A *Golfer*
1316 Garden Grove Ct, Plano, TX 75075
Weick, Paul C *Judge*
%US Courthouse, 2 S Main St, Akron, OH 44308
Weicker, Lowell P, Jr *Governor/Senator, CT*
%Governor's Office, State Capitol, 210 Capitol Ave, Hartford, CT 06106
Weidenbaum, Murray L *Government Official, Economist*
1531 Heirloom Ct, Creve Coeur, MO 63141
Weidenfeld of Chelsea, Arthur G *Publisher*
9 Chelsea Embankment, London SW3, England
Weider, Joe *Publisher*
%Weider Health & Fitness, 21100 Erwin St, Woodland Hills, CA 91367
Weidlinger, Paul *Engineer*
301 E 47th St, New York, NY 10017
Weidman, Jerome *Writer*
1966 Pacific Ave, San Francisco, CA 94109
Weikl, Bernd *Opera Singer*
%Lies Askonas Ltd, 186 Drury Ln, London WC2B 5QD, England
Weill, Claudia *Movie Director, Cinematographer*
%Cyclops Films, 1697 Broadway, #1109, New York, NY 10019
Weill, Cynthia *Songwriter*
%National Academy of Songwriters, 6381 Hollywood Blvd, Los Angeles, CA 90028
Weill, Sanford I *Businessman, Lawyer*
50 E 79th St, New York, NY 10021
Wein, George *Musical Producer*
%Festival Productions, 311 W 74th St, New York, NY 10023
Weinbach, Lawrence A *Businessman*
%Arthur Andersen & Co, 1345 Ave of Americas, New York, NY 10105
Weinberg, Alvin M *Physicist*
111 Moylan Ln, Oak Ridge, TN 37830
Weinberg, Harry *Businessman*
%Maui Land & Pineapple Co, Kane St, Kahului, HI 96732
Weinberg, John L *Financier*
%Goldman Sachs Co, 55 Broad St, New York, NY 10004
Weinberg, Robert A *Cancer Researcher, Biochemist*
%Massachusetts Institute of Technology, Whitehead Institute, Cambridge, MA 02139
Weinberg, Steven *Nobel Physics Laureate*
%University of Texas, Physics Dept, Austin, TX 78712
Weinberger, Caspar W *Secretary, Defense, HEW; Publisher*
%Forbes Magazine, 60 5th Ave, New York, NY 10011
Weiner, Tim *Journalist*
%Philadelphia Inquirer, 400 N Broad St, Philadelphia, PA 19101
Weinig, Robert W *Businessman*
%Eastern Enterprises, 1 Beacon St, Boston, MA 02108
Weinig, Sheldon *Businessman*
%Materials Research Corp, Rt 303, Orangeburg, NY 10962

W

Weinmeister – Weitz

Weinmeister, Arnie *Football Player*
PO Box 70149, Seattle, WA 98117

Weinstein, Milton N *Businessman*
%National Service Industries, 1180 Peachtree St NE, Atlanta, GA 30309

Weintraub, Jerry *Movie Producer*
%Jerry Weintraub Productions, Lorimar Plz, Burbank, CA 91505

Weir, Morton W *Educator*
%Illinois University, President's Office, Urbana, IL 61801

Weir, Peter *Movie Director*
Post Office, Palm Beach 2108, Australia

Weir, Thomas C *Financier*
%Home Federal Savings & Loan, 32 N Stone Ave, Tucson, AZ 85701

Weis, Arthur M *Businessman*
%Capintec Inc, 6 Arrow Rd, Ramsey, NJ 07446

Weis, Joseph F, Jr *Judge*
%US Court of Appeals, US Courthouse, 700 Grant St, Pittsburgh, PA 15219

Weis, Konrad M *Businessman*
%Mobay Chemical Corp, Mobay Rd, Pittsburgh, PA 15205

Weisberg, Ruth *Artist*
2421 3rd St, Santa Monica, CA 90405

Weisbord, Sam *Entertainment Executive*
9255 Doheny Dr, #2206, Los Angeles, CA 90069

Weisgall, Hugo *Composer, Conductor*
81 Maple Dr, Great Neck, NY 11021

Weiskopf, Tom *Golfer*
5412 E Morrison Ln, Paradise Valley, AZ 85253

Weisman, Edward A *Businessman*
%Allegheny Beverage Corp, Allegheny Cir, Cheverly, MD 20781

Weisman, Sam *Actor*
4448 Tujunga Ave, North Hollywood, CA 91602

Weiss, Bob *Basketball Coach*
%Atlanta Hawks, 100 Techwood Dr NW, Atlanta, GA 30303

Weiss, Daniel E *Religious Leader*
%American Baptist Churches, PO Box 851, Valley Forge, PA 19482

Weiss, Melvyn I *Attorney*
%Milberg Weiss Bershad, 1 Pennsylvania Plz, New York, NY 10119

Weiss, Morry *Businessman*
%American Greetings Corp, 10500 American Rd, Cleveland, OH 44144

Weiss, Paul *Philosopher*
2000 "N" St NW, Washington, DC 20036

Weiss, Theodore *Poet, Editor*
%QRL Poetry Series, Princeton University, 26 Haslet St, Princeton, NJ 08540

Weiss, Theodore S *Representative, NY*
37 W 65th St, New York, NY 10023

Weiss, William L *Businessman*
%Ameritech Corp, 225 W Randolph St, Chicago, IL 60606

Weissberg, Lawrence *Financier*
%Homestead Financial Corp, 1777 Murchison Dr, Burlingame, CA 94010

Weissenberg, Alexis *Concert Pianist*
%Columbia Artists Mgmt Inc, 165 W 57th St, New York, NY 10019

Weisskopf, Victor F *Physicist*
36 Arlington St, Cambridge, MA 02140

Weissman, George *Businessman*
%Philip Morris Companies, 120 Park Ave, New York, NY 10017

Weissman, Robert E *Businessman*
%Dun & Bradstreet Corp, 299 Park Ave, New York, NY 10171

Weisweller, Franz Josef *Businessman*
%Mannesmann, Mannesmannufer 2, 4000 Dusseldorf 1, Germany

Weisz, William J *Businessman*
%Motorola Inc, 1303 E Algonquin Rd, Schaumburg, IL 60196

Weitz, Bruce *Actor*
2385 Castilian Dr, Los Angeles, CA 90068

Weitz, John *Fashion Designer*
600 Madison Ave, New York, NY 10022

Weitz, Paul J *Astronaut*
%NASA, Johnson Space Ctr, Houston, TX 77058

Weitzman, Howard 2049 Central Park East, #1400, Los Angeles, CA 90067	*Attorney*
Weizman, Ezer 28 Hageffen St, Ramat Hasheram, Israel	*Air Force General, Israel*
Welbergen, Johannes C %Standard Elektrik Lorenz, Hellmuth-Hirth-Strasse 42, Stuttgart, Germany	*Businessman*
Welch, Bob 4150 Delphi Cir, Huntington Beach, CA 92649	*Baseball Player*
Welch, Elisabeth 4-A Carpenters Close, London SW1, England	*Actress, Singer*
Welch, James O %RJR Nabisco Inc, Reynolds Blvd, Winston-Salem, NC 27102	*Businessman*
Welch, John F, Jr %General Electric Co, 3135 Easton Turnpike, Fairfield, CT 06451	*Businessman*
Welch, Louie 21 Briar Hollow Ln, #803, Houston, TX 77027	*Mayor*
Welch, Raquel PO Box 26472, Prescott Valley, AZ 86312	*Actress*
Welch, Tahnee %Gersh Agency, 232 N Canon Dr, Beverly Hills, CA 90210	*Actress*
Weld, Tuesday 300 Central Park West, #5-E, New York, NY 10019	*Actress*
Weld, William %Governor's Office, State House, Boston, MA 02133	*Governor, MA*
Weldon, Casey %Florida State University, Athletic Dept, Tallahassee, FL 32306	*Football Player*
Weldon, Fay 24 Ryland Rd, London NW5 3EA, England	*Writer*
Welk, Lawrence %Welk Syndication, 1299 Ocean Ave, #800, Santa Monica, CA 90401	*Orchestra Leader*
Weller, Michael 215 E 5th St, New York, NY 10003	*Playwright*
Weller, Peter %Bill Treusch Assoc, 853 7th Ave, #9-A, New York, NY 10019	*Actor*
Weller, Thomas H 56 Winding River Rd, Needham, MA 02192	*Nobel Medicine Laureate*
Weller, Walter Doblinger Hauptstrasse 40, 1190 Vienna, Austria	*Conductor*
Wellford, Harry W %US Court of Appeals, Federal Bldg, 167 N Main St, Memphis, TN 38103	*Judge*
Wellington, Robert H %Amsted Industries, 3700 Prudential Plz, Chicago, IL 60601	*Businessman*
Wellman, Mark %Visitor's Bureau, Yosemite National Park, CA 95389	*Rock Climber*
Wellman, William, Jr 410 N Barrington Ave, Los Angeles, CA 90049	*Actor*
Wells, Carole %Burton Moss Agency, 113 N San Vicente Blvd, #202, Beverly Hills, CA 90211	*Actress*
Wells, Charles W %Illinois Power Co, 500 S 27th St, Decatur, IL 62525	*Businessman*
Wells, Dawn PO Box 423, Burlington, WI 53105	*Actress*
Wells, Frank G %Walt Disney Productions, 500 S Buena Vista St, Burbank, CA 91521	*Entertainment Executive*
Wells, Harry K %McCormick & Co, 11350 McCormick Rd, Hunt Valley, MD 21031	*Businessman*
Wells, Herman B 1321 E 10th St, Bloomington, IN 47401	*Educator*
Wells, Kitty 352 Cumberland Hills Dr, Madison, TN 37115	*Singer*
Wells, Mary 9200 Sunset Blvd, #1220, Los Angeles, CA 90069	*Singer*
Wells, Thomas B %US Tax Court, 400 2nd St NW, Washington, DC 20217	*Judge*
Wells, Wayne PO Box 3938, Edmond, OK 73083	*Wrestler*

W

Wellstone, Paul D — *Senator, MN*
%US Senate, Washington, DC 20510

Welsh, George — *Football Player, Coach*
%University of Virginia, Athletic Dept, Charlottesville, VA 22903

Welsh, Matthew — *Governor, IN*
4546 N Park Ave, Indianapolis, IN 46205

Weltner, Charles L — *Representative, GA; Judge*
%Georgia Supreme Court, 244 Washington St SW, Atlanta, GA 30334

Welty, Eudora — *Writer*
1119 Pinehurst St, Jackson, MS 39202

Wences, Senor — *Ventriloquist*
204 W 55th St, #701-A, New York, NY 10019

Wendelin, Rudolph — *Cartoonist (Smokey the Bear)*
4516 7th St N, Arlington, VA 22203

Wendelstedt, Harry H, Jr — *Baseball Umpire*
88 S St Andrews Dr, Ormond Beach, FL 32074

Wenden, Michael — *Swimmer*
%Palm Beach Currumbin Ctr, Thrower Dr, Palm Beach Queens, Australia

Wenders, Wim — *Movie Director*
%Paul Kohner Inc, 9169 Sunset Blvd, Los Angeles, CA 90069

Wendt, George — *Actor*
3856 Vantage Ave, Studio City, CA 91604

Wendt, Henry — *Businessman*
%SmithKline Beckman Corp, 1 Franklin Plz, Philadelphia, PA 19101

Wenge, Ralph — *Commentator*
%Cable News Network, 1 CNN Center, PO Box 105366, Atlanta, GA 30348

Wenner, Jann — *Publisher*
%Rolling Stone Magazine, 745 5th Ave, New York, NY 10151

Went, Frits W — *Botanist*
Lodestar Lane 3450, Reno, NV 89503

Went, Joseph J — *Marine Corps General*
%Office of Assistant Commandant, Marine Corps Headquarters, Washington, DC 20380

Wentz, Howard B, Jr — *Businessman*
%Amstar Corp, 1251 Ave of Americas, New York, NY 10020

Wenzel, Andreas — *Skier*
Oberhul 151, Liechtenstein-Gamprin, Liechtenstein

Wenzel, Fred W — *Businessman*
%Kellwood Co, 600 Kellwood Pkwy, St Louis, MO 63017

Wenzel, Hanni — *Skier*
%General Delivery, Planken, Liechtenstein

Werner, Charles G — *Editorial Cartoonist*
4445 Brown Rd, Indianapolis, IN 46226

Werner, Ernest G G — *Businessman*
%Shell Petroleum Co, 30 Carel Van Bylandtaan, The Hague, Netherlands

Werner, Helmut — *Businessman*
%Continental Gummi-Werke, Postfach 169, 3000 Hanover 1, Germany

Werner, Jesse — *Businessman*
%GAF Corp, 140 W 51st St, New York, NY 10020

Werner, Pierre — *Prime Minister, Luxembourg*
%Prime Minister's Office, 4 Rue de la Congregation, Luxembourg

Werner, Roger — *Television Executive*
%ESPN, ESPN Plz, Bristol, CT 06010

Werries, E Dean — *Businessman*
%Fleming Companies, 6301 Waterford Blvd, Oklahoma City, OK 73126

Werthan, Bernard, Jr — *Businessman*
%Werthan Industries, 1400 8th Ave N, Nashville, TN 37203

Wertheimer, Fred — *Association Executive*
%Common Cause, 2030 "M" St NW, Washington, DC 20036

Wertheimer, Linda — *Commentator*
%National Public Radio, News Dept, 2025 "M" St NW, Washington, DC 20036

Wertheimer, R E — *Businessman*
%Longview Fibre Co, PO Box 639, Longview, WA 98632

Wertheimer, Thomas — *Entertainment Executive*
%MCA Inc, 100 Universal City Plz, Universal City, CA 91608

Werthen, Hans — *Businessman*
%L M Ericsson Telephone, Telefonplan, 126 25 Stockholm, Sweden

Wescoe, W Clarke *Businessman*
%Sterling Drug Co, 90 Park Ave, New York, NY 10016

Wescott, Glenway *Writer*
Hay Meadows, Rosemont, NJ 08556

Wesker, Arnold *Writer*
37 Ashley Rd, London N19 3AG, England

Wesselmann, Tom *Artist*
RD 1, Box 36, Long Eddy, NY 12760

Wessner, Kenneth T *Businessman*
%ServiceMaster Industries, 2300 Warrenville Rd, Downers Grove, IL 60515

West, Adam *Actor*
PO Box 3446, Ketchum, ID 83340

West, Ernest E *Korean War Army Hero (CMH)*
912 Adams Ave, Wurtland, KY 41144

West, Frederic W, Jr *Businessman*
Saucon Valley Rd, Bethlehem, PA 18015

West, Jake *Labor Leader*
%International Assn of Iron Workers, 1750 New York Ave NW, Washington, DC 20006

West, Jerry *Basketball Player, Executive*
%Los Angeles Lakers, Great Western Forum, 3900 W Manchester, Inglewood, CA 90306

West, Mark *Basketball Player*
%Phoenix Suns, 2910 N Central, Phoenix, AZ 85012

West, Morris *Writer*
%Maurice Greenbaum, 575 Madison Ave, New York, NY 10022

West, Robert H *Businessman*
%Butler Manufacturing Co, BMA Tower, Penn Valley Park, Kansas City, MO 64141

West, Robert V, Jr *Businessman*
%Tesoro Petroleum Co, 8700 Tesoro Dr, San Antonio, TX 78286

Westerberg, Verne *Publisher*
%Vogue Magazine, 350 Madison Ave, New York, NY 10017

Westerfield, Putney *Publisher*
360 Robinwood Ln, Hillsborough, CA 94010

Westermann, H C *Artist*
PO Box 28, Brookfield Center, CT 06805

Westhead, Paul *Basketball Coach*
%Denver Nuggets, McNichols Arena, 1635 Clay St, Denver, CO 80204

Westheimer, David *Writer*
11722 Darlington Ave, Los Angeles, CA 90049

Westin, Av *Television Executive, Journalist*
%King World Productions, 1700 Broadway, New York, NY 10019

Westmoreland, James *Actor*
8019 1/2 W Norton Ave, Los Angeles, CA 90046

Westmoreland, William *Army General*
107 1/2 Tradd St, Charleston, SC 29401

Weston, Brett *Photographer*
PO Box 694, Carmel Valley, CA 93924

Weston, G H *Businessman*
%George Weston Holdings, 68 Knightsbridge, London SW1X 7LR, England

Weston, J Fred *Educator*
258 Tavistock Ave, Los Angeles, CA 90024

Weston, Jack *Actor*
%A Kozak, 468 Park Ave S, New York, NY 10016

Weston, Josh S *Businessman*
%Automatic Data Processing, 1 ADP Blvd, Roseland, NJ 07068

Weston, Paul *Musician, Composer*
2339 Century Hill, Los Angeles, CA 90067

Westphal, James A *Space Scientist*
%California Institute of Technology, Planetary Sciences Dept, Pasadena, CA 91125

Westphal, Paul *Basketball Player, Coach*
%Phoenix Suns, 2910 N Central, Phoenix, AZ 85012

Westwood, Jean *Figure Skater*
795 Meaford Ave, Victoria BC V9B 2P7, Canada

Wetherbee, James D *Astronaut*
%NASA, Johnson Space Ctr, Houston, TX 77058

Wetherby, Lawrence W *Governor, KY*
Weehawken Ln, Frankfort, KY 40601

W

Wethington, Charles T, Jr %University of Kentucky, President's Office, Lexington, KY 40506	*Educator*
Wetter, Friedrich Cardinal Domberg 1, 8050 Freising, Germany	*Religious Leader*
Wetterau, Ted C %Wetterau Inc, 8920 Pershall Rd, Hazelwood, MO 63042	*Businessman*
Wettig, Patricia %Gersh Agency, 232 N Canon Dr, Beverly Hills, CA 90210	*Actress*
Wetzel, John %Portland Trail Blazers, 700 NE Multnomah St, Portland, OR 97232	*Basketball Coach*
Wexler, Alex 1341 Ocean Blvd, #53, Santa Monica, CA 90401	*Cinematographer*
Wexler, Anne 1616 "H" St NW, Washington, DC 20006	*Government Official*
Wexler, Haskell 1341 Ocean Ave, #111, Santa Monica, CA 90401	*Cinematographer*
Wexler, Jacqueline G 222 Park Ave S, New York, NY 10003	*Educator*
Wexler, Jerry %Warner Bros Records, 3 E 54th St, New York, NY 10022	*Record Producer*
Wexner, Leslie H %Limited Stores, 1 Limited Pkwy, Columbus, OH 43216	*Businessman*
Weyand, Frederick C %First Hawaiian Bank, 165 S King St, Honolulu, HI 96813	*Army General*
Weyerhaeuser, George H %Weyerhaeuser Co, 33663 32nd Ave S, Tacoma, WA 98003	*Businessman*
Whalen, Laurence J %US Tax Court, 400 2nd St NW, Washington, DC 20217	*Judge*
Whalley-Kilmer, Joanne PO Box 363, Tesuque, NM 87574	*Actress*
Wharton, Clifton R, Jr %TIAA-CREF, 730 3rd Ave, New York, NY 10017	*Educator, Businessman*
Wharton, David %University of Southern California, Heritage Hall, Los Angeles, CA 90089	*Swimmer*
Whatley, James R %Kaneb Services, 1 Sugar Creek Pl, Sugar Land, TX 77478	*Businessman*
Wheat, Alan %House of Representatives, Washington, DC 20515	*Representative, MO*
Wheat, Francis %Gibson Dunn Crutcher, 333 S Grand Ave, Los Angeles, CA 90071	*Attorney*
Wheaton, Wil 2603 Seapine Ln, La Crescenta, CA 91214	*Actor*
Wheeler, C E %Railway Carmen Brotherhood, 4929 Main St, Kansas City, MO 64112	*Labor Leader*
Wheeler, Daniel S %American Legion Magazine, 700 N Pennsylvania St, Indianapolis, IN 46206	*Editor*
Wheeler, John 4741 Laurel Canyon Blvd, #109, Studio City, CA 91607	*Actor*
Wheeler, John A 1410 Wildcat Hollow, Austin, TX 78746	*Physicist*
Wheeler, Thomas B %Massachusetts Mutual Life Insurance, 1295 State St, Springfield, MA 01111	*Businessman*
Wheeler-Bennett, R C %Thomas Borthwick & Sons, St John's Ln, London EC1M 4BX, England	*Businessman*
Whelan, William A %Pope & Talbot Inc, 1500 SW 1st Ave, Portland, OR 97201	*Businessman*
Whelchel, Lisa %William Morris Agency, 151 El Camino, Beverly Hills, CA 90212	*Actress*
Whinnery, Barbara %Harry Gold Assoc, 3500 W Olive Ave, #1400, Burbank, CA 91505	*Actress*
Whinnery, John R 1 Daphne Ct, Orinda, CA 94563	*Electrical Engineer*
Whipple, Fred L 35 Elizabeth Rd, Belmont, MA 02178	*Astronomer*
Whitaker, Forest %Creative Artists Agency, 9830 Wilshire Blvd, Beverly Hills, CA 90212	*Actor*

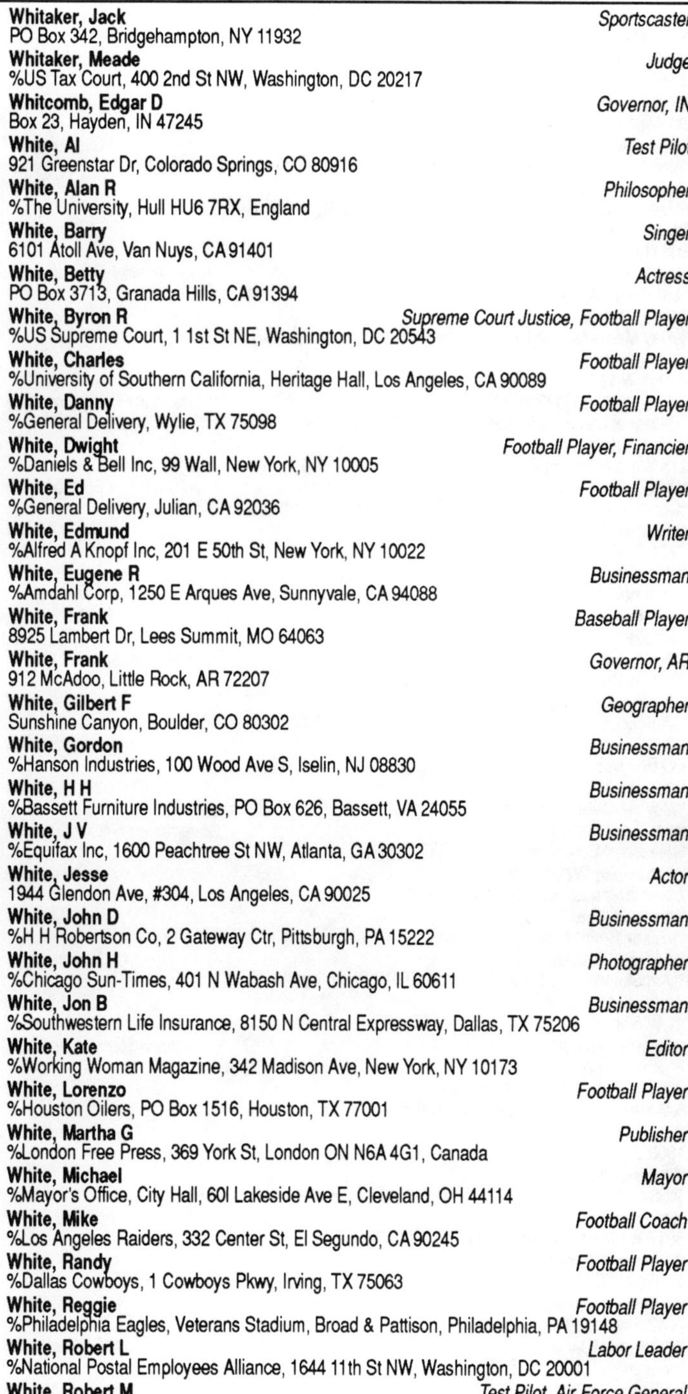

Whitaker, Jack *Sportscaster*
PO Box 342, Bridgehampton, NY 11932
Whitaker, Meade *Judge*
%US Tax Court, 400 2nd St NW, Washington, DC 20217
Whitcomb, Edgar D *Governor, IN*
Box 23, Hayden, IN 47245
White, Al *Test Pilot*
921 Greenstar Dr, Colorado Springs, CO 80916
White, Alan R *Philosopher*
%The University, Hull HU6 7RX, England
White, Barry *Singer*
6101 Atoll Ave, Van Nuys, CA 91401
White, Betty *Actress*
PO Box 3713, Granada Hills, CA 91394
White, Byron R *Supreme Court Justice, Football Player*
%US Supreme Court, 1 1st St NE, Washington, DC 20543
White, Charles *Football Player*
%University of Southern California, Heritage Hall, Los Angeles, CA 90089
White, Danny *Football Player*
%General Delivery, Wylie, TX 75098
White, Dwight *Football Player, Financier*
%Daniels & Bell Inc, 99 Wall, New York, NY 10005
White, Ed *Football Player*
%General Delivery, Julian, CA 92036
White, Edmund *Writer*
%Alfred A Knopf Inc, 201 E 50th St, New York, NY 10022
White, Eugene R *Businessman*
%Amdahl Corp, 1250 E Arques Ave, Sunnyvale, CA 94088
White, Frank *Baseball Player*
8925 Lambert Dr, Lees Summit, MO 64063
White, Frank *Governor, AR*
912 McAdoo, Little Rock, AR 72207
White, Gilbert F *Geographer*
Sunshine Canyon, Boulder, CO 80302
White, Gordon *Businessman*
%Hanson Industries, 100 Wood Ave S, Iselin, NJ 08830
White, H H *Businessman*
%Bassett Furniture Industries, PO Box 626, Bassett, VA 24055
White, J V *Businessman*
%Equifax Inc, 1600 Peachtree St NW, Atlanta, GA 30302
White, Jesse *Actor*
1944 Glendon Ave, #304, Los Angeles, CA 90025
White, John D *Businessman*
%H H Robertson Co, 2 Gateway Ctr, Pittsburgh, PA 15222
White, John H *Photographer*
%Chicago Sun-Times, 401 N Wabash Ave, Chicago, IL 60611
White, Jon B *Businessman*
%Southwestern Life Insurance, 8150 N Central Expressway, Dallas, TX 75206
White, Kate *Editor*
%Working Woman Magazine, 342 Madison Ave, New York, NY 10173
White, Lorenzo *Football Player*
%Houston Oilers, PO Box 1516, Houston, TX 77001
White, Martha G *Publisher*
%London Free Press, 369 York St, London ON N6A 4G1, Canada
White, Michael *Mayor*
%Mayor's Office, City Hall, 601 Lakeside Ave E, Cleveland, OH 44114
White, Mike *Football Coach*
%Los Angeles Raiders, 332 Center St, El Segundo, CA 90245
White, Randy *Football Player*
%Dallas Cowboys, 1 Cowboys Pkwy, Irving, TX 75063
White, Reggie *Football Player*
%Philadelphia Eagles, Veterans Stadium, Broad & Pattison, Philadelphia, PA 19148
White, Robert L *Labor Leader*
%National Postal Employees Alliance, 1644 11th St NW, Washington, DC 20001
White, Robert M *Test Pilot, Air Force General*
PO Box 2488, APO, New York, NY 09063

W

White – Whitney

White, Robert M *Meteorologist*
8306 Melody Ct, Bethesda, MD 20034

White, Robert M, II *Journalist*
8 Melody Ln, Mexico, MO 65265

White, Roy *Baseball Player*
30 Aspen Way, Upper Saddle River, NJ 07458

White, Russell P *Businessman*
%Indiana Farm Bureau Cooperative, 120 E Market, Indianapolis, IN 46204

White, Sammy *Football Player*
%Minnesota Vikings, 9520 Viking Dr, Eden Prairie, MN 55344

White, Slappy *Comedian*
933 N La Brea Ave, Los Angeles, CA 90038

White, Steven A *Navy Admiral, Businessman*
%Stone & Webster Engineering Corp, 245 Summer St, Boston, MA 02210

White, Vanna *Actress*
%Ray Manzella, 9454 Wilshire Blvd, #PH, Beverly Hills, CA 90212

White, William *Journalist, Editor*
25860 W 14 Mile Rd, Franklin, MI 48205

White, William D (Bill) *Baseball Player, Executive*
%National League, President's Office, 350 Park Ave, New York, NY 10022

White, William S *Journalist*
115 W Campbell St, Frankfurt, KY 40601

White, Willis S, Jr *Businessman*
%American Electric Power Co, 1 Riverside Plz, Columbus, OH 43215

White, Willye *Track Athlete*
7221 S Calumet, Chicago, IL 60619

Whitehead, Alfred K *Labor Leader*
%International Assn of Fire Fighters, 1750 New York Ave NW, Washington, DC 20006

Whitehead, George W *Mathematician*
25 Bellevue Rd, Arlington, MA 02174

Whitehead, John C *Financier, Government Official*
131 Old Chester Rd, Essex Falls, NJ 07021

Whitehead, Richard F *Navy Admiral*
%American Cage & Machine Co, 135 S LaSalle St, Chicago, IL 60603

Whitehurst, George W *Representative, VA*
PO Box 685, Sea Pines Station, Virginia Beach, VA 23451

Whitelaw, Billie *Actress*
%Joy Jameson, 7 W Eaton Place Mews, London SW1X 8LY, England

Whitelaw, William *Government Official, England*
%House of Commons, London SW1, England

Whitemore, Willet F, Jr *Cancer Researcher*
2 Hawthorne Ln, Plandome, NY 11030

Whitfield, Lynn *Actress*
%Susan Smith Assoc, 121 N San Vicente Blvd, Beverly Hills, CA 90211

Whitfield, Robert *Businessman*
%Airbus Industrie, 5 Ave de Villiers, 75017 Paris, France

Whiting, Margaret *Singer*
41 W 58th St, #5-A, New York, NY 10019

Whitlam, Gough *Prime Minister, Australia*
Westfield Towers, 100 William St, Sydney NSW 2011, Australia

Whitman, Marina Von Neumann *Economist*
%General Motors, 767 5th Ave, New York, NY 10022

Whitman, Slim *Singer*
1300 Division St, #103, Nashville, TN 37203

Whitman, Stuart *Actor*
%Stone Manners Agency, 9113 Sunset Blvd, Los Angeles, CA 90069

Whitmire, Donald B *Football Player*
3817 Winterset Dr, Annandale, VA 22003

Whitmore, James *Actor*
%Harris & Goldberg Agency, 1999 Ave of Stars, #2850, Los Angeles, CA 90067

Whitmore, James, Jr *Actor*
7642 Etiwanda Ave, Reseda, CA 91335

Whitmore, Kay R *Businessman*
%Eastman Kodak Co, 343 State St, Rochester, NY 14650

Whitney, CeCe *Actress*
840 N Ogden Dr, Los Angeles, CA 90046

Whitney, Claude %Allen-Bradley Co, 1201 S 2nd St, Milwaukee, WI 53204	*Businessman*
Whitney, Hassler %Institute for Advanced Study, Princeton, NJ 08540	*Educator*
Whitney, Ruth %Glamour Magazine, 350 Madison Ave, New York, NY 10017	*Editor*
Whitsell, Dave 2441 W 79th St, Long Grove, IL 60047	*Football Player*
Whittaker, Roger 50 Regents Park Rd, Primrose Hill, London NW1 75X, England	*Singer*
Whitten, Jamie L %House of Representatives, Washington, DC 20515	*Representative, MS*
Whittingham, Charles A %Life Magazine, Rockefeller Ctr, New York, NY 10020	*Publisher*
Whittle, Christopher %Whittle Communications, 505 Market, Knoxville, TN 37902	*Publisher*
Whitwam, David R %Whirlpool Corp, 2000 US 33 N, Benton Harbor, MI 49022	*Businessman*
Whitwell, Joseph E %Culbro Corp, 387 Park Ave S, New York, NY 10016	*Businessman*
Whitworth, Kathy %General Delivery, Roanoke, TX 76262	*Golfer*
Whyte, William H 175 E 94th St, New York, NY 10028	*Writer*
Wiatt, Jim %International Creative Mgmt, 8899 Beverly Blvd, Los Angeles, CA 90048	*Entertainment Executive*
Wiberg, Kenneth B 160 Carmalt Rd, Hamden, CT 06517	*Educator, Chemist*
Wiborg, James H %Univar Corp, 1600 Norton Bldg, Seattle, WA 98104	*Businessman*
Wichmann, Herbert Ohnhorstrasse 29, 2000 Hamburg 52, Germany	*Government Official, Germany*
Wick, Charles Z %US Information Agency, 400 "C" St NW, Washington, DC 20547	*Government Official*
Wick, Paul A %Landmark Savings Assn, 335 5th Ave, Pittsburgh, PA 15222	*Financier*
Wicker, Thomas G %New York Times, 229 W 43rd St, New York, NY 10036	*Writer, Journalist*
Wickes, Mary 2160 Century Park East, #503, Los Angeles, CA 90067	*Actress*
Wicks, Ben 38 Yorkville Ave, Toronto ON M4W 1L5, Canada	*Editorial Cartoonist*
Wicks, Sue %Rutgers University, Athletic Dept, East Rutherford, NJ 08903	*Basketball Player*
Widdoes, Kathleen %STE Representation, 9301 Wilshire Blvd, #312, Beverly Hills, CA 90210	*Actress*
Wideman, John Edgar %University of Massachusetts, English Dept, Amherst, MA 01003	*Writer*
Widener, H Emory, Jr %US Court of Appeals, PO Box 868, Abingdon, VA 24210	*Judge*
Widerberg, Bo %Svenska Filminstitutet, Kingsgatan 48, Stockholm, Sweden	*Movie Director*
Widmark, Richard %International Creative Mgmt, 8899 Beverly Blvd, Los Angeles, CA 90048	*Actor*
Widseth, Edwin C 2919 Arthur St NE, Minneapolis, MN 55418	*Football Player*
Wiechern, Howard J, Jr %FirstSouth FA, 121 W 6th Ave, Pine Bluff, AK 71611	*Financier*
Wiederkehr, Joseph A %Roofers Waterproofers & Allied Workers, 1125 17th NW, Washington, DC 20036	*Labor Leader*
Wieghan, James G %New York Daily News, 220 E 42nd St, New York, NY 10017	*Editor*
Wiehn, Helmut %Deutsche Babcock, Duisburger Strasse 375, 42000 Oberhausen 1, Germany	*Businessman*
Wieland, Robert R %Huffy Corp, 7701 Byers Rd, Miamisburg, OH 45342	*Businessman*

Wiener, Jacques L, Jr *Judge*
%US Court of Appeals, 500 Fannin St, Shreveport, LA 71101

Wiese, John P *Judge*
%US Claims Court, 717 Madison Pl NW, Washington, DC 20005

Wiesel, Elie *Writer, Nobel Peace Laureate*
%Boston University, Humanities Dept, 745 Commonwealth Ave, Boston, MA 02215

Wiesel, Torsten N *Nobel Medicine Laureate*
%Harvard University Medical School, 25 Shattuck St, Boston, MA 02115

Wiesen, Bernard *Movie Director*
Wiessgerberstrasse 2, Munich 23, Germany

Wiesenthal, Simon *War Crimes Activist*
%Jewish Documentation Ctr, Salztorgasse 6, 1010 Vienna, Austria

Wiesner, Jerome *Communications Engineer*
61 Shattuck Rd, Watertown, MA 02172

Wiest, Dianne *Actress*
%International Creative Mgmt, 40 W 57th St, New York, NY 10019

Wigger, Lones W, Jr *Rifle Marksman*
%US Shooting Team, Olympic Training Ctr, Colorado Springs, CO 80909

Wiggin, Paul *Football Player, Coach*
%Minnesota Vikings, 9520 Viking Dr, Eden Prairie, MN 55344

Wiggins, Charles E *Judge, Representative, CA*
%US Court of Appeals, 50 W Liberty St, Reno, NV 89501

Wigglesworth, Marian McKean *Skier*
%General Delivery, Wilson, WY 83014

Wight, Albert B *Businessman*
%Sanders Assoc, Daniel Webster Pkwy, South Nashua, NH 03061

Wightman, Arthur S *Mathematician, Physicist*
16 Balsam Ln, Princeton, NJ 08540

Wigle, Ernest D *Cardiologist*
101 College St, Toronto ON M56 1L7, Canada

Wigner, Eugene P *Nobel Physics Laureate*
8 Ober Rd, Princeton, NJ 08540

Wiik, Sven *Skier*
PO Box 774484, Steamboat Springs, CO 80477

Wilander, Mats *Tennis Player*
%Einar Wilander, Vickersvagen 2, Vaxjo, Sweden

Wilbur, Doreen *Archery Athlete*
1401 W Lincoln Way, Jefferson, IA 50129

Wilbur, Richard P *Writer, Educator*
Dodswells Rd, Cummington, MA 01026

Wilcox, Larry *Actor*
13 Appaloosa Ln, Bell Canyon, Canoga Park, CA 91305

Wilcox, William W *Financier*
%Society for Savings, 31 Pratt St, Hartford, CT 06103

Wilcutt, Terence W *Astronaut*
%NASA, Johnson Space Ctr, Houston, TX 77058

Wild, Earl *Concert Pianist*
2233 Fernleaf Ln, Worthington, OH 43085

Wild, Jack *Actor*
Charlesworth, 68 Old Brompton Rd, London SW7 3LP, England

Wilder, Billy *Movie Director*
10375 Wilshire Blvd, Los Angeles, CA 90024

Wilder, Brooks *Businessman*
3000 Sand Hill Rd, Menlo Park, CA 94025

Wilder, Don *Cartoonist (Crock)*
%North America Syndicate, 235 E 45th St, New York, NY 10017

Wilder, Gene *Actor, Movie Director*
%Pal-Mel Productions, 9350 Wilshire Blvd, #316, Beverly Hills, CA 90212

Wilder, James *Football Player*
%Washington Redskins, Dulles Airport, Box 17247, Washington, DC 20041

Wilder, James *Actor*
%InterTalent Agency, 131 S Rodeo Dr, #300, Beverly Hills, CA 90212

Wilder, L Douglas *Governor, VA*
%Governor's Office, State Capital Bldg, Richmond, VA 23219

Wildmon, Donald *Religious Leader*
%National Federation of Decency, PO Box 1398, Tupelo, MS 38801

Wildung, Richard K *Football Player*
10368 Rich Rd, Bloomington, MN 55437

Wiley, Lee *Singer*
%Marlow Productions, PO Box 156, Hicksville, NY 11802

Wiley, Richard E *Government Official*
3818 Woodrow St, Arlington, VA 22207

Wiley, William B *Publisher*
57 Prospect Hill Ave, Summit, NJ 07901

Wiley, William T *Artist*
PO Box 654, Woodacre, CA 94973

Wilford, John Noble *Journalist*
%New York Times, 229 W 43rd St, New York, NY 10036

Wilhelm, Hoyt *Baseball Player*
3102 N Himes Ave, Tampa, FL 33607

Wilhelmina (Cooper) *Model*
%Wilhelmina Models, 9 E 37th St, New York, NY 10016

Wilkens, Lenny *Basketball Player, Coach*
%Cleveland Cavaliers, 2923 Statesboro Rd, Richfield, OH 44286

Wilkes, Glen *Basketball Coach*
%Stetson University, Athletic Dept, Campus Box 8359, DeLand, FL 32720

Wilkes, Jamal *Basketball Player*
7846 W 81st St, Playa del Rey, CA 90291

Wilkie, David *Swimmer*
Oaklands, Queens Hill, Ascot, Berkshire, England

Wilkins, Dominque *Basketball Player*
%Atlanta Hawks, 105 Techwood Dr NW, Atlanta, GA 30303

Wilkins, Gerald *Basketball Player*
%New York Knicks, Madison Square Grdn, 4 Pennsylvania Plz, New York, NY 10001

Wilkins, Graham J *Businessman*
%Beecham Group, Great West Rd, Brentford, Middlesex TW8 9BD, England

Wilkins, Maurice H F *Nobel Medicine Laureate*
30 St John's Park, London SE3, England

Wilkins, Roger C *Businessman*
791 Prospect Ave, West Hartford, CT 06105

Wilkins, Williams V, Jr *Judge*
%US Court of Appeals, PO Box 10857, Greenville, SC 29603

Wilkinson Miles, Tichi *Editor/Publisher*
%Hollywood Reporter, 6715 Sunset Blvd, Los Angeles, CA 90028

Wilkinson, Bud (Charles B) *Football Coach*
%Public Employees Benefit Services Corp, 2241 Edwards St, St Louis, MO 63110

Wilkinson, Geoffrey *Nobel Chemistry Laureate*
%Imperial College, London SW7 2AY, England

Wilkinson, J Harvie, III *Judge*
%US Court of Appeals, 255 W Main St, Charlottesville, VA 22901

Wilkinson, June *Actress*
%Aimee Entertainment Assn, 13743 Victory Blvd, Van Nuys, CA 91401

Wilkinson, Signe *Editorial Cartoonist*
%Philadelphia Daily News, 400 N Broad St, Philadelphia, PA 22209

Will, George F *Columnist*
%Washington Post, 1150 15th St NW, Washington, DC 20071

Will, James F *Businessman*
%Cyclops Corp, 650 Washington Rd, Pittsburgh, PA 15228

Will, Maggie *Golfer*
217 Maple St, Whiteville, NC 28472

Willard, Fred C *Actor, Comedian*
%William Morris Agency, 151 El Camino, Beverly Hills, CA 90212

Willebrands, Johannes Cardinal *Religious Leader*
%Council for Promoting Christian Unity, Via dell'Erba I, 00120 Rome, Italy

Willem-Alexander Claus George Ferdinand *Crown Prince, Netherlands*
%Huis ten Bosch, The Hague, Netherlands

Willes, Mark H *Businessman*
%General Mills Inc, 9200 Wayzata Blvd, Minneapolis, MN 55426

Willet, E Crosby *Stained Glass Artist*
%Willet Stained Glass Studios, 10 E Moreland Ave, Philadelphia, PA 19118

Willey, Gordon Randolph *Archaeologist*
25 Gray Gdns E, Cambridge, MA 02138

W

Willhite – Williams

Willhite, Gerald — *Football Player*
%Denver Broncos, 13655 E Dove Valley Pkwy, Englewood, CO 80112

William — *Prince, England*
%Kensington Palace, London W8, England

William, Edward — *Religious Leader*
%Bible Way Church, 5118 Clarendon Rd, Brooklyn, NY 11226

Williams, Alexander M — *Businessman*
%Campbell Soup Co, Campbell Pl, Camden, NJ 08101

Williams, Alfred — *Football Player*
%Cincinnati Bengals, 200 Riverfront Stadium, Cincinnati, OH 45202

Williams, Andy — *Singer*
%Triad Artists, 10100 Santa Monica Blvd, #1600, Los Angeles, CA 90067

Williams, Anson — *Actor*
%David Shapira Assoc, 15301 Ventura Blvd, #345, Sherman Oaks, CA 91403

Williams, B John, Jr — *Judge*
%US Tax Court, 400 2nd St NW, Washington, DC 20217

Williams, Barry — *Actor, Singer*
21006 Pacific Coast Hwy, Malibu, CA 90265

Williams, Ben — *Football Player*
%Buffalo Bills, 1 Bills Dr, Orchard Park, NY 14127

Williams, Betty — *Nobel Peace Laureate*
Orchardville Gdns, Finaghy, Belfast 10, Northern Ireland

Williams, Bill — *Actor*
%Associated Talent International, 1320 Armacost Ave, Los Angeles, CA 90025

Williams, Bill — *Astronaut*
%Environmental Protection Agency, 200 SW 35th St, Corvallis, OR 97333

Williams, Billy — *Baseball Player*
586 Prince Edward Rd, Glen Ellyn, IL 60137

Williams, Billy — *Cinematographer*
%Coach HS, Hawkshill Pl, Esher, Surrey KT10 9HY, England

Williams, Billy Dee — *Actor*
1240 Loma Vista Dr, Beverly Hills, CA 90210

Williams, Bob — *Football Player*
602 Stone Barn Rd, Towson, MD 21204

Williams, Buck — *Basketball Player*
%Portland Trail Blazers, 700 NE Multnomah St, Portland, OR 97232

Williams, C Wayne — *Educator*
%University of NY State, Regents College, President's Office, Albany, NY 12203

Williams, Charles P — *Businessman*
%Williams Companies, 1 Williams Ctr, Tulsa, OK 74172

Williams, Cindy — *Actress*
709 19th St, Santa Monica, CA 90402

Williams, Clarence, III — *Actor*
%Flick East-West Talents, 1608 Las Palmas Ave, Los Angeles, CA 90028

Williams, Colleen — *Commentator*
%KNBC-TV, News Dept, 3000 W Alameda Ave, Burbank, CA 91523

Williams, Darnell — *Actor*
400 Madison Ave, #2000, New York, NY 10017

Williams, David — *Football Player*
%Chicago Bears, 250 N Washington Rd, Lake Forest, IL 60045

Williams, David P — *Businessman*
%Associated Dry Goods Corp, 417 5th Ave, New York, NY 10016

Williams, Dean E — *Businessman*
%General American Life Insurance, PO Box 396, St Louis, MO 63166

Williams, Deniece — *Singer*
%Agency for Performing Arts, 888 7th Ave, New York, NY 10106

Williams, Dick (Richard H) — *Baseball Manager*
98 Union, #507, Seattle, WA 98101

Williams, Don — *Singer, Songwriter*
%Jim Halsey Co, 3225 S Norwood Ave, Tulsa, OK 74135

Williams, Donald E — *Astronaut*
%SAIC, 17049 El Camino Real, #202, Houston, TX 77058

Williams, Doug — *Football Player*
PO Box 515, Zachary, LA 70791

Williams, Dudley — *Ballet Dancer*
%Alvin Ailey Dance Theatre, 1519 Broadway, New York, NY 10036

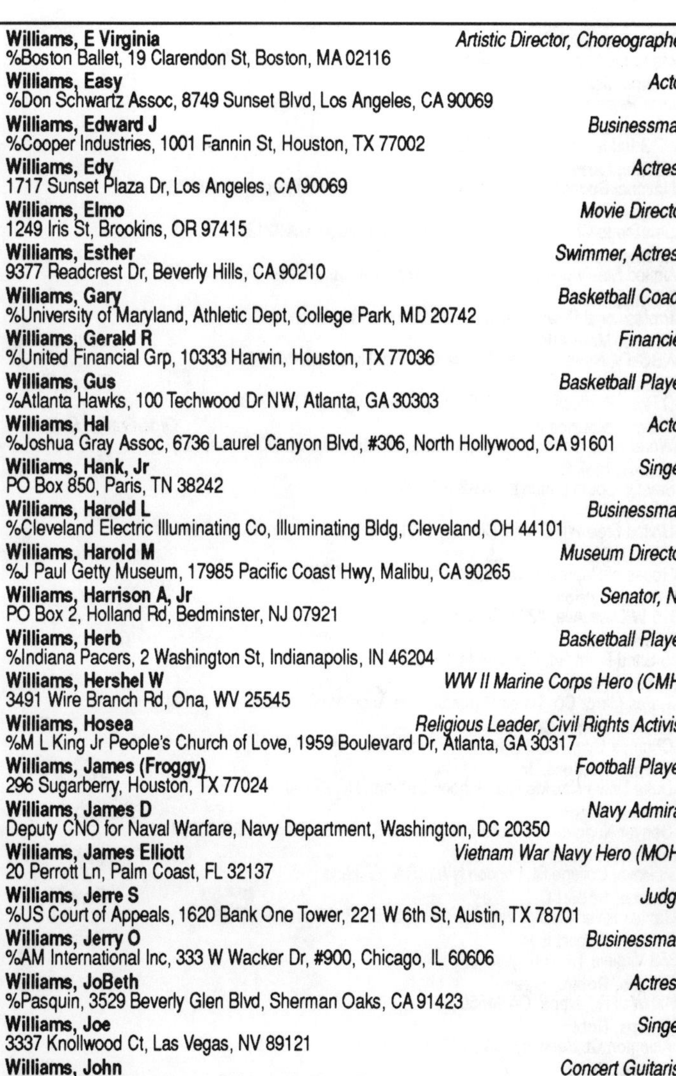

Williams, E Virginia *Artistic Director, Choreographer*
%Boston Ballet, 19 Clarendon St, Boston, MA 02116

Williams, Easy *Actor*
%Don Schwartz Assoc, 8749 Sunset Blvd, Los Angeles, CA 90069

Williams, Edward J *Businessman*
%Cooper Industries, 1001 Fannin St, Houston, TX 77002

Williams, Edy *Actress*
1717 Sunset Plaza Dr, Los Angeles, CA 90069

Williams, Elmo *Movie Director*
1249 Iris St, Brookins, OR 97415

Williams, Esther *Swimmer, Actress*
9377 Readcrest Dr, Beverly Hills, CA 90210

Williams, Gary *Basketball Coach*
%University of Maryland, Athletic Dept, College Park, MD 20742

Williams, Gerald R *Financier*
%United Financial Grp, 10333 Harwin, Houston, TX 77036

Williams, Gus *Basketball Player*
%Atlanta Hawks, 100 Techwood Dr NW, Atlanta, GA 30303

Williams, Hal *Actor*
%Joshua Gray Assoc, 6736 Laurel Canyon Blvd, #306, North Hollywood, CA 91601

Williams, Hank, Jr *Singer*
PO Box 850, Paris, TN 38242

Williams, Harold L *Businessman*
%Cleveland Electric Illuminating Co, Illuminating Bldg, Cleveland, OH 44101

Williams, Harold M *Museum Director*
%J Paul Getty Museum, 17985 Pacific Coast Hwy, Malibu, CA 90265

Williams, Harrison A, Jr *Senator, NJ*
PO Box 2, Holland Rd, Bedminster, NJ 07921

Williams, Herb *Basketball Player*
%Indiana Pacers, 2 Washington St, Indianapolis, IN 46204

Williams, Hershel W *WW II Marine Corps Hero (CMH)*
3491 Wire Branch Rd, Ona, WV 25545

Williams, Hosea *Religious Leader, Civil Rights Activist*
%M L King Jr People's Church of Love, 1959 Boulevard Dr, Atlanta, GA 30317

Williams, James (Froggy) *Football Player*
296 Sugarberry, Houston, TX 77024

Williams, James D *Navy Admiral*
Deputy CNO for Naval Warfare, Navy Department, Washington, DC 20350

Williams, James Elliott *Vietnam War Navy Hero (MOH)*
20 Perrott Ln, Palm Coast, FL 32137

Williams, Jerre S *Judge*
%US Court of Appeals, 1620 Bank One Tower, 221 W 6th St, Austin, TX 78701

Williams, Jerry O *Businessman*
%AM International Inc, 333 W Wacker Dr, #900, Chicago, IL 60606

Williams, JoBeth *Actress*
%Pasquin, 3529 Beverly Glen Blvd, Sherman Oaks, CA 91423

Williams, Joe *Singer*
3337 Knollwood Ct, Las Vegas, NV 89121

Williams, John *Concert Guitarist*
%Harold Holt Ltd, 31 Sinclair Rd, London W14, England

Williams, John *Basketball Player*
%Washington Bullets, Capital Ctr, 1 Truman Dr, Landover, MD 20785

Williams, John (Hot Rod) *Basketball Player*
%Cleveland Cavaliers, 2923 Statesboro Rd, Richfield, OH 44286

Williams, John G, Jr *Navy Admiral*
2300 "E" St NW, Washington, DC 20037

Williams, John J *Representative, IA*
4001 47th St NW, Washington, DC 20016

Williams, John L *Football Player*
%Seattle Seahawks, 5305 Lake Washington Blvd, Kirkland, WA 98033

Williams, John T *Conductor, Composer*
%Boston Pops Orchestra, Symphony Hall, Boston, MA 02115

Williams, Joseph D *Businessman*
%Warner-Lambert Co, 201 Tabor Rd, Morris Plains, NJ 07950

Williams, Joseph H *Businessman*
%Williams Companies, 1 Williams Ctr, Tulsa, OK 74172

W

Williams, Joseph R *Publisher*
%Memphis Commerical Appeal, 495 Union Ave, Memphis, TN 38101

Williams, Joseph T *Businessman*
%Lear Petroleum Corp, 4925 Greenville Ave, #950, Dallas, TX 75206

Williams, L Stanton *Businessman*
%PPG Industries, 1 PPG Pl, Pittsburgh, PA 15272

Williams, Larry E *Businessman*
%National Cooperative Refinery, 2000 S Main St, McPherson, KS 67460

Williams, Lee *Football Player*
%San Diego Chargers, 9449 Friars Rd, San Diego, CA 92120

Williams, Lynn R *Labor Leader*
%United Steelworkers of America, 5 Gateway Ctr, Pittsburgh, PA 15222

Williams, Mark *Bowler*
%Professional Bowlers Assn, 1720 Merriam Rd, Akron, OH 44313

Williams, Mary Alice *Commentator*
%NBC-TV, News Dept, 30 Rockefeller Plz, New York, NY 10112

Williams, Mason *Singer, Pianist*
%D Ross Productions, 3097 Floral Hill Rd, Eugene, OR 97403

Williams, Maurice J *Organization Executive*
%World Food Council, Via della Terme di Caracalla, 00100 Rome, Italy

Williams, Nick B *Editor*
3 Bay Dr, South Laguna, CA 92677

Williams, O L *Religious Leader*
%United Free Will Baptist Church, 1101 University St, Kinston, NC 28501

Williams, Pat *Representative, MT*
%House of Representatives, Washington, DC 20515

Williams, Patrick *Composer*
3815 W Olive Ave, #202, Burbank, CA 91505

Williams, Paul *Composer, Actor*
645 Sand Point Rd, Carpinteria, CA 93013

Williams, Phillip L *Publisher*
%Times Mirror Co, Times Mirror Sq, Los Angeles, CA 90053

Williams, Prince Charles *Boxer*
%Champs Gym, 1243 N 26th St, Philadelphia, PA 19121

Williams, Redford, Jr *Internist*
%Duke University, Medical School, Durham, NC 27706

Williams, Reggie *Basketball Player*
%Denver Nuggets, McNichols Arena, 1635 Clay St, Denver, CO 80204

Williams, Richard *Cartoonist (Pink Panther)*
138 Royal College St, London NW1 0TA, England

Williams, Robert C *Businessman*
%James River Corp of Virginia, Tredegar St, Richmond, VA 23217

Williams, Robert E *Businessman*
1359 Virginia Trl, Youngstown, OH 44505

Williams, Robin *Comedian*
1100 Wall Rd, Napa, CA 94550

Williams, Robley C *Biophysicist*
1 Arlington Ct, Berkeley, CA 94707

Williams, Roger *Pianist*
%Virtuoso, 5710 Wallis Ln, Woodland Hills, CA 91364

Williams, Ron *Bowler*
5700 Westchase Dr, North Richland Heights, TX 76180

Williams, Roshumba *Model*
%Bethann Model Mgmt, 36 N Moore St, New York, NY 10013

Williams, Shirley *Government Official, England*
%House of Commons, Westminster, London SW1, England

Williams, Stephen *Anthropologist*
103 Old Colony Rd, Wellesley, MA 02181

Williams, Stephen F *Judge*
%US Court of Appeals, 3rd & Constitution Ave NW, Washington, DC 20001

Williams, Steven *Actor*
%Geddes Agency, 8457 Melrose Pl, #200, Los Angeles, CA 90069

Williams, T Franklin *Physician*
%National Institute on Aging, 9000 Rockville Pike, Bethesda, MD 20205

Williams, Ted *Baseball Player, Manager*
PO Box 5127, Clearwater, FL 34618

Williams, Thomas Cardinal *Religious Leader*
Viard, 21 Eccleston Hill, PO Box 198, Wellington, New Zealand

Williams, Tony *Jazz Drummer*
%Ted Kurland Assoc, 173 Brighton Ave, Boston, MA 02134

Williams, Treat *Actor*
1501 Broadway, #2600, New York, NY 10036

Williams, Ulis *Track Athlete*
%Compton Community College, Athletic Dept, Compton, CA 90221

Williams, Van *Actor*
%KHM Communications, 1630 Ocean Park Blvd, Santa Monica, CA 90405

Williams, Vanessa *Actress, Model*
%Gersh Agency, 232 N Canon Dr, Beverly Hills, CA 90210

Williams, W Clyde *Religious Leader*
%Christian Methodist Episcopal Church, 2805 Shoreland Dr, Atlanta, GA 30331

Williams, Walter F *Businessman*
%Bethlehem Steel Corp, 701 E 3rd St, Bethlehem, PA 18016

Williams, Walter Ray, Jr *Bowler*
%Professional Bowlers Assn, 1720 Merriman Rd, Akron, OH 44313

Williams, Walter W *Businessman*
%Rubbermaid Inc, 1147 Akron Rd, Wooster, OH 44691

Williams, William B *Actor*
1175 Park Ave, New York, NY 10021

Williams, William J *Businessman*
%Republic Steel Corp, 1707 Republic Bldg, Cleveland, OH 44145

Williamson, David G, Jr *Businessman*
%Hospital Corp of America, 1 Park Plz, Nashville, TN 37203

Williamson, E L *Businessman*
%Louisiana Land & Exploration Co, 225 Baronne St, New Orleans, LA 70112

Williamson, Fred *Actor, Football Player*
%H David Moss Assoc, 8019 1/2 Melrose Ave, #3, Los Angeles, CA 90046

Williamson, Gilbert P *Businessman*
%NCR Corp, 1700 S Patterson Blvd, Dayton, OH 45479

Williamson, Hugh H, III *Businessman*
%Revere Copper & Brass Inc, High Ridge Park, Stamford, CT 06904

Williamson, Marianne *Psychotherapist*
%Los Angeles Center for Living, 650 N Robertson Blvd, Los Angeles, CA 90069

Williamson, Mykel T *Actor*
%Abrams Artists, 9200 Sunset Blvd, #625, Los Angeles, CA 90069

Williamson, Nicol *Actor*
%International Creative Mgmt, 388-396 Oxford St, London W1X 3LD, England

Williamson, Richard *Football Coach*
%Cincinnati Bengals, 200 Riverfront Stadium, Cincinnati, OH 45202

Williamson, Samuel R, Jr *Educator*
%University of the South, President's Office, Sewanee, TN 37375

Williford, John H *Businessman*
%CooperVision Inc, 3145 Porter Dr, Palo Alto, CA 94304

Willis, Austin *Actor*
%BDP Assoc, 10637 Burbank Blvd, North Hollywood, CA 91601

Willis, Baron Ted *Writer*
5 Shepherds Green, Chislehurst, Kent, England

Willis, Bill (William K) *Football Player*
1158 S Waverly, Columbus, OH 43227

Willis, Bruce *Actor*
%Triad Artists, 10100 Santa Monica Blvd, #1600, Los Angeles, CA 90067

Willis, Gordon *Cinematographer*
%Gersh Agency, 232 N Canon Dr, Beverly Hills, CA 90210

Willis, Kevin *Basketball Player*
%Atlanta Hawks, 100 Techwood Dr NW, Atlanta, GA 30303

Willoch, Kare I *Prime Minister, Norway*
%Hoyres Stortingsgruppe, Stortinget, Oslo, Norway

Wills Moody Roark, Helen *Tennis Player*
PO Box 22095, Carmel, CA 93922

Wills, Garry *Writer*
%Andrews & McMeel, 6700 Squibb Rd, Mission, KS 66202

Wills, Maury *Baseball Player*
30100 Town Center Dr, #0209, Laguna Niguel, CA 92677

Wilmer, Harry A — *Psychiatrist*
%University of Texas, Health Science Ctr, San Antonio, TX 78284

Wilson, Allan B — *Molecular Biologist*
%University of California, Molecular Biology Dept, Berkeley, CA 94724

Wilson, Ann — *Singer (Heart)*
219 1st Ave N, #333, Seattle, WA 98109

Wilson, Bobby (Robert E) — *Football Player*
5235 Carew, Houston, TX 77096

Wilson, Brian — *Singer (Beach Boys), Songwriter*
%Brains & Genius, 12217 W Pico Blvd, Los Angeles, CA 90064

Wilson, C Ivan — *Financier*
%First City Bancorp of Texas, 1001 Fannin St, #400, Houston, TX 77002

Wilson, C Kemmons — *Businessman*
3615 S Galloway Dr, Memphis, TN 38111

Wilson, Carl — *Singer (Beach Boys), Songwriter*
8860 Evan View Dr, Los Angeles, CA 90069

Wilson, Charles — *Representative, TX*
%House of Representatives, Washington, DC 20515

Wilson, Colin — *Writer*
Tetherdown, Trewallock Ln, Gorran Haven, Cornwall, England

Wilson, David — *Actor*
%Susan Smith Assoc, 121 N San Vicente Blvd, Beverly Hills, CA 90211

Wilson, David K — *Businessman*
%Cherokee Equity Corp, 3022 Vanderbilt Plz, Nashville, TN 37212

Wilson, David Mackenzie — *Museum Director*
%British Museum, London WC1, England

Wilson, Doug — *Hockey Player*
%Chicago Black Hawks, 1800 W Madison St, Chicago, IL 60612

Wilson, E Bright — *Chemist*
12 Oxford St, Cambridge, MA 02138

Wilson, Earl — *Baseball Player*
Box 662, Ponchatoula, LA 70454

Wilson, Earle L — *Religious Leader*
%The Wesleyan Church, PO Box 50434, Indianapolis, IN 46250

Wilson, Edward O — *Writer, Educator*
9 Foster Rd, Lexington, MA 02173

Wilson, Eric C T — *WW II British Army Hero (VC)*
Woodside Cottage, Stowell, Sherborne, Dorset, England

Wilson, Eugene — *Skier*
PO Box 912, Coleraine, NH 55722

Wilson, F Perry — *Chemical Engineer*
11656 Lake House Ct, North Palm Beach, FL 33408

Wilson, Flip — *Comedian*
21970 Pacific Coast Hwy, Malibu, CA 90265

Wilson, Gahan — *Cartoonist, Writer*
%Michelle Urry, 747 3rd Ave, New York, NY 10017

Wilson, Geoffrey H — *Businessman*
%Delta Grp, 1 Kingsway, London WC1B 6XF, England

Wilson, George B (Mike), Jr — *Football Player, Army General*
1062 Lancaster Ave, Rosemont, PA 19010

Wilson, Gerald — *Jazz Trumpeter, Composer*
4625 Brynhurst Ave, Los Angeles, CA 90043

Wilson, H C — *Religious Leader*
%The Wesleyan Church, PO Box 50434, Indianapolis, IN 46250

Wilson, Harold — *Prime Minister, England*
%House of Commons, London SW1, England

Wilson, Harold E — *Korean War Marine Corps Hero (CMH)*
125 Shadydale Dr, Lexington, SC 29073

Wilson, Harry — *Football Player*
209 Rush St, New Smyrna Beach, FL 32069

Wilson, Hillsman V — *Businessman*
%McCormick & Co, 11350 McCormick Rd, Hunt Valley, MD 21031

Wilson, J Tuzo — *Geologist*
27 Pricefield Rd, Toronto ON M4W 1Z8, Canada

Wilson, J Tylee — *Businessman*
%RJR Nabisco Inc, Reynolds Blvd, Winston-Salem, NC 27102

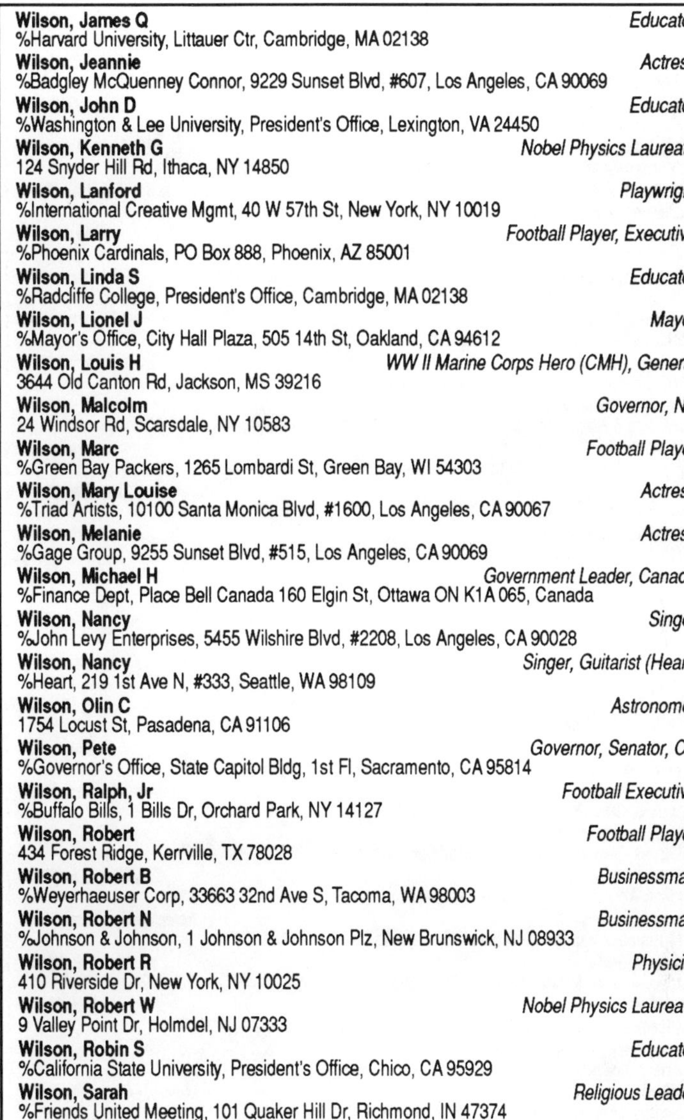

Wilson, James Q *Educator*
%Harvard University, Littauer Ctr, Cambridge, MA 02138

Wilson, Jeannie *Actress*
%Badgley McQuenney Connor, 9229 Sunset Blvd, #607, Los Angeles, CA 90069

Wilson, John D *Educator*
%Washington & Lee University, President's Office, Lexington, VA 24450

Wilson, Kenneth G *Nobel Physics Laureate*
124 Snyder Hill Rd, Ithaca, NY 14850

Wilson, Lanford *Playwright*
%International Creative Mgmt, 40 W 57th St, New York, NY 10019

Wilson, Larry *Football Player, Executive*
%Phoenix Cardinals, PO Box 888, Phoenix, AZ 85001

Wilson, Linda S *Educator*
%Radcliffe College, President's Office, Cambridge, MA 02138

Wilson, Lionel J *Mayor*
%Mayor's Office, City Hall Plaza, 505 14th St, Oakland, CA 94612

Wilson, Louis H *WW II Marine Corps Hero (CMH), General*
3644 Old Canton Rd, Jackson, MS 39216

Wilson, Malcolm *Governor, NY*
24 Windsor Rd, Scarsdale, NY 10583

Wilson, Marc *Football Player*
%Green Bay Packers, 1265 Lombardi St, Green Bay, WI 54303

Wilson, Mary Louise *Actress*
%Triad Artists, 10100 Santa Monica Blvd, #1600, Los Angeles, CA 90067

Wilson, Melanie *Actress*
%Gage Group, 9255 Sunset Blvd, #515, Los Angeles, CA 90069

Wilson, Michael H *Government Leader, Canada*
%Finance Dept, Place Bell Canada 160 Elgin St, Ottawa ON K1A 065, Canada

Wilson, Nancy *Singer*
%John Levy Enterprises, 5455 Wilshire Blvd, #2208, Los Angeles, CA 90028

Wilson, Nancy *Singer, Guitarist (Heart)*
%Heart, 219 1st Ave N, #333, Seattle, WA 98109

Wilson, Olin C *Astronomer*
1754 Locust St, Pasadena, CA 91106

Wilson, Pete *Governor, Senator, CA*
%Governor's Office, State Capitol Bldg, 1st Fl, Sacramento, CA 95814

Wilson, Ralph, Jr *Football Executive*
%Buffalo Bills, 1 Bills Dr, Orchard Park, NY 14127

Wilson, Robert *Football Player*
434 Forest Ridge, Kerrville, TX 78028

Wilson, Robert B *Businessman*
%Weyerhaeuser Corp, 33663 32nd Ave S, Tacoma, WA 98003

Wilson, Robert N *Businessman*
%Johnson & Johnson, 1 Johnson & Johnson Plz, New Brunswick, NJ 08933

Wilson, Robert R *Physicist*
410 Riverside Dr, New York, NY 10025

Wilson, Robert W *Nobel Physics Laureate*
9 Valley Point Dr, Holmdel, NJ 07333

Wilson, Robin S *Educator*
%California State University, President's Office, Chico, CA 95929

Wilson, Sarah *Religious Leader*
%Friends United Meeting, 101 Quaker Hill Dr, Richmond, IN 47374

Wilson, Sloan *Writer*
%Pretty Baby III, Richmond Yacht Basin, 9954 Hoke Brady Rd, Richmond, VA 23231

Wilson, Thornton A *Businessman*
%Boeing Co, 7755 E Marginal Way S, Seattle, WA 98108

Wilson, W Robert *Businessman*
%Lukens Inc, 50 S 1st Ave, Coatesville, PA 19320

Wilson, Willie *Baseball Player*
3905 W 110th St, Leawood, KS 66211

Wilson, Woody *Cartoonist (Rex Morgan, MD)*
%North America Syndicate, 235 E 45th St, New York, NY 10017

Wilt, Fred *Track Athlete*
2525 Kickapoo Dr, Lafayette, IN 47905

Wimmer, Brian *Actor*
641 Swarthmore Ave, Pacific Palisades, CA 90272

W

Winans, BeBe *Singer*
%Triad Artists, 10100 Santa Monica Blvd, #1600, Los Angeles, CA 90067

Winans, CeCe *Singer*
%Triad Artists, 10100 Santa Monica Blvd, #1600, Los Angeles, CA 90067

Winbergh, Gosta *Opera Singer*
%Columbia Artists Mgmt Inc, 165 W 57th St, New York, NY 10019

Winbigler, Leon F *Businessman*
%Mercantile Stores Co, 1100 N Market St, Wilmington, DE 19801

Winder, Sammy *Football Player*
%Denver Broncos, 13655 E Dove Valley Pkwy, Englewood, CO 80112

Winders, Wim *Movie Director*
%Paul Kohner Inc, 9169 Sunset Blvd, Los Angeles, CA 90069

Windle, William F *Anatomist*
229 Cherry St, Granville, OH 43023

Windom, William *Actor*
6535 Langdon Ave, Van Nuys, CA 91406

Windsor, Marie *Actress*
9501 Cherokee Ln, Beverly Hills, CA 90210

Windust, Penelope *Actress*
%Writers & Artists Agency, 11726 San Vicente, #300, Los Angeles, CA 90049

Winegardner, Roy E *Businessman*
%Holiday Inns Inc, 3742 Lamar Ave, Memphis, TN 38195

Winfield, Dave *Baseball Player*
367 W Forest, Teaneck, NJ 07666

Winfield, John A *Businessman*
%Brockway Inc, 1 Enterprise Ctr, 225 Water St, Jacksonville, FL 77079

Winfield, Paul *Actor*
5693 Holly Oak Dr, Los Angeles, CA 90068

Winfield, Rodney M *Artist*
444 Laclede Pl, St Louis, MO 63108

Winfrey, Oprah *Entertainer*
%Harpo Inc, 110 N Carpenter St, Chicago, IL 60607

Wing, Toby *Actress*
PO Box 1197, Lake Elsinore, CA 92330

Wingate, David A *Businessman*
%Hi-Shear Industries, 3333 New Hyde Park Rd, North Hills, NY 11042

Winger, Debra *Actress*
PO Box 1368, Pacific Palisades, CA 90272

Wingerter, Robert G *Businesman*
%Libbey-Owens-Ford Co, 811 Madison Ave, Toledo, OH 43695

Winkler, Hans-Gunter *Equestrian Rider*
Dr Rau Allee 48, 4410 Warendorf, Germany

Winkler, Henry *Actor, Television Director*
%Monument Pictures, PO Box 1764, Studio City, CA 91604

Winkler, Irwin *Movie Producer*
%Irwin Winkler Productions, 10125 W Washington Blvd, Culver City, CA 90230

Winkler, K C *Actress, Model*
%Phillips Moore Entertainment, PO Box 3673, Santa Monica, CA 90403

Winn, Kitty *Actress*
%Artists Agency, 10000 Santa Monica Blvd, #305, Los Angeles, CA 90067

Winner, Michael *Movie Director, Producer*
%Scimitar Films, 6-8 Sackville St, Piccadilly, London W1X 1DD, England

Winningham, Mare *Actress*
10120 Lasaine Ave, Northridge, CA 91325

Winningstad, C Norman *Businessman*
%Floating Point Systems, 3601 SW Murray Blvd, Beaverton, OR 97005

Winokur, Herbert S, Jr *Businessman*
%Penn Central Corp, 500 W Putnam Ave, Greenwich, CT 06836

Winpisinger, William W *Labor Leader*
%Machinists & Aerospace Union, 1300 Connecticut Ave NW, Washington, DC 20036

Winship, Thomas *Editor*
Old Concord Rd, South Lincoln, MA 01773

Winslow, Kellen *Football Player*
%San Diego Chargers, 9449 Friars Rd, San Diego, CA 92108

Winslow, Michael *Comedian*
5750 Wilshire Blvd, #580, Los Angeles, CA 90036

Winsor, Kathleen *Writer*
115 E 67th St, New York, NY 10021
Winsor, Ralph E *Businessman*
%Curtice-Burns Inc, 1 Lincoln First Sq, Rochester, NY 14603
Winston, George *Pianist, Composer*
%Dancing Cat Productions, PO Box 639, Santa Cruz, CA 95061
Winston, Patrick H *Computer Scientist*
%Massachusetts Institute of Technology, Technology Sq, Cambridge, MA 02139
Winter, Edgar *Singer*
PO Box 6380, Albany, NY 12206
Winter, Edward D *Actor*
%Winterset Inc, 4359 Hayvenhurst Ave, Encino, CA 91316
Winter, Frederick Thomas *Thorougbred Racing Jockey, Trainer*
Uplands, Lambourn, Berks, England
Winter, Harrison L *Judge*
%US Court of Appeals, 101 W Lombard St, Baltimore, MD 21201
Winter, Max *Football Executive*
%Minnesota Vikings, 9520 Viking Dr, Eden Prairie, MN 55344
Winter, Ralph K, Jr *Judge*
%US Court of Appeals, Audubon Court Bldg, 55 Whitney Ave, New Haven, CT 06511
Winter, William B *Businessman*
%Becor Western Inc, PO Box 56, South Milwaukee, WI 53172
Winter, William F *Governor, MS*
633 N State St, Jackson, MS 39201
Winters, Brian *Basketball Player, Coach*
%Cleveland Cavaliers, PO Box 5000, Cleveland, OH 44286
Winters, Jonathan *Comedian*
4310 Arcola Ave, Toluca Lake, CA 91602
Winters, Robert C *Businessman*
%Prudential Insurance Co, Prudential Plz, Newark, NJ 07101
Winters, Shelley *Actress*
457 N Oakhurst Dr, Beverly Hills, CA 90210
Wintour, Anna *Editor*
%Vogue Magazine, 350 Madison Ave, New York, NY 10017
Winwood, Steve *Singer*
%Island Records, 22 St Peters Sq, London W6, England
Wire, William S, II *Businessman*
%Genesco Inc, Genesco Park, Nashville, TN 37202
Wirth, Timothy E *Senator, CO*
%US Senate, Washington, DC 20510
Wirtz, W Willard *Secretary, Labor*
5009 39th St NW, Washington, DC 20016
Wirtz, William W *Hockey Executive*
DeWindt Rd, Winnetka, IL 60093
Wisdom, John Minor *Judge*
%US Court of Appeals, US Courthouse, 600 Camp St, New Orleans, LA 70130
Wisdom, Norman *Comedian*
28 Berkeley Sq, London 6HD, England
Wise, George S *Educator*
5500 Collins Ave, Miami Beach, FL 33140
Wise, Robert *Movie Director, Producer*
31220 Broad Beach Rd, Malibu, CA 90265
Wise, Robert E, Jr *Representative, WV*
%House of Representatives, Washington, DC 20515
Wiseman, Joseph *Actor*
382 Central Park West, New York, NY 10019
Wishnick, William *Businessman*
%Witcon Corp, 520 Madison Ave, New York, NY 10022
Wisniewski, Steve *Football Player*
%Los Angeles Raiders, 332 Center St, El Segundo, CA 90245
Wisoff, Peter J *Astronaut*
%NASA, Johnson Space Ctr, Houston, TX 77058
Wistert, Albert *Football Player*
2100 Whetstone Ct, Thousand Oaks, CA 91362
Wistert, Alvin *Football Player*
10250 W Seven Mile Rd, Northville, MI 48167

W

Withers, Jane *Actress*
1801 N Curson Ave, Los Angeles, CA 90046

Witherspoon, Jimmy *Singer*
%Hoffer, 233 1/2 E 48th St, New York, NY 10017

Witherspoon, Tim *Boxer*
%Carl King, 32 E 69th St, New York, NY 10021

Witkop, Bernhard *Chemist*
3807 Montrose Drwy, Chevy Chase, MD 20015

Witt, Katerina *Figure Skater*
Reichenheimer Strasse, D-Chemnitz, Germany

Witt, Mike *Baseball Player*
8042 San Leon Circle Dr, Buena Park, CA 90620

Witten, Edward *Physicist*
%Institute for Advanced Study, Olden Ln, Princeton, NJ 08540

Wittig, Georg *Nobel Chemistry Laureate*
Bergstrasse 35, 69 Heidelberg, Germany

Wittman, Randy *Basketball Player*
%Sacramento Kings, 1515 Sports Dr, Sacramento, CA 95834

Woelfle, Arthur W *Businessman*
%Dart & Kraft Inc, Kraft Ctr, Glenview, IL 60025

Woessner, Mark *Businessman, Publisher*
%Bertelsmann, Carl-Bertelsmann-Strasse 270, 4830 Guetersloh, Germany

Wohl, Dave *Basketball Coach*
%New Jersey Nets, Meadowlands Arena, East Rutherford, NJ 07073

Wohlstetter, Charles *Businessman*
%Continental Telecom Inc, 245 Perimeter Center Pkwy, Atlanta, GA 30346

Woit, Dick *Physical Fitness Expert*
%Lehman Sports Ctr, 2700 N Lehmann Ct, Chicago, IL 60614

Woiwode, Larry *Writer, Poet*
%State University of New York, English Dept, Binghamton, NY 13901

Wojciechowicz, Alex *Football Player*
1105 Skiff Way Dr, Forked River, NJ 08731

Wolcott, Arthur S *Businessman*
%S S Pierce Co, 74 Seneca St, Dundee, NY 14837

Wolcott, John W *Businessman*
%Transway International Corp, 81 Main St, White Plains, NY 10601

Wolcott, Robert W, Jr *Businessman*
%IU International Corp, 1500 Walnut St, Philadelphia, PA 19102

Wolf, David A *Astronaut*
%NASA, Johnson Space Ctr, Houston, TX 77058

Wolf, Don A *Businessman*
%Hardware Wholesalers Inc, Box 868, Fort Wayne, IN 46801

Wolf, Frank *Publisher*
%Seventeen Magazine, 850 3rd Ave, New York, NY 10022

Wolf, Frank R *Representative, VA*
%House of Representatives, Washington, DC 20515

Wolf, Sigrid *Skier*
General Delivery, 6652 Elbigenalp 45-A, Austria

Wolf, Stephen M *Businessman*
%United Airlines, 1200 Algonquin Rd, Mount Prospect, IL 60056

Wolfe, John F *Publisher*
%Columbus Dispatch, 34 S 3rd St, Columbus, OH 43216

Wolfe, Kenneth L *Businessman*
%Hershey Foods Corp, 100 Mansion Rd E, Hershey, PA 17033

Wolfe, Tom *Writer*
%Farrar Straus & Giroux, 19 Union Sq W, New York, NY 10003

Wolfenden of Westcott, John F *Educator*
White House, Guildford Rd, Westcott Near Dorking, Surrey, England

Wolfensohn, James D *Financier*
%James D Wolfensohn Co, 599 Lexington Ave, New York, NY 10022

Wolfermann, Klaus *Track Athlete*
%Puma Sportschu, Postfach 1420, 8522 Herzogenraurach, Germany

Wolff, Hugh *Conductor*
%Affiliate Artists, 37 W 65th St, #601, New York, NY 10023

Wolff, Roger *Baseball Player*
1307 Knott, Chester, IL 62233

Wolff, Sanford I — *Labor Leader*
%TV & Radio Artists Federation, 1350 Ave of Americas, New York, NY 10019

Wolfman Jack (Robert Weston Smith) — *Radio Entertainer*
%Belvidere Plantation, Rt 1, Box 56, Belvidere, NC 27919

Wolford, Will — *Football Player*
%Buffalo Bills, 1 Bills Dr, Orchard Park, NY 14127

Wolfson, Louis E — *Businessman, Thoroughbred Racing Owner*
10205 Collins Ave, Bal Harbour, FL 33154

Wollenberg, R P — *Businessman*
%Longview Fibre Co, PO Box 639, Longview, WA 98632

Wollman, Harvey — *Governor, SD*
RR 1, Box 43, Hitchcock, SD 57348

Wollman, Roger L — *Judge*
%US Court of Appeals, Federal Bldg, Pierre, SD 57501

Wolpe, Howard E — *Representative, MI*
%House of Representatives, Washington, DC 20515

Wolper, David L — *Movie Producer*
10847 Bellagio Rd, Los Angeles, CA 90024

Womack, Bobby — *Singer*
%Truth Records, 2841 Firenze Pl, Los Angeles, CA 90048

Wonder, Stevie — *Singer*
2270 Astral Dr, Los Angeles, CA 90068

Woo, Peter K C — *Businessman*
%Hongkong & Kowloon Wharf & Godown Co, 7 Canton Rd, Kowloon, Hong Kong

Wood, Arthur M — *Businessman*
%Sears Roebuck & Co, Sears Tower, Chicago, IL 60684

Wood, C Norman — *Air Force General*
Director, Intelligence Community Staff, CIA, PO Box 571, Washington, DC 20044

Wood, Godfrey — *Hockey Executive*
%Boston Bruins, 150 Causeway St, Boston, MA 02114

Wood, Harland G — *Biochemist*
%Case Western Reserve University, Medical School, Cleveland, OH 44106

Wood, Harlington, Jr — *Judge*
%US Court of Appeals, 600 E Monroe St, Springfield, IL 62705

Wood, Harold — *Businessman*
%Michigan Milk Producers Assn, PO Box 5087, Southfield, MI 48037

Wood, James — *Businessman*
%Great Atlantic & Pacific Tea Co, 2 Paragon Dr, Montvale, NJ 07645

Wood, Kimba M — *Judge*
%US District Court House, Foley Square, 40 Centre St, New York, NY 10007

Wood, Leon — *Basketball Player*
%San Antonio Spurs, 600 E Market, San Antonio, TX 78025

Wood, Nigel — *Astronaut, England*
%Defense Ministry, 98 High Holburn, London WC1V 6LL, England

Wood, Quentin E — *Businessman*
%Quaker State Oil Refining Corp, 255 Elm St, Oil City, PA 16301

Wood, Richard — *Football Player, Coach*
%Philadelphia Eagles, Veterans Stadium, Broad & Pattison, Philadelphia, PA 19148

Wood, Richard D — *Businessman*
%Eli Lilly Co, Lilly Corporate Ctr, Indianapolis, IN 46285

Wood, Robert — *Astronaut*
%McDonnell Douglas Corp, Box 516, St Louis, MO 63166

Wood, Robert E — *Publisher*
%Peninsula Times Tribune, 245 Lytton Ave, Palo Alto, CA 94301

Wood, Sidney B B — *Tennis Player*
300 Murray Pl, Southhampton, NY 11068

Wood, Thomas H — *Publisher*
%Atlanta Constitution, 72 Marietta St NW, Atlanta, GA 30302

Wood, Wilbur — *Baseball Player*
8 Wachusett Dr, Lexington, MA 02173

Wood, William B, III — *Biologist*
%University of Colorado, Molecular Biology Dept, Boulder, CO 80309

Wood, Willie — *Football Player*
%Willie Wood Mechanical Systems, 1335 11th St NW, Washington, DC 20001

Woodall, Jack — *Army General*
Commanding General, US Army Japan/IX Corps, APO, AP 96343

Woodard, Alfre *Actress*
802 Bay St, Santa Monica, CA 90405

Woodard, Lynette *Basketball Player*
%University of Kansas, Athletic Dept, Lawrence, KS 66045

Woodard, Max W *Businessman*
%Lear Petroleum Corp, 4925 Greenville Ave, #950, Dallas, TX 75206

Woodcock, Leonard *Labor Leader, Diplomat*
2404 Vinewood, Ann Arbor, MI 48104

Wooddy, L D, Jr *Businessman*
%Exxon Pipeline Co, Exxon Bldg, Houston, TX 77252

Wooden, John *Basketball Player, Coach*
17711 Margate St, #102, Encino, CA 91316

Woodhead, Cynthia *Swimmer*
PO Box 1193, Riverside, CA 92501

Woodhouse, John F *Businessman*
%Sysco Corp, 1177 West Loop S, Houston, TX 77027

Woodiwiss, Kathleen E *Writer*
%Avon Books, 959 8th Ave, New York, NY 10019

Woodley, David *Football Player*
%Pittsburgh Steelers, Three Rivers Stadium, Pittsburgh, PA 15212

Woodling, Gene *Baseball PLayer*
926 Remsen Rd, Medina, OH 44256

Woodring, Wendell P *Geologist, Paleontologist*
6647 El Colegio Rd, Goleta, CA 93117

Woodruff, John *Track Athlete*
822 Mary Manuel Cir, Sacramento, CA 95831

Woodruff, Judy *Commentator*
%MacNeil/Lehrer News Hour, 3620 27th St S, Arlington, VA 22206

Woods, Donald *Social Activist*
%Atheneum Publishers, 597 5th Ave, New York, NY 10017

Woods, Ickey *Football Player*
%Cincinnati Bengals, 200 Riverfront Stadium, Cincinnati, OH 45202

Woods, James *Actor*
%Creative Artists Agency, 9830 Wilshire Blvd, Beverly Hills, CA 90212

Woods, James D *Businessman*
%Baker International Corp, 500 City Pkwy W, Orange, CA 92668

Woods, Michael *Actor*
%Harris & Goldberg Agency, 1999 Ave of Stars, #2850, Los Angeles, CA 90067

Woods, Nan *Actress*
%Geddes Agency, 8457 Melrose Pl, #200, Los Angeles, CA 90069

Woods, Phil *Jazz Clarinetist, Saxophonist*
PO Box 278, Delaware Water Gap, PA 18327

Woods, Rose Mary *Presidential Secretary*
2500 Virginia Ave NW, Washington, DC 20037

Woodside, William S *Businessman*
%Primerica Corp, PO Box 3610, Greenwich, CT 06838

Woodson, Mike *Basketball Player*
%Houston Rockets, Summit, Greenway Plz, #10, Houston, TX 77046

Woodson, Rod *Football Player*
%Pittsburgh Steelers, Three Rivers Stadium, Pittsburgh, PA 15212

Woodson, Warren *Football Coach*
7076 Briarmeadow Dr, Dallas, TX 75230

Woodward, Bob *Journalist*
%Washington Post, 1150 15th St NW, Washington, DC 20005

Woodward, C Vann *Historian*
83 Rogers Rd, Hamden, CT 06517

Woodward, Edward *Actor, Singer*
%Eric Glass Ltd, 28 Berkeley Sq, London W1X 6HD, England

Woodward, James H, Jr *Educator*
%University of North Carolina, President's Office, Charlotte, NC 28223

Woodward, John *Navy Admiral, England*
%Navy Secretary, Defense Ministry, Whitehall, London SW1, England

Woodward, M Cabell, Jr *Businessman*
%ITT Corp, 320 Park Ave, New York, NY 10022

Woolard, Edgar S, Jr *Businessman*
%E I du Pont de Nemours Co, 1007 Market St, Wilmington, DE 19898

Wooldridge, Dean E *Businessman*
4545 Via Esperanza, Santa Barbara, CA 93110

Woolery, Chuck *Entertainer*
620 N Linden Dr, Beverly Hills, CA 90210

Wooley, Sheb *Singer, Songwriter*
%Tessier, 264 Old Hickory Blvd, Madison, TN 37115

Woolley, Catherine *Writer*
Higgins Hollow Rd, Truro, MA 02666

Woolridge, Orlando *Basketball Player*
%Detroit Pistons, The Palace, 1 Championship Dr, Auburn Hills, MI 48057

Woolsey, Clinton N *Neurophysiologist*
106 Virginia Terr, Madison, WI 53705

Woolsey, Elizabeth D *Skier*
Trail Creek Ranch, Wilson, WY 83014

Woosnam, Ian *Golfer*
Dyffryn, Morda Rd, Oswestry, Shropshire SY11 2AY, Wales

Wooten, Jim *Commentator*
%ABC-TV, News Dept, 1717 De Sales St NW, Washington, DC 20036

Wootten, Morgan *Basketball Coach*
%De Matha High School, Athletic Dept, Hyattsville, MD 20781

Wootton, Charles Greenwood *Diplomat*
%OECD, Chateau de la Muette, 2 Rue Andre-Pascal, 75775 Paris, France

Wopat, Tom *Actor*
12245 Morrison St, North Hollywood, CA 91607

Word, Weldon R *Engineer (Paveway Smart Bomb)*
Northshore Dr Brookhaven, Rt 2, Box 293-BB, Hawkins, TX 75765

Worden, Alfred M *Astronaut*
%Jet Electronic & Technology, 5353 52nd St SE, Grand Rapids, MI 49588

Worgull, David *Religious Leader*
%Wisconsin Evangelical Lutheran Synod, 1270 N Dobson Chandler, AZ 85224

Worley, Joanne *Actress*
4363 Ledge Ave, North Hollywood, CA 91602

Worley, Tim *Football Player*
%Pittsburgh Steelers, Three Rivers Stadium, Pittsburgh, PA 15212

Worner, Manfred *Government Official, Germany*
%NATO, Secretary-General's Office, 78380 Bougival, France

Worsham, James E *Businessman, Aeronautical Engineer*
%Douglas Aircraft Co, 3855 Lakewood Blvd, Long Beach, CA 90846

Worsley, Lorne (Gump) *Hockey Player*
%Minnesota North Stars, 7901 Cedar Ave S, Bloomington, MN 55420

Worthen, John E *Educator*
%Ball State University, President's Office, Muncie, IN 47306

Worthington, Melvin *Religious Leader*
%Free Will Baptists, PO Box 1088, Nashville, TN 37202

Worthy, James *Basketball Player*
%Los Angeles Lakers, Great Western Forum, 3900 W Manchester, Inglewood, CA 90306

Wortley, George C *Representative, NY*
%House of Representatives, Washington, DC 20515

Wouk, Herman *Writer*
%BSW Literary Agency, 3255 "N" St NW, Washington, DC 20007

Wray, Fay *Actress*
2080 Century Park East, #406, Los Angeles, CA 90067

Wright, Charles Alan *Attorney*
5304 Western Hills Dr, Austin, TX 78731

Wright, Clyde *Baseball Player*
528 Jeanine Ave, Anaheim, CA 92806

Wright, Cobina, Jr *Actress*
1326 Dove Meadow Rd, Solvang, CA 93463

Wright, Don *Editorial Cartoonist*
%Palm Beach Post, 2751 S Dixie Hwy, West Palm Beach, FL 33405

Wright, Donald F *Publisher*
%Los Angeles Times, Times Mirror Sq, Los Angeles, CA 90053

Wright, Eugene A *Judge*
%US Courthouse, 1010 5th Ave, Seattle, WA 98104

Wright, Felix E *Businessman*
%Leggett & Platt Inc, 1 Leggett Rd, Carthage, MO 64836

W

Wright – Wussler

Wright, Gerald *Theatre Director*
%Guthrie Theatre, 725 Vineland Pl, Minneapolis, MN 55403

Wright, Irving S *Physician*
450 E 69th St, New York, NY 10021

Wright, James C, Jr *Representative, TX*
Lanham Federal Office Bldg, 819 Taylor St, Fort Worth, TX 76102

Wright, Jay *Poet*
%General Delivery, Piermont, NH 03779

Wright, Lawrence A *Judge*
%US Tax Court, 400 2nd St NW, Washington, DC 20217

Wright, Louis *Football Player*
%Denver Broncos, 13655 E Dove Valley Pkwy, Englewood, CO 80112

Wright, Louis B *Historian*
3702 Leland St, Chevy Chase, MD 20815

Wright, Max *Actor*
%Bresler Kelly Kipperman, 15760 Ventura Blvd, #1730, Encino, CA 91436

Wright, Michael W *Businessman*
%Super Valu Stores, 11840 Valley View Rd, Eden Prairie, MN 55344

Wright, Mickey *Golfer*
%Ladies Professional Golf Assn, 2570 Volusia Ave, #B, Daytona Beach, FL 32114

Wright, Myron A *Businessman*
%Cameron Iron Works, 130013 Northwest Fwy, Houston, TX 77040

Wright, Oliver *Government Official, England*
%British Embassy, 3100 Massachusetts Ave NW, Washington, DC 20008

Wright, Paul E *Businessman*
%Fairchild Industries, Dulles Airport, 300 W Service Rd, Chantilly, VA 22021

Wright, Robert C *Television Executive*
%National Broadcasting Co, 30 Rockefeller Plz, New York, NY 10020

Wright, Robert F *Businessman*
%Ameralda Hess Corp, 1185 Ave of Americas, New York, NY 10036

Wright, Robin *Actress, Model*
PO Box 2630, Malibu, CA 90265

Wright, Teresa *Actress*
19 W 44th St, #1500, New York, NY 10036

Wright, V Orville *Businessman*
%MCI Communications Corp, 1133 19th St NW, Washington, DC 20036

Wrighton, Mark S *Chemist*
%Massachusetts Institute of Technology, Chemistry Dept, Cambridge, MA 02139

Wrightson, Bernie *Diver*
924 Birch Ave, Escondido, CA 92027

Wrigley, William *Businessman*
%William Wrigley Jr Co, 410 N Michigan Ave, Chicago, IL 60611

Wriston, Walter B *Financier*
%Citicorp, 399 Park Ave, New York, NY 10043

Wszola, Jacek *Track Athlete*
Ul Chrzanowskiego 7 m 70, 04-381, Warsaw, Poland

Wu Cheng-Chung, John B Cardinal *Religious Leader*
%Catholic Diocese Center, 16 Caine Rd, Hong Kong

Wu Xiuqan *Government Official, China*
%Ministry of Foreign Affairs, Beijing, China

Wu, Chien-Shiung *Physicist*
15 Claremont Ave, New York, NY 10027

Wu-Yi Hsiang *Topologist*
%University of California, Mathematics Dept, Berkeley, CA 94720

WuDunn, Sheryl *Journalist*
%New York Times, 229 W 43rd St, New York, NY 10036

Wulff, Kai *Actor*
%Barr Agency, PO Box 69590, Los Angeles, CA 90069

Wunderlich, Paul *Artist*
Haynstrasse 2, 2000 Hamburg 20, Germany

Wuorinen, Charles *Composer*
%Howard Stokar Mgmt, 870 West End Ave, New York, NY 10025

Wurster, William *Architect*
1459 Greenwood Terr, Berkeley, CA 94708

Wussler, Bob *Television Executive*
%Comsat Video Enterprises, 950 L'Enfant Plz SW, Washington, DC 20024

Wyatt, Jane *Actress*
651 Siena Way, Los Angeles, CA 90024

Wyatt, Joe B *Educator*
%Vanderbilt University, President's Office, Nashville, TN 37240

Wyatt, Katy Rodolph *Skier*
3824 Golf Ln, Las Vegas, NV 89108

Wyatt, Oscar S, Jr *Businessman*
%Coastal Corp, 9 Greenway Plz, Houston, TX 77046

Wyatt, Whit *Baseball Player*
Box 56, Buchanan, GA 30113

Wyche, Sam *Football Coach*
%Tampa Bay Buccaneers, 1 Buccaneer Pl, Tampa, FL 33607

Wyckoff, Ralph W G *Physicist*
%Duvall Corp, 4715 E Fort Lowell Rd, Tucson, AZ 85712

Wycoff, Robert E *Businessman*
%Atlantic Richfield Co, 515 S Flower St, Los Angeles, CA 90071

Wyden, Ronald L *Representative, OR*
%House of Representatives, Washington, DC 20515

Wyeth, Andrew *Artist*
%General Delivery, Chadds Ford, PA 19317

Wyeth, James Browning *Artist*
%General Delivery, Chadds Ford, PA 19317

Wyeth, Willard H *Businessman*
%Provident Life & Accident Insurance, Fountain Sq, Chattanooga, TN 37402

Wyle, Frank *Businessman*
%Wyle Laboratories, 128 Maryland St, El Segundo, CA 90245

Wyler, Gretchen *Actress*
15115 Weddington St, Van Nuys, CA 91411

Wylie, Chalmers P *Representative, OH*
%House of Representatives, Washington, DC 20515

Wylie, Laurence William *Educator*
997 Memorial Dr, Cambridge, MA 02138

Wyman, James T *Businessman*
%Super Valu Stores, 11840 Valley View Rd, Eden Prairie, MN 55344

Wyman, Jane *Actress*
PO Box 540148, Orlando, FL 32854

Wyman, Louis C *Senator, NH; Judge*
121 Shaw St, Manchester, NH 03104

Wymore, Patrice *Actress*
Port Antonio, Jamaica, British West Indies

Wynbrandt, James *Radio Executive*
%Progressive Radio Network, 321 Ruder Ave, Bronx, NY 10451

Wynder, E L *Internist*
Twin Chimneys, 50 Revolutionary Rd, Scarborough, NY 10510

Wyner, George *Actor*
3450 Laurie Pl, Studio City, CA 91604

Wynette, Tammy *Singer*
1222 16th Ave S, Nashville, TN 37203

Wynn, Early *Baseball Player*
525 Bayview Pkwy, PO Box 218, Nokomis, FL 33551

Wynn, Si Richard *Businessman*
%Helene Curtis Industries, 325 N Wells St, Chicago, IL 60610

Wynn, Stephen A *Businessman*
%Mirage Hotel & Casino, 3400 Las Vegas Ave S, Las Vegas, NV 89109

Wynn, William H *Labor Leader*
%Food & Commercial Workers Union, 1775 "K" St NW, Washington, DC 20006

Wynter, Dana *Actress*
9206 Monte Mar Dr, Los Angeles, CA 90035

Wyse, Hank *Baseball Player*
1133 SE 14th St, Pryor, OK 74361

Wysocki, Charles *Artist*
PO Box 441, Cedar Glen, CA 92321

X-Y

Xenakis – Yarborough

Xenakis, Iannis *Composer, Architect, Engineer*
9 Rue Chaptal, 75009 Paris, France

Yaeger, Andrea *Tennis Player*
%General Delivery, Lincolnshire, IL 60015

Yagi, Yasuhiro *Businessman*
%Kawasaki Steel Corp, 2-3 Uchisaiwaicho, Chiyodaku, Tokyo, Japan

Yago, Bernard Cardinal *Religious Leader*
Arceveche, Ave Jean-Paul II, 01 BP 1287, Abidjan 01, Ivory Coast

Yalow, Rosalyn S *Nobel Medicine Laureate*
130 W Kingsbridge Rd, Bronx, NY 10468

Yamada, Eiichi *Businessman*
%Citizen Watch Co, 2-1-1 Nishi, Shinjulu, Tokyo 160, Japan

Yamada, Hajime *Financier*
%Mitsubishi Bank, 2-7-1 Marunouchi, Chiyodaku, Tokyo 100, Japan

Yamada, Osamu (Sam) *Financier*
%Bank of California, 400 California St, San Francisco, CA 94104

Yamaguchi, Yoshio *Financier*
%Yasuda Trust & Banking Co, 1-2-1 Tarsu, Chuoku, Tokyo 103, Japan

Yamamoto, Kichibei *Businessman*
%Shiseido Co, 7-5-5 Ginza, Chuoku, Tokyo 104, Japan

Yamamoto, Takuma *Businessman*
%Fujitsu Ltd, 2-6-1 Marunouchi, Chiyodaku, Tokyo, Japan

Yamamoto, Yoichi *Businessman*
%Snow Brand Milk Products, 13 Honshiocho, Shinjuku, Tokyo 160, Japan

Yamanaka, Seiichiro *Financier*
%Mitsui Trust & Banking Ltd, 2-1-1 Nihonbashi, Muromachi, Tokyo 103, Japan

Yamanaka, Tetsuo *Financier*
%Kyowa Bank, 1-1-2 Otemachi, Chiyodaku, Tokyo 100, Japan

Yamanaka, Tsuyoshi *Swimmer*
6-10-33-212 Akasaka, Minatoku, Tokyo, Japan

Yamani, Shaikh Ahmed Zaki *Government Official, Saudi Arabia*
General Delivery, Chermignon nr Crans-Montana, Valais, Switzerland

Yamano, Tanematsu *Businessman*
%Rengo Co, 4-18 Hiranomuchi, Higashiku, Osaka 541, Japan

Yamaoka, Seigen H *Religious Leader*
%Buddhist Churches of America, 1710 Octavia St, San Francisco, CA 94109

Yamasaki, Yoshiki *Businessman*
%Mazda Motor Corp, 3-1 Fuchacho-Shinchi, Akigun, Hiroshima, Japan

Yamashita, Hideaki *Businessman*
%Ashai Glass Co, 2-1-2 Marunouchi, Chiyodaku, Tokyo 100, Japan

Yamashita, Isamu *Businessman*
%Mitsui Engineering & Shipbuilding, 5-6-4 Tsukiji, Tokyo 104, Japan

Yamashita, Toshihiko *Businessman*
%Matsushita Electric Industrial, 1006 Kadoma City, Osaka 571, Japan

Yamazaki, Rokuya *Businessman*
%Citizen Watch Co, 2-1-1 Nishi-Shinjuku, Shinjuku, Tokyo 160, Japan

Yancey, Bert *Golfer*
%Professional Golf Assn, Box 109601, Palm Beach Gardens, FL 33410

Yancy, Emily *Actress*
%Henderson/Hogan Agency, 247 S Beverly Dr, #102, Beverly Hills, CA 90210

Yang Dezhi *Army General, China*
%General Staff, Liberation Army, Beijing, China

Yang Shangkun *President, China*
%National People's Congress, Beijing, China

Yang, Chen Ning *Nobel Physics Laureate*
%State University of New York, Physics Dept, Stony Brook, NY 11794

Yankovic, (Weird) Al *Comedian*
925 Westmount Dr, Los Angeles, CA 90069

Yankovic, Frankie *Accordianist*
%Cleveland International Records, 51 W 52nd St, New York, NY 10019

Yannas, I V *Mechanical Engineer, Medical Researcher*
%Massachusetts Institute of Technology, Engineering School, Cambridge, MA 02139

Yanofsky, Charles *Biologist*
725 Mayfield Ave, Stanford, CA 94305

Yarborough, Cale *Auto Racing Driver*
724 Scott Dr, Fredrocksburg, VA 22405

Yarborough, Ralph W *Senator, TX*
721 Brown Bldg, W 8th & Colorado, Austin, TX 78701

Yarbrough, Glenn *Singer (Limelighters)*
2835 Woodstock Ave, Los Angeles, CA 90046

Yardley, George *Basketball Player*
%George Yardley Co, 18401 Mt Langley, Fountain Valley, CA 92708

Yariv, Aharon *Army General*
20 Rimon St, Neve Magen, Ramat Hasharon, Israel

Yarmolinsky, Adam *Government Official, Attorney*
3307 Highland Pl NW, Washington, DC 20008

Yarnell, Kenneth A, Jr *Businessman*
%Primerica Corp, PO Box 3610, Greenwich, CT 06838

Yarnell, Lorene *Mime (Shields & Yarnell)*
9220 Sunset Blvd, #306, Los Angeles, CA 90069

Yarrow, Peter *Singer (Peter, Paul & Mary)*
27 W 67th St, #5-E, New York, NY 10023

Yary, Ron *Football Player*
18 Kenilworth Dr, Cresskill, NJ 07626

Yasui, Tadashi *Financier*
%Mitsubishi Trust & Banking, 4-5 Marunouchi, Tokyo 100, Japan

Yates, Cassie *Actress*
%Susan Smith Assoc, 121 N San Vicente Blvd, Beverly Hills, CA 90211

Yates, Peter *Movie Director*
%Chasin Agency, 190 N Canon Dr, #201, Beverly Hills, CA 90210

Yates, Richard *Writer*
%University of Southern California, English Dept, Los Angeles, CA 90089

Yates, Ronald W *Air Force General*
Comdr, Air Force Systems Command, Andrews Air Force Base, Washington, DC 20334

Yates, Sidney R *Representative, IL*
%House of Representatives, Washington, DC 20515

Yatron, Gus *Representative, PA*
1908 Hessian Rd, Reading, PA 19602

Yauch, Adam *Singer (Beastie Boys)*
%Rush Productions, 1133 Broadway, New York, NY 10010

Yawkey, Jean R *Baseball Executive*
%Boston Red Sox, 24 Yawkey Way, Boston, MA 21218

Yeager, Charles E *Test Pilot*
PO Box 128, Cedar Ridge, CA 95924

Yeager, Jeana *Experimental Airplane Pilot*
%Voyager Aircraft Inc, Mojave Airport, Hangar 77, Mojave, CA 93501

Yearwood, Trisha *Singer*
%MCA Records, 70 Universal City Plz, Universal City, CA 91608

Yegorov, Boris B *Cosmonaut*
141 160 Svyosdny Gorodok, Moskovskoi Oblasti, Potchta Kosmonavtov, Russia

Yeliseyev, Alexei *Cosmonaut*
141 160 Svyosdny Gorodok, Moskovskoi Oblasti, Potchta Kosmonavtov, Russia

Yeltsin, Boris N *President, Russia*
%Russian Central Committee, 4 Staraya Ploshchad, Moscow, Russia

Yeoman, Bill *Football Coach*
%University of Houston, Athletic Dept, Houston, TX 77204

Yeosock, John J *Army General*
DCG, Forces Command, CG, 3rd US Army, Fort McPherson, GA 30330

Yepremian, Garo *Football Player*
8821 SW 69th Ct, #A, Miami, FL 33156

Yerkovich, Anthony *Television Producer*
1802 Ashland Ave, Santa Monica, CA 90405

Yerxa, Charles T *Businessman*
%Sun-Diamond Growers, 1050 S Diamond St, Stockton, CA 95205

Yeston, Maury *Composer*
%Yale University, Music Dept, New Haven, CT 06520

Yetnikoff, Walter *Record Company Executive*
%CBS/Records Group, 51 W 52nd St, New York, NY 10019

Yeutter, Clayton *Secretary, Agriculture*
%White House, 1600 Pennsylvania Ave NW, Washington, DC 20500

Yevtushenko, Yevgeniy *Poet*
%Union of Writers, Ul Vorovskogo 52, Moscow, Russia

Y

Yingling – Young

Yingling, William E, III *Businessman*
%Thrifty Corp, 5051 Rodeo Rd, Los Angeles, CA 90016

Yoakam, Dwight *Singer*
%Dwight Yoakam Tours, 6363 Sunset Blvd, #712, Los Angeles, CA 90028

Yochum, Leo W *Businessman*
%Westinghouse Electric Corp, Gateway Ctr, Pittsburgh, PA 15222

Yock, Robert J *Judge*
%US Claims Court, 717 Madison Pl NW, Washington, DC 20005

Yoder, Hatten Schuyler, Jr *Petrologist*
%Carnegie Institution, Geophysical Laboratory, Washington, DC 20008

Yoken, Mel *Writer*
261 Carroll St, New Bedford, MA 02740

Yokoyama, Soichi *Financier*
%Bank of Tokyo, 6-3 Nihombashi, Hongokucho, Chuoku, Tokyo 103, Japan

Yontz, Kenneth F *Businessman*
%Sybron Corp, Park 80 West, Plaza I, Saddle Brook, NJ 07662

York, Dick *Actor*
PO Box 499, Rockford, MI 49341

York, Francine *Actress*
%William Carroll Agency, 120 S Victory Blvd, #104, Burbank, CA 91501

York, Herbert F *Physicist*
6110 Camino de la Costa, La Jolla, CA 92037

York, Michael *Actor*
9100 Cordell Dr, Los Angeles, CA 90069

York, Michael M *Journalist*
%Lexington Herald-Leader, Main & Midland, Lexington, KY 40507

York, Susannah *Actress*
%International Creative Mgmt, 388/396 Oxford St, London W1, England

York, W Thomas *Businessman*
%AMF Inc, 777 Westchester Ave, White Plains, NY 10604

Yorkin, Alan (Bud) *Movie Producer, Director*
124 Delfern Dr, Los Angeles, CA 90024

Yorty, Samuel W *Mayor*
320 N Vermont Ave, Los Angeles, CA 90004

Yorzyk, William *Swimmer*
417 Forest Hills Rd, Springfield, MA 01128

Yoshikuni, Jiro *Financier*
%Bank of Yokohama, 5-47 Honcho, Nakaku, Yokohoma 231, Japan

Yoshimura, Kanbei *Financier*
%Long-Term Credit Bank of Japan, 1-2-4 Otemachi, Tokyo 100, Japan

Yoshitoshi, Kazuo *Businessman*
%Shionogi & Co, 12 Doshomachi Sanchome, Higashiku, Osaka 541, Japan

Yoshiyama, Hirokichi *Businessman*
%Hitachi Ltd, 1-5-1 Marunouchi, Chiyodaku, Tokyo 100, Japan

Yoshizawa, Takeshi *Businessman*
%NTN Toyo Bearing Co, 3-17 Kyomachibor, Nishiku, Osaka 500, Japan

Yost, Eddie *Baseball Player*
48 Oak Ridge Rd, Wellesley, MA 02181

Yost, Paul A, Jr *Coast Guard Admiral*
%Commandant's Office, US Coast Guard, Washington, DC 20593

Yothers, Tina *Actress*
%Dale Garrick Agency, 8831 Sunset Blvd, #402, Los Angeles, CA 90069

Youman, Roger *Editor*
%TV Guide Magazine, 100 Matsonford Rd, Radnor, PA 19088

Younce, Len *Football Player*
300 S River St, Enterprise, OK 97828

Young, Alan *Actor*
33872 Barcelona Pl, Dana Point, CA 92629

Young, Andrew *Mayor; Ambassador to UN*
%Mayor's Office, City Hall, 68 Mitchell St SW, Atlanta, GA 30303

Young, Bert *Actor*
324 S Spaulding Dr, Beverly Hills, CA 90212

Young, C W (Bill) *Representative, FL*
%House of Representatives, Washington, DC 20515

Young, Charles *Entertainment Executive*
%Fox Television, 5746 Sunset Blvd, Los Angeles, CA 90028

Young, Charles E *Educator*
%University of California, Chancellor's Office, Los Angeles, CA 90024

Young, Coleman A *Mayor*
%Mayor's Office, 2 Woodward Ave, Detroit, MI 48226

Young, Conrad S *Businessman*
%United of Omaha Life Insurance, Mutual of Omaha Plz, Omaha, NE 68175

Young, Dean *Cartoonist (Blondie)*
%King Features Syndicate, 235 E 45th St, New York, NY 10017

Young, Donald E *Businessman*
%Unisys Corp, Burroughs Pl, Detroit, MI 48232

Young, Donald E *Representative, AK*
PO Box 119, Fort Yukon, AK 99740

Young, Donna Caponi *Golfer*
%Ladies Professional Golf Assn, 2570 Volusia Ave, #B, Daytona Beach, FL 32114

Young, Faron *Singer*
%Tessier Mgmt, 505 Canyon Pass, Madison, TN 37115

Young, Frank E *Research Scientist, Government Official*
%Health & Human Services Dept, 200 Independence Ave SW, Washington, DC 20201

Young, Fredd *Football Player*
%Indianapolis Colts, 7001 W 56th St, Indianapolis, IN 46254

Young, Freddie *Cinematographer*
3 Roehampton Close, London SW15 5LU, England

Young, George *Track Athlete*
Rt 1, Box 479, Casa Grande, AZ 85222

Young, Gerald O *Vietnam War Air Force Hero (CMH)*
317 Eden Rd, Anacortes, WA 98221

Young, J Warren *Publisher*
%Boys Life Magazine, 1325 Walnut Hill Rd, Irving, TX 75062

Young, Jerry *Religious Leader*
%Grace Brethren Church Fellowship, 855 Trunbull St, Delona, FL 32725

Young, Jim *Football Coach*
%US Military Academy, Athletic Dept, West Point, NY 10966

Young, John A *Businessman*
%Hewlett-Packard Co, 3000 Hanover St, Palo Alto, CA 94304

Young, John W *Astronaut*
%NASA, Johnson Space Ctr, Houston, TX 77058

Young, John Zachary *Zoologist*
The Crossroads, Brill, Bucks HP18 9TL, England

Young, Lewis H *Editor*
%Business Week Magazine, 1221 Ave of Americas, New York, NY 10020

Young, Loretta *Actress*
1705 Ambassador Dr, Beverly Hills, CA 90210

Young, Marguerite *Writer*
375 Bleecker St, New York, NY 10014

Young, Martin D *Parasitologist*
8421 NW 4th Pl, Gainesville, FL 32601

Young, Otis *Actor*
6716 Zumirez Dr, Malibu, CA 90265

Young, Richard S *Space Administrator, Educator*
200 Douglas Pl, Mount Vernon, NY 10552

Young, Robert *Actor*
31589 Saddletree Dr, Westlake Village, CA 91361

Young, Robert A *Representative, MO*
12248 Turkey Creek Ct, Marilyn Heights, MO 63043

Young, Robert A, III *Businessman*
%Arkansas Best Corp, 1000 S 21st St, Fort Smith, AK 72901

Young, Sean *Actress*
300 Mercer St, #7-E, New York, NY 10003

Young, Sheila *Speed Skater*
PO Box 176, Pewaukee, WI 53027

Young, Terence *Movie Director*
61 Eaton Sq, London SW1, England

Young, Tom *Basketball Coach*
%Old Dominion University, Athletic Dept, Norfolk, VA 23508

Young, William Allen *Actor*
%Artists Agency, 10000 Santa Monica Blvd, #305, Los Angeles, CA 90067

Y

Young-Herries – Yzerman

Young-Herries, Michael *Financier*
%Royal Bank of Scotland, 36 St Andrew Sq, Edinburgh EH2 2YB, Scotland

Youngblood, Jack *Football Player, Sportscaster*
%Los Angeles Rams, 2327 W Lincoln Ave, Anaheim, CA 92801

Youngblood, John L *Businessman*
%Kollmorgen Corp, 10 Mill Pond Ln, Simsbury, CT 06070

Younger, K G *Businessman*
%Carolina Freight Corp, North Carolina Hwy 150 E, Cherryville, NC 28021

Younger, Paul (Tank) *Football Player*
%Los Angeles Rams, 2327 W Lincoln Ave, Anaheim, CA 92801

Youngerman, Jack *Artist*
%Washburn Gallery, 41 E 57th St, New York, NY 10022

Youngman, Henny *Comedian*
77 W 55th St, New York, NY 10019

Yount, Robin *Baseball Player*
5010 E Shea Blvd, D-200, Scottsdale, AZ 85254

Yow, Kay *Basketball Coach*
%North Carolina State University, Athletic Dept, Raleigh, NC 27695

Yu Chuanyong *Architect*
%Urban & Rural Construction Committee, Weihai, China

Yu Kuo-Hwa *Financier*
%Central Bank of China, 2 Roosevelt Rd, Section 1, Taipei, Taiwan

Yunich, David L *Businessman*
Five Birches, 26 Cooper Rd, Scarsdale, NY 10583

Yunick, Smokey *Auto Racing Builder*
957 N Beach St, Daytona Beach, FL 32017

Yunis, Jorge J *Cancer Researcher*
%University of Minnesota, Medical School, Minneapolis, MN 55455

Yzerman, Steve *Hockey Player*
%Detroit Red Wings, 600 Civic Center Dr, Detroit, MI 48226

Zabaleta, Nicanor *Concert Harpist*
%Mariedi Anders Artists Mgmt, 535 El Camino Del Mar St, San Francisco, CA 94121

Zaban, Erwin *Businessman*
%National Service Industries, 1180 Peachtree St NE, Atlanta, GA 30309

Zabic, Walter C *Businessman*
%Cubic Corp, 9333 Balboa Ave, San Diego, CA 92123

Zabic, Walter J *Businessman*
%Cubic Corp, 9333 Balboa Ave, San Diego, CA 92123

Zaborowski, Robert R J M *Religious Leader*
%Mariavite Old Catholic Church, 2803 10th St, Wynadotte, MI 48192

Zachara, Jan *Boxer*
Sladkovicova 13, 018 51 Nova Dubnica, Czechoslovakia

Zacharias, Donald W *Educator*
%Mississippi State University, President's Office, Mississippi State, MS 39762

Zachary, Frank *Editor*
%Town & Country Magazine, 1700 Broadway, New York, NY 10019

Zadora, Pia *Singer, Actress*
418 Robert Ln, Beverly Hills, CA 90210

Zaentz, Saul *Movie Producer*
%Saul Zaentz Co, 2600 10th St, Berkeley, CA 94710

Zaffaroni, Alejandro C *Biochemist*
%Alza Corp, 950 Page Mill Rd, Palo Alto, CA 94304

Zahn, Geoff *Baseball Player*
26004 Moreno Dr, Valencia, CA 91355

Zahn, Joachim *Businessman*
%Motoren-Und Turbinen Union, 8000 Munich 50, Germany

Zahn, Paula *Commentator*
%CBS-TV, News Dept, 51 W 52nd St, New York, NY 10019

Zahn, Wayne *Bowler*
%Professional Bowlers Assn, 1720 Merriman Rd, Akron, OH 44313

Zaklinsky, Konstantin *Ballet Dancer*
%Kirov Ballet Theatre, 1 Ploshchad Iskusstv, St Petersburg, Russia

Zale, Tony *Boxer*
3001 S King Dr, #809, Chicago, IL 60616

Zamba, Frieda *Surfboard Athlete*
2706 S Central Ave, Flagler Beach, FL 32036

Zamecnik, Paul C *Physician*
%Worcester Foundation, 22 Maple, Shrewsbury, MA 01545

Zanuck, Lili Fini *Movie Producer, Director*
%Zanuck Co, 202 N Canon Dr, Beverly Hills, CA 90210

Zanuck, Richard D *Movie Producer*
%Zanuck Co, 202 N Canon Dr, Beverly Hills, CA 90210

Zanussi, Krzysztof *Movie Director*
Kaniowska 114, 01-529, Warsaw, Poland

Zapata, Carmen *Actress*
6107 Ethel Ave, Van Nuys, CA 91406

Zapf, Hermann *Book, Type Designer*
1 Lomb Memorial Dr, Rochester, NY 14623

Zappa, Dweezil *Actor*
PO Box 5265, North Hollywood, CA 91616

Zappa, Frank *Singer*
7885 Woodrow Wilson Dr, Los Angeles, CA 90046

Zappa, Moon *Actress*
%Agency for Performing Arts, 9000 Sunset Blvd, #1200, Los Angeles, CA 90069

Zarb, Frank G *Government Official, Financier*
%Smith Barney Harris Upham Co, 1345 Ave of Americas, New York, NY 10105

Zariski, Oscar *Mathematician*
122 Sewall Ave, Brookline, MA 02146

Zarkhi, Aleksandr *Movie Director*
%Mosfilm Studio, 1 Mosfilmovskaya Ul, Moscow, Russia

Zarnas, August *Football Player*
850 Jennings St, Bethlehem, PA 18017

Zasloff, Michael *Geneticist*
%National Child Health Institute, 9000 Rockville Pike, Bethesda, MD 20205

Zaslow, Jeff *Columnist*
%Chicago Sun-Times, 401 N Wabash, Chicago, IL 60611

Z

Zatopek, Emil — *Track Athlete*
Nad Kazankov 3, 170 00 Prague 7, Czechslovakia

Zatopkova, Dana — *Track Athlete*
Troja, 17100 Prague 7, Czechoslovakia

Zawoluk, Robert — *Basketball Player*
%General Delivery, Mineola, NY 11501

Zayak, Elaine — *Figure Skater*
298 McHenry Dr, Paramus, NJ 07652

Zdatny, Benjamin — *Businessman*
%Di Giorgio Corp, 1 Maritime Plz, San Francisco, CA 94111

Zeamer, Jay — *WW II Army Air Corps Hero (MOH)*
PO Box 602, Boothbay Harbor, ME 04538

Zech, Lando — *Government Official*
%Nuclear Regulatory Commission, 1717 "H" St NW, Washington, DC 20555

Zeffirelli, Franco — *Movie Director*
Via Pignatelli 448, 00194 Rome, Italy

Zeien, Alfred M — *Businessman*
%Gillette Co, Prudential Tower, Boston, MA 02199

Zeitlin, Zvi — *Concert Pianist*
204 Warren Ave, Rochester, NY 14618

Zeliff, Bill — *Representative, NH*
%House of Representatives, Washington, DC 20515

Zell, Samuel — *Businessman*
%Itel Corp, 1 Embarcadero Ctr, San Francisco, CA 94111

Zellars, John B — *Financier*
%Georgia Federal Bank, 20 Marietta St NW, Atlanta, GA 30303

Zellerbach, William J — *Businessman*
%Zellerbach Paper Co, 55 Hawthorne St, San Francisco, CA 94120

Zeman, Jacklyn — *Actress*
12024 Sarah St, Studio City, CA 91607

Zeman, Karel — *Movie Director*
%Film Studio/Kudlov, Gottwaldov, Czechoslovakia

Zemke, E Joseph — *Businessman*
%Amdahl Corp, 1250 E Arques Ave, Sunnyvale, CA 94088

Zendejas, Tony — *Football Player*
%Houston Oilers, PO Box 1516, Houston, TX 77251

Zerbe, Anthony — *Actor*
%Susan Smith Assoc, 121 N San Vicente Blvd, Beverly Hills, CA 90211

Zernial, Gus — *Baseball Player*
5902 E Belmont Ave, Fresno, CA 93727

Zetlin, Lev — *Civil Engineer*
6 Fairway Dr, Manhasset, NY 11030

Zetterling, Mai — *Director, Actress*
%Douglas Rae Mgmt, 20 Charing Cross Rd, London W1, England

Zevon, Warren — *Singer*
1880 Century Park East, #900, Los Angeles, CA 90067

Zhambyn Batmunkh — *Chairman of Presidium, Mongolia*
%Government Palace, Ulan Bator, Mongolia

Zhang Aiping — *Government Official, China*
%Ministry of Defense, State Council, Beijing, China

Zhao Ziyang — *Prime Minister, China*
%State Council, Beijing, China

Zhelev, Zhelyu — *President, Bulgaria*
%President's Office, Sofia, Bulgaria

Zhikov, Todor — *President, Bulgaria*
Durzhaven Suvet, Sofia, Bulgaria

Zholobov, Vitali — *Cosmonaut*
141 160 Svyosdny Gorodok, Moskovskoi Oblasti, Potchta Kosmonavtov, Russia

Zhu Jianhua — *Track Athlete*
%Chinese Olympic Committee, 9 Tiyuguan Rd, Beijing, China

Ziegler, Henri A L — *Aviation Engineer, Businessman*
55 Blvd Lannes, 75116 Paris, France

Ziegler, Jack — *Cartoonist*
%New Yorker Magazine, 25 W 43rd St, New York, NY 10036

Ziegler, John — *Hockey Executive*
%National Hockey League, 650 5th Ave, #301, New York, NY 10019

Ziegler, Larry *Golfer*
6209 Dartmoor Ct, Orlando, FL 32819
Ziegler, Ronald L *Government Official, Journalist*
%National Assn of Chain Drug Stores, 413 N Lee St, Alexandria, VA 22314
Ziegler, William, III *Businessman*
%American Maize-Products Co, 41 Harbor Plaza Dr, Stamford, CT 06904
Ziemann, Sonja *Actress*
Niederdorfstrasse 10, 8032 Zurich, Switzerland
Ziff, William B *Publisher*
%Ziff-Davis Publishing Co, 1 Park Ave, New York, NY 10016
Zikes, Les *Bowler*
%Beverly Lanes, 8 S Beverly Ln, Arlington Heights, IL 60004
Zimbalist, Efrem, Jr *Actor*
4750 Encino Ave, Encino, CA 91316
Zimbalist, Stephanie *Actress*
%Triad Artists, 10100 Santa Monica Blvd, #1600, Los Angeles, CA 90067
Zimerman, Krystian *Concert Pianist*
%Deutsche Grammophon Records, 810 7th Ave, New York, NY 10019
Zimm, Bruno H *Chemist*
2605 Ellentown Rd, La Jolla, CA 92037
Zimmer, Dick *Representative, NJ*
%House of Representatives, Washington, DC 20515
Zimmer, Don *Baseball Manager*
10124 Yacht Club Dr, St Petersburg, FL 33706
Zimmer, William L, III *Businessman*
%A H Robins Co, 1407 Cummings Dr, Richmond, VA 23261
Zimmerman, Charles J *Businessman*
70 Mohawk Dr, West Hartford, CT 06117
Zimmerman, Gary *Football Player*
%Minnesota Vikings, 9520 Vikings Dr, Eden Prairie, MN 55344
Zimmerman, John T *Neuroscientist*
%University of Colorado, Medical School, Denver, CO 80202
Zimmerman, Kent *Publisher*
%Friendly Exchange Magazine, 1999 Shepard Rd, St Paul, MN 55116
Zimmerman, Mary Beth *Golfer*
%Ladies Professional Golf Assn, 2570 Volusia Ave, #B, Daytona Beach, FL 32114
Zimmerman, Raymond *Businessman*
%Service Merchandise Co, 2968 Foster Creighton Dr, Nashville, TN 37204
Zimmerman, Richard A *Businessman*
%Hershey Foods Corp, 100 Mansion Rd E, Hershey, PA 17003
Zindel, Paul *Playwright*
%Harper & Row, 10 E 53rd St, New York, NY 10022
Zinder, Norton D *Geneticist*
450 E 63rd St, New York, NY 10021
Zindler, Marvin *Commentator*
%KTRK-TV, News Dept, 3310 Bissonnet, Houston, TX 77005
Zinman, David *Conductor*
%Baltimore Symphony, 1212 Cathedral St, Baltimore, MD 21210
Zinnemann, Fred *Movie Director*
128 Mount St, London W1, England
Zion, Roger H *Representative, IN*
834 Plaza Dr, Evansville, IN 47715
Zmed, Adrian *Actor*
8370 Wilshire Blvd, #310, Beverly Hills, CA 90211
Zoeller, Frank (Fuzzy) *Golfer*
12 Bellewood Ct, New Albany, IN 47150
Zoff, Dino *Soccer Player*
%Juventus F C, Galleria S Federico, 10121 Torino, Italy
Zoran *Fashion Designer*
214 Sullivan St, New York, NY 10012
Zorich, Chris *Football Player*
%Chicago Bears, 250 N Washington Rd, Lake Forest, IL 60045
Zorich, Louis *Actor*
222 Upper Montclair, Upper Montclair, NJ 07043
Zorina, Vera *Actress, Ballet Dancer*
10 Gracie Sq, New York, NY 10028

Z

Zorn - Zykes

Zorn, Jim *Football Player, Coach*
%Utah State University, Athletic Dept, Logan, UT 84322

Zorrilla, Alberto *Swimmer*
580 Park Ave, New York, NY 10021

Zoungrana, Paul Cardinal *Religious Leader*
Archeveche, BP 1472, Ouagadougou, Burkina Faso

Zschau, Ed *Representative, CA; Businessman*
%Censtor Corp, 530 Race, San Jose, CA 95126

Zsigmond, Vilmos *Cinematograper*
%Smith-Gosnell-Nicholson, 1515 Palisades Dr, #N, Pacific Palisades, CA 90272

Zubrod, C Gordon *Physician*
177 Ocean Lane Dr, Key Biscayne, FL 33149

Zucaro, A C *Businessman*
%Old Republic International Corp, 307 N Michigan Ave, Chicago, IL 60601

Zucker, Jerry *Movie Director*
481 Denslow Ave, Los Angeles, CA 90049

Zuckerman of Burnham Thorpe, Solly *Anatomist*
%University of East Anglia, Norwich NR4 7TJ, England

Zuckerman, Mortimer B *Publisher*
%Boston Properties, 599 Lexington Ave, New York, NY 10022

Zuckert, Bill *Actor*
%Allen Goldstein Assoc, 5015 Lemona Ave, Sherman Oaks, CA 91423

Zuckert, Donald M *Businessman*
%Ted Bates Co, 1515 Broadway, New York, NY 10036

Zudov, Vyachselav *Cosmonaut*
141 160 Svyosdny Gorodok, Moskovskoi Oblasti, Potchta Kosmonavtov, Russia

Zukerman, Eugenia *Concert Flutist*
%International Creative Mgmt, 40 W 57th St, New York, NY 10019

Zukerman, Pinchas *Concert Violinist, Conductor*
173 Riverside Dr, New York, NY 10024

Zukofsky, Paul *Concert Violinist*
%University of Southern California, Schoenberg Institute, Los Angeles, CA 90089

Zulu, Alphaeus H *Religious Leader*
PO Box 177, Edendale, Natal 4505, South Africa

ZumFelde, Donald B *Financier*
%Nafco Financial Grp, 5801 Pelican Bay Blvd, Naples, FL 33940

Zumwalt, Elmo R, Jr *Navy Admiral*
1500 Wilson Blvd, Arlington, VA 22209

Zuniga, Daphne *Actress*
PO Box 1249, White River Junction, VT 05001

Zur Loye, Dieter *Businessman*
%American Hoechst Corp, Rt 202-206 N, Somerville, NJ 08876

Zurbriggen, Pirmin *Skier*
%Hotel Larchenhof, 3905 Saas-Almagell, Switzerland

Zurn, David M *Businessman*
%Zurn Industries, 1 Zurn Pl, Erie, PA 16512

Zurn, James A *Businessman*
%Zurn Industries, 1 Zurn Pl, Erie, PA 16505

Zwanzig, Robert W *Chemical Physicist*
5314 Sangamore Rd, Bethesda, MD 20816

Zweig, George *Theoretical Physicist*
%California Institute of Technology, Lauritsen Laboratory, Pasadena, CA 91125

Zwerling, Darrell *Actor*
250 E 3rd St, New York, NY 10021

Zwick, Charles J *Financier*
%Southeast Banking Corp, 100 S Biscayne Blvd, Miami, FL 33131

Zwick, Edward M *Movie Director, Producer*
%Bedford Falls Productions, CBS/MTM Studios, 4024 Radford, Studio City, CA 91604

Zwick, Edward M *Movie Director, Producer*
%Skywalker Sound, 1861 S Bundy, #314, Los Angeles, CA 90025

Zwilich, Ellen Taaffe *Composer*
%Music Assoc of America, 224 King St, Englewood, NJ 07631

Zygmund, Antoni *Mathematician*
5420 East View Park, Chicago, IL 60615

Zykes, Les *Bowler*
%Professional Bowlers Assn, 1720 Merriman Rd, Akron, OH 44313

NECROLOGY

Abbott, Berenice	Photographer
Abdul Rahman Putra	President, Maylasia
Abe, Shintaro	Government Official, Japan
Ackerman, Harry S	Movie Producer
Akhromeyev, Sergei F	Army Marshal, USSR
Alcorn, H Meade, Jr	Government Official
Alexander, John	Opera Singer
Allen, George	Football Coach
Anderson, Carl D	Nobel Physics Laureate
Anderson, Judith	Actress
Appling, Luke	Baseball Player
Arden, Eve	Actress, Comedienne
Arpino, Giovanni	Writer
Arrau, Claudio	Concert Pianist
Arrupe, Pedro	Religious Leader, Activist
Arthur, Jean	Actress
Ashcroft, Peggy	Actress
Ashton, Frederick	Choreographer, Dancer
Athanasiadis-Novas, Georgios	Prime Minister, Greece
Auric, Georges	Composer
Axthelm, Pete	Columnist, Sportscaster
Bailey, Pearl	Singer
Ball, William	Actor, Theater Director
Ballard, Lucien	Cinematographer
Bancroft, Harding	Publisher, Diplomat
Bardeen, John	Nobel Physics Laureate
Barghoorn, Frederick C	Educator
Barrett, Charles (Red)	Baseball Player
Baruch, Andre	Entertainer
Bell, James (Cool Papa)	Baseball Player
Bellamy, Ralph	Actor
Bennett, Joan	Actress
Bere, James F	Businessman
Berghof, Herbert	Actor
Bernstein, Leonard	Conductor, Composer
Binns, Edward	Actor
Birch, A Francis	Geophysicist
Bixler, Dallas	Gymnast
Blakey, Art	Jazz Drummer
Bliss, Anthony A	Opera Executive, Attorney
Boardman, Eleanor	Actress
Boggs, Phil	Diver
Bolet, Jorge	Concert Pianist
Bolling, Richard W	Representative, MO
Boskovsky, Willi	Conductor
Brodie, Steve	Actor
Brown, Paul	Football Coach, Executive
Browne, Coral	Actress
Brownell, Samuel Miller	Educator
Brunet, Pierre	Figure Skater
Bunshaft, Gordon	Architect
Burch, Dean	Government Official
Busch, Niven	Writer
Calder, Alexander, Jr	Businessman
Capra, Frank	Movie Director, Producer
Carter, John B	Businessman
Carter, Manley L, Jr	Astronaut
Carvel, Tom	Businessman
Castle, William Bosworth	Educator
Caulfield, Joan	Actress
Chaikin, Sol C	Labor Leader
Chandler, A B (Happy)	Governor, KY
Charlap, E Paul	Businessman
Cherry, Wendell	Businessman
Chusmir, Janet	Editor
Cleveland, James	Singer, Songwriter
Clifton, Nat (Sweetwater)	Basketball Player
Cloud, Preston	Biogeologist
Coleman, James P	Governor, MS
Collins, LeRoy	Governor, FL
Combs, Bert T	Governor, KY
Conchon, Georges	Writer
Connelly, John F	Businessman
Conte, Silvio O	Representative, MA
Convy, Bert	Actor
Cooper, John Sherman	Senator, KY
Cooper, Walker	Baseball Player
Copland, Aaron	Composer
Coppola, Carmine	Composer
Cousins, Norman	Writer, Editor
Cramer, Roger (Doc)	Baseball Player
Crawford, John	Tennis Player
Crosby, John Campbell	Writer
Crown, Henry	Businessman
Cummings, Robert	Actor
Curtis, Ken	Actor
Dahl, Roald	Writer

Daly, John	Journalist
Danaher, John A	Senator, CT; Judge
Dante, Nicholas	Playwright
Dascoli, Frank	Baseball Umpire
Davis, Brad	Actor
Davis, Deane C	Governor, VT
Davis, Miles	Jazz Trumpeter
De L'Isle, Viscount	WW II Army Hero (VC)
De Lubac, Henri Cardinal	Religious Leader
De Witt, Lew	Singer, Songwriter
Dehner, John	Actor
Demy, Jacques	Movie Director
Dewhurst, Colleen	Actress
Di Giorgio, Robert J	Businessman
Dichter, Ernest	Psychologist
Dickey, John Sloan	Educator
Diehl, Walter F	Labor Leader
Dimitrios I	Religious Leader
Dixon, Willie	Singer, Songwriter
Dodd, Ed	Cartoonist
Doe, Samuel K	Head of State, Liberia
Donovan, Hedley W	Journalist
Dubbins, Don	Actor
Duff, Howard	Actor
Dunne, Irene	Actress
Dunnock, Mildred	Actress
Durocher, Leo	Baseball Player, Manager
Durrell, Lawrence	Writer
Durrenmatt, Friedrich	Writer
Edwards, Douglas	Commentator
Eggan, Fred Russell	Anthropologist
Elias, Taslim O	Judge
Elliott, Keith	WW II Army Hero (VC)
Elsasser, Walter M	Geophysicist
Etten, Nick	Baseball Player
Evers, Hoot	Baseball Player
Fanning, John H	Government Official
Fedeli, Frederick	Businessman
Fender, Leo	Inventor, Musician
Ferrer, Jose	Actor
Ferri, Roger	Architect
Fetzer, John E	Baseball Executive
Fildes, Robert A	Businessman
Fish, Hamilton	Football Player, Representative, NY
Flamson, Richard J, III	Financier
Fletcher, Gilbert H	Radiotherapist
Fletcher, James C	Space Administrator
Fodor, Eugene	Editor, Publisher
Fonssagrives, Lisa	Model
Fonteyn de Arias, Margot	Ballerina
Ford, Tennessee Ernie	Singer
Foxx, Redd	Comedian
Francescatti, Zino	Concert Violinist
Francisco, George J	Labor Leader
Franciscus, James	Actor
Frankovich, Mike J	Movie Producer
Freeman, James Cardinal	Religious Leader
Frisch, Max R	Writer, Architect
Fuller, Roy B	Writer, Poet
Gandhi, Rajiv	Prime Minister, India
Gann, Ernest	Writer
Garcia Robles, Alfonso	Nobel Peace Laureate
Geisel, Theodor S	Writer, Artist (Dr Seuss)
Getz, Stan	Jazz Saxophonist
Ginzburg, Natalia	Writer
Glover, Charles C	Editor
Gobel, George	Comedian
Gordis, Robert	Religious Leader
Goren, Charles	Bridge Expert
Gorkin, Jess	Editor
Graham, Bill	Musical Promoter
Graham, Martha	Dancer, Choreographer
Grange, Harold (Red)	Football Player
Greene, Graham	Writer
Gross, Chaim	Sculptor
Grosvenor, Melville Bell	Editor
Guthrie, A B, Jr	Writer
Hagen, John P	Astronomer
Haley, Alex	Writer
Hammer, Armand	Businessman
Harris, Harwell Hamilton	Architect
Hartley, Fred L	Businessman
Hay, Alexandre	International Official, Switzerland
Head, Howard	Ski, Tennis Equipment Designer
Heidelberger, Michael	Immunochemist
Hein, Mel	Football Player
Heinz, H John, III	Senator, PA
Hengsbach, Franz Cardinal	Religious Leader
Hobson, Howard A	Basketball Coach
Hofstadter, Robert	Nobel Physics Laureate
Hogan, Daniel E	Businessman

Hogan, Daniel E	Businessman
Hollaender, Alexander	Biophysicist
Holmes a Court, Robert	Businessman
Honda, Soichiro	Businessman
Hopper, Grace B M	Mathematician, Navy Admiral
Husak, Gustav	President, Czechoslovakia
Hyde-White, Wilfred	Actor
Imai, Tadashi	Movie Director
Irving, Robert A	Conductor, Concert Pianist
Irwin, James B	Astronaut
Jagger, Dean	Actor
Johnson, Bob	Hockey Coach, Executive
Johnson, Joseph E	Foundation Executive
Joyce, Eileen	Concert Pianist
Kaer, Morton	Football Player
Kahane, Meir	Religious Activist
Kaper, Bronislaw	Composer
Kaplan, Joseph	Physicist
Karasz, Arthur	Financier
Kaufman, Irving R	Judge
Kaye, Sylvia Fine	Lyricist, Composer
Kelberer, John J	Businessman
Keltner, Ken	Baseball Player
Kinski, Klaus	Actor
Kirk, Lisa	Singer, Actress
Kiviat, Abel	Track Athlete
Kliban, B(ruce)	Cartoonist
Klien, Walter	Concert Pianist
Knight, James L	Publisher
Knox, Seymour H, III	Financier, Art Patron, Hockey Executive
Kohler, Foy D	Diplomat
Kosinski, Jerzy	Writer
Kreisky, Bruno	Chancellor, Austria
Krenek, Ernst	Composer
Kulp, Nancy	Actress
Land, Edwin H	Businessman
Landon, Michael	Actor
Larkin, Felix E	Businessman
Larkin, Tippy	Boxer
Lauter, Harry	Actor
Le Duc Tho	Nobel Peace Laureate
Le Gallienne, Eva	Actress
Lean, David	Movie Director
Lefebvre, Marcel	Religious Leader
Leger, Paul Emile Cardinal	Religious Leader

LeMay, Curtis	Air Force General
Lewis, Richard	Opera Singer
Lewis, Robert Q	Comedian
Lewis, W Arthur	Nobel Economics Laureate
Lewis, W Bennett	Physicist
Liedtke, William C, Jr	Businessman
Lilly, Doris	Writer
Lobel, Arnold	Writer, Illustrator
Lockwood, Margaret	Actress
Long, Dale	Baseball Player
Lott, George M, Jr	Tennis Player
Luke, Keye	Actor
Luria, Salvador	Nobel Medicine Laureate
Lurie, Robert A	Baseball Executive
Lynch, Edward M	Labor Leader
Lynes, Russell	Editor, Author
Macioce, Thomas M	Businessman
Mackail, Dorothy	Actress
MacMurray, Fred	Actor
Manzu, Giacomo	Sculptor
Marble, Alice	Tennis Player
Martin, Kiel	Actor
Martin, Mary	Singer, Actress
Masursky, Harold	Geologist
Maw, Herbert B	Governor, UT
Maxwell, Robert	Publisher
Maytag, Lewis B	Businessman
Mazurki, Mike	Actor
McCone, John A	Director, C I A
McCrea, Joel	Actor
McIntire, John	Actor
McKay, Robert B	Attorney, Educator
McKissick, Floyd	Civil Rights Activist
McLaughlin, Emily	Actress
McMillan, Edwin	Nobel Chemistry Laureate
McNeely, E L	Businessman
Meany Gravis, Helen	Diver
Menninger, Karl A	Psychiatrist
Mercury, Freddie	Singer (Queen)
Michener, D Roland	Government Official, Canada
Miller, Edgar (Rip)	Football Player
Miller, Paul	Publisher
Milliken, Frank R	Businessman
Mirabito, Paul S	Businessman
Mockler, Colman M, Jr	Businessman
Mollenhoff, Clark R	Journalist

Moravia, Alberto	Writer
Morse, David A	International Official
Moses, Wally	Baseball Player
Motherwell, Robert	Artist
Muggeridge, Malcolm	Editor, Writer
Murray, Arthur	Dancer
Namuth, Hans	Photographer
Natwick, Grimm	Animator
Nelson, Dave	Football Coach
Nemerov, Howard	Poet
Netter, Frank H	Medical Artist
North, Alex	Composer
Nova, Lou	Boxer
Nsubuga, Emmanuel Cardinal	Religious Leader
O'Brien, Lawrence F	Postmaster General, Basketball Executive
O'Faolain, Sean	Writer
Olav V	King, Norway
Oosterbaan, Bennie	Football Player, Coach
Ormsby, Gary	Hot Rod Racing Driver
Page, Irvine H	Physician
Paley, Wiliam S	Communications Executive
Pan, Hermes	Choreographer
Pandit, Vijaya Lakshmi	Government Official, India
Pao, Yue-Kong	Businessman
Papp, Joseph	Theatre Producer, Director
Parks, Bert	Entertainer
Parr, Albert Eide	Oceanographer
Pasternak, Joseph	Movie Director, Producer
Perlman, Isadore	Chemist
Piazza, Ben	Actor
Pierce, Webb	Singer
Platten, Donald C	Financier
Porter, Eliot F	Photographer
Porter, Sylvia	Financial Columnist
Quillan, Eddie	Comedian
Quist, Adrian	Tennis Player
Racker, Efraim	Biochemist
Reasoner, Harry	Commentator
Reischauer, Edwin O	Historian, Diplomat
Remick, Lee	Actress
Revelle, Roger	Oceanographer
Revere, Ann	Actress
Revolta, Johnny	Golfer
Rice, J Gregory (Greg)	Track Athlete
Richardson, Tony	Movie, Stage Director
Riding Jackson, Laura	Writer
Ritt, Martin	Movie Director, Producer
Rizzo, Frank L	Mayor
Robinson, Earl	Composer, Singer
Rodale, Robert	Editor
Roddenberry, Gene	Television Producer
Roddis, Louis H, Jr	Naval Atomic Engineer
Rodriguez, Cleto L	WW II Army Hero (CMH)
Rolvaag, Karl F	Governor, MN
Roosevelt, James	Representative, CA
Rose, David	Composer
Rossi-Lemeni, Nicola	Opera Singer
Rubin, Alvin B	Judge
Rubin, Wladyslaw Cardinal	Religious Leader
Runnels, Pete	Baseball Player
Russell, John	Actor
Salazar Lopez, Jose Cardinal	Religious Leader
Salzman, Herbert	Diplomat, Businessman
Sansom, Art	Cartoonist
Sansone, Robert	Businessman
Schafer, Natalie	Actress
Schriner, David	Hockey Player
Schwartz, Marchmont	Football Player
Scott, Simon	Actor
Serkin, Rudolf	Concert Pianist
Seton, Anya	Writer
Shemin, David	Biochemist
Sherman, George	Movie Director
Shero, Fred	Hockey Coach
Shoemaker, Vaughn	Editorial Cartoonist
Short, Chris	Baseball Player
Siegel, Don	Movie Director
Singer, Isaac Bashevis	Nobel Literature Laureate
Sinkwich, Frank	Football Player
Siskind, Aaron	Artist, Photographer
Skinner, B F	Psychologist
Smith, Cladys (Jabbo)	Jazz Trumpeter
Smith, William French	Attorney General
Snelling, Richard A	Governor, VT
Soustelle, Jacques	Government Official, France
Sperti, George S	Engineer
St Jacques, Raymond	Actor
Staggers, Harley O	Representative, WV
Starcevich, Leslie T	WW II Army Hero (VC)
Starcevich, Max	Football Player
Stigler, George J	Nobel Economics Laureate

Stigler, George J	Nobel Economics Laureate
Stilwell, Richard G	Army General
Storey, June	Actress
Stratton, Samuel S	Representative, NY
Stravropoulos, George	Fashion Designer
Strout, Richard L	Journalist
Suits, Chauncey Guy	Physicist
Sunderland, Thomas E	Businessman
Swearer, Howard R	Educator
Tamayo, Rufino	Artist
Taylor, A J P	Historian, Journalist
Teague, Bertha	Basketball Coach
Thomas, Danny	Comedian
Thompson, John A (Cat)	Basketball Player
Thorkilsen, Harold	Businessman
Tierney, Gene	Actress
Tippet, Clark	Ballet Dancer
Tognazzi, Ugo	Actor
Toomey, Regis	Actor
Toor, Harold O	Businessman
Torgeson, Earl	Baseball Player
Tortelier, Paul	Concert Cellist
Tower, John G	Senator, TX
Tryon, Thomas	Writer, Actor
Tsedenbal, Yumjaagiyn	Chairman Mongolia
Urban, Jerome A	Surgeon, Oncologist
Van Alen, James H	Tennis Contributor
Vogler, Rich	Auto Racing Driver
Wagner, Robert F	Mayor; Diplomat
Walcha, Helmut	Concert Organist
Walters, Bucky (William H)	Baseball Player
Waters, Aaron C	Geologist
Weir, Ed	Football Player
Welensky, Roy	Prime Minister, Rhodesia
West, Dottie	Singer
White, David	Actor
White, Patrick	Nobel Literature Laureate
Williams, Carroll M	Biologist
Williams, Smallwood E	Religious Leader
Wilson, Angus	Writer
Wilson, Teddy	Jazz Pianist, Composer
Wolfe, Ian	Actor
Wright, Peter H	WW II Army Hero (VC)
Wulff, Lee	Fisherman
Yancey, Robert E	Businessman
Yerby, Frank	Writer
Zampa, Luigi	Movie Director

BIBLIOGRAPHY

OTHER REFERENCE SOURCES FOR CELEBRITIES, DIGNITARIES AND ORGANIZATIONS

Academy Players Directory, Academy of Motion Picture Arts & Sciences, 8949 Wilshire Blvd, Beverly Hills, CA 90211

International Dictionary of Films & Filmmakers, St James Press, 175 5th Ave, New York, NY 10010

African Who's Who, African Journal Ltd, Kirkman House, 54-A Tottenham Court Rd, London W1P 08T, England

Biographical Dictionary of Governors of the US, Meckler Publishing, Ferry Ln W, Westport, CT 06880

Biographical Dictionary of US Executive Branch, Greenwood Press, 51 Riverside Ave, Westport, CT 06880

Celebrity Access - The Directory, Celebrity Access Publications, 20 Sunnyside Ave., Mill Valley, CA 94941.

Christensen's Ultimate Movie, TV & Rock Directory, Cardiff-by-the Sea Publishing Co, 6065 Mission Gorge Rd, San Diego, CA 92120

Congressional Directory, Superintendent of Documents, US Government Printing Office, Washington, DC 20402

Contemporary Architects, St Martin's Press, 175 5th Ave, New York, NY 10010

Contemporary Designers, Gale Research Co, Book Tower, Detroit, MI 48226

Contemporary Theatre, Film & Television, Gale Research Co, Book Tower, Detroit, MI 48226

Corporate 1000, Washington Monitor, 1301 Pennsylvania Ave NW, Washington, DC 20004

Editor & Publisher International Yearbook, 575 Lexington Ave, New York, NY 10022

IMS/Ayer Directory, IMS Press, 426 Pennsylvania Ave, Fort Washington, PA 19034

International Who's Who, Europa Publications Ltd, 18 Bedford Sq, London WC1B 3JN, England

Kraks BlaBog, Nytorv 17, 1450 Copenhagen K, Denmark

Major Companies of the Far East, Graham & Trotman Ltd, Sterling House, 66 Wilton Rd, London SW1V 1DE, England

Major Companies of Europe, Graham & Trotman Ltd, Sterling House, 66 Wilton Rd, London SW1V 1DE, England

Martindale-Hubbell Law Directory, Reed Publishing, Summit, NJ 07902

U.S. Court Directory, Government Printing Office, Washington, DC 20401

U.S. Government Manual, National Archives & Records Service, General Services Administration, Washington, DC 20408

Who's Who, A & C Black Ltd, St Martin's Press, 175 5th Ave, New York, NY 10010

Who's Who in America, Marquis Who's Who, 200 E Ohio St, Chicago, IL 60611

Who's Who in American Art, R R Bowker Co, 1180 Ave of Americas, New York, NY 10036

Who's Who in American Politics, R R Bowker Co, 1180 Ave of Americas, New York, NY 10036

Who's Who in Canada, Global Press, 164 Commanden Blvd, Agincourt ON M1S 3C7, Canada

Who's Who in France, Editions Jacques Lafitte SA, 75008 Paris, France

Who's Who in Germany, Verlag AG Zurich, Germany

Who's Who in Israel, Bronfman Publishers Ltd, 82 Levinsky St, Tel Aviv 61010, Israel

Who's Who in Poland, Graphica Comense Srl, 22038 Taverreiro, Italy

Who's Who in Scandinavia, A Sutter Druckerei GmbH, 4300 Essen, Germany

Who's Who in Switzerland, Nagel Publishers, 5-5 bis de l'Orangeris, Geneva, Switzerland

Who's Who in the Theatre, Pitman Press, 39 Parker St, London WC2B 5PB, England

Who's Who in Washington, Tiber Reference Press, 4340 East-West Hwy, Bethesda, MD 20814

Writer's Directory, St James Press, 213 W Institute Pl, Chicago, IL 60610

ORDER CARD

THE V.I.P. ADDRESS BOOK

Associated Media Companies Ltd.

P.O. Box 10190

Marina del Rey, CA 90295-8864

Please send ____________________ copies of the 1992-93 V.I.P. ADDRESS BOOK at

$________________ each. Price includes shipping and handling costs.

Quantity orders are priced as follows:

1 copy	$89.95 each.
2-4 copies	$79.95 each.
5-12 copies	$75.46 each.
13-49 copies	$71.96 each.
50-99 copies	$63.70 each.
100 -199 copies	$58.47 each.
200 or more copies	$44.88 each

California residents add 7.5 percent for sales tax. Foreign orders write for information on overseas shipping costs.

My check/money order for $____________________________________ is enclosed.

Purchase Order Number____

Name____

Title____

Organization____

Address____

City______________________________ State____________ Zip____________

Signature____

NOMINATIONS - REVISIONS

Do you wish to nominate someone for inclusion in the **V.I.P. ADDRESS BOOK** or revise an entry? Mail this form to:

THE V.I.P. ADDRESS BOOK

%Associated Media Companies, Ltd.

P.O. Box 10190

Marina del Rey, CA 90295-8864

1. (Check One) Nomination ____________________ Revision ________________________

Name____

Organization____

Address____

City ________________________________ State ______________ Zip____________

2. (Check One) Nomination _____________________ Revision _____________________

Name ____

Organization____

Address____

City ______________________________________ State ___________ Zip__________

For additional names, use separate page for the information.

Submitted by:____

Title____

Organization____

Address____

City ________________________________ State ______________ Zip____________

Telephone: Area Code____________ Number ___________________________________

V.I.P. ADDRESS BOOK UPDATES

KEEP YOUR V.I.P. ADDRESS BOOK CURRENT ! ! !

The U.S. Bureau of Statistics says almost 20 percent of people move yearly. Not only do people change places of residence, many change business affiliations.

- athletes get traded
- entertainers change agents
- businesspeople change jobs
- politicians leave or change office

How do you stay abreast of changes? . . . Through the **V.I.P. ADDRESS BOOK UPDATES**! These updates will keep you on top of:

- changed addresses
- invalid addresses
- new V.I.P.s
- deaths

The **V.I.P. ADDRESS BOOK UPDATES** is the same size and format as the **1992-1993 V.I.P. ADDRESS BOOK**. Cost of the updates is $34.95 per year postpaid (California residents add $2.97 for sales tax). Fill out and mail the coupon below **today.** Foreign orders add $6.00 for overseas shipping. Be sure to include your check or money order. No C.O.D. orders.

Please add me as a subscriber to **V.I.P. ADDRESS BOOK UPDATES** at $34.95 per year (California residents add $2.97 sales tax).

NAME____

ADDRESS_____________________________________

CITY__________________ STATE_________ ZIP________

Mail this coupon with check or money order to:

V.I.P. ADDRESS BOOK UPDATES

%Associated Media Companies Ltd.

P.O. Box 10190

Marina del Rey, CA 90295-8864

ADDRESS CORRECTIONS

If your letters are returned due to an expired or incorrect address listed in the **V.I.P. ADDRESS BOOK**, we will try to help you obtain updated addresses.

We will check our files to see if a later or alternate address is available if you do the following:

1 - Send the front of the returned envelope **and** any postal service markings on the envelope.

2 - Requests must be limited to **one** address.

3 - List additional names in case there are no later or alternate addresses in our files.

4 - If more than one name is included, only the first name will be researched for later or alternate addresses.

5 - For each address request, send **$1.00 and a self-addressed, stamped envelope** to:

V.I.P. ADDRESS CORRECTIONS

Associated Media Companies Ltd.

P.O. Box 10190

Marina del Rey, CA 90295-8864

Requests without the handling fee and the self-addressed, stamped envelope will not receive replies.

Book design by Lee Ann Nelson. Cover logo is Trooper Extra Bold. Body type is Helvetic and Helvetica Condensed. Production by Nelson Design of Oakland, California. Printed in the United States of America